Official American Map

ZIP CODE DIRECTORY

COVERING ALL FIFTY STATES

- Area Code Directory by State, City and Area Code
- Detailed Zip Code ... Cities
- Sp...
- Alpha... Towns
- Latest Po... ...estic & Foreign
- Conve... ...ights and Measures Metric Conversion Charts

WARNING

Published by
Dome Publishing Co., Inc.
Ten New England Way
Warwick, RI 02887
In cooperation with
Arrow Map, Inc.
Division of American Map Corp.
46-35 54th Road
Maspeth, N.Y. 11378
(Not Affiliated with U.S. Postal Service)

PUBLISHER'S NOTES

This Official Dome/American Map Zip Code Directory has been compiled from reliable federal, state, county and local government information. Additional data have been obtained from non-governmental sources. Considerable time and effort have been expended to make this publication as accurate as is humanly possible. However, we cannot guarantee complete accuracy, nor do we assume liability for damages arising from errors or omissions.

The publisher wishes to acknowledge and thank the many readers who took the time to send us corrections, additions and helpful suggestions on how to improve this publication.

We appreciate hearing from you. Any errors or omissions brought to our attention will be corrected in the next edition. Please submit information to: Dome Publishing Co., Inc., 10 New England Way, Warwick, RI 02887.

13th Edition, 1995

Previous editions copyright 1972, 1974, 1984, 1985, 1986, 1987, 1988, 1989, 1990, 1992, 1994 by Arrow Map, Inc.

ISBN: 0-913450-85-5

Printed in the United States of America

CONTENTS

ZIP CODE MAP LIST

INDEX to STATE LISTS and CITY APPENDICES

INDEX to STATE LISTS and CITY APPENDICES -(Cont.)

INTRODUCTION

WHAT IS A ZIP CODE?

A ZIP Code is a five-digit geographic code that identifies areas within the United States and its possessions for purposes of simplifying the distribution of mail by the U.S. Postal Service.

The United States and its possessions are divided into 10 large geographic areas. Each area consists of three or more States or possessions and is given a number between 0 and 9.

ZIP CODE NATIONAL AREAS

Because of favorable transportation facilities, key post offices in each area are designated as Sectional Centers. Each Sectional Center post office receives and transmits mail moving between post offices within its section. It also receives and transmits all mail moving into or out of the section.

WHAT YOUR ZIP CODE MEANS

• Together, the first three digits of any ZIP Code number stand for either a particular Sectional Center or a metropolitan city.
• The last two digits of a Sectional Center ZIP Code number stand for one of the associated post offices served by the Sectional Center.
• The last two digits of a metropolitan city ZIP Code stand for one of the delivery areas served by the city post office, its branches and stations.

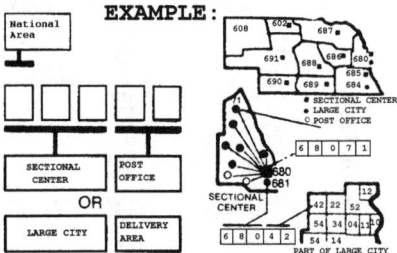

FINDING A ZIP CODE IN THIS BOOK

Each State contains two parts, a STATE LIST containing all post offices in that state and a section which lists Hospitals, Colleges, and Universities.

HELPFUL HINT

If the user of this Zip Code Directory cannot ascertain a Zip Code for an addressee in a given area, especially a "multi-zipped" city, the following suggestion might be in order. Look up the five-digit Zip Code for the community in the "State List of Post Offices". Add to this five-digit number a hyphen and the numerals "9998". This Zip + 4 Code will then deliver the letter to the Postmaster's office of the community in question. It will then be sorted to its final destination. This method should be used only as a temporary measure, until the sender learns the proper Zip Code of the addressee.

DOMESTIC FIRST-CLASS RATES

(Effective January 1, 1995)

FIRST CLASS

LETTER RATES - 11 OUNCES OR LESS

1st ounce .... .32
Each additional ounce .... .23

For Pieces Not Exceeding (oz.)	The Rate Is	For Pieces Not Exceeding (oz.)	The Rate Is
1	$0.32	7	$1.70
2	0.55	8	1.93
3	0.78	9	2.16
4	1.01	10	2.39
5	1.24	11	2.62
6	1.47		

FOR PIECES OVER 11 OUNCES SEE FIRST-CLASS ZONE RATED (PRIORITY) MAIL RATES

CARD RATES:

Single postal cards sold by the post office .... .20 each.
Double postal cards sold by the post office .... .40 (.20 each half)
Single post cards .... .20 each.
Double post cards (reply-half of reply post card does
   not have to bear postage when originally mailed) .... .40 (.20 each half)
Presort rate .... Consult Postmaster
Business reply mail .... Consult Postmaster
Note: To qualify for "card rates", a card may not be larger than 4¼ x 6 inches, or more than .0095 inch thick.

FIRST-CLASS ZONE RATED (PRIORITY) MAIL

Weight over 11 ounces and not exceeding Pound(s)	Local Zones 1 2, and 3	Zone 4	Zone 5	Zone 6	Zone 7	Zone 8
1	$3.00	$3.00	$3.00	$3.00	$3.00	$3.00
2	3.00	3.00	3.00	3.00	3.00	3.00
3	4.00	4.00	4.00	4.00	4.00	4.00
4	5.00	5.00	5.00	5.00	5.00	5.00
5	6.00	6.00	6.00	6.00	6.00	6.00
6	6.35	6.90	7.10	7.20	7.80	8.00
7	6.65	7.80	8.10	8.40	9.20	9.80
8	6.95	8.70	9.05	9.50	10.40	11.60
9	7.40	9.35	10.00	10.60	11.30	13.00
10	7.85	10.00	10.75	11.40	12.15	14.05
11	8.25	10.65	11.45	12.20	13.00	15.10
12	8.70	11.30	12.20	13.00	13.90	16.15
13	9.10	11.95	12.90	13.80	14.75	17.20
14	9.55	12.60	13.65	14.55	15.60	18.25
15	10.00	13.25	14.35	15.35	16.50	19.30
16	10.40	13.90	15.05	16.15	17.35	20.35
17	10.85	14.55	15.80	16.95	18.20	21.40
18	11.30	15.20	16.50	17.75	19.05	22.45
19	11.70	15.85	17.25	18.55	19.95	23.50
20	12.15	16.50	17.95	19.30	20.80	24.55

INTERNATIONAL FIRST-CLASS RATES

A. *Regular Surface Mail* - Letters and Post Cards (For Canada and Mexico see C.)

> 70 cents for the first ounce;
> 25 cents for each additional ounce up to 8 ozs;
> $3.95 for 12 ozs;
> $5.55 for 16 ozs;
> $7.65 for 24 ozs;
> $9.75 for 32 ozs;
> $11.85 for 40 ozs;
> $13.95 for 48 ozs;
> $16.05 for 56 ozs;
> $18.15 for 64 ozs;

Weight limit: 4 pounds.

B: *Air Mail Rates for Letters and Letter Packages* (For Canada and Mexico see C.)

> 50 cents for 1/2 ounce;
> 95 cents for 1 ounce;
> 39 cents for each additional 1/2 ounce up to and including 32 ozs;
> 39 cents for each additional ounce over 32 ozs.

Weight limit: 4 pounds.

C. *Surface Rates for Letters and Letter Packages*

Canada

> 40 cents for the first ounce;
> 23 cents for each additional ounce up to 16 ozs;
> 60 cents for each additional 1/2 pound (8 ozs.) up to 2 pounds.
> 93 cents for each additional 1/2 pound (8 ozs.) up to 4 pounds.

Mexico

> 45 cents for the first ounce;
> 65 cents for two ounces;
> 25 cents for each additional ounce up to 16 ozs;
> $2.00 for each additional 1/2 pound (8 ozs.) up to 4 pounds.

Weight limit: 4 pounds

> *Note:* Letter class mail to Canada and Mexico receives First-Class service in the United States and air service in Canada and Mexico.

D. *Post and Postal Cards*

Canada - 30 cents each

Mexico - 30 cents each

All Other Countries

> Surface - 35 cents each
> Air - 40 cents each

E. *Aerogramme* - 45 cents each

DOMESTIC PARCEL POST

Service by the U.S. Postal Service

> Rates for parcel post are governed by a zone structure. You must request the "Official Zone Chart" and the table of rates from your local post office. There are eight zones, each with sixty-nine rate steps.

U.P.S. MAILING INFORMATION

Service by the United Parcel Service (UPS)

> This organization, a private company, offers a service in the parcel delivery field which competes favorably with the U.S. Postal Service. UPS distinctive brown vans are seen almost as often in metropolitan areas as those of the U.S. Postal Service.

UPS is very competitive on both rates and service, particularly if the destination is within 500 miles. They also handle expeditiously parcels outside the U.S. Postal Service's weight and size regulations.

Call your local UPS office for further information. 1-800-222-8333

STATE ABBREVIATIONS

Alabama	AL	New Jersey	NJ
Alaska	AK	New Mexico	NM
Arizona	AZ	New York	NY
Arkansas	AR	North Carolina	NC
California	CA	North Dakota	ND
Colorado	CO	Ohio	OH
Connecticut	CT	Oklahoma	OK
Delaware	DE	Oregon	OR
District of Columbia	DC	Pennsylvania	PA
Florida	FL	Rhode Island	RI
Georgia	GA	South Carolina	SC
Hawaii	HI	South Dakota	SD
Idaho	ID	Tennessee	TN
Illinois	IL	Texas	TX
Indiana	IN	Utah	UT
Iowa	IA	Vermont	VT
Kansas	KS	Virginia	VA
Kentucky	KY	Washington	WA
Louisiana	LA	West Virginia	WV
Maine	ME	Wisconsin	WI
Maryland	MD	Wyoming	WY
Massachusetts	MA		
Michigan	MI		
Minnesota	MN		
Mississippi	MS		
Missouri	MO		
Montana	MT	Guam	GU
Nebraska	NE	Puerto Rico	PR
Nevada	NV	Virgin Islands	VI
New Hampshire	NH		

In addition, the following abbreviations are used:

Alley	Aly & Al	Expressway	Expy	Plaza	Plz
Arcade	Arc		& Expwy	Point	Pt
Avenue	Ave & Av	Extension	Ext	Road	Rd
Boulevard	Blvd	Freeway	Fwy & Frwy	Rural	R
Branch	Br	Gardens	Gdns	Square	Sq
Bypass	Byp	Grove	Grv	Street	St
Causeway	Cswy	Heights	Hts & Hgts	Terrace	Ter
Center	Ctr	Highway	Hwy & Hgwy	Trail	Tr
Circle	Cir	Lane	Ln & La	Turnpike	Tpke
Court(s)	Ct(s)	Manor	Mnr	Viaduct	Via
Crescent	Cres	Parkway	Pky & Pkwy	Vista	Vis
Drive	Dr	Place	Pl		

North Florence 35630
Foley 36535-536
  Huggers Landing 36535
  Oyster Bay 36535
  Vernant Park 36535
Forest Home 36030
Forestdale (Birmingham) .. 35214
Forkland 36740
Fort Davis 36031
Fort Deposit 36032
Fort Mc Clellan 36205, 36201
  (Anniston)
Fort Mitchell 36856
Fort Morgan (Gulf Shores) 36542
Fort Payne 35967
Fort Rucker 36362
Fosters 35463
Franklin 36444
Frankville 36538
Frisco City 36445
Fruitdale 36539
Fruithurst 36262
Fulton (Dickinson) .. 36436, 36446
Fulton Springs 35068
  (Fultondale)
Fultondale 35068
Furman 36741
Fyffe 35971
Gadsden 35901-906, 35999
  East Gadsden 35903
  Glencoe 35905
  Hokes Bluff 35903
  Rainbow City 35901
  Southside 35901
Gainestown 36540
Gainesville 35464
Gallant 35972
Gallion 36742
Gantt 36038
Garden City 35070
Gardendale 35071
Garland (Mc Kenzie) 36456
Gateswood (Robertsdale) . 36567
Gayfers (Mobile) 36626
Gaylesville 35973
Geiger (Emelle) 35459
Geneva 36340
Georgetown 36521, 36587
  (Chunchula)
Georgiana 36033
Geraldine 35974
Gibsonville (Ashland) 36251
Gilbertown 36908
Glen Allen 35559
Glen City (Pell City) 35125
Glencoe (Gadsden) 35905
Glenwood 36034
Golden Springs (Anniston) 36201
Goldville (Wadley) 36276
Goodsprings 35560
Goodwater 35072
Goodway 36449
Gordo 35466
Gordon 36343
Goshen 36035
Gosport (Whatley) 36482
Graball (Abbeville) 36310
Grady 36036
Graham 36263
Grand Bay 36541
Grangeburg (Gordon) 36343

Grant 35747
Gravleeton (Sumiton) 35148
Grayson (Houston) 35572
Grayson Valley 35235
  (Birmingham)
Graysville 35073
Green Pond 35074
Greensboro 36744
Greenville 36037
Grimes (Dothan) 36301
Grove Hill (Allen) 36419, 36451
  Antioch 36451
  Hebron 36451
  Pine Acres 36451
  Sandflat 36451
  Union 36451
Groveoak 35975
Guin 35563
Gulf Crest (Chunchula) 36521
Gulf Shores 36542, 36547
  Fort Morgan 36542
Guntersville 35976
Gurley 35748
Hackleburg 35564
Hacoda (Florala) 36442
Haleburg (Columbia) 36319
Haleyville 35565
Hamilton 35570
Hanceville 35077
Hardaway 36039
Harkins Crossroads 36251
  (Ashland)
Harpersville 35078
Harrisburg (Brent) .. 35034, 35125
Hartford 36344
Hartselle 35640
Harvest 35749
Hatchechubbee 36858
Havana (Moundville) 35474
Hawk (Woodland) 36280
Hawthorn (Wagarville) 36585
Hawthorne (Deer Park) 36529
Hayden 35079
Hayneville 36040
Haywood (Wedowee) 36278
Hazel Green 35750
Headland 36345
Healing Springs (Millry) ... 36558
Hebron (Grove Hill) 36451
Heflin 36264
Helena 35080
Henagar 35978
Heron Bay (Coden) 36523
Hickory Flat (Roanoke) 36274
Higdon 35979
Highbluff (Hartford) 36344
Highland (Lineville) 36266
Highland Home 36041
Highland Lake (Oneonta) .. 35121
Hightower (Graham) 36263
Hillsboro 35643
Hobson City (Anniston) 36201
Hodges 35571
Hodgesville (Dothan) 36301
Hokes Bluff (Gadsden) 35903
Hollins 35082
Hollis Crossroads 36264
  (Heflin)
Holly Pond 35083
Hollytree 35751
Hollywood 35752

Holt (Tuscaloosa) 35404
Homewood 35209, 35259
  (Birmingham)
Honoraville 36042
Hoods Crossroads 35121
  (Oneonta)
Hoover 35216, 35236, 35244
  (Birmingham)
Hope Hull 36043
Hopewell (Bessemer) 35023
Horton 35980
Houston 35572
Hueytown 35020, 35023
  (Bessemer)
Huffman (Birmingham) 35235
Huggers Landing (Foley) .. 36535
Huntsville 35800-816, 35824
  Redstone Arsenal 35808-809
Hurtsboro 36860
Huxford 36543
Hybart (Vredenburgh) 36481
Hytop (Scottsboro) 35768
Idaho (Ashland) 36251
Ider 35981
Independence 36003
  (Autaugaville)
Indian Springs (Pelham) .. 35124
Irondale (Birmingham) 35210
Irvington 36544
Ivalee (Attalla) 35954
Jachin 36910
Jack 36346
Jackson 36501, 36515, 36545
  (Alma)
Jacksons Gap 36861
Jacksonville 36265
Jasper 35501-502
Jefferson 36745
Jefferson Park 35210
  (Birmingham)
Jemison 35085
Jones 36749
Joppa 35087
Josephine (Elberta) 36530
Kansas 35573
Keego (Brewton) 36426
Kellerman 35468
Kelly Springs (Dothan) 36301
Kellyton 35089
Kennedy 35574
Kent 36045
Ketona (Birmingham) 35217
Keystone (Alabaster) 35007
Keyton (Enterprise) 36330
Killen 35645
Kimberly 35091
Kingville (Kennedy) 35574
Kinsey (Dothan) 36303
Kinston 36453
Knoxville 35469
Koenton (Millry) 36558
Laceys Spring 35754
Lafayette 36862
Lamison 36747
Lanett 36863
Langston 35755
Lapine 36046
Lavaca 36911
Lawley 36793
Lawrenceville (Abbeville) .. 36310
Leeds 35094

Wadley 36276	Wedowee 36278	Wilkes (Birmingham) 35228
Wagarville 36585	Wehadkee (Roanoke) 36274	Wills Crossroads 36310
Walker Springs 36586	Wellington 36279	(Abbeville)
Wallace (Brewton) 36426	Wenonah (Birmingham) 35211	Wilmer 36587
Walnut Grove 35990	Weogufka 35183	Wilsonville 35186
Ward 36922	West Blocton 35184	Wilton 35187
Warrior 35180	West Greene 35491	Winfield 35594
Waterford (Newton) 36352	Westover 35185	Wing 36483
Waterloo 35677	Wetumpka 36092	Winslow (Autaugaville) 36003
Watson 35181	Whatley 36482	Woodland 36280
Watts Mill (Lineville) 36266	Whistler (Mobile) 36612	Woodstock 35188
Wattsville 35182	White Hall (Hayneville) 36040	Woodville 35776
Waverly 36879	White Oak (Abbeville) 36310	Yantley (Lisman) 36912
Weaver 36277	Whitehead (Rogersville) 35652	Yarbo (Millry) 36558
Webb 36376	Whitfield (York) 36925	Yellow Pine (Fruitdale) 36539
		York 36925

IMPORTANT BUILDINGS

ANNISTON

BUILDINGS

City Hall
1200 Gurnee Ave 36201

Co Courthouse
25 W 11th St 36201

County Admin Office
1702 Noble St 36201

Federal Building
1129 Noble St 36201

Ne Ala Regional Med Ctr
400 E 10th St 36201

AVALON PARK

BUILDINGS

Jefferson Co Ct House
1801 3rd Ave N 35020

BIRMINGHAM

BUILDINGS

Amsouth Harbert Plaza
1901 6th Ave N 35203

Amsouth Sonat Tower
1900 5th Ave N 35203

Bank For Savings Building
1919 Morris Ave 35203

Brown Marx Tower
2000 1st Ave N 35203

City Federal Building
2026 2nd Ave N 35203

City Hall
710 20th St N 35203

Colonial Bank Building
1928 1st Ave N 35203

Commerce Center
2027 1st Ave N 35203

Daniel Building
15 20th St S 35233

Eastwood Mall
7703 Crestwood Blvd 35210

Financial Center
505 20th St N 35203

First Ala Bank Building
417 20th St N 35203

Frank Nelson Building
205 20th St N 35203

John Hand Building
17 20th St N 35203

Massey Building
2025 3rd Ave N 35203

Park Place Towers
2001 Park Pl 35203

Southtrust Tower
420 20th St N 35203

GOVERNMENT

Fed Building U S Courthouse
1800 5th Ave N 35203

Hugo Black U S Courthouse
1729 5th Ave N 35203

DECATUR

BUILDINGS

City Hall Tower
402 Lee St NE 35601

Federal Building
400 Well St NE 35601

HOSPITALS

Med Surg Center
2828 Highway 31 S 35603

DOTHAN

GOVERNMENT

Houston County Court Hous
100 N Oates St 36303

FLORENCE

APARTMENTS

Una Apts
403 Circular Dr 35630

BUILDINGS

Federal Building
426 E Spring St 35630

Municipal Building
110 W College St 35630

GOVERNMENT

Lauderdale Co Courthouse
200 S Court St 35630

GADSDEN

BUILDINGS

City Hall
90 Broad St 35901

Federal Building
600 Broad St 35901

Gadsden Business College
750 Forrest Ave 35901

New World Bus College
434 Broad St 35901

GOVERNMENT

Court House
800 Forrest Ave 35901

HUNTSVILLE

APARTMENTS

Mayfair Towers
4701 Whitesport Cir SW ... 35801

Parkview Nursing Home
2004 Max Luther Dr NW ... 35810

Summit Apts
111 Walker Ave NE 35801

Todd Towers
204 Greene St NE 35801

BUILDINGS

Amsouth Center
200 Clinton Ave W 35801

Central Bank Building
200 Westside Sq 35801

Colonial Bank Building
101 Governors Dr SE 35801

Madison Sq Mall
5901 University Dr NW 35806

Park Plaza Office Center
303 Williams Ave SW 35801

Parkway City Mall
2801 Memorial Pky SW 35801

The Mall
1001 Memorial Pky NW 35801

GOVERNMENT

Federal Courthouse
101 Holmes Ave NE 35801

Madison Co Courthouse
100 Courthouse Sq SE 35801

MOBILE

GOVERNMENT

County Court House
109 Government St 36602

HOSPITALS

Mobile Medical Center Bld
1720 Springhill Ave 36604

MONTGOMERY

COLLEGES

Alabama State University
271 Po Box 36101

TUSCALOOSA

BUILDINGS

Amsouth Bank Building
2330 University Blvd 35401

GOVERNMENT

Tuscaloosa Cty Ct House
714 Greensboro Ave 35401

Us Federal Building
1118 24th Ave 35401

Us Federal Building
1118 Greensboro Ave 35401

Platinum	99651	Sheldon Point	99666	Border	99780
Point Baker	99927	Shishmaref	99772	Mentasta Lake	99780
Point Hope	99766	Shungnak	99773	Toksook Bay	99637
Point Lay	99759	Sitka	99835-836	Trapper Creek	99683
Port Alexander	99836	Skagway	99840	Tuluksak	99679
Port Alsworth	99653	Skwentna	99667	Tuntutuliak	99680
Port Graham (Homer)	99603	Slana (Gakona)	99586	Tununak	99681
Port Heiden	99549	Sleetmute	99668	Twin Hills (Dillingham)	99576
Port Lions	99550	Soldotna	99669	Two Rivers	99716
Prudhoe Bay	99734	South Naknek	99670	Tyonek	99682
Quinhagak	99655	Stebbins	99671	Unalakleet	99684
Rampart	99767	Steese (Fairbanks)	99710	Unalaska	99685, 99692
Red Devil	99656	Sterling	99672	Uscgs (Kodiak)	99619
Ruby	99768	Stevens Village	99774	Valdez	99686
Russian Mission	99657	Stony River (Aniak)	99557	Venetie	99781
Saint George Island	99591	Sutton	99674	Wainwright	99782
Saint Marys	99658, 99666	Takotna	99675	Wales	99783
Saint Michael	99659	Talkeetna	99676	Ward Cove	99928
Saint Paul Island	99591, 99660	Tanacross	99776	Wasilla	99652, 99654, 99687
(Saint George Island)		Tanana	99777		99694
Salcha	99714	Tatitlek	99677	White Mountain	99784
Sand Point	99661	Teller	99778	Whittier	99693
Savoonga	99769	Tenakee Springs	99841	Willow	99683, 99688
Scammon Bay	99662	Tetlin	99779	(Trapper Creek)	
Selawik	99770	Thorne Bay	99919	Wrangell	99929
Seldovia	99663	Togiak	99678	Yakutat	99689
Seward	99664	Tok	99776, 99779-780		
Shageluk	99665	(Tanacross)			
Shaktoolik	99771				

ANCHORAGE

APARTMENTS

Nelchina Point
1601 Nelchina St 99501

The Cassel
1040 W 27th Ave 99503

The Chandalar
1055 W 27th Ave 99503

BUILDINGS

101 Benson Building
101 W Benson Blvd 99503

1st National Bank Building
425 G St 99501

420 L Building
420 L St 99501

Austalaska Building
360 K St 99501

Calais Office Center
3201 C St 99503

Calais Office Center
3301 C St 99503

Carr Gottstein Building
310 K St 99501

Cook Inlet Region Building
2525 C St 99503

Denali Towers North
2550 Denali St 99503

Denali Towers South
2600 Denali St 99503

Dimond Center
800 E Dimond Blvd 99515

Enserch Center
550 W 7th Ave 99501

Financial Plaza
601 W 5th Ave 99501

Frontier Building
3601 C St 99503

Peterson Towers
510 L St 99501

Sohio Building
3111 C St 99503

GOVERNMENT

Federal Building
222 W 7th Ave 99513

Friendly Corners (Eloy)	85231
Fry (Sierra Vista)	85635
Gadsden	85336
Ganado 86505, 86540	
Cornfields	86505
Greasewood	86505
Hubbell Trading Post ..	86505
Kin-li-chee	86505
Klagetoh	86505
Mennonite Mission	86505
Nazlini	86505
Steamboat Canyon	86505
Sunrise Springs	86505
Toyei	86505
Woodsprings	86505
Geronimo (Fort Thomas) ...	85536
Gila Bend	85337
Gilbert 85233-234	
.... 85296, 85299	
Gisela (Payson)	85541
Gleeson (Elfrida)	85610
Glendale 85301-313, 85318	
Globe 85501-502	
Cutter	85501
Little Acres	85501
Parker Creek	85501
Gold Canyon	85219
(Apache Junction)	
Golden Shores (Topock) ...	86436
Golden Valley	86413
Goodyear	85338
Graham (Thatcher)	85552
Grand Canyon	86023
Grand View (Prescott)	86301
Grasshopper Junction	86401
(Kingman)	
Gray Mountain ... 86001, 86016	
(Flagstaff)	
Cameron	86016
Greasewood (Ganado)	86505
Greasewood Springs	86507
(Lukachukai)	
Greaterville (Sonoita)	85637
Green Valley 85614, 85622	
Greenhaven (Page)	86040
Greer	85927
Groom Creek 86301, 86303	
(Prescott)	
Gu Achi (Sells)	85634
Guadalupe (Tempe)	85283
Guthrie (Clifton)	85533
Hackberry	86411
Hano (Polacca)	86042
Happy Jack	86024
Hard Rock	86039
(Kykotsmovi Village)	
Harshaw (Patagonia)	85624
Havasu City	86403
(Lake Havasu City)	
Hawley Lake (Mc Nary)	85930
Hayden	85235
Heber 85928, 85931	
Hereford	85615
Higley	85236
Hillside (Prescott)	86301
Hilltop (San Simon)	85632
Ho Kay Gan (Prescott)	86301
Holbrook 85942, 86025	
.... 86028-029, 86031	
(Woodruff)	
Hollywood (Safford)	85546

Hopi Indian Reservation	86039
(Kykotsmovi Village)	
Horse Thief (Mayer)	86333
Hotevilla	86030
Houck 86506, 86508	
Allentown	86506
Oak Springs	86506
Pine Springs	86506
Querino	86506
Huachuca City	85616
Huachuca Terrace (Chinle)	86503
Hualapai	86412
Hubbell Trading Post National	
(Ganado)	86505
Humboldt	86329
Hunters Point	86511
(Saint Michaels)	
Indian Wells	86031
Inspiration (Claypool)	85532
Iron Springs	86330
Jacob Lake (Fredonia)	86022
Jakes Corner (Payson)	85541
Jeddito (Keams Canyon) ..	86034
Jerome	86331
Johnson (Dragoon)	85609
Joseph City	86032
Kachina Village	86001
(Flagstaff)	
Kaibab (Fredonia)	86022
Kaibito	86053
Kansas Settlement	85643
(Willcox)	
Kayenta	86033
Keams Canyon	86034
Kearny	85237
Kin-li-chee (Ganado)	86505
Kingman 86401-402	
..... 86411-413, 86437, 86445	
Grasshopper Junction	86401
Lake Mead Rancheros	86401
Kino (Tucson)	85705
Kinsley Ranch	85640
(Tumacacori)	
Kirkland	86332
Klagetoh (Ganado)	86505
Klondyke (Willcox)	85643
Kykotsmovi Village	86039
Lake Havasu City 86403-406	
Desert Hills	86403
Havasu City	86403
Lake Mary (Flagstaff)	86001
Lake Mead Rancheros	86401
(Kingman)	
Lake Montezuma	86342
Lakeside	85929
Laveen	85339
Leupp	86035
Leupp Corner (Winslow)	86047
Litchfield Park	85340
Little Acres (Globe)	85501
Little Tucson (Sells)	85634
Littlefield	86432
Lochiel (Patagonia)	85624
Lone Star (Safford)	85546
Low Mountain (Chinle)	86503
Lowell (Bisbee)	85603
Lower Miami (Miami)	85539
Lukachukai	86507
Lukeville	85341
Lupton	86508
Mammoth	85618

Many Farms	86538
Marana	85653
Marble Canyon	86036
Maricopa	85239
Martinez Lake (Yuma)	85365
Maverick (Show Low)	85901
Mayer 86333, 86343	
Bumble Bee	86333
Cleator	86333
Cordes Lakes	86333
Horse Thief	86333
Poland Junction	86333
Spring Valley	86333
Mc Nary	85930
Mc Neal	85617
Mcguireville (Rimrock)	86335
Meadview	86444
Mennonite Mission	86505
(Ganado)	
Mesa 85201-208, 85210-216	
... 85240, 85274-275, 85277	
Mexican Water	86514
(Teec Nos Pos)	
Miami	85539
Middle Verde (Camp Verde)	86322
Midland City (Miami)	85539
Miller Valley (Prescott)	86301
Miracle Valley (Hereford) ...	85615
Mishongnovi	86043
(Second Mesa)	
Mission 85706, 85714, 85746	
(Tucson)	
Mobile (Maricopa)	85239
Moccasin (Fredonia)	86022
Moenave (Tuba City)	86045
Moenkopi (Tuba City)	86045
Mohave Valley	86440
Morenci	85540
Mormon Lake	86038
Morristown	85342
Mount Lemmon	85619
Mountainaire (Flagstaff)	86001
Munds Park	86017
Naco	85620
Nau (Flagstaff)	86011
Nazlini (Ganado) ... 86505, 86540	
Ganado	86540
New Oraibi	86039
(Kykotsmovi Village)	
New River (Phoenix)	85027
Nicksville (Hereford)	85615
Nogales 85621, 85628	
.... 85648, 85662	
Fairbank	85621
Rio Rico	85621
North Rim	86052
Nowhere (Kirkland)	86332
Nutrioso	85932
Oak Creek Canyon	86336
(Sedona)	
Oak Springs (Houck)	86506
Oatman	86433
Old Oraibi	86039
(Kykotsmovi Village)	
Oljato (Kayenta)	86033
Oracle	85623
Oraibi	86039
(Kykotsmovi Village)	
Oro Valley 85704, 85737	
(Tucson)	
Overgaard	85933

Tintown (Bisbee)	85603
Tolacon (Teec Nos Pos)	86514
Tolani (Winslow)	86047
Tolleson	85353
Toltec (Eloy)	85231
Tombstone	85638
Tonalea	86044, 86053-054
Red Lake	86044
Tonopah	85354
Tonto Basin	85553
Topawa	85639
Topock	86436
Toreva (Second Mesa)	86043
Tortilla Flat	85290
Toyei (Ganado)	86505
Truxton (Peach Springs)	86434
Tsail (Chinle)	86503
Tsaile	86556
Tse Bonita (Window Rock)	86515
Tuba City	86045
Tubac	85640, 85646
(Tumacacori)	
Tumacacori	85646
Tucson	85700-726
	85722, 85728, 85730-738
	85740-749, 85751-752
	85754, 85775, 85777
Casas Adobes	85704
Casas Adobes	85718
Casas Adobes	85741
Casas Adobes	85743
Coronado	85711
Fort Lowell	85715
Fort Lowell	85749
Kino	85705
Mission	85706
Mission	85714
Mission	85746
Oro Valley	85704

Oro Valley	85737
Rincon	85710
Rincon	85730
Rincon	85747-85748
South Tucson	85713
Sun	85716
Sun	85719
Tumacacori	85640, 85645-646
Agua Linda	85640
Amado	85640
Carmen	85640
Continental	85640
Kinsley Ranch	85640
Santa Rita	85640
Tubac	85640
Tusayan (Grand Canyon)	86023
Twin Arrows (Flagstaff)	86001
Two Story	86511
(Saint Michaels)	
Upper Wheatfields	86507
(Lukachukai)	
Vail	85641
Valentine	86437
Valley Farms	85291
Vamori (Sells)	85634
Vernon	85940
Village Meadows	85635
(Sierra Vista)	
Village Of Oak Creek	86341
(Sedona)	
Waddell	85355
Walker (Prescott)	86301
Walnut Grove (Kirkland)	86332
Walpi (Polacca)	86042
Warren (Bisbee)	85603
Wellton	85356
Wenden	85357
West Sedona (Sedona)	86340
Whipple (Prescott)	86313

Whispering Hills	85635
(Sierra Vista)	
White Clay	86504
(Fort Defiance)	
White Mountain Lake	85912
Whiteriver	85941
Why (Ajo)	85321
Wickenburg	85358, 85390
Wide Ruins (Chambers)	86502
Wikieup	85360
Wilhoit (Kirkland)	86332
Willcox	85643-644
Bonita	85643
Dos Cabezas	85643
Fort Grant	85643
Kansas Settlement	85643
Klondyke	85643
Sierra Bonita	85643
Sunset	85643
Williams	86046
Willow Beach	86445
Window Rock	86515
Winkelman	85292
Winona (Flagstaff)	86001
Winslow	86047
Winwood (Bisbee)	85603
Witch Wells (Saint Johns)	85936
Wittmann	85361
Woodruff	85942
Woodsprings (Ganado)	86505
Yarnell	85362
York (Duncan)	85534
Young	85554
Youngtown	85363
Yucca	86438
Yuma	85364-367, 85369
Martinez Lake	85365

APACHE JUNCTION

BUILDINGS

Palmas Del Sol East
3400 S Ironwood Dr 85220

HOTELS

Countryside Trvl Trlr Pk
2701 S Idaho Rd 85219

Grand Recreation Center
201 W Apache Trl 85220

MHP
400 N Plaza Dr 85220

Rock Shadow Trlr Pk
600 S Idaho Rd 85219

The View Mhp
7151 E Us Highway 60 85219

CORONADO

BUILDINGS

Great Western Bank Building
5151 E Broadway Blvd 85711

Pioneer Title Building
6245 E Broadway Blvd 85711

Security Savings Building
101 N Wilmot Rd 85711

MESA

BUILDINGS

Valley Bank Building
66 W Main St 85201

Valley Bank Building
13 N Macdonald 85201

GOVERNMENT

Federal Building
26 N Macdonald 85201

HOSPITALS

Desert Vista Hospital
570 W Brown Rd 85201

Mesa Lutheran
500 W 10th Pl 85201

MESA

BUILDING

Bank One
66 Main Street 85201

PHOENIX

APARTMENTS

Camelback Towers
4750 N Central Ave 85012

BUILDINGS

1 North First Street
1 N 1st St 85004

1st Interstate Building
114 W Adams St 85003

Arizona Center
400 E Van Buren St 85004

AZ Title Building
111 W Monroe St 85003

Bank One Center
201 Central Street 85073

Citibank Building
3300 N Central Ave 85012

First Interstate Bank Plz
100 W Washington St 85003

Greater Ariz Savings Building
112 N Central Ave 85004

I Columbus Plaza
3636 N Central Ave 85012

Lawyer Title Building
2200 N Central Ave 85004

Luhrs Building
11 W Jefferson St 85003

Luhrs Central
132 S Central Ave 85004

Luhrs Tower
45 W Jefferson St 85003

Security Building
234 N Central Ave 85004

Security Center
222 N Central Ave 85004

GOVERNMENT

County Courthouse
125 W Washington St 85003

Federal Building
230 N 1st Ave 85025

State Capitol Building
1700 W Washington St 85007

Superior Court Building
201 W Jefferson St 85003

TUCSON

BUILDINGS

Bank One Building
2 Congress Street 85701

Citibank Tower
1 S Church Ave 85701

Great American Tower
32 N Stone Ave 85701

Pioneer Plaza
100 N Stone Ave 85701

Transamerica Building
177 N Church Ave 85701

GOVERNMENT

Federal Building
300 W Congress St 85701

State Office Building
402 W Congress St 85701

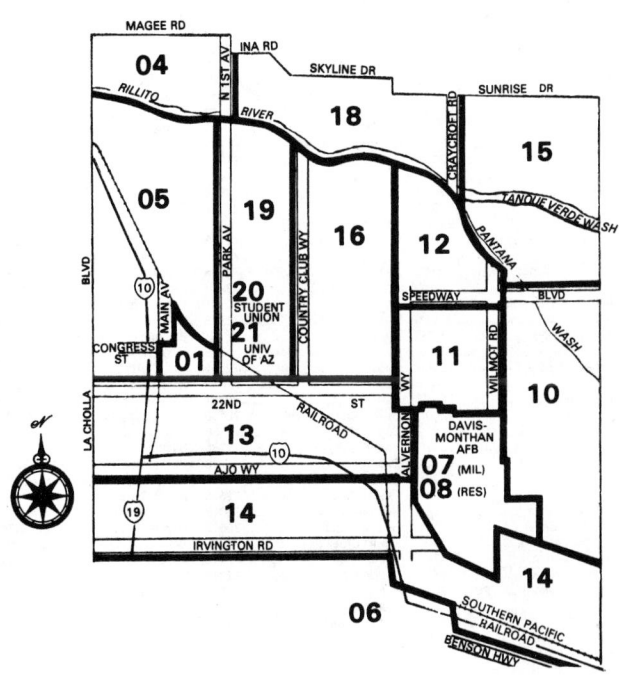

ZIP CODES

TUCSON, AZ

857 + TWO DIGITS SHOWN = ZIP CODE

ARKANSAS
Abbreviation AR

Abbott (Mansfield) 72944
Aberdeen (Roe) 72134
Acorn (Mena) 71953
Ada (Adona) 72001
Adams Field (Little Rock) .. 72202
Adona 72001
Agnos (Ash Flat) 72513
Alabam (Huntsville) 72740
Albert Pike 71913
   (Hot Springs National Park)
Albion (Searcy) 72143
Alco 72610
Alexander 72002
Alfrey (Brinkley) 72021
Algoa (Newport) 72112
Alicia 72410
Alix 72820
Allbrook 71851
   (Mineral Springs)
Alleene 71820
Allport (England) 72046
Alma 72921
Almyra 72003
Alpena 72611
Alpine (Amity) 71920
Alread (Clinton) 72031
Altheimer 72004
Altus 72821
Aly (Plainview) 72857
Amagon 72005
Amity 71920-921
   Alpine 71920
   Caney Valley 71921
   Center Ridge 71921
   Elm 71921
   Fendley 71921
   Point Cedar 71921
   Rosboro 71921
Amy (Camden) 71701
Anthony (Hope) 71801
Antioch (Beebe) 72012, 72070
Antoine 71922
Aplin (Perryville) 72126
Appleton (Atkins) 72822
Arcadia (Prescott) 71857
Arden (Ashdown) 71822
Arkadelphia 71998-99
Arkana (Bradley) 71826
Arkansas City 71630
Arkinda (Foreman) . 71836, 71838
Armorel 72310
Arsenal (Pine Bluff) 71601
Arthur (Solgohachia) 72156
Ash Flat 72513
Ashdown 71822
Asher (Little Rock) 72204
Ashton (Lake Village) 71653
Athens (Umpire) 71971
Atkins 72822-823
   Appleton 72822
   Bells Chapel 72823
   Economy 72823
   Galla Rock 72823
   Happy Bend 72823
   Kenwood 72823
   Wilson 72823
Atlanta (Emerson) 71740
Aubrey 72311

Augusta 72006
Aurelle (Strong) 71765
Aurora (Huntsville) 72740
Austin 72007, 72027
   Oak Grove 72007
   Old Austin 72007
Auvergne (Newport) 72112
Avery (Dumas) 71639
Avila (Alexander) 72002
Avoca 72711
Avon (De Queen) 71832
Azor (Emmet) 71835
Back Gate (Dumas) 71639
Balch 72009
Bald Knob 72010
Baldwin (Fayetteville) 72701
Banks 71631
Barber (Booneville) 72927
Barling 72923
Barney (Enola) 72047
Barrentine Corner (Beebe) 72012
Barringer (Gurdon) 71743
Barton 72312
Bass 72612, 72655
Bassett 72313
Bates 72924
Batesville ... 72501, 72503, 72522
Baucum 72117
   (North Little Rock)
Bauxite 72011
Baxter (Dermott) 71638
Bay 72411
Bayou Meto (Stuttgart) 72160
Bayou Metro (Lonoke) 72086
Bear (Royal) 71968
Bearden 71720
Beaudry (Jessieville) 71949
Beaver 72613
Bee Branch 72013
Beebe 72012
Beech Creek (Hamburg) 71646
Beech Grove 72412
Beedeville 72014
Beirne 71721
Bella Vista 72714
Bellaire (Dermott) 71638
Belleville 72824
Bells Chapel (Atkins) 72823
Bellville (Lockesburg) 71846
Belton (Nashville) 71852
Ben Hur (Pelsor) 72856
Ben Lomond 71823
Bengal (Newport) 72112
Benton 72015, 72018, 72158
   Congo 72015
   Haskell 72015
   Kentucky 72015
   Tull 72015
Bentonville . 72712, 72714, 72716
   Centerton 72712
   Healing Springs 72712
   Mason Valley 72712
   Vaughn 72712
Berea (Hamburg) 71646
Bergman 72615
Berlin (Hamburg) 71646
Berryville 72616
Beryl (Conway) 72032
Bethany (Dierks) 71833
Bethel Heights 72745, 72764
   (Lowell)

Beulah (Biscoe) 72017
Beverage Town (Cleveland) 72030
Bexar 72515
Big Flat 72617
Big Fork (Mena) 71953
Bigelow 72016
Biggers 72413
Billingsleys Corner 71866
   (Winthrop)
Billstown (Murfreesboro) ... 71958
Bingen (Nashville) 71852
Bird Town (Springfield) 72157
Birdeye 72314
Biscoe 72017
Bismarck 71929
Black Fork (Mena) 71953
Black Oak ... 72386, 72414, 72701
   (Tyronza)
Black Rock 72415
Blackfish (Heth) 72346
Blackland (Foreman) 71836
Blackton (Holly Grove) 72069
Blackville (Newport) 72112
Blaicely (Blakely) 71931
Blakely 71931
Blakemore (England) 72046
Blevins 71825
Bloomer (Charleston) 72933
Blue Hill 72118
   (North Little Rock)
Blue Mountain 72826
Blue Springs 71901
   (Hot Springs National Park)
Bluff City 71722
Bluffton 72827
Blytheville 72315-317, 72319
   Gosnell 72315
Board Camp 71932
Bodcaw (Rosston) 71858
Bolding (Huttig) 71747
Boles 72926
Bonanza (Fort Smith) 72916
Bonnerdale 71933
Bono (Greenbrier) .. 72058, 72416
Booker 72117
   (North Little Rock)
Booneville 72927
Boston (Pettigrew) 72752
Boswell 72516
Botkinburg (Clinton) 72031
Boueff (Eudora) 71640
Boughton (Prescott) 71857
Bovine (Hamburg) 71646
Bowen (Delight) 71940
Boxley (Kingston) 72742
Boyd (Fouke) 71837, 71845
Boydell (Montrose) 71658
Bradford 72020
Bradley 71826
Brady (Little Rock) 72205
Bragg City (Chidester) 71726
Branch 72928
Brasfield (Biscoe) 72017
Bredlow Corner (England) .. 72046
Brentwood (Winslow) 72959
Brewer (Edgemont) 72044
Brickeys 72320
Briggsville (Rover) 72828
Bright Star 71851
   (Mineral Springs)
Brightwater (Rogers) 72756

Brinkley 72021
Brister (Emerson) 71740
Brockwell 72517
Brookland 72417
Brown Springs (Malvern) .. 72104
Brownstown (Lockesburg) 71846
Brownsville (Booneville) 72927
Brumley (Conway) 72032
Brummitt (Stuttgart) 72160
Bruno 72618
Brush Creek (Leola) 72084
Bryant 72022, 72089
Buck Range 71851
   (Mineral Springs)
Buckner 71827
Buckville (Mountain Pine) . 71956
Buena Vista (Stephens) 71764
Buie (Prattsville) 72129
Bull Shoals 72619
Burdette 72321
Burg (Dierks) 71833
Burnville (Greenwood) 72936
Burton Mill 71839
   (Garland City)
Busch (Eureka Springs) 72632
Bussey (Stamps) 71860
Butlerville (Ward) 72176
Butterfield (Malvern) 72104
Byron (Salem) 72576
Cabot 72023
Caddo Gap 71935
Caddo Valley 71923
   (Arkadelphia)
Calamine (Strawberry) 72469
Caldwell 72322
Cale 71828
Calhoun (Magnolia) 71753
Calico Rock 72519
Calion 71724
Calmer (Rison) 71665
Camden 71701
Cammack Village 72207
   (Little Rock)
Camp 72520
Canaan (Marshall) 72650
Canale (Bradley) 71826
Cane Creek (Sheridan) 72150
Canehill 72717
Caney 71858, 71929, 72032
   (Rosston)
Caney Valley (Amity) 71921
Caraway 72419
Carbon City (Paris) 72855
Carlisle 72024
Carmel (Warren) 71671
Carolan (Booneville) 72927
Carrollton (Alpena) 72611
Carthage 71725
Casa 72025
Cash 72421
Cass (Ozark) 72949
Casscoe 72026
Catcher (Van Buren) 72956
Catholic Point 72027
   (Center Ridge)
Cato (North Little Rock) 72116
Caulksville (Ratcliff) 72951
Cauthron (Waldron) 72958
Cave City 72521
Cave Springs 72718
Cecil 72930

Cedar Creek (Parks) 72950
Cedarville 72932
Center Grove (Sheridan) ... 72150
Center Hill 72143, 72450
   (Searcy)
Center Point 71743
   (Gurdon)
Center Ridge 71921, 72027
   (Amity)
   Austin 72027
   Catholic Point 72027
   Lick Mountain 72027
   Middleton 72027
Centerton 72712, 72719
   (Bentonville)
Centerville .. 71835, 72058, 72829
   (Emmet)
Central 71842, 71923, 72104
Central City 71901
   .... 71913, 72941
   (Hot Springs National Park)
Cerrogordo (Winthrop) 71866
   (Lake Village)
Chapel Hill (De Queen) 71832
Charleston 72933
Charlotte 72522
Chatfield 72323
Cherokee Village ...72525, 72529
   Hardy 72525
   Hardy 72529
Cherry Hill (Perryville) 72126
Cherry Valley 72324
Chester 72934
Chicot (Eudora) 71640
Chicot Terrace 72209
   (Little Rock)
Chidester 71726
Childress (Des Arc) 72040
Chimes (Leslie) 72645
Chismville 72927, 72943
   (Booneville)
Choctaw 72028
Cincinnati (Summers) 72769
Clarendon 72029
Clarkedale 72325
Clarkridge 72623
Clarksville 72830
Clay (Searcy) 72143
Cleveland 72030
Clifty (Rogers) 72756
Clinton 72031
Clow (Ozan) 71855
Coal Hill 72832
Cobbs (England) 72046
Coffeeville (Bradford) 72020
Cole Spur (Gould) 71643
Coleman (Monticello) 71655
College City 72476
   (Walnut Ridge)
College Station 72053
Collegehill (Mc Neil) 71752
Collegeville (Alexander) 72002
Collins 71634, 71638
Colt 72326
Columbus 71831
Combs 72721
Cominto (Monticello) 71655
Compton 72624
Concord 72523
Congo (Benton) 72015

Conway 72032-033, 72035
   Beryl 72032
   Brumley 72032
   Caney 72032
   Gleason 72032
   Gold Creek 72032
   Preston 72032
   Saltillo 72032
   Skunkhollow 72032
Cord 72524
Corinth (Belleville) 72824
Corley (Paris) 72855
Cornerstone (Altheimer) ... 72004
Cornerville (Star City) 71667
Cornhill (Lockesburg) 71846
Corning 72422
Cotter 72626
Cotton Belt Junction 72021
   (Brinkley)
Cotton Plant 72036
Cove 71937
Cowlingsville 71846
   (Lockesburg)
Coy 72037
Cozahome (Harriet) 72639
Crabtree (Clinton) 72031
Crawfordsville 72327
Crigler (Star City) 71667
Critten Ridge (Foreman) ... 71836
Crocketts Bluff 72038
Cross Roads 71751
   .... 71933, 72069
   (Louann)
Crosses (Fayetteville) 72701
Crossett 71635
Crossroads 72040, 72131, 72150
   (Des Arc)
Crumrod 72328
Crystal Hill 72118
   (North Little Rock)
Cullendale (Camden) 71701
Culpeper (Clinton) 72031
Curtis 71728
Cushman 72526
Cypress Valley 72156
   (Solgohachia)
Dabney (Morrilton) 72110
Dalark (Arkadelphia) 71923
Dallas (Mena) 71953
Dalton (Pocahontas) 72455
Damascus 72039
Danville 72833
Dardanelle 72834
Datto 72424
Davenport (Pangburn) 72121
Dayton (Huntington) 72940
De Ann (Hope) 71801
De Luce (De Witt) 72042
De Queen 71832
De Valls Bluff 72041
De Witt 72042
Deaneyville (Prescott) 71857
Deberrie (Perryville) 72126
Decatur 72722
Deep Elm 71653, 72069
   (Lake Village)
Deer 72628
Degray (Arkadelphia) 71923
Delaney (Elkins) 72727
Delaplaine 72425
Delaware 72835

Delight	71940	
Dell	72426	
Denmark (Bradford)	72020	
Dennard	72629	
Denning (Altus)	72821	
Dermott	71638	
Des Arc	72040	
Desha	72527	
Detonti (Bauxite)	72011	
Dewey (Pangburn)	72121	
Dialion (Rison)	71665	
Diamond City	72630	
Dian (Prescott)	71857	
Diaz	72043	
Dierks	71833	
Divide (Casa)	72025	
Dixie (Augusta)	72006	
Doddridge	71834	
Dodson (Magnolia)	71753	
Dogpatch	72648	
Dollarway (Pine Bluff)	71602	
Dolph	72528	
Donaldson	71941	
Dongola (Marshall)	72650	
Doniphan (Searcy)	72143	
Dora (Van Buren)	72956	
Dover	72837	
Drakes Creek (Huntsville)	72740	
Drasco	72530	
Driggs (Magazine)	72943	
Driver	72329	
Duce (Mc Gehee)	71666	
Dumas	71639	
Durham (Fayetteville)	72701	
Durian (Malvern)	72104	
Dutch Mills (Lincoln)	72744	
Dutton (Saint Paul)	72760	
Dyer	72935	
Dyess	72330	
Eagle Mills (Bearden)	71720	
Earle	72331	
East Camden (Camden)	71701	
East Cotter (Gassville)	72635	
East End (Hensley)	72065	
Ebenezer (Stephens)	71764	
Economy (Atkins)	72823	
Eden Isle (Heber Springs)	72543	
Edgemont	72044	
Edmondson	72332	
Eglantine (Shirley)	72153	
Egypt	72427	
El Dorado	71730-731, 71768	
Goodwin Field	71730	
Lisbon	71730	
Newell	71730	
Old Union	71730	
Quinn	71730	
Ritchie	71730	
Rock Island Quarters	71730	
Sandyland	71730	
Shuler	71730	
Urbana	71768	
El Paso	72045	
Elaine	72333	
Elizabeth	72531	
Elk Ranch	72632	
(Eureka Springs)		
Elkins	72727	
Ellison (Sherrill)	72152	
Elm (Amity)	71921	
Elm Springs	72728, 72762	

Emanuel (Almyra)	72003	
Emerson	71740	
Emmet	71835	
Empire (Parkdale)	71661	
Enders (Quitman)	72131	
Endoka (Eudora)	71640	
England	72046	
English (Altheimer)	72004	
Enola	72047	
Enright (Searcy)	72143	
Erbie (Dogpatch)	72648	
Erwin (Des Arc)	72040, 72112	
Estes (England)	72046	
Ethel	72048	
Etowah	72428	
Euclid Heights	71901	
(Hot Springs National Park)		
Eudora	71640	
Eureka Springs	72632	
Evansville	72729	
Evelyn Hills	72701	
(Fayetteville)		
Evening Shade	72532	
Everton	72633	
Excelsior (Greenwood)	72936	
Fair Oaks (Wynne)	72397	
Fairbanks (Quitman)	72131	
Fairfield (Little Rock)	72209	
Fairfield Bay	72088, 72153	
Shirley	72088	
Fairindale (Carthage)	71725	
Fairview	71653, 71701	
	71763, 72086, 72634	
(Lake Village)		
Falcon (Buckner)	71827	
Falls Chapel (Lockesburg)	71846	
Fancy Hill (Caddo Gap)	71935	
Farelly Lake (Stuttgart)	72160	
Fargo (Brinkley)	72021	
Farmington	72730	
Farmville (Warren)	71671	
Fayetteville	72701-704	
Baldwin	72701	
Black Oak	72701	
Crosses	72701	
Durham	72701	
Evelyn Hills	72701	
Habberton	72701	
Harmon	72701	
Harris	72701	
Hicks	72701	
Mayfield	72701	
Savoy	72701	
Sulphur City	72701	
Wedington	72701	
Wyman	72701	
Felsenthal (Huttig)	71747	
Fendley (Amity)	71921	
Fenter (Traskwood)	72167	
Ferda (England)	72046	
Ferguson Crossroads	71837	
(Fouke)		
Ferndale	72208	
Fifty Six	72533	
Figure Five (Van Buren)	72956	
Fisher	72429	
Fitzgerald (Newport)	72112	
Fitzhugh (Augusta)	72006	
Flag (Leslie)	72645	
Flat Rock (London)	72847	
Flippin	72634	

Floral	72534	
Florence (Monticello)	71655	
Floyd (Searcy)	72143	
Fomby (Ashdown)	71822	
Fordyce	71742	
Foreman	71836	
Forest Grove (Taylor)	71861	
Forest Park (Little Rock)	72207	
Formosa (Clinton)	72031	
Forrest City	72335	
Fort Chaffee	72901, 72905	
(Fort Smith)		
Fort Hill (Fountain Hill)	71642	
Fort Lynn (Fouke)	71837	
Fort Smith	72901-046	
	72913-914, 72916-919	
Bonanza	72916	
Fort Chaffee	72901, 72905	
South Fort Smith	72906	
Forty Four (Calico Rock)	72519	
Forum (Huntsville)	72740	
Fouke	71837	
Fountain Hill	71642	
Fountain Lake	71901	
(Hot Springs National Park)		
Fountain Prairie	71646	
(Hamburg)		
Four Mile Corner	72040	
(Des Arc)		
Fourche (Bigelow)	72016	
Fourmile Hill (Searcy)	72143	
Fox	72051	
Franklin	72512, 72536	
Horseshoe Bend	72512	
Free Hope (Magnolia)	71753	
Frenchmans Bayou	72338	
Friendship	71860, 71942	
(Stamps)		
Friley (Pettigrew)	72752	
Frog Town (Hartford)	72938	
Fulton	71838	
Furlow (Lonoke)	72086	
Gaines Landing	71653	
(Lake Village)		
Galla Rock (Atkins)	72823	
Gallitin (Siloam Springs)	72761	
Galloway	72117	
(North Little Rock)		
Gamaliel	72537	
Gardner (Strong)	71765	
Garfield	72732	
Garland City	71839	
Garland Springs	72111	
(Mount Vernon)		
Garlandville (Prescott)	71857	
Garner	72052	
Garrett Bridge (Dumas)	71639	
Gassville	72635	
Gaston (Mount Ida)	71957	
Gateway	72733	
Geneva (De Queen)	71832	
Genevia (College Station)	72053	
Genoa	71840	
Gentry	72734	
Georgetown	72143, 72773	
	72847	
(Searcy)		
Gepp	72538	
Geridge (England)	72046	
Gethsemane (Altheimer)	72004	
Gibbs (Sims)	71969	

Mays Mission 72545
   (Heber Springs)
Maysville 72747
Mazarn (Bonnerdale) 71933
Mc Almont 72117
   (North Little Rock)
Mc Arthur (Mc Gehee) 71654
Mc Caskill 71847
Mc Clelland (Augusta) 72006
Mc Crory 72101, 72189
   Grays 72101
   Hillemann 72101
   Morton 72101
   Overcup 72101
   Pumpkin Bend 72101
   Riverside 72101
   Wiville 72101
Mc Dougal 72441
Mc Gehee 71654, 71666
   Duce 71666
   Masonville 71654
   Mcarthur 71654
   Possum Fork 71666
   Rohwer 71666
   Trippe 71654
Mc Gintytown (Greenbrier) 72058
Mc Jester (Pangburn) 72121
Mc Kamie (Stamps) 71860
Mc Kinney (Warren) 71671
Mc Milan Corner 71653
   (Lake Village)
Mc Nab (Fulton) 71838
Mc Neil 71752
Mc Rae 72102
Melbourne 72556
Mellwood 72367
Mena 71953
Menifee 72107
Menos (Mena) 71953
Meridian (Crossett) 71635
Meroney (Gould) 71643
Merrivale (Little Rock) 72204
Metalton (Berryville) 72616
Mid America 71913
   (Hot Springs National Park)
Middleton (Center Ridge) .. 72027
Midland 72945
Midway 71845, 71941, 72651
   (Lewisville)
Midway Corner (Proctor) ... 72376
Milford (Lockesburg) 71846
Millers Bluff (Louann) 71751
Milltown (Greenwood) 72936
Milo (Hamburg) 71646
Mineral (Gillham) 71841
Mineral Springs 71851
Minturn 72445
Mist (Hamburg) 71646
Mitchellville (Dumas) 71639
Moko 72557
Monette 72447
Monkey Run (Gassville) 72635
Monroe 72108
Monte Ne (Rogers) 72756
Monticello 71655, 71565
Montongo (Monticello) 71655
Montrose 71658
Moore (Pelsor) 72856
Morganton (Bee Branch) ... 72013
Morning Star 71901, 72650
Morning Sun (Searcy) 72ᵢ43

Moro 72368
Morobay (Jersey) 71651
Morrilton 72110
Morrow 72749
Morton (Mc Crory) 72101
Moscow 71659
Mossville (Jasper) 72641
Mount Gayler (Winslow) 72959
Mount Hersey 72685
   (Western Grove)
Mount Holly 71758
Mount Ida 71957
Mount Judea 72655
Mount Moriah 71958
   (Murfreesboro)
Mount Olive (Hermitage) ... 71647
Mount Pisgah (Searcy) 72143
Mount Pleasant 72561
Mount Sherman (Jasper) ... 72641
Mount Tabor (Monticello) .. 71655
Mount Vernon 72111
Mountain Fork (Mena) 71953
Mountain Home 72121, 72653
   (Pangburn)
Mountain Pine 71956
Mountain Top (Ozark) 72949
Mountain Valley 71901
   (Hot Springs National Park)
Mountain View 72533, 72560
   (Fifty Six)
   Hanover 72560
Mountainburg 72946
Mozart (Fox) 72051
Muddyfork (Nashville) 71852
Mulberry 72947
Murfreesboro 71958
Murphys Corner (Newport) 72112
Mustin Lake (Camden) 71701
Nady (Tichnor) 72166
Nail (Deer) 72628
Nashville 71852
Nathan (Nashville) 71852
Natural Dam 72948
Natural Steps (Roland) 72135
Naylor (Vilonia) 72173
Neal Springs (Horatio) 71842
Nebo (Star City) 71667
Needmore (Waldron) 72958
New Augusta (Augusta) 72006
New Blaine 72851
New Dixie (Bigelow) 72016
New Edinburg 71660
New Gascony (Altheimer) . 72004
New London (Strong) 71765
New Salme (Augusta) 72006
New Summit (Bauxite) 72011
Newark 72562
Newell (El Dorado) 71730
Newhope 71959
Newnata (Timbo) 72680
Newport 72112
Newtown (Altheimer) 72004
Nimrod (Perryville) 72126
Noble Lake (Pine Bluff) 71601
Nola (Gravelly) 72838
Norfork 72658-659
   Old Joe 72658
Norman 71960
Norphlet 71759
Norristown (Russellville) ... 72801
North (Crossett) 71635

North Bingen (Nashville) ... 71852
North Brinkley (Brinkley) ... 72021
North Cedar (Pine Bluff) ... 71601
North Crossett (Crossett) .. 71635
North Lewisville 71845
   (Lewisville)
North Little Rock
   ... 72100, 72113-120, 72124,
   72190, 72199
   Baucum 72117
   Blue Hill 72118
   Booker 72117
   Cato 72116
   Crystal Hill 72118
   Galloway 72117
   Gibson 72116
   Jeffery 72118
   Main Street 72119
   Marche 72117
   Maumelle 72113
   Maumelle 72118
   Mcalmont 72117
   Oak Grove 72118
   Park Hill 72116
   Rixey 72117
   Rose City 72117
   Sherwood 72116-72117
   Sylvan Hills 72116
   West Marche 72118
Northpoint (Roland) 72135
Nunley (Mena) 71953
O Kean 72449
Oak Grove 71665, 71846
   .... 72104, 72118, 72660
   (Rison)
   Oakgrove 72660
Oak Park (Pine Bluff) 71603
Oakgrove 72070, 72660
   (Houston)
Oakhaven (Hope) 71801
Oakland 72661
Oaklawn 71901
   (Hot Springs National Park)
Oark 72852
Oden 71961, 71966
   Huddleston 71961
   Pine Ridge 71966
   Whitetown 71961
Ogden 71853
Ogemaw (Stephens) 71764
Oil Trough 72564
Okean (O Kean) 72449
Okolona 71962
Ola 72853
Old Alabam (Huntsville) 72740
Old Austin (Austin) 72007
Old Grand Glaise 72020
   (Bradford)
Old Hickory (Hattieville) 72063
Old Joe (Norfork) 72658
Old Milo (Hamburg) 71646
Old Union (El Dorado) 71730
Olmstead (Jacksonville) 72076
Olyphant (Bradford) 72020
Oma (Pearcy) 71964
Omaha 72662
Onda (West Fork) 72774
Oneida 72369
Onia 72663
Onyx (Plainview) 72857
Opal 71932, 72012

31

(Board Camp)
Oppelo (Morrilton) 72110
Orion (Redfield) 72132
Orlando (New Edinburg) ... 71660
Osage (Green Forest) 72638
Osceola 72370
Otto (Vilonia) 72173
Ouachita (Sparkman) 71763
Overcup 72101, 72110
(Mc Crory)
Owensville (Lonsdale) 72087
Oxford 72565
Oxley (Leslie) 72645
Ozan 71855
Ozark 72949
Ozark Lithia 71901
(Hot Springs National Park)
Ozone 72854
Pace City (Louann) 71751
Palestine 72372
Palmer (Holly Grove) 72069
Palmyra (Star City) 71667
Pangburn 72121
Pankey (Little Rock) 72207
Pansy (Rison) 71665
Panther Forest 71653
(Lake Village)
Paragould 72439, 72450-451
(Light)
Center Hill 72450
Light 72450
Stonewall 72450
Paraloma (Lockesburg) 71846
Paris 72855
Park Hill 72116
(North Little Rock)
Parkdale 71661
Parkin 72373
Parks 72950
Parma (Edgemont) 72044
Parnell (Cabot) 72023
Paron 72122
Partee (Magnolia) 71753
Parthenon 72666
Pastoria (Sherrill) 72152
Patmos (Hope) 71801
Patrick (Elkins) 72727
Patsville (Hermitage) 71647
Patterson 72123
Payne (Strong) 71765
Payneway (Trumann) 72472
Pea Ridge 72751
Peach Orchard 72453
Pearcy 71964
Pearson (Quitman) 72131
Peel 72668
Pelsor 72856
Pencil Bluff 71965
Pendleton (Dumas) 71639
Pennington (Amagon) 72005
Pennys (Lockesburg) 71846
Perla (Malvern) 72104
Perry 72125
Perrytown (Hope) 71801
Perryville 72126
Pettigrew 72752
Pettus (Lonoke) 72086
Philadelphia (Magnolia) 71753
Pickens 71662, 72143
Gourd 71662
Tyro 71662

Piercetown (Jasper) 72641
Piggott 72454
Pike (Delight) 71940
Pindall 72669
Pine Bluff 71601-603
.... 71611, 71613
Arsenal 71601
Dollarway 71602
Hardin 71601
Hooker 71601
Jefferson Square 71601
Ladd 71601
Leitner 71601
Noble Lake 71601
North Cedar 71601
Oak Park 71603
Pinecrest 71601
South Pine Bluff 71601
Sulphur Springs 71601
Wampler 71601
West End 71601
White Hall 71601-71602
Pine City (Holly Grove) 72069
Pine Grove (Sparkman) 71763
Pine Ridge (Oden) 71966
Pinecrest (Pine Bluff) 71601
Pineville 72566
Piney 71901, 72847
(Hot Springs National Park)
Piney Grove 71845, 71940
(Lewisville)
Pinnacle (Roland) 72135
Pisgah (Delight) 71940
Plainfield (Emerson) 71740
Plainview 72081, 72857
(Judsonia)
Aly 72857
Hollis 72857
Onyx 72857
Steve 72857
Plant (Clinton) 72031
Pleasant Grove ... 72030, 72567
(Cleveland)
Pleasant Hill 71857, 71901
(Prescott)
Pleasant Hills (Onia) 72663
Pleasant Plains 72568
Pleasant Valley ... 71826, 72058
(Bradley)
Pleasure Heights (Lowell) . 72745
Plum Bayou (Wright) 72182
Plumerville 72127
Plunketts (Biscoe) 72017
Pocahontas 72455, 72478
Dalton 72455
Point Cedar (Amity) 71921
Pollard 72456
Ponca 72670
Pontoon (Casa) 72025
Poplar Grove 72374
Portia 72457
Portland 71663
Possum Fork (Mc Gehee) . 71666
Possum Grape (Bradford) . 72020
Potter (Mena) 71953
Pottsville 72858
Poughkeepsie 72569
Powhatan 72458
Poyen 72128
Prague (Sheridan) 72150
Prairie Creek (Hartford) 72938

Prairie Grove 72753
Prairie View (Scranton) 72863
Prattsville 72129
Prescott 71857
Preston (Conway) 72032
Preston Ferry (Roe) 72134
Price 71901
(Hot Springs National Park)
Prim 72130
Princeton (Carthage) 71725
Process City (De Queen) .. 71832
Proctor 72376
Providence (Judsonia) 72081
Provo (Lockesburg) 71846
Pruitt (Dogpatch) 72648
Pullman (De Queen) 71832
Pumpkin Bend (Mc Crory) . 72101
Purdy (Huntsville) 72740
Pyatt 72672
Quinn (El Dorado) 71730
Quitman 72131
Ramsey (Fordyce) 71742
Randall (Rison) 71665
Ratcliff 72951
Ravenden 72459
Ravenden Springs 72460
Raymond (Holly Grove) 72069
Rea Valley (Flippin) 72634
Reader (Chidester) 71726
Readland (Eudora) 71640
Rector 72461
Red Fork (Watson) 71674
Red Leaf (Lake Village) 71653
Red Oak 71901
(Hot Springs National Park)
Red Springs (Gurdon) 71743
Red Star (Pettigrew) 72752
Red Wing (De Queen) 71832
Redemption (Bigelow) 72016
Redfield 72132
Redland (Prescott) 71857
Reed (Tillar) 71670
Reedville (Dumas) 71639
Relfs Bluff (Star City) 71667
Remmel (Newport) 72112
Rena (Van Buren) 72956
Republican (Greenbrier) ... 72058
Revel (Augusta) 72006
Rex (Clinton) 72031
Reydell 72133
Reyno 72462
Rhea (Lincoln) 72744
Rich (Brinkley) 72021
Richland (Little Rock) 72206
Richmond (Ashdown) 71822
Richwood (Arkadelphia) 71923
Rio Vista (Bald Knob) 72010
Rison 71665
Ritchie (El Dorado) 71730
River Mountain (Delaware) . 72835
Riverside (Mc Crory) 72101
Rivervale 72377
Riverview (Morrilton) 72110
Rixey (North Little Rock) ... 72117
Rob Roy (Altheimer) 72004
Robertsville 72063
(Hattieville)
Robinson (Siloam Springs) . 72761
Rock Hill (Lockesburg) 71846
Rock Island Junction 71647
(Hermitage)

Rock Island Quarters 71730
(El Dorado)
Rock Springs (Wilmar) 71675
Rockport (Malvern) 72104
Rocky (Mena) 71953
Rocky Mound 71753
(Magnolia) 71801, 71837
Roe 72134
Rogen (Rogers) 72756, 72758
Rogers 72756-757
Brightwater 72756
Clifty 72756
Larue 72756
Little Flock 72756
Monte Ne 72756
Rogen 72756
Rohwer (Mc Gehee) 71666
Roland 72135
Rolla (Malvern) 72104
Romance 72136
Rosboro (Amity) 71921
Rose Bud 72137
Rose City 72117
(North Little Rock)
Rose Meadow (Little Rock) 72206
Roseland (Manila) 72442
Rosie 72571
Rosston 71858
Round Mountain (Casa) 72025
Round Pond 72394
Rover 72828, 72860
Briggsville 72828
Rowell (Rison) 71665
Roy (Nashville) 71852
Royal 71968
Royal Oak (Mabelvale) 72103
Rudd (Berryville) 72616
Rudy 72952
Rule (Green Forest) 72638
Rumley (Leslie) 72645
Rupert (Clinton) 72031
Rushing (Shirley) 72153
Russell 72139
Russellville 72801, 72811
Norristown 72801
Ryan (England) 72046
Rye (Rison) 71665
Saffell 72572
Sage 72573
Saginaw (Donaldson) 71941
Saint Charles 72140
Saint Francis 72464
Saint Joe 72675
Saint Paul 72760
Salado 72575
Salem 71943, 72576
(Glenwood)
Byron 72576
Saline (Kingsland) 71652
Saltillo (Conway) 72032
Salus (Ozone) 72854
Sand Hill (Des Arc) 72040
Sandtown (Morrilton) 72110
Sandy Bend (Strong) 71765
Sandyland (El Dorado) 71730
Saratoga 71859
Sardis (Bauxite) 72011
Savoy (Fayetteville) 72701
Sayre (Chidester) 71726
Schaal (Mineral Springs) ... 71851
Scotland 72141

Scott 72142
Scranton 72863
Screeton (Hazen) 72064
Searcy 72143, 72145, 72149
Seaton (England) 72046
Sedgwick 72465
Selma (Tillar) 71670
Shady Grove 71857, 72205
(Prescott)
Shannon (Grady) 71644
Shannon Hills (Mabelvale) 72103
Sharman (Stamps) 71860
Shell Lake (Heth) 72346
Sheppard (Fulton) 71838
Sheridan 72150
Sherrill 72152
Sherwood 72116-117
(North Little Rock)
Sherwood Hills 72105
(Jones Mills)
Shiloh (Buckner) 71827, 71851
Shirley 72088, 72153
(Fairfield Bay)
Eglantine 72153
Fairfield Bay 72153
Lexington 72153
Rushing 72153
Shives (Lake Village) 71653
Shover Springs (Hope) 71801
Shuler (El Dorado) 71730
Sidney 72577
Sidon (Rose Bud) 72137
Siloam Springs 72761
Silver (Mount Ida) 71957
Silver Ridge (Lockseburg) . 71846
Sims 71969
Skunkhollow (Conway) 72032
Slovac (Stuttgart) 72160
Smackover 71762
Smale (Brinkley) 72021
Smearney (Hermitage) 71647
Smithton (Gurdon) 71743
Smithville 72466
Snow Hill (Louann) 71751
Snow Lake 72379
Snyder (Montrose) 71658
Social Hill (Malvern) 72104
Solgohachia 72156
Sondra (Springdale) 72764
South Crossett (Crossett) .. 71635
South Fort Smith 72906
(Fort Smith)
South Hot Springs 71901
(Hot Springs National Park)
South Pine Bluff 71601
(Pine Bluff)
South Sheridan (Sheridan) 72150
South Side (Little Rock) 72206
Southside (Bee Branch) 72013
Sparkman 71763
Spirit Lake (Lewisville) 71845
Spotville (Magnolia) 71753
Spring Hill (Hope) 71801
Springdale 72762, 72764-766
Bethel Heights 72764
Elm Springs 72762
Sondra 72764
Tontitown 72762
Springfield 72157
Springhill (Greenbrier) 72058
Springtown 72734, 72767

(Gentry)
Stamps 71860
Star City 71667
State Capitol 72201
(Little Rock)
State Line 71740, 71861
(Emerson)
Staves (Rison) 71665
Stephens 71764
Steprock 72159
Steve (Plainview) 72857
Stevens Creek (Bald Knob) 72010
Stonewall (Paragould) 72450
Stony Point 72012, 72070
(Beebe)
Story 71970
Strawberry 72469
Strickler (West Fork) 72774
Stringtown (Horatio) 71842
Strong 71765
Sturkie 72578
Stuttgart 72160
Subiaco 72865
Success 72470
Sugar Grove (Booneville) .. 72927
Sugar Hill (Lincoln) 72744
Sulphur City 72701
(Fayetteville)
Sulphur Rock 72579
Sulphur Springs 71601, 72768
(Pine Bluff)
Summers 72769
Summit 72677
Sumpter (Hermitage) 71647
Sunny Hill (Searcy) 72143
Sunnydale (Steprock) 72159
Sunset (Winslow) 72959
Sunshine 71661, 71968
(Parkdale)
Sutton (Emmet) 71835
Swan Lake (Altheimer) 72004
Sweden (Altheimer) 72004
Sweet Home 72164
Swifton 72471
Sycamore (Gurdon) 71743
Sylvan Hills 72116
(North Little Rock)
Sylvania (Ward) 72176
Tafton (Wrightsville) 72183
Tamo (Grady) 71644
Tarry (Star City) 71667
Tate (Booneville) 72927
Taylor 71861
Tennessee (Monticello) 71655
Terrytown (Little Rock) 72206
Texarkana 75502
Thebes (Montrose) 71658
Thida 72165
Thornburg (Perryville) 72126
Thornton 71766
Tichnor 72166
Tillar 71670
Tilly 72679
Timbo 72657, 72680
Newnata 72680
Tinsman (Hampton) 71767
Tobin (Delight) 71940
Tokio (Nashville) 71852
Toledo (Rison) 71665
Tollette 71851
(Mineral Springs)

33

Tollville 72041
  (De Valls Bluff)
Toltec (Scott) 72142
Tomato 72381
Tomberlin (England) 72046
Toneyville (Jacksonville) ... 72076
Tontitown 72762, 72770
  (Springdale)
Traskwood 72167
Trippe (Mc Gehee) 71654
Troy (Stephens) 71764
Trumann 72472
Tucker 72168
Tuckerman 72473
Tukertown (Burdette) 72321
Tulip (Carthage) 71725
Tull (Benton) 72015
Tumbling Shoals 72581
Tupelo 72169
Turner 72383
Turrell 72384
Tuttle (Elkins) 72727
Twentythree (Bald Knob) .. 72010
Twin Groves (Damascus) .. 72039
Twin Springs 72205
  (Little Rock)
Twist 72385
Tyro (Pickens) 71662
Tyronza 72386
Ua Monticello 71655
  (Monticello)
Ulm 72170
Umpire 71971
Union (Strong) 71765, 71832
Unionhill (Bradford) 72020
Uniontown 72955
Urbana (El Dorado) 71768
Urbanette (Berryville) 72616
Valley Springs 72682
Van Buren 72956
Vandervoort 71972
Vanity Corner (Searcy) 72143
Vanndale 72387
Vaughn (Bentonville) 72712
Velie (Camden) 71701
Velvet Ridge (Bald Knob) .. 72010
Vendor 72683
Verona (Bruno) 72618
Vick (Hermitage) 71647
Village 71769
Vilonia 72173
Vimy Ridge (Alexander) 72002
Viola 72583
Violet Hill 72584
Wabash 72389
Wabbaseka 72175
Walcott 72474
Waldenburg 72475
Waldo 71770
Waldron (Bates) 72924, 72958
    Cauthron 72958

Hon 72958
Needmore 72958
Winfield 72958
Walker (Magnolia) ..71753, 72143
Walkers Creek (Taylor) 71861
Walkerville (Emerson) 71740
Wallace (Foreman) 71836
Walnut Grove 71822, 72031
  (Ashdown)
Walnut Hill (Bradley) 71826
Walnut Ridge 72476
Walnut Springs (Horatio) .. 71842
Waltreak (Danville) 72833
Wampler (Pine Bluff) 71601
Wampoo (England) 72046
Ward 72176
Warm Springs 72478
Warner (Camden) 71701
Warren 71671
Washburn (Greenwood) 72936
Washington 71862
Waterloo (Rosston) 71858
Watkins (Searcy) 72143
Watson 71674
Wattensaw (Lonoke) 72086
Waveland 72842, 72867
  (Havana)
Wayton (Deer) 72628
Weathers (Kingston) 72742
Webb City (Ozark) 72949
Wedington (Fayetteville) ... 72701
Weiner 72479
Welcome (Taylor) 71861
Wesley 72773
Wesley Chapel (Morrilton) . 72110
West Bauxite (Bauxite) 72011
West Camden Heights 71701
  (Camden)
West Crossett (Crossett) ... 71635
West End (Pine Bluff) 71601
West Fork 72774
West Gum Springs 71923
  (Arkadelphia)
West Hartford (Hartford) 72938
West Helena 72390
West Marche 72118
  (North Little Rock)
West Memphis 72301, 72303
West Otis (De Queen) 71832
West Point 72178
West Ridge 72391
Western Grove 72685
Westside (Little Rock) 72211
Wheatley 72392
Wheeler 72775
Whelen Springs 71772
Whipple (Bee Branch) 72013
White (Crossett) 71635
White Hall 71601-602
  (Pine Bluff)
Whitecliffs (Lockesburg) 71846

Whiterock (Mulberry) 72947
Whitetown (Oden) 71961
Whiteville (Gassville) 72635
Wickes 71973
Wideman 72585
Widener 72394
Wiederkehr Village 72821
  (Altus)
Wilburn 72179
Williams Junction 72126
  (Perryville)
Williamson (Horatio) 71842
Williford 72482
Willisville 71864
Willow (Leola) 72084
Willow Creek (Bee Branch) 72013
Wilmar 71675
Wilmot 71676
Wilson 72395, 72823
Wilton 71865
Winchester 71677
Winfield (Waldron) 72958
Winslow 72959
Winthrop 71866
Wiseman 72587
Witcherville (Huntington) ... 72940
Witherspoon (Arkadelphia) 71923
Witter 72776
Witts Springs 72686
Wiville (Mc Crory) 72101
Wolf Bayou (Drasco) 72530
Woodberry (Hampton) 71744
Woodland Heights 72207
  (Little Rock)
Woodrow (Prim) 72130
Woodson 72180
Woolsey (West Fork) 72774
Wooster 72181
Worden (Bald Knob) 72010
Wright 72182
Wrightsville 72183
Wye (Bigelow) 72016
Wyman (Fayetteville) 72701
Wynne 72396-397
  Fair Oaks 72397
Yale (Pettigrew) 72752
Yancopin (Watson) 71674
Yardelle (Western Grove) .. 72685
Yellville 72687
Yocana (Mena) 71953
Yorktown 71678
Yukon (Winchester) 71677
Zent (Brinkley) 72021
Zinc (Harrison) 72601
Zion (Melbourne) 72556

BRADY

HOSPITALS

Baptist Medical Center
9601 I 630 Exit 7 72205

LITTLE ROCK

BUILDINGS

Federal Building
700 W Capitol Ave 72201

Post Office Building.
600 W Capitol Ave 72201

Pulaski Co Courthouse
401 W Markham St 72201

State Capitol Building
1 State Capitol 72201

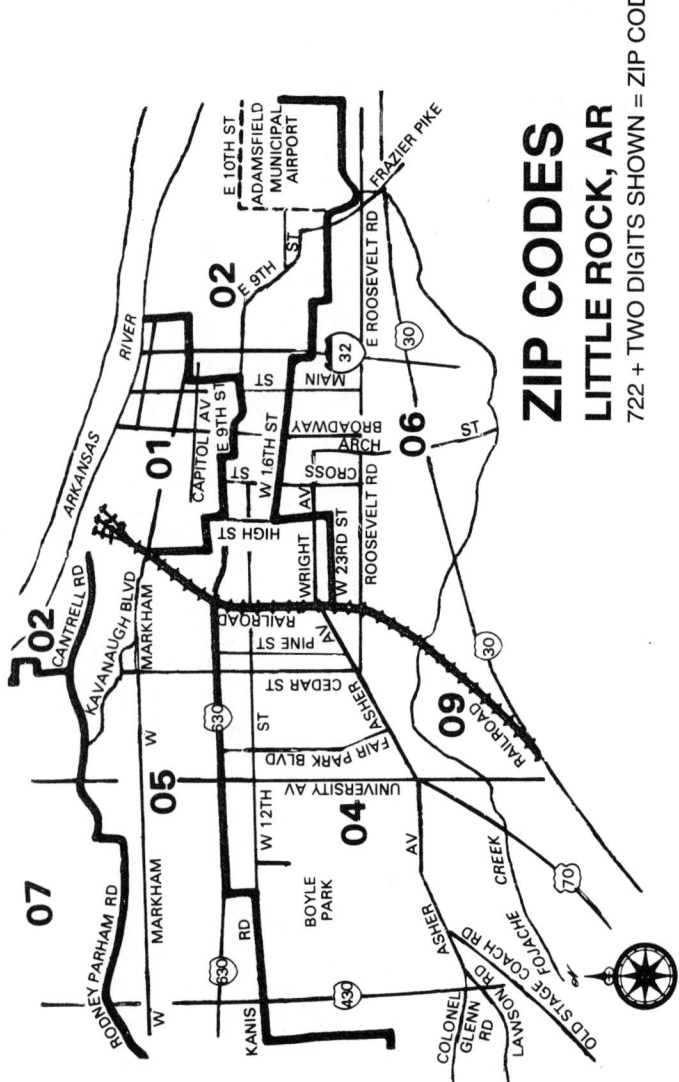

ZIP CODES
LITTLE ROCK, AR
722 + TWO DIGITS SHOWN = ZIP CODE

Butte Creek (Chico) 95926
Butte Meadows 95942
(Forest Ranch)
Buttonwillow 93206
Byron (Discovery Bay) 94514
C S U Dom Hls (Carson) ... 90747
C South U Long Beach 90840
(Long Beach)
CA State DMV 95894
Cabazon 92230, 92282
Cabazon Indian Res 92201
(Indio)
Cable Data (Sacramento) . 95873
Cabrillo (Long Beach) 90810
Cadiz 92319
Cain Ranch (Lee Vining) .. 93541
Cairns Corner (Lindsay) 93247
Cajon Junction 92407
(San Bernardino)
Cal Poly Student Dorms 93410
(San Luis Obispo)
Cal Poly University 93407
(San Luis Obispo)
Cal State Univ Dom Hills ... 90747
(Carson)
Cal Tech (Pasadena) .. 91125-126
Calabasas .. 91302, 91372, 91399
Hidden Hills 91302
Monte Nido 91302
Woodland Hills 91302, 91372
Calabasas Hills 91301
(Agoura Hills)
Caldors Corner 93312
(Bakersfield)
Calexico 92231-232
Mount Signal 92231
Caliente 93518
California City 93504-505
California Conservation Ctr 96130
(Susanville)
California Correctional Inst 93561
(Tehachapi)
California Hot Springs 93207
California Pines 96101
(Alturas)
California State University
(Northridge) 91330, 92096
California Valley 93453
(Santa Margarita)
California Water Service ... 95194
(San Jose)
Calimesa 92320
Calipatria 92233
Calistoga 94515
Callahan 96014
Calpella 95418
Calpine 96124
Calwa (Fresno) 93725, 93745
Camanche Lake (Ione) 95640
Camarillo 93010-012
Cambria 93428
Cameron Park 95682
(Shingle Springs)
Camino 95709
Camp Connell (Arnold) 95223
Camp Meeker 95419
Camp Nelson 93208
Camp Pendleton 92055
Camp Richardson 96156
(South Lake Tahoe)
Camp Roberts (San Miguel) 93451

Campbell 95008-009, 95011
Campo 91906, 91987
Campo Seco 95226
Camptonville 95922
Campus Crusade For Christ
(San Bernardino)
.... 92414, 92424
Canby 96015
Canoga Park 91303-309
Bell Canyon 91307
Box Canyon 91304
West Hills 91304
.... 91307-91308
Woodland Hills 91303
Cantil 93519
Cantua Creek 93608
Canyon 94516
Canyon Country 91351, 91386
Santa Clarita ... 91351, 91386
Canyon Crest (Riverside) .. 92507
Canyon Lake (Sun City) ... 92587
Canyondam 95923
Capay 95607
Cape Horn (Colfax) 95713
Capistrano Beach 92624
Capitola 95010
Carbondale (Ione) 95640
Cardiff 92007
Cardiff By The Sea 92007
Caribou (Belden) 95915
Carlotta 95528
Carlsbad 92008-009, 92018
Carmel 93921-923
Carmel By The Sea 93921
(Carmel)
Carmel Highlands (Carmel) 93923
Carmel Valley 93924
Carmel Valley Village 93924
(Carmel Valley)
Carmet (Bodega Bay) 94923
Carmichael 95608-609
Carnelian Bay 96140
Carpinteria 93013-014
Carson . 90745-47, 90749, 90810
C S U Dom Hls 90747
Long Beach 90749
Cartago (Olancha) 93549
Carter Hawley Hale 91841
(Alhambra)
Caruthers 93609
Casa Blanca (Riverside) ... 92504
Caseys-carnation 90665
(Pico Rivera)
Casmalia 93429
Caspar 95420
Cassel 96016
Castaic 91310, 91384
Santa Clarita ... 91310, 91384
Castella 96017
Castle Air Force Base 95342
Castro Valley 94546, 94552
Hayward 94546, 94552
Castroville 95012
Catalina (Avalon) 90704
Cathedral City 92234-235
Catheys Valley 95306
Cayucos 93430
Cazadero 95421
Cedar (Lancaster) 93534
Cedar Flat 96140
(Carnelian Bay)

Cedar Glen 92321
Cedar Grove (Camino) 95709
Cedar Ravine 95667
(Placerville)
Cedar Ridge 95924
Cedarpines Park 92322
Cedarville 96104
Center Ave 92605
(Huntington Beach)
Centerville (Sanger) 93657
Central Valley (Shasta Lake)
.... 96019, 96079
Century City 90067
(Los Angeles)
Ceres 95307
Cerritos (Artesia) ... 90701, 90703
Chalfant (Bishop) 93514
Challenge 95925
Chambless (Cadiz) 92319
Chapmantown (Chico) 95926
Charter Oak (Covina) 91724
Chatsworth 91311-313
Deluxe Check Printers 91312
Chemehuevi (Needles) 92363
Chemehuevi Valley 92363
(Needles)
Cherokee (Nevada City)
.... 95959, 95965
Cherry Valley (Beaumont) . 92223
Chester 96020
Chicago Park 95712
Chico .. 95926-929, 95973, 95976
Blue Shield Of Cal 95976
Butte Creek 95926
CSU Chico 95929
Chapmantown 95926
Cohasset 95926
Dayton 95926
Midtown 95928
Nord 95926
Chico Vecino (Chico) 95926
Chilcoot 96105
Childeth U South A 91370
(Woodland Hills)
China Lake (Ridgecrest)
.... 93555-556
Chinese Camp 95309
Chino 91708-710
Chino Hills 91709
Chiriaco Smt (Indio) 92201
Chiriaco Summit (Indio) 92201
Cholame (Shandon) 93461
Chowchilla 93610
Christian Valley (Auburn) .. 95602
Chualar 93925
Chula Vista 91909-915
Cima 92323
Cisco (Soda Springs) 95728
Citrus Heights . 95610-611, 95621
City Hall 92418
(San Bernardino)
City Light And Water 92522
(Riverside)
City Of Commerce (Los Angeles)
.... 90040, 90091
City Of Industry 91714-716
... 91744-746, 91748, 91899
Claremont 91711
Clarksburg 95612
Clay (Herald) 95638
Clayton 94517

(Susanville)	
Eagle Mountain	92239
(Desert Center)	
Eagle Rock (Los Angeles)	90041
Eagle Tree (Walnut Grove)	95690
Eagleville	96110
Earlimart	93219
Earp	92242
East Bakersfield	93305
(Bakersfield)	
East Bay Mun Util D	94649
(Oakland)	
East Blythe (Blythe)	92225
East Gridley (Gridley)	95948
East Guernewood	95446
(Guerneville)	
East Highland (Highland)	92346
East Irvine	92650
East Long Beach	90804
(Long Beach)	
East Los Angeles	90022
(Los Angeles)	
East Nicolaus	95622
East Orosi (Orosi)	93647
East Palo Alto	94303
(Palo Alto)	
East Quincy (Quincy)	95971
East Rancho Dominguez	90221
(Compton)	
Easton (Fresno)	93706
Echo Lake	95721
Echo Park (Los Angeles)	90026
Eden Valley (Colfax)	95713
Edendale (Los Angeles)	90026
Edgewood (Weed)	96094
Edison	93220
Edward (Edwards)	93523-524
Edwards	93523-524
Aerial Acres	93523
Edward	93523-93524
North Edwards	93523
Edwards Air Force Base	
(Edwards)	93523-524
Eight Mile House (Camino)	95709
El Bonita (Guerneville)	95446
El Cajon	92019-022, 92090
Bostonia	92021
Crest	92021
Travel Lodge	92090
El Centro	92243-244
El Centro Naval Air	92243
(El Centro)	
El Cerrito	94530
El Dorado	95623
El Dorado Hills	95762
El Granada	94018
El Macero	95618
El Modena (Orange)	92669
El Monte	91731-735
Wells Fargo Bank	91735
El Nido	95317
El Portal	95318
El Segundo	90245
El Sereno (Los Angeles)	90032
El Sobrante	94803, 94820
Richmond	94803
Richmond	94820
El Toro (Foothill Ranch)	
	92610, 92630
El Toro M C A South	92709
(Irvine)	

El Toro Marine Corps Air	92709
(Irvine)	
El Verano	95433
Eldridge	95431
Electronic Data Systems	90398
(Inglewood)	
Elizabeth Lake	93532
(Lake Hughes)	
Elk	95432
Elk Creek	95939
Elk Grove	95624, 95758-759
Elkhorn Village	95605
(Broderick)	
Elmira	95625
Elverta	95626
Emandal (Willits)	95490
Emeryville	94608, 94662
Oakland	94608, 94662
Emigrant Gap	95715
Emigrant Trail	96120
(Markleeville)	
Empire	95319
Encinitas	92023-024
Leucadia	92024
Olivenhain	92024
Encino	91316, 91335, 91416
	91426, 91436
Van Nuys	91316, 91416
	91426, 91436
Equit Life Assc Soc	93759
(Fresno)	
Escalon	95320
Escondido	92025-027
	92029-030, 92033, 92046
Esparto (Capay)	
	95607, 95627, 95679
Essex	92332
Etiwanda	91739
(Rancho Cucamonga)	
Etna	96027
Eureka	95501-503, 95534
Cutten	95501
Exeter	93221
Fair Oaks	95628
Fairfax	94930, 94978
Manor	94930
Fairfield	94533, 94535, 94585
Fairmead (Chowchilla)	93610
Fairmont (Lancaster)	93534,536
Fairplay (Somerset)	95684
Fall River Mills	96028
Fallbrook	92028, 92088
Rainbow	92028
Fallen Leaf	96151
(South Lake Tahoe)	
Fallon (Petaluma)	94952
Fallsvale (Forest Falls)	92339
Far (Long Beach)	90888
Farmers Ins (Simi Valley)	93099
Farmers Ins Group	95343
(Merced)	
Farmers Market	90036
(Los Angeles)	
Farmersville	93223
Farmington	95230
Fawnskin	92333
Feather Falls	95940
Federal (Los Angeles)	
	90012-013, 92805
Federal Boxes	90053
(Los Angeles)	

Federal Home Loan Bank	
(Walnut)	91795, 94650
Felicity (Winterhaven)	92283
Fellows	93224
Felton	95018
Ferndale	95536
Fetters Hot Springs	95416
(Boyes Hot Springs)	
Fiddletown	95629
Fields Landing	95537
Fig Garden Village	93704
(Fresno)	
Fillmore	93015-016
Finley	95435
Firebaugh	93622
Fireman Fund Ins	94911
(San Rafael)	
Firemans Fund Ins Co	94998
(Novato)	
Firestone Park	90001
(Los Angeles)	
Firm Holdouts	94106
(San Francisco)	
First Chicago Service Corp	91189
(Pasadena)	
First Interstate Bancorp	93097
(Simi Valley)	
First Interstate Bank	
(Los Angeles)	90084, 94139
Fish Camp	93623
Five Brooks (Olema)	94950
Five Mile Terrace	95667
(Placerville)	
Five Points	93624
Flick Point	96140
(Carnelian Bay)	
Flint (Los Angeles)	90057
Flintridge	91011
(La Canada Flintridge)	
Floriston	96111
Flournoy	96029
Fluor Corp (Irvine)	92730
Focus On The Family	91799
(Pomona)	
Folsom	95630, 95671, 95762-63
Lake Natoma	95630
Mormon Island	95630
Pine Bluff	95630
White Rock	95630
Folsom Prison (Represa)	95671
Fontana	92334-337
Foothill Ranch	92610
Forbestown	95941
Forest City (Alleghany)	95910
Forest Falls	92339
Forest Knolls	94933
Forest Ranch	95942
Foresthill	95631
Forestville	95436
Forks Of Salmon	96031
Fort Baker (Sausalito)	94965
Fort Barry (Sausalito)	94965
Fort Bidwell	96112
Fort Bragg (Caspar)	
	95420, 95437, 95488
Cleone	95437
Inglenook	95437
Noyo	95437
Pine Grove	95437
Pudding Creek	95437
Redwood Lodge	95437

Sherwood Valley Rancheria .
.... 95437
Fort Cronkhite 94965
(Sausalito)
Fort Dick 95538
Fort Hunter Liggett 93928
(Jolon)
Fort Irwin 92310
Fort Jones 96032
Fort Macarthur 90731
(San Pedro)
Fort Ross (Jenner) 95450
Fortuna 95540
Foster City (San Mateo) 94404
Foundation Airborne Relief 90888
(Long Beach)
Fountain Valley 92708, 92728
Santa Ana 92708, 92728
Four Corners (Boron) 93516
Fouts Springs (Stonyford) . 95979
Fowler 93625
Foy (Los Angeles) 90017
Franchise Tax Board 95840
(Sacramento)
Frazier Park 93222, 93225
Pine Mountain Club 93222
Fredricksburg 96120
(Markleeville)
Freedom 95019
Freestone (Sebastopol) 95472
Fremont 94536-539, 94555
Fremont Valley (Mojave) .. 93501
French Camp 95231
French Corral 95977
(Smartville)
French Gulch 96033
Fresh Pond 95726
(Pollock Pines)
Fresno 93650, 93700-712
.... 93714-718, 93720-722
.... 93724-729, 93740-741
.... 93744-745, 93747, 93750
.... 93755, 93759-762
.... 93764-765, 93771-780
.... 93782, 93784, 93786
.... 93790-794, 93844, 93888
Aetna Life And Casualty 93765
Calwa 93725
Calwa 93745
Easton 93706
Equit Life Assc Soc 93759
Fig Garden Village 93704
Gottschalks 93780
Industrial Indemnity ... 93782
IRS 93844
Liberty Mutual 93784
Malaga 93725
Pacific Bell 93762
Pacific Gas And Elec .. 93760
Pinedale 93650
Rolinda 93706
United Faith Found 93761
Fresno Bee (Fresno) 93786
Fresno City College 93741
(Fresno)
Fresno City Utilities 93764
(Fresno)
Fresno State University 93740
(Fresno)
Friant 93626
Friendly Valley (Newhall) .. 91321

Frontera (Corona) 91720
Fruitridge (Sacramento) 95820
Fruitvale (Bakersfield) 93308
Fruto (Willows) 95988
Fuller Theological Semi 91182
(Pasadena)
Fullerton 92631-635
Commonwealth 92632
Orangehurst 92633
Sunny Hills 92635
Fulton 95439
Fulton Acres 96140
(Carnelian Bay)
Gallinas (San Rafael) 94903
Galt 95632
Ganser Bar (Belden) 95915
Garberville 95542
Garden Grove 92640-645
West Garden Grove 92645
Garden Valley 95633
Gardena 90247-249
Garey (Santa Maria) 93454
Garlock (Randsburg) 93554
Gasquet 95543
Gaviota (Goleta) 93117
Gazelle 96034
General Telephone 90313
(Inglewood)
Genesee (Taylorsville) 95983
Georgetown 95634
Gerber 96035
Geyserville 95441
Giant Forest 93262
(Sequoia National Park)
Gilman Hot Springs 92583
(San Jacinto)
Gilroy 95020-021
Glassell (Los Angeles) 90065
Glen Ellen 95442
Glenbrook Heights 95945
(Grass Valley)
Glencoe 95232
Glendale 91200-210, 91214
.... 91221-222, 91224-226
Glendale Galleria 91210
(Glendale)
Glendora 91740-741
Glenhaven 95443
Glenn 95943
Glennville 93226
Glenoaks (Burbank) 91504
Glenshire (Truckee) 96161
Goffs (Essex) 92332
Gold Hill (Placerville) 95667
Gold River 95670
(Rancho Cordova)
Gold Run 95717
Golden Hills (Tehachapi) ... 93561
Goleta 93116-118
Gaviota 93117
Isla Vista 93117
Santa Barbara .. 93116-93118
Gonzales 93926
Goodyears Bar 95944
Gorda (Big Sur) 93920
Gorman (Lebec) 93243
Goshen 93227
Gottschalks (Fresno) 93780
Graeagle (Blairsden) 96103
Granada Hills 91344, 91394
San Fernando 91344

Grand Island 95690
(Walnut Grove)
Grand Terrace 92313, 92324
Granite Bay (Roseville)
.... 95661, 95746
Roseville 95746
Graniteville 95959
(Nevada City)
Grant Grove 93633
(Kings Canyon National Pk)
Grass Valley 95945, 95949
Alta Hill 95945
Alta Sierra 95945
Bear River Pines 95945
Boston Ravine 95945
Glenbrook Heights 95945
Hills Flat 95945
La Barr Meadows 95945
Peardale 95945
Spring Hill 95945
Sunset View 95945
Union Hill 95945
Willaura Estates 95945
Graton 95444
Great American 92183
(San Diego)
Greeley (Bakersfield) 93312
Green Valley 91350
(Santa Clarita)
Green Valley Lake 92341
Greenacres (Bakersfield) .. 93312
Greenbrae 94904, 94914
Del Mesa 94904
Kent Woodlands 94904
Kentfield 94904
San Rafael 94904
Greenfield 93927
Greenmead (Los Angeles) 90059
Greenview 96037
Greenville 95947
Greenwood 95635
Grenada 96038
Gridley 95948
Griffith (Los Angeles) 90039
Grimes 95950
Grindstone Creek Rancheria
(Elk Creek) 95939
Grizzly Flats 95636
Groveland 95321
Grover Beach 93433, 93483
Grover City 93433
Grover City 93433
(Grover Beach)
Guadalupe 93434
Gualala 95445, 95497
Anchor Bay 95445
Guasti 91743
Guatay 91931
Guerneville 95446
Guernewood (Guerneville) 95446
Guernewood Park 95446
(Guerneville)
Guinda 95637
Gustine 95322
Hacienda (Forestville) 95436
Hacienda Heights 91745
Haiwee (Olancha) 93549
Halcyon (Arroyo Grande) .. 93420
Half Moon Bay 94019
Halloran Springs (Baker) ... 92309
Hallwood (Marysville) 95901

Hamilton City	95951
Hammil Valley (Bishop)	93514
Hammonton (Marysville)	95901
Hams Station (Kirkwood)	95646
Hancock (Los Angeles)	90044
Hanford	93230-232
Beacon Oil Co	93231
Hansen Hills (Pacoima)	91331
Happy Camp	96039
Harbor City	90710
Hardman Center	92504
(Riverside)	
Harmony	93435
Harris Co	92416
(San Bernardino)	
Hat Creek	96040
Hathaway Pines	95233
Havilah (Caliente)	93518
Hawaiian Gardens	90716
Hawthorne	90250-251
Holly Park	90250
Hayfork	96041
Hayward	
... 94540-546, 94552, 94557	
Mount Eden	94557
Hazard (Los Angeles)	90063
Healdsburg	95448
Heather Glen (Applegate)	95703
Heber	92249
Helena (Junction City)	96048
Helendale	92342
Helm	93627
Hemet	92543-546
Herald	95638
Hercules	94547
Herlong	96113
Hermosa Beach	90254
Hesperia	92340, 92345
Hi Vista (Lancaster)	93534-535
Hickman	95323
Hidden Hills (Calabasas)	91302
Hidden Valley	91361
(Westlake Village)	
Highland	92346
Highland Park	90042
(Los Angeles)	
Hilarita	94920
(Belvedere Tiburon)	
Hillcrest Center	93306
(Bakersfield)	
Hills Flat (Grass Valley)	95945
Hillsborough (Burlingame)	94010
Hilltop (Bakersfield)	93307
Hilmar	95324
Hilt (Hornbrook)	96044
Hilton (Forestville)	95436
Hinkley	92347
Hobart Mills (Truckee)	96161
Hodge (Barstow)	92311
Holcomb Village (Aguanga)	92536
Holiday (Anaheim)	92802
Hollister	95023-024
Holly Park (Hawthorne)	90250
Hollydale (Forestville)	95436
Hollywood (Los Angeles)	
... 90027-028, 90038, 90068	
Holt	95234
Holtville	92250
Holy City	95026
Home Federal Svng Loan	92185
(San Diego)	

Homeland	92548
Homestead Valley	94941
(Mill Valley)	
Homewood	96141-142
Tahoe Pines	96141
Honcut (Oroville)	95965
Honeydew	95545
Hood	95639
Hoopa	95546
Hoopa Valley Indian Res	95546
(Hoopa)	
Hope Valley	96120
(Markleeville)	
Hopland	95449
Hornbrook	96044
Hornitos	95325
Horse Creek	96050
(Klamath River)	
Howard Landing	95690
(Walnut Grove)	
Hughson	95326
Hume	93628
Huntington	92646
Huntington Beach	
... 92605, 92615, 92646-649	
Beach Center	92648
Center Ave	92605
Huntington	92646
Huntington Lake	93629
Huntington Park	90255
Hurleton (Oroville)	95965
Huron	93234
Hyampom	96046
Hydesville	95547
I B M (San Jose)	95193
I R South (Fresno)	93888
Idyllwild	92549
Ignacio (Novato)	94949
Igo	96047
Imperial	92251
Imperial Beach	91932-933
Independence	93526
Indian Hills (Riverside)	92509
Indian Wells	92210
Indio	92201-203
Bermuda Dunes	92201
Cabazon Indian Res	92201
Chiriaco Summit	92201
Industrial (Santa Ana)	92705
Industrial Indemnity	93782
(Fresno)	
Industry (La Puente)	
... 91744-746, 91748	
Inglenook (Fort Bragg)	95437
Inglewood ... 90300-13, 90397-98	
General Telephone	90313
Lennox	90304
Shared Firm Zip Code	90397
Internal Revenue Service	
Fresno	93844
Rancho Cordova	95743
Remittance	94151
Inverness	94937
Inverness Park	94956
(Point Reyes Station)	
Inyokern ... 93527, 93542	
Pearsonville	93527
Ione	95640
Iowa Hill (Colfax)	95713
Iron Mountain (Kirkwood)	95646
Irvine .. 92619, 92650, 92709-710	

... 92713-718, 92720, 92730	
El Toro M C A South	92709
Fluor Corp	92730
Tustin Marine Corps	92710
U C Irvine	92717
Irwindale (Baldwin Park)	91706
Isla Vista (Goleta)	93117
Isleton	95641
Ivanhoe	93235
J B Lansing Co	91329
(Northridge)	
Jackson	95642, 95654
Clinton	95642
Jacumba	91934
Jamestown	95327
Jamul	91935
Janesville ... 96114, 96136	
Wendel	96136
Jarbo (Oroville)	95965
Jenner	95450
Jimtown (Healdsburg)	95448
Johannesburg ... 93528, 554, 558	
Johnson Park (Burney)	96013
Johnson Valley (Landers)	92285
Johnstonville	96130
(Susanville)	
Johnsville (Blairsden)	96103
Jolon	93928
Joshua Tree	92252
Julian	92036
Junction City	96048
June Lake Junction	93529
(June Lake)	
Juniper Hills (Littlerock)	
... 93543, 93553	
Jurupa (Riverside)	92509
Kagel Canyon (Sylmar)	91342
Kaiser Alum & Chem	94643
(Oakland)	
Kaiser Foundation Health	91188
(Pasadena)	
Kaiser Services (Oakland)	94666
Kaweah	93237
Keeler	93530
Keene	93531, 93570
Keene Summit (Comptche)	95427
Kelsey	95643
Kelseyville	95451
Kelso (Baker)	92309
Kensington (Berkeley)	94707-708
Kent Woodlands	94904
(Greenbrae)	
Kentfield (Greenbrae)	
... 94904, 94914	
San Rafael	94914
Kenwood	95452
Kerman	93630
Kernville	93238
Keswick (Redding)	96001
Kettleman City	93239
Keyes	95328
King (Santa Ana)	92706
King City	93930
Kings Beach	96143
Kings Canyon National Pk	93633
Kingsburg	93631
Kingvale (Soda Springs)	95728
Kirkwood	95646
Kit Carson	95644
Klamath	95548
Klamath Air Force Station	95548

43

Mcdonnell Douglas	90846
Naples	90803
North Long Beach	90805
Press Telegram	90844
Signal Hill	90804
Signal Hill	90806-90807
Long Beach Naval Ship	90822
(Long Beach)	
Long Beach Naval Station	90822
(Long Beach)	
Long Island	95690
(Walnut Grove)	
Longvale (Willits)	95490
Lookout	96054
Loomis	95650
Loraine (Caliente)	93518
Los Alamitos	90720-721
Rossmoor	90720
Los Alamos	93440
Los Altos	94022-024
Los Altos Hills	94022
(Los Altos)	
Los Angeles	90000-080
.... 90082-084, 90086-089	
... 90091, 90093-097, 90099	
.... 90101-102, 90185	
1st Interstate Bk	90088
Ambassador	90070
ARCO-plaza	90071
Atlantic Richfield Plaza	90071
Bank Of America	90074
Bar Code Term Annex .	90099
Barrington	90049
Bicentennial	90048
Boyle	90033
Boyle Heights	90033
Bradley International ...	90045
Brentwood	90049
Briggs	90048
Broadway Manchester	90003
Brylane	90102
Bulk Mail Center	90101
Century City	90067
City Of Commerce	90040
....	90091
Cole	90046
Crenshaw 90008, 90056	
Del Valle	90015
Dockweiler	90007
Dowtown Carrier Annex	
....	90014-90015
Eagle Rock	90041
East Los Angeles	90022
Echo Park	90026
Edendale	90026
El Sereno	90032
Farmers Market	90036
Federal 90012-90013	
Federal Boxes	90053
Firestone Park	90001
First Interstate Bank ...	90084
Flint	90057
Foy	90017
Glassell	90065
Greenmead	90059
Griffith	90039
Hancock	90044
Hazard	90063
Highland Park	90042
Hollywood 90038, 90068	
La Tijera	90043

Ladera Heights	90045
Lincoln Heights	90031
Los Feliz	90027
Lugo	90023
Mar Vista	90066
Market	90021
Miracle Mile	90036
Oakwood	90004
Palms	90034
Pico Heights	90006
Playa Vista	90094
Preuss	90035
Rancho Park	90064
Rimpau	90019
Sanford 90005, 90010	
....	90020
Santa Western	90072
Silver Lake	90026
South	90061
Textile	90015
Textile Boxes	90079
UCLA	90095
Vermont	90029
Vernon	90058
Veterans Admin	90073
View Park	90043
Village	90024
Village	90077
Wagner	90047
Watts ... 90002, 90044, 90059	
....	90061
West Adams	90016
West Los Angeles	90025
Westchester	90045
Westvern	90062
Wilcox	90038
Wilshire-la Brea	90036
Windsor Hills	90056
Worldway Postal Ctr ...	90009
Los Angeles International Airport	
(Los Angeles)	90009
Los Banos	93635
Los Feliz (Los Angeles)	90027
Los Gatos	95030-032
Monte Sereno	95030
Los Molinos	96055
Los Nietos (Whittier)	
.... 90606, 90610	
Los Olivos	93441
Los Osos	93402, 93412
Baywood Park	93402
San Luis Obispo	93402
San Luis Obispo	93412
Los Ranchitos	94903
(San Rafael)	
Lost Hills	93249
Lost Lake (Blythe)	92225
Lotus	95651
Lower Lake	95457
Loyalton	96118
Lucas Valley (San Rafael) .	94903
Lucerne	95458
Lucerne Valley	92356
Lucia (Big Sur)	93920
Ludlow	92338
Lugo (Los Angeles)	90023
Lundy (Lee Vining)	93541
Lynwood	90262
Lytle Creek	92358
Lytton (Healdsburg)	95448
Macdoel	96058

Macys Of California	94155
(San Francisco)	
Mad River	95552
Madeline	96119
Madera	93637-639
Madison	95653
Magalia	95954
Magnolia Center	92506
(Riverside)	
Magra (Gold Run)	95717
Malaga (Fresno)	93725
Malibu	90263-265
Mammoth Lakes	93546
Manchester	95459
Manchester Rancheria ...	95459
(Manchester)	
Manhattan Beach	90266-267
Manila (Arcata)	95521
Manor (Fairfax)	94930
Manteca	95336-337
Manton	96059
Manzanita (Gridley)	95948
Mar Vista (Los Angeles) ...	90066
March Air Force Base ...	92518
Maricopa	93252
Marigold (Redlands)	92373
Marin City (Sausalito) ...	94965
Marin Country Club Est	94949
(Novato)	
Marina	93933
Marina Del Rey (Venice)	
.... 90291-292, 90295	
Venice 90292, 90295	
Marine Corp Base	92055
(Camp Pendleton)	
Marine Corps Base	92278
(Twentynine Palms)	
Marinwood (San Rafael) ..	94903
Mariposa	95338
Mark West (Santa Rosa) ..	95404
Market (Los Angeles)	90021
Markleeville	96120
Marshall	94940
Martell	95654
Martinez	94553
Marysville	95901, 95903
Arboga	95901
Hallwood	95901
Hammonton	95901
Loma Rica	95901
Massack (Quincy)	95971
Master Charge (San Diego)	92180
Mather	95655
Maxwell	95955
Maywood	90270
Mc Farland	93250
Mc Kinleyville (Arcata) ...	95521
Mc Kittrick	93251
Mcarthur (Little Valley)	
.... 96053, 96056	
Pittville	96056
Mcclellan Air Force Base ..	95652
Mccloud	96057
Mcdonnell Douglas	90846
(Long Beach)	
Mckinleyville (Arcata)	95521
Mead Valley (Perris)	92570
Meadow Valley	95956
Meadow Vista	95722
Meadows Field	93308
(Bakersfield)	

Meadowsweet 94925
(Corte Madera)
Mecca 92254
Media Zip (Van Nuys) . 91461-463
Medicine Lake Lodge 96134
(Tulelake)
Meeks Bay (Tahoma) 96142
Mellon Financial Services .. 91187
(Pasadena)
Mellon Regional Lockbox Netw ...
91185 (Pasadena)
Mendocino 95460
Mendota 93640
Menifee 92584
Menlo Park 94025-029
West Menlo Park 94025
Mentone 92359
Merced 95340-344, 95348
Farmers Ins Group 95343
Red Top 95340
Meridian 95957
Mesa Center (Costa Mesa) 92627
Mesa Verde (Blythe) 92225
Mesa Vista (Markleeville) .. 96120
Metler Valley (Lancaster) .. 93536
Mettler (Bakersfield) 93301
Meyers (South Lake Tahoe) 96155
Mi Wuk Village 95346
Michigan Bluff 95631
(Foresthill)
Middletown 95461
Middletown Rancheria 95461
(Middletown)
Midlake (Ukiah) 95482
Midpines 95345
Midtown (Chico) 95928
Midway City 92655
Milford 96121
Mill Creek 96061
Mill Valley 94941-942
Almonte 94941
Homestead Valley 94941
Locust 94941
Mt Tamalpais 94941
Muir Woods 94941
Strawberry Manor 94941
Strawberry Point 94941
Tamalpais Valley 94941
Mill Valley Air Force Sta 94941
(Mill Valley)
Millbrae 94030-031
Mills Orchard 95951
(Hamilton City)
Millville 96062
Milpitas 95035-036
Mineral (Mill Creek)
.... 96061, 96063
Minkler (Sanger) 93657
Mint Canyon 91350
(Santa Clarita)
Mira Loma 91752
Mirabel Heights 95436
(Forestville)
Mirabel Park 95436
(Forestville)
Miracle Mile 90036
(Los Angeles)
Miramonte (Badger)
93603, 93628, 93633, 93641
Pinehurst 93641
Miranda 95553

Mission Hills ... 91345-346, 91395
Mission City 91345
San Fernando . 91345-91346
Mission Rafael (San Rafael)
.... 94901, 94915
Mission Viejo .. 92675, 92690-692
(San Juan Capistrano)
Moccasin 95347
Modesto 95350-358, 95397
Modesto Ca Bus Reply 95397
(Modesto)
Modjeska (Silverado) 92676
Modjeska Canyon 92676
(Silverado)
Moffett Field 94035
(Mountain View)
Moffett Field Naval Air Stat 94035
(Mountain View)
Mojave 93501-502, 93519
Fremont Valley 93501
Mokelumne Hill 95245
Monarch Bay (Dana Point) 92629
Monarch Beach 92629
(Dana Point)
Mono City (Lee Vining) 93541
Mono Hot Springs 93642
Mono Lake (Lee Vining) 93541
Monolith (Tehachapi) 93561
Monrovia 91016-017
Montague 96064
Montara 94037
Montclair 91763
Monte Nido (Calabasas) ... 91302
Monte Rio 95462
Monte Sereno (Los Gatos) 95030
Monte Vista (Cupertino) ... 95014
Montebello 90640
Montecito (Santa Barbara) 93108
Monterey 93940-944
Del Rey Oaks 93940
New Monterey 93940
Point Sur 93940
Presidio Of Monterey .. 93940
Presidio Of Monterey .. 93944
Monterey Park 91754-756
Montesano (Guerneville) ... 95446
Montgomery Creek 96065
Montgomery Village 95405
(Santa Rosa)
Montgomery Ward Co 94616
(Oakland)
Montrose 91020-021
Moorpark 93020-021
Moraga 94556, 94570, 94575
Moreno Valley 92551-557
Morgan Hill 95037-038
Mormon Island (Folsom) ... 95630
Morongo Valley 92256
Morro Bay 93442-443
Moss Beach 94038
Moss Landing 95039
Mount Aukum 95656, 95675
Mount Eden (Hayward) 94557
Mount Hamilton 95140
Mount Hermon 95041
Mount Laguna 91948
Mount Shasta 96067
Mount Signal (Calexico) 92231
Mount Wilson 91023
Mountain Center 92561
Mountain Home Village 92359

(Mentone)
Mountain Mesa 93240
(Lake Isabella)
Mountain Pass 92366
Mountain Ranch 95246
Mountain View . 94035, 94039-43
Blossom Valley 94040
Moffett Field 94035
Mt View 94040
Muir (Willits) 95490
Muir Beach (Sausalito) 94965
Muir Woods (Mill Valley) ... 94941
Muir Woods Nat Monument 94941
(Mill Valley)
Murphys 95247
Murray Park (Larkspur) 94939
Murrieta 92562-564
Murrieta Hot Springs (Murrieta)
.... 92562-564
Muscoy (San Bernardino) .. 92405
Myers Flat 95554
Napa 94558-559, 94581
Spanish Flat 94558
Naples (Long Beach) 90803
Nas Alameda (Alameda) ... 94501
Nashville (El Dorado) 95623
National City 91950-951
National Pen Corp 92181
(San Diego)
Naval Hospital (Oakland) .. 94627
Navarro 95463
Navelencia (Reedley) 93654
Needles 92363
Neenach (Lancaster) 93536
Nelson 95958
Nestor (San Diego) 92153
Nevada City 95959
New Almaden 95042
New Cuyama 93254
New Idria (Paicines) 95043
New Monterey (Monterey) . 93940
Newark 94560
Newberry Springs (Ludlow)
.... 92338, 92365
Newbury Park 91319-320
Thousand Oaks 91319-91320
Newcastle 95658
Newell (Tulelake) 96134
Newhall ... 91321-322, 91381-382
Friendly Valley 91321
Santa Clarita 91321-91322
Newman 95360
Newport Beach
(Newport Coast) . 92657-663
Balboa 92661
Newport Coast 92657
Newtown (Placerville)
.... 95667, 95959
Newville (Orland) 95963
Nicasio 94946
Nice 95464
Nicolaus (East Nicolaus)
.... 95622, 95659
Trowbridge 95659
Verona 95659
Verona Landing 95659
Niland 92257
Nimbus (Rancho Cordova) 95670
Nimshew (Magalia) 95954
Nipinnawassee (Ahwahnee)93601
Nipomo 93444

Ranchita 92066
Rancho Bernardo 92128
 (San Diego)
Rancho California (Temecula)
 92589-593
Rancho Cordova
 .... 95670, 95741-743
 Gold River 95670
 IRS 95743
 Nimbus 95670
Rancho Cucamonga (Alta Loma)
 .... 91701, 91729-730, 91737
 91739
 Cucamonga 91729-91730
 Etiwanda 91739
Rancho Dominguez (Compton)
 .... 90220, 90224
Rancho La Tuna Canyon .. 91352
 (Sun Valley)
Rancho Mirage 92270
Rancho Murieta 95683
 (Sloughhouse)
Rancho Palos Verdes 90274-275
 (Palos Verdes Peninsula)
 Palos Verdes Estates . 90275
 Rolling Hills Estates 90275
Rancho Park 90064
 (Los Angeles)
Rancho Santa Fe 92067
Rancho Santa Margarita .. 92688
Randall Island 95615
 (Courtland)
Randsburg 93554
Ravendale 96123, 96132
Raymond 93653
Red Bluff 96080
Red Mountain 93558
Red Top (Merced) 95340
Redcrest 95569
Redding . 96001-3, 96049, 96099
 Keswick 96001
 Shasta Lake 96003
Redlands 92373-375
 Marigold 92373
 Smiley Heights 92373
Redondo Beach 90277-278
Redway 95560
Redwood City 94059, 94061-065
 Woodside 94062
Redwood Estates 95044
Redwood Lodge 95437
 (Fort Bragg)
Redwood Valley 95470
Reedley 93654
Renaissance 95962
 (Oregon House)
Represa 95671
Rescue 95672
Reseda 91335, 91337
 Encino 91335
 Tarzana 91335
Resighini Rancheria 95546
 (Hoopa)
Rialto 92376-377
Richardson Springs 95973
Richgrove 93261
Richmond
 .... 94801-808, 94820, 94850
 North Richmond 94801
 Point Richmond ... 94801, 807
 San Francisco BMC 94850

Richvale 95974
Ridgecrest 93555-556
 China Lake 93555-93556
Ridgewood (Carnelian By) 96140
Rimforest 92378
Rimpau (Los Angeles) 90019
Rimrock (Pioneertown) 92268
Rio Campo (Monte Rio) 95462
Rio Del Mar (Aptos) 95003
Rio Dell 95562
Rio Linda 95673
Rio Nido 95471
Rio Oso 95674
Rio Vista 94571
Ripley 92272
Ripon 95366
Ritter Ranch (Palmdale) ... 93551
River Bank (Broderick) 95605
River Kern (Kernville) 93238
River Pines 95675
Riverbank 95367, 95390
 Blue Shield 95390
Riverdale (Burrel) .. 93607, 93656
Riverside . 92501-509, 92513-519
 92521-522
 Arlanza Village 92505
 Belltown 92509
 Box Springs 92507
 Canyon Crest 92507
 Casa Blanca 92504
 City Light And Water ... 92522
 Crestmore Heights 92509
 Hardman Center 92504
 Indian Hills 92509
 Jurupa 92509
 Magnolia Center 92506
 Rubidoux 92509
 Sunnyslope 92509
 U C At Riverside 92521
Robbins 95676
Robinson Ranch 92679
 (Trabuco Canyon)
Robinsons Corner 95965
 (Oroville)
Robles Del Rio 93924
 (Carmel Valley)
Rock Creek (Storrie) 95980
Rock Crest (Storrie) 95980
Rocklin 95677, 95765
 Stanford Ranch 95677
 Sunset Whitney Ranch 95677
Rockport (Westport) 95488
Rodeo (Hercules) ... 94547, 94572
Rogers Flat (Storrie) 95980
Rogina Heights (Ukiah) ... 95482
Rohnert Park (Cotati) . 94926-928
Rolinda (Fresno) 93706
Rolling Hills 90274
 (Palos Verdes Peninsula)
Rolling Hills Estates ... 90274-275
 (Palos Verdes Peninsula)
Romoland (Sun City) 92585
Roosevelt Corner 93535
 (Lancaster)
Rosamond 93560
Roseland (Santa Rosa) ... 95407
Rosemead 91770-772
 South Cal Edison Co .. 91771
 South San Gabriel ... 91770
Roseville 95661, 95678
 95746-747

Granite Bay 95661
Rosewood (Compton) 90222
Ross 94957
Rossmoor (Los Alamitos) .. 90720
Rough And Ready 95975
Round Mountain 96084
Round Valley (Bishop) 93514
Rovana (Bishop) 93514
Rowland Heights 91748
Rubicon Bay (Tahoma) 96142
Rubidoux (Riverside) 92509
Rumsey 95679
Running Springs 92382
Russian River (San Mateo) 94401
Russian River Mdws 95462
 (Monte Rio)
Russian River Terrace 95436
 (Forestville)
Ruth (Bridgeville) 95526
Rutherford 94573
Ryde 95680
Ryer Island 95690
 (Walnut Grove)
Sacramento 94203-209, 94211
 .... 94229-230, 94232
 .... 94234-237, 94239-240
 .... 94243-250, 94252-254
 .... 94256-259, 94261-263
 .... 94267-269, 94271
 .... 94273-274, 94277-280
 .... 94282-291, 94293-299
 .... 95798-800, 95812-838
 .... 95840-842, 95851-853
 .... 95857, 95860, 95864-867
 95873, 95887, 95894, 95899
 Arcade 95821
 Business Reply Mail ... 95899
 Ca State Dmv 95894
 Cable Data 95873
 Franchise Tax Board .. 95840
 Franchise Tax Brd Ref 95867
 Fruitridge 95820
 North Sacramento 95815
 Pacific Bell 95887
 Walsh Station 95826
Safeway Stores (Oakland) 94660
Saint Helena 94574
Salida 95368
Salinas ... 93901-902, 93905-908,
 .... 93911-912, 93915, 93962
 Alisal 93905
 Prunedale 93907
 Social Security Data 93911
 Spreckels 93962
Salmon Creek (Bodega By) 94923
Salton City 92275
Saltus (Amboy) 92304
Salyer 95563
Samoa 95564
San Andreas 95249-250
San Anselmo 94960, 94979
 Lansdale 94960
 Sleepy Hollow 94960
 Yolanda 94960
San Ardo 93450
San Benito (Paicines) 95043
San Bernardino .. 92400-408
 .... 92410-416, 92418, 92420
 .... 92423-424, 92427
 Base Line 92410
 Cajon Junction 92407

City Hall 92418
Devore Heights 92407
Harris Co 92416
Muscoy 92405
Shearson Lehman Am Exp
.... 92420
South B County Off 92415
San Bruno 94066-067, 94096
.... 94098-099
San Carlos 94070-071
San Clemente 92672-674
Vista Del Mar 92672
San Diego 92100-124
.... 92126-140, 92142-143
.... 92145, 92147, 92149-150
..... 92152-155, 92158-199
Donovan Correctional Facility
.... 92179
Great American 92183
Home Federal Sng Ln   92185
Master Charge 92180
National Pen Corp 92181
Nestor 92153
Ocean Beach 92107
Pacific Beach 92109
Paradise Hills 92139
Rancho Bernardo 92128
V A Hospital 92161
San Diego County Jail 92158
(San Diego)
San Diego Gas And Elec .. 92184
(San Diego)
San Diego State Univ 92182
(San Diego)
San Diego Water Utilities .. 92187
(San Diego)
San Dimas 91773
San Fernando 91340-346
San Francisco 94100-112
.... 94114-147, 94150-157
.... 94159-172, 94175, 94177
.... 94188
Airport 94128
At & T 94151, 94171
Bank Cal/union Bank .. 94145
Bank Of America 94137
.... 94154, 94160
Express Mail Rep Sys   94135
Firm Holdouts 94106
First Interstate Bank 94139
IRS Remittance 94151
Letterman Army Medical Junct
94129
Macys Of California ...   94155
Pacific Gas & Electric . 94152
Pacific Gas & Electric . 94177
Presidio 94129
Security Pacific Natl Bk ....
.... 94161
Selective Service 94136
Union Oil Co Of Cal 94150
Univ Of Cal Medical Junction
.... 94143
US Bureau Of The Mint 94175
Wells Fargo Bank 94138
.... 94144, 94153, 94156
.... 94162-163
San Francisco BMC 94850
(Richmond)
San Francisco Intnl Airport 94128
(San Francisco)

San Gabriel 91775-776, 91778
San Geronimo 94963
San Gregorio 94074
San Jacinto 92581-583
Gilman Hot Springs ... 92583
Soboba Hot Springs ... 92583
Soboba Indian Reservation ..
.... 92583
San Joaquin 93660
San Jose 95100-103, 95106
. 95108-42, 95148, 95150-61
95164, .. 95170-73, 95190-94
.... 95196
A M O R C 95191
California Water Serv .. 95194
I B M 95193
San Jose Mercury News .. 95190
(San Jose)
San Jose State University . 95192
(San Jose)
San Jose Water Company 95196
(San Jose)
San Juan Bautista 95045
San Juan Capistrano
.... 92675, 92688, 92690-693
Mission Viejo 92675
San Leandro 94577-579
San Lorenzo 94580
San Lucas 93954
San Luis Obispo 93401-403
.... 93405-410, 93412
Cal Poly Student Dms 93410
Cal Poly University 93407
San Luis Rey 92068
San Manuel Indian Res 92346
(Highland)
San Marcos
.... 92069, 92079, 92096
California State Univ ... 92096
Lake San Marcos 92069
San Marin (Novato) 94945
San Marino 91108, 91118
Pasadena 91108, 91118
San Martin 95046
San Mateo 94400-409, 94497
Foster City 94404
Postal Data Center 94497
Russian River 94401
San Miguel 93451
San Pablo 94806
San Pedro 90731-734
Fort Macarthur 90731
Terminal Island 90731
San Quentin 94964, 94974
San Rafael 94901, 94903-904
.... 94911-915
Fireman Fund Ins 94911
Gallinas 94903
Los Ranchitos 94903
Lucas Valley 94903
Marinwood 94903
Mission Rafael 94901
Mission Rafael 94915
Peacock Gap 94901
Santa Venetia 94903
Terra Linda 94903
San Ramon 94583
San Simeon 93452
San Ysidro 92143, 92173
San Diego 92143, 92173
Sand Canyon (Tehachapi) 93561

Sand City (Seaside) 93955
Sandberg (Lake Hughes) .. 93532
Sandy Korner (Thermal) .. 92274
Sanford (Los Angeles)
.... 90005, 90010, 90020
Sanger 93657
Santa Ana 92701-08, 92711-12
.... 92728, 92735, 92799
Bristol 92703
Cowan Heights 92705
Diamond 92704
Industrial 92705
King 92706
South Main 92707
Santa Ana Heights 92707
(Santa Ana)
Santa Barbara 93101-103
.... 93105-111, 93116-118
...... 93120-121, 93130, 93140
.... 93150, 93160, 93190
Montecito 93108
UCSB Student Dorm Boxes
.... 93107
Univ Cal Santa Barb .. 93106
Santa Catalina (Avalon) 90704
Santa Clara 95050-056
Santa Clara University .. 95053
(Santa Clara)
Santa Clarita (Castaic) 91310
.... 91321-322, 91350-351
..... 91354-355, 91380-386
Agua Dulce 91350
Bouquet Canyon 91350
Green Valley 91350
Mint Canyon 91350
Newhall 91382
Saugus 91350
Val Verde Park 91350
Valencia 91380
Santa Cruz 95060-067
Bonny Doon 95060
Paradise Park 95060
Scotts Valley 95060
Santa Fe Springs 90670-671
Santa Margarita 93453
Santa Maria 93454-457
Garey 93454
Orcutt 93455, 93457
Sisquoc 93454
Santa Monica 90400-411
Santa Nella (Gustine) 95322
Santa Paula 93006-061
Santa Rita Park 93661
Santa Rosa 95401-409
Bellevue 95407
Coddingtown 95401
Crossroads 95401
Larkfield 95403
Mark West 95404
Montgomery Village ... 95405
Roseland 95407
South Park 95404
Trenton 95401
Wilfred 95407
Santa Susana 93063
(Simi Valley)
Santa Venetia 94903
(San Rafael)
Santa Western 90072
(Los Angeles)
Santa Ynez 93460

Santa Ysabel 92070
Santee 92071-072
Saratoga 95070-071
Saratoga Hills 91301
    (Agoura Hills)
Sattley (Calpine) 96124
Saugus (Santa Clarita) 91350
Sausalito 94965-966
    Fort Baker 94965
    Fort Barry 94965
    Fort Cronkhite 94965
    Marin City 94965
    Muir Beach 94965
Sawyers Bar (Etna) 96027
Schellville (Sonoma) 95476
Scotia 95565
Scott Bar 96085
Scotts Valley (Santa Cruz)
    .... 95060, 95066-067
Sea Ranch 95497
Seacliff (Aptos) 95003
Seahaven (Inverness) 94937
Seal Beach 90740
Sears Merchandise Group . 91186
    (Pasadena)
Seascape (Aptos) 95003
Seaside 93955
Sebastiani (Sonoma) 95476
Sebastopol 95472-473
    Cunningham 95472
    Daywalt 95472
    Freestone 95472
Security Pacific Natl Bank . 94161
    (San Francisco)
Seeley 92273
Seiad Valley 96086
Seigler Springs 95461
    (Middletown)
Selective Service 94136
    (San Francisco)
Selma 93662
Seneca (Canyondam) 95923
Sepulveda (North Hills)
    .... 91343, 91393
Sequoia National Park 93262
Serene Lakes 95728
    (Soda Springs)
Seven Oaks 92305
    (Angelus Oaks)
Shadow Hills (Sunland) 91040
Shady Glen (Colfax) 95713
Shafter 93263
Shandon 93461
Shared Firm Zip Code (LA)
    90185, 90397, 91110, 91797
Sharon (Chowchilla) 93610
Sharp Park (Pacifica) 94044
Shasta 96087
Shasta Lake (Redding) 96003
    .... 96019, 96079, 96089
    Central Valley .. 96019, 96079
    Project City 96079
Shaver Lake (Lakeshore)
    .... 93634, 93642, 93664
    Dinkey Creek 93664
Shearson Lehman Am Exp 92420
    (San Bernardino)
Sheepranch 95250
Shell Beach (Pismo Beach) 93449
Sheridan (Villa Grande)
    .... 95486, 95681

Sherman Oaks (Van Nuys)
    .... 91401, 91403, 91411
    .... 91413, 91423
Sherwood Valley Rancheria 95437
    (Fort Bragg)
Shingle Springs 95682
Shingletown 96088
Shoshone 92384
Sierra Army Depot 96113
    (Herlong)
Sierra City 96125
Sierra Madre 91024-025
Sierraville 96126
Signal Hill (Long Beach)
    .... 90804, 90806-807
Silver Fork (Kyburz) 95720
Silver Lake (Los Angeles)
    .... 90026, 95666
Silver Lakes (Helendale) ... 92342
Silverado 92676
Simi Valley 93062-065, 93093
    .... 93097, 93099
    Farmers Ins 93099
    First Interstate Bancorp 93097
    Santa Susana 93063
Sisquoc (Santa Maria) 93454
Sites (Stonyford) 95979
Skaggs Island (Sonoma) ... 95476
Skaggs Island Naval Sec .. 95476
    (Sonoma)
Sky Valley 92241
    (Desert Hot Springs)
Skyforest 92385
Sleepy Hollow 94960
    (San Anselmo)
Sloughhouse 95683
Smartville 95977
Smiley Heights (Redlands) 92373
Smith River 95567
Smoke Tree (Palm Springs) 92262
Snelling 95369
Snow Creek (White Water) 92282
Snowline Camp (Camino) .. 95709
Soboba Hot Springs 92583
    (San Jacinto)
Soboba Indian Reservation 92583
    (San Jacinto)
Social Security Data Jtn 93911
    (Salinas)
Soda Bay (Kelseyville) 95451
Soda Springs (Norden)
    .... 95724, 95728
    Cisco 95728
    Kingvale 95728
    Serene Lakes 95728
    The Cedars 95728
Solana Beach 92075
Soledad 93960
Solvang 93463-464
    Ballard 93463
Somerset 95684
Somes Bar 95568
Somesbar (Somes Bar) 95568
Somis 93066
Sonoma 95476
Sonoma Vista (Sonoma) ... 95476
Sonora 95370, 95373
Soquel 95073
Soulsbyville 95372
South (Los Angeles) 90061
South B County Offices 92415

    (San Bernardino)
South Cal Edison Co .. 91771-772
    (Rosemead)
South Dos Palos 93665
South El Monte 91733
South Gate ,,,,,,,,,,,,,,,,,,,,,,,,,, 90280
South Laguna 92677
    (Laguna Niguel)
South Laguna Beach 92677
    (Laguna Niguel)
South Lake Tahoe 96150-158
    Bijou 96156
    Camp Richardson 96156
    Fallen Leaf 96151
    Meyers 96155
    Stateline 96157
    Tahoe Paradise 96155
    Tahoe Valley 96158
South Main (Santa Ana) ... 92707
South Oroville (Oroville) ... 95965
South Park (Santa Rosa) .. 95404
South Pasadena 91030-031
South San Francisco
    .... 94080, 94083
South San Gabriel 91770
    (Rosemead)
Southern California Gas Comp
    (Monterey Park) 91756
Southern California Gas Comp
    (Van Nuys) 91497
Southport 95691
    (West Sacramento)
Spanish Flat (Napa) 94558
Spanish Ranch 95956, 95971
    (Meadow Valley)
Spaulding (Susanville) 96130
Spreckels (Salinas) 93962
Spring Garden (Quincy) 95971
Spring Hill 95945
    (Grass Valley)
Spring Valley 91976-979
Spring Valley Lake 92392
    (Victorville)
Springville (Camp Nelson)
    .... 93208, 93265
Squaw Valley 93675
Stallion Springs 93561
    (Tehachapi)
Standard 95373
Standard Oil Co (Concord) 94529
Standish 96128
Stanford (Palo Alto) 94305
Stanford Ranch (Rocklin) .. 95677
Stanton 90680
Starcrest Of Cal (Perris) ... 92599
Starlight Hills (Burbank) ... 91501
State Farm 91363
    (Westlake Village)
State Farm Ins (Cotati) 94926
Stateline 96157
    (South Lake Tahoe)
Stevenson Ranch 91381
Stevinson 95374
Stewarts Point 95480
Stewarts Point Rancheria . 95480
    (Stewarts Point)
Stinson Beach 94970
Stirling City 95978
Stockdale (Bakersfield) 93309
Stockton 95201-213, 95215
    95219, 95267, 95269, 95290

Whispering Pines 95461
   (Middletown)
White Rock (Folsom) 95630
White Water 92282
Whitethorn 95589
Whitmore 96096
Whittier 90601-610, 90612
   Los Nietos 90606
   Los Nietos 90610
Wilbur Springs (Williams) .. 95987
Wilcox (Los Angeles) 90038
Wildomar 92595
Wildwood (Platina) 96076
Wilfred (Santa Rosa) 95407
Willaura Estates 95945
   (Grass Valley)
Williams 95987
Willits (Dos Rios) 95429, 95490
   Emandal 95490
   Longvale 95490
   Muir 95490
Willow Creek 95573
Willow Ranch 96108
   (Davis Creek)
Willow Springs 93560
   (Rosamond)
Willows 95988
Wilmington 90744, 90748
Wilseyville 95257
Wilshire-la Brea 90036
   (Los Angeles)
Wilsona Gardens (Lancaster)

.... 93534-535
Wilsonia 93633
   (Kings Canyon National Pk)
Wilton 95693
Winchester 92596
Windsor 95492
Windsor Hills 90056
   (Los Angeles)
Winnetka 91306, 91396
   Canoga Park 91306
Winterhaven 92283
Winters 95694
Winton 95388
Wishon 93669
Witter Springs 95493
Wofford Heights 93285
Woodacre 94973
Woodbridge 95258
Woodfords (Markleeville) .. 96120
Woodlake 93286
Woodland 95695, 95776
Woodland Hills (Calabasas)
   .... 91302-303, 91364-365
   .... 91367, 91370-372, 91399
   Calabasas 91399
   Childhelp U South A ... 91370
   Lockheed Corp 91399
   Pierce College 91371
Woodleaf (Challenge) 95925
Woodside (Redwood City) 94062
Woody 93287
World Vision Inc Brm 91191

   (Pasadena)
World Vision International .. 91131
   (Pasadena)
Worldway Postal Center ... 90009
   (Los Angeles)
Wrightwood 92397
Wyandotte (Oroville) 95965
Xl Ranch Indian Res 96101
   (Alturas)
Yankee Hill (Oroville) 95965
Yankee Jims (Colfax) 95713
Yermo 92398
Yettem 93670
Yolanda (San Anselmo) 94960
Yolo 95697
Yorba Linda 92686-687
Yorkville 95494
Yosemite Lodge 95389
   (Yosemite National Park)
Yosemite National Park ... 95389
Young America (Potrero)
   91990-995
Yountville 94599
Yreka 96097
Yuba City 95991-993
   Tierra Buena 95991
Yucaipa 92399
Yucca Valley 92284-286
Zamora 95698
Zenia 95595

ALAMEDA

BUILDINGS

City Of Alameda
2263 SANTA CLARA AVE . 94501

South Shore Shopping Cent
2202 S SHORE CTR 94501

GOVERNMENT

Alameda Courthouse
2417 CENTRAL AVE 94501

Federal Center Building
620 CENTRAL AVE 94501

ARCADIA

HOSPITAL

Methodist Hospital
300 HUNTINGTON 91007

ARTESIA

GOVERNMENT

City Of Cerritos
18125 BLOOMFIELD AVE 90701

HOSPITALS

Pioneer Hospital
17831 PIONEER BLVD 90701

BAKERSFIELD

GOVERNMENT

Bakersfield City Hall
1501 TRUXTUN AVE 93301

Federal Building
800 TRUXTUN AVE 93301

Kern County Civic Center
1415 TRUXTUN AVE 93301

BEACH CENTER

HOSPITALS

Pacifica Community Hosp
18792 DELAWARE ST 92648

HOTELS

Waterfront Hilton
21100 PACIFIC COAST HWY92648

BERKELEY

BUILDINGS

Great Western Savings
2150 SHATTUCK AVE 94704

Wells Fargo Bank
2144 SHATTUCK AVE ......^94704

HOSPITALS

Herrick Hospital
2500 MILVIA ST 94704

HOTELS

Shattuck Hotel
2086 ALLSTON WAY 94704

BETTERAVIA

GOVERNMENT

Orcutt Branch
155 S 1ST ST 93455

BEVERLY HILLS

GOVERNMENT

Beverly Hills Court House
9355 BURTON WAY 90210

City Hall
455 N REXFORD DR 90210

BIXBY KNOLLS

APARTMENTS

Bixby Knolls Towers
3737 ATLANTIC AVE 90807

BONNY DOON

GOVERNMENT

Santa Cruz City Hall
809 CENTER ST 95060

Santa Cruz County Building
701 OCEAN ST 95060

BUENA PARK

BUILDINGS

Buena Park Commerce Plaza
6280 MANCHESTER BLVD 90621

CABRILLO

APARTMENTS

American Gold Star Home
3001 N GOLD STAR DR ... 90810

CAMARILLO

GOVERNMENT

Camarillo City Hall
601 CARMEN DR 93010

HOSPITALS

Camarillo State Hospital
1878 S LEWIS RD 93012

Pleasant Valley Hospital
2309 ANTONIO AVE 93010

Pleasant Valley Hospital
2415 ANTONIO AVE 93010

COLLEGES

St Johns Seminary College
5118 SEMINARY RD 93012

CAMPBELL

GOVERNMENT

Campbell City Hall
70 N 1ST ST 95008

CARMEL

GOVERNMENT

Carmel Police Dept
600 PO BOX 93921

City Of Carmel
0 PO BOX 93921

CASITAS SPRINGS

GOVERNMENT

Ventura City Hall
501 POLI ST 93001

CLOVIS

GOVERNMENT

City Hall
1033 5TH ST 93612

COLONIA

BUILDINGS

Amtrak/greyhound Station
201 E 4TH ST 93030

North Coast Executive Ctr
1000 TOWN CENTER DR 93030

Union Bank Building
500 E ESPLANADE DR 93030

Ventura Co Nat Bank Building
300 E ESPLANADE DR 93030

GOVERNMENT

Oxnard City Hall
305 W 3RD ST 93030

Oxnard Public Library
251 S A ST 93030

HOSPITALS

St John Outpatient Clinic
540 HOBSON WAY 93030

St Johns Regional Med Ctr
1600 N ROSE AVE 93030

GOVERNMENT

Federal Building Station
340 S A ST 93030

Oxnard Main Post Office
1961 N C ST 93030

HOTELS

Financial Plaza Hilton
600 E ESPLANADE DR 93030

COLLEGES

Watterson College
815 N OXNARD BLVD 93030

COMPTON

GOVERNMENT

City Hall
205 S Willowbrook Ave 90220

L A County Courts Building
200 W COMPTON BLVD .. 90220

COSTA MESA

BUILDINGS

South Coast Plaza
3333 BRISTOL ST 92626

HOSPITALS

Fairview State Hospital
2501 HARBOR BLVD 92626

HOTELS

Red Lion Inn
3050 BRISTOL ST 92626

Westin South Coast Plaza
686 ANTON BLVD 92626

COLLEGES

Coast Community College
1370 ADAMS AVE 92626

Orange Coast College
2701 FAIRVIEW RD 92626

Southern California Colg
55 FAIR DR 92626

COWAN HEIGHTS

HOTELS

Irvine Host Hotel
1717 E DYER RD 92705

Ramada Hotel
2726 S GRAND AVE 92705

CULVER CITY

GOVERNMENT

City Hall
4095 OVERLAND AVE 90232

DOWNEY

GOVERNMENT

City Hall
11111 BROOKSHIRE AVE . 90241

Downey Municipal Court
7500 IMPERIAL HWY 90242

HOSPITALS

Rio Hondo Hospital
8300 TELEGRAPH RD 90240

EAST VENTURA

HOSPITALS

Community Memorial Hosp
147 N BRENT ST 93003

Ventura Co Med Center
3291 LOMA VISTA RD 93003

EL CAJON

GOVERNMENT

County Building
250 E MAIN ST 92020

EMERYVILLE

APARTMENTS

Pacific Park Plaza
6363 CHRISTIE AVE 94608

BUILDINGS

Emeryville Market Place
5820 SHELLMOUND ST .. 94608

Shaklee Building
1900 POWELL ST 94608

FITCHBURG

BUILDINGS

Oakport Executive Center
7677 OAKPORT ST 94621

HOTELS

Hyatt House
455 HEGENBERGER RD . 94621

FORT MACARTHUR

GOVERNMENT

City Hall
638 S BEACON ST 90731

Federal Building
839 S BEACON ST 90731

San Pedro Municipal Court
505 S CENTRE ST 90731

US Customs House
300 FERRY ST 90731

FOSTER CITY

BUILDINGS

Metro Tower
950 TOWER LN 94404

FOUNTAIN VALLEY

HOSPITALS

Fountain Valley Regional
17100 EUCLID ST 92708

COLLEGES

Coastline Community Colg
11460 WARNER AVE 92708

FREMONT

GOVERNMENT

Fremont Public Library
2400 STEVENSON BLVD . 94538

FRESNO

GOVERNMENT

City Hall
2600 FRESNO ST 93721

County Courthouse
1100 VAN NESS AVE 93721

County Hall Of Records
2281 TULARE ST 93721

Federal Building
1130 O ST 93721

Golden State County Plaza
2220 TULARE ST 93721

State Building
2550 MARIPOSA MALL 93721

GARDENA

HOSPITALS

Memorial Hospital Of Gard
1145 W RedondoBch Blvd 90247

GAREY

COLLEGE

Allan Hancock College
800 COLLEGE 93454

GAVIOTA

GOVERNMENT

Ellwood Branch
7127 HOLLISTER AVE 93117

GLENDALE

BUILDINGS

F I B Towers
535 N BRAND BLVD 91203

GOVERNMENT

City Hall
613 E BROADWAY 91206

L A County Court
600 E BROADWAY 91206

HAYWARD

BUILDINGS

City Center
22300 FOOTHILL BLVD ... 94541

Hayward Airport Plaza
22693 HESPERIAN BLVD 94541

HOLLYWOOD

BUILDING

Clampett Building
729 SEWARD 90038

HUNTINGTON BEACH

COLLEGES

Goldenwest College
15744 GOLDENWEST ST 92647

INGLEWOOD

GOVERNMENT

City Hall
1 W MANCHESTER BLVD 90301

IRVINE

COLLEGES

Concordia University
1530 CONCORDIA 92715

KING

COLLEGES

Rancho Santiago College
1530 W 17TH ST 92706

LA HABRA

HOSPITALS

Friendly Hills Medical Ce
1251 W LAMBERT RD 90631

LA MESA

HOSPITALS

Grossmont Medical
5565 Grossmont Center Dr 91942

LADERA HEIGHTS

BUILDINGS

Sheraton Hotel
6101 W CENTURY BLVD . 90045

HOTELS

Marriott Hotel
5855 W CENTURY BLVD . 90045

LAWNDALE

GOVERNMENT

Federal Building
15000 AVIATION BLVD 90261

LEMORE

GOVERNMENT

Livermore Unified School
685 E Jack London Blvd ... 94550

LOMPOC

GOVERNMENT

Lompoc City Hall
100 CIVIC CENTER PLZ .. 93436

LONG BEACH

APARTMENTS

Brethren Manor
3333 N PACIFIC PL 90806

BUILDINGS

F And M Building
320 PINE AVE 90802

Fidelity Federal Plaza
555 E OCEAN BLVD 90802

L B Harbor Admin Building
925 HARBOR PLZ 90802

Ocean Center Building
110 W OCEAN BLVD 90802

Security Pacific Building
110 PINE AVE 90802

Sumitomo Bank Building
444 W OCEAN BLVD 90802

GOVERNMENT

Cal Vet Memorial State Bl
245 W BROADWAY 90802

County Court Building
415 W OCEAN BLVD 90802

Federal Building
501 W OCEAN BLVD 90802

Police Dept Building
400 W BROADWAY 90802

HOTELS

Hilton Hotel
2 WORLD TRADE CTR 90831

LOS ANGELES

HOTELS

Bonaventure Hotel
404 S FIGUEROA ST 90071

METRO

GOVERNMENT

Federal Building
801 I ST 95814

US Courthouse And Fed Bld
650 CAPITOL MALL 95814

MIRA VISTA

GOVERNMENT

Contra Costa County
100 37TH ST 94805

MISSION HILLS

HOSPITALS

Indian Hills Medical Ctr
14935 RINALDI ST 91345

MONTEREY

HOSPITALS

Community Hosp Monterey
0 PO BOX 93942

MORAGA

COLLEGES

Saint Marys College
4240 PO BOX 94575

NAPA

GOVERNMENT

City Of Napa
660 PO BOX 94559

HOTELS

Inn At Napa Valley
1075 CALIFORNIA BLVD . 94559

NEWPORT BEACH

BUILDINGS

Fashion Island
901 Newport Center Dr 92660

HOTELS

Four Seasons Hotel
690 Newport Center Dr 92660

Marriott Hotel
900 Newport Center Dr 92660

Sheraton Newport Hotel
4545 MACARTHUR BLVD 92660

OAKLAND

APARTMENTS

Lakeshore Building
1200 LAKESHORE AVE ... 94606

Lakeside Regency Plaza
1555 LAKESIDE DR 94612

Noble Tower
1515 LAKESIDE DR 94612

Oakland Housing Building
1621 HARRISON ST 94612

Oakmont Towers
110 41ST ST 94611

Rose Of Sharon
1600 LAKESHORE AVE ... 94606

Valdez Plaza
280 28TH ST 94611

BUILDINGS

Bank Of America Building
1212 BROADWAY 94612

Bermuda Building
2150 FRANKLIN ST 94612

Broadway Building
1419 BROADWAY 94612

Caltrans Building
111 GRAND AVE 94612

Central Building
436 14TH ST 94612

Clorox Building
1221 BROADWAY 94612

El Dorado Building
360 22ND ST 94612

Federal Towers Building
1515 CLAY ST 94612

Franklin Building
1904 FRANKLIN ST 94612

Great Western Bank Building
1700 BROADWAY 94612

Holland Building
1404 FRANKLIN ST 94612

Kaiser Center Building
300 LAKESIDE DR 94612

Latham Square Building
508 16TH ST 94612

Leamington Building
1814 FRANKLIN ST 94612

Macarthur/broadway Mall
235 W MACARTHUR BLVD 94611

Manifest Building
1916 BROADWAY 94612

Park Plaza Building
1939 HARRISON ST 94612

Trans Pacific Center Building
1000 BROADWAY 94607

Tribune Building
409 13TH ST .... 94′ 12

Wells Fargo Bank Building
1333 BROADWAY 94612

World Saving Tower Building
1970 BROADWAY 94612

GOVERNMENT

Alameda County Admin Building
1221 OAK ST 94612

Alameda County Courthouse
1225 FALLON ST 94612

City Of Oakland
1 CITY HALL PLZ 94612

Federal Buliding
1301 CLAY ST 94612

HOTELS

Hotel Oakland
270 13TH ST 94612

OXNARD

COLLEGES

Oxnard College
4000 S ROSE AVE 93033

PASADENA

BUILDINGS

Pasadena Federal Building
125 GRAND 91105

PLEASANTON

GOVERNMENT

City Of Pleasanton
520 PO BOX 94566

PORT HUENEME

GOVERNMENT

Port Hueneme City Hall
250 N VENTURA RD 93041

HOSPITALS

Port Hueneme Adventist
307 E CLARA ST 93041

RANCHO PALOS VERDES

BUILDINGS

Fidelity Fed Building
29000 S WESTERN AVE .. 90732

RIVERSIDE

BUILDINGS

Raincross Square
3443 N ORANGE ST 92501

Riverside Co Court House
4050 N MAIN ST 92501

SACRAMENTO

GOVERNMENT

Assembly
942849 PO BOX 94249

Attorney General
944255 PO BOX 94244

Board Of Equilization
942879 PO BOX 94279

California Highway Patrol
942898 PO BOX 94298

California State Library
942837 PO BOX 94237

Caltrans Public Works
942873 PO BOX 94273

Dept Of Conservation
944268 PO BOX 94244

Dept Of Corrections
942883 PO BOX 94283

Dept Of Education
944272 PO BOX 94244

Dept Of Food And Ag
942871 PO BOX 94271

Dept Of Forestry
944246 PO BOX 94244

Dept Of Highways
942874 PO BOX 94274

Dept Of Motor Veh Dr Lic
942890 PO BOX 94290

Dept Of Motor Veh Reg
942894 PO BOX 94294

Dept Of Parks And Rec
942896 PO BOX 94296

Dept Of Veterans Affairs
942895 PO BOX 94295

Dept Of Water Resources
942836 PO BOX 94236

Developmental Services
944202 PO BOX 94244

Energy Commission
944295 PO BOX 94244

Fish And Game Dept
944209 PO BOX 94244

Franchise Tax Gen Corresp
942840 PO BOX 94240

Franchise Tax Hra Claims
942886 PO BOX 94286

Franchise Tx Bank Inc Tax
942857 PO BOX 94257

Franchise Tx Per Incom Tx
942867 PO BOX 94267

General Services
942804 PO BOX 94204

Governors Office
942868 PO BOX 94268

Housing & Community Devel
952050 PO BOX 94252

Justice B N E
903397 PO BOX 94203

Justice B O C I
903357 PO BOX 94203

Justice C I I Branch
903387 PO BOX 94203

Justice Central Registry
903199 PO BOX 94203

Justice Central Services
903367 PO BOX 94203

Justice Charitable Trusts
903447 PO BOX 94203

Justice Criminal Stats
903427 PO BOX 94203

Justice Field Services
903281 PO BOX 94203

Justice Forensic Service
903337 PO BOX 94203

Justice Invest Enforce Br
903327 PO BOX 94203

Justice Latent Prints
903437 PO BOX 94203

Justice Law Enf Data Ctr
903307 PO BOX 94203

Justice Parent Locator
903300 PO BOX 94203

Justice Special Services
903417 PO BOX 94203

Lottery Comm Admin
942807 PO BOX 94207

Personnel Board
944234 PO BOX 94244

Public Emp Retirement Sys
942715 PO BOX 94229

Secretary Of State
944260 PO BOX 94244

Senate
942848 PO BOX 94248

State Controller
942850 PO BOX 94250

State Lottery Comm Lotto
942100 PO BOX 94211

Student Aid Commission
510845 PO BOX 94245

Treasury Dept
942809 PO BOX 94209

Vets Affrs Farm And Home
942888 PO BOX 94288

SALINAS

GOVERNMENT

Monterey Co Courthouse
240 CHURCH ST 93901

SAN BERNARDINO

GOVERNMENT

Federal Building
699 N ARROWHEAD AVE 92401

SAN DIEGO

BUILDINGS

5th Ave Financial Center
2550 5TH AVE 92103

Bank Of America Plaza
450 B ST 92101

Calif State Building
1350 FRONT ST 92101

Centre City Building
233 A ST 92101

Gaslamp Building
520 E ST 92101

Spreckles Building
121 BROADWAY 92101

Wells Fargo Building
101 W BROADWAY 92101

GOVERNMENT

County Court House
220 W BROADWAY 92101

San Diego County Building
1600 PACIFIC HWY 92101

MILITARY

Nas North Island
357033 PO BOX 92135

SAN FRANCISCO

APARTMENTS

Alexander Hamilton
631 OFARRELL ST 94109

Alexander Residence
230 EDDY ST 94102

Buckelew Building (apts)
155 JACKSON ST 94111

Carillon Towers
1100 GOUGH ST 94109

Cathedral Hills West
1333 GOUGH ST 94109

Comstock Apts
1333 JONES ST 94109

Dana Building (apts)
550 BATTERY ST 94111

Gramercy Tower
1177 CALIFORNIA ST 94108

Macondray House
405 DAVIS CT 94111

Mc Allister Tower Apts
100 MCALLISTER ST 94102

Silvercrest Res
133 SHIPLEY ST 94107

Wm Heath Davis
440 DAVIS CT 94111

Woolf House
801 HOWARD ST 94103

BUILDINGS

100 Pine St Building
100 PINE ST 94111

100 Spear St Building
100 SPEAR ST 94105

100 Van Ness Building
100 VAN NESS AVE 94102

111 Sutter Building
111 SUTTER ST 94104

1st Interstate Bank Building
405 MONTGOMERY ST ... 94104

350 Sansome Building
350 SANSOME ST 94104

550 Calif Building
550 CALIFORNIA ST 94104

601 Montgomery Building
601 MONTGOMERY ST 94111

Alcoa Building
1 MARITIME PLZ 94111

Alexander Building
155 MONTGOMERY ST ... 94104

B Of A Building
555 CALIFORNIA ST 94104

Bank Of Orient Building
233 SANSOME ST 94104

Bechtel-fremont Building
45 FREMONT ST 94105

Brooks Bro Building
209 POST ST 94108

Cal Academy Science Building
833 MARKET ST 94103

Cathedral Hill East
1200 GOUGH ST 94109

Central Towers
703 MARKET ST 94103

China Basin Building
185 BERRY ST 94107

David Hewes Building
995 MARKET ST 94103

Ecker Square Building
25 ECKER PL 94105

Flood Building
870 MARKET ST 94102

Fremont Center Building
50 FREMONT ST 94105

French Medical Center
4141 GEARY BLVD 94118

Hartford Building
650 CALIFORNIA ST 94108

Herbst Building
30 VAN NESS AVE 94102

Hobart Building
582 MARKET ST 94104

Hong Kong Bank Building
160 SANSOME ST 94104

Humboldt Bank Building
785 MARKET ST 94103

Industrial Indemnity Building
255 CALIFORNIA ST 94111

Insurance Exchange Building
433 CALIFORNIA ST 94104

Insurance Securities Building
100 CALIFORNIA ST 94111

Internationall Building
601 CALIFORNIA ST 94108

Kohl Building
400 CALIFORNIA ST 94104

Mckesson Plaza
1 POST ST 94104

Medical Building
450 SUTTER ST 94108

Medical-dental Building
490 POST ST 94102

Merchants Exchange
465 CALIFORNIA ST 94104

Metropolitan Building
425 MARKET ST 94105

Mills Building
220 MONTGOMERY ST ... 94104

Mills Tower
220 BUSH ST 94104

Monadnock Building
681 MARKET ST 94105

Montg/wash Tower
655 MONTGOMERY ST 94111

Montgomery Plaza
456 MONTGOMERY ST ... 94104

Mutual Benefit Life Building
1 CALIFORNIA ST 94111

New Montgomery Building
33 New Montgomery St 94105

One Montgomery St
1 MONTGOMERY ST 94104

P G & E Building
123 MISSION ST 94105

Pacific Gateway Building
201 MISSION ST 94105

Qantas Building
360 POST ST 94108

Shaklee Building
444 MARKET ST 94111

Shell Building
100 BUSH ST 94104

Shreve Building
210 POST ST 94108

Spear St Terrace
201 SPEAR ST 94105

Spear Tower
1 MARKET PLZ 94105

St Compensation Building
1275 MARKET ST 94103

Standard Oil Building
225 BUSH ST 94104

Standard Oil Building
575 MARKET ST 94105

Stevenson Building
71 STEVENSON ST 94105

The Gift Center
888 BRANNAN ST 94103

Tishman Building
525 MARKET ST 94105

Transamerica Building
600 MONTGOMERY ST 94111

Two Transamerica Center
505 SANSOME ST 94111

Wells Fargo Building
44 MONTGOMERY ST 94104

West Merchandise Mart
1355 MARKET ST 94103

GOVERNMENT

Appraisers Building
630 SANSOME ST 94111

City Hall
400 VAN NESS AVE 94102

Federal Building
450 GOLDEN GATE AVE .. 94102

Federal Office Building
50 UNITED NATIONS PLZ 94102

Hall Of Justice
850 BRYANT ST 94103

State Building
350 MCALLISTER ST 94102

State Building
455 GOLDEN GATE AVE .. 94102

V A Building
211 MAIN ST 94105

War Memorial Veterans Bld
401 VAN NESS AVE 94102

HOSPITALS

Ralph K. Davies Med. Ctr
45 CASTRO ST 94114

HOTELS

Minna Lee Hotel
149 6TH ST 94103

SAN JOSE

GOVERNMENT

San Jose City Hall
801 N 1ST ST 95110

Us Federal Building/court
280 S 1ST ST 95113

SAN LUIS OBISPO

GOVERNMENT

San Luis Obispo City Hall
990 PALM ST 93401

SANTA ANA

BUILDINGS

John Wayne Airport
18601 AIRPORT WAY 92707

SANTA BARBARA

BUILDINGS

Balboa Building
735 STATE ST 93101

El Paseo
814 STATE ST 93101

Freitas Building
200 E CARRILLO ST 93101

Granada Building
1216 STATE ST 93101

Howard Canfield Building
831 STATE ST 93101

La Arcada
1114 STATE ST 93101

Lobero Building
924 ANACAPA ST 93101

San Marcos Building
1129 STATE ST 93101

Victoria Court
1221 STATE ST 93101

GOVERNMENT

County Admin Building
105 E ANAPAMU ST 93101

County Engineering Building
123 E ANAPAMU ST 93101

Public Library
40 E ANAPAMU ST 93101

Victoria Court Station
1221 STATE ST 93101

COLLEGES

City College
721 CLIFF DR 93109

SANTA SUSANA

GOVERNMENT

Simi Valley City Hall
2929 TAPO CANYON RD . 93063

Santa Susana Station
4212 E Los Angeles Ave ... 93063

HOSPITAL

Valley Vista Conv. Hosp
5270 LOS ANGELES 93063

SIMI VALLEY

GOVERNMENT

Simi Valley Courthouse
3200 COCHRAN ST 93065

HOSPITALS

Simi Valley Adventist Hos
1575 ERRINGER RD 93065

Simi Valley Adventist Hsp
2975 SYCAMORE DR 93065

West Valley Medical Ctr
1376 ERRINGER RD 93065

TORRANCE

GOVERNMENT

South Bay Municipal Court
825 MAPLE AVE 90503

VALLEJO

GOVERNMENT

City Hall
555 SANTA CLARA ST 94590

VAN NUYS

GOVERNMENT

City Hall
14410 SYLVAN ST 91401

Federal Building
6230 VAN NUYS BLVD 91401

State Office Building
6150 VAN NUYS BLVD 91401

VENTURA

GOVERNMENT

Ventura Co Govt Center
800 S VICTORIA AVE 93009

WHITTIER

HOTELS

Whittier Hilton
7320 GREENLEAF AVE 90602

WOODLAND

GOVERNMENT

Yolo County Admin Building
625 COURT ST 95695

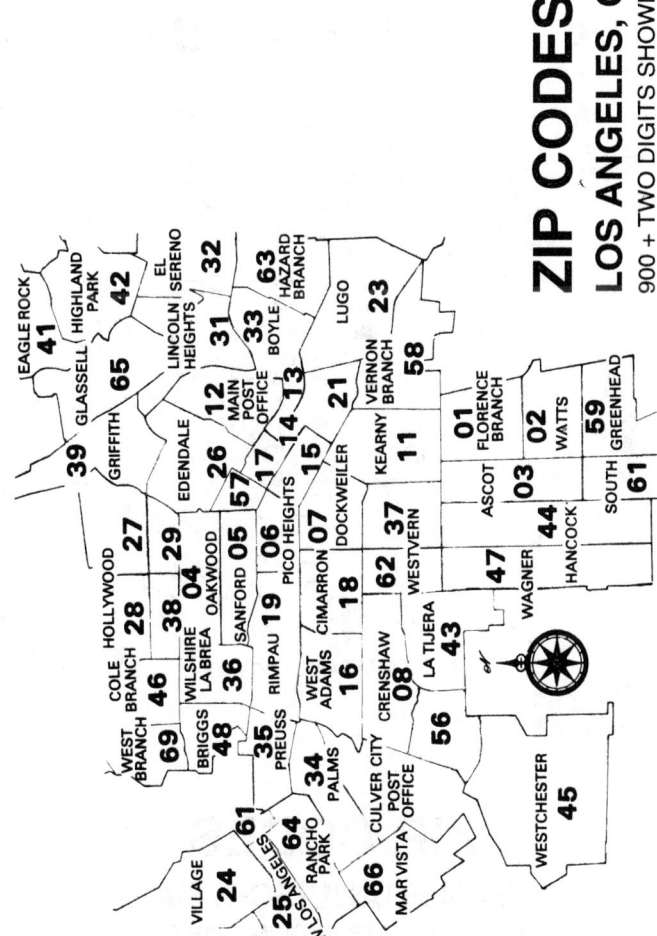

ZIP CODES
LOS ANGELES, CA
900 + TWO DIGITS SHOWN = ZIP CODE

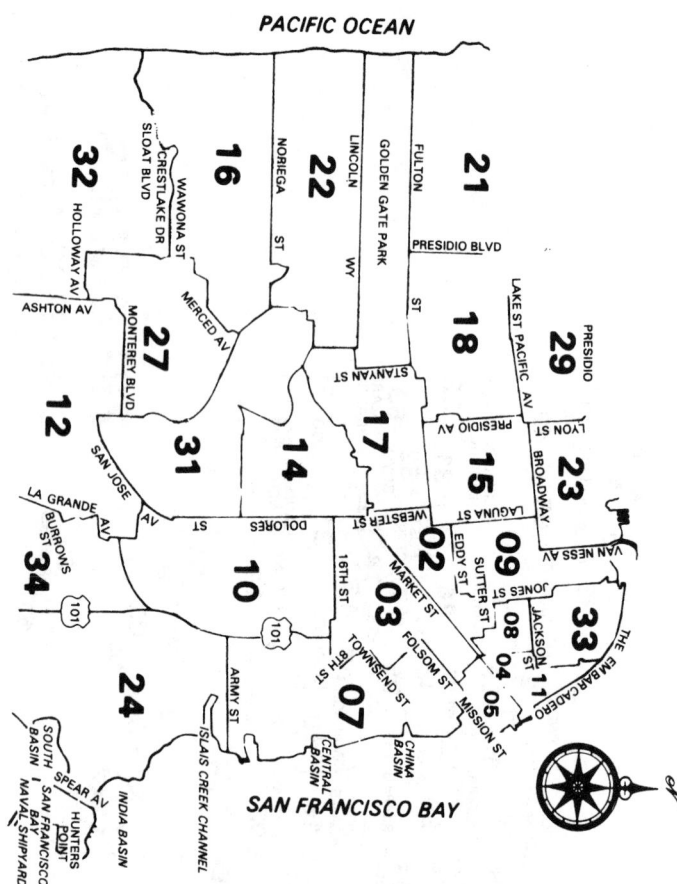

ZIP CODES
SAN FRANCISCO, CA
941 + TWO DIGITS SHOWN = ZIP CODE

COLORADO
Abreviation CO

Adams City 80022
   (Commerce City)
Adams State College 81102
   (Alamosa)
Affiliated Banks Service Co 80263
   (Denver)
Agate 80101
Aguilar 81020
Akron 80720
Alamosa 81101-102
   Adams State College .. 81102
   Carmel 81101
   East Alamosa 81101
   Estrella 81101
   Great Sand Dunes 81101
   Henry 81101
   Stanley 81101
   Washington 81101
   Waverly 81101
Allenspark 80510
Allison (Ignacio) 81137
Alma 80420
Almont 81210
Alpine (South Fork) 81154
Alpine Village (Nathrop) ... 81236
Amherst 80721
Amo (Peyton) 80831
Antlers (Rifle) 81650
Anton 80801
Antonito 81120
Appleton (Grand Junction) 81505
Aqua Ramon (Del Norte) ... 81132
Arapahoe 80802
Arapahoe County Offices . 80166
   (Littleton)
Arboles 81121
Arickaree (Anton) 80801
Ark Valley Corr Facl 81034
   (Crowley)
Arlington 81021
Aroya (Wild Horse) 80862
Arriba 80804
Arriola (Cortez) 81321
Arvada 80001-006, 80403
   Westminster 80003
   Westminster 80005
   Wheat Ridge 80002
Aspen 81611-612
Aspen-gerbaz (Aspen) 81611
ATT Information Systems .. 80275
   (Denver)
Atwood 80722
Ault 80610
Aurora
      80010-019, 80040-042
   80044-047, 80220, 80231
   Buckley ANG Base 80011
   Denver 80014
   Fitzsimons Army Med ... 80045
Austin 81410
Avon 81620
Avondale 81022
Axel (Meeker) 81641
Bailey 80421
Baldwin (Gunnison) 81230
Bank Americard (Denver) . 80252
Barton (Granada) 81041
Basalt 81621

Battlement Mesa (Parachute)
   81635-636
Baxter (Pueblo) 81006
Baxterville (Del Norte) 81132
Bayfield 81122
Bear Creek (La Veta) 81055
Bear Mine (Somerset) 81434
Beaver Creek (Avon) 81620
Bedrock 81411
Belle Plain (Pueblo) 81001
Bellvue 80512
Belmont (Pueblo) 81001
Bennett 80102
Bents Fort (La Junta) 81050
Bents Old Fort (La Junta) . 81050
Berthoud 80513
Beshoar Junction 81082
   (Trinidad)
Bessemer (Pueblo) 81004
Bethune 80805
Beulah 81023
Big Bend (Wiley) 81092
Black Forest 80908
   (Colorado Springs)
Black Hawk (Golden) 80403, 422
Blanca 81123
Blende (Pueblo) 81006
Blue Cross Blue Shield 80273
   (Denver)
Blue Mountain (Dinosaur) . 81610
Bonanza City 81155
   (Villa Grove)
Boncarbo 81024
Bond 80423
Boone 81025
Boulder ... 80301-304, 80306-310
    .... 80314, 80321-323
    80328-329
   I B M 80314
   Neodata 80329
   Neodata Business Rep 80321
   Neodata Business Rep 80328
   Residence Halls UC ... 80310
   University Of Colorado 80309
Bountiful (La Jara) 81140
Bovina (Genoa) 80818
Bow Mar (Littleton) 80123
Bowie (Paonia) 81428
Boyero 80806
Brandon 81026, 81036
   Eads 81026
Branson 81027
Breckenridge 80424
Breen (Hesperus) 81326
Brewster (Florence) 81226
Briggsdale 80611
Brighton 80601
Bristol 81028, 81047
   Holly 81028
Broadacre (Avondale) 81022
Broomfield 80020-021, 80038
    80234
   Thornton 80020
   Westminster 80020-80021
Browns Park (Maybell) 81640
Brush 80723
Buckley Air Natl Guard 80011
   (Aurora)
Buckskin Joe (Canon City) 81212
Buena Vista 81211
Buffalo Creek 80425

Buford (Meeker) 81641
Burlington 80807
Burns 80426
Byers 80103
C O Interstate Gas 80944
   (Colorado Springs)
Cablevision 80945
   (Colorado Springs)
Caddoa (Hasty) 81044
Cadet Station 80841
   (U S A F Academy)
Cahone 81320
Calhan 80808
Campo 81029
Canon City 81212, 81215, 81246
   Buckskin Joe 81212
   Ilse 81212
   Parkdale 81212
   Penitentiary 81212
   Prospect Heights 81212
   Royal Gorge 81246
Capulin 81124
Carbondale 81623
Cardiff 81601
   (Glenwood Springs)
Carlton (Lamar) 81052
Carmel (Alamosa) 81101
Carr 80612
Cascade 80809
Castle Rock 80104
Cedaredge 81413
Cedarwood (Rye) 81069
Cement Creek 81224
   (Crested Butte)
Center 81125
Central Bank & Trust 80292
   (Denver)
Central City 80427
Chama 81126
Cheney Center (Holly) 81047
Cheraw 81030
Cherry Hills Village (Englewood)
   80110-111
Cheyenne Mt Complex 80914
   (Colorado Springs)
Cheyenne Mtn A. F. B. 80914
   (Colorado Springs)
Cheyenne Wells 80810
Chimney Rock 81127
Chipita Park (Cascade) 80809
Chivington (Eads) 81036
Chromo 81128
Cimarron 81220
Cinderella City 80154
   (Englewood)
Clark 80428
Cleora (Salida) 81201
Clifton 81520
Climax 80429
CO Spgs Utilities 80947
   (Colorado Springs)
Coal Creek 81221
Coalby (Cedaredge) 81413
Coaldale 81222
Coalmont 80430
Cokedale 81032
Collbran 81624
College Heights (Durango) 81301
Colona (Montrose) 81401
Colorado City 81019
Colorado College 80946

Denver 80110
Greenwood Village 80110-112
Sheridan 80110
Ent Air Force Base 80912
(Colorado Springs)
Erie80516
Espinoza (Antonito) 81120
Estes Park 80511, 80517
Rocky Mountain Pk 80517
Estrella (Alamosa) 81101
Evans 80620
Evergreen 80439
Exchange Natl Bank 80943
(Colorado Springs)
Fair View (La Junta) 81050
Fairmont (La Junta) 81050
Fairplay (Como)
.... 80432, 80440, 80456
Falcon (Peyton) 80831
Falcon Air Force Base 80912
(Colorado Springs)
Farisita (Gardner) ... 81040, 81089
Farista (Walsenburg) 81089
Federal Bldg/US Courthouse
(Denver) 80294
Federal Correctional Cpx .. 81290
(Florence)
Federal Heights (Denver) .. 80221
Firestone 80520
First Interstate Bank (Denver)
.... 80270-271
First Interstate Twr South .. 80293
(Denver)
First National Bank 80942
(Colorado Springs)
First View 80810
(Cheyenne Wells)
Fitzsimons Army Med Junc 80045
(Aurora)
Flagler 80815
Fleming 80728
Florence 81226, 81290
Brewster 81226
Federal Correctional Complex
.... 81290
Portland 81226
Williamsburg 81226
Florida (Antonito) 81120
Florissant 80816
Florissant Fossil Beds Nat Pk
(Florissant) 80816
Focus On The Family 80995
(Colorado Springs)
Forbes Park 81133
(Fort Garland)
Fort Bent (La Junta) 81050
Fort Carson 80913
(Colorado Springs)
Fort Collins .. 80521-527, 80553
Colorado State Univ ... 80523
Teledyne Water Pik 80553
Fort Garland 81133
Fort Logan (Denver) 80236
Fort Lupton 80621
Fort Lyon 81038
Fort Morgan
.... 80701, 80705, 80742
Fountain 80817
Fowler 81039
Fox Creek (Antonito) 81120
Foxton 80441

Franktown 80116
Fraser 80442
Frederick 80530
Freeman (Del Norte) 81132
Frisco 80443
Fruita 81521
Fruitvale 81504
(Grand Junction)
G P O (Pueblo) 81009
Galeton 80622
Garcia 81134
Garden City (Greeley) 80631
Gardner 81040
Gateway 81522
Gem Village (Bayfield) 81122
Genoa 80818
Georgetown 80444
Gilcrest 80623
Gill 80624
Gilman (Minturn) 81645
Glade Park 81523
Glen Haven 80532
Glendale (Denver) 80222
Glenwood Springs
.... 81601-602, 81628
Cardiff 81601
North Name 81601
West Glenwood 81601
Golden 80401-403, 80419
Arvada 80403
Black Hawk 80403
Jefferson County 80419
Lakewood 80401
Pine Cliff 80403
Rollinsville 80403
Goldfield (Victor) 80860
Granada 81041
Granby 80446
Grand Junction . 81501-06, 81523
Appleton 81505
Fruitvale 81504
Orchard Mesa 81503
Redlands 81503
Grand Lake (Granby) . 80446-447
Grand Mesa (Cedaredge) . 81413
Grand Valley (Parachute) .. 81635
Granite 81228
Grant 80448
Great Sand Dunes Nat Mo . 81101
(Alamosa)
Greeley ... 80631-634, 80638-639
Garden City 80631
State Farm Ins 80638
Univ Of No Colo 80639
Green Mtn. (Lakewood) 80228
Green Mountain Falls 80819
Greenwood (Rye) ... 81069, 81253
Greenwood Village (Englewood)
.... 80110-112, 80121
Greystone (Maybell) 81640
Grover 80729
Guffey 80820
Gulnare 81042
Gunnison 81230-231, 81247
Baldwin 81230
Doyleville 81230
Iola 81230
Sapinero 81247
Taylor Park 81230
Western State College . 81231
Windy Point 81247

Gypsum 81637
Hale (Idalia) 80735
Hamilton 81638
Hartman 81043, 81047
Holly 81043
Hartsel 80449
Hasty 81044
Haswell 81045
Hawley (Rocky Ford) 81067
Haxtun 80731
Hayden 81639
Heeney (Silverthorne) 80498
Henderson 80640
Henry (Alamosa) 81101
Hereford 80732
Hermosa (Durango) 81301
Hesperus 81326
Higbee (La Junta) 81050
Highlands Ranch 80126
(Littleton)
Hillrose 80733
Hillside 81232
Hoehne 81046
Holly (Bristol)
.... 81028, 81043, 81047
Bristol 81047
Cheney Center 81047
Hartman 81047
Holyoke 80734
Homelake 81135
Hooper 81136
Horn Creek (Westcliffe) 81252
Hot Sulphur Springs 80451
Hotchkiss 81419
Hovenweep National Mnt
(Cortez) 81321
Howard 81233
Hoyt (Wiggins) 80654
Hudson 80642
Hugo 80821
Hygiene 80533
I B M (Boulder) 80314
Idaho Springs 80452
Idalia 80735
Idledale 80453
Ignacio 81137
Iliff 80736
Ilse (Canon City) 81212
Indian Agency (Ignacio) 81137
Indian Creek (La Veta) 81055
Indian Hills 80454
Iola (Gunnison) 81230
Iron City (Nathrop) 81236
Irondale (Commerce City) . 80022
Jacks Cabin (Almont) 81210
Jamestown 80455
Jansen (Trinidad) 81082
Jaroso 81138
Jefferson 80456
Jefferson County (Golden) . 80419
Joes 80822
John Martin Reservoir 81044
(Hasty)
Johnson Village 81211
(Buena Vista)
Johnstown 80534
Julesburg 80737
Karval 80823
Keenesburg 80643
Kersey 80644
Keystone (Dillon) 80435

Kim 81049
Kiowa 80117
Kirk 80824
Kit Carson 80825
Kittredge 80457
Kline (Hesperus) 81326
Koen (Granada) 81041
Kornman (Lamar) 81052
Kremmling 80459
La Isla (Antonito) 81120
La Jara 81140
La Junta 81050
La Salle 80645
La Valley (San Pablo) 81153
La Veta 81055
Lafayette 80026
Laird (Wray) 80758
Lake City 81235
Lake George 80827
Lakewood (Wheat Ridge) . 80033
.... 80214-215, 80225-228
.... 80232, 80235, 80401
    Green Mountain 80228
    Morrison 80228
    Wheat Ridge 80215
Lamar 81052
Laporte 80535
Lariat (Monte Vista) 81144
Larkspur 80118
Las Animas 81054
Las Mesitas (Antonito) 81120
Lasauses (Sanford) 81151
Lascar (Rye) 81069
Last Chance (Woodrow) .. 80757
Lay (Craig) 81625
Lazear 81420
Leadville (Climax) .. 80429, 80461
Lewis 81327
Limon 80826, 80828
Limon Correctional Facility 80826
    (Limon)
Lincoln Center Bldg 80264
    (Denver)
Lincoln Tower Bldg 80295
    (Denver)
Lindon 80740
Littleton ... 80120-127, 80160-162
.... 80165-166
    Arapahoe County Off .. 80166
    Bow Mar 80123
    Columbine Valley 80123
    Denver 80123
    Denver 80127
    Greenwood Village 80121
    Highlands Ranch 80126
Littleton City Offices 80165
    (Littleton)
Livermore 80536, 80545
    Red Feather Lakes 80536
    Virginia Dale 80536
Lobatos (Antonito) 81120
Lochbuie (Brighton) 80601
Log Lane Village 80705
Loma 81524
Longmont 80501-504
Los Fuertes (San Pablo) 81153
Los Pinas (Antonito) 81120
Louisville 80027-028
    Storage Technology Corp
    80028
    Superior 80027

Louviers 80131
Loveland 80537-539
Lowry Air Force Base 80230
Lubers (Mc Clave) 81057
Lucerne 80646
Ludlow (Trinidad) 81082
Lycan (Two Buttes) 81084
Lyons 80540
Mack 81525
Maher 81421
Main Office (Pueblo)
    .... 81002-003, 81008
Manassa 81141
Mancos 81328
Manitou Springs 80829
Manzanola 81058
Marble (Carbondale) 81623
Marvel 81329
Masonic Park (South Fork) . 81154
Masonville 80541
Massadona (Dinosaur) 81610
Matheson 80830
Maxey (Springfield) 81073
Maxeyville (Monte Vista) 81144
May Valley (Lamar) 81052
Maybell 81640
Maysville (Salida) 81201
Mc Clave 81057
Mc Coy 80463
Mead 80542
Meeker 81641
Meredith 81642
Meridian Lake 81225
    (Crested Butte)
Merino 80741
Mesa (Pueblo) 81004, 81643
Mesa Verde National Park . 81330
Mesita (San Luis) 81152
Milliken 80543
Minturn 81645
Mirage (Moffat) 81143
Model 81059
Moffat 81143
Mogote (Antonito) 81120
Molina 81646
Monarch 81227
Monte Vista (Homelake)
    .... 81135, 81144
    Lariat 81144
    Maxeyville 81144
    Sargents School 81144
Montrose 81401-402
    Colona 81401
Monument 80132
Monument Lake Park 81091
    (Weston)
Monument Park (Weston) . 81091
Morgan (La Jara) 81140
Morrison (Lakewood)
    .... 80228, 80465
Mosca 81146
Mount Crested Butte 81225
    (Crested Butte)
Mount Princeton (Nathrop) 81236
Mountain Bell (Denver) 80244
Mountain View (Denver) ... 80212
Mt Crested Butte 81225
    (Crested Butte)
Mutual (Walsenburg) 81089
Nast (Meredith) 81642
Nathrop 81236

National Farmers Union 80251
    (Denver)
Naturita 81422
Navajo State Park 81121
    (Arboles)
Nederland 80466
Neodata (Boulder)
    .... 80322-323, 80329
Neodata Business Reply
    (Boulder) 80321, 80328
New Castle 81647
New Liberty (Mack) 81525
New Raymer 80742
Ninaview (Las Animas) 81054
Niwot 80544
Norrie (Meredith) 81642
North Avondale (Avondale) 81022
North La Junta (La Junta) . 81050
North Name 81601
    (Glenwood Springs)
North Pole (Cascade) 80809
Northglenn (Denver)
    ... 80221, 80233-234, 80241
Norwest Bank Denver (Denver)
    .... 80274, 80281, 80291
Norwood 81423
Nucla 81424
Numa (Ordway) 81063
Nunn 80648
Oak Creek 80467
Ohio City 81237
Ojo (La Veta) 81055
Olathe 81425
Old Snowmass 81654
    (Snowmass)
Olney Springs 81062
Olympic Comm 80950
    (Colorado Springs)
Ophir 81426
Orchard 80649
Orchard City (Austin)
    .... 81410, 81418
Orchard Mesa 81503
    (Grand Junction)
Ordway 81063
Ortiz (Antonito) 81120
Otis 80743
Ouray 81427
Ovid 80744
Oxford (Ignacio) 81137
Padroni 80745
Pagoda (Hamilton) 81638
Pagosa Springs ... 81147, 81157
Paisaje (Antonito) 81120
Palisade 81526
Palmer Lake 80133
Pandora (Telluride) 81435
Paoli 80746
Paonia 81428
Parachute 81635-636
    Battlement Mesa 81635
    Grand Valley 81635
    Rulison 81635
Paradox 81429
Parkdale (Canon City) 81212
Parker 80134
Parlin 81239
Parshall 80468
Peetz 80747
Penitentiary (Canon City) .. 81212
Penrose 81240

Peterson Air Force Base ... 80914	Residence Halls Univ Of CO	Sheridan Lake 81071
(Colorado Springs)	(Boulder) 80310	Silt 81652
Peyton 80831	Richfield (La Jara) 81140	Silver Cliff 81249
Phippsburg 80469	Rico 81332	Silver Plume 80476
Piedra (Chimney Rock) 81127	Ridgway 81432	Silverthorne 80498
Piedre Park (Arboles) 81121	Rifle 81650	Silverton 81433
Pierce 80650	Rio Blanco (Rifle) 81650	Simla 80835
Pine (Buffalo Creek)	Riverbend (Crested Butte) . 81225	Skyland (Crested Butte) ... 81225
.... 80425, 80470	Roberta (La Junta) 81050	Slater 81653
Pine Cliff (Golden) 80403	Rockrimmon 80949	Slick Rock 81333
Pinecliffe 80471	(Colorado Springs)	Small Business Adm 80259
Pinon (Pueblo) 81008	Rockvale 81244	(Denver)
Pinon Canyon (Trinidad) ... 81082	Rocky Ford 81067	Smeltertown (Salida) 81201
Pitkin 81241	Rocky Mountain National Pk	Snowmass 81654
Placerville 81430	(Estes Park) 80517	Snowmass Village 81615
Plateau City (Collbran) 81624	Rogers Mesa (Hotchkiss) .. 81419	Snyder 80750
Platteville 80651	Roggen 80652	Somerset 81434
Plaza (Del Norte) 81132	Rollinsville (Golden)	Sopris (Trinidad) 81082
Pleasant View 81331	.... 80403, 80474	South Fork 81154
Poncha Springs 81242	Romeo 81148	South Ute Indian Res 81137
Portland (Florence) 81226	Rosita (Westcliffe) 81252	(Ignacio)
Powderhorn 81243	Royal Gorge (Canon City) . 81246	Spar City (Creede) 81130
Pritchett 81064	Ruedi (Basalt) 81621	Spring Creek (Almont) 81210
Prospect Heights 81212	Rulison (Parachute)	Springfield 81073
(Canon City)	.... 81635, 81650	Squaw Point (Dove Creek) 81324
Prowers (Lamar) 81052	Rush 80833	Stanley (Alamosa) 81101
Prudential Plaza Bldg 80265	Rye81069	Starkville 81074
(Denver)	Saguache 81149	State Farm Ins (Greeley) ... 80638
Pryor 81065, 81089	Saint Elmo (Nathrop) 81236	Steamboat Springs
Public Service Company ... 80255	Salida 81201, 81227-228	.... 80477, 80487-488
(Denver)	.... 81232, 81237, 81251	Sterling 80751
Pueblo 81001-015	Cleora 81201	Stoneham 80754
Baxter 81006	Maysville 81201	Stoner (Dolores) 81323
Belle Plain 81001	Smeltertown 81201	Stonewall (Weston) 81091
Belmont 81001	Swissvale 81201	Stonington 81075, 81090
Bessemer 81004	Turret 81201	Storage Technology Corp .. 80028
Blende 81006	Wellsville 81201	(Louisville)
Colorado Lottery 81010-12	San Acacio 81150	Strasburg 80136
Columbia House ... 81013-15	San Antonio (Antonito) 81120	Stratton 80836
Devine 81001	San Francisco (San Pablo) . 81153	Sugar City 81076
G P O 81009	San Isabel (Rye) 81069	Summitville (Del Norte) 81132
Main Office 81008	San Juan (Segundo) 81070	Sunset (Pueblo)
Mesa 81004	San Luis (Garcia) 81134, 81152	.... 81004, 81006
Pinon 81008	Mesita 81152	Superior (Louisville) 80027
Sunset 81004	Wildhorse Mesa 81152	Sweetwater (Gypsum) 81637
Sunset 81006	San Miguel (Antonito) 81120	Swink 81077
Vineland 81006	San Pablo 81153	Swissvale (Salida) 81201
West Pueblo 81007	San Pedro (San Pablo) 81153	Tabernash 80478
Pueblo Army Depot 81001	San Rafael (Antonito) 81120	Tamarron (Durango) 81301
(Pueblo)	Sanford 81151	Tanglewood Acres 81252
Pueblo Depot Activity 81001	Sangre De Cristo Ranches 81133	(Westcliffe)
(Pueblo)	(Fort Garland)	Tarryall (Lake George) 80827
Pueblo West (Pueblo) 81007	Sapinero (Gunnison) 81247	Taylor Park (Almont)
Punkin Center (Hugo)	Sargents 81248	.... 81210, 81230
.... 80821, 81063	Sargents School 81144	Teledyne Water Pik 80553
Purgatory (Durango) 81301	(Monte Vista)	(Fort Collins)
Rainbow (Almont) 81210	Sawpit (Placerville)	Telluride 81435
Ramah 80832	.... 81430, 81435	Tercio (Weston) 81091
Rand 80473	Security (Colorado Springs)	Texas Creek (Cotopaxi) 81223
Rangely 81648	.... 80911, 80925	Thatcher (Model) 81059
Raymer (New Raymer) 80742	Sedalia 80135	Thornton (Broomfield)
Red Cliff 81649	Sedgwick 80749	.... 80020, 80221, 80229
Red Feather Lakes (Livermore)	Segundo 81070, 81082	.... 80233, 80241, 80601
.... 80536, 80545	San Juan 81070	Tiffany (Ignacio) 81137
Livermore 80545	Valdez 81070	Timber Lake (La Junta) 81050
Red Mountain (Ouray) 81427	Seibert 80834	Tinnath 80547
Red Wing 81066	Severance 80546	Timpas (La Junta) 81050
Redlands (Grand Junction) 81503	Shady Camp (Lamar) 81052	Tincup (Almont) 81210
Redmesa (Hesperus) 81326	Shawnee 80475	Toltec (Walsenburg) 81089
Redstone (Carbondale) 81623	Sheridan (Englewood)	Toonerville (Las Animas) ... 81054
Redvale 81431	.... 80110, 80236	Toponas 80479

Torres Canon (Weston)	81091
Towaoc	81334
Towner (Sheridan Lake)	81071
Track City (Antonito)	81120
Trinchera	81081
Trinidad (Starkville)	
.... 81074,	81082
Beshoar Junction	81082
El Moro	81082
Jansen	81082
Ludlow	81082
Pinon Canyon	81082
Segundo	81082
Sopris	81082
Truckton (Yoder)	80864
Turret (Salida)	81201
Twin Lakes	81251
Twin Rock (Florissant)	80816
Two Buttes	81084
Two United Bank Junction	80290
(Denver)	
Tyrone (Model)	81059
USAF Academy 81654,	80840
Univ Of Colorado Med Jtn .	80262
(Denver)	
Univ Of Denver (Denver) ..	80208
Univ Of No Colo (Greeley)	80639
University Of Colorado	80309
(Boulder)	
US Court Of Appeals 10th Cir	
(Denver)	80257
US Olympic Committee	80977
(Colorado Springs)	
Ute Mountain Indian Res ..	81334
(Towaoc)	
Ute Pass	80819
(Green Mountain Falls)	
Utleyville (Pritchett)	81064
Vail 81657-658	
East Vail	81657
West Vail	81657
Valdez (Segundo)	81070
Vallecito (Bayfield)	81122
Vernon	80755

Victor	80860
Vigil (Weston)	81091
Vilas	81087
Villa Grove	81155
Villegreen (Kim)	81049
Vineland (Pueblo)	81006
Virginia Dale (Livermore) ..	80536
Vona	80861
Vroman (Rocky Ford)	81067
Wagon Wheel Gap	81154
(South Fork)	
Wahatoya (La Veta)	81055
Walden (Coalmont)	
.... 80430,	80480
Walsenburg (Red Wing)	
.... 81066,	81089
Farisita	81089
Mutual	81089
Pryor	81089
Toltec	81089
Walsh	81090
Walter Drake	80940
(Colorado Springs)	
Ward	80481
Washington (Alamosa)	81101
Watkins	80137
Wattenburg (Fort Lupton) ..	80621
Waverly (Alamosa)	81101
Welby (Denver)	80229
Weldona	80653
Wellington	80549
Wellsville (Salida)	81201
West Farm (Lamar)	81052
West Glenwood	81601
(Glenwood Springs)	
West Pueblo (Pueblo)	81007
West Vail (Vail)	81657
West Village	81615
(Snowmass Village)	
Westcliffe	81252
Western Area (Denver)	80299
Western State College	81231
(Gunnison)	
Westminster (Arvada)	

.... 80003, 80005, 80020-021	
.... 80030-031, 80035-036	
.... 80221, 80234	
Weston	81091
Westwood Lake	80863
(Woodland Park)	
Wetmore	81253
Wheat Ridge (Arvada)	
.... 80002, 80033-034, 80212	
.... 80214-215	
Lakewood	80033
Wheatridge	80034
Wheatridge (Wheat Ridge)	80034
White Pine (Sargents)	81248
Whitewater	81527
Widefield	80911
(Colorado Springs)	
Wiggins	80654
Wild Horse	80862
Wildhorse Mesa (San Luis)	81152
Wiley	81092
Willard (Merino)	80741
Williamsburg (Florence)	81226
Windsor 80550-551	
Eastman Kodak Co	80551
Windy Point (Gunnison)	81247
Winter Park	80482
Wolcott	81655
Woodland Park 80863, 80866	
Crystola	80863
Westwood Lake	80863
Woodmoor (Monument)	80132
Woodrow	80757
Woody Creek	81656
Wray	80758
Yampa	80483
Yellow Jacket	81335
Yoder	80864
Yuma	80759

Stafford	06075
Stafford Springs	06076
Staffordville	06077
Stamford . 06900-907, 06910-914	
...... 06920-922, 06925-028	
Glenbrook	06906
Ridgeway	06905
Springdale	06907
Stepney (Monroe)	06468
Sterling	06377
Stevenson	06491
Stonington	06378
Storrs Mansfield	06268-269
Stratford	06497
Suffield 06078, 06080, 06093	
Taconic	06079
Taftville	06380
Talcott Village	06032
(Farmington)	
Talcottville	06066
(Vernon Rockville)	
Tariffville	06081
Terryville	06786
Thomaston 06778, 06787	
(Northfield)	
Northfield	06787
Thompson	06277
Thompsonville (Enfield)	06082
Tokeneke (Darien)	06820
Tolland	06084
Torrington	06790-791
Trumbull	06611
Turnpike	06066
(Vernon Rockville)	
Twin Lakes (Taconic)	06079
Uncasville	06382
Union (Stafford Springs)	06076
Union City (Naugatuck)	06770
Unionville ... 06013, 06085, 06087	
(Burlington)	
Burlington	06085

Farmington	06085
Lake Garda	06085
Upper Stepney (Monroe)	06468
Vernon (Vernon Rockville)	06066
Vernon Rockville	06066
Versailles	06383
Voluntown	06384
Wallingford	06492-494
Wapping (South Windsor) . 06074	
Warehouse Point	06088
(East Windsor)	
Warren 06754, 06777	
(Cornwall Bridge)	
Warrenville (Ashford)	06278
Washington ... 06777, 06793-794	
(New Preston Marble Dale)	
Washington Green	06793
(Washington Depot)	
Waterbury ... 06701-706, 06708	
.... 06710, 06712, 06716	
.... 06720-726, 06749	
East End	06705
Plaza	06704
Waterford	06385-386
Watertown 06779, 06795	
Oakville	06795
Wauregan	06387
Weatogue	06089
Wesleyan (Middletown)	06459
West Ashford	06250
(Mansfield Center)	
West Cornwall	06796
West Granby	06090
West Hartford .. 06105-107, 06110	
.... 06117, 06119	
...... 06127, 06133, 06137	
(Hartford)	
West Hartland	06091
West Haven	06516
West Mystic	06388
West Redding (Redding) ... 06896	

West Simsbury	06092
West Stafford	06076
(Stafford Springs)	
West Suffield	06093
West Wauregan	06387
(Wauregan)	
West Willington	06279
West Woods (Sharon)	06069
Westbrook	06498
Weston	06883
Westport	06880-88
.... 06888-06889	
Saugatuck	06880
Westville (New Haven)	06515
Wethersfield 06109, 06129	
Hartford	06109
Hartford	06129
Whitneyville (Hamden)	06517
Willimantic	06226
Willington	06279
(West Willington)	
Wilson (Windsor)	06095
Wilton	06897
Winchester (Winsted)	06098
Winchester Center	06094
Windham 06256, 06280	
(North Windham)	
Windsor 06006, 06095	
Windsor Locks	06096
Windsorville	06016
(Broad Brook)	
Winsted 06094, 06098	
(Winchester Center)	
Winchester	06098
Wolcott	06716
Woodbridge	06525
Woodbury	06798
Woodstock	06281
Woodstock Valley	06282
Yalesville (Wallingford)	06492
Yantic	06389

BISHOPS CORNER

COLLEGES

Saint Joseph College
1678 Asylum Ave 06117

University Of Conn
1800 Asylum Ave 06117

University Of Hartford
200 Bloomfield Ave 06117

BLUE HILLS

HOSPITALS

Mount Sinai Hospital
500 Blue Hills Ave 06112

BUCKLAND

GOVERNMENT

Town Hall
41 Center St 06040

CENTRAL

APARTMENTS

Bushnell Ii
100 Wells St 06103

Bushnell Towers
1 Gold St 06103

BUILDINGS

100 Pearl St
100 Pearl St 06103

American Plaza
915 Main St 06103

City Hall Building
550 Main St 06103

Cityplace
185 Asylum St 06103

Civic Center Plz
225 Trumbull St 06103

Constitution Plaza
100 Constitution Plz 06103

Financial Plz
755 Main St 06103

Metro Ctr
1 Metro Ctr 06103

One State St
1 State St 06103

State House Sq
10 State House Sq 06103

GOVERNMENT

Federal Building
135 High St 06103

Federal Building
450 Main St 06103

HOTELS

Sheraton Hotel
315 Trumbull St 06103

DANBURY

APARTMENTS

Birchwood Condo Building 1
27 Crows Nest Ln 06810

Crossroads
1 Beaver Brook Rd 06810

Lake Place
11 Boulevard Dr 06810

Putnam Towers
25 Beaver St 06810

Triangle Apts Building 1
126 Triangle St 06810

BUILDINGS

Danbury Fair Mall
7 Backus Ave 06810

GOVERNMENT

Court House
146 White St 06810

Danbury City Hall
155 Deer Hill Ave 06810

EAST END

APARTMENTS

119 East Apts
119 Store Ave 06705

Chelsea Sq Condos
975 Meriden Rd 06705

Countrywood Hill Est
380 Hitchcock Rd 06705

East Line Condo
1568 Meriden Rd 06705

Eastgate Apts
2171 E Main St 06705

Eastgate Apts #2
2221 E Main St 06705

Eastwood Ter Apt
329-366 Schraffts Dr 06705

Eastwood Ter Apts
3-6 Gayridge Rd 06705

Hamilton Park Apts
1660 E Main St 06705

Hillcrest Condo
138 Hillcrest Ave 06705

Laur Ray Apts
136 Store Ave 06705

Mall View Apts
30 Framingham Dr 06705

Maplewood Manor Apts
1030 Meriden Rd 06705

BUILDINGS

625 Plaza
625 Wolcott St 06705

Naugatuck Valley Mall
920 Wolcott St 06705

Shoppers Plaza
835 Wolcott St 06705

HARTFORD

APARTMENTS

Hampshire House
887 Farmington Ave 06119

Hampshire House
893 Farmington Ave 06119

Woodland House
31 Woodland St 06105

BUILDINGS

Hartford Sq North
10 Columbus Blvd 06106

Jefferson Medical Building
85 Seymour St 06106

Medical Building
1000 Asylum Ave 06105

Seymour St Medical Building
85 Seymour St 06106

State Legislature
300 Capitol Ave 06106

Woodland Medical Center
140 Woodland St 06105

Xerox Centre
25 Sigourney St 06106

GOVERNMENT

CT Legislative Building
300 Capitol Ave 06106

State Office Building
165 Capitol Ave 06106

Town Hall
131 Cedar St 06111

HOSPITALS

Institute Of Living
200 Retreat Ave 06102

Newington Childrens Hosp
181 E Cedar St 06111

Saint Francis Hospital
114 Woodland St 06105

Veterans Hospital
555 Willard Ave 06111

COLLEGES

Hartford College For Women
1265 Asylum Ave 06105

Trinity College
300 Summit St 06106

NEW BRITAIN

BUILDINGS

City Hall
185 Main St 06051

NEW HAVEN

BUILDINGS

Yale New Haven Hospital
789 Howard Ave 06519

NORWALK

APARTMENTS

Carlton Ct
133 Monterey Pl 06854

Norwalk West Apts
80 County St 06851

Rolling Ridge Condo
50 Aiken St 06851

Roodner Ct
261 Ely Ave 06854

Winnipauk Village
71 Aiken St 06851

PLAZA

APARTMENTS

Barkley Sq Condo
450 Hill St 06704

Bergin Apts
70 Lakewood Rd 06704

Frances Manor
48 Craftwood Rd 06704

Ledgewood Est Condo
488 Perkins Ave 06704

Perkins Hills Condo
388 Perkins Ave 06704

Pine Village Condo
100 Mark Ln 06704

Schoolhouse Apts
90 Platt St 06704

Woodland Heights Condos
200 Yale St 06704

BUILDINGS

Wtby Industrial Commons
1875 Thomaston Ave 06704

WATERBURY

APARTMENTS

Abbott Towers Apts
255 N Main St 06702

Arrowhead By The Lake
12 Spindle Hill Rd 06716

Beggs Apt
1106 Bank St 06708

Carlton Towers Apts
120 Hillside Ave 06710

Carrollton Apts
80 Willow St 06710

Clearview Hills Condo
20 Wolf Hill Rd 06716

Countryside Apts
12 Wolf Hill Rd 06716

Exchange Place Towers
44 Center St 06702

Ferncliff At Cables
65 Cables Ave 06710

Garden Hall Apts
168 E Main St 06702

Hilltop Tower Apts
259 Oakville Ave 06708

Hilltop Tower Apts
279 Oakville Ave 06708

Hitchcock Apts
164 W Main St 06702

Hitchcock Apts
182 W Main St 06702

Josephine Towers
24 Union St 06706

Lake Hill Village
264 Lyman Rd 06716

Mount Olive Tower
173 Grove St 06710

One Enterprise Pl
13 Cherry Ave 06702

Oronoke Ridge Condo
925 Oronoke Rd 06708

Oronoke Woods
827 Oronoke Rd 06708

Parkview Condo
585 Park Rd 06708

Piping Rock Apts
1579 Hamilton Ave 06706

Plaza-on-the-green Building
2 N Main St 06702

Robinridge Apts
990 W Main St 06708

St Regis Apts
330 E Main St 06702

Trinity Apts
41 Prospect St 06702

Villa Sol Dor Condo
222 Bradley Ave 06708

Watorian Apts
144 Grove St 06710

Westview House
170 Hillside Ave 06710

Wilby House Apts
42 Pine St 06710

Woodrich Condo
128 Lyman Rd 06716

BUILDINGS

Anaconda Brass Building
414 Meadow St 06702

Elton Building
30 W Main St 06702

Grand Professional Building
182 Grand St 06702

One Exchange Pl
30 Bank St 06702

One Exchange Pl
21 W Main St 06702

Prospect Tower Building
34 Prospect St 06702

Savings Tower Building
45 Savings St 06702

Westville Plaza
1650 Watertown Ave 06708

GOVERNMENT

City Hall Of Wtby
235 Grand St 06702

City Hall Of Wtby
236 Grand St 06702

Federal Building
14 Cottage Pl 06702

Superior Court
300 Grand St 06702

HOSPITALS

St Marys Hospital
56 Franklin St 06706

Waterbury Hospital
64 Robbins St 06708

COLLEGES

Mattatuck Community Coll
750 Chase Pky 06708

Post College
800 Country Club Rd 06708

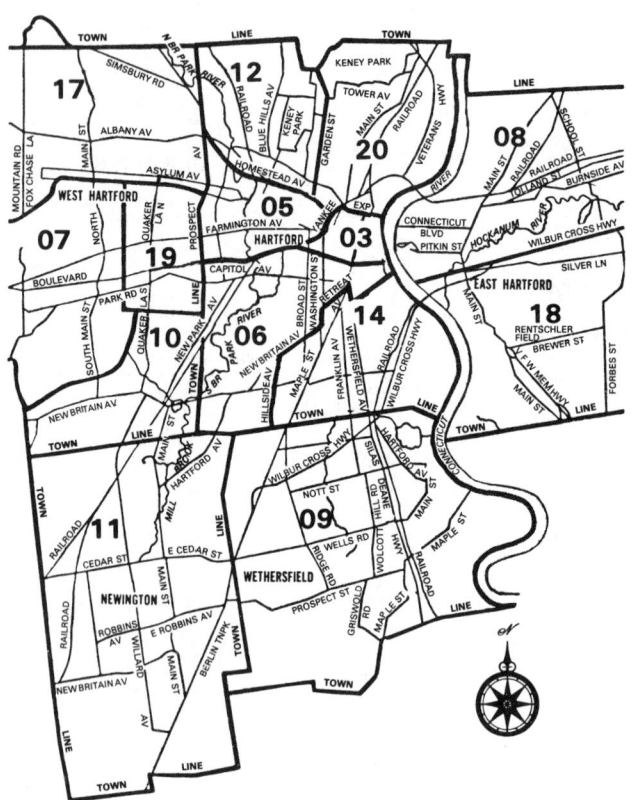

ZIP CODES
HARTFORD, CT
061 + TWO DIGITS SHOWN = ZIP CODE

DELAWARE
Abbreviation DE

Arden (Wilmington) 19810
Bear 19701
Bethany Beach 19930
Bethel 19931
Blackbird (Townsend) 19734
Blades (Seaford) 19973
Bridgeville 19933
Brookside (Newark) 19713
Camden Wyoming 19934
Cheswold 19936
Christiana (Newark) 19702
Claymont 19703
Clayton 19938
Dagsboro 19939
Delaware City 19706
Delmar 19940
Delmarva Power 19895
  (Wilmington)
Dewey Beach 19971
  (Rehoboth Beach)
Dover 19901-905
Edgemoor 19802, 19809-810
  (Wilmington)
Ellendale 19941
Elsmere (Wilmington) 19805
Fairfax (Wilmington) 19803
Farmington 19942
Felton 19943
Fenwick Island 19944, 19975
  Selbyville 19944
Frankford 19945
Frederica 19946
Georgetown 19947
Greenville (Wilmington) 19807
Greenwood 19950
Harbeson 19951

Harrington 19952
Hartly 19953
Henlopen Acres 19971
  (Rehoboth Beach)
Hockessin 19707
Holly Oak (Wilmington) 19809
Houston 19954
Kenton 19955
Kirkwood 19708
Laurel 19956
Lewes 19958
Lincoln 19960
Little Creek 19961
Long Neck (Millsboro) 19970
Magnolia 19962
Manor (New Castle) 19720
Marshallton (Wilmington) .. 19808
Marydel 19964
Middletown 19709
Midway (Rehoboth Beach) 19971
Milford 19963
Millsboro 19966
Millville 19967, 19970
  Ocean View 19967
Milton 19968
Minquadale (New Castle) .. 19720
Montchanin 19710
Nassau 19969
New Castle 19720-721
Newark 19702
  .... 19711-712, 19713-718
  19725-727
  Brookside 19713
  Christiana 19702
Newport (Wilmington) 19804
North Shores 19971
  (Rehoboth Beach)
Ocean View 19967, 19970
  (Millville)

Millville 19970
Odessa 19730
Port Penn 19731
Rehoboth Beach 19971
Rockland 19732
Saint Georges 19733
Seaford 19973
Selbyville 19944, 19975
  (Fenwick Island)
  Fenwick Island 19975
Smyrna 19977
Stanton (Wilmington) 19804
Talleyville (Wilmington) 19803
Townsend 19734
Viola 19979
Westover Hills 19807
  (Wilmington)
Wilmington 19800-810
  ... 19850, 19880, 19884-899
  Arden 19810
  Delmarva Power 19895
  Edgemoor 19802
  Edgemoor 19809-19810
  Elsmere 19805
  Fairfax 19803
  Greenville 19807
  Holly Oak 19809
  Marshallton 19808
  Newport 19804
  Stanton 19804
  Talleyville 19803
  Westover Hills 19807
Winterthur 19735
Woodside 19980
Wyoming 19934
  (Camden Wyoming)
Yorklyn 19736

CHRISTIANA

BUILDINGS

Bristol Building
248 Chapman Rd 19702

Chopin Building
258 Chapman Rd 19702

Christiana Building North
252 Chapman Rd 19702

Christiana Building South
250 Chapman Rd 19702

Commonwealth Building
260 Chapman Rd 19702

Oxford Building
256 Chapman Rd 19702

Stockton Building
261 Chapman Rd 19702

Topkis Building
254 Chapman Rd 19702

GOVERNMENT

Bellevue Building
262 Chapman Rd 19702

Dept Of Labor Building
263 Chapman Rd 19702

DOVER

GOVERNMENT

City Of Dover
475 Po Box 19903

Delaware State Gov Ofc
1401 Po Box 19903

Kent County Building
414 Federal St 19901

HOSPITALS

Kent General Hospital
640 S State St 19901

COLLEGES

Delaware State College
1200 N Dupont Hwy 19901

Wesley College
120 N State St 19901

FAIRFAX

BUILDINGS

Concord Mall
4737 Concord Pike 19803

Foulkstone Plaza
1401 Foulk Rd 19803

Independence Mall
1601 Concord Pike 19803

Lombardi Building
410 Foulk Rd 19803

Rollins Plaza
2200 Concord Pike 19803

Tigani Building
300 Foulk Rd 19803

HOSPITALS

A I Dupont Institute
1600 Rockland Rd 19803

NEWARK

GOVERNMENT

City Of Newark
220 Elkton Rd 19711

Hudson Center
501 Ogletown Rd 19711

Newark Police Station
294 E Main St 19711

WILMINGTON

APARTMENTS

Park Plaza
1100 Lovering Ave 19806

BUILDINGS

Bank Of Delaware Building
300 Delaware Ave 19801

Delaware Trust Building
900 N Market St 19801

Disabitino Building
200 W 9th St 19801

Dupont Building
1007 N Market St 19801

Market Tower Building
901 N Market St 19801

Mellon Bank Ctr
919 N Market St 19801

Montchanin Building
100 W 10th St 19801

Wilmington Tower
1105 N Market St 19801

Wilmington Trust Center
1100 N Market St 19801

GOVERNMENT

Carvel State Building
820 N French St 19801

Federal Building
844 N King St 19801

Lewis L Reeding Building
800 N French St 19801

Municipal Building
1000 N King St 19801

Public Building
1020 N King St 19801

COLLEGES

Goldey Beacom College
4701 Limestone Rd 19808

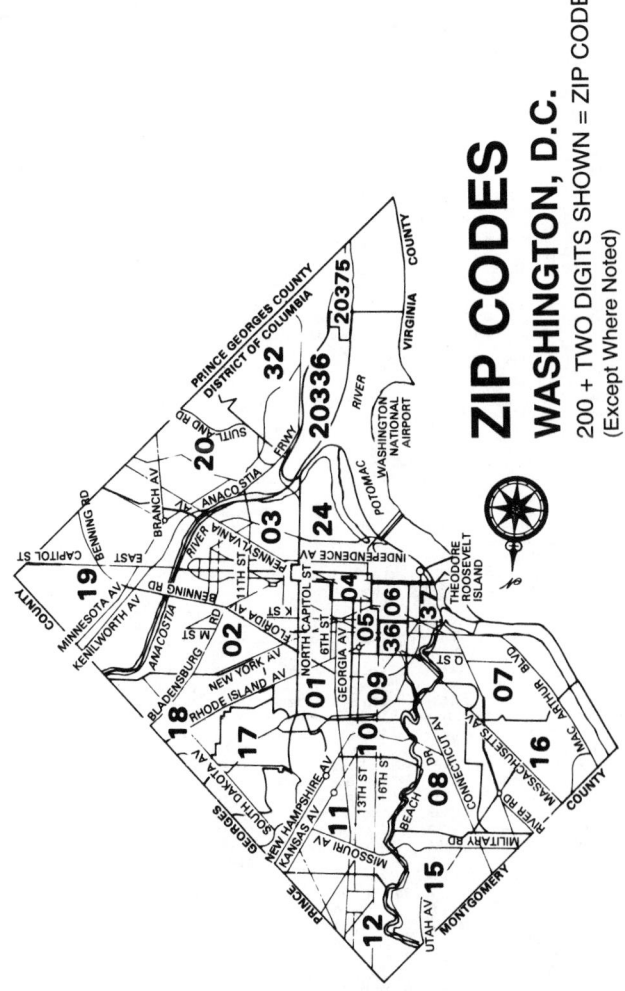

ZIP CODES
WASHINGTON, D.C.
200 + TWO DIGITS SHOWN = ZIP CODE
(Except Where Noted)

Carlton	34625
Cleveland Plaza	34615
Feather Sound	34622
Northwood Plaza	34621
Sunshine Mall	34616
Clermont	34711-712
Cleveland Plaza	34615
(Clearwater)	
Clewiston	33440
Cocoa	32922-927
Port Saint John	32927
Cocoa Beach	32931-932
Coconut Creek	33063
	33066, 33073
(Pompano Beach)	
Coconut Grove	33133-134
	33146, 33233
(Miami)	
Coleman	33521
College Parkway	33919
(Fort Myers)	
College Plaza (Bradenton)	34207
Conch Key	33001, 33050
(Long Key)	
Connersville (Bartow)	33830
Cooper City	33024, 33026
	33328, 33330
(Hollywood)	
Copeland	33926
Coral Gables	33114
	33124, 33133-134
	33143-146, 33156
(Miami)	
Coral Springs	33065, 33067
	33071, 33073, 33075-077
(Pompano Beach)	
Cortez	34215
Cottondale	32431
Crawfordville	32326-327
Crescent Bch (Sarasota)	34242
Crescent City	32112
Crestview	32536, 32539
Croom-a-coochee	33597
(Webster)	
Cross City	32628
Cross Key (Key Largo)	33037
Crossings (Miami)	33186
Crossroads	33710
(Saint Petersburg)	
Crystal Beach	34681
Crystal Lake (Lakeland)	33801
Crystal River	34423, 34428-429
Crystal Springs	33524
Cutler Ridge	33157
(Miami)	33170, 33189-190
Cypress	32432
Cypress Gardens	33884
(Winter Haven)	
Dade City	33525-526
Ridge Manor	33525
Dania	33004, 33312
Davenport	33837
Davie	33024, 33312, 33314
	33317, 33324-326
(Hollywood)	33328-332
Day	32013
Daytona Beach	32114-125
	32126-127, 32129, 32198
Downtown	32115
Dunlawton	32119
Holly Hill	32117

Port Orange	32124, 32127
South Daytona	32121
De Bary (Debary)	32713
De Funiak Springs	32433
De Leon Springs	32130
De Soto Square Mall	34607
(Spring Hill)	
Debary	32713
Deerfield Beach	33064
	33073, 33441-443, 33482
(Pompano Beach)	
Deland	32720-724
Glenwood	32720
Delray Beach	33444-447
	33483-484
Deltona	32725, 32728, 32738
Enterprise	32725, 32728, 32738
Orange City	
	32725, 32728, 32738
Destin	32540-541
Sandestin	32541
Dixieland (Lakeland)	33803
Dona Vista (Umatilla)	32784
Dover	33527
Dowling Park (Live Oak)	32060
Downtown	32115
(Daytona Beach)	
Duck Key (Marathon)	33050
Duette (Bowling Green)	33834
Dundee	33838
Dunedin	34697-698
Dunlawton	32119
(Daytona Beach)	
Dunnellon	34430-434
Citrus Springs	34433-34434
Durant	33530
Eagle Lake	33839
Earleton	32631
East Auburndale	33823
(Auburndale)	
East Lake (Tampa)	33610
East Palatka	32131
East Rockland Key	33040
(Key West)	
East Winter Haven	33880
(Winter Haven)	
Eastlake Weir	32133
Eastpoint	32328
Eaton Park	33840
Eatonville (Maitland)	32751
Eau Gallie	32934-936, 32940
(Melbourne)	
Ebro	32437
Edgar (Interlachen)	32149
Edgewater	32132, 32141
Edgewood	32809, 32839
(Orlando)	
Eglin Air Force Base	32542
Egypt Lake (Tampa)	33614
El Jobean (Punta Gorda)	33927
El Portal (Miami)	33138, 33150
Elfers	34680
Elkton	32033
Ellenton	34222
Eloise (Winter Haven)	33880
Englewood	34223-224, 34295
Grove City	34224
Enterprise	32725, 32738
(Deltona)	
Estero	33928
Euclid (Saint Petersburg)	33704

Eustis	32726-727
Everglades City	33929
Evinston	32633
Fairfield	32634
Fairvilla (Orlando)	32804
Feather Sound	34622
(Clearwater)	
Fedhaven	33854
Felda	33930
Fellsmere	32948
Fern Beach	32034
(Fernandina Beach)	
Fern Park (Casselberry)	32730
Fernandina Beach	32034-035
Amelia Island	32034
Amelia Village	32035
Fern Beach	32034
Ferndale	34729
Fiesta Key (Long Key)	33001
Fifty Seventh Avenue	34207
	34282
(Bradenton)	
Fisher Island	33109, 33139
(Miami)	
Flagler Beach	32135-137, 32142
(Palm Coast)	32151
Flamingo	33030, 33034
(Homestead)	
Flemington (Reddick)	32686
Fletcher (Tampa)	33612, 33695
Florahome	32140
Floral City	34436
Florence Villa	33880-881
(Winter Haven)	
Florida City (Homestead)	33034
Forest City	32714
(Altamonte Springs)	
Forest Hills (Tampa)	33612
Forest Lakes (Sarasota)	34232
Fort Lauderdale	33300-332
	33334-335, 33337-340
	33345, 33349-351, 33388
	33394
Bonaventure	33326
Broward Mall	33388
City Of Sunrise	33313
Cooper City	33328, 33330
Davie	33312, 33314, 33317
	33328-332
Galt Ocean Mile	33308
Hacienda Village	33312
Hacienda Village	33314
Inverrary	33313
Lauderdale By The Sea	
	33308
Lauderdale Isles	33312
Lauderdale Lakes	
	33311, 33313, 33319
Lauderhill	33311, 33313
	33319, 33321, 33351
Oakland Park	33334
Pine Ridge	33324
Plantation	33322-327
Port Everglades	33316
Sea Ranch Lakes	33308
Sunrise	33304, 33313
	33325, 33338, 33345, 33351
Tamarac	
	33309, 33323, 33351
Weston	33326, 33331
Wilton Manors	

.... 33305, 33311, 33334
Fort Mc Coy 32134
Fort Meade 33841
Fort Myers 33901-919
.... 33990-991
   College Parkway 33919
   North Fort Myers 33903
   Tice 33905
Fort Myers Beach 33931-932
Fort Ogden 33842
Fort Pierce 34945-954
.... 34979, 34981-988
Fort Walton Beach 32547-549
Fort White 32038
Forty Ninth Street 33707
   (Saint Petersburg)
Fountain 32438
Freeport 32439
Frostproof 33843
Fruitland Park 34731
Fruitville 34232, 34278
   (Sarasota)
Gainesville 32600-614
.... 32641, 32653
Galloway (Lakeland) 33805
Galt Ocean Mile 33308
   (Fort Lauderdale)
Garden Grove 34609
   (Brooksville)
Gateway Mall 33702
   (Saint Petersburg)
Geneva 32732
Georgetown 32139
Gibsonia (Lakeland) 33805
Gibsonton 33534
Gifford 32960-961, 32967
   (Vero Beach)
Glen Ridge 33406
   (West Palm Beach)
Glen Saint Mary 32040
Glenwood (Deland) 32720, 32722
   Deland 32722
Golden Beach (Miami) 33160
Golden Isles (Hallandale) .. 33009
Golden Shores (Miami) 33160
Goldenrod 32733
Gonzalez 32560
Goodland 33933
Gordonville (Bartow) 33830
Gotha 34734
Goulds 33170, 33187, 33189-190
   (Miami)
Graceville 32440
Graham 32042
Grand Island 32735
Grand Ridge 32442
Grandin 32138
Grant 32949
Grassy Key (Marathon) 33050
Green Cove Springs 32043
Greenacres (Lake Worth) ... 33463
Greensboro 32330
Greenville 32331
Greenwood 32443
Grenelefe (Haines City) 33844
Gretna 32332
Griffin (Lakeland) 33805
Grove City (Englewood) 34224
Grove Park (Lakeland) 33801
Groveland 34736
Gulf Breeze 32561-562, 32566

Navarre 32566
Pensacola Beach 32561
Gulf Gate East 34233, 34241
   (Sarasota)
Gulf Hammock 32639
Gulf Harbors 34652
   (New Port Richey)
Gulfport 33707, 33711, 33737
   (Saint Petersburg)
Hacienda Village ... 33312, 33314
   (Fort Lauderdale)
Haines City 33844-845
   Grenelefe 33844
Haines Creek (Leesburg) .. 34788
Hallandale 33008-009
   Golden Isles 33009
   Pembroke Park 33009
Hampton 32044
Harold 32563
Hastings 32145
Havana 32333
Haverhill 33409, 33415, 33417
   (West Palm Beach)
Hawthorne 32640
Heathrow (Lake Mary) 32746
Hernando 34442
Hernando Beach 34607
   (Spring Hill)
Hialeah 33010-017, 33054
   Miami 33010-33017
   Opa Locka 33014
   Palm Springs North ... 33015
High Springs 32643
Highland Beach 33487
   (Boca Raton)
Highland City 33846
Highland Park 33853
   (Lake Wales)
Hillcrest Heights 33827
   (Babson Park)
Hilldale (Tampa) 33614
Hilliard 32046
Hillsboro Beach 33062, 33072
   (Pompano Beach)
Hobe Sound 33455, 33475
Holder 34445
Holiday 34690-691
   Tarpon Springs 34690-691
Hollister 32147
Holly Hill 32117
   (Daytona Beach)
Hollywood 33312, 33314
.... 33019-029, 33332
.... 33081-084
   Cooper City 33024, 33026
   Davie 33024
   Miramar 33023, 33025
.... 33027, 33029, 33083
   Pembroke Lakes 33026
   Pembroke Park
.... 33021, 33023
   Pembroke Pines
.... 33022, 33084
   West Hollywood
.... 33023, 33083
Holmes Beach 34218
Holt 32564
Homeland 33847
Homestead 33030-035
.... 33039, 33090, 33092
   Flamingo 33030, 33034

Florida City 33034
Leisure City 33030, 33033
Modello 33030
Naranja 33092
Princeton
.... 33030, 33032, 33092
Homosassa 34446
.... 34448, 34487
Homosassa Springs 34447
Horseshoe Beach 32648
Hosford 32334
Hudson 34667, 34669
   (Port Richey)
Hunt Club (Apopka) 32703
Hurlburt Field 32544
Hypoluxo (Lake Worth) 33462
Ilexhurst 34217
   (Bradenton Beach)
Immokalee 33934
Indialantic 32903
Indian Harbor Beach 32937
   (Satellite Beach)
Indian Lake Estates 33855
Indian River Shores 32963
   (Vero Beach)
Indian Rocks Beach 34635
Indiantown 34956
Inglis 34449
Interbay (Tampa) 33611
Interlachen 32148-149
   Edgar 32149
Inverness 34450-453
Inverrary 33313
   (Fort Lauderdale)
Inwood (Winter Haven) 33880
Irvine (Reddick) 32686
Islamorada 33036
Island Grove 32654
Istachatta 34636
Jacksonville ... 32099, 32200-212
.... 32215-234, 32236-241
.... 32244-247, 32250
.... 32254-259, 32266-267
.... 32276-277, 32294
.... 32296-297
   Baldwin 32234
   Cecil Field 32215
   Jax Beach 32200
   Mayport 32227-228
   Sears Roebuck 32297
   Whitehouse 32220
Jasper 32052
Jax Beach 32200, 32250
   (Jacksonville)
Jay 32565
Jennings 32053
Jensen Beach 34957-958
Johns Pass 33708
   (Saint Petersburg)
Juno Beach 33408
   (North Palm Beach)
Jupiter 33458
.... 33468-469, 33477-478
   Tequesta 33469
Kathleen 33849
Kenansville 34739
Kendall 33156, 33158, 33175
.... 33176, 33183, 33186
.... 33193, 33196, 33256
.... 33283, 33296
   (Miami)

Aventura
.... 33160, 33180, 33280
Bal Harbour 33154
Bay Harbor Islands 33154
Biscayne Gardens 33168
Biscayne Park . 33161, 33181
.... 33261
Coconut Grove 33146
.... 33233
Coral 33145
Coral Gables ... 33124, 33156
Crossings 33186
Cutler Ridge
... 33157, 33170, 33189-190
Dr Martin Luther King . 33147
Eastern Airlines 33148
El Portal 33138, 33150
First Union Bank 33195
Flagship Banks Of M ... 33121
Flinternatioal Univ 33199
Florida International U . 33199
Gables By The Sea 33156
Golden Beach 33160
Golden Shores 33160
Goulds 33170
Kendall 33156, 33158
.... 33173, 33176, 33183
.... 33186, 33193, 33196
.... 33256, 33283, 33296
Keystone Islands . 33161, 261
Ludlam 33255
Master Charge 33107
Medley 33166, 33178
Normandy 33141
Normandy Isle 33141
North Bay Village 33141
North Miami 33181, 33261
North Miami Beach 33169
North Miami Beach 33261
Ojus 33163, 33180
Olympia Heights 33165
.... 33194, 33265
Perrine 33157, 33170
.... 33177, 33187, 33257
Quail Heights .. 33170, 33177
.... 33187, 33197
Richmond Heights 33156
.... 33158, 33176
South Miami 33143, 33146
.... 33173, 33176, 33183
.... 33243, 33256
South Miami Heights ... 33157
Southern Bell 33110
Sunny Isles 33160
Sunset Island 33140
Surfside 33154
Sweetwater 33144, 33172
.... 33174, 33182, 33184
.... 33194
Uleta 33162, 33164
University Of Miami 33124
.... 33146
Virginia Gardens 33166
West Kendall 33183
West Miami 33144, 33155
.... 33172, 33174, 33182
.... 33194
Westchester 33165
Williams Island 33160
Miami Beach 33109, 33119
.... 33139-141, 33154, 33160

(Miami)
Micanopy 32667
Micco (Sebastian) 32976
Mid Venice (Venice) 34292
Middle Florida 32799
(Mid Florida)
Middle Torch Key 33042
(Summerland Key)
Middleburg 32050, 32068
Midway 32343
Milligan 32537
Milton 32570-572, 32583
Pace 32571
Mims 32754
Minneola 34755
Miramar 33023, 33025
.... 33027, 33029, 33083
(Hollywood)
Modello (Homestead) 33030
Molino 32577
Monticello 32344
Montverde 34756
Moore Haven 33471
Morriston 32668
Mossy Head 32434
Mount Dora 32745, 32757
(Lake Jem)
Mount Pleasant 32352
Mount Plymouth (Sorrento) 32776
Mountain Lake 33853
(Lake Wales)
Mulberry 33860
Mullinsville (Frostproof) 33843
Munson Island (Key West) 33040
Murdock (Punta Gorda) ... 33938
Myakka City 34251
Myakka Head (Ona) 33865
Nalcrest 33856
Naples 33939-942
.... 33961-964, 33999
Towne Center 33962
Naranja 33032-033, 33092
(Homestead)
Navarre (Gulf Breeze) 32566
Neptune Beach 32266
New Port Richey 34652-656
Gulf Harbors 34652
Seven Springs 34655
Woodtrail Plaza 34652
New Smyrna Beach .. 32168-170
New Zion (Ona) 33865
Newberry 32669
Niceville 32578, 32588
Nichols 33863
Nobleton 34661
Nocatee 33864
Nokomis 34274-275
Noma 32452
Normandy (Miami) 33141
North Bay Village (Miami) . 33141
North Coral Springs 33067
(Pompano Beach)
North Fort Myers 33903
(Fort Myers)
North Lauderdale 33068
(Pompano Beach)
North Merritt Island 32953
(Merritt Island)
North Miami 33161-162
.... 33168-169, 33181, 33261
(Miami)

North Miami Beach 33160
.... 33179-180
(Miami)
North Palm Beach 33408
North Port 34287
North Redington Beach 33708
(Saint Petersburg)
North Winter Haven 33880
(Winter Haven)
Northdale (Tampa) . 33624, 33694
Northeast Park 33704
(Saint Petersburg)
Northside (Lakeland) 33805
Northwood Plaza 34621
(Clearwater)
O Brien 32071
Oak Hill 32759
Oakland 34760
Oakland Park .. 33304-311, 33334
(Fort Lauderdale)
Ocala 34470-482
Ocean Reef (Key Largo) ... 33037
Ocean Ridge 33435
(Boynton Beach)
Ochopee 33943
Ocklawaha 32179
Ocoee 34761
Odessa 33556
Ojus (Miami) 33163, 33180
Okahumpka 34762
Okeechobee 34972-974
Basinger 34972
Oklawaha (Ocklawaha) 32179
Old Town 32680
Oldsmar 34677
Olustee 32072
Olympia Heights 33165
.... 33174-175, 33184-185
.... 33194, 33265
(Miami)
Ona 33865
Oneco 34264
Opa Locka 33014, 33054-056
(Hialeah)
Carol City 33055-056
Hialeah 33054
Miami 33054-056
Orange City 32725, 32728
.... 32738, 32763, 32774
(Deltona)
Orange Lake 32681
Orange Park 32065
.... 32067, 32073
Orange Springs 32182
Orlando ... 32800-822, 32824-837
.... 32839, 32853-862
.... 32867-869, 32872, 32878
.... 32886-887, 32889-891
.... 32893, 32897-899
Azalea Park 32807
Barnett Bank 32889
Belle Isle 32809
Edgewood 32809, 32839
Fairvilla 32804
First Union 32886
Harcourt Brace & Co Inc
.... 32887
HBJ 32887
Hiawassee 32818
J C Penney Co 32890
Kennedy Space Center 32815

Lake Buena Vista 32830
Lockhart 32810
Mastercard 32898
Naval Training Center . 32813
Navy Recruit Command
.... 32893
North A South A 32899
Orlo Vista 32811
Pine Castle 32809
Pine Hills 32808, 32818
Pinecastle 32809
Recruit Training Command
.... 32813, 32893
Sand Lake 32819
Sun First 32897
Sun First National Bank 32897
Sun Mortgage Co 32891
Taft 32824
UCF 32816
Union Park 32817, 32831
.... 32833
University Of Central .. 32816
Ventura 32822
Westside Crossing 32808
Orlo Vista (Orlando) 32811
Ormond Beach 32173-176
Osprey 34229
Osteen 32764
Otter Creek 32683
Overstreet 32453
Oviedo 32765-766
Chuluota 32766
Oxford 34484
Ozona 34660
Pace (Milton) 32571
Pahokee 33476
Paisley 32767
Palatka 32177-178
Palm Bay 32905-910
Melbourne ... 32905-910
Palm Beach 33480
Palm Beach Gardens ... 33410
.... 33418, 33420
Palm Beach Shores 33404
(West Palm Beach)
Palm City 34990
Palm Coast 32135, 32137, 32142
Flagler Beach
.... 32135, 32137, 32142
Palm Harbor 34682-685
Lake Tarpon 34684
Tarpon Woods 34685
Palm River (Tampa) 33619
Palm Springs (Lake Worth) 33461
Palm Springs North 33015
(Hialeah)
Palma Ceia 33609, 33629
(Tampa)
Palma Sola 34209, 34280
(Bradenton)
Palmdale 33944
Palmetto 34220-221
Rubonia 34221
Panacea 32346
Panama City 32400-409
..... 32411-413, 32417, 32461
Southport 32409
Parkland 33067, 33076
(Pompano Beach)
Parrish 34219
Pasadena 33707

(Saint Petersburg)
Pass A Grill Beach . 33706, 33741
(Saint Petersburg)
Paxton 32538
Pelican Lake 33491
(Canal Point)
Pembroke Lakes 33026
(Hollywood)
Pembroke Park 33009
.... 33021, 33023
(Hallandale)
Pembroke Pines 33019-020
.... 33022, 33024-025
.... 33027-029, 33082, 33084
(Hollywood)
Peninsula (Tampa) 33609
Penney Farms 32079
Pensacola 32500-509
.... 32511-514, 32516
... 32520-524, 32526, 32534
.... 32559, 32573-576
.... 32581-582, 32589-598
City Of Pensacola 32521
Pensacola Beach 32561
(Gulf Breeze)
Perrine 33157, 33170, 33177
.... 33187, 33189-190, 33257
(Miami)
Perry 32347
Pierson 32180
Pine Castle (Orlando) 32809
Pine Hills 32808, 32818
(Orlando)
Pine Ridge 33324
(Fort Lauderdale)
Pinecastle (Orlando) 32809
Pinecraft 34239, 34278
(Sarasota)
Pineland 33945
Pinellas Park 34664-666
Pinetta 32350
Placida 33946-947
Plant City 33564-567
Walden Lake 33566
Walden Woods 33567
Plantation 33311-313
.... 33317-318, 33322-327
(Fort Lauderdale)
Plantation Key 33036, 33070
(Islamorada)
Plymouth 32768
Poinciana (Kissimmee)
34759, 34758
Point Washington 32454
Polk City 33868
Pomona Park 32181
Pompano Beach 33060-069
.... 33071-077, 33093
Atlantic Boulevard 33077
Coconut Creek
.... 33063, 33066, 33073
Coral Springs ... 33065, 33067
.... 33071, 33073, 33075-077
Deerfield Beach
.... 33064, 33073
Hillsboro Beach
.... 33062, 33072
Lighthouse Point
.... 33064, 33074
Margate 33063
.... 33066, 33068, 33073

North Coral Springs 33067
North Lauderdale 33068
Parkland 33067, 33076
West Atlantic 33065, 33077
West Coral Springs 33065
Ponce De Leon 32455
Ponte Vedra Beach ....
.... 32004, 32082
Port Charlotte 33948-949
.... 33952-954, 33980-981
Punta Gorda ... 33980-981
Port Everglades 33316
(Fort Lauderdale)
Port La Belle (Labelle) 33935
Port Orange 32118-119, 32124
(Daytona Beach) 32127
Port Richey 34667-669
.... 34673-674
Bayonet Point 34667
Hudson 34667, 34669
Port Saint Joe 32456
Port Saint John (Cocoa) ... 32927
Port Saint Lucie 34952-953
.... 34983-988
Fort Pierce ... 34983-988
Port Salerno 34992
Port St John (Cocoa) 32927
Port Tampa City (Tampa) ... 33616
Princeton ... 33030, 33032, 33092
(Homestead)
Produce (Tampa) 33610
Progress Village (Tampa) .. 33619
Punta Gorda 33927, 33938
.... 33948-955, 33980-983
El Jobean 33927
Murdock 33938
Putnam Hall 32185
Quail Heights 33170, 33177
.... 33187, 33189-190, 33197
(Miami)
Quincy 32351, 32353
Raccoon Key (Key West) .. 33040
Raiford 32083
Ralston Beach (Tampa) 33614
Ramrod Key 33042
(Summerland Key)
Reddick 32686
Redington Shores 33708
(Saint Petersburg)
Richmond Heights 33156
.... 33158, 33176
(Miami)
Ridge Manor (Dade City) .. 33525
Ridge Manor Estates 33597
(Webster)
Ridge Manor West 34602
(Brooksville)
River Ranch 33867
River Ranch Shores 33853
(Lake Wales)
Riverview 33569
Riverview Plaza 34231
(Sarasota)
Riviera Beach 33404, 33419
(West Palm Beach)
Rockledge 32955-956
Rolling Acres 34602
(Brooksville)
Roseland 32957
Royal Palm Beach 33411
(West Palm Beach)

Rubonia (Palmetto) 34221
Ruskin 33570-573
   Apollo Beach .. 33570, 33572
   Bahia Beach 33570
   Sun City Center ... 33570-571
Safety Harbor 34695
Saint Augustine 32086
.... 32092, 32095
Saint Augustine South 32086
  (Saint Augustine)
Saint Cloud 34769-773
Saint George Island 32328
  (Eastpoint)
Saint James City 33956
Saint Leo 33574
Saint Marks 32355
Saint Pete 33784
  (Saint Petersburg)
Saint Petersburg 33700-716
.... 33730-734
.... 33736-743, 33784
   Bay Vista 33712
   Big Bayou 33705
   Crossroads 33710
   Euclid 33704
   Forty Ninth Street 33707
   Gateway Mall 33702
   Gulfport
   .... 33707, 33711, 33737
   Johns Pass 33708
   Madeira Beach
   .... 33708, 33738
   North Redington Beach 33708
   Northeast Park 33704
   Pasadena 33707
   Pass A Grill Beach
   .... 33706, 33741
   Redington Shores 33708
   Saint Pete 33784
   South Pasadena 33707
   Tierra Verda 33715
   Treasure Island
   .... 33706, 33740
Salem 32356
Salt Springs 32134
  (Fort Mc Coy)
Samoset (Bradenton) 34208
San Antonio 33576
San Mateo 32187
Sand Lake (Orlando) 32819
Sanderson 32087
Sandestin (Destin) 32541
Sanford 32771-773
Sanibel 33957
Santa Fe (Alachua) 32615-616
Santa Rosa Beach 32459
Sarasota 34230-243, 34276-278
   Airgate 34243, 34278
   Crescent Beach 34242
   Forest Lakes 34232
   Fruitville 34232, 34278
   Gulf Gate East 34233, 34241
   Meadows Village 34234
   Pinecraft 34239, 34278
   Riverview Plaza 34231
   Siesta 34242
   South Trail 34231
Satellite Beach 32937
Satsuma 32189
Scottsmoor 32775
Sea Ranch Lakes 33308

.... 33573
(Fort Lauderdale)
Sears Roebuck 32297
(Jacksonville)
Searstown (Lakeland) 33801
Sebastian 32958
.... 32976, 32978
   Barefoot Bay 32976
   Micco 32976
Sebring 33870-872
Seffner 33584
Seminole (Largo) 34642-643
Seminole Heights (Tampa) 33603
Seven Springs 34655
(New Port Richey)
Seville 32190
Shady Grove 32357
Shady Hills (Brooksville) .. 34610
Shalimar 32579
Sharpes 32959
Siesta (Sarasota) 34242
Silver Springs 34488-489
Sneads 32460
Socrum (Lakeland) 33805
Sopchoppy 32358
Sorrento 32776
South Bay 33493
South Daytona 32121
(Daytona Beach)
South Florida 33082
South Lake Wales 33853
(Lake Wales)
South Miami 33143, 33146
.... 33155-156, 33173, 33176
.... 33183, 33243, 33256
South Miami Heights 33157
(Miami)
South Pasadena 33707
(Saint Petersburg)
South Trail (Sarasota) 34231
South Venice (Venice) 34293
Southeast (Winter Haven) 33880
Southport (Panama City) .. 32409
Southside . 33807, 33811, 33813
(Lakeland)
Southwest (Miami) 33165
Sparr 32192
Spring Hill 34606-609
   Brooksville 34606-608
   De Soto Square Mall .. 34607
   Hernando Beach 34607
Springs Plaza (Longwood) 32779
Starke 32091
Steinhatchee 32359
Stock Island 33040-041
(Key West)
Stuart 34994-997
Sugarloaf Key 33042, 33044
(Summerland Key)
Sulphur Springs (Tampa) .. 33604
Sumatra 32335
Summerfield 34491-492
Summerland Key 33042-044
   Big Torch Key 33042
   Cudjoe 33042
   Little Torch Key 33042
   Middle Torch Key 33042
   Ramrod Key 33042
   Sugarloaf Key . 33042, 33044
Sumterville 33585
Sun City 33586
Sun City Center 33570-571

.... 33573
Ruskin 33573
Sunny Isles (Miami) 33160
Sunnyside 32461
Sunrise 33304, 33313
.... 33321-323, 33325
.... 33338, 33345, 33351
(Fort Lauderdale)
Sunset Island (Miami) 33140
Sunshine Mall 34616
(Clearwater)
Surfside (Miami) 33154
Suwanee (Suwannee) 32692
Suwannee 32692
Sweetwater 33144, 33172
  33174, 33182, 33184, 33194
(Miami)
Sweetwater Creek (Tampa) 33614
Sydney 33587
Taft (Orlando) 32824
Tallahassee 32301-304
.... 32306-308, 32310-317
.... 32359, 32399
Centerville
.... 32308, 32312, 32317
Tallevast 34270
Tamarac 33309, 33319-321
.... 33323, 33351
(Fort Lauderdale)
Tampa 33600-626, 33629-631
... 33633-635, 33637, 33647
.... 33650-651, 33655
.... 33660-662, 33672-675
.... 33677, 33679-682
.... 33684-688, 33690
.... 33694-695, 33697
   Bears Plaza 33697
   Broadway 33605
   Business Reply 33633
   Carrollwood 33618, 33688
   Citrus Park 33625
   Clair Mel City 33619
   East Lake 33610
   East Lake Park 33610
   Egypt Lake 33614
   First National Bank 33651
   Fletcher 33695
   Forest Hills 33612
   Hilldale 33614
   Home Shopping Club .. 33650
   Interbay 33611
   Lake Carroll 33618
   Lake Magdalene 33612
   Mac Dill AFB ... 33608, 33621
   NCNB National Bank ... 33655
   Northdale 33694
   Palm River 33619
   Palma Ceia 33609, 33629
   Peninsula 33609
   Port Tampa City 33616
   Produce 33610
   Progress Village 33619
   Ralston Beach 33614
   Seminole Heights 33603
   Sulphur Springs 33604
   Sweetwater Creek 33614
   Temple Terrace
   .... 33617, 33637, 33687
   Time Inc 33660-33662
   Town N Cntry 33615
   Twin Lake 33604

Univ Of So Florida	33620
University Collection ...	33612
University Of Tampa ...	33606
YBOR City	33605
Tampa Palms (Tampa)	33647
Tangerine	32777
Tarpon Springs	34688-691
Tarpon Woods	34685
(Palm Harbor)	
Tarrytown (Webster)	33597
Tavares	32778
Tavernier	33070
Telogia	32360
Temple Terrace	33617
.... 33637,	33687
(Tampa)	
Tequesta (Jupiter)	33469
Terra Ceia	34250
Thonotosassa	33592
Tice (Fort Myers)	33905
Tierra Verde	33715
(Saint Petersburg)	
Titusville 32780-783,	32796
Towne Center (Naples)	33962
Trailer Estates	34281
(Bradenton)	
Tranquility Park	33880
(Winter Haven)	
Treasure Island 33706,	33740
(Saint Petersburg)	
Trenton	32693
Trilby	33593
Tuscawilla	32708
(Winter Springs)	
Twin Lake (Tampa)	33604
Uleta (Miami) 33162,	33164
Umatilla	32784
Union Park 32817,	32820
.... 32825-826, 32828-829	
.... 32831,	32833
(Orlando)	
Upper Key Largo	33037
(Key Largo)	
Upper Matecumbe Key	33036
(Islamorada)	
Valkaria (Grant)	32949
Valparaiso	32580
Valrico	33594
Venetian Islands (Miami) ...	33139
Venetian Shores	33036
(Islamorada)	
Venice 34284-285	
.... 34287, 34292-293	
Mid Venice	34292
South Venice	34293
Venice Beach (Venice)	34285
Ventura (Orlando)	32822
Venus	33960
Vernon	32462
Vero Beach 32960-968	
Gifford	32967
Indian River Shores ...	32963
Virginia Gardens (Miami) ..	33166
Wabash (Lakeland)	33801
Wabasso	32970
Wacissa	32361
Wahneta (Winter Haven) ...	33880
Wakulla Springs	32305
Walden Lake (Plant City) ..	33566
Walden Woods (Plant City)	33567
Waldo	32694
Walnut Hill (Mc David)	32568
Warm Mineral Springs	34287
(North Port)	
Wauchula	33873
Wausau	32463
Waverly	33877
Webster	33597
Weeki Wachee	34613
(Brooksville)	
Weirsdale	32195
Welaka	32193
Wellborn	32094
West Atlantic 33065,	33077
(Pompano Beach)	
West Auburndale	33823
(Auburndale)	
West Bradenton	34205
(Bradenton)	
West Coral Springs	33065
(Pompano Beach)	
West Frost Proof	33843
(Frostproof)	
West Hollywood 33023,	33083
(Hollywood)	
West Kendall (Miami)	33183
West Lake Wales	33853
(Lake Wales)	
West Melbourne	32904
(Melbourne)	
West Miami 33144,	33155
.... 33172,	33174
.... 33182,	33194
West Palm Beach 33401-421	
Glen Ridge	33406
Haverhill	
.... 33409, 33415,	33417
Lake Park	33403
Palm Beach Gardens	
.... 33410, 33418,	33420
Palm Beach Shores	33404
Riviera Beach .. 33404,	33419
Royal Palm Beach	33411
West Scenic Park	33853
(Lake Wales)	
Westchester (Miami)	33165
Westgate (Bradenton)	34205
Weston 33326,	33331
(Fort Lauderdale)	
Westside Crossing	32808
(Orlando)	
Westville	32464
Wewahitchka	32465
White Springs	32096
Whitehouse (Jacksonville)	32220
Whitney Beach	34228
(Longboat Key)	
Wildwood	34785
Williams Island (Miami)	33160
Williston	32696
Willow Oak (Mulberry)	33860
Wilton Manors	33305
.... 33311,	33334
(Fort Lauderdale)	
Wimauma	33598
Windermere	34786
Windley Key (Islamorada) .	33036
Winter Beach	32971
Winter Garden 34777,	34787
Winter Haven . 33880-885,	33888
Cypress Gardens	33884
East Winter Haven	33880
Eloise	33880
Florence Villa 33880-881	
Inwood	33880
Lake Maude	33880
Lake Shipp Heights	33880
Lucerne Park	33880
North Winter Haven	33880
Southeast	33880
Tranquility Park	33880
Wahneta	33880
Winter Park	32789-790
....	32792-793
Aloma	32792
Winter Springs 32708,	32719
Casselberry ... 32708,	32719
Tuscawilla	32708
Woodland (Boca Raton)	33481
Woodtrail Plaza	34652
(New Port Richey)	
Woodville	32362
Worthington Springs	32697
Xmas (Christmas)	32709
Yalaha	34797
Yankeetown	34498
Ybor City (Tampa)	33605
Youngstown	32466
Yulee	32097
Zellwood	32798
Zephyrhills	
.... 33539-541, 33543-544	
Zolfo Springs	33890

ALOMA

APARTMENTS

Four Seasons Condos
200 Saint Andrews Blvd 32792

La Aloma Apt
3040 ALOMA AVE 32792

Signal Point Apartments
2500 Howell Branch Rd 32792

Winter Park Towers
1111 S LAKEMONT AVE ... 32792

BASINGER

GOVERNMENT

County Court House
304 NW2ND ST 34972

BELLEAIR

GOVERNMENT

Pinellas County Ct House
315 COURT ST 34616

BRADENTON

BUILDINGS

Crossland Center
1301 6TH AVE W 34205

Nationsbank Building
1201 6TH AVE W 34205

Professional Building
1023 MANATEE AVE W 34205

Southeast Natl Bank Building
920 MANATEE AVE W 34205

CARL FISHER

BUILDINGS

1 Lincoln Rd Building
169 LINCOLN RD 33139

Financial Fed Building
407 LINCOLN RD 33139

Lincoln Medical Building
605 LINCOLN RD 33139

Meridian Medical Building
1680 N MERIDIAN AVE 33139

Sun Bank Building
1111 LINCOLN RD 33139

CENTERVILLE

APARTMENTS

Miccosukee Arms Apartment
1839 MICCOSUKEE RD ... 32308

COCOA

BUILDINGS

Cocoa Commercial Center
3815 N US HIGHWAY 1 32926

Mariner Sq
96 WILLARD ST 32922

GOVERNMENT

City Municipal Building
603 BREVARD AVE 32922

Federal Building
435 BREVARD AVE 32922

COCONUT GROVE

BUILDINGS

Corinthian Plaza
22 SALAMANCA AVE 33134

First Union Bank Building
169 MIRACLE MILE 33134

Franklin Intl Plaza
255 ALHAMBRA CIR 33134

CORAL GABLES

BUILDINGS

Datran Building
9100 S DADELAND BLVD 33156

COLLEGES

University Of Miami
248025 PO BOX 33124

CORAL SPRINGS

HOSPITALS

Coral Springs Medical Ctr
3000 CORAL HILLS DR ... 33065

DAYTONA BEACH

HOSPITALS

Halifax Med Ctr
2830 PO BOX 32120

Humana Hospital
9000 PO BOX 32120

COLLEGES

Daytona Bch Cmnty College
2811 PO BOX 32120

DEERFIELD BEACH

APARTMENTS

Deerfield Pines South
1428 SE 4TH AVE 33441

Ocean Harbor
800 SE 20TH AVE 33441

Ocean Harbor
800 S A 1 A 33441

Ocean Harbor
800 S OCEAN BLVD 33441

Penthouse South
745 SE 19TH AVE 33441

Tiara East
333 NE 21ST AVE 33441

Tiara East
333 N A 1 A 33441

Tiara East
333 N OCEAN BLVD 33441

DELAND

GOVERNMENT

Volusia Co Court House
125 W NEW YORK AVE 32720

COLLEGE

Stetson University
421 WOODLAND 32720

Ft Laud City Hall
100 N ANDREWS AVE 33301

Doctors
1859 VAN BUREN ST 33020

DELRAY BEACH

GOVERNMENT

Delray Beach City Hall
100 NW 1ST AVE 33444

South County Court House
200 W ATLANTIC AVE 33444

EAU GALLIE

APARTMENTS

Courtyard On The Green
2700 CROTON RD 32935

Eagles Nest Condos
1225 N WICKHAM RD 32935

Ramshur Towers
1279 HOUSTON ST 32935

Sun-n-green Villa
2727 N WICKHAM RD 32935

GOVERNMENT

Brevard Co. Government Ctr
2725 SAINT JOHNS 32940

FLORENCE VILLA

GOVERNMENT

City Hall
451 3RD ST NW 33881

FORT LAUDERDALE

BUILDINGS

Broward Financial Centre
500 E BROWARD BLVD ... 33394

One Financial Plaza
1 FINANCIAL PLZ 33394

GOVERNMENT

Brwd Cty Courthouse
201 SE6TH ST 33301

Federal Building
299 E BROWARD BLVD ... 33301

FORT PIERCE

GOVERNMENT

Clerk Of The Circuit Cour
221 S INDIAN RIVER DR . 34950

Saint Lucie Co Civic Ctr
2300 VIRGINIA AVE 34982

HOSPITALS

Lawnwood Medical Center
188 PO BOX 34954

Lawnwood Psychiatric Pavi
1540 PO BOX 34954

GAINESVILLE

GOVERNMENT

Alachua County Adm Building
21 E UNIVERSITY AVE 32601

Federal Building
401 SE 1ST AVE 32601

GIFFORD

GOVERNMENT

County Courthouse
2145 14TH AVE 32960

GULF BREEZE

GOVERNMENT

Gulf Breeze City Hall
1070 SHORELINE DR 32561

HIALEAH

HOSPITALS

Palm Springs Hospital
1475 W 49TH ST 33012

COLLEGES

Florida Memorial College
15800 NW 42ND AVE 33054

HOLLYWOOD

HOSPITALS

INDIALANTIC

APARTMENTS

Villager Condos
877 N A1A HWY 32903

INDIAN HARBOR BEACH

APARTMENTS

Buccaneer Beach Club
1125 A1A HWY 32937

Buccaneer Condos
1175 A1A HWY 32937

INVERNESS

APARTMENTS

Hill & Pine Apts
400 S PINE AVE 34452

Inverness Village Condo
2400 FOREST DR 34453

GOVERNMENT

Citrus County Courthouse
110 N APOPKA AVE 34450

Citrus Memorial Hospital
6003 PO BOX 34451

JACKSONVILLE

APARTMENTS

Cathedral Towers
601 N NEWNAN ST 32202

BUILDINGS

Daniel Building
111 E COASTLINE DR 32202

Southern Bell Building
301 W BAY ST 32202

GOVERNMENT

Federal Building
400 W BAY ST 32202

HOSPITALS

Baptist Medical Center
800 PRUDENTIAL DR 32207

JUNO BEACH

BUILDINGS

No Palm Bch Village Hall
501 US HIGHWAY 1 33408

KISSIMMEE

GOVERNMENT

City Hall
101 CHURCH ST 34741

Osceola Co Courthouse
12 S VERNON AVE 34741

LAKE WORTH

APARTMENTS

Lake Worth Towers
1500 LUCERNE AVE 33460

Village Club Building B
550 PURDY LN 33461

MELBOURNE

APARTMENTS

Trinity Towers E
700 E STRAWBRIDGE AVE 32901

Trinity Towers W
650 E STRAWBRIDGE AVE 32901

BUILDINGS

Melb Regional Airport
1 AIR TERMINAL PKY 32901

Sabal Palm Square
4700 BABCOCK ST NE 32905

GOVERNMENT

S Brev Br Cnty Courthouse
50 NIEMAN AVE 32901

HOSPITAL

Holmes Regional MEdical Center
1350 HICKORY 32901

MERRITT ISLAND

GOVERNMENT

Brevard County Courthouse
2575 N COURTENAY PKY 32953

MIAMI

BUILDINGS

American Title Building
1101 BRICKELL AVE 33131

Amerifirst Federal Building
1 SE 3RD AVE 33131

Atico Financial Center
200 SE 1ST ST 33131

Barnett Tower
701 BRICKELL AVE 33131

Bayside
401 BISCAYNE BLVD 33132

Bayside Office Center
141 NE 3RD AVE 33132

Bayside Plaza
330 BISCAYNE BLVD 33132

Biscayne Building
19 W FLAGLER ST 33130

Brickell Bay
1001 S BAYSHORE DR 33131

Brickell Building
1110 BRICKELL AVE 33131

Brickell Center
799 BRICKELL PLZ 33131

Brickell Concours Building
1401 BRICKELL AVE 33131

Capital Bank Building
3550 BISCAYNE BLVD 33137

Capital Building
117 NE 1ST AVE 33132

Caribank Tower
848 BRICKELL AVE 33131

Centrust Building
101 E FLAGLER ST 33131

Citizens Financial Center
999 BRICKELL AVE 33131

City National Bank Building
25 W FLAGLER ST 33130

City Of Miami Building
275 NW 2ND ST 33128

Concord Building
66 W FLAGLER ST 33130

GOVERNMENT

Congress Building
111 NE 2ND AVE 33132

Consolidated Bank Building
168 SE 1ST ST 33131

Continental Bank
888 BRICKELL AVE 33131

Courthouse Center
175 NW 1ST AVE 33128

Courvoisier
501 BRICKELL KEY DR ... 33131

Dade County Bar Asso Building
111 NW 1ST AVE 33128

Dupont Building
169 E FLAGLER ST 33131

Dupont Plaza
300 Biscayne Boulevard ... 33131

First Union Center
800 BRICKELL AVE 33131

First Union Financial Ctr
200 S BISCAYNE BLVD 33131

Five-fifty Building
550 BRICKELL AVE 33131

Flagler Center Building
44 W FLAGLER ST 33130

Ingraham Building
25 SE 2ND AVE 33131

International Place
100 SE 2ND ST 33131

Israel Discount Bank Building
14 NE 1ST AVE 33132

Langford Building
121 SE 1ST ST 33131

Maritime Building
1001 N AMERICA WAY 33132

Metro Mall
1 NE 1ST ST 33132

Miami Center
201 S BISCAYNE BLVD 33131

NCNB Building
150 SE 3RD AVE 33131

New World Tower
100 BISCAYNE BLVD 33132

Northeast Airlines Building
150 SE 2ND AVE 33131

Northern Trust Building
700 BRICKELL AVE 33131

Olympia Building
174 E FLAGLER ST 33131

One Biscayne Tower
2 S BISCAYNE BLVD 33131

One Brickell Square
801 BRICKELL AVE 33131

Plaza Building
245 SE 1ST ST 33131

Rhode Building
401 NW 2ND AVE 33128

Rivergate Plaza
444 BRICKELL AVE 33131

Roberts Building
28 W FLAGLER ST 33130

Roper Building
20 SE 3RD AVE 33131

Seybold Building
36 NE 1ST ST 33132

Sun Bank Center
777 BRICKELL AVE 33131

United National Bank Building
1399 SW 1ST AVE 33130

White Building
1 NE 2ND AVE 33132

World Trade Center
80 SW 8TH ST 33130

GOVERNMENT

Dade County Courthouse
73 W FLAGLER ST 33130

Federal Building
51 SW 1ST AVE 33130

Federal Courthouse
300 NE 1ST AVE 33132

Federal Courthouse Sq
301 N MIAMI AVE 33128

Metro Dade Building
111 NW 1ST ST 33128

State Fla Office Building
1350 NW 12TH AVE 33136

GOVERNMENT

Airport Mail Facility
599000 PO BOX 33159

OCALA

BUILDINGS

Concord Square
7 E SILVER SPRINGS BLVD ......
.... 34470

GOVERNMENT

Marion Cty Sheriffs
1987 PO BOX 34478

OKEECHOBEE

APARTMENTS

4 Acres Trailer Park
2727 HIGHWAY 441 SE ... 34974

Town & Country Trlr Park
4425 HIGHWAY 441 S ... 34974

ORLANDO

APARTMENTS

Kinneret Towers Apts
515-517 DELANEY AVE ... 32801

Lucerne Tower Apts
20 W LUCERNE CIR 32801

Magnolia Towers
100 E ANDERSON ST 32801

Orlando Lutheran Towers
300 E CHURCH ST 32801

BUILDINGS

First Union Tower
20 N ORANGE AVE 32801

Sun Bank Center
200 S ORANGE AVE 32801

The Park Building
250 S ORANGE AVE 32801

GOVERNMENT

County Admin Building
100 E PINE ST 32801

Federal Building
80 N HUGHEY AVE 32801

Orange County Admin Ctr
201 S ROSALIND AVE 32801

Orange County Courthouse
65 E CENTRAL BLVD 32801

State Building
400 W ROBINSON ST 32801

PENSACOLA

GOVERNMENT

Chappie James Building
160 W GOVERNMENT ST 32501

County Court House
223 PALAFOX PL 32501

Federal Court House
100 N PALAFOX ST 32501

Governmental Center
190 W GOVERNMENT ST 32501

SAINT AUGUSTINE

GOVERNMENT

County Court House
99 CORDOVA ST 32084

SAINT PETERSBURG

APARTMENTS

Presbyterian Towers
430 BAY ST NE 33701

BUILDINGS

State Office
525 MIRROR LAKE DR N 33701

SANFORD

GOVERNMENT

Sem Cty Cthse Annex
1101 E 1ST ST 32771

SARASOTA

BUILDINGS

Federal Building
111 S ORANGE AVE 34236
Main Building
1900 MAIN ST 34236

Nationsbank Building
1605 MAIN ST 34236

STUART

GOVERNMENT

Martin County Court House
120 E OCEAN BLVD 34994

Stuart City Hall
121 SWFLAGLER AVE 34994

HOSPITALS

Martin Memorial Hospital
615 SEOSCEOLA ST 34994

TALLAHASSEE

APARTMENTS

Worthington Park Apts
1112 S MAGNOLIA DR 32301

BUILDINGS

Barnett Bank Building
315 S CALHOUN ST 32301

Exchange Building
201 S MONROE ST 32301

I B M Building
660 APALACHEE PKY 32301

Monroe Park Towers Building
101 N MONROE ST 32301

GOVERNMENT

Agriculture Complex
3125 CONNER BLVD 32399

Bloxham Building
727 S CALHOUN ST 32399

Bryant Building
620 S MERIDIAN ST 32399

Burns Building
605 SUWANNEE ST 32399

Caldwell Building
107 E MADISON ST 32399

Capitol Building
400 S MONROE ST 32399

Carlton Building
501 S CALHOUN ST 32399

City Center Building
227 N BRONOUGH ST 32301

City Hall
300 S ADAMS ST 32301

Claude Deason Pepper Bldg
111 MADISON 32399

Collins Building
107 W GAINES ST 32399

Commonwealth Building
3900 Commonwealth Blvd 32399

Dept Of Educ Building
325 W GAINES ST 32399

Fletcher Building
101 E GAINES ST 32399

Forest Building
2728 CENTERVIEW DR ... 32399

Hartman Building
2012 CAPITAL CIR SE 32399

Holland Building
600 S CALHOUN ST 32399

Johns Building
725 S BRONOUGH ST 32399

Knight Building
2737 CENTERVIEW DR ... 32399

Knott Building
111 W Saint Augustine St .. 32399

Larson Building
200 E GAINES ST 32399

Leon County Courthouse
301 S MONROE ST 32301

Lottery Complex
250 MARRIOTT DR 32399

Mayo Building
407 S CALHOUN ST 32399

Montgomery Building
2562 E Executive Center .. 32399

Neil Kirkman Building
2900 APALACHEE PKY 32399

Rhyne Building
2740 CENTERVIEW DR ... 32399

Supreme Court Building
500 S DUVAL ST 32399

Twin Towers
2600 BLAIRSTONE RD 32399

HOTELS

Sheraton Hotel
101 S ADAMS ST 32301

TITUSVILLE

GOVERNMENT

Brevard Co Courthouse
400 SOUTH ST 32780

WEST PALM BEACH

BUILDINGS

Citizens
105 S NARCISSUS AVE ... 33401

Comeau
319 CLEMATIS ST 33401

Commerce Center
324 DATURA ST 33401

Forum Iii
1675 Palm Bch Lakes Blvd 33401

Guaranty
120 S OLIVE AVE 33401

Harvey Building
224 DATURA ST 33401

GOVERNMENT

Paul E Rogers Federal Bld
701 CLEMATIS ST 33401

Pbc Courthouse
300 N DIXIE HWY 33401

WINTER PARK

APARTMENTS

Calvary Towers
1099 CLAY ST 32789

Cloisters Condos
100 S INTERLACHEN AVE 32789

Lake Killarney Condo
151 N ORLANDO AVE 32789

Lake Virginia Condos
690 OSCEOLA AVE 32789

Sutton Place South
500 OSCEOLA AVE 32789

BUILDINGS

New England Building
157 E New England Ave ... 32789

Winter Park Mall
500 N ORLANDO AVE 32789

COLLEGES

Rollins College
1000 HOLT AVE 32789

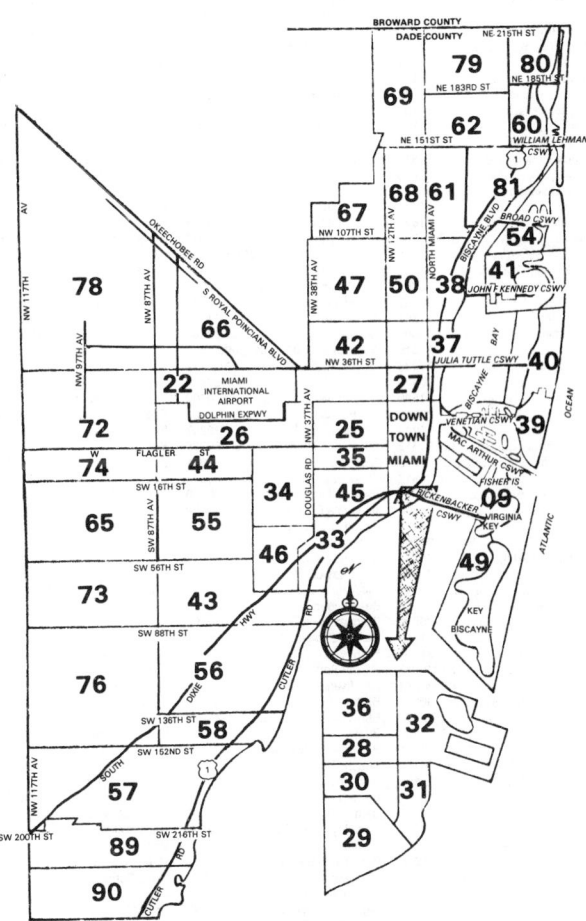

ZIP CODES

MIAMI, FL

331 + TWO DIGITS SHOWN = ZIP CODE

(Gainesville)	
Chickamauga	30707
Chula	31733
Cisco	30708
Clarkdale	30020
Clarkesville	30523
Clarkston	30021
Claxton	30414, 30417, 30438
(Bellville)	
Clayton	30525
Clermont	30527
Cleveland	30528
Climax	31734
Clinchfield	31013
Cloudland (Menlo)	30731
Clyattville (Valdosta)	31601
Clyo	31303
Cobb	31735
Cobbtown	30420
Cochran	31014, 31026
Empire	31026
Cogdell (Homerville)	31634
Cohutta	30710
Colbert	30628
Coleman	31736
Colemans Lake (Midville)	30441
College Park	30337, 30349
(Atlanta)	
Collins	30421
Colquitt	31737
Columbus	31829
	31900-909, 31993-999
Custer Terrace	31905
Fort Benning	31905
Upatoi	31829
Comer	30629
Commerce	30529, 30599
Concord	30206
Conley	30027
Conyers	30207-208
Milstead	30207
South Conyers	30208
Coolidge	31738
Coosa	30129
Cordele	31015
Cornelia	30531
Cotton	31739
Covington	30209-210
Cox (Townsend)	31331
Crandall	30711
Crawford	30630
Crawfordville	30631
Crescent	31304, 31332
Crossroads (Riceboro)	31323
Culloden	31016
Cumberland (Atlanta)	30339
Cumming	30130-131
Tri County	30130
Cusseta	31805
Custer Terrace (Columbus)	31905
Cuthbert	31740
Dacula	30211
Dahlonega	30533, 30597
Daisy	30423
Dallas	30132
Dalton	30719-722
Damascus	31741
Danburg (Tignall)	30668
Danielsville	30633
Danville	31017
Darien	31305

Dasher (Valdosta)	31601
Davisboro	31018
Dawson	31742
Dawsonville	30534
De Soto	31743
Dearing	30808
Decatur	30030-038, 30089
Belvedere	30032
Dunaire	30032
North Decatur	30033
Snapfinger	30035
South Decatur	30034
Vista Grove	30033
Deepstep (Sandersville)	31082
Dellwood (Swainsboro)	30401
Demorest	30535, 30544
Habersham	30544
Denmark (Brooklet)	30415
Denton	31532
Devereux (Sparta)	31087
Dewy Rose	30634
Dexter	31019
Dillard	30537
Dixie	31629
Doerun	31744
Donald (Ludowici)	31316
Donalsonville	31745
Doraville (Atlanta)	30340
Double Branches	30817
(Lincolnton)	
Douglas	31533
Douglasville	30133-135
Dover	30424
Druid Hills (Atlanta)	30333
Dry Branch	30822, 31020
(Perkins)	
Du Pont	31630
Dublin	31021, 31040
East Dublin	31021
Lollie	31021
Dudley	31022
Duluth	30136, 30158-159
	30198, 30199
Berkeley Lake	30136
Dunaire (Decatur)	30032
Dunwoody	30338, 30350
(Atlanta)	
East Dublin (Dublin)	31021
East Ellijay	30539
East Lake Center	30062
(Marietta)	
East Point (Atlanta)	30344, 30364
Eastanollee	30538
Eastman	31023
Eatonton	31024
Eden	31307
Edge Hill (Gibson)	30810
Edison	31746
Elberton	30635
Elim (Ludowici)	31316
Elko	31025
Ellabell	31308
Ellaville	31806
Ellenton	31747
Ellenwood	30049
Ellerslie	31807
Ellijay	30540
Ellwood (Blythe)	30805
Elmodel (Newton)	31770
Embry Hills (Atlanta)	30341
Emerson	30137

Emmalane (Millen)	30442
Empire (Cochran)	31026
Enigma	31749
Ephesus (Roopville)	30170
Epworth	30541
Esom Hill	30138
Eton	30724
Eulonia (Townsend)	31331
Evans	30809
Everett (Brunswick)	31520
Excelsior (Metter)	30439
Executive Park (Atlanta)	30347
Experiment	30212
Fair Oaks (Marietta)	30060
Fairburn	30213
Fairfax (Millwood)	31552
Fairmount	30139
Fairview Road (Ellenwood)	30049
Fargo	31631
Farmington	30638
Farrar (Shady Dale)	31085
Fayetteville	30214, 30232
Inman	30232
Woolsey	30214
Felton	30140
First Union (Atlanta)	31193
Fitzgerald	31750
Fleming	31309
Flemington (Hinesville)	31313
Flintstone	30725
Flovilla	30216
Flowery Branch	30542, 50502
Floyd Junction (Marietta)	30060
Folkston	31537
Forest Hills (Augusta)	30909
Forest Park	30050-051
Fort Gillem	30050
Forsyth	31029
Fort Benning (Columbus)	31905
Fort Gaines	31751
Fort Gillem (Forest Park)	30050
Fort Gordon (Augusta)	30905
Fort Mc Pherson	30310, 30330
(Atlanta)	
Fort Oglethorpe	30742
Fort Screven	31328
(Tybee Island)	
Fort Stewart	31313-314
(Hinesville)	
Fort Valley	31030
Fortson	31808
Fowlstown	31752
Franklin	30217
Franklin Springs	30639
Fry (Mc Caysville)	30555
Funston	31753
Gainesville	30501, 30503-507
Chestnut Mountain	30502
Westside	30501
Garden City	31408, 31418
(Savannah)	
Gardi (Jesup)	31545
Garfield	30425
Gary (Swainsboro)	30401
Gay	30218
Geneva	31810
Georgetown	31754
Gibson	30810
Gillsville	30543
Girard	30426
Glenn (Franklin)	30217, 30219

Glennville	30427	
Glenwood	30428	
Glynco (Brunswick)	31520	
Good Hope	30641	
Gordon	31031	
Gough	30811	
Gracewood	30812	
Graham (Baxley)	31513	
Grange (Louisville)	30434	
Grantville	30220	
Graves (Dawson)	31742	
Gray	31032	
Grayson	30221	
Graysville	30726	
Greensboro	30642	
Greenville	30222, 31548	
Stovall	30222	
Greenway (Midville)	30441	
Griffin	30223-224	
Grovania (Hawkinsville)	31036	
Grovetown	30813	
Gumbranch (Hinesville)	31313	
Guysie (Alma)	31510	
Guyton	31312	
Habersham (Demorest)	30544	
Haddock	31033	
Hagan	30429	
Hahira	31632	
Hamilton	31811	
Hampton	30228	
Hapeville (Atlanta)	30354	
Haralson	30229	
Hardwick	31034	
Harlem	30814	
Harrison	31035	
Hartsfield	31756	
Hartville (Hartsfield)	31756	
Hartwell	30643	
Hawkinsville	31036	
Hayneville (Hawkinsville)	31036	
Hazlehurst	31539	
Helen	30545	
Helena	31037	
Hephzibah	30815	
Herndon (Midville)	30441	
Hiawassee	30546	
Hickory Bluff (Waverly)	31565	
Hickox (Nahunta)	31553	
Higgston (Ailey)	30410	
High Shoals	30645	
Hill City (Resaca)	30735	
Hillsboro	31038	
Hiltonia (Sylvania)	30467	
Hinesville	31313-314	
Flemington	31313	
Fort Stewart	31313-314	
Gumbranch	31313	
Hinsonton (Meigs)	31765	
Hiram	30141	
Hoboken	31542	
Hogansville	30230	
Holly Springs	30142	
Homer	30547	
Homerville	31634	
Honora (Lincolnton)	30817	
Hortense	31543	
Hoschton	30548	
Howard	31039	
Huber (Macon)	31201	
Hubert (Brooklet)	30415	
Hull	30646	

Ideal	31041	
Ila	30647	
Indian Springs (Flovilla)	30216	
Industrial (Atlanta)	30336	
Inman (Fayetteville)	30232	
Iron City	31759	
Irwinton	31042	
Irwinville	31760	
Ivanhoe (Brooklet)	30415	
Jackson	30233	
Jacksonville	31544	
Jakin	31761	
Jasper	30143	
Jefferson	30549	
Jeffersonville	31044	
Jekyll Island	31520, 31527	
(Brunswick)		
Brunswick	31527	
Jenkinsburg	30234	
Jersey	30235	
Jesup	31545, 31599	
Jewell	31045	
Johnson Corner (Lyons)	30436	
Jones (Riceboro)	31323	
Jonesboro	30236-237	
Juliette	31046	
Junction City	31812	
Juniper (Box Springs)	31801	
Juno (Dawsonville)	30534	
Kathleen	31047	
Kelly (Shady Dale)	31085	
Kemp (Swainsboro)	30401	
Kennesaw	30144	
Keysville (Gough)	30811, 30816	
Kibbee (Vidalia)	30474	
Kings Bay (Kingsland)	31547	
Kingsland	31547-548	
Greenville	31548	
Kings Bay	31547	
Kingston	30145	
Kite	31049	
Klondike (Hawkinsville)	31036	
Knoxville	31050	
La Fayette	30728	
La Grange	30240-241, 30261	
Mountville	30261	
Lake Arrowhead (Waleska)	30183	
Lake City (Morrow)	30260	
Lake Park	31636	
Lakeland	31635	
Lakemont	30552	
Lavonia	30553	
Lawrenceville	30243-246	
Shannon Oaks	30245	
Leah (Appling)	30802	
Leary	31762	
Leathersville	30817	
(Lincolnton)		
Lebanon	30146	
Leesburg	31763	
Lenox	31637	
Leslie	31764	
Lexington	30648	
Lexsy (Swainsboro)	30401	
Lilburn	30226, 30247	
Lilly	31051	
Lincolnton	30817	
Lindale	30147	
Lithia Springs	30057	
Lithonia	30038, 30058	
Decatur	30038	

Lizella	31052	
Lockheed (Marietta)	30063	
Loco (Lincolnton)	30817	
Locust Grove	30248	
Loganville	30249	
Lollie (Dublin)	31021	
Lookout Mountain	30750	
Lotts (Broxton)	31519	
Louisville	30434	
Louvale	31814	
Lovejoy	30250	
Ludowici	31316	
Lula	30554	
Lulaton (Nahunta)	31553	
Lumber City	31549	
Lumpkin	31815	
Luthersville	30251	
Lyerly	30730	
Lyons	30436	
Mableton	30059	
Macon	31200-213, 31294-299	
Huber	31201	
Payne City	31204	
Madison	30650	
Madray Springs (Jesup)	31545	
Manassas	30438	
Manchester	31816	
Manor	31550	
Mansfield	30255	
Marble Hill	30148	
Marietta	30007, 30060-069	
	30090	
Canton Plaza	30066	
East Lake Center	30062	
Fair Oaks	30060	
Floyd Junction	30060	
Lockheed	30063	
Northeast	30062	
Sprayberry	30062	
Sprayberry	30066	
West Gate	30060	
Windy Hill	30067	
Marlow (Guyton)	31312	
Marshallville	31057	
Martin	30557	
Martinez (Augusta)	30907	
Matthews	30818	
Mauk	31058	
Maxeys (Union Point)	30671	
Maxim (Lincolnton)	30817	
Mayfield (Sparta)	31087	
Maysville	30558	
Mc Caysville	30555	
Mc Donough	30253	
Mc Gregor (Ailey)	30410	
Mc Intyre	31054	
Mc Kinnon (Jesup)	31545	
Mc Rae	31055	
Meansville	30256	
Meigs	31765	
Meldrim	31318	
Mendes (Glennville)	30427	
Menlo	30731	
Meridian	31319	
Mershon	31551	
Mesena	30819	
Metter	30439	
Midland	31820	
Midville	30441	
Midway	31320	
Milan	31060	

Milledgeville	31061-062	
Millen	30442	
Millwood	31552	
Milner	30257	
Milstead (Conyers)	30207	
Mineral Bluff	30559	
Mitchell	30820	
Modoc (Swainsboro)	30401	
Molena	30258	
Monroe	30655-656	
Montezuma	31063	
Monticello	31064	
Montrose	31065	
Moreland	30259	
Morgan	31766	
Morganton	30560	
Morris	31767	
Morrow	30260, 30287	
Lake City	30260	
Park Place	30287	
Morven	31638	
Moultrie	31768, 31776	
Mount Airy	30563	
Mount Berry	30149	
Mount Vernon	30445	
Mount Zion	30150	
Mountain City	30562	
Mountville (La Grange)	30261	
Moxley (Wadley)	30477	
Munnerlyn (Waynesboro)	30830	
Murrayville	30564	
Musella	31066	
Mystic	31769	
Nahunta	31553	
Nashville	31639	
Naylor	31641	
Nelson	30151	
New Branch (Lyons)	30436	
New Hope (Lincolnton)	30817	
Newborn	30262	
Newington	30446	
Newnan	30263-265	
Raymond	30263	
Shenandoah	30265	
Newton	31770	
Nicholls	31554	
Nicholson	30565	
Noah (Matthews)	30818	
Norcross	30071, 30091-093	
Parkway	30092	
Peachtree Corners	30092	
Rockbridge	30093	
Norman Park	31771	
Normantown (Vidalia)	30474	
Norris (Warrenton)	30828	
Norristown	30447	
North Atlanta (Atlanta)	30319	
North Corners	30120	
(Cartersville)		
North Decatur (Decatur)	30033	
North Metro	30158-159	
Duluth	30158-159	
North Springs (Atlanta)	30338	
Northeast (Marietta)	30062	
Northlake (Atlanta)	30345	
Northside (Warner Robins)	31093	
Norwood	30821	
Nunez	30448	
Oak Grove (Acworth)	30101	
Oak Park (Swainsboro)	30401	
Oakfield	31772	
Oakman	30732	
Oakwood	30566	
Ochlocknee	31773	
Ocilla	31774	
Oconee	31067	
Odum	31555	
Offerman	31556	
Oglethorpe	31068	
Ohoopee (Lyons)	30436	
Okefenokee (Waycross)	31501	
Old National (Atlanta)	30349	
Oliver	30449	
Omaha	31821	
Omega	31775	
Orchard Hill	30266	
Oxford	30267	
Palmetto	30268	
Park Place (Morrow)	30287	
Parkway (Norcross)	30092	
Parrott	31777	
Patterson	31557	
Pavo	31778	
Payne City (Macon)	31204	
Peach Orchard (Augusta)	30906	
Peachtree City	30269	
Peachtree Corners	30092	
(Norcross)		
Pearson	31642	
Pelham	31779	
Pembroke	31321	
Pendergrass	30567	
Penfield (Union Point)	30669	
Perimeter (Atlanta)	30346	
Perkins	30822	
Perry	31069	
Petross (Vidalia)	30474	
Philomath (Rayle)	30660	
Phinizy (Appling)	30802	
Pine Grove (Baxley)	31513	
Pine Lake	30072	
Pine Log (Rydal)	30171	
Pine Mountain	31822	
Pine Mountain Valley	31823	
Pinehurst	31070	
Pineora (Guyton)	31312	
Pineview	31071	
Piney Bluff (Waverly)	31565	
Pitts	31072	
Plainfield	31073	
Plains	31780	
Plainville	30733	
Pollards Corner (Appling)	30802	
Pooler	31322	
Port Wentworth (Savannah)	31407	
Portal	30450	
Porterdale	30270	
Poulan	31781	
Powder Springs	30073	
Powersville (Byron)	31008	
Preston	31824	
Pridgen (Broxton)	31519	
Pulaski	30451	
Pumpkin Center (Harlem)	30814	
Putney	31782	
Quitman	31643	
Rabun Gap	30568	
Radium Springs (Albany)	31705	
Ranger	30734	
Ray City	31645	
Raybon (Nahunta)	31553	
Rayle	30660	
Raymond (Newnan)	30263	
Rebecca	31783	
Red Oak	30272	
Redan	30074	
Reese (Warrenton)	30828	
Register	30452	
Reidsville	30453, 30499	
Remerton (Valdosta)	31601	
Rentz	31075	
Resaca	30735	
Retreat (Riceboro)	31323	
Rex30273		
Reynolds	31076	
Rhine	31077	
Riceboro	31323	
Richland	31825	
Richmond Hill	31324	
Ridgeville (Townsend)	31331	
Rincon	31326	
Ringgold	30736	
Riverdale	30274, 30296	
Roberta	31078	
Rochelle	31079	
Rock Spring	30739	
Rockbridge (Norcross)	30093	
Rockingham (Alma)	31510	
Rockledge	30454	
Rockmart	30153	
Rocky Face	30740	
Rocky Ford	30455	
Rome	30149, 30161-165	
(Mount Berry)		
Roopville	30170	
Roper (Hazlehurst)	31539	
Rosier (Louisville)	30434	
Rossville	30741-742	
Roswell	30075-077	
Sandy Plains	30075	
Round Oak (Hillsboro)	31038	
Royston	30662	
Rupert	31081	
Rutledge	30663	
Rydal	30171	
Saint George	31646	
Saint Marys	31558	
Saint Mountain	30083, 30086	
(Stone Mountain)		
Saint Simons Island	31522	
Sale City	31784	
Salem Road (Covington)	30209	
Sandersville	31082	
Sandy Plains (Roswell)	30075	
Sandy Springs	30328, 30358	
(Atlanta)		
Santa Claus (Lyons)	30436	
Sapelo Island	31327	
Sardis	30456	
Sargent	30275	
Sasser	31785	
Sautee Nacoochee	30571	
Savannah	31400-412, 31414	
	31416, 31418-420	
	31498-499	
Garden City	31408	
Garden City	31418	
Port Wentworth	31407	
Thunderbolt	31404	
Village Station	31411	
Wilmington Island	31410	
Scarboro (Millen)	30442	
Scotland	31083	

Scottdale	30079	
Screven	31560	
Sea Island	31561	
Senoia	30276	
Sessoms (Nicholls)	31554	
Seville	31084	
Shady Dale	31085	
Shannon	30172	
Shannon Oaks	30245	
(Lawrenceville)		
Sharon	30664	
Sharpsburg	30277	
Shell Bluff (Waynesboro)	30830	
Shellman	31786	
Shenandoah (Newnan)	30265	
Shiloh	31826	
Shoals (Mitchell)	30820	
Siloam	30665	
Silver Creek	30173	
Six Flags (Austell)	30001	
Smarr	31086	
Smithville	31787	
Smyrna	30080-082	
Snapfinger (Decatur)	30035	
Snellville	30278	
Snipesville (Denton)	31532	
Social Circle	30279	
Soperton	30457	
South Base	31098	
(Warner Robins)		
South Conyers (Conyers)	30208	
South Decatur (Decatur)	30034	
South Newport (Riceboro)	31323	
Southern Bell	30375, 30385	
(Atlanta)		
Southwire (Carrollton)	30119	
Sparks	31647	
Sparta	31087	
Sprayberry	30062, 30066	
(Marietta)		
Spring Bluff (Waverly)	31565	
Springfield	31329	
Springvale (Morris)	31767	
Stapleton	30823	
Starrsville (Covington)	30209	
Statenville	31648	
Statesboro	30458-460	
Statham	30666	
Stephens	30667	
Stillmore	30464	
Stilwell (Springfield)	31329	
Stilson (Brooklet)	30415	
Stockbridge	30281	
Stockton	31649	
Stone Mountain	30083	
	30086-088	
Saint Mountain	30083	
Saint Mountain	30086	
Stovall (Greenville)	30222	
Suches	30572	
Sugar Hill (Buford)	30518	
Sugar Valley	30746	
Summertown	30466	
Summerville	30747	
Sumner	31789	
Sunny Side	30284	
Surrency	31563	

Suwanee	30174	
Swainsboro	30401, 30466	
Blun	30401	
Blundale	30401	
Dellwood	30401	
Gary	30401	
Kemp	30401	
Lexsy	30401	
Modoc	30401	
Oak Park	30401	
Wesley	30401	
Sybert (Lincolnton)	30817	
Sycamore	31790	
Sylvania	30467	
Sylvester	31791	
Talbotton	31827	
Talking Rock	30175	
Tallapoosa	30176	
Tallulah Falls	30573	
Talmo	30575	
Tarrytown	30470	
Tate	30177	
Taylorsville	30178	
Tazewell (Buena Vista)	31803	
Temple	30179	
Tennga	30751	
Tennille	31089	
The Rock	30285	
Thomaston	30286	
Thomasville	31792, 31799	
Thomson	30824	
Thrift (Millen)	30442	
Thunderbolt (Savannah)	31404	
Tifton	31793-794	
Abac	31794	
Tiger	30576	
Tignall	30668	
Tison (Glennville)	30427	
Toccoa	30577, 30598	
Toomsboro	31090	
Townsend	31331	
Trenton	30752	
Tri County (Cumming)	30130	
Trion	30753	
Tucker	30084-085	
Tunnel Hill	30755	
Turin	30289	
Turnerville	30580	
Tuxedo (Atlanta)	30342	
Twin City	30471	
Ty Ty	31795	
Tybee Island	31328	
Tyrone	30290	
Unadilla	31091	
Union City	30291	
Union Point	30669, 30671	
Maxeys	30671	
Penfield	30669	
Upatoi (Columbus)	31829	
Uvalda	30473	
Valdosta	31601-604, 31698-399	
Bemiss	31602	
Clyattville	31601	
Dasher	31601	
Remerton	31601	
Valona	31332	
Varnell	30756	

Vidalia	30474	
Vidette (Louisville)	30434	
Vienna	31092	
Villa Rica	30180	
Village Station	31411	
(Savannah)		
Vinnings (Atlanta)	30339	
Vista Grove (Decatur)	30033	
Waco	30182	
Wadley	30477	
Waleska	30183	
Walnut Grove (Covington)	30209	
Walthourville	31333	
Waresboro	31564	
Warm Springs	31830	
Warner Robins	31028, 31088	
	31093, 31095, 31098-099	
(Centerville)		
Northside	31093	
South Base	31098	
Warrenton	30828	
Warthen	31094	
Warwick	31796	
Washington	30673	
Watkinsville	30677	
Waverly	31565	
Waverly Hall	31831	
Waycross	31501-503	
Okefenokee	31501	
Waynesboro	30830	
Waynesville	31566	
Wesley (Swainsboro)	30401	
West Bainbridge	31717	
(Bainbridge)		
West Gate (Marietta)	30060	
West Green	31567	
West Point	31833	
Weston	31832	
Westside (Gainesville)	30501	
Whigham	31797	
White	30184	
White Oak	31568	
White Plains	30678	
Whitesburg	30185	
Wildwood	30757	
Wiley	30581	
Willacoochee	31650	
Williamson	30292	
Wilmington Island	31410	
(Savannah)		
Wilsonville (Nicholls)	31554	
Winder	30680	
Windy Hill (Marietta)	30067	
Winfield (Thomson)	30824	
Winston	30187	
Winterville	30683	
Woodbine	31569	
Woodbury	30293	
Woodland	31836	
Woodstock	30188	
Woolsey (Fayetteville)	30214	
Wray	31798	
Wrens (Matthews)	30818, 30833	
Wrightsville	31096	
Yatesville	31097	
Young Harris	30582	
Zebulon	30295	

ALBANY

HOSPITALS

HCA Palmyra Park Hospital
1908 Po Box 31703

Phoebe Putney Hospital
1828 Po Box 31703

ATHENS

GOVERNMENT

Athens City Hall
301 College Ave 30601

County Court House
300 E Washington St 30601

Federal Building
355 E Hancock Ave 30601

U S Post Office Court Hou
115 E Hancock Ave 30601

ATLANTA

GOVERNMENT

Fulton County Health
99 Butler St SE 30303

HOSPITALS

Emory School Of Med
69 Butler St SE 30303

Grady Memorial Hosp
80 Butler St SE 30303

AUGUSTA

BUILDINGS

Augusta Mall
3450 Wrightsboro Rd 30909

City County
530 Greene St 30911

Federal
816 Walker St 30901

First Union Bank
699 Broad St 30901

Lamar
753 Broad St 30901

Marion
739 Broad St 30901

Mid South
360 Bay St 30901

Regency Mall
1700 Gordon Hwy 30904

Trust Company Bank
801 Broad St 30901

GOVERNMENT

Main Post Office
525 8th St 30901

HOSPITALS

Charter Hospital Of Augus
3100 Perimeter Pky 30909

DALTON

APARTMENTS

Executive Apts
1104 Walston St 30720

Georgian Apts
1219 W Emory St 30720

Huntington Place
1702 Crow Valley Rd NW . 30720

GOVERNMENT

Courthouse
300 W Crawford St 30720

DECATUR

GOVERNMENT

Dekalb County Court House
556 N Mcdonough St 30030

DOUGLASVILLE

GOVERNMENT

Douglas County Courthouse
6754 Broad St 30134

FAIR OAKS

MILITARY

Base Official
0 Naval Air Station Atl 30060

GAINESVILLE

GOVERNMENT

Hall County Court House
116 Spring St E 30501

MACON

HOSPITALS

Medical Ctr Of Central Ga
6000 Po Box 31208

SAVANNAH

BUILDINGS

American
7 Drayton St 31401

C & S Bank
300 Bull St 31401

Candler Profofessional
5354 Reynolds St 31405

First Union Bank
2 E Bryan St 31401

Oglethorpe Mall
7804 Abercorn St 31406

Palmer & Cay
25 Bull St 31401

Provident Professional
4750 Waters Ave 31404

Realty
24 Drayton St 31401

Savannah Financial Ctr
7 E Congress St 31401

Savannah Mall
14045 Abercorn St 31419

Trust Co Bank Building
33 Bull St 31401

Two Whitaker
2 Whitaker St 31401

Whitaker Congress
31 W Congress St 31401

GOVERNMENT

Chatham Co Courthouse
133 Montgomery St 31401

Federal
100 W Oglethorpe Ave 31401

Federal Building Annex
120 Barnard St 31401

Federal Building Annex
124 Barnard St 31401

Human Resources Building
2 E Henry St 31401

Main Post Office
2 N Fahm St 31402

Old Courthouse Building
124-125 Bull St 31401

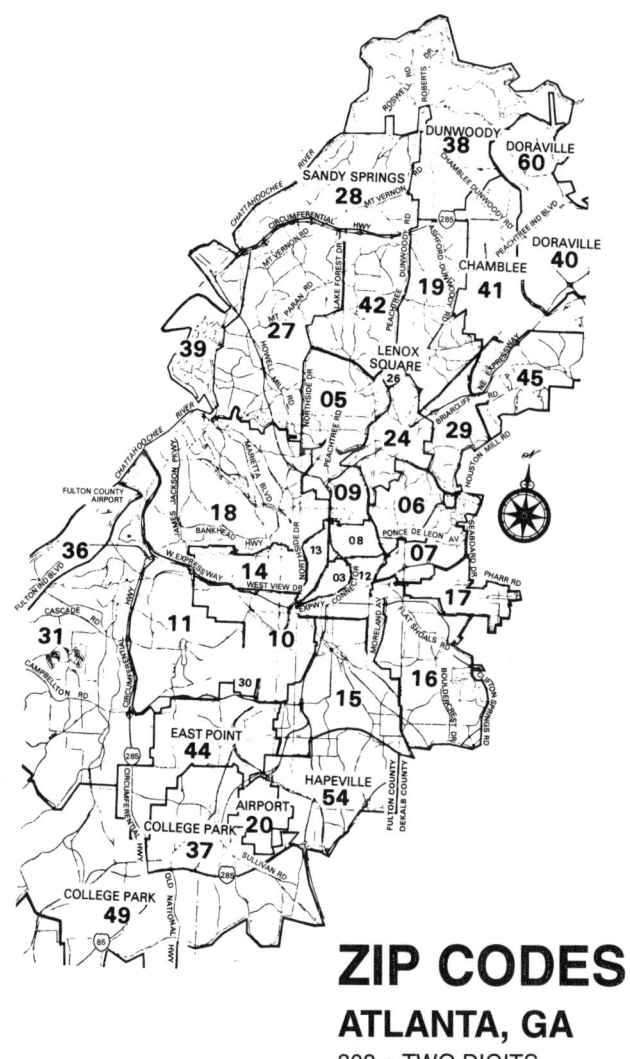

ZIP CODES

ATLANTA, GA

303 + TWO DIGITS
SHOWN = ZIP CODE

GUAM
Abbreviation GU

HAWAII
Abbreviation HI

Aiea 96701, 96861
Anahola 96703
Bancorp Hawaii (Honolulu) 96849
Camp Smith 96861
(Camp H M Smith)
Captain Cook 96704, 76737
Downtown Station .. 96721, 96767
(Hilo)
East West Center 96848
(Honolulu)
Eleele 96705
Ewa Beach 96706, 96862
Fort Shafter (official) 96858
(Fort Shafter)
Haiku 96708
Hakalau 96710
Haleiwa 96712
Hana 96713
Hanalei 96714
Hanamaulu 96715
Hanapepe 96716
Hauula 96717
Hawaii National Park 96718
Hawi 96719
Hilo 96720-721
Downtown Station 96721
Holualoa 96725
Honaunau 96726
Honokaa 96727
Honolulu 96800-828, 96830
.... 96835-850
Bancorp Hawaii 96849
East West Center 96848
Liberty House 96845
University Of Hawaii ... 96844
Honomu 96728

Hoolehua 96729
Kaaawa 96730
Kahuku 96731
Kahului 96732-733
Kailua 96734, 96863
Kailua Kona ... 96739-740, 96745
Keauhou 96739
Kalaheo 96741
Kalaupapa 96742
Kamuela 96738, 96743
(Waikoloa)
Kaneohe 96744
Kapaa 96746
Kapaau 96755
Kapolei 96707
Kaumakani 96747
Kaunakakai 96748
Keaau 96749
Kealakekua 96750
Kealia 96751
Keauhou (Kailua Kona) 96739
Kekaha 96752
Kihei 96753
Kilauea 96754
Koloa 96756
Kualapuu 96757
Kula 96790
Kunia 96759
Kurtistown 96760
Lahaina 96761, 96767
Downtown Station 96767
Laie 96762
Lanai City 96763
Laupahoehoe . 96764, 96773-774
Lawai 96765
Liberty House (Honolulu) .. 96845
Lihue 96766
Makawao 96768

Makaweli 96769
Maunaloa 96770
Mililani 96789
Mountain View 96771
Naalehu 96772
Ninole 96773
Ookala 96774
Paauhau 96775
Paauilo 96776
Pahala 96777
Pahoa 96778
Paia 96779
Papaaloa 96780
Papaikou 96781
Pearl City 96782
Pearl Harbor (official) 96860
(Pearl Harbor)
Pepeekeo 96783
Princeville 96722
Pukalani 96788
Puunene 96784
Schofield Barracks 96857
(Schofield Barracks)
Tripler Mc (official) 96859
(Tripler Army Medical Ctr)
University Of Hawaii 96844
(Honolulu)
Volcano 96785
Wahiawa 96786
Waialua 96791
Waianae 96792
Waikoloa 96738
Wailuku 96793
Waimanalo 96795
Waimea 96796
Waipahu 96797
Wake Island 96898
Wheeler Army Airfield 96854

HONOLULU

BUILDINGS

1833 Kalakaua
1833 KALAKAUA AVE 96815

Ala Moana Building
1441 KAPIOLANI BLVD 96814

Ala Moana Pacific Center
1585 KAPIOLANI BLVD 96814

Aliiolani Hale
417 S KING ST 96813

Alioto's Building
1580 MAKALOA ST 96814

American Savings Building
915 FORT STREET MALL 96813

Amfac Center
700 BISHOP ST 96813

Atlas Ins Building
1150 S KING ST 96814

Bank Of America Building
677 ALA MOANA BLVD 96813

Bank Of Hawaii Building
2222 KALAKAUA AVE 96815

Bishop Building
1164 BISHOP ST 96813

Bishop Trust Building
1000 BISHOP ST 96813

Castle & Cooke Building
130 MERCHANT ST 96813

Central Pacific Plaza
220 S KING ST 96813

Century Square
1188 BISHOP ST 96813

Community Service Ctr
200 N VINEYARD BLVD ... 96817

Davies Pacific Center
841 BISHOP ST 96813

Dillingham Trans Building
735 BISHOP ST 96813

Executive Center
1088 BISHOP ST 96813

Finance Factors Building
195 S KING ST 96813

First Hawaiian Bank Building
165 S KING ST 96813

Grosvenor Ctr Mauka Tower
737 BISHOP ST 96813

Grosvenor Ctr Pri Tower
733 BISHOP ST 96813

Hasegawa Komuten Building
820 MILILANI ST 96813

Hawaii Building
745 FORT STREET MALL 96813

Hawaiian Life Building
1311 KAPIOLANI BLVD 96814

HMSA Building
818 KEEAUMOKU 96814

Honolulu Police Dept Building
801 S BERETANIA ST 96813

Interstate Building
1314 S KING ST 96814

Kapiolani Medical Center
1319 PUNAHOU 96826

Kawaiahao Plaza
567 S KING ST 96813

Kendall Building
888 MILILANI ST 96813

Kuakini Medical Plaza
321 N KUAKINI ST 96817

Medical Arts Building
1010 S KING ST 96814

Pacific Tower
1001 BISHOP ST 96813

Pan Am Building
1600 KAPIOLANI BLVD 96814

Pauahi Tower
1001 BISHOP ST 96813

Pioneer Plaza Building
900 FORT STREET MALL 96813

Queens Physician Office
1380 LUSITANA ST 96813

Sperry Univac Building
3049 UALENA ST 96819

The Eight Fifty Building
850 RICHARDS ST 96813

Waikiki Trade Center
2255 KUHIO AVE 96815

Waterfront Plaza
500 ALA MOANA BLVD 96813

District Court Building
1111 ALAKEA ST 96813

Keelikolani Building
830 PUNCHBOWL ST 96813

Municipal Building C & C
650 S KING ST 96813

Prince J K Kuhio Fed Building
300 ALA MOANA BLVD 96850

State Capitol Building
415 S BERETANIA ST 96813

GOVERNMENT

City Hall
530 S KING ST 96813

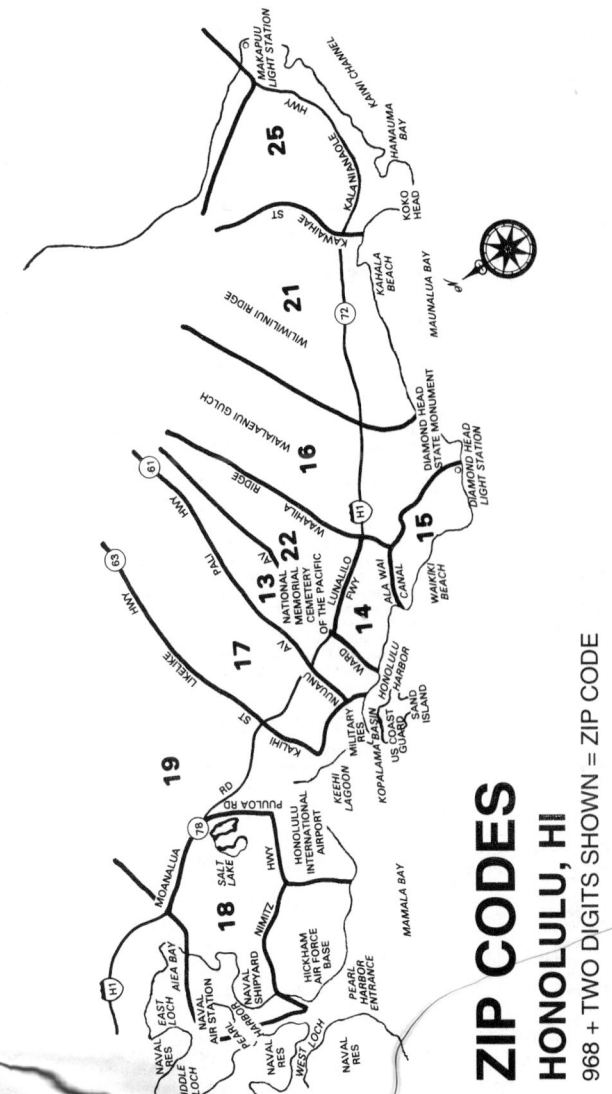

ZIP CODES
HONOLULU, HI
968 + TWO DIGITS SHOWN = ZIP CODE

IDAHO
Abbreviation ID

Aberdeen	83210
Acequia (Rupert)	83350
Ahsahka	83520
Alameda 83201, 83206	
(Pocatello)	
Albertsons (Boise)	83726
Albion	83311
Almo	83312
Alpha (Cascade)	83611
Alpine (Cambridge)	83610
Alta (Driggs)	83422
American Falls	83211
Ammon (Idaho Falls)	83401
Anderson Dam	83647
(Mountain Home)	
Annis (Rigby)	83442
Antelope (Ririe)	83443
Anthony (Saint Anthony)	83445
Apple Valley (Parma)	83660
Appleton (Jerome)	83338
Arbon	83212
Archer (Rexburg)	83440
Arco	83213
Argora (Dubois)	83423
Arimo	83214
Ashton 83420, 83447	
Drummond	83420
Lamont	83420
Marysville	83420
Warm River	83420
Athol	83801
Atlanta	83601
Atomic City	83215
Avery	83802
Baker (Salmon)	83467
Bancroft	83217
Banks	83602
Bannock (Pocatello)	83204
Barrymore (Jerome)	83338
Basalt	83218
Basin (Oakley)	83346
Bates (Driggs)	93422
Bayview	83803
Beachs Corner	83401
(Idaho Falls)	
Bear (Council)	83612
Bellevue	83313
Belmont (Athol)	83801
Bench (Grace)	83241
Bennington (Montpelier)	83254
Bern	83220
Big Springs (Macks Inn)	83433
Blackfoot 83221, 83277	
Groveland	83221
Riverside	83221
Rockford	83221
Rose	83221
Taber	83221
Thomas	83221
Wapello	83221
Blanchard	83804
Bliss	83314
Bloomington	83223
Blue Dome (Leadore)	83464
Boise 83700-709, 83711-713	
.... 83714-715, 83719-735	
.... 83744, 83756-757, 83788	
Albertsons	83726

Collister	83703
Garden City	83714
Mayfield	83706
Ustick	83704
Bonanza (Stanley)	83278
Bone (Idaho Falls)	83401
Bonners Ferry	83805
Bovill	83806
Bowmont (Nampa)	83686
Box Canyon (Island Park)	83429
Bridge (Malta)	83342
Broadford (Bellevue)	83313
Bruneau	83604
Buhl	83316
Burgdorf (Mc Call)	83638
Burley	83318
Burmah (Richfield)	83349
Burton (Rexburg)	83440
Cabinet (Clark Fork)	83811
Calder	83808
Caldwell 83605-606	
Doles	83605
Enrose	83605
Knowlton Heights	83605
Sunnyslope	83605
Weitz	83605
Cambridge	83610
Canyon Creek (Newdale)	83436
Carey	83320
Careywood	83809
Carmen	83462
Cascade	83611
Castleford	83321
Cataldo	83810
Centerville (Idaho City)	83631
Central (Grace)	83241
Challis 83226, 83229	
Cherry Creek (Malad City)	83252
Chester	83421
Chesterfield (Bancroft)	83217
Chilco (Athol)	83801
Chilly (Mackay)	83251
Chubbuck (Pocatello)	83202
Churchill (Oakley)	83346
Clark Fork	83811
Clarkia	83812
Clawson (Tetonia)	83452
Clayton	83227
Clearwater (Kooskia)	83539
Clementsville (Newdale)	83436
Clifton	83228
Clover (Buhl)	83316
Clyde (Howe)	83244
Cobalt	83229
Cocolalla	83813
Coeur D Alene 83814, 83816	
Colburn	83865
Collister (Boise)	83703
Coltman (Idaho Falls)	83401
Conda	83230
Conner (Malta)	83342
Coolin	83821
Cooperville (White Bird)	83554
Copeland (Bonners Ferry)	83805
Corral	83322
Cotterel (Declo)	83323
Cottonwood	83522
.... 83533, 83538	
Keuterville	83538
Council	83612
Craigmont	83523

Crouch (Garden Valley)	83622
Crystal (Weiser)	83672
Culdesac 83524, 83548	
Cuprum (Council)	83612
Curry (Filer)	83328
Daniels (Malad City)	83252
Darlington	83231
Dayton	83232
Deary	83823
Declo	83323
Deep Creek (Buhl)	83316
Desmet	83824
Dietrich	83324
Dingle	83233
Dixie (Elk City)	83525
Doles (Caldwell)	83605
Donnelly	83615
Dover	83825
Downey	83234
Driggs	83422
Drummond (Ashton)	83420
Dubois 83423, 83446	
Argora	83423
Idman	83423
Kilgore	83423
Lidy Hot Springs	83423
Reno	83423
Small	83423
Eagle	83616
Eagle Rock (Idaho Falls)	83402
East Hope (Hope)	83836
East Lewiston (Lewiston)	83501
Eastport	83826
Eaton (Weiser)	83672
Eden	83325
Edmonds (Rexburg)	83440
Egin (Saint Anthony)	83445
Elba	83326
Elk Bend (Salmon)	83467
Elk City	83525
Elk Horn (Sun Valley)	83354
Elk River	83827
Ellis	83235
Elmira (Samuels)	83862
Emmett	83617
Enaville (Kingston)	83839
Enrose (Caldwell)	83605
Fairfield (Corral) 83322, 83327	
Fairview (Preston) .. 83263, 83316	
Falls City (Jerome)	83338
Featherville	83647
(Mountain Home)	
Felt	83424
Fenn	83531
Ferdinand	83526
Fernwood	83830
Filer	83328
Firth	83236
Fish Haven	83287
Fort Hall	83203
Fox Creek (Victor)	83455
Franklin	83237
Fruitland	83619
Fruitvale	83620
Gannett (Bellevue)	83313
Garden City (Boise)	83714
Garden Creek (Arimo)	83214
Garden Valley	83622
Gardena (Horseshoe Bend)	83629
Garfield (Idaho Falls)	83401
Garwood (Hayden)	83835

Genesee	83832	
Geneva	83238	
Georgetown	83239	
Gibbonsville	83463	
Gibson (Fort Hall)	83203	
Glencoe (Paris)	83261	
Glendale (Preston)	83263	
Glenns Ferry	83623	
Gooding	83330	
Goodrich (Council)	83612	
Goshen (Shelley)	83274	
Grace	83241, 83283	
Bench	83241	
Central	83241	
Lago	83241	
Niter	83241	
Turner	83241	
Grand View	83624	
Grangeville	83530-531	
Harpster	83530	
Granite (Athol)	83801	
Grant (Idaho Falls)	83401	
Grasmere (Bruneau)	83604	
Gray (Wayan)	83285	
Greencreek	83533	
Greenleaf	83626	
Greenwood (Hazelton)	83335	
Greer (Orofino)	83544	
Gross (Ola)	83657	
Grouse (Moore)	83255	
Groveland (Blackfoot)	83221	
Gwenford (Malad City)	83252	
Hagerman	83332	
Hailey	83333	
Hamer	83425	
Hamilton Corner	83655	
(New Plymouth)		
Hammett	83627	
Hansen	83334	
Harpster	83530, 83539	
(Grangeville)		
Harrison	83833, 83842	
Harvard	83834	
Hauser (Post Falls)	83854	
Hawkins (Arimo)	83214	
Hayden	83835	
Hazelton	83335	
Heglar (American Falls)	83211	
Heise (Ririe)	83443	
Helmer (Deary)	83823	
Heman (Saint Anthony)	83445	
Henry (Conda)	83230	
Heyburn	83336	
Hill City	83337	
Hillview (Idaho Falls)	83401	
Holbrook	83243	
Hollister (Twin Falls)	83301	
Homedale	83628	
Hope	83836	
Hornet (Council)	83612	
Horseshoe Bend	83629	
Howe	83244	
Humphrey (Spencer)	83446	
Hunt (Hazelton)	83335	
Huston	83630	
Idaho City	83631	
Idaho Falls	83401-406, 83415	
Ammon	83401	
Beachs Corner	83401	
Bone	83401	
Coltman	83401	

Eagle Rock	83402	
Garfield	83401	
Grant	83401	
Hillview	83401	
Lincoln	83401	
New Sweden	83401	
Osgood	83401	
Saint Leon	83401	
Shelton	83401	
Skyline	83401	
Taylor	83401	
Idahome (Declo)	83323	
Idman (Dubois)	83423	
Indian Cove (Hammett)	83627	
Indian Valley	83632	
Inkom	83245	
Iona	83427	
Irwin	83428	
Island Park	83429, 83433	
Box Canyon	83429	
Ponds Resort	83429	
Jackson (Rupert)	83350	
Jamestown (Shelley)	83274	
Jerome	83338	
Jonathan (Weiser)	83672	
Juliaetta	83535	
Kamiah	83536	
Kellogg	83837	
Kendrick	83537	
Ketchum	83340	
Keuterville (Cottonwood)	83538	
Kilgore (Dubois)	83423	
Kimball (Firth)	83236	
Kimberly	83341	
King Hill	83633	
Kingston	83839	
Knowlton Heights	83605	
(Caldwell)		
Kooskia	83539	
Kootenai	83840	
Kuna	83634	
Labelle (Rigby)	83442	
Laclede	83841	
Lago (Grace)	83241	
Lake Fork	83635	
Lamont (Ashton)	83420	
Lanark (Ovid)	83260	
Lapwai	83540	
Lardo (Mc Call)	83638	
Lava Hot Springs	83246	
Leadore	83464	
Lemhi	83465	
Lenore	83541	
Leslie (Moore)	83255	
Letha	83636	
Lewiston	83501	
Lewiston Orchards	83501	
(Lewiston)		
Lewisville	83431	
Liberty (Ovid)	83260	
Lidy Hot Springs (Dubois)	83423	
Lincoln (Idaho Falls)	83401	
Linrose (Weston)	83286	
Lone Pine (Leadore)	83464	
Lone Star (Shoshone)	83352	
Lorenzo (Rigby)	83442	
Lowell (Kooskia)	83539	
Lower Presto (Firth)	83236	
Lower Stanley (Stanley)	83278	
Lowman	83637	
Lucile	83542	

Lund (Bancroft)	83217	
Lyman (Rexburg)	83440	
Lynwood (Twin Falls)	83301	
Mackay	83251	
Magic City (Hailey)	83333	
Malad City	83252, 83280	
Cherry Creek	83252	
Daniels	83252	
Gwenford	83252	
Pleasantview	83252	
Samaria	83252	
Woodruff	83252	
Malta	83342	
Mapleton (Preston)	83263	
Marion (Oakley)	83346	
Marsing	83639	
Marysville (Ashton)	83420	
May	83253	
Mayfield (Boise)	83706	
Mc Call	83635, 83638	
(Lake Fork)		
Burgdorf	83638	
Lardo	83638	
Mc Cammon	83250	
Meadows (New Meadows)	83654	
Medimont	83842	
Melba	83641	
Mellon Valley (Bliss)	83314	
Menan	83434	
Meridian	83642, 83680	
Mesa	83643	
Middleton	83644	
Midvale	83645	
Minidoka	83343	
Mink Creek (Preston)	83263	
Monteview	83435	
Montour (Emmett)	83617	
Montpelier	83254	
Moore	83231, 83255	
(Darlington)		
Grouse	83255	
Leslie	83255	
Mora (Kuna)	83634	
Moreland	83256	
Morgans Alley (Lewiston)	83501	
Moscow	83843, 83844	
Mountain Home	83647	
Moyie Springs	83845	
Mud Lake (Terreton)	83450	
Muldoon (Carey)	83320	
Mullan	83846	
Murphy	83650	
Murray	83874	
Murtaugh	83344	
Nampa	83651-653, 83686-687	
Bowmont	83686	
Naples	83847	
Neeley (American Falls)	83211	
New Centerville	83631	
(Idaho City)		
New Meadows	83654	
New Plymouth	83655	
New Sweden (Idaho Falls)	83401	
Newdale	83436	
Newport (Old Town)	83822	
Nezperce	83543	
Niter (Grace)	83241	
Nordman	83848	
North Fork	83466, 83469	
North Lewiston (Lewiston)	83501	
Northside (Emmett)	83617	

Notus	83656
Nounan (Montpelier)	83254
Oakley	83346
Obsidian (Ketchum)	83340
Ola	83657
Old Town	83822, 83856
Newport	83822
Oreana (Murphy)	83650
Orofino	83544
Osburn	83849
Osgood (Idaho Falls)	83401
Ovid (Bern)	83220, 83260
Lanark	83260
Liberty	83260
Sharon	83260
Oxford (Preston)	83263
Palisades	83437
Paris	83261, 83287
Glencoe	83261
Parker	83438
Parma	83660
Patterson (May)	83253
Paul	83347
Payette	83661
Pearl (Eagle)	83616
Pebble (Bancroft)	83217
Peck	83545
Pegram (Montpelier)	83254
Pella (Burley)	83318
Picabo	83348
Pierce	83546
Pine (Mountain Home)	83647
Pine Ridge (Council)	83612
Pinehurst	83850
Pingree	83262
Pioneerville (Idaho City)	83631
Placerville	83666
Plano (Rexburg)	83440
Pleasantview (Malad City)	83252
Plummer	83851
Pocatello	83201-206, 83209
Alameda	83201
Alameda	83206
Bannock	83204
Chubbuck	83202
Tyhee	83201
Westwood Village	83201
Pollock	83547
Ponderay	83852
Ponds Resort	83429
(Island Park)	
Porthill	83853
Post Falls	83854
Potlatch	83855
Prairie (Mountain Home)	83647
Preston	83263
Prichard (Wallace)	83873
Priest River	83856
Princeton	83857
Raft River	83211
(American Falls)	
Rathdrum	83858
Raymond (Geneva)	83238
Redfish Lake (Stanley)	83278
Reno (Dubois)	83423
Reubens	83548
Rexburg	83440, 83441, 83460
Rexcraft (Rexburg)	83441
Reynolds (Murphy)	83650
Richfield	83349
Riddle (Bruneau)	83604

Rigby	83442
Riggins	83549
Ririe	83443
Riverdale (Preston)	83263
Riverside (Blackfoot)	83221
Roberts	83444
Robin (Arimo)	83214
Rock Creek (Hansen)	83334
Rockford (Blackfoot)	83221
Rockland	83271
Rocky Bar	83647
(Mountain Home)	
Rogerson	83302
Rose (Blackfoot)	83221
Rose Lake (Cataldo)	83810
Roseberry (Donnelly)	83615
Roseworth (Castleford)	83321
Roswell (Parma)	83660
Roy (Rockland)	83271
Rupert (Minidoka)	83343, 83350
Acequia	83350
Jackson	83350
Sagle	83860
Saint Anthony	83445
Saint Charles	83272
Saint Leon (Idaho Falls)	83401
Saint Maries	83861
Salmon	83467
Samaria (Malad City)	83252
Samuels	83862
Sanders (Tensed)	83870
Sandpoint	83809, 83840
	83862, 83864-865
(Careywood)	
Santa	83866
Sharon (Ovid)	83260
Shelley	83274
Shelton (Idaho Falls)	83401
Shoshone	83324, 83352
(Dietrich)	
Lone Star	83352
Shoup	83469
Silver City (Murphy)	83650
Silver Creek Plunge	83622
(Garden Valley)	
Silverton	83867
Skyline (Idaho Falls)	83401
Small (Dubois)	83423
Smelterville	83868
Smiths Ferry (Cascade)	83611
Soda Springs	83230
	83276, 83285
(Conda)	
Southwick (Kendrick)	83537
Spalding	83551
Spencer	83446
Spirit Lake	83869
Springdale (Burley)	83318
Springfield	83277
Squirrel	83447
Stanley	83278
Star	83669
Starrhs Ferry (Burley)	83318
State Line (Post Falls)	83854
Steirman (Idaho City)	83631
Sterling (Aberdeen)	83210
Stibnite (Yellow Pine)	83677
Stites	83552
Stoddard (Melba)	83641
Stone	83280
Sublett (Malta)	83342

Sugar City	83448
Sugar Loaf (Jerome)	83338
Sun Valley	83353-354
Elk Horn	83354
Sunbeam (Stanley)	83278
Sunnydell (Rexburg)	83440
Sunnyslope (Caldwell)	83605
Swan Valley	83449
Swanlake	83281
Sweet	83670
Sweetwater (Lapwai)	83540
Syringa (Kooskia)	83539
Taber (Blackfoot)	83221
Tamarack (Council)	83612
Taylor (Idaho Falls)	83401
Tendoy	83468
Tensed	83870
Terreton	83450
Teton	83451
Tetonia (Felt)	83424, 83452
Clawson	83452
Thatcher	83283
Thomas (Blackfoot)	83221
Thornton (Rexburg)	83440
Three Creek (Twin Falls)	
83301-302	
Topaz (Lava Hot Springs)	83246
Torrey (Clayton)	83227
Treasureton (Preston)	83263
Triumph (Hailey)	83333
Troy	83871
Turner (Grace)	83241
Tuttle (Bliss)	83314
Twin Falls	83301-303
Hollister	83301
Lynwood	83301
Three Creek	83301
Twin Groves	83445
(Saint Anthony)	
Twin Lakes (Rathdrum)	83858
Tyhee (Pocatello)	83201
Ucon	83454
University (Moscow)	83843
Ustick (Boise)	83704
Vernon (Victor)	83455
Victor	83455
View (Burley)	83318
Viola	83872
Virginia (Downey)	83234
Wallace	83873-874
Prichard	83873
Wapello (Blackfoot)	83221
Wardboro (Montpelier)	83254
Wardner (Kellogg)	83837
Warm Lake (Cascade)	83611
Warm River (Ashton)	83420
Warren	83671
Wayan	83285
Weippe	83553
Weiser	83672
Weitz (Caldwell)	83605
Wendell	83355
West Mountain (Cascade)	83611
Weston	83286
Westwood Village	83201
(Pocatello)	
White Bird	83554
Whitney (Preston)	83263
Wilder	83676
Wilford (Saint Anthony)	83445
Winchester	83555

Woodruff (Malad City) 83252
Woodville (Shelley) 83274
Worley 83876
Yellow Pine 83677

ALAMEDA

GOVERNMENT

City Building
902 E SHERMAN ST 83201

Court House
624 E CENTER ST 83201

Federal Building
250 S 4TH AVE 83201

BOISE

BUILDINGS

Boise Towne Square Mall
350 N MILWAUKEE ST 83788

First Interstate Building
877 MAIN ST 83702

First Security Building
119 N 9TH ST 83702

Idaho Tower Building
702 W IDAHO ST 83702

Key Bank Plaza
101 S CAPITOL BLVD 83702

Medical Arts Building
999 N CURTIS RD 83706

One Capital Center
999 MAIN ST 83702

GOVERNMENT

Ada County Building
650 MAIN ST 83702

Ada County Courthouse
514 W JEFFERSON ST 83702

City Hall
150 N CAPITOL BLVD 83702

BOWMONT

HOSPITALS

Mercy Medical Center
1512 12TH AVE RD 83686

COLLEGES

Nw Nazarine College
623 HOLLY ST 83686

Biggs (Easton)	62633	
Biggsville	61418	
Bigneck (Loraine)	62349	
Billet (Lawrenceville)	62439	
Bingham	62011	
Binghampton (Amboy)	61310	
Birds	62415	
Birkbeck (Clinton)	61727	
Birmingham (Plymouth)	62367	
Bishop (Forest City)	61532	
Bishop Hill	61419	
Bismarck	61814	
Bissell (Springfield)	62707	
Black (Albion)	62806	
Blackhawk (Milan)	61264	
Blackstone	61313	
Blaine (Poplar Grove)	61065	
Blair (Sparta)	62286, 62858	
Blairsville	62859, 62918	
(Mc Leansboro)		
Blandinsville	61420, 61475	
Bloomingdale	60108	
Bloomington	61701-702, 61704	
	61709-710, 61799	
Barnes	61701	
Covell	61701	
Eastland Commons	61701	
Fletcher	61701	
Gillum	61701	
IRS	61799	
Kerrik	61701	
Oldtown	61701	
State Farm Ins	61710	
State Farm Ins Region	61709	
Yuton	61701	
Blue Island	60406	
Blue Mound	62513	
Blue Point (Effingham)	62401	
Bluff City	62471, 62624	
(Vandalia)		
Bluff Hall (Payson)	62360	
Bluff Springs	62622	
Bluffs	62621	
Bluford	62814	
Blyton (Smithfield)	61477	
Boaz (Karnak)	62956	
Boden (Sherrard)	61281	
Boggsville (Effingham)	62401	
Bogota (Newton)	62448	
Boles	62909	
Bolingbrook	60440	
Bolivia (Mechanicsburg)	62545	
Bolo (Ashley)	62808	
Bolton (Freeport)	61032, 62987	
Bond (Lawrenceville)	62439	
Bondville	61815	
Bone Gap	62815	
Bonfield	60913	
Bonnie	62816	
Bonpas (Calhoun)	62419	
Bonus (Garden Prairie)	61038	
Boody	62514	
Boskydell (Carbondale)	62901	
Boulder (Shattuc)	62283	
Boulder Hill (Montgomery)	60538	
Bourbonnais	60914	
Bowen	62316	
Bowlesville	62984	
(Shawneetown)		
Bowling (Milan)	61264	

Bowling Green (Cowden)	62422	
Boyd (Dix)	62830	
Boyleston (Fairfield)	62837	
Boynton (Delavan)	61734	
Braceville	60407	
Bradbury (Toledo)	62468	
Bradford	61421	
Bradfordton (Springfield)	62707	
Bradley	60915, 62907	
Braidwood	60408	
Breckenridge (Rochester)	62563	
Breeds (Canton)	61520	
Breese	62230	
Bremen (Chester)	62233	
Brereton (Canton)	61520	
Briar Bluff (Coal Valley)	61240	
Briarwood Trace	62901	
(Carbondale)		
Brickton (Ottawa)	61350	
Bridgeport	62417	
Bridgeview (Oak Lawn)	60455	
Brighton	62012	
Brimfield	61517-518	
Oak Hill	61518	
Southport	61517	
Bristol	60512	
Broadlands	61816	
Broadmoor (Bradford)	61421	
Broadview (Maywood)	60153	
Broadwell (Elkhart)	62634	
Brocton	61917	
Brookfield	60513	
Brookhaven (Prophetstown)	61277	
Brookport	62910	
Brooks Isle (Oregon)	61061	
Brookville (Polo)	61064	
Broughton	62817	
Brownfield (Golconda)	62938	
Browning	62624, 62812	
Bader	62624	
Bluff City	62624	
Sheldons Grove	62624	
Browns	62818	
Brownstown	62418	
Brownsville (Carmi)	62821	
Brunswick (Findlay)	62534	
Brush Hill (Carbondale)	62901	
Brushy (Galatia)	62935	
Brussels	62013	
Bryant	61519	
Buckhart	62545, 62563	
(Mechanicsburg)		
Buckingham	60917	
Buckley	60918	
Buckner	62819	
Buda	61314	
Buena Vista	61032, 62946	
(Freeport)		
Buffalo	62515	
Buffalo Grove	60089	
Buffalo Hart	62693	
(Williamsville)		
Buffalo Prairie	61237	
Bull Valley	60050, 60098	
(Mc Henry)		
Bulpit	62517	
Buncombe	62912	
Bungay (Springerton)	62887	
Bunker Hill	62014	
Burbank (Oak Lawn)	60459	
Bureau	61315	

Burgess (Aledo)	61231, 62275	
Burksville (Waterloo)	62298	
Burlington	60109	
Burnham (Chicago)	60633	
Burnside	62318	
Burnt Prairie	62820	
Burr Ridge	60521	
(Hinsdale)		
Burt (Armington)	61721	
Burton (Quincy)	62301, 62347	
Bush (De Soto)	62924	
Bushnell	61422	
Butler	62015	
Byron	61010	
Byron Hills (Port Byron)	61275	
Cabery	60919	
Cable (Sherrard)	61281	
Cache	62913-914	
Cahokia	62206	
(East Saint Louis)		
Cairo	62914	
Caledonia	61011	
Calhoun	62419	
Calumet City	60409	
Calumet Park (Chicago)	60643	
Calvin (Crossville)	62827	
Camargo	61919	
Cambria	62915	
Cambridge	61238	
Camden	62319	
Cameron	61423	
Camp Epworth	61038	
(Garden Prairie)		
Camp Ground	62864	
(Mount Vernon)		
Camp Grove	61424	
Camp Point	62320	
Campbell Hill	62916	
Campbells Island	61244	
(East Moline)		
Campus	60920	
Canoe Creek (Hillsdale)	61257	
Canton	61520	
Cantrall	62625	
Capron	61012	
Carbon Cliff	61239	
Carbon Hill (Coal City)	60416	
Carbondale	62901-903	
Boskydell	62901	
Briarwood Trace	62901	
Brush Hill	62901	
Lake Tacoma	62901	
Lakewood Park	62901	
Carlinville	62626	
Carlock	61725	
Carlyle	62231	
Carman	61425	
Carmi	62821	
Carol Stream	60100, 60116	
	60125, 60128, 60132, 60155	
	60158, 60188, 60197-199	
	60351, 60353	
Citicorp	60132	
North Suburban		
	60128, 60132, 60155	
	60158, 60351, 60353	
Carpentersville	60110	
Carriers Mills	62917	
(Carrier Mills)		
Carrigan (Patoka)	62875	
Carrollton	62016	

Galena Knolls	61523
(Chillicothe)	
Galesburg	61401-402
Henderson Grove	61401
Galt	61037
Galva	61434
Ganntown (Grantsburg)	62943
Garber (Gibson City)	60936
Garden Heights	62946
(Harrisburg)	
Garden Hill (Xenia)	62899
Garden Plain (Fulton)	61252
Garden Prairie	61038
Gardner	60424
Garfield (Wenona)	61377
Garfield Park (Chicago)	60624
Garrett (Atwood)	61913
Gays	61928
Geff	62842
Genesee (Morrison)	61270
Geneseo	61254
Geneva	60134
Genoa	60135
Georgetown	61846
Gerlaw	61435
German (Claremont)	62421
German Valley	61039
Germantown	61548, 62245
(Metamora)	
Gibson City	60936
Gifford	61847
Gila (Montrose)	62445
Gilberts	60136
Gilchrist (Viola)	61486
Gilead (Batchtown)	62006
Gillespie	62033
Gillum (Bloomington)	61701
Gilman	60938
Gilmore (Mason)	62443
Gilson	61436
Ginger Hill (Milan)	61264
Girard	62640
Gladstone	61437
Glasford	61533
Glasgow (Winchester)	62694
Glen (Glen Carbon)	62034
Glen Avon (Bellflower)	61724
Glen Carbon	62025, 62034
(Edwardsville)	
Glen	62034
Peters	62034
Glen Ellyn	60137-138
Glen Ridge (Sandoval)	62882
Glenarm	62536
Glencoe	60022
Glendale Heights	60139
Glenn (Rockwood)	62280
Glenview	60025-026
Glenwood	60425
Godfrey (Alton)	62002, 62035
Godley (Braceville)	60407
Golconda	62938
Gold Hill (Shawneetown)	62984
Golden	62339
Golden Eagle	62036
Golden Gate	62843
Golf	60029
Good Hope	61438
Goode (Sesser)	62884
Goodenow (Beecher)	60401

Goodfield	61742
Goodwine	60939
Goofy Ridge (Topeka)	61567
Gordons (Robinson)	62454
Goreville	62939
Gorham	62940
Goshen (Toulon)	61483
Gossett (Norris City)	62869
Graceland (Chicago)	60657
Grafton	62037
Grand Chain	62941
Grand Crossing (Chicago)	60619
Grand Detour (Dixon)	61021
Grand Oaks (Groveland)	61535
Grand Prairie (Woodlawn)	62898
Grand Ridge	61325
Grand Tower	62942
Grandview	61258, 62702
(Hooppole)	
Granite City	62040
Grant Park	60940
Grantfork (Highland)	62249
Grantsburg	62943
Granville	61326
Graymont	61743
Grayslake	60030
Grayville	62844
Great Lakes	60088
Green Creek (Effingham)	62401
Green Oaks	60031, 60048
(Gurnee)	
Green River (Colona)	61241
Green Valley	61534
Greenbush (Avon)	61415
Greene (Viola)	61486
Greenfield	62044
Greenup	62428
Greenview	62642
Greenville	62246
Gridley	61744
Grigg (Red Bud)	62278
Griggsville	62340
Grimes Addition	61081
(Sterling)	
Grimsby (Gorham)	62940
Grisham (Panama)	62077
Groveland	61535
Grover (Fairfield)	62837
Guilford (Scales Mound)	61075
Gurnee	60031
Hafer (Carterville)	62918
Hagaman (Chesterfield)	62630
Hagarstown	62247
Hahnaman (Tampico)	61283
Haines (Kell)	62853
Hainesville	60030, 60073
(Grayslake)	
Haldane (Forreston)	61030
Half Day (Lincolnshire)	60069
Hallidayboro (Elkville)	62932
Hallsville (Clinton)	61727
Hamburg	62045, 62935
Hamel	62046
Hamilton	62341
Hamlet (Aledo)	61231
Hamletsburg	62944
Hammond	61929
Hampshire	60140
Hampton	61256
Hanaford (Logan)	62856
Hanks Station	62092

(White Hall)	
Hanna (Geneseo)	61254
Hanna City	61536
Hanover	61041
Hanover Park (Bartlett)	60103
Harco	62945
Hardin	62047
Harding (Earlville)	60518
Hardinville	62449, 62454
(Oblong)	
Harmon	61042
Harmony (Carthage)	62321
Harp Township (Clinton)	61727
Harper (Forreston)	61030
Harrisburg	62946
Harrison (Rockton)	61072, 62966
Harrisonville (Valmeyer)	62295
Harristown	62537
Hartford	62048
Hartsburg	62643
Harvard	60033
Harvel	62538
Harvey	60426
Harwood Heights	60656
(Chicago)	
Havana	62644
Hawthorn Woods	60047, 60060
(Lake Zurich)	
Hawthorne (Chicago)	60623
Haymarket (Chicago)	60606
Hazel Crest	60429
Hazel Dell (Greenup)	62428
Hazelhurst (Polo)	61064
Heartville (Effingham)	62401
Heathsville (Flat Rock)	62427
Hebron	60034
Hecker	62248
Hegewisch (Chicago)	60633
Helena (Sumner)	62466
Helm (Iuka)	62849
Helmar (Newark)	60541
Heman (Warrensburg)	62573
Henderson	61439
Henderson Grove	61401
(Galesburg)	
Hennepin	61327
Henning	61848
Henry	61537
Henton (Shelbyville)	62565
Herald	62845
Heralds Prairie	62869
(Norris City)	
Herborn (Strasburg)	62465
Hermon (Maquon)	61458
Herod	62947
Herrick	62431
Herrin	62948
Herscher	60941
Hersman (Mount Sterling)	62353
Hervey City (Mount Zion)	62549
Hettick	62649
Hewittsville	62568
(Taylorville)	
Heyworth	61745
Hickory Hills (Oak Lawn)	60457
Hidalgo	62432
High Meadows (Peoria)	61607
Highland	62249
Highland Park	60035
	60037, 62930
Ravinia	60035

Lake Forest 60045	Lincolnshire 60069	Lyons 60534
Lake Fork 62541	Lincolnshire Woods 60045	Lyttleville (Heyworth) 61745
Lake Lancelot (Mapleton) . 61547	(Lake Forest)	Macedonia 62860
Lake Sara (Effingham) 62401	Lincolnwood ... 60645-646, 60659	Machesney Park 61115
Lake Tacoma (Carbondale) 62901	(Chicago)	Mackinaw 61755
Lake Thunderbird (Putnam) 61560	Lindenhurst (Lake Villa) 60046	Macomb 61455
Lake Villa 60046	Lindenwood 61049	Macon 62544
Lake Wildwood (Magnolia) 61336	Lisbon (Newark) 60541	Madison 62060
Lake Zurich 60047, 60049	Lisle 60532	Madonnaville (Waterloo) ... 62298
Lakemoor (Mc Henry) 60050	Litchfield 62056	Maeystown 62256
Lakeview (Chicago) 60613	Literberry 62660	Magnolia 61336
Lakewood 60014, 62438	Little America 61542	Mahomet 61853
(Crystal Lake)	(Lewistown)	Makanda 62958
Lakewood Park 62901	Little Indian (Virginia) 62691	Malden 61337
(Carbondale)	Little Mackinaw (Minier) 61759	Malta 60150
Lamard (Geff) 62842	Little Rock (Plano) 60545	Malvern (Morrison) 61270
Lamb (Cave In Rock) 62919	Little York 61453	Manchester 62663
Lamotte (Palestine) 62451	Littleton 61452	Manhattan 60442
Lanark 61046	Lively Grove (Oakdale) 62268	Manito 61546
Lancaster 62855	Liverpool 61543	Manlius 61338
Lane 61750	Livingston 62058, 62441	Mansfield 61854
Lanesville (Buffalo) 62515	Loami 62661	Manteno 60950
Langleyville 62568	Lockport 60441, 60446	Manville (Cornell) 61319
(Taylorville)	Romeoville 60441	Maple Lane (Sterling) 61081
Lansing 60438	Loda 60948	Maple Park 60151
Larchland (Monmouth) 61462	Logan 61536, 62856	Maple Point (Greenup) 62428
Larkinsburg (Edgewood) ... 62426	(Hanna City)	Maples Mill (Lewistown) ... 61542
Latham 62543	Hanaford 62856	Mapleton 61547
Latham Park (Rockford) 61103	Logan Square (Chicago) ... 60647	Maquon 61458
Laura 61451	Lomax 61454	Marblehead (Quincy) 62301
Lawn Ridge (Edelstein) 61526	Lombard 60148	Marcelline (Ursa) 62376
Lawndale 61751	Lombardville (Bradford) 61421	Marcoe (Mount Vernon) 62864
Lawrenceville 62439	London Mills 61544	Mardell Manor (Peoria) 61607
Layton (Rushville) 62681	Lone Grove (Saint Peter) .. 62880	Marengo 60152
Le Roy 61752	Lone Tree (Tiskilwa) 61368	Marietta 61459
Leaf River 61047	Long Branch (Galatia) 62935	Marine 62061
Lebanon 62254	Long Grove 60047, 60049	Marion 62959
Ledford (Harrisburg) 62946	(Lake Zurich) ... 60060, 60069	Marissa 62257
Lee 60530	Long Lake (Ingleside) 60041	Mark 61340
Lee Center 61331	Long Point 61333	Markham (Harvey) 60426
Leeds (Wenona) 61377	Longview 61852	Marlow (Opdyke) 62872
Leland 60531	Loogootee 62857	Maroa 61756
Leland Grove 62706	Loop (Chicago) 60604	Marquette Heights (Pekin) 61554
(Springfield)	Loop Station 60601-605	Marseilles 61341
Lemont 60439	(Chicago)	Marshall 62423, 62441
Lena 61048	Loraine 61277, 62349	(Dennison)
Lenzburg 62255	(Prophetstown)	Albright 62441
Leon Corners 61277	Bigneck 62349	Anderson 62441
(Prophetstown)	Loran (Pearl City) 61062	Auburn 62441
Leonore 61332	Lorenzo (Wilmington) 60481	Clark Center 62441
Lerna 62440	Lost Nation (Dixon) 61021	Clarksville 62441
Levan (Murphysboro) 62966	Lostant 61334	Livingston 62441
Lewistown 61542	Lou Del (Waterloo) 62298	Mckeen 62441
Lexington 61753	Louisville 62858	Oliver 62441
Liberty 62347, 62946	Lovejoy 62059	Marston (Reynolds) 61279
Adams 62347	Loves Park 61111, 61130-132	Martin (Colfax) 61728
Beverly 62347	Lovington 61937	Martinsville 62442
Burton 62347	Lowder 62662	Martinton 60951
Chestline 62347	Lowell (Tonica) 61370	Maryland (Polo) 61064
Richfield 62347	Lowpoint 61545	Maryville 62062
Libertyville 60048, 60092	Ludlow 60949	Mascoutah 62224, 62258
Green Oaks 60048	Lukin (Bridgeport) 62417	Mason 62443
Mettawa 60048	Lumaghi Heights 62234	Mason City 62664
Lick Creek (Buncombe) 62912	(Collinsville)	Massbach (Elizabeth) 61028
Lilly (Mackinaw) 61755	Luther (Mason City) 62664	Matherville 61263
Lillyville (Effingham) 62401	Lynchburg (Bath) 62617	Matteson 60443
Lima 62348	Lyndon 61261	Mattoon 61938
Limerick (Ohio) 61349	Lynn (Lynn Center) 61262	Maud (Mount Carmel) 62863
Limestone (Peoria) 61607	Lynnville (Jacksonville) 62650	Maunie 62861
Lincoln 62656	Lynwood 60411	Mayberry (Broughton) 62817
Lincoln Park (Chicago) 60614	(Chicago Heights)	Mayfair (Morton) 61550

...... 61112, 61114, 61125-126	
Hutchins Park	61103
Latham Park	61103
Morristown	61109
New Milford	61109
Rockport	62370
Rockton	61072
Rockwell (La Salle)	61301
Rockwood	62280
Rodden (Hanover)	61041
Rogers Park	60626, 60660
(Chicago)	
Rolling Meadows	60008
Rollo (Earlville)	60518
Rome	61562
Rome Heights	61523
(Chillicothe)	
Romeoville	60441, 60446
(Lockport)	
Lockport	60446
Roodhouse	62082
Rooks Creek (Pontiac)	61764
Rosamond	62083
Roscoe	61073
Rose Hill (Hidalgo)	62432
Rosebud (Golconda)	62938
Rosecrans (Wadsworth)	60083
Rosedale (Fieldon)	62031
Rosefield (Elmwood)	61529
Roseland (Chicago)	60628
Roselle (Schaumburg)	60172
Rosemont (Des Plaines)	60018
Roseville	61473
Rosewood (East Alton)	62024
Rosiclare	62982
Rossville	60963
Round Grove (Morrison)	61270
Round Knob (Metropolis)	62960
Round Lake	60073
Rowe (Pontiac)	61764
Roxana	62084
Royal	61871
Royal Lake (Carlyle)	62231
Royal Lakes (Shipman)	62685
Royalton	62983
Rozetta (Kirkwood)	61447
Rudement (Harrisburg)	62946
Rugby (Pontiac)	61764
Ruma (Red Bud)	62278
Rural (Coal Valley)	61240
Rushville	62681
Russell	60075
Russelville	62439
(Lawrenceville)	
Rustic Acre (Colona)	61241
Rutland	61358
Sabina (Arrowsmith)	61722
Sacramento (Enfield)	62835
Sadorus	61872
Sailor Springs	62879
Saint Anne	60964
Saint Augustine	61474
Saint Charles	60174-175
Valley View	60174
Saint David	61563
Saint Elmo	62458
Saint Francis	62467
(Teutopolis)	
Saint Francisville	62460
Saint Jacob	62281
Saint James (Loogootee) ..	62857

Saint Joe (Waterloo)	62298
Saint Joseph	61873
Saint Libory	62282
Saint Marys (Effingham)	62401
Saint Morgan (Trenton)	62293
Saint Paul	62880, 62885
(Saint Peter)	
Saint Peter	62880
Saint Rose (Breese)	62230
Sainte Marie	62459
Salem	62881
Salisbury	62677
(Pleasant Plains)	
Samoth (Grantsburg)	62943
Samsville (West Salem)	62476
San Jose	62682
Sand Barrens	62460
(Saint Francisville)	
Sand Ridge (Gorham)	62940
Sandoval	62882
Sandwich	60548
Santa Fe (Bartelso)	62218
Saratoga (Anna)	62906
Sauget (East Saint Louis) .	62201
Sauk Village	60411
(Chicago Heights)	
Saunemin	61769
Savanna	61074
Savoy	61874
Sawyerville	62085
Saxton (Toulon)	61483
Saybrook	61770
Scales Mound	61075
Scarboro (Steward)	60553
Schaeferville (Pekin)	61554
Schapville (Elizabeth)	61028
Schaumburg	60159, 60168
.... 60172-173, 60179	
.... 60192-196	
Hoffman Estates	
.... 60192, 60194-195	
Keeneyville	60172
Roselle	60172
Scheller	62883
Schiller Park	60176
Schram City (Hillsboro)	62049
Schulines (Sparta)	62286
Sciota	61475
Scioto Mills	61076
Scottville	62683
Scovel (Saunemin)	61769
Seaton	61476
Seatonville	61359
Secor	61771
Seneca	61360
Sepo (Lewistown)	61542
Serena	60549
Sesser	62884
Seville (Smithfield)	61477
Seward	61077
Seymour	61875
Shabbona	60550
Shady Grove (Brookport) ..	62910
Shafter (Vandalia)	62471
Shakerag (Johnston City) .	62951
Shale City (Aledo)	61231
Shanghai City (Alexis)	61412
Shannon	61078
Sharpsburg (Taylorville)	62568
Shattuc	62283
Shawneetown	62984

Shaws (Amboy)	61310
Sheffield	61361
Shelbyville	62565
Sheldon	60966
Sheldons Grove	62624
(Browning)	
Sheridan	60551
Sherman	62684
Sherrard	61281
Shields (Keenes)	62851
Shiloh (O Fallon)	62269
Shiloh Hill	62916
(Campbell Hill)	
Shipman	62685
Shirland	61079
Shirley	61772
Shobonier	62885
Shokokon (Carman)	61425
Shore Acres	61071, 61523
(Rock Falls)	
Shorewood (Joliet)	60435-436
Shumway	62461
Sibley	61773
Sicily (Pawnee)	62558
Sidell	61876
Sidney	61877
Sigel	62462
Signal Hill (Belleville)	62223
Silvis	61282
Simpson	62985
Sims	62886
Sinclair (Jacksonville)	62650
Six Mile (Zeigler)	62999
Skokie	60076-077
Slap Out (Iuka)	62849
Sleepy Hollow (Dundee)	60118
Smithboro	62284
Smithfield	61477
Smithshire	61478
Smithton	62243, 62285
(Freeburg)	
Smithville (Hanna City)	61536
Snicarte (Bath)	62617
Snyder (West Union)	62477
Sollitt (Beecher)	60401
Solon Mills	60080
Somerset	62946, 62966
(Harrisburg)	
Somonauk	60552
Songer (Xenia)	62899
Sorento	62086
South Barrington	60010
(Barrington)	
South Beloit	61080
South Chicago (Chicago) ..	60617
South Clinton (Clinton)	61727
South Crouch	62859
(Mc Leansboro)	
South Elgin	60177
South Fillmore (Fillmore) ..	62032
South Holland	60473
South Moline	61244
(East Moline)	
South Pekin	61564
South Rome (Chillicothe) ..	61523
South Roxana	62087
South Shore (Chicago)	60649
South Standard	62686
(Standard City)	
South Streator (Streator) ...	61364
South Suburban	60499

Vera (Ramsey) 62080
Vergennes 62994
Vermilion 61955
Vermilionville (Tonica) 61370
Vermont 61484
Vernon 62892
Vernon Hills 60061
Verona 60479
Versailles 62378
Victoria 61485
Vienna 62995
Villa Grove 61956
Villa Park 60181
Villa Ridge 62996
Viola 61486
Virden 62690
Virgil 60182
Virginia 62691
Visa (Elgin) 60122
Voio (Round Lake) 60073
Vonachen Knolls 61523
    (Chillicothe)
Wacker (Mount Carroll) 61053
Waddams Grove (Lena) 61048
Wadsworth 60083
Waggoner 62572
Wakefield (Newton) 62448
Waldo (Gridley) 61744
Walkerville 62050, 62092
    (Hillview)
Walnut 61376
Walnut Grove 61438, 61470
    (Good Hope)
Walnut Hill 62893
Walnut Prairie 62477
    (West Union)
Walpole (Broughton) 62817
Walsh 62297
Walshville 62091
Walton (Dixon) 61021
Waltonville 62894
Wamac (Centralia) 62801
Wanlock (Aledo) 61231
Wapella 61777
Ware (Jonesboro) 62952
Warner (Orion) 61273
Warren 61087
Warrensburg 62573
Warrenville 60555
Warsaw 62379
Wartburg (Waterloo) 62298
Wartrace (Grantsburg) 62943
Wasco 60183
Washburn 61570
Washington 61571
Washington Park 62204
    (East Saint Louis)
Wasson (Eldorado) 62930
Wataga 61488
Waterford (Lewistown) 61542
Waterloo 62298
Waterman 60556
Watertown (East Moline) ... 61244
Watseka 60970
Watson 62473
Wauconda 60084
Waukegan 60079
.... 60085, 60087

Mc Gaw Park 60085
    Park City 60085
Waverly 62692
Wayne 60184
Wayne City 62895
Waynesville 61778
Wayside (Makanda) 62958
Webster (Carthage) 62321
Webster Park 61362
    (Spring Valley)
Wedron 60557
Weldon 61882
Welge (Steeleville) 62288
Weller (Cambridge) 61238
Wellington 60973
Wendelin (Newton) 62448
Wenona 61377
Wenonah (Nokomis) 62075
West (Arrowsmith) 61722
West Brooklyn 61378
West Chicago 60185-186
West City (Benton) 62812
West Dundee (Dundee) 60118
West End (Thompsonville) . 62890
West Frankfort 62896
West Hallock (Edelstein) .. 61526
West Jersey (Toulon) 61483
West Liberty 62475
West Miltmore 60046
    (Lake Villa)
West Peoria (Peoria) 61604
West Point 62380
West Salem 62476
West Union 62477
West York 62478
Westchester 60154
Western (Orion) 61273
Western Springs 60558
Westervelt 62565, 62574
    (Shelbyville)
Westfield 62474
Westmont 60559, 60561
    Darien 60559
Weston (Chenoa) 61726
Westport (Lawrenceville) .. 62439
Westville 61883
Wetaug (Dongola) 62926
Wethersfield 61277
    (Prophetstown)
Wheaton 60187, 60189
Wheeler 62479
Wheeling 60090
Whispering Oaks 61535
    (Groveland)
White City (Mount Olive) ... 62069
White Hall 62092
White Heath 61884
Whites Addition 61244
    (East Moline)
Whittington 62897
Wicker Park (Chicago) 60622
Wilbern (Washburn) 61570
Wilberton (Shobonier) 62885
Wildwood (Grayslake) 60030
Willeys (Taylorville) 62568
Williamsfield 61489
Williamson (Staunton) 62088
Williamsville 62693

Willisville 62997
Willow (Stockton) 61085
Willow Hill 62480
Willow Springs 60480
Willowbrook 60514, 60521
    (Clarendon Hills)
Wilmette 60091
Wilmington 60481
Wilsonville 62093
Winchester 62694
Windsor 61957
Wine Hill (Steeleville) 62288
Winfield 60190
Wing (Forrest) 61741
Winkle (Coulterville) 62237
Winnebago 61088
Winneshiek (Freeport) 61032
Winnetka 60093
Winslow 61089
Winthrop Harbor 60096
Wisetown (Greenville) 62246
Witt 62094
Woburn (Greenville) 62246
Wolf Lake 62998
Womac (Carlinville) 62626
Wonder Lake 60097
Wood Dale 60191
Wood River 62095
Woodbine (Stockton) 61085
Woodburn (Bunker Hill) 62014
Woodbury (Montrose) 62445
Woodford (Minonk) 61760
Woodhull 61490
Woodland 60974
Woodlawn 62898
Woodridge 60517
    (Downers Grove)
Woodson 62695
Woodstock 60098
Woodville (Eldred) 62027
Woodyard (Shobonier) 62885
Woosung 61091
Worden 62097
Worth 60465, 60482, 61548
    Palos Hills 60465
Wrights 62098
Wrights Corner 62414
    (Beecher City)
Wyanet 61379
Wynoose (Noble) 62868
Wyoming 61491
Xenia 62899
Yale 62481
Yantisville (Findlay) 62534
Yates (Chenoa) 61726
Yates City 61572
Yatesville (Ashland) 62612
Yeowardville (Rock Falls) .. 61071
York (Thomson) 61285, 62477
Yorktown 61277, 61283
    (Prophetstown)
Yorkville 60560
Youngstown (Roseville) 61473
Yuton (Bloomington) 61701
Zearing (Malden) 61337
Zeigler 62999
Zenith (Xenia) 62899
Zion 60099
Zuma (Hillsdale) 61257

ALTA

BUILDINGS

Community Bank Building
4516 N STERLING AVE 61615

AURORA

HOTELS

Galena Hotel
116 W GALENA BLVD 60506

BARNES

APARTMENTS

Lincoln Towers Apt
202 S ROOSEVELT AVE .. 61701

Woodhill Towers
101 E MACARTHUR AVE . 61701

BUILDINGS

Eastland Mall
1615 E EMPIRE ST 61701

Illinois Ag Building
1701 N TOWANDA AVE 61701

Towanda Plaza
1206 N TOWANDA AVE 61701

GOVERNMENT

City Hall
109 E OLIVE ST 61701

Mclean Co Law & Justice
104 W FRONT ST 61701

BEARSDALE

APARTMENTS

Concord House
333 E CENTER ST 62526

Oxford House
2700 N MONROE ST 62526

BELLEVILLE

BUILDINGS

Belleville Medical Building
301 W LINCOLN ST 62220

Belleville Medical Building
311 W LINCOLN ST 62220

Doctors Building
110 N HIGH ST 62220

Kil Mar Building
8601 W MAIN ST 62223

Med Centre Building
7210 W MAIN ST 62223

Olde Town Mall North
310 E MAIN ST 62220

Richland Plaza I
521 W MAIN ST 62220

Richland Plaza II
525 W MAIN ST 62220

Richland Plaza III
720 W MAIN ST 62220

Saint Clair Cnty Courthse
10 PUBLIC SQ 62220

Saint Elizabth Medcl Building
300 W LINCOLN ST 62220

Schaufler Building
4 S CHURCH ST 62220

GOVERNMENT

Belleville City Hall
101 S ILLINOIS ST 62220

BOSKYDELL

GOVERNMENT

Federal Building
250 W CHERRY ST 62901

CHAMPAIGN

BUILDINGS

Armory Building
505 E ARMORY AVE 61820

City Building
102 N NEIL ST 61820

Huntington Towers
201 W SPRINGFIELD AVE 61820

Robeson Building
206 N RANDOLPH ST 61820

CHESTNUT STREET

APARTMENTS

Elliot House
1255 N CLARK ST 60610

Faulkner House
70 W BURTON PL 60610

BUILDINGS

Marina City East
300 N STATE ST 60610

Quaker Tower
321 N CLARK ST 60610

HOTELS

Ambassador Hotel East
1301 N STATE ST 60610

Ambassador Hotel West
1300 N STATE ST 60610

Cedar Hotel
1118 N STATE ST 60610

Olympia Hotel
613 N WELLS ST 60610

COLLEGES

Scholl College Podiatry
1001 N DEARBORN ST ... 60610

CHICAGO

APARTMENTS

Buckingham Plaza
360 E RANDOLPH ST 60601

Burnham Park Plaza
40 E 9TH ST 60605

Donohue Building
711 S DEARBORN ST 60605

Michigan Terr
535 N MICHIGAN AVE 60611

Outer Drive East
400 E RANDOLPH ST 60601

Presidential Towers
625 W MADISON ST 60661

River City
800 S WELLS ST 60607

The Seneca
200 E CHESTNUT ST 60611

BUILDINGS

1 N Dearborn Building
22 W MADISON ST 60602

2 N Lasalle Building
2 N LA SALLE ST 60602

200 Madison Plaza Building
200 W MADISON ST 60606

208 S La Salle Building
208 S LA SALLE ST 60604

29 E Madison Building
29 E MADISON ST 60602

310 W Polk
310 W POLK ST 60607

American Dental Building
211 E CHICAGO AVE 60611

American National Bank Building
33 N LA SALLE ST 60602

Amoco Building
200 E RANDOLPH ST 60601

Apparel Center Building
350 N ORLEANS ST 60654

Association Building
19 S LA SALLE ST 60603

Bankers Building
105 W ADAMS ST 60603

Barrister Hall
29 S LA SALLE ST 60603

Bell Building
212 W WASHINGTON ST . 60606

Bell Savings Building
79 W MONROE ST 60603

Board Of Trade Building
141 W JACKSON BLVD 60604

Borg Warner Building
200 S MICHIGAN AVE 60604

Britannica Center
310 S MICHIGAN AVE 60604

Brunswick Building
69 W WASHINGTON ST ... 60602

Builders Building
222 N LA SALLE ST 60601

Butler Building
162 N STATE ST 60601

Carbon Carbide Building
230 N MICHIGAN AVE 60601

Century Building
202 S STATE ST 60604

Champlain Building
37 S WABASH AVE 60603

Chgo Bd Options Exch Building
400 S LA SALLE ST 60605

Chicago Public Library
78 E WASHINGTON ST 60602

Chicago Temple
77 W WASHINGTON ST ... 60602

Chicago Title Trust Building
111 W WASHINGTON ST . 60602

Chicago Tribune Building
435 N MICHIGAN AVE 60611

Circle Shopping Center
500 S RACINE AVE 60607

Civic Opera House
20 N WACKER DR 60606

Civic Tower
32 W RANDOLPH ST 60601

CNA Building
333 S WABASH AVE 60604

Connecticut Mutual Building
33 N DEARBORN ST 60602

Consumers Building
220 S STATE ST 60604

Continental II Bank Building
231 S LA SALLE ST 60604

Cook County Building
118 N CLARK ST 60602

Corn Products Building
201 N WELLS ST 60606

Doral Plaza
155 N MICHIGAN AVE 60601

Douglas Building
20 E JACKSON BLVD 60604

Edison Building
72 W ADAMS ST 60603

Eiger Building
1255 S WABASH AVE 60605

Engineering Building
205 W WACKER DR 60606

Equitable Building
401 N MICHIGAN AVE 60611

Executive House
71 E WACKER DR 60601

Federal Building
536 S CLARK ST 60605

Finchley Building
23 E JACKSON BLVD 60604

Fine Art Building
410 S MICHIGAN AVE 60605

First Federal Building
7 S DEARBORN ST 60603

Fisher Building
343 S DEARBORN ST 60604

Flomer Building
1020 S WABASH AVE 60605

Frank J Lewis Building
25 E JACKSON BLVD 60604

Franklin Building
525 S DEARBORN ST 60605

Gage Building
18 S MICHIGAN AVE 60603

Garland Building
111 N WABASH AVE 60602

Gateway Building
10 S RIVERSIDE PLZ 60606

Gateway Iv Building
300 S RIVERSIDE PLZ 60606

Graphic Arts Building
732 S FINANCIAL PL 60605

Great Lakes
180 N WACKER DR 60606

Greek Bank Building
168 N MICHIGAN AVE 60601

Harris Bank Building
115 S LA SALLE ST 60603

Harris Bank Building
111 W MONROE ST 60603

Hartford Plaza Building
100 S WACKER DR 60606

Hartford Plaza Building
150 S WACKER DR 60606

Heitman Centre
180 N LA SALLE ST 60601

Home Federal Building
11 E ADAMS ST 60603

Inland Steel Building
30 W MONROE ST 60603

Insurance Center Building
330 S WELLS ST 60606

Insurance Exchange Building
175 W JACKSON BLVD 60604

Isabella Building
21 E VAN BUREN ST 60605

John Hancock Building
875 N MICHIGAN AVE 60611

Lakeview Building
116 S MICHIGAN AVE 60603

Lasalle Natl Bk Building
135 S LA SALLE ST 60603

Lasalle-wacker Building
221 N LA SALLE ST 60601

Lemoyne Building
180 N WABASH AVE 60601

Lincoln Tower
75 E WACKER DR 60601

Loop End Building
177 N STATE ST 60601

Lyon And Healy Building
64 E JACKSON BLVD 60604

Lytton Building
14 E JACKSON BLVD 60604

Madison Bank Building
2 N RIVERSIDE PLZ 60606

Majestic Building
22 W MONROE ST 60603

Mallers Building
5 S WABASH AVE 60603

Manhattan Building
431 S DEARBORN ST 60605

Marmon Building
39 S LA SALLE ST 60603

Marquette Building
140 S DEARBORN ST 60603

Marsh & Mclennan Building
222 S RIVERSIDE PLZ 60606

Marshall Field Annex Building
25 E WASHINGTON ST 60602

Masonite Building
29 N WACKER DR 60606

Mc Cormick Building
332 S MICHIGAN AVE 60604

Mc Clurg Court Center
333 E ONTARIO ST 60611

Mechanics Union Building
133 S ASHLAND AVE 60607

Mercantile Exchange Building
30 S WACKER DR 60606

Merchandise Mart Building
222 Merchandise Mart Plz 60654

Mid Continental Plaza
55 E MONROE ST 60603

Midland Building
176 W ADAMS ST 60603

Monadnock Building
53 W JACKSON BLVD 60604

Monroe Building
104 S MICHIGAN AVE 60603

Morton Building
538 S DEARBORN ST 60605

Morton Salt Building
110 N WACKER DR 60606

Moser Building
621 S PLYMOUTH CT 60605

Motor Club Building
66 E WACKER PL 60601

Nattional Surety Building
200 W MONROE ST 60606

Neiman Marcus Building
737 N MICHIGAN AVE 60611

North American Building
36 S STATE ST 60603

Northern Trust Building
125 S WACKER DR 60606

Northern Trust Co
50 S LA SALLE ST 60603

Oakes Building
650 S CLARK ST 60605

Old Colony
407 S DEARBORN ST 60605

Old Republic Building
307 N MICHIGAN AVE 60601

One Illinois Center
111 E WACKER DR 60601

One Park Place Building
150 N MICHIGAN AVE 60601

One S Wacker Drive Building
1 S WACKER DR 60606

Pakula Building
218 S WABASH AVE 60604

Pan Am Building
30 S MICHIGAN AVE 60603

Patten Building
161 W HARRISON ST 60605

Peoples Gas Light & Coke
122 S MICHIGAN AVE 60603

Peterson Building
523 S PLYMOUTH CT 60605

Pittsfield Building
55 E WASHINGTON ST 60602

Plumbers Union Building
1340 W Washington Blvd .. 60607

Pontiac Building
542 S DEARBORN ST 60605

Pope Building
633 S PLYMOUTH CT 60605

Prudential Building
130 E RANDOLPH ST 60601

Publishers Aux Building
210 S DESPLAINES ST ... 60661

Randolph Tower
188 W RANDOLPH ST 60601

Richard J Daley Center
50 W WASHINGTON ST ... 60602

River City Plaza
555 W ROOSEVELT RD ... 60607

River Plaza
405 N WABASH AVE 60611

Roanoke Building
11 S LA SALLE ST 60603

Rookery Building
209 S LA SALLE ST 60604

Santa Fe Building
80 E JACKSON BLVD 60604

Sears Tower
233 S WACKER DR 60606

Silversmith Building
10 S WABASH AVE 60603

Stark Building
234 S WABASH AVE 60604

State Madison Prop Inc
7 W MADISON ST 60602

State Of Il Center
100 W RANDOLPH ST 60601

State-lake Building
190 N STATE ST 60601

Steger Building
28 E JACKSON BLVD 60604

Stevens Building
17 N STATE ST 60602

Stock Exchange Building
120 S LA SALLE ST 60603

Stone Container Building
360 N MICHIGAN AVE 60601

Suntimes Building
401 N WABASH AVE 60611

Teamsters City
300 S ASHLAND AVE 60607

Three First National Plaz
70 W MADISON ST 60602

Three Illinois Center
303 E WACKER DR 60601

Traders Bld
401 S LA SALLE ST 60605

Trans Union Building
111 W JACKSON BLVD 60604

Two First Natl Plaza
20 S CLARK ST 60603

Two Illinois Center
233 N MICHIGAN AVE 60601

U S Gypsum
101 S WACKER DR 60606

Union Station
516 W JACKSON BLVD 60661

United Of America Building
1 E WACKER DR 60601

Utilities Building
327 S LA SALLE ST 60604

Wacker Randolph Building
150 N WACKER DR 60606

Wacker Wash Plaza Building
101 N WACKER DR 60606

Water Tower Place
835 N MICHIGAN AVE 60611

Willoughby Towers
8 S MICHIGAN AVE 60603

Wood Building
54 W RANDOLPH ST 60601

Wrigley Building
400 N MICHIGAN AVE 60611

Xerox Centre
55 W MONROE ST 60603

GOVERNMENT

Chicago City Hall
121 N LA SALLE ST 60602

Custom House
610 S CANAL ST 60607

Dirksen Building
219 S DEARBORN ST 60604

Kluczynski Building
230 S DEARBORN ST 60604

Irving Park Rd P&d Ctr
11560 W Irving Park Rd 60701

Main Post Office Building
433 W VAN BUREN ST 60607

HOSPITALS

University Of Il Hospital
1740 W TAYLOR ST 60612

Weiss Memorial Hospital
4646 N MARINE DR 60640

HOTELS

Allerton Hotel
701 N MICHIGAN AVE 60611

Arcade Hotel
1013 W MADISON ST 60607

Ascot Motel
1100 S MICHIGAN AVE 60605

Barclay Hotel
166 E SUPERIOR ST 60611

Blackstone Hotel
636 S MICHIGAN AVE 60605

Cass Hotel
640 N WABASH AVE 60611

Chicago Hilton & Towers
720 S MICHIGAN AVE 60605

Congress Hotel
520 S MICHIGAN AVE 60605

Days Inn
644 N LAKE SHORE DR ... 60611

Essex Inn Motel
800 S MICHIGAN AVE 60605

Harrison Hotel
65 E HARRISON ST 60605

Hotel Intercontinental
505 N MICHIGAN AVE 60611

Inn Of Chicago
162 E OHIO ST 60611

Knickerbocker Hotel
163 E WALTON ST 60611

Lion Hotel
4250 W NORTH AVE 60639

Major Hotel
660 W MADISON ST 60661

Marriott Hotel
540 N MICHIGAN AVE 60611

Mayfair Regent
181 E LAKE SHORE DR ... 60611

Midland Hotel
172 W ADAMS ST 60603

Ohio East Hotel
15 E OHIO ST 60611

Palmer House
17 E MONROE ST 60603

Park Hyatt
800 N MICHIGAN AVE 60611

Raphael Hotel
201 E DELAWARE PL 60611

Richmont Hotel
162 E ONTARIO ST 60611

Ritz-carlton
160 E PEARSON ST 60611

Sheraton Plaza Hotel
160 E HURON ST 60611

St James Hotel
1234 S WABASH AVE 60605

The Drake Hotel
140 E WALTON ST 60611

Tokyo Hotel
19 E OHIO ST 60611

Westin Hotel
909 N MICHIGAN AVE 60611

COLLEGES

Chicago Kent College Of Law
77 S WACKER DR 60606

CREVE COEUR

APARTMENTS

Raintree Apts
2811 SPRINGFIELD RD 61611

Riverview Apts
500 CENTENNIAL DR 61611

CRYSTAL LAKE

HOSPITALS

Crystal Lake Ambutal
4900 S STATE ROUTE 31 60012

DECATUR

APARTMENTS

Hartford House
1096 W DECATUR ST 62522

BUILDINGS

Citizens Building
250 N WATER ST 62523

Decatur Airport
910 S AIRPORT RD 62521

Millikin Court Building
132 S WATER ST 62523

Professional Building
363 S MAIN ST 62523

GOVERNMENT

Macon County Building
253 E WOOD ST 62523

EAST SAINT LOUIS

APARTMENTS

Brenton Building
2901 WAVERLY AVE 62204

North Park Towers
1415 N PARK DR 62204

Ruggerri Building
2901 WAVERLY AVE 62204

Rukavina Building
2901 WAVERLY AVE 62204

Starnes Building
2901 WAVERLY AVE 62204

BUILDINGS

First Illinois Bank Building
327 MISSOURI AVE 62201

Illini Federal Building
6550 N ILLINOIS ST 62208

Landmark Bank Building
10950 LINCOLN TRL 62208

New Federal Building
650 MISSOURI AVE 62201

One Central Bank Building
6701 N ILLINOIS ST 62208
Saint Marys Medical Ctr
4601 STATE ST 62205

U S Courthouse
750 MISSOURI AVE 62201

JOLIET

APARTMENTS

Burnham Towers
247 CATERPILLAR DR 60436

Salem Towers
1315 ROWELL AVE 60433

Salem Village
1314 ROWELL AVE 60433

BUILDINGS

Barber
68 N CHICAGO ST 60431

Chalstrom
25 N OTTAWA ST 60431

Chicago Jefferson
58 N CHICAGO ST 60431

Crystal
81 N CHICAGO ST 60431

Emco Plaza
57 N OTTAWA ST 60431

Pioneer
54 N OTTAWA ST 60431

GOVERNMENT

Federal Building
101 N JOLIET ST 60431

OAK PARK

HOSPITALS

West Suburban Plaza
1 ERIE CT 60302

PEORIA

APARTMENTS

Bnai Brith Apts
215 W 6TH AVE 61605

Gardner Lane Apts
1501 E GARDNER LN 61614

Glen Oak Towers
926 MAIN ST 61602

Hickory Ridge Apts
7150 N TERRA VISTA DR 61614

International Place
6500 N UNIVERSITY ST .. 61614

Pennsylvania Terrace
1505 N PEORIA AVE 61603

Windsor At Gaslight Sq
6516 N UNIVERSITY ST .. 61614

Windsor At Seven Oaks
4010 N BRANDYWINE DR 61614

BUILDINGS

Bank One Building
124 SW ADAMS ST 61602

Board Of Trade
330 SW WASHINGTON ST 61602

Caterpillar Building
200 NE ADAMS ST 61602

Commerce Bank Building
416 MAIN ST 61602

Community Bank Plaza
401 MAIN ST 61602

Cullinan Building
300 HAMILTON BLVD 61602

First Financial Plaza
411 HAMILTON BLVD 61602

First Of America Bk Building
301 SW ADAMS ST 61602

Janssen Building
333 MAIN ST 61602

Junction City Town Hall
5901 N PROSPECT RD ... 61614

River Valley Plaza
331 FULTON ST 61602

Stockyards
0 SOUTH ST 61602

Twin Towers
123 SW JEFFERSON AVE 61602

GOVERNMENT

Federal Building
100 NEMONROE ST 61602

Peoria County Courthouse
324 MAIN ST 61602

Peoria City Hall
419 FULTON ST 61602

Peoria Police Dept
542 SW ADAMS ST 61602

ROCKFORD

GOVERNMENT

Illinois State Building
200 S WYMAN ST 61101

Public Safety Building
420 W STATE ST 61101

US Federal Government
211 S COURT ST 61101

Winnebago Co Courthouse
400 W STATE ST 61101

SPRINGFIELD

BUILDINGS

County Building
200 S 9TH ST 62701

Reisch Building
117 S 5TH ST 62701

GOVERNMENT

Municipal Building
300 S 7TH ST 62701

Municipal Building
700 E MONROE ST 62701

Paul Finley Building
600 E MONROE ST 62701

HOTELS

Forum Thirty
700 E ADAMS ST 62701

Springfield Hilton
700 E ADAMS ST 62701

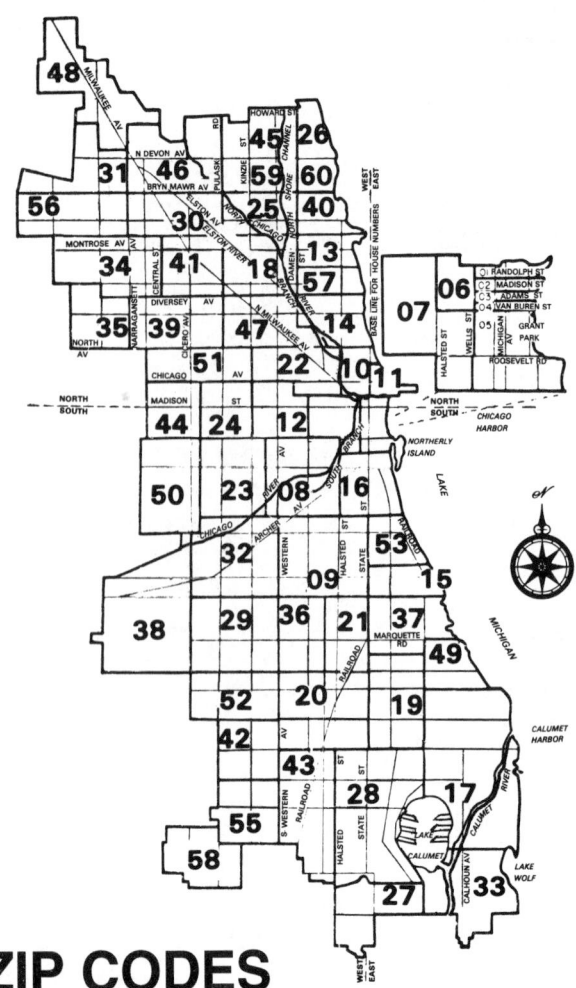

ZIP CODES

CHICAGO, IL

606 + TWO DIGITS SHOWN = ZIP CODE

INDIANA
Abbreviation IN

Abbey Dell	47469
(West Baden Springs)	
Abington (Centerville)	47330
Acton (Indianapolis)	46259
Adams	47240, 47872
(Greensburg)	
Adams Lake (Wolcottville)	46795
Adel (Spencer)	47460
Advance	46102
Akron	46910
Alamo	47916
Albany	47320
Albion	46701
Alert (Westport)	47283
Alexandria	46001
Alford (Petersburg)	47567
Alfordsville (Loogootee)	47553
Algiers (Petersburg)	47567
Allen (Kendallville)	46755
Allendale (Terre Haute)	47802
Alma Lake (Brazil)	47834
Alpine (Connersville)	47331
Alquina (Connersville)	47331
Alta (Hillsdale)	47854
Alton (Fremont)	46737
Altona (Garrett)	46738
Alvarado (Hamilton)	46742
Ambia	47917
Amboy	46911
Amity (Franklin)	46131
Amo	46103
Anderson	46011-018
	47586, 47630
Chesterfield	46017
Andersonville (Laurel)	47024
Andrews	46702
Angola	46703
Annapolis (Bloomingdale)	47832
Anthony (Muncie)	47303
Antioch (Portland) .. 47371, 47438	
Antiville (Portland)	47371
Apache Acres	47805
(Terre Haute)	
Arba (Lynn)	47355
Arcadia	46030
Arcola	46704
Argos	46501
Ari (Churubusco)	46723
Arlington	46104, 47042
Armiesburg (Montezuma)	47862
Arney (Freedom)	47431
Aroma (Atlanta)	46031
Art (Brazil)	47834
Arthur (Winslow)	47598
Artic (Butler)	46721
Ashboro (Centerpoint)	47840
Asherville (Brazil)	47834
Ashland	46151, 47362
(Martinsville)	
Ashley	46705
Athens	46912
Atherton (Rosedale)	47874
Atkinsonville (Poland)	47868
Atlanta	46031
Attica	47918
Atwood	46502
Auburn	46706
Augusta (Winslow)	47598

Aurora	47001
Austin	47102
Avilla	46710
Avoca	47420
Avon (Plainfield) ... 46168, 46234	
Avonburg (Bennington)	47011
Ayrshire (Winslow)	47598
Baer Field (Fort Wayne)	46809
Bainbridge	46105, 47546
Baker (Gosport)	47433
Bakertown (Albion)	46701
Balbee (Pennville)	47369
Bandon (Branchville)	47514
Bargersville	46106
Barnard (Roachdale)	46172
Barnhart Town	47885
(West Terre Haute)	
Barr (Cannelburg)	47519
Barrick Corner	47841
(Clay City)	
Barrington Woods	46733
(Decatur)	
Bartlettsville (Bedford)	47421
Bartley (Terre Haute)	47805
Bartonia (Union City)	47390
Bass Lake (Knox)	46534
Batesville	47006
Bath	47010
Battle Ground	47920
Bean Blossom 46160, 47429	
(Morgantown)	
Bear Branch (Dillsboro)	47018
Bear Lake (Albion)	46701
Becks Mill (Salem)	47167
Bee Ridge (Brazil)	47834
Beech Grove	46107
Belle Union (Cloverdale)	46120
Bellefountain (Portland)	47371
Belleville (Clayton)	46118
Bellmore	47830
Belmont	47362, 47448
(New Castle)	
Belshaw (Lowell)	46356
Bengal (Franklin)	46131
Bennington	47011
Benton (Bloomington)	47401
Bentonville	47322
Benwood (Brazil)	47834
Berlien (Angola)	46703
Berne 46711, 46769	
Linn Grove	46711
Bethel (Fountain City)	47341
Bethlehem	47104
Beverly Shores	46301
Bicknell	47512
Big Lake (Columbia City)	46725
Bigger (North Vernon)	47265
Billingsville (Liberty)	47353
Billtown (Brazil)	47834
Billville (Brazil)	47834
Bippus	46713
Birdseye	47513
Blackhawk 46815, 47866	
(Fort Wayne)	
Blaine (Portland)	47371
Blairsville (Wadesville)	47638
Blanford	47831
Bloomfield	47424
Blooming Grove	47012
(Brookville)	
Bloomingdale 46808, 47832	

(Fort Wayne)	
Annapolis	47832
Penn	47832
Sylvania	47832
Bloomingport (Lynn)	47355
Bloomington	47401-408
Arlington	47401
Benton	47401
Cascade Heights	47401
Clear Creek	47401
Dolan	47401
Eastern Heights	47401
Garden Acres	47401
Handy	47401
Highland Village	47401
Hindustan	47401
Hoosier Acres	47401
Indian Creek	47401
Kirksville	47401
Lancaster Park	47401
Marlin Hills	47401
Matlock Heights	47401
Modesto	47401
Park Ridge	47401
Perry	47401
Ridgemede	47401
Salt Creek	47401
Sanders	47401
Van Buren	47401
Washington	47401
West Brook Downs	47401
Whitehall	47401
Woodbridge	47408
Woodville Hills	47401
Blountsville	47354
(Losantville)	
Blue Creek 46772, 47041	
(Monroe)	
Blue Lake (Churubusco)	46723
Bluff Point (Portland)	47371
Bluffton	46714
Bo Bo (Decatur)	46733
Bogard (Plainville)	47568
Boggstown	46110
Bogle Corner (Jasonville)	47438
Bonnell (Guilford)	47022
Bono (Mitchell) 47446, 47847	
Boone (Jasper)	47546
Boone Grove	46302
Boonville	47601
Borden	47106
Boston	47324
Boston Corner	46773
(Monroeville)	
Boswell	47921
Boundry (Portland)	47371
Bourbon	46504
Bowerstown (Huntington)	46750
Bowling Green	47833
Bowman (Petersburg)	47567
Boyleston (Michigantown)	46057
Bracken (Huntington)	46750
Bradford	47107
Bramble (Loogootee)	47553
Branchville	47514
Braxton (Paoli)	47454
Braytown (Vevay)	47043
Brazil	47834
Bremen	46506
Bretzville (Huntingburg)	47542
Brice (Portland)	47371

133

Bridgeport 46231, 47117
  (Indianapolis)
Bridgeton 47836
Brighton (Howe) 46746
Brimfield 46720, 46755
  Kendallville 46720
Brinckley (Farmland) 47340
Bringhurst 46913
Bristol 46507
Bristow 47515
Broad Ripple 46220
  (Indianapolis)
Bromer (Orleans) 47452
Brook 47922
Brook Knoll (Bedford) 47421
Brooklyn 46111
Brookside Estates .. 46835, 47802
  (Fort Wayne)
Brookston 47923
Brookville 47012
Brookville Heights 46163
  (New Palestine)
Brown (Campbellsburg) 47108
Brown Jug Corner (Lewis) 47858
Brownsburg 46112
Brownstown 47118, 47220
  (English)
Brownsville 47325
Bruceville 47516
Brunswick (Gary) ... 46406, 47841
Brushy Prairie (Lagrange) . 46761
Bryant 47326
Bryantsville (Mitchell) 47446
Brylane (Indianapolis) 46283
Buck Creek 47924
Buckeye (Warren) 46792
Buckskin 47647
Bucktown (Carlisle) 47838
Buddha (Bedford) 47421
Buena Vista (Laurel) 47024
Buffalo 47925
Buffaloville (Lamar) 47550
Bugtown (Poseyville) 47633
Bullocktown (Boonville) 47601
Bunker Hill 46914
  .... 47167, 47331
Burglen Hills (Tell City) 47586
Burket 46508
Burlington 46915
Burnett (Terre Haute) 47805
Burnettsville 47926
Burney 47222, 47240
Burns City (Loogootee) 47553
Burr Oak (Culver) .. 46511, 46701
Burrows 46916
Busseron (Oaktown) 47561
Butler 46721
Butler Center (Garrett) 46738
Butlerville 47223
Cadiz (New Castle) 47362
Caesar Creek (Dillsboro) .. 47018
Cale (Shoals) 47581
Calvertville (Bloomfield) 47424
Cambridge City 47327
Camby 46113
Camden 46917
Cammack (Muncie) 47304
Campbellsburg 47108
Canaan 47224
Cannelburg 47519
Canton (Salem) 47167

Capehart (Washington) 47501
Carbon 47837
Cardonia (Brazil) 47834
Carefree (Leavenworth) 47137
Carlisle 47838
Carlos City (Lynn) 47355
Carmel 46032-033
Carp (Spencer) 47460
Carpentersville 46172
  (Roachdale)
Carrollton (Finly) 46129
Carter (Dale) 47523
Cartersburg 46114, 46168
Carthage 46115
Carwood (Borden) 47106

Cass (Newberry) 47449
  .... 47541, 47868, 47882
Castleton 46250, 46256
  (Indianapolis)
Cataract (Spencer) 47460
Cates (Kingman) 47952
Catlin (Rockville) 47872
Cato (Winslow) 47598
Cayuga 47928
Cedar Canyon (Leo) 46765
Cedar Creek (Garrett) 46738
Cedar Grove 47016
Cedar Lake 46303
Cedarville (Leo) 46765
Celestine 47521
Cemar Estates 47805
  (Terre Haute)
Cementville 47129-130
  (Clarksville)
Centenary (Clinton) 47842
Center (Portland) 47371
  .... 47424, 47553
Centerpoint 47840
Centerton (Martinsville) 46151
Centerville 47330
Central 47110
Ceylon (Geneva) 46740
Chalmers 47929
Chambersburg (Paoli) 47454
Champion 47885
  (West Terre Haute)
Chandler 47610
Chapelhill (Heltonville) 47436
Charlestown 47111
Charlottesville 46117
Chester (Richmond) 47374
Chesterfield (Anderson) 46017
Chesterton 46304
Chili (Denver) 46926
Chrisney 47611
Churubusco 46723
Cicero 46034
Cincinnati (Bloomfield) 47424
Circle Park (Hamilton) 46742
City (Michigan City) 46360
Clarks Hill 47930
Clarks Landing (Hamilton) 46742
Clarksburg 47225
Clarksville 47129-131
  Cementville 47129
  Jeff 47129
  Jeffersonville 47129
Clay 47345, 47460
  (Greens Fork)
Clay City (Lamar) ... 47550, 47841

Barrick Corner 47841
  Brunswick 47841
  Harrison 47841
  Martz 47841
Claypool 46510
Claysville 47108
  (Campbellsburg)
Clayton 46118
Clear Creek 47401, 47426
  (Bloomington)
Clear Lake (Fremont) 46737
Clermont (Indianapolis) 46234
Clifford 47226
Clinton 47842
Cloverdale 46120
Cloverland (Brazil) 47834
Coal Bluff (Rosedale) 47874
Coal City 47427
Coalmont 47845
Coatesville 46121
Coe (Winslow) 47598
Coesse (Columbia City) 46725
Colburn 47931
Cold Springs (Hamilton) ... 46742
Colfax 46035
Collamer (South Whitley) .. 46787
Collegeville (Rensselaer) .. 47978
Collett (Portland) 47371
Collins (Columbia City) 46725
Coloma (Rockville) 47872
Columbia (Columbia City) . 46725
  .... 47331, 47527
Columbia City 46725
Columbus 47201-203
Commiskey 47227
Como (Portland) 47371
Concord (Elkhart) ... 46517, 46785
Concordia Gardens 46825
  (Fort Wayne)
Connersville 47331
Converse 46919
Cook (Cedar Lake) 46303
Coppess Corner (Monroe) 46772
Cornettsville 47568
  (Plainville)
Corning (Montgomery) 47558
Cortland 47228
Corunna 46730
Cory 47846
Corydon 47112
Cosperville (Wawaka) 46794
Cottagegrove (Liberty) 47353
Coveyville (Bedford) 47421
Covington 47932
Cowan (Muncie) 47302
Coxville (Rosedale) 47874
Craigville 46731
Crandall 47114
Crawford (Bedford) 47421
Crawfordsville 47933-939
Cree Lake (Kendallville) 46755
Creston (Lowell) 46356
Crete (Lynn) 47355
Crompton Hill (Clinton) 47842
Cromwell 46732
Crooked Lake (Angola) 46703
Cross Plains 47017
Cross Roads 47006, 47356
  (Batesville)
Crothersville 47229
Crown Point 46307

Crystal (Dubois) 47527
Cuba (Grabill) 46741, 47460
Culver 46511
Cumberland (Indianapolis) 46229
Cunot (Cloverdale) 46120
Curry (Shelburn) 47879
Curryville (Craigville)
    46731, 47879
Curtisville (Elwood) 46036
Cutler 46920
Cuzco (French Lick) 47432
Cynthiana 47612
Dabney (Holton) 47023
Daggett (Coal City) 47427
Daisy Hill (Borden) 47106
Dale 47523
Daleville 47334
Dallas (Andrews) 46702
Dalton (Hagerstown) 47346
Dana 47847
Danville 46122
Dark Hollow (Bedford) 47421
Darlington 47940
Daylight (Evansville) 47711
Dayton 47941
Dayville (Newburgh) 47630
De Gonia (Boonville) 47601
Decatur 46733
Decker 47524
Deedsville 46921
Deer Creek (Camden) 46917
Deerfield 47380, 47802
    (Ridgeville)
Delong 46922
Delphi 46923
Demotte 46310
Denham 46925
Denmark (Coal City) 47427
Denver 46926
Depauw 47115
Deputy 47230
Derby 47525
Desoto (Muncie) 47303
Dexter (Derby) 47525
Diamond (Rosedale) 47874
Diamond Lake (Wawaka) .. 46794
Dick Johnson (Brazil) 47834
Dillman (Warren) 46792
Dillsboro 47018
Diplomat 46806, 46816
    (Fort Wayne)
Dixon (Monroeville) 46773
Doans (Bloomfield) 47424
Dodd (Tobinsport) 47587
Dodds Bridge (Fairbanks) . 47849
Dogwood (Laconia) 47135
Dolan (Bloomington) 47401
Domestic (Bluffton) 46714
Donaldson 46513
Dover (Guilford) 47022
Dover Hill (Shoals) 47581
Dowden Acres 47802
    (Terre Haute)
Dresden (Owensburg) 47453
Dresser 47885
    (West Terre Haute)
Dublin 47335
Duck Creek (Elwood) 46036
Dudley (Straughn) 47387
Duff (Huntingburg) 47542
Dugger 47848

Dunfee (Fort Wayne) 46818
Dunkirk 47336
Dunlap (Elkhart) 46517
Dunlapsville (Liberty) 47353
Dunreith 47337
Dupont 47231
Dutch Town (Garrett) 46738
Dyer 46311
Eagle Creek ... 46214, 46253-254
    (Indianapolis)
Earl Park 47942, 47976
Earlham (Richmond) 47374
East Cedar Lake 46303
    (Cedar Lake)
East Chicago 46312
East Connersville 47331
    (Connersville)
East Enterprise 47019
East Haven (Richmond) 47374
East Oolitic (Bedford) 47421
East Shelburn (Shelburn) .. 47879
East Shoals (Shoals) 47581
East Union (Atlanta) 46031
Eastern Heights 47401
    (Bloomington)
Eaton 47338
Eckerty 47116
Economy 47339
Eden (Greenfield) 46140
Edgerton (Woodburn) 46797
Edgewood (Bedford) 47421
Edgewood Park 46818
    (Fort Wayne)
Edinburgh 46124
Edwardsport 47528
Edwardsville (Georgetown) 47122
Eel River (Churubusco) 46723
Ege (Laotto) 46763
Ehrmandale (Terre Haute) . 47805
Ekin (Atlanta) 46031
Elberfeld 47613
Elizabeth 47117
Elizabethtown 47232, 47236
    Grammer 47232
    Grammer 47236
Elkhart 46514-517
    Concord 46517
    Dunlap 46517
Elkinsville (Nashville) 47448
Ellettsville 47429
Ellis (Dugger) 47848
Elliston (Bloomfield) 47424
Ellisville (Fort Wayne) 46804
Elmira (Lagrange) 46761
Elmore (Elnora) 47529
Elnora 47529
Elrod (Dillsboro) 47018
Elwood 46036
Eminence 46125
Emison 47530
Emporia (Markleville) 46056
Enchanted Hills 46732
    (Cromwell)
Englewood (Bedford) 47421
English 47118
English Lake 46366
    (North Judson)
Enochsburg (Greensburg) . 47240
Epsom (Plainville) 47568
Etna (Columbia City) 46725
Etna Green 46524

Eureka (Rockport) 47635
Evanston 47531
Evansville 47700-706, 47708
    .... 47710-716, 47719-728
    ..... 47730-737, 47739-47741
    .... 47744, 47747, 47750
    Daylight 47711
    Knight 47711
    Mccutchanville 47711
    North Park 47710
Everton (Connersville) 47331
Fair Oaks 47943
Fairbanks 47849
Fairfield (Corunna) 46730
    .... 46807, 47012
Fairland 46126
Fairmount 46928
Fairplay (Switz City) 47465
Fairview 47331, 47373
    (Connersville)
Fairview Park (Clinton) 47842
Falmouth 46127
Farlen (Odon) 47562
Farmers (Freedom) 47431
Farmersburg 47850
Farmland 47340
Fayette 47885
    (West Terre Haute)
Fayetteville (Bedford) 47421
Fenn Haven (Tell City) 47586
Ferdinand 47532
Ferguson Hill 47885
    (West Terre Haute)
Fiat (Bryant) 47326
Fillmore 46128
Fincastle (Roachdale) 46172
Finly 46129
Fish Lake (Lagrange) 46763
Fishers 46038, 46060
    Noblesville 46038
Five Points 46797, 47557
    (Woodburn)
Flat Rock 47234
Flint (Angola) 46703
Flora 46929
Florence 47020
Florida (Rosedale) 47874
Floyds Knobs 47119
Folsomville 47614
Fontanet 47851
Foraker (Goshen) 46526
Forest 46039
Fort Branch 47648
Fort Ritner 47430
Fort Wayne 46800-809
    .... 46815-816, 46818-819
    .... 46825, 46835, 46845
    .... 46850-869, 46885
    .... 46895-897, 46898-899
    Baer Field 46809
    Blackhawk 46815
    Bloomingdale 46808
    Brookside Estates ... 46835
    Concordia Gardens . 46825
    Diplomat 46806
    Diplomat 46816
    Dunfee 46818
    Edgewood Park 46818
    Ellisville 46804
    Fairfield 46807
    Georgetown Square . 46815

(Fort Wayne)	.... 46209, 46211, 46214,	Madison 47546
Hessville (Hammond) 46323	.... 46216-227, 46229-231	Marion 47546
Hibernia (Charlestown) 47111	.... 46234, 46236-237	Portersville 47546
High Lake (Albion) 46701	.... 46239-242, 46244	Jay City (Bryant) 47326
Highland (Hammond) 46322	.... 46247, 46249-251	Jeff (Clarksville) 47129-130
.... 47424, 47854	.... 46253-256, 46259-260	Jefferson (Albion) ... 46701, 46725
Highland Center 47012	. 46266 46268, 46275, 46277	.... 47108, 47346, 47371
(Brookville)	.... 46278, 46280, 46282-283	.... 47388, 47427, 47471
Hillham (French Lick) 47432	.... 46285, 46290-291, 46295	.... 47513, 47564, 47838
Hillisburg 46041, 46046	Acton 46259	Jeffersonville 47129-131
(Frankfort)	Avon 46234	(Clarksville)
Hillsboro 47362, 47949	Bridgeport 46231	Cementville 47130
(New Castle)	Broad Ripple 46220	Clarksville 47130-131
Hillsdale 47854	Brylane 46283	Jeff 47130
Hindustan (Bloomington) .. 47401	Castleton 46250	Utica 47130
Hitchcock (Salem) 47167	Castleton 46256	Watson 47130
Hoagland 46745	Clermont 46234	Jennings (Connersville) 47331
Hobart 46342	Cumberland 46229	Jessup (Rosedale) 47874
Hobbieville (Springville) 47462	Drexel Gardens 46241	Johnsburg (Huntingburg) .. 47542
Hobbs 46047	Eagle Creek 46214	Johnson (Eckerty) 47116
Hogtown (Marengo) 47140	Eagle Creek 46253-46254	Johnstown 47471, 47512
Holiday (Garrett) 46738	Irvington 46219	(Worthington)
Holland 47541	Lawrence 46216	Jonesboro 46938
Hollandsburg (Rockville) ... 47872	Lawrence 46226	Jonestown (Clinton) 47842
Holly Hills (Terre Haute) ... 47802	Linwood 46201	Jonesville 47247
Hollybrook Lake (Gosport) 47433	Mars Hill 46241	Jordan (Poland) 47868
Holton 47023	Maywood 46241	Judah (Bedford) 47421
Homer 46146	New Augusta 46268	Judson 47856
Hondorus (Decatur) 46733	New Augusta 46278	Keller (Terre Haute) 47802
Honey Creek 47356, 47802	Nora 46240	Kellerville (Dubois) 46049
(Middletown)	Nora 46260	Kempton 46049
Hoosier Acres 47401	Nora 46280	Kendallville 46720, 46755
(Bloomington)	Nora 46290	(Brimfield)
Hoosier Highlands 47868	Oaklandon 46236	Allen 46755
(Poland)	Park Fletcher 46241	Brimfield 46755
Hoosierville (Brazil) 47834	Southport 46217	Cree Lake 46755
Hope 47246	Southport 46227	Lisbon 46755
Hopewell (Franklin) 46131	Southport 46237	Round Lake 46755
Howard (Marshall) 47859	Southport 46247	Wayne 46755
Howe 46746	Speedway 46224	Kennard 47351
Howesville (Jasonville) 47438	Speedway 46254	Kennedy (Lamar) 47550
Hubbell (Coal City) 47427	Traders Point 46278	Kentland 47951
Hubbells Corner (Sunman) 47041	Uptown 46205	Kenwood 47885
Hudson (Helmer) 46744, 46747	Wanamaker 46239	(West Terre Haute)
Gravel Beach 46747	West Indianapolis 46221	Kersey (Demotte) 46310
Helmer 46747	Indianola (Wolcottville) 46795	Kewanna 46935, 46939
Salem Center 46747	Ingalls 46048	(Grass Creek)
Hudson Lake 46552	Inglefield 47618	Keyser (Garrett) 46738
(New Carlisle)	Inwood (Plymouth) 46563	Keystone 46759
Hudsonville (Montgomery) 47558	Ireland 47545	Kimmell 46760
Huffman (Troy) 47588	Ironton (Shoals) 47581	Kingman 47952
Huntersville (Batesville) 47006	Irvington (Indianapolis) 46219	Kingsbury 46345
Huntertown 46748	Island City (Linton) 47441	Kingsford Heights 46346
Huntingburg 47542	Island Park (Hamilton) 46742	Kingsland (Ossian) 46777
Huntington 46750	Iva (Otwell) 47564	Kingston (Greensburg) 47240
Huntsville (Pendleton) 46064	Jackson (Monroeville) 46773	Kingswood Terra 47802
Huron 47437	.... 47327, 47331	(Terre Haute)
Hurshtown (Spencerville) .. 46788	.... 47348, 47432, 47448	Kirklin 46050
Hyde Park (Muncie) 47302	.... 47462, 47537, 47542	Kirksville (Bloomington) 47401
Hymera 47855	.... 47834, 47837, 47855	Kitchell (Liberty) 47353
Idaho (Terre Haute) 47802	Jackson Hill (Shelburn) 47879	Klondike (Clinton) . 47842, 47862
Idaville 47950	Jacksonburg 47327	Knapp Lake (Cromwell) 46732
Indian Creek 47401, 47421	(Cambridge City)	Knight (Evansville) 47711
(Bloomington)	Jacksonville (Clinton) 47842	Knightstown 46148
Indian Lake (Corunna) 46730	Jamestown 46147, 46737	Knightsville 47857
Indian Springs (Shoals) 47581	Jasonville 47438	Knox 46534
Indian Village (Cromwell) .. 46732	Jasper 47546-547	Kokomo 46901-904
Indiana Beach 47960	Bainbridge 47546	Koleen 47439
(Monticello)	Boone 47546	Kossuth (Salem) 47167
Indianapolis 46107	Hall 47546	Kouts 46347
.... 46142-143, 46200-209	Haysville 47546	Kurtz 47249

Kyana (Saint Anthony) 47575	
La Crosse 46348	
La Fontaine 46940	
La Porte 46350-351, 46367	
Pinola 46350	
Pleasant 46350	
Laconia 47135	
Ladoga 47954	
Lafayette (Floyds Knobs) ... 47119	
.... 47460, 47901-907, 47996	
Lagrange 46761	
Lagro 46941	
Lake Cicott 46942	
Lake Dalecarlia (Lowell) ... 46356	
Lake Dilldear (Dillsboro) ... 47018	
Lake Edgewood 46151	
(Martinsville)	
Lake Everett (Fort Wayne) 46818	
Lake James (Angola) 46703	
Lake Lincoln 47552	
(Lincoln City)	
Lake Maxine (Quincy) 47456	
Lake Mccoy (Greensburg) . 47240	
Lake Mohee 47348	
(Hartford City)	
Lake Noji (Terre Haute) 47802	
Lake Station (Gary) 46405	
Lake Sullivan (Sullivan) 47882	
Lake Village 46349	
Lakeside (Wolcottville) 46795	
Laketon 46943	
Lakeview (Wolcottville) 46795	
Lakeview Estates 47802	
(Terre Haute)	
Lakeville 46536	
Lakewood (Terre Haute) ... 47802	
Lamar 47550	
Lancaster (Huntington) 46750	
Lancaster Park 47401	
(Bloomington)	
Landess 46944, 46691	
Lanesville 47136	
Laotto 46763	
Lapaz 46537	
Lapel 46051	
Larimer Hill 47885	
(West Terre Haute)	
Larwill 46764	
Laud (Columbia City) 46725	
Laurel 47024	
Lawrence 46216, 46226	
(Indianapolis)	
Lawrenceburg 47025	
Lawrenceport (Mitchell) 47446	
Lawrenceville (Sunman) ... 47041	
Leavenworth 47137	
Lebanon 46052	
Leesburg 46538	
Leesville (Bedford) 47421	
Leisure (Elwood) 46036	
Leiters Ford 46945	
Lena (Brazil) 47834	
Leo 46765	
Leopold 47551	
Leroy 46355	
Lewis (Jasonville) .. 47438, 47858	
Brown Jug Corner 47858	
Lewisville 46120, 47352	
(Cloverdale)	
Lexington 47138	
Liber (Portland) 47371	

Liberty 47353, 47362, 47383	
Billingsville 47353	
Cottagegrove 47353	
Dunlapsville 47353	
Kitchell 47353	
Lotus 47353	
Roseburg 47353	
Salem 47353	
Witts 47353	
Liberty Center 46766	
Liberty Mills 46946	
Libertyville 47885	
(West Terre Haute)	
Licking (Hartford City) 47348	
Liggett 47885	
(West Terre Haute)	
Ligonier 46767	
Lilly Dale (Tell City) 47586	
Lima (Howe) 46746	
Limedale (Greencastle) 46135	
Lincoln City 47552	
Linden 47955	
Linn Grove (Berne) 46711, 46769	
Berne 46769	
Linton 47441, 47802	
Island City 47441	
Stockton 47441	
Vicksburg 47441	
Victoria 47441	
West Linton 47441	
Whites Crossing 47441	
Wright 47441	
Linwood (Indianapolis) 46201	
Lisbon (Kendallville) 46755	
Little (Petersburg) 47567	
Little Point 47464	
(Stinesville)	
Little York 47139	
Livonia (Campbellsburg) ... 47108	
Lizton 46149	
Lockhart (Stendal) 47585	
Logan (Petersburg) 47567	
Logansport 46947	
Lonetree (Jasonville) 47438	
Long Lake (Fremont) 46737	
Loogootee 47553	
Loon Lake (Columbia City) 46725	
Lorane (Columbia City) 46725	
Losantville 47354	
Lost River (French Lick) 47432	
Lotus (Liberty) 47353	
Lowell 46356, 46399	
Belshaw 46356	
Creston 46356	
Lake Dalecarlia 46356	
North Hayden 46356	
Lucerne 46950	
Luray (Springport) 47386	
Luther (South Whitley) 46787	
Lutheran Lake (Seymour) . 47274	
Lydick (South Bend) 46628	
Lyford (Rosedale) 47874	
Lynn 47355	
Lynnville 47619	
Lyons 47443	
Lyonsville (Connersville) ... 47331	
Mackey 47654	
Macy 46951	
Madison (Campbellsburg) . 47108	
47250, 47546, 47562, 47567	
North Madison 47250	

Magnet 47555	
Mahon (Huntington) 46750	
Majenica (Huntington) 46750	
Maltersville 47542	
(Huntingburg)	
Manchester (Aurora) 47001	
Manhattan (Greencastle) .. 46135	
Manilla 46150	
Mansfield (Rockville) 47872	
Maples (Fort Wayne) 46816	
Maplewood 46167, 47885	
(Pittsboro)	
Maplewood Park 46815	
(Fort Wayne)	
Marco (Lyons) 47443	
Marengo 47140	
Mariah Hill 47556	
Marion 46952-953, 47446	
.... 47455, 47546, 47590	
Markle 46770	
Markleville 46056	
Marlin Hills 47401	
(Bloomington)	
Mars Hill (Indianapolis) 46241	
Marshall (Bedford) . 47421, 47859	
Howard 47859	
Sugar Creek 47859	
Washington 47859	
Marshfield (Williamsport) ... 47993	
Martinsburg (Pekin) 47165	
Martinsville 46151	
Martz (Clay City) 47841	
Maryland (Terre Haute) 47802	
Marysville 47141, 47598	
Marywood (Terre Haute) ... 47802	
Matlock Heights 47401	
(Bloomington)	
Matthews 46957	
Mauckport 47142	
Maumee (Woodburn) 46797	
Maxville (Farmland) 47340	
Maxwell 46154	
Mays 46155	
Maysville (Washington) 47501	
Maywood (Indianapolis) 46241	
Mc Cordsville 46055	
Mccutchanville 47711	
(Evansville)	
Mckinley (Campbellsburg) 47108	
Mcnatts (Montpelier) 47359	
Meadowbrook 46774	
(New Haven)	
Mecca 47860	
Mechanicsburg (Kirklin) 46050	
.... 46056, 47356	
Medaryville 47957	
Medford (Muncie) 47302	
Medora 47260	
Mellott 47958	
Memphis 47143	
Mentone 46539	
Mentor (Birdseye) 47513	
Merom 47861	
Merriam (Albion) 46701	
Merrillville (Gary) 46410-411	
Messick (New Castle) 47362	
Metamora 47030	
Metz (Angola) 46703	
Mexico 46958	
Miami 46959	
Michigan City 46360	

Orestes	46063
Oriole (Leopold)	47551
Orland	46776
Orleans	47452
Ormas (Columbia City)	46725
Osceola	46561
Osgood	47037
Ossian	46777
Otis	46367
Otisco	47163
Otsego (Hamilton)	46742
Otter Creek	47023, 47805
(Holton)	
Otter Lake (Fremont)	46737
Otter Village (Holton)	47023
Otterbein	47970
Otto (New Washington)	47162
Otwell	47564
Owensburg	47453
Owensville	47665
Oxford	47971
Palestine (Brookville)	47012
Palmer (Crown Point)	46307
Palmyra	47164
Paoli	47454
Paradise (Newburgh)	47630
Paradise Lake	46151
(Martinsville)	
Paragon	46166
Paris Crossing	47270
Park (Bloomfield)	47424
Park Fletcher	46241
(Indianapolis)	
Park Ridge (Bloomington)	47401
Parker City	47368
Parkerdale (Fort Wayne)	46835
Patoka (Huntingburg)	47542
	47598, 47666
Patricksburg	47455
Patriot	47038
Patronville (Rockport)	47635
Patton Hill (Bedford)	47421
Paxton	47865
Paynesville (Hanover)	47243
Peabody (Columbia City)	46725
Pearsontown (Marengo)	47140
Peerless (Bedford)	47421
Pekin	47165
Pelzer (Boonville)	47601
Pence	47973, 47993
Pendleton	46064
Penn (Pennville)	47369, 47832
Penn Park (Hamilton)	46742
Penntown (Sunman)	47041
Pennville	47327, 47369
(Cambridge City)	
Balbee	47369
Penn	47369
Peoga (Trafalgar)	46181
Peppertown (Metamora)	47030
Perry (Economy)	47339, 47401
	47462, 47553, 47846
Perrysville	47974
Pershing	47370
Perth (Carbon)	47837
Peru	46970-971
Petersburg	47567
Peterson (Decatur)	46733
Petroleum	46778
Pheasant Run	46819
(Fort Wayne)	

Philomath (Brownsville)	47325
Pierceton	46562, 46566
Pierceville	47039
Pigeon (Dale)	47523
Pimento	47866
Pine Ridge	47885
(West Terre Haute)	
Pine Valley	46825, 47454
(Fort Wayne)	
Pine Village	47975
Pinhook (Bedford)	47421
Pinola (La Porte)	46350
Pipe Creek (Elwood)	46036
Pittsboro	46167
Plainfield	46168
Plainville	47568
Plato (Lagrange)	46761
Pleasant (La Porte)	46350
	46703, 47224
Pleasant Lake	46779
Pleasant Mills	46780
Pleasant Plain (Warren)	46792
Pleasant Ridge (Borden)	47106
Pleasant Run	47436
(Heltonville)	
Pleasantville (Carlisle)	47838
Plum Tree (Warren)	46792
Plummer (Bloomfield)	47424
Plymouth	46563
Poe (Fort Wayne)	46819
Point Commerce	47471
(Worthington)	
Poland	47868
Poling (Bryant)	47326
Polk (Huntington)	46750, 47436
Poneto	46781
Pontiac (Carbon)	47837
Popcorn (Springville)	47462
Portage	46368
Porter (Chesterton)	46304
Portersville (Jasper)	47546
Portland	47371
Posey	47331, 47834
(Connersville)	
Poseyville	47633
Potter Brumfield	47671
(Princeton)	
Pottersville (Spencer)	47460
Powers (Portland)	47371
Prairie City (Brazil)	47834
Prairie Creek	47869
Prairie Village	47802
(Terre Haute)	
Prairieton	47870
Preble	46782
Pretty Lake	46795
(Wolcottville)	
Princeton	47670
Progress (Muncie)	47302
Progress Acres	47805
(Terre Haute)	
Prospect	47469
(West Baden Springs)	
Providence (Bargersville)	46106
Prowsville	47108
(Campbellsburg)	
Putnamville	46170
Quailtown (Westport)	47283
Quaker (Dana)	47847
Queensville	47265
(North Vernon)	

Quincy	47456
Raber (Columbia City)	46725
Raccoon	46172, 47874
(Roachdale)	
Raglesville (Odon)	47562
Ragsdale	47573
Ramsey	47166
Randolph (Ridgeville)	47380
Raub	47976
Ray (Fremont)	46737
Raysville (Knightstown)	46148
Redkey	47373
Reelsville	46171
Reeve (Loogootee)	47553
Rego (Hardinsburg)	47125
Reiffsburg (Bluffton)	46714
Remington	47977
Reno (Coatesville)	46121
Rensselaer	47978
Reo (Rockport)	47635
Reserve (Montezuma)	47862
Retreat (Crothersville)	47229
Reynolds	47980
Riceville (Birdseye)	47513
Richland (Larwill)	46764
	47424, 47429, 47634
Richmond	47374-375
Chester	47374
Earlham	47374
East Haven	47374
Middleboro	47374
Spring Grove	47374
Whitewater	47374
Ridgemede (Bloomington)	47401
Ridgeport (Bloomfield)	47424
Ridgeville	47380
Ridgeway (Fort Wayne)	46809
Rigdon (Elwood)	46036
Riley	47871
Rising Sun	47040
River Vale (Mitchell)	47446
Riverton (Merom)	47861
Riverview (Fairbanks)	47849
Roachdale	46172
Roann	46974
Roanoke	46783
Robertsdale (Whiting)	46394
Rochester	46975
Rock Creek	46714, 46750
(Bluffton)	
Rockfield	46977
Rockford (Bluffton)	46714
Rockport	47635
Rockville	47872
Rocky Fork Lake (Brazil)	47834
Roland	47469
(West Baden Springs)	
Roll (Hartford City)	47348
Rolling Prairie	46371
Rollins (Shoals)	47581
Rome	47574
Rome City	46784
Romney	47981
Romona (Spencer)	47460
Roseburg (Liberty)	47353
Rosedale	47874
Roseland (South Bend)	46637
Roselawn	46372
Rosewood (Elizabeth)	47117
Rossville	46065
Round Lake (Kendallville)	46755

Royal Center	46978
Royal Oaks (Fort Wayne) ..	46815
Royer Lake (Lagrange)	46761
Royerton (Muncie)	47303
Rural (Winchester)	47394
Rushville	46173
Russellville	46175
Russels Point (Hamilton) ..	46742
Russiaville	46979
Rutherford (Loogootee)	47553
Saint Anthony	47755
Saint Bernice	47875
Saint Croix	47576
Saint Henry (Ferdinand) ...	47532
Saint Joe	46785
Saint John	46373
Saint Johns (Garrett)	46738
Saint Joseph Hill	47172
(Sellersburg)	
Saint Marks 47575, 47586	
(Saint Anthony)	
Saint Mary Of The Woods .	47876
Saint Marys (Notre Dame)	46556
.... 46808, 46818	
Saint Meinrad	47577
Saint Paul	47272
Salamonia	47381
Salamonie (Warren)	46792
Salem (Decatur)	46733
.... 47167, 47334, 47353	
Becks Mill	47167
Bunker Hill	47167
Canton	47167
Harristown	47167
Hitchcock	47167
Kossuth	47167
New Philadelphia	47167
Salem Center (Hudson)	46747
Saline City (Centerpoint) ..	47840
Salomonia (Salamonia)	47381
Salt Creek 47024, 47401	
(Laurel)	
Saltillo (Campbellsburg)	47108
Samaria (Trafalgar)	46181
San Pierre	46374
Sandborn	47578
Sandcut (Terre Haute)	47805
Sanders (Bloomington)	47401
Sandford 47877, 47885	
Sandusky (Greensburg)	47240
Sandytown (Clinton)	47842
Santa Claus	47579
Saratoga	47382
Sardinia (Westport)	47283
Scenic Heights	47586
(Tell City)	
Scenic Hill (Loogootee)	47553
Schererville	46375
Schneider	46376
Schnellville	47580
Scipio	47273
Scotland	47457
Scott (Angola)	46703
Scott City (Shelburn)	47879
Scottsburg	47170
Scottsville (Borden)	47106
Sedalia	46067
Sedan (Waterloo)	46793
Seelyville	47878
Sellersburg	47172
Selma	47383

Selvin (Dale)	47523
Servia	46980
Seymour	47274
Shady Nook (Wolcottville) .	46795
Sharpsville	46068
Shawswick (Bedford)	47421
Shawville (Terre Haute)	47805
Shelburn	47879
Shelby	46377
Shelbyville	46176
Shepardsville	47880
Sheridan	46069
Shideler (Eaton)	47338
Shipshewana	46565
Shirkleville	47885
(West Terre Haute)	
Shirley	47384
Shoals	47581
Siberia (Bristow)	47515
Sidney	46566
Silver Lake	46982
Silverville (Williams)	47470
Simpson (Huntington)	46750
Sims	46983
Skinner Lake (Albion)	46701
Smedley (Campbellsburg) ..	47108
Smith 46723, 47471	
(Churubusco)	
Smithfield (Selma)	47383
Smithville	47458
Smockville (Carbon)	47837
Snow Hill (Winchester)	47394
Solitude (Mount Vernon) ...	47620
Solsberry	47459
Somerset	46984
Somerville	47683
South Bend (Notre Dame)	46556
.... 46600-601, 46612-617	
.... 46619, 46624	
.... 46628-629, 46634-635	
.... 46637, 46660, 46680	
Lydick	46626
Roseland	46637
South Lake	47885
(West Terre Haute)	
South Milford	46786
South Salem (Union City) ..	47390
South Wanatah (Wanatah)	46390
South Washington	47501
(Washington)	
South Whitley	46787
Southport (Indianapolis) ...	46217
.... 46227, 46237, 46247	
Southtown (Fort Wayne) ...	46816
Southwood (Terre Haute) ..	47802
Sparta (Kimmell)	46760
Spartanburg (Lynn)	47355
Spearsville (Trafalgar)	46181
Speed (Sellersburg)	47172
Speedway 46224, 46254	
(Indianapolis)	
Spelterville	47805
(Terre Haute)	
Spencer	47460
Spencerville	46788
Spiceland	47385
Spring Grove (Richmond) .	47374
Spring Valley Estates	47802
(Terre Haute)	
Springersville	47325
(Brownsville)	

Springfield 46743, 46771	
(Harlan)	
Springport	47386
Springville	47462
Springwood (Terre Haute) .	47805
Spurgeon	47584
Stafford (Butler) 46721, 47578	
Stanford	47463
Star City	46985
Starlight (Borden)	47106
State Line 47885, 47982	
(West Terre Haute)	
Staunton	47881
Stavetown (Brookville)	47012
Stearleyville (Brazil)	47834
Steele (Monroe) 46772, 47501	
Steen (Wheatland)	47597
Stendal	47585
Steubenville (Ashley)	46705
Stewartsville	47633
(Poseyville)	
Stilesville	46180
Stillwell	46351
Stinesville	47464
Stockton (Linton)	47441
Stockwell	47983
Stone (Winchester)	47394
Stone Head (Nashville)	47448
Stonington (Mitchell)	47446
Story (Nashville)	47448
Straughn	47387
Strawtown (Noblesville)	46060
Stroh	46789
Sugar Creek 47859, 47885	
(Marshall)	
Sugar Ridge (Centerpoint)	47840
Sullivan 47864, 47882	
(New Lebanon)	
Cass	47882
Hamilton	47882
Lake Sullivan	47882
Turman	47882
Sulphur	47174
Sulphur Springs	47388
Summit Grove (Clinton)	47842
Summitville	46070
Sunman	47041
Sunny Acres (Decatur)	46733
Sunnybrook Acres	46835
(Fort Wayne)	
Sunnymede (Fort Wayne) .	46803
Swan (Laotto)	46763
Swayzee	46986
Sweetser	46987
Switz City	47465
Sycamore Park	47885
(West Terre Haute)	
Sylvania (Bloomingdale) ...	47832
Syndicate (Clinton)	47842
Syracuse	46567
Syria (Orleans)	47452
Tabertown (Seelyville)	47878
Talbot	47984
Tampico (Crothersville)	47229
Tanglewood (New Haven) .	46774
Taswell	47175
Taylor 47424, 47460	
(Bloomfield)	
Taylorsville	47280
Tecumseh	47885
(West Terre Haute)	

Tefft	46380
Tell City	47586
Temple (English)	47118
Templeton	47986
Tennyson	47637
Tera North (Terre Haute)	47805
Terre Haute	47801-805
	47807-808
Allendale	47802
Apache Acres	47805
Bartley	47805
Brookside Estates	47802
Burnett	47805
Cemar Estates	47805
Deerfield	47802
Dowden Acres	47802
Ehrmandale	47805
Grouseland	47805
Harrison	47807
Holly Hills	47802
Honey Creek	47802
Idaho	47802
Keller	47802
Kingswood Terra	47802
Lake Noji	47802
Lakeview Estates	47802
Lakewood	47802
Linton	47802
Maryland	47802
Marywood	47802
North Terre Haute	47805
Northwood	47805
Oak Grove	47802
Otter Creek	47805
Prairie Village	47802
Progress Acres	47805
Sandcut	47805
Shawville	47805
Southwood	47802
Spelterville	47805
Spring Valley Estates	47802
Springwood	47805
Tera North	47805
Wonder Lake	47802
Woodgate	47802
Youngstown	47802
Thayer	46381
Thomaston (Wanatah)	46390
Thorncreek	46725
(Columbia City)	
Thorntown	46071
Thurman (New Haven)	46774
Tillman (Monroeville)	46773
Timberhurst	46795
(Wolcottville)	
Times Corner	46804
(Fort Wayne)	
Tippecanoe	46570
Tipton	46072
Toad Hop	47885
(West Terre Haute)	
Tobin (Rome)	47574
Tobinsport	47587
Tocsin (Ossian)	46777
Toledo (Huntington)	46750
Topeka	46571
Toto (Knox)	46534
Townley (Monroeville)	46773
Traders Point	46278
(Indianapolis)	
Trafalgar	46181

Travisville (Bluffton)	46714
Trenton (Hartford City)	47348
Trevlac (Nashville)	47448
Tri Lakes (Columbia City)	46725
Troy	47588
Tulip (Bloomfield)	47424
Tunker (South Whitley)	46787
Tunnelton	47467
Turman (Sullivan)	47882
Turner (Brazil)	47834
Twelve Mile	46988
Tyner	46572
Underwood	47177
Union (Columbia City)	46725
	47555, 47872
Union City	47390
Union Mills	46382
Uniondale	46791
Unionport (Farmland)	47340
Uniontown	47229, 47515
(Crothersville)	
Unionville	47468
Universal	47884
Upland	46989
Upper Long Lake (Albion)	46701
Uptown (Indianapolis)	46205
Urbana	46990
Urmeyville (Franklin)	46131
Utica (Jeffersonville)	47130
Valeene	47125, 47140
(Hardinsburg)	
Valentine (Lagrange)	46761
Vallonia	47281
Valparaiso	46383-384
Valpo	46383
Valpo (Valparaiso)	46383
Van Buren	46991, 47401
	47448, 47553, 47837
Landess	46991
Vandalia (Spencer)	47460
Veale (Washington)	47501
Veedersburg	47987
Velpen	47590
Vera Cruz (Bluffton)	46714
Vernon	47108, 47282
(Campbellsburg)	
Versailles	47042
Vevay	47043
Vicksburg (Linton)	47441
Victoria (Linton)	47441
Vigo (Bicknell)	47512, 47870
Vilas (Spencer)	47460
Villa North (Bluffton)	46714
Vincennes	47591
Wabash	46992, 47860
Wadesville	47638
Wakarusa	46573
Walden (Fort Wayne)	46815
Waldron	46182
Waldron Lake (Wawaka)	46794
Walkerton	46574
Wall Lake (Orland)	46776
Wallace	47988
Wallen (Fort Wayne)	46818
Walton	46994
Wanamaker (Indianapolis)	46239
Wanatah	46390
Wanda Lake	47885
(West Terre Haute)	
Warren	46792
Warrenton (Haubstadt)	47639

Warrington (Wilkinson)	46186
Warsaw	46580-581
Washington	46725, 46760
	46818, 47162, 47348
	47401, 47443, 47448
	47460, 47501, 47516
	47567, 47833, 47859
(Columbia City)	
Capehart	47501
Harrison	47501
Maysville	47501
South Washington	47501
Steele	47501
Veale	47501
Waterloo	46793, 47331
Sedan	46793
Watson (Jeffersonville)	47130
Waveland	47989
Waverly (Martinsville)	46151
Wawaka	46794
Wayne	46755, 47433
(Kendallville)	
Waynedale	46809, 46819
(Fort Wayne)	
Waynesburg (Hartsville)	47244
Waynetown	47990
Webster	47392
Weisburg (Sunman)	47041
Wellsboro (Union Mills)	46382
West Acres (Muncie)	47304
West Atherton (Rosedale)	47874
West Baden Springs	47469
West Brook Acres	47006
(Batesville)	
West Brook Downs	47401
(Bloomington)	
West Elwood (Elwood)	46036
West Harrison	47060
(W Harrison)	
West Indianapolis	46221
(Indianapolis)	
West Lafayette	47906-907
	47996
Lafayette	47996
West Lebanon	47991
West Liberty (Bryant)	47326
West Linton (Linton)	47441
West Middleton	46995
West Muncie (Yorktown)	47396
West Newton	46183
West Petersburg	47567
(Petersburg)	
West Terre Haute	47885
West Union (Montezuma)	47862
Westchester (Portland)	47371
Westfield	46074
Westlawn (Fort Wayne)	46804
Westphalia	47596
Westpoint	47992
Westport	47283
Westville	46391
Westwood (New Castle)	47362
Wey Lake (Brazil)	47834
Wheatfield	46392
Wheatland	47597
Wheatonville (Elberfeld)	47613
Wheeler	46393
Wheeling (Gaston)	47342
Whitcomb (Brookville)	47012
Whitcomb Heights	47885
(West Terre Haute)	

White Swan (Fort Wayne) . 46818
Whitehall (Bloomington) 47401
Whiteland 46184
Whiteoak (Winslow) 47598
Whitestown 46075
Whitewater (Richmond) 47374
Whitfield (Loogootee) 47553
Whiting 46394
Wickliffe (Eckerty) 47116
Widner (Oaktown) 47561
Wildwood Lake (Paoli) 47454
Wildwood Landing (Stroh) . 46789
Wilfred (Shelburn) 47879
Wilkinson 46186
Williams (Decatur) .. 46733, 47470
    Silverville 47470
Williamsburg 47393
Williamsport 47993
Williamstown (Greensburg) 47240
Willisville (Petersburg) 47567
Willow Branch 46187
Willow Valley (Shoals) 47581
Wilmington (Butler) 46721, 47001
Wilson Lake 46725
    (Columbia City)
Wilson Switch (Borden) 47106
Winamac 46996
Winchester 47394
Windemere Lake 47885
    (West Terre Haute)
Windfall 46076
Windom (Shoals) 47581
Windsor (Parker City) 47368
Wingate 47994
Winona Lake 46590
Winslow 47598
Witmer Manor 46795
    (Wolcottville)
Witts (Liberty) 47353

Wolcott 47995
Wolcottville 46795
Wolf Lake (Wolflake) 46796
Wolflake 46796
Wonder Lake (Terre Haute) 47802
Woodbridge (Bloomington) 47408
Woodburn 46797
Woodbury (Mc Cordsville) . 46055
Woodgate (Terre Haute) 47802
Woodland Park 46795
    (Wolcottville)
Woodlawn Park (Muncie) .. 47303
Woodruff (Wolcottville) 46795
Worthington 47471
Wright (Linton) 47441
Wrights Corners (Aurora) .. 47001
Wyatt 46595
Yankeetown (Newburgh) ... 47630
Yeoman 47997
Yockey (Mitchell) 47446
Yoder 46798
York (Angola) 46703, 47022
Yorktown 47396
Yorkville (Guilford) 47022
Yost Woods (Decatur) 46733
Youngs Creek (Paoli) 47454
Youngstown (Terre Haute) . 47802
Zanesville 46799
Zionsville 46077
Zoar (Stendal) 47585
Zulu (Monroeville) 46773

ALLENDALE

APARTMENTS

Westminster Village
1120 E DAVIS DR 47802

BUILDINGS

Dixie Bee Plaza
5149 S US HIGHWAY 41 .. 47802

Honey Creek Square
3401 S US HIGHWAY 41 .. 47802

Southland Shopping Center
3001 S 7TH ST 47802

ANDERSON

APARTMENTS

Abbott
1003 E 8TH ST 46012

Anderson Chase Apt
2505 E 10TH ST 46012

Arbor Village Apt
2012 E 7TH ST 46012

Arbor Village South
1823 E 8TH ST 46012

Autumn Winds Apt
1716 E 50TH ST 46013

Beverly Terrace Apt
1102 CENTRAL AVE 46016

Brock Apt
23 W 11TH ST 46016

Community Square Apt
1641 N MADISON AVE 46011

Crystal Glen Apt
2800 CRYSTAL ST 46012

Delaware Ct Apt
120 W 10TH ST 46016

Eberhart
1412 MERIDIAN ST 46016

Edgewood Plaza Apt
2725 W 16TH ST 46011

Edgewood Plaza Apt
1710 BRENTWOOD DR 46011

Farrington Apt
1426 E 60TH ST 46013

Gas Light Apt
814 W 53RD ST 46013

Giant Oaks Apt
1300 W 8TH ST 46016

Leigh Apt
1324 W 11TH ST 46016

Lincolnshire Apt
330 W 12TH ST 46016

Longfellow Plaza
319 E 12TH ST 46016

Mansfield Apt
1700 E 1ST ST 46012

Pinetree Village Apts
2801 RAIBLE AVE 46011

Southdale Towers
524 W 53RD ST 46013

Tower Apts
1109 JACKSON ST 46016

Vickers
1808 E 8TH ST 46012

BUILDINGS

Anderson Bank Building
931 MERIDIAN ST 46016

Citizens Plaza
800 MAIN ST 46016

First Savings Tower
33 W 10TH ST 46016

Union Building
1106 MERIDIAN ST 46016

Warner Press Admin
1200 E 5TH ST 46012

GOVERNMENT

Anderson City Building
120 E 8TH ST 46016

Courthouse
16 E 9TH ST 46016

ARLINGTON

APARTMENTS

Ambassador Apt
2511 E 2ND ST 47401

Ardmore Apt
100 E MILLER DR 47401

B & W Apt
208 E 2ND ST 47401

Bart Villa
2301-307 E 2ND ST 47401

Beau Trace Apt
415-425 S GRANT ST 47401

Bellevue Apt
400 E 2ND ST 47401

Burnham Apt
808 E HUNTER AVE 47401

College Mall Apt
2611-639 E 2ND ST 47401

Colstone Square
421 E 3RD ST 47401

Diplomat Apt
2521 E 2ND ST 47401

Heritage Apt
1600 E HILLSIDE DR 47401

Hunter #1 Apt
801 E HUNTER AVE 47401

Hunter #2 Apt
809 E HUNTER AVE 47401

Jackson Creek Apt
720 S College Mall Rd 47401

Knightridge Apt
612 S KNIGHTRIDGE RD   47401

Landmark Apt
507 S FESS AVE 47401

Landmark Apt
508 S FESS AVE 47401

Maple Grove Apt
408 S DUNN ST 47401

Maple Leaf Apt
407 S GRANT ST 47401

Margrave Apt
736 E 3RD ST 47401

Mays Apt
405 S WALNUT ST 47401

Plantation Apt
421-41 S DUNN ST 47401

Plantation Apt
413-27 S HENDERSON ST 47401

Poolside Apt
430 S DUNN ST 47401

Southern Valley Apt
411 E SOUTHERN DR 47401

University Square
316-20 E UNIVERSITY ST 47401

Willow Manor Apt
3910 S Walnut Street Pike   47401

Woodcrest Apt
2602-610 E 2ND ST 47401

BUILDINGS

Professional Building
400 E 3RD ST 47401

Wilson Building
809 S HENDERSON ST ... 47401

BAER FIELD

BUILDINGS

Baer Field Terminal
3801 W FERGUSON RD .. 46809

BLOOMINGTON

APARTMENTS

Allentown Village Apt
601 W ALLEN ST 47403

Arcadia Heights
915-1015 N ROGERS ST . 47404

Aspen Chalet
422 E 11TH ST 47408

Cambridge Square Apt
301-305 N Pete Ellis Dr 47408

Canadian Apt
327-329 W 1ST ST 47403

Chateau Van Buren Apt
2911 S Leonard Springs Rd 47403

Chateau Van Buren Apt
3203 S MARKET PL 47403

Chateau Van Buren Apt
3214-227 S MARKET PL .. 47403

Chateau Van Buren Apt
3911-21 W Maybury Mall .. 47403

Colonial Crest
703 W GOURLEY PIKE 47404

Colonial East
3405 E LONGVIEW AVE ... 47408

Colonial Hill
301 E 20TH ST 47408

Continental Terrace
3315 E LONGVIEW AVE ... 47408

Country Club Apt
1004 COUNTRY CLUB DR 47403

Country View Apt
2500 S ROCKPORT RD ... 47403

Dunn Hill
405 E 17TH ST 47408

Eastwood Apt
305 E 17TH ST 47408

Empire Apt
225 E 20TH ST 47408

Fairview Apt
714 S FAIRVIEW ST 47403

Fountain Park
3209 E 10TH ST 47408

Full-o-pep Apt
222 W 2ND ST 47403

Full-o-pep Apt
422 S COLLEGE AVE 47403

Garden Terrace
205 E 17TH ST 47408

Gibson Apt
2938 N SMITH PIKE 47404

Green Tree Apt
727-29 W DIXIE ST 47403

Hall Apt
828 W DIXIE ST 47403

Hazel Bud Apt
409 E 10TH ST 47408

Hilltop Apt
1201 W ALLEN ST 47403

Holiday Apt
205 E 20TH ST 47408

Jackson Heights Apt
503-73 W GRANITE DR ... 47404

Jackson Heights Apt
505-65 W LAVA WAY 47404

Jackson Heights Apt
601-45 N MARBLE LN 47404

Jackson Heights Apt
603-11 W SLATE DR 47404

Jackson Heights Apt
501-41 TERRY LN 47404

Jamestown Village
3015 E LONGVIEW AVE ... 47408

Kingston Manor
3200 E LONGVIEW AVE ... 47408

Lexington House
411-13 E 8TH ST 47408

Libey Apt
321 W HILLSIDE DR 47403

Lincoln Apt
510 N LINCOLN ST 47408

Lincoln Manor
1015 N LINCOLN ST 47408

Maplecrest Apt
720 W DODDS ST 47403

Meadow Park Apt
800 N SMITH RD 47408

Meadowood Apt
2455 TAMARACK TRL 47408

Meadows Apt
432 S COLLEGE AVE 47403

Northcrest Apt
1440 N WOODBURN AVE 47404

Northview Apt
1212 N GRANT ST 47408

Nutt Apt
0 NUTT APTS 47406

Park Dorel
2602-620 EASTGATE LN . 47408

Park Sq & Gifford Apt
4540 W GIFFORD RD 47403

Pigskin #1
421 E 19TH ST 47408

Pigskin #2
420 E 19TH ST 47408

Pigskin #3
412 E 19TH ST 47408

Pigskin #4
408 E 17TH ST 47408

Pine Terrace
1211 W 2ND ST 47403

Plantation Apt
417 N GRANT ST 47408

Plantation North
303-15 E 8TH ST 47408

Ridgeline Apt
2775 N SMITH PIKE 47404

Shannon Isles Apt
530 N LINCOLN ST 47408

Springmill Apt
238 N SMITH RD 47408

Stadium View #2
310-30 E 20TH ST 47408

Stadium View #3
319 E 20TH ST 47408

Stadium View Apt
416 E 17TH ST 47408

Stadium View Apt #4
416 E 17TH ST 47408

Sunbelt Apt
516-20 N GRANT ST 47408

Sunflower Apt
1306-08 N MAPLE ST 47404

Terra Trace
321 E 14TH ST 47408

Terra Trace
426 E 15TH ST 47408

Trafalgar Square
405 E Cottage Grove Ave 47408

University East Apts
1603 E 3RD ST 47406

University West Apts
1415 E 3RD ST 47406

Virgo Apt
504-23 N LINCOLN ST 47408

Washington Terrace Apt
316 N WASHINGTON ST . 47408

BUILDINGS

Bloomington Med Art Ctr
822 W 1ST ST 47403

Graham Plaza
205 N COLLEGE AVE 47404

Medical Arts Building
619 W 1ST ST 47403

Monroe Co Courthouse
100 W KIRKWOOD AVE ... 47404

The Justice Building
301 N COLLEGE AVE 47404

CANNELTON

APARTMENTS

Golden Years Apt
125 S 4TH ST 47520

CARMEL

BUILDINGS

Fidelity Plaza
11590 N MERIDIAN ST 46032

Meridian Mark
11611 N MERIDIAN ST 46032

Meridian Technical Center
111 Congressional Blvd 46032

Pennmark Plaza
11595 N MERIDIAN ST 46032

Pennwood Office Park
11495 N Pennsylvania St .. 46032

CONCORD

APARTMENTS

Elkhart Greens Apt
123 W HIVELY AVE 46517

Farmington Hills Apt
1000 MISHAWAKA 46517

BUILDINGS

Concord Mall
3701 S MAIN ST 46517

Pierre Moran Mall
154 W HIVELY AVE 46517

DIPLOMAT

BUILDINGS

Southtown Mall
7800 S ANTHONY BLVD .. 46816

ELKHART

APARTMENTS

20 East Apt
2125 TOLEDO RD 46516

Claridge House Apt
250 E BRISTOL ST 46514

Greenleaf Apt
1077 GREENLEAF BLVD . 46514

Greenleaf Manor Apt
2100 E BRISTOL ST 46514

Le Chateau Apt
1501 LOCUST ST 46514

Middlebury Village Apt
740 PRAIRIE ST 46516

Riverside Terrace Apt
181 N ELKHART AVE 46516

Rosedale Apt
501 W INDIANA AVE 46516

Village Sq Apts
2301 W LEXINGTON AVE 46514

Waterfall Apt
303 WATERFALL DR 46516

BUILDINGS

Communicana Building
421 S 2ND ST 46516

Executive 500 Building
500 N NAPPANEE ST 46514

Indiana Building
405 S 2ND ST 46516

Midwest Commerce Bank Bld
121 W FRANKLIN ST 46516

GOVERNMENT

County Courts Building
315 S 2ND ST 46516

Municipal Building
229 S 2ND ST 46516

FORT WAYNE

BUILDINGS

Central Building
203 W WAYNE ST 46802

Commerce Building
127 W BERRY ST 46802

Foellinger Building
227 E Washington Blvd 46802

Fort Wayne National Bank Building
110 W BERRY ST 46802

Glenbrook Mall
4201 COLDWATER RD 46805

Lincoln Bank Tower
116 E BERRY ST 46802

Metro Building
202 W BERRY ST 46802

Strauss Building
809 S CALHOUN ST 46802

GOVERNMENT

Allen County Court House
715 S CALHOUN ST 46802

City-county Building
1 E MAIN ST 46802

Federal Building
1300 S HARRISON ST 46802

GREENWOOD

APARTMENTS

Greenwood Village Arms
295 VILLAGE LN 46143

Greenwood Village Manor
271 VILLAGE LN 46143

Greenwood Village Tower
278 VILLAGE LN 46143

Mission Hills
1084 SIERRA MADRE DR 46143

BUILDINGS

Corporate Square
1000 N MADISON AVE 46142

Executive Park Building
710 Executive Park Dr 46143

Greenwood Nat'l Bank Building
300 S MADISON AVE 46142

Greenwood Park Mall
1251 US HIGHWAY 31 N . 46142

Greenwood Prof Park
622 N MADISON AVE 46142

Polk Place
435 E MAIN ST 46143

Thomas Building
520 N MADISON AVE 46142

Valle Vista Indus Park
500 POLK AVE 46143

Vantage Centre
720 Executive Park Dr 46143

GOVERNMENT

Greenwood City Building
2 N MADISON AVE 46142

HARRISON

BUILDINGS

Foulkes Square
401 OHIO ST 47807

Merchants Bank Building
701 WABASH AVE 47807

Star Building
601 OHIO ST 47807

Sycamore Building
19 S 6TH ST 47807

Tribune Building
721 WABASH AVE 47807

Wabash Park Plaza
1509 WABASH AVE 47807

INDIANAPOLIS

BUILDINGS

American United Life Building
1 AMERICAN SQ 46282

Capitol Center
251 N ILLINOIS ST 46204

Century Building
36 S PENNSYLVANIA ST . 46204

Chamber Of Commerce Building
320 N MERIDIAN ST 46204

Conrail Building
31 E GEORGIA ST 46204

Consolidated Building
115 N PENNSYLVANIA ST 46204

Electric Building
25 MONUMENT CIR 46204

English Foundation Building
615 N ALABAMA ST 46204

First Indiana Building
11 N PENNSYLVANIA ST . 46204

Guaranty Building
20 N MERIDIAN ST 46204

Harrison Building
143 W MARKET ST 46204

Illinois Building
17 W MARKET ST 46204

Ind Farm Bureau
130 E WASHINGTON ST .. 46204

Ind Farm Bureau Building
120 E MARKET ST 46204

Indiana National Bk Tower
1 INDIANA SQ 46204

Indiana State Teachers
150 W MARKET ST 46204

Inland Building
156 E MARKET ST 46204

Investors Trust
107 N PENNSYLVANIA ST 46204

Jefferson National Building
1 VIRGINIA AVE 46204

King Cole Building
7 N MERIDIAN ST 46204

Landmark Building
1099 N MERIDIAN ST 46204

Majestic Building
47 S PENNSYLVANIA ST . 46204

Market Sq Center
151 N DELAWARE ST 46204

Merchant Bank Building
11 S MERIDIAN ST 46204

Merchants Plaza
101 W WASHINGTON ST . 46204

Ober Building
38 N PENNSYLVANIA ST . 46204

Peoples Bank Building
136 E MARKET ST 46204

Test Building
54 MONUMENT CIR 46204

Two Market Sq Center
251 E OHIO ST 46204

Union Federal Building
45 N PENNSYLVANIA ST . 46204

GOVERNMENT

City County Building
200 E WASHINGTON ST .. 46204

Federal Building
575 N PENNSYLVANIA ST 46204

Federal Building/courthouse
46 E OHIO ST 46204

Indiana Government Center S
402 W WASHINGTON ST . 46204

Indiana State Capitol
200 W WASHINGTON ST . 46204

State Office Building
100 N SENATE AVE 46204

KOKOMO

GOVERNMENT

City Building
100 S UNION ST 46901

Howard County Building
120 E MULBERRY ST 46901

Howard County Court House
104 N BUCKEYE ST 46901

LAFAYETTE

BUILDINGS

Bank One
201 MAIN ST 47901

Lafayette Life
300 MAIN ST 47901

GOVERNMENT

Halleck Fed Building
232 N 4TH ST 47901

MARION

GOVERNMENT

Courthouse
101 E 4TH ST 46952

Grant County Off Building
401 S ADAMS ST 46953

Municipal Building
301 S BRANSON ST 46952

MISHAWAKA

APARTMENTS

100 Ctr Hi Rise Apt
100 N CENTER ST 46544

500 Hi Rise
500 LINCOLN WAY E 46544

Parkview Apt
529-620 E 12TH ST 46544

Tanglewood Trace
530 TANGLEWOOD LN 46545

BUILDINGS

Medical Arts Building
303 S MAIN ST 46544

University Center
6502 GRAPE RD 46545

University Park Mall
6501 GRAPE RD 46545

GOVERNMENT

Municipal Building
219 LINCOLN WAY W 46544

MUNCIE

GOVERNMENT

City Hall
300 N HIGH ST 47305

Delaware Cty Courthouse
100 W MAIN ST 47305

Justice Center
100 W WASHINGTON ST . 47305

ROSELAND

APARTMENTS

Campus View Apt
54585 IRISH WAY 46637

SOUTH BEND

APARTMENTS

Greensprings Manor Apt
1112 S 20TH ST 46615

Karl King Apt
515 E MONROE ST 46601

St Joe Towers
316 S SAINT JOSEPH ST 46601

St Pauls Retire Comm
3602 S IRONWOOD DR ... 46614

Topsfield Apt
2500 TOPSFIELD RD 46614

Western Manor
628 W WESTERN AVE 46601

BUILDINGS

Commerce Building
103 W WAYNE ST 46601

First Bank Building
205 W JEFFERSON BLVD 46601

First Source Building
100 N MICHIGAN ST 46601

Gateway Center
425 N MICHIGAN ST 46601

Hazlitt/lasalle W Building
120 W LA SALLE AVE 46601

Jefferson Centre
105 E JEFFERSON BLVD 46601

Jms Building
108 N MAIN ST 46601

Lafayette Building
115 S LAFAYETTE BLVD .. 46601

Marycrest Building
2015 W WESTERN AVE ... 46629

Medical Arts Building
919 E JEFFERSON BLVD 46617

Medical Office Building
2505 E Jefferson Blvd 46615

Medical Pavilion
720 CEDAR ST 46617

Medical Pavilion #2
707 CEDAR ST 46617

Memorial Medical Plaza
707 N MICHIGAN ST 46601

Memorial Professional Bld
513 N MICHIGAN ST 46601

Norwest Bank Building
112 W JEFFERSON BLVD 46601

One Michiana Sq
100 E WAYNE ST 46601

Society Bank Building
202 S MICHIGAN ST 46601

Trigon Building
224 W Jefferson Blvd 46601

Valley American Bank Building
211 W WASHINGTON ST . 46601

Van Mele Building
1030 E Jefferson Blvd 46617

Whitcomb Keller Building
340 COLUMBIA ST 46601

GOVERNMENT

County-city Building
227 W JEFFERSON BLVD 46601

Court House
101 S MAIN ST 46601

Federal Building
204 S MAIN ST 46601

TERRE HAUTE

APARTMENTS

Garfield Gardens
1200 MAPLE AVE 47804

Garfield Towers
2200 N 12TH 1/2 ST 47804

Garfield Towers
2200 GARFIELD AVE 47804

Latta Apt
10199 E US HIGHWAY 40 47803

WOODBRIDGE

APARTMENTS

Park Doral
2602-2620 EASTGATE 47408

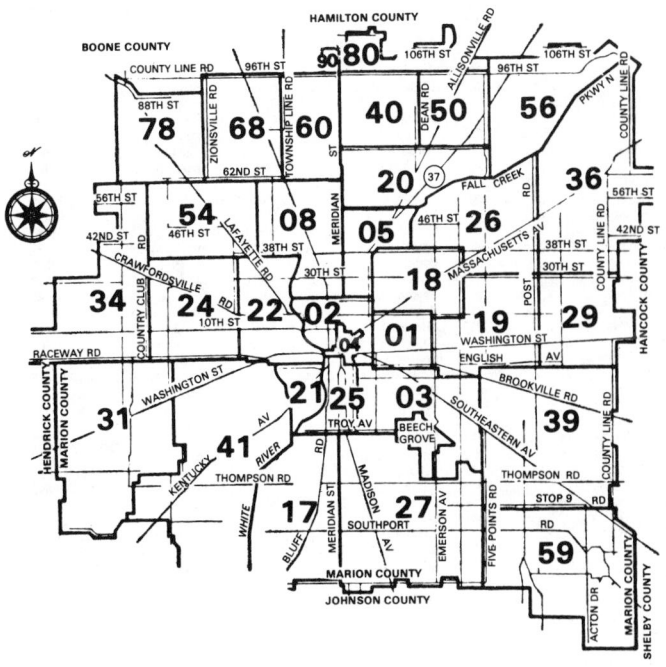

ZIP CODES
INDIANAPOLIS, IN
462 + TWO DIGITS SHOWN = ZIP CODE

IOWA
Abbreviation IA

Abingdon (Batavia) 52533
Ackley 50601
Ackworth 50001
Adair 50002
Adaville (Westfield) 51062
Adaza (Churdan) 50050
Adel 50003
Adelphi (Runnells) 50237
Afton 50830
Agency 52530
Ainsworth 52201
Akron 51001
Albany (Fayette) 52142
Albert City 50510
Albia 52531
Albion 50005
Alburnett 52202
Alden 50006, 50043
   Burdette 50006
Alexander 50420
Algona 50511
Alleman 50007
Allendorf 51330
Allerton 50008
Allison 50602
Alpha 52130, 52177
   Waucoma 52130
Alta 51002
Alta Vista 50603
Alton 51003
Altoona 50009
Alvord 51230
Amana 52203-204
Amber (Anamosa) 52205
Amboy (Newton) 50208
Ames 50010, 50011-014
   Napier 50010
   North Grand 50010
   Ontario 50010
   Welch Avenue 50010
Anamosa 52205
Andover 52701
Andrew 52030
Anita 50020
Ankeny 50021
Anthon 51004
Aplington 50604
Arbor Hill (Stuart) 50250
Arcadia 51430
Archer 51231
Aredale 50605
Argo (Le Claire) 52753
Argyle 52619
Arion 51520
Arispe 50831
Arlington 50606
Armstrong 50514
Arnolds Park 51331
Artesian (Waverly) 50677
Arthur 51431
Asbury (Dubuque) ... 52001-002
Ashton 51232
Aspinwall 51432
Atalissa 52720
Athelstan (Blockton) 50836
Atkins 52206
Atlantic 50022
Auburn 51433, 52175

Grant City 51433
   Yetter 51433
Audubon 50025
Augusta (Wever) 52658
Aurelia 51005
Aureola (Marble Rock) 50653
Aurora 50607
Austinville 50608
Avery (Albia) 52531
Avoca 51521
Avon (Carlisle) 50047
Ayrshire 50515
Badger 50516
Bagley 50026
Baldwin 52207
Balltown (Sherrill) 52073
Bancroft 50517
Bangor (Union) 50258
Bankston (Epworth) 52045
Barnes City 50027
Barney (Lorimor) 50149
Barnum 50518
Bartlett 51655
Bassett (Ionia) 50645
Batavia 52533
Battle Creek 51006
Baxter 50028
Bayard 50029
Beacon 52534
Beaconsfield 50030
Beaman 50609
Beaver 50031
Beaverdale (Des Moines) . 50310
Beaverdale Heights 52655
   (West Burlington)
Beckwith (Fairfield) 52556
Bedford 50833
Beech (Pleasantville) 50225
Belknap (Bloomfield) 52537
Bellevue 52031
Belmond 50421
Bennett 52721
Benton 50835
Bentonsport (Keosauqua) . 52565
Berea (Anita) 50020
Berkley (Perry) 50220
Bernard 52032
Berne (Ute) 51060
Bertram (Cedar Rapids) ... 52401
Berwick 50032
Bethlehem (Russell) 52538
Bettendorf 52722
Bevington 50033
Big Rock 52725, 52745
   Dixon 52725
Birmingham 52535
Bladensburg (Ottumwa) ... 52501
Blairsburg 50034
Blairstown 52209
Blakesburg 52536
Blanchard 51630
Blencoe 51523
Blockton 50836
Bloomfield 52537-538
   Belknap 52537
   Mark 52537
   Monterey 52537
   Savannah 52537
   Stiles 52537
   Troy 52537
   West Grove 52537

Blue Grass 52726
Bluff Park (Montrose) 52639
Bluffton (Decorah) 52101
Bode 50519
Bolan (Kensett) 50448
Bonair (Lime Springs) 52155
Bonaparte 52620
Bondurant 50035
Boone 50036
Booneville 50038
Botna (Manilla) 51454
Bouton 50039
Boxholm 50040
Boyd (New Hampton) 50659
Boyden 51234
Boyer (Kiron) 51448
Braddyville 51631
Bradford 50041
Bradgate 50520
Brainard (Elgin) 52141
Brandon 52210
Brayton 50042
Brazil (Mystic) 52574
Breda 51436
Bremer (Waverly) 50677
Bridge Port (Eddyville) 52553
Bridgewater 50837
Brighton 52540
Bristow 50611
Britt 50423
Bronson 51007
Brooklyn 52211
Brooks (Corning) 50841
Brookside (Cedar Falls) 50613
Brunsville 51008
Brushy (Duncombe) 50532
Bryant 52727
Buchanan (Tipton) 52772
Buckcreek (Sumner) 50674
Buckeye 50043
Buckingham 50612
Buffalo 52728
Burchinal (Rockwell) 50469
Burdette (Alden) 50006
Burlington 52601
Burnside 50521
Burr Oak 52101, 52131
   (Decorah)
   Decorah 52131
Burt 50522
Bussey 50044
Cairo (Columbus Junction) . 52738
Calamus 52729
Callender 50523
Calmar 52132
Calumet 51009
Camanche 52730
Cambria (Corydon) 50060
Cambridge 50046
Camp Dodge (Johnston) ... 50131
Canby (Casey) 50048
Canton (Monmouth) 52309
Cantril 52542, 52575
   Mount Sterling 52542
Capitol Heights 50317
   (Des Moines)
Capitol Square 50393
   (Des Moines)
Carbon 50839
Carbondale (Des Moines) . 50317
Carl (Corning) 50841

Carlisle	50047
Carmel (Rock Valley)	51247
Carnarvon	51437
Carnes (Alton)	51003
Carney (Ankeny)	50021
Carnforth (Victor)	52347
Carpenter	50426
Carroll	51401
Carson	51525
Carter Lake	51510
Cartersville (Rockwell)	50469
Cascade	52033
Casey	50048
Casino Beach	50588
(Storm Lake)	
Castalia	52133
Castana	51010
Cedar	52543
Cedar Bluff (Tipton)	52772
Cedar City (Cedar Falls)	50613
Cedar Falls	50613-614
Cedar Rapids	52400-411
52498-499	
Bertram	52401
Konigsmark	52401
Linn Junction	52401
Rockwell Collins	52498
Western	52401
Cedar Valley	52358
(West Branch)	
Center Grove (Dubuque)	52001
Center Junction	52212
Center Point	52213
Centerdale (West Liberty)	52776
Centerville	50036, 52544
(Boone)	
Clarkdale	52544
Darbyville	52544
Forbush	52544
Jerome	52544
Rathbun	52544
Sedan	52544
Sunshine	52544
Thirty	52544
Central (Davenport)	52801
Central City	52214
Central Heights	50401
(Mason City)	
Centralia (Peosta)	52068
Chapin	50427
Chariton	50049
Charles City	50616, 50620
Maple Heights	50616
Charleston (Argyle)	52619
Charlotte	52731
Charter Oak	51439
Chatsworth	51011
Chelsea	52215
Cherokee	51012
Chester	52134
Chickasaw (Ionia)	50645
Chillicothe	52548
Church (Lansing)	52151
Churchville (Norwalk)	50211
Churdan	50050
Adaza	50050
Cincinnati	52549
Clare	50524
Clarence	52216
Clarinda	51632
Clarion	50525-526

Clarkdale (Centerville)	52544
Clarksville	50619
Clayton (Garnavillo)	52049
Clayton Center (Elkader)	52043
Clayworks (Fort Dodge)	50501
Clear Creek (Keota)	52248
Clear Lake	50428
Clearfield	50840
Cleghorn	51014
Clemons	50051
Clermont	52135
Cleves (Ackley)	50601
Cliffland (Ottumwa)	52501
Climbing Hill	51015
Clinton	52732-733, 52336,52771
Elvira	52732
Hauntown	52732
Lyons	52732
Six Mile	52732
Teeds Grove	52732
Clio	50052
Clive (Des Moines)	50325
Clover Hills	50265
(West Des Moines)	
Cloverdale (Sibley)	51249
Clutier	52217
Clyde (Collins)	50055
Coal Creek (What Cheer)	50268
Coalville (Fort Dodge)	50501
Coggon	52218
Coin	51636
Colesburg	52035
Colfax	50054
College Springs	51637
College Square	50613
(Cedar Falls)	
Collins	50055
Colo	50056
Columbia	50057
Columbus City	52737
Columbus Junction	52738
Colwell	50620
Commerce	50265
(West Des Moines)	
Communia (Elkader)	52043
Conesville	52739
Confidence	50238, 52569
(Russell)	
Conger (Saint Charles)	50240
Conover (Calmar)	52132
Conrad	50621
Conroy	52220
Conway (Bedford)	50833
Cool (Indianola)	50125
Coon Rapids	50058
Cooper	50059
Coppock (Wayland)	52654
Coralville	52241
Cornelia (Clarion)	50525
Cornell (Sioux Rapids)	50585
Corning	50841
Correctionville	51016
Corwith	50430
Corydon	50060
Cosgrove (Oxford)	52322
Cotter	52738
(Columbus Junction)	
Cou Falls (Swisher)	52338
Coulter	50431
Council Bluffs	51501-503
Manawa	51501

Covington (Palo)	52324
Craig	51017
Cranston (Letts)	52754
Crawfordsville	52621
Crescent	51526
Cresco	52136
Creston	50801
Crocker (Polk City)	50226
Cromwell	50842
Croton (Farmington)	52626
Crystal Lake	50432
Culver (Muscatine)	52761
Cumberland	50843
Cumming	50061
Curlew	50527
Cushing	51018
Cylinder	50528
Dahlonega (Ottumwa)	52501
Dakota City	50529
Dalby (Waterville)	52170
Dale (Stuart)	50250
Dallas	50062, 50163
Melcher	50062
Dana	50064
Danbury	51019
Danville	52623
Darbyville (Centerville)	52544
Davenport	52800-809
Central	52801
Davis City	50065
Dawson	50066
Dayton	50530
Daytonville (Wellman)	52356
De Soto	50069
De Witt	52742
Dean (Moulton)	52572
Decatur	50067
Decorah	52101, 52131
Bluffton	52101
Burr Oak	52101
Freeport	52101
Hesper	52101
Locust	52101
Nordness	52101
Quandahl	52101
Sattre	52101
Dedham	51440
Deep River	52222
Defiance	51527, 51530
Earling	51527
Delaware	52036
Delhi	52223
Delmar	52037
Deloit	51441
Delphos	50844
Delta	52550
Denhart (Kanawha)	50447
Denison	51442
Denmark	52624
Denver	50622
Depew (Cylinder)	50528
Derby	50068
Des Moines	50300-323, 50325
	50328-336, 50338-340
	50347, 50350, 50359-364
	50367-369, 50380-381
	50391-398, 50936, 50940
	50947, 50950, 50980-981
Amoco Oil	50367-50369
Capitol Heights	50317
Carbondale	50317

Kossuth (Mediapolis) 52637	Linden 50146
Koszta (Belle Plaine) 52208	Lineville 50147
La Moille (Marshalltown) ... 50158	Linn Grove 51033
La Motte 52054	Linn Junction 52401
La Porte City 50651	(Cedar Rapids)
Lacelle (Osceola) 50213	Lisbon 52253
Lacey (New Sharon) 50207	Liscomb 50148
Lacona 50139	Little Cedar 50454
Ladora 52251	Little Rock 51243
Lake City 51449	Little Sioux 51545
Lake Mills 50450	Little Turkey (Lawler) 52154
Lake Panorama (Panora) .. 50216	Littleport 52055
Lake Park 51347	Littleton (Jesup) 50648
Lake View 51450	Livermore 50558
Lakeside (Storm Lake) 50588	Livingston (Cincinnati) 52549
Lakewood (Norwalk) 50211	Lockridge 52635
Lakota 50451	Locust (Decorah) 52101
Lambs Grove (Newton) 50208	Logan 51546, 51550
Lamoni 50140	Logansport (Boone) 50036
Lamont 50650	Lohrville 51453
Lancaster (Sigourney) 52591	Lone Rock 50559
Lanedale (Rockwell City) .. 50579	Lone Tree 52755
Lanesboro 51451	Long Grove 52756
Langdon (Spencer) 51301	Lorah (Atlantic) 50022
Langworthy 52252, 52310	Lorimor 50149
Monticello 52252	Lost Island Lake 51358
Lansing 52151	(Ruthven)
Lanyon (Harcourt) 50544	Lost Nation 52254
Larchwood 51241	Lotts Creek (Lone Rock) ... 50559
Larrabee 51029	Lourdes (Elma) 50628
Last Chance (Derby) 50068	Lovilia 50150
Latimer 50452	Lovington (Des Moines) 50322
Latty (Burlington) 52601	Low Moor 52757
Laurel 50141	Lowden 52255
Laurens 50554	Lowell (New London) 52645
Lavinia (Rockwell City) 50579	Lu Verne 50560
Lawler 52154	Luana 52156
Lawn Hill 50206	Lucas 50151
(New Providence)	Ludlow (Waukon) 52172
Lawton 51030	Lundstrom Heights 50021
Le Claire 52753	(Ankeny)
Le Grand 50142	Luther 50152
Le Mars (Craig) 51017	Luton (Salix) 51052
.... 51031, 51057	Luxemburg 52056
Seney 51031	Luzerne 52257
Union Center 51031	Lynnville 50153
West Le Mars 51031	Lyons (Marion) 52302, 52732
Le Roy (Humeston) 50123	Lytton 50561
Leando (Douds) 52551	Macedonia 51549
Lebanon 51250, 52565	Mackey (Boone) 50036
(Sioux Center)	Macksburg 50155
Ledyard 50556	Macy (Ackley) 50601
Leeds (Sioux City) 51108	Madrid 50156
Lehigh 50557	Magnolia 51550
Leighton 50143	Malcom 50157
Leland 50453	Mallard 50562
Lemars (Craig) 51017	Malone (De Witt) 52742
Lenox 50851	Maloy 50852
Leon 50144	Malvern 51551
Lester 51242	Manawa (Council Bluffs) ... 51501
Letts 52754	Manchester 52057
Lewis 51544	Manilla 51454
Liberty (New Virginia) 50210	Manly 50456
Liberty Center 50145	Manning 51432, 51455
Libertyville 52567	(Aspinwall)
Lidderdale 51452	Manson 50563
Lima (Fayette) 52142	Maple Heights 50616
Limby (Packwood) 52580	(Charles City)
Lime City (Wilton) 52778	Maple Hill (Armstrong) 50514
Lime Springs 52155	Maple River (Carroll) 51401
Lincoln 50652	Mapleton 51034

Maquoketa 52060
Marathon 50565
Marble Rock 50653
Marcus 51035
Marengo 52301
Marietta (Marshalltown) 50158
Marion 52302, 52328
Indian Creek 52302
Lyons 52302
Midway 52302
Robins 52302
Mark (Bloomfield) 52537
Marne 51552
Marquette 52158
Marquisville (Des Moines) . 50313
Marshalltown 50158
Martelle 52305
Martensdale 50160
Martinsburg 52568
Martinstown (Numa) 52575
Marysville (Hamilton) 50116
Maryville (Arlington) 50606
Mason City 50401-402, 50467
Central Heights 50401
Emery 50401
Freeman 50401
Hanford 50401
Portland 50401
Rock Falls 50467
Winnebago Heights 50401
Masonville 50654
Massena 50853
Massey (Dubuque) 52001
Massillon (Lowden) 52255
Matlock 51244
Maurice 51036
Maxwell 50161
May City 51349
Maynard 50655
Maysville (Walcott) 52773
Mc Callsburg 50154
Mc Causland 52758
Mc Clelland 51548
Mc Gregor 52157
Mc Intire 50455
Mcnally (Ireton) 51027
Mechanicsville 52306
Mederville (Elkader) 52043
Mediapolis 52637
Medora (Indianola) 50125
Melbourne 50162
Melcher (Dallas) 50062, 50163
Dallas 50163
Melrose 52569
Meltonville 50472
(Saint Ansgar)
Melvin 51350
Menlo 50164
Meriden 51037
Meroa (Osage) 50461
Merrill 51038
Meservey 50457
Meyer (Mc Intire) 50455
Middle (Middle Amana) 52307
Middle Amana 52307
Middleburg (Orange City) .. 51041
Middletown 52638
Midvale (Huxley) 50124
Midway (Marion) 52302
Midway Beach (Muscatine) 52761
Miles 52064

Persia 51563	Redding 50860	Meltonville 50472
Peru 50222	Redfield 50233	Otranto 50472
Petersburg (Dyersville) 52040	Reinbeck 50669	Saint Anthony 50239
Peterson 51047	Rembrandt 50576	Saint Benedict (Algona) 50511
Petersville (Charlotte) 52731	Remsen 51050	Saint Charles 50240
Pierson 51048	Renwick 50577	Saint Donatus 52071
Pilot Grove 52648	Rhodes 50234	Saint Joseph (Bode) 50519
Pilot Mound 50223	Riceville 50466	Saint Lucas 52166
Pioneer (Gilmore City) 50541	Richards (Rockwell City) ... 50579	Saint Marys 50241
Piper (Rockwell City) 50579	Richland 52585	Saint Olaf 52072
Pisgah 51564	Richmond (Kalona) 52247	Saint Paul 52657, 52756
Pittsburg (Keosauqua) 52565	Rickardsville (Durango) 52039	West Point 52657
Pitzer (Earlham) 50072	Ricketts 51460	Salem 52649
Plain View (Walcott) 52773	Ridgeport (Boone) 50036	Salina (Fairfield) 52556
Plainfield 50666	Ridgeway 52165	Salix 51052
Plano 52581	Rinard 50587	Sanborn 51248
Platteville (Blockton) 50836	Ringsted 50578	Sand Prairie (Argyle) 52619
Pleasant Hill 50317	Rippey 50235	Sand Spring (Hopkinton) ... 52237
(Des Moines)	Risingsun (Des Moines) 50317	Sandusky (Keokuk) 52632
Pleasant Plain (Brighton) .. 52540	Ritter (Sheldon) 51201	Sandyville (Ackworth) 50001
Pleasant Prairie 52761	River Junction 52755	Santiago (Mitchellville) 50169
(Muscatine)	(Lone Tree)	Saratoga (Lime Springs) ... 52155
Pleasant Valley 52767	Riverdale (Bettendorf) 52722	Sattre (Decorah) 52101
Pleasantgrove 52645	Riverside 52327	Saude (Lawler) 52154
(New London)	Riverton 51650	Savannah (Bloomfield) 52537
Pleasanton (Davis City) 50065	Roberts (Otho) 50569	Sawyer (Fort Madison) 52627
Pleasantville 50225	Robertson (Ackley) 50601	Saydel (Des Moines) 50313
Plover 50573	Robins (Marion) 52302, 52328	Saylorville (Des Moines) 50313
Plymouth 50464	Marion 52328	Scarville 50473
Pocahontas 50574	Robinson (Ryan) 52330	Schaller 51053
Polk City 50226	Rochester (Tipton) 52772	Schleswig 51461
Pomeroy 50575	Rock Creek (Osage) 50461	Schley (Cresco) 52136
Popejoy 50227	Rock Falls (Mason City) 50467	Scotch Grove 52331
Portland (Mason City) 50401	Rock Rapids 51246	Scotch Ridge (Carlisle) 50047
Portsmouth 51565	Rock Valley 51247	Scranton 51462
Postville 52162	Rockdale (Dubuque) 52001	Searsboro 50242
Powersville (Greene) 50636	Rockford 50468	Sedan (Centerville) 52544
Prairie City 50228	Rockwell 50469	Selma 52588
Prairie Grove 52655	Rockwell City 50579	Seneca (Fenton) 50539
(West Burlington)	Rockwell Collins 52498	Seney (Le Mars) 51031
Prairieburg 52219, 52310	(Cedar Rapids)	Sergeant Bluff 51054
Monticello 52219	Rodman 50580	Sewal (Corydon) 50060
Prescott 50859	Rodney 51051	Sexton (Wesley) 50483
Preston 52069	Roelyn (Moorland) 50566	Seymour 52590
Primghar 51245	Roland 50236	Shady Grove (Jesup) 50648
Primrose (Donnellson) 52625	Rolfe 50581	Shaffton (Camanche) 52730
Princeton 52768	Rome 52641-642	Shambaugh 51651
Prole 50229	(Mount Pleasant)	Shannon City 50861
Promise City 52583	Mount Pleasant 52642	Sharon (Audubon) 50025
Prospect Hill 52601	Rose Hill 52586	Sharpsburg 50862
(Burlington)	Roselle (Carroll) 51401	Shawondasse (Dubuque) . 52001
Protivin 52163	Ross (Audubon) 50025	Sheffield 50475
Pulaski 52584	Rossie (Royal) 51357	Shelby 51570
Quandahl (Decorah) 52162	Rossville 52159, 52172	Sheldahl 50243
Quarry (Marshalltown) 50158	(Monona)	Sheldon 51201, 51244
Quasqueton 52326	Rowan 50470	Ritter 51201
Quimby 51049	Rowley 52329	Shell Rock 50670
Radcliffe 50230	Royal 51357	Shellsburg 52332
Rake 50465	Rubio (Richland) 52585	Shenandoah .. 51601-603, 51693
Ralston 51459	Ruble (Akron) 51001	Sheridan (Malcom) 50157
Randalia 52164	Rudd 50471	Sherrill 52073
Randall 50231	Runnells 50237	Sherwood (Rockwell City) .. 50579
Randolph 51649	Russell 50238	Shipley (Nevada) 50201
Rands (Rockwell City) 50579	Ruthven 51358	Siam (Bedford) 50833
Rathbun (Centerville) 52544	Rutland 50582	Sibley 51249
Raymar (Waterloo) 50707	Rutledge (Ottumwa) 52501	Sidney 51652
Raymond 50667	Ryan 52330	Sigourney 52591
Readlyn 50668	Sabula 52070	Silver City 51571
Reasnor 50232	Sac City 50583	Silver Lake (Northwood) 50459
Red Line (Kirkman) 51447	Sageville (Dubuque) 52001	Sinclair (Parkersburg) 50665
Red Oak 51566, 51591	Saint Ansgar 50472, 50481	Sioux Center 51250

Sioux City	51100-111	
James	51108	
Leeds	51108	
Morningside	51106	
North Side	51104	
Wickham Spur	51101	
Sioux Rapids	50585	
Six Mile (Clinton)	52732	
Slater	50244	
Slifer (Gowrie)	50543	
Sloan	51055	
Smithland	51056	
Soldier	51572	
Solon	52333	
Somers	50586-587	
South Amana	52334	
South Des Moines	50315	
	50320-321	
(Des Moines)		
South English	52335	
South Muscatine	52761	
(Muscatine)		
South Ottumwa (Ottumwa)	52501	
Spaulding (Creston)	50801	
Spencer	51301, 51343	
Langdon	51301	
Sperry	52650	
Spillville	52168	
Spirit Lake	51360	
Spragueville	52074	
Spring Grove (Burlington)	52601	
Spring Hill (Indianola)	50125	
Springbrook	52075	
Springdale (West Branch)	52358	
Springville	52336	
Stacyville	50476	
Stanhope	50246	
Stanley	50671	
Stanton	51573	
Stanwood	52337	
Stanzel (Greenfield)	50849	
Steamboat Rock	50672	
Stiles (Bloomfield)	52537	
Stilson (Britt)	50423	
Stockport	52651	
Stockton	52769	
Stone City (Anamosa)	52205	
Storm Lake	50588	
Story City	50248	
Stout	50673	
Stratford	50249	
Strawberry Point	52076	
Stringtown (Lenox)	50851	
Struble	51057	
Stuart	50250	
Sugar Creek (Charlotte)	52731	
Sully	50251	
Sulphur Springs	50588	
(Storm Lake)		
Summerset (Indianola)	50125	
Summitville (Keokuk)	52632	
Sumner	50674	
Sunshine (Centerville)	52544	
Superior	51363	
Sutherland	51058	
Sutliff (Lisbon)	52253	
Swaledale	50477	
Swan	50252	
Swea City	50590	
Swedesburg	52652	
Swisher	52338	

Tabor	51653	
Taintor	50253	
Talleyrand (Keota)	52248	
Talmage (Thayer)	50254	
Tama	52339	
Tara (Fort Dodge)	50501	
Teeds Grove	52732, 52771	
(Clinton)		
Clinton	52771	
Templar Park	51360	
(Spirit Lake)		
Templeton	51463	
Ten Mile (Bryant)	52727	
Tennant	51574	
Tenville Junction	50864	
(Villisca)		
Terril	51364	
Thayer	50254	
The Meadows (Woodward)	50276	
Thirty (Centerville)	52544	
Thompson	50478	
Thor	50591	
Thornburg	50255	
Thornton	50479	
Thorpe (Manchester)	52057	
Thurman	51654	
Ticonic (Castana)	51010	
Tiffin	52340	
Tingley	50863	
Tipton	52772	
Titonka	50480	
Toddville	52341	
Toeterville	50481	
Toledo	52342	
Toolesboro (Wapello)	52653	
Toronto	52343	
Tracy	50256	
Traer	50675	
Trenton (Mount Pleasant)	52641	
Treynor	51575	
Triboji Beach	51360	
(Spirit Lake)		
Tripoli	50676	
Troy (Bloomfield)	52537	
Troy Mills	52344	
Truax (Eddyville)	52553	
Truesdale	50592	
Truro	50257	
Turin	51059	
Turkey River (Guttenberg)	52052	
Tuskeego (Kellerton)	50133	
Twin View Heights (Solon)	52333	
Udell	52593	
Ulmer (Lake View)	51450	
Underwood	51576	
Union	50258-259	
Bangor	50258	
Union Center (Le Mars)	51031	
Union Mills (New Sharon)	50207	
Unionville	52594	
University Park	52595	
University Place	50311	
(Des Moines)		
Urbana	52345	
Urbandale (Des Moines)	50322	
Ute	51060	
Vail	51465	
Valeria (Colfax)	50054	
Van Cleve (Melbourne)	50162	
Van Horne	52346	
Van Meter	50261	

Van Wert	50262	
Vandalia (Prairie City)	50228	
Varina	50593	
Ventura	50482	
Veo (Richland)	52585	
Vernon (Keosauqua)	52565	
Vernon Springs (Cresco)	52136	
Victor	52347	
Village Creek (Lansing)	52151	
Villisca	50864	
Vincent	50594	
Vining	52348	
Vinton	52349	
Viola (Audubon)	50025, 52350	
Volga	52077	
Volney (Monona)	52159	
Voorhies (Hudson)	50643	
Wadena	52169	
Wahpeton (Milford)	51351, 51360	
Walcott	52773	
Walford	52351	
Walker	52352	
Wall Lake	51466	
Wallingford	51365	
Walnut	51577	
Walnut City (Mystic)	52574	
Wapello	52653	
Ware (Havelock)	50546	
Washburn (Waterloo)	50706	
Washington	52353	
Washta	51061	
Waterloo	50700-704	
	50706-707	
Evansdale	50707	
Orange	50701	
Raymar	50707	
Washburn	50706	
Waterville	52170	
Watkins	52354	
Watson (Monona)	52159	
Waubeek (Central City)	52214	
Waucoma (Alpha)	52130, 52171	
Alpha	52171	
Waukee	50263	
Waukon	52172	
Waukon Junction	52146	
(Harpers Ferry)		
Waupeton (Sherrill)	52073	
Waverly	50677	
Wayland	52654	
Webb	51366	
Webster	50273, 52355	
(Winterset)		
Webster City	50595	
Welch Avenue (Ames)	50010	
Weldon	50264	
Weller (Lovilia)	50150	
Wellman	52356	
Wellsburg	50680	
Welton	52774	
Wesley	50483	
West Amana	52357	
West Bend	50597	
West Branch	52358	
West Burlington	52655	
West Chester	52359	
West Des Moines	50265-266	
Clover Hills	50265	
Commerce	50265	
West Fort Dodge	50501	
(Fort Dodge)		

IMPORTANT BUILDINGS

IOWA

ASBURY

APARTMENTS

Alverno Apartments Inc
3525 WINDSOR AVE 52001

Angella Apartments
444 ANGELLA ST 52001

Clin Que Apt
1850 ELLIS ST 52001

Cooper Apt
610 COOPER PL 52001

Coventry Court
201 W 17TH ST 52001

Don Apartments
1717 KANE ST 52001

Ecumenical Towers
250 W 6TH ST 52001

Fulton Apartments
2535 CENTRAL AVE 52001

Granda Gardens Trlr Park
11948 SHERRILL RD 52002

Hillcrest Apts
3290 HILLCREST RD 52001

Kennedy Manor
2641 OWEN CT 52002

Key Apartments
1600 BUTTERFIELD DR .. 52001

Knapp Trlr Ct
17909 PERU RD 52001

Lore Trlr Ct
15462 LEWIS RD 52002

Luther Manor
3129 HILLCREST RD 52001

St Marys Apartments
2955 KAUFMANN AVE 52001

Valley Hill Trailer Ct
11420 Rupp Hollow Rd 52001

Washington Park Place
605 BLUFF ST 52001

Windsor Park Apt
801 DAVIS ST 52001

Woodland Arms Apts
2160 WOODLAND DR 52002

BUILDINGS

Area Residential Care
2935 KAUFMANN AVE 52001

Bethany Home
1005 LINCOLN AVE 52001

Cycare Plaza
700 LOCUST ST 52001

Dubuque Health Care Ctr
2935 KAUFMANN AVE 52001

Duq County Nursing Home
2375 ROOSEVELT ST 52001

Ennoble Manor Care Ctr
2000 PASADENA DR 52001

Executive West Dentists
3455 STONEMAN RD 52002

Federal Building
350 W 6TH ST 52001

Fischer Arcade Building
880 LOCUST ST 52001

Fischer Building
909 MAIN ST 52001

Heritage Manor
4885 ASBURY RD 52002

Holy Family Hall
3340 WINDSOR AVE 52001

Julien Care Facility
13066 SEIPPEL RD 52002

Kennedy Mall
555 John F Kennedy Rd ... 52002

Luther Manor
3131 HILLCREST RD 52001

Manor Care Nursing Center
901 W 3RD ST 52001

Mt Loretta Convent
2360 CARTER RD 52001

Mt Pleasant Home
1695 Mount Pleasant St 52001

Mt St Francis
3390 WINDSOR AVE 52001

Nesler Center
799 MAIN ST 52001

Professional Arts Plaza
200 MERCY DR 52001

Security Building
151 W 8TH ST 52001

St Dominic Villa
600 MAZZUCHELLI PL 52001

Stonehill Care Center
3485 WINDSOR AVE 52001

Visitation Convent
900 ALTA VISTA ST 52001

Wacker Plaza
806 WACKER DR 52002

GOVERNMENT

City Hall
50 W 13TH ST 52001

City Hall Annex
1300 MAIN ST 52001

Corps Of Engineers
11 LIME STREET EXT 52001

Dubuque County Courthouse
720 CENTRAL AVE 52001

Dubuque County Sheriff
770 IOWA ST 52001

HOTELS

Clarion Hotel
450 MAIN ST 52001

Julien Inn
200 MAIN ST 52001

Redstone Inn
504 BLUFF ST 52001

BEAVERDALE

APARTMENTS

Apartment
2800 30TH ST 50310

Ashley Square
5505 AURORA AVE 50310

Birchwood
3720 MARTIN LUTHER KING JR
PKY 50310

Carmel Heights
3800 MARTIN LUTHER KING JR
PKY 50310

Cedarview
2525 LINCOLN AVE 50310

Chateau
2212 MERLE HAY RD 50310

Clarkson
2525 CLARKSON AVE 50310

Cortese
2620 BEAVER AVE 50310

Country Club Estates
3620 TWANA DR 50310

Country Club Estates
4530 Lower Beaver Rd 50310

Douglas Oaks
2829 DOUGLAS AVE 50310

Douglas Terrace
3000 DOUGLAS AVE 50310

Dover Park
2519 CLARKSON AVE 50310

Franklin Court
4925 FRANKLIN AVE 50310

Franklin West
1900 50TH ST 50310

Hickman Village
2400 HICKMAN RD 50310

Housing For Handicaped
2916 30TH ST 50310

Jacobs Place
2400 30TH ST 50310

Mcneal
5703 URBANDALE AVE ... 50310

Oakview Terrace
2907 BOSTON AVE 50310

Oakview Terrace
3211 30TH ST 50310

Rowecienda
3710 56TH ST 50310

Royal Oaks
2201 26TH ST 50310

Silhouette
3720 57TH ST 50310

Thirty Oaks
3201 30TH ST 50310

Westchester Square
5524 MEREDITH DR 50310

Westchester Village
5413 AURORA AVE 50310

BERTRAM

BUILDINGS

1st Avenue Building
411 1ST AVE SE 52401

201 Town Centre
201 3RD AVE SE 52401

221 Town Centre
221 3RD AVE SE 52401

American Building
101 2ND ST SE 52401

Arco Building
308 3RD ST SE 52401

Brenton Financial Center
150 1ST AVE NE 52401

Cedar River Tower
100 1ST ST. 52401

Dows Building
210 2ND ST SE 52401

Firstar Bank Building
115 3RD ST SE 52401

Five Seasons Center
370 1ST AVE NE 52401

Granby Building
224 2ND ST SE 52401

Guaranty Bank Building
216 3RD ST SE 52401

Higley Building
118 3RD AVE SE 52401

Le Tower
200 1ST ST SE 52401

Iowa Building
221 4TH AVE SE 52401

Iowa Theater Building
108 3RD ST SE 52401

Irvine Building
417 1ST AVE SE 52401

Law Building
225 2ND ST SE 52401

Paramount Building
305 2ND ST SE 52401

Professional Park Building
119 3RD ST NE 52401

SGA Building
122 2ND ST SE 52401

The Center
425 2ND ST SE 52401

United Fire & Casualty
118 2ND AVE SE 52401

GOVERNMENT

City Hall
50 2ND AVENUE BRG 52401

Federal Building
101 1ST ST SE 52401

Linn County Courthouse
51 3RD AVENUE BRG 52401

Linn County Office Building
305 2ND AVE SE 52401

CAPITOL HEIGHTS

APARTMENTS

Canterbury
720 SHERRY LYNN BLVD 50317

Eastridge
3913 HUBBELL AVE 50317

Eastview Cir
3908 E 23RD ST 50317

Eastview Manor
3700 E 31ST ST 50317

Embassy
3418 E 26TH ST 50317

Horizons East
4010 HUBBELL AVE 50317

Stonecrest
3330 E 25TH ST 50317

Wedgewood
2555 WEDGEWOOD RD .. 50317

CEDAR RAPIDS

APARTMENTS

Blair House Condos
2222 1ST AVE NE 52402

Chalet Apts
210 19TH ST NE 52402

Commonwealth
1400 2ND AVE SE 52403

Gateway
2901 6TH ST SW 52404

Hawthorne Hills
2263 C ST SW 52404

Oakland Court
1500 OAKLAND RD NE 52402

Oakland Gardens
1300 OAKLAND RD NE 52402

Pheasant Run
550 QUAIL CT SW 52404

Wildwood Pool Apts
911 OLD MARION RD NE   52402

BUILDINGS

Old Cr Airport Terminal
2501 Wright Brths. Blvd W   52404

Commerce Exchange Building
2720 1ST AVE NE 52402

Corporate Center East
2750 1ST AVE NE 52402

Executive Building
385 COLLINS RD NE 52402

Executive Plaza Building
4403 1ST AVE SE 52402

Glenbrook Centre
4341 1ST AVE SE 52402

Lindale Mall
4444 1ST AVE NE 52402

St Andrews Office Building
1930 Saint Andrews Ct NE 52402

GOVERNMENT

Linn County Adm Building
930 1ST ST SW 52404

CENTRAL

APARTMENTS

Langwith
320 W 4TH ST 52801

Linden
219 SCOTT ST 52801

Schricker
403 W 4TH ST 52801

BUILDINGS

Bicentennial Building
428 WESTERN AVE 52801

Citizens Federal Building
101 W 3RD ST 52801

Davenport Bank Building
220 N MAIN ST 52801

First Bank Building
201 W 2ND ST 52801

Kahl Building
326 W 3RD ST 52801

Main Street Building
517 N MAIN ST 52801

Northwest Bank Building
101 W 2ND ST 52801

Parker Building
102 W 2ND ST 52801

Putnam Building
215 N MAIN ST 52801

Union Arcade Building
111 E 3RD ST 52801

GOVERNMENT

City Hall
226 W 4TH ST 52801

Federal Building
131 E 4TH ST 52801

Police Department
420 N HARRISON ST 52801

Scott County Courthouse
416 W 4TH ST 52801

HOTELS

Blackhawk Hotel Building
200 E 3RD ST 52801

CLOVER HILLS

APARTMENTS

Ashworth Manor
1020 ASHWORTH RD 50265

Bennett Grandwoods
1813 BENNETT DR 50265

Briarwood Grand
2132 GRAND AVE 50265

Briarwood Iv
317 S 19TH ST 50265

Camelot West
1420 20TH ST 50265

Cloverhills
830 12TH ST 50265

Con & Jean Manor
800 13TH ST 50265

Country Club Village
1202 OFFICE PARK RD ... 50265

Country Club Village
1180 11TH ST 50265

Garden Ridge
1831 FULLER RD 50265

Glorianne
712 13TH ST 50265

Hamlet
2200 EP TRUE PKY 50265

Old English Village
1201 OFFICE PARK RD ... 50265

Park West
1155 OFFICE PARK RD ... 50265

Regency Woods
1101 11TH ST 50265

Robin Hills
2000 WESTOWN PKY 50265

West Woods
218 52ND ST 50265

BUILDINGS

Ashworth Plaza
1025 ASHWORTH RD 50265

CORALVILLE

APARTMENTS

Alexandria Apt
1500 5TH ST 52241

Carol Ann Apt
1205 5TH ST 52241

Coral Manor Apt
1211 2ND ST 52241

Coral Village Apt
1799 5TH ST 52241

Econo Apt
1209 2ND ST 52241

Elmwood Terrace Apt
502 5TH ST 52241

Fullman Apt
612 5TH ST 52241

Julber Apt
508 5TH ST 52241

Lakewood Hills Apt
209 HOLIDAY RD 52241

Lakewood Village Apts
1512 1ST AVE 52241

Lantern Court Apt
727 20TH AVE 52241

Lantern Park Apt
902 20TH AVENUE PL 52241

Le Chateau Apt
300 4TH AVE 52241

Park Motel Apt
2711 2ND ST 52241

Parkside Manor Apt
612 12TH AVE 52241

Parkview Apt
1616 5TH ST 52241

Paul Tudor Apt
1648 5TH ST 52241

Penningroth Apt
1106 5TH ST 52241

Scotch Pine Apt
199 6TH ST 52241

Valley Forge Apt
2030 9TH ST 52241

Villa Brun
720 4TH AVENUE PL 52241

GOVERNMENT

City Hall
1512 7TH ST 52241

HOTELS

Cantebury Inn
704 1ST AVE 52241

Comfort Inn
205 9TH ST 52241

Days Inn Ironmen
1200 1ST AVE 52241

Heartland Inn
87 2ND ST 52241

Kinseth Hotel Corp
1895 27TH AVE 52241

COUNCIL BLUFFS

APARTMENTS

Bennett Ave Estates
131 BENNETT AVE 51503

Camelot
1105 S 3RD ST 51503

Colonial Plaza
38 DILLMAN DR 51503

Cozy Court
2725 N BROADWAY 51503

Dot Apt
715 E BROADWAY 51503

Echo Park
1110 MARSHALL AVE 51503

Elder Court
207 ELDER ST 51503

Indian Hill Apt
1455 MCPHERSON AVE .. 51503

Macinerry Apts
2809 MACINEERY DR 51501

Monticello Apts
37 BLUFF ST 51503

Oakland Court
255 OAKLAND AVE 51503

Parkwild Apt
1921 PARKWILD W 51503

Pine Ridge
36 DILLMAN DR 51503

Sherwood Apt
2008 SHERWOOD CT 51503

Sherwood Apts
1615 LITTLE JOHN CIR ... 51503

Sylvan Arms
101 ZENITH DR 51503

Wolf Apt
1404 MCPHERSON AVE .. 51503

Woodbury Pines
548 WOODBURY AVE 51503

Zenith Arms
103 ZENITH DR 51503

BUILDINGS

801 Building
801 HARMONY ST 51503

Bluffs Towers
38 PEARL ST 51503

Council Bluff Sav & Loan
11 PEARL ST 51503

Dr Building
201 RIDGE ST 51503

Executive Building
427 E WASHINGTON AVE 51503

Executive Building
427 E KANESVILLE BLVD 51503

First National Bank
500 W BROADWAY 51503

Mall Of The Bluffs
1751 MADISON AVE 51503

Mc Pherson Office Building
1705 MCPHERSON AVE .. 51503

Metropolitan Fed Bank
421 W BROADWAY 51503

North Ave Towers
103 NORTH AVE 51503

Park Building
500 WILLOW AVE 51503

Park Building
101 PEARL ST 51503

Park Plaza
532 1ST AVE 51503

Willow & Main Building
125 S MAIN ST 51503

HOTELS

Heartland Inn
1000 WOODBURY AVE 51503

Motel 6
1846 N 16TH ST 51501

DAVENPORT

APARTMENTS

Breckenridge
4323 N DIVISION ST 52806

Castlewood
2030 EMERALD DR 52804

Chateau
121 W 8TH ST 52803

Courtland
321 E 7TH ST 52803

Crown
807 W 2ND ST 52802

Davenport Manor
7102 HILLANDALE RD 52806

Fisher Crest
227 E 35TH ST 52806

Harrison Manor
2502 N HARRISON ST 52803

Holiday Terrace
1935 W 40TH ST 52806

Indian Ridge
3301 JERSEY RIDGE RD   52807

Kimberly Club
3290 E KIMBERLY RD 52807

Sherwood Forest
1000 BLYTHWOOD PL 52804

Westview Terrace
7202 HILLANDALE RD 52806

BUILDINGS

1 River Place
1225 E RIVER DR 52803

Brenton Bank Building
1606 BRADY ST 52803

Central Park Plaza
2906 W Central Park Ave .. 52804

Corporate East
1910 E KIMBERLY RD 52807

Medical Art
1333 W LOMBARD ST 52804

Mercy Medical Pavillion
1351 W Central Park Ave .. 52804

Midtown Plaza
1706 BRADY ST 52803

Northgate Shopping Ctr
1801 E KIMBERLY RD 52807

Northpark Mall
320 W KIMBERLY RD 52806

Northtown Plaza
102 E KIMBERLY RD 52806

Northwest Plaza
1416 W 16TH ST 52804

Northwest Towers
100 E KIMBERLY RD 52806

Old Town Mall
901 E KIMBERLY RD 52807

Paul Revere Square
2322 E KIMBERLY RD 52807

Priester Building
601 BRADY ST 52803

Professional Arts
121 W LOCUST ST 52803

St Lukes Mc Pavillion
1228 E RUSHOLME ST 52803

Valley Fair Plaza
2720 W LOCUST ST 52804

Walnut Center
4811 N BRADY ST 52806

HOSPITALS

Mercy Hospital
1401 W Central Park Ave .. 52804

HOTELS

Standard
712 W 2ND ST 52802

COLLEGES

Teikyo Marycrest Univ
1607 W 12TH ST 52804

DES MOINES

APARTMENTS

Acadian Manor
2801 GRAND AVE 50312

Alpine Village
7800 ILTIS DR 50322

Ambassador
3610 ELM DR 50322

Ambassador West
7600 DENNIS DR 50322

Amber Ridge
2100 EVERGREEN AVE ... 50320

Argonne
1729 GRAND AVE 50309

Arlington Apt
1301 LOCUST ST 50309

Ayrshire
1815 6TH AVE 50314

Barbican
3920 GRAND AVE 50312

Birch
2315 GRAND AVE 50312

Brady
650 16TH ST 50314

Brentwood
1359 24TH ST 50311

Butler
510 15TH ST 50309

Candle Ridge
4427 86TH ST 50322

Candle Ridge Ii
4515 NW 86TH ST 50322

Cape Cod
1731 HIGH ST 50309

Capitol Heights
1424 E WALNUT ST 50316

Capitol Hill
820 LYON ST 50309

Century Park
717 4TH ST 50309

Chad Estates
6316 URBANDALE AVE ... 50322

City View
1010 SCHOOL ST 50309

Civic Center Court
200 GRAND AVE 50309

Civic Center Court
401 3RD ST 50309

Civic Ctr Ct
201 LOCUST ST 50309

Concord
732 18TH ST 50314

Del Ray Heights
1100 E 6TH ST 50316

Drake Court
1126 25TH ST 50311

Drake Park
1304 34TH ST 50311

Drake Park Apts
1306 34TH ST 50311

Eddy
1120 POLK BLVD 50311

Elliott
219 4TH ST 50309

Elms
2225 GRAND AVE 50312

Elsie Mason Manor
430 GRAND AVE 50309

Ewing
917 LOCUST ST 50309

Fleur Place
2800 FLEUR DR 50321

Fort South
6800 SW 9TH ST 50315

Forty Three Twnty Three
4323 GRAND AVE 50312

Four Season
3001 WOODLAND AVE 50312

Four Thousand Four
4004 GRAND AVE 50312

Goldbriar Chateau
5555 SW 9TH ST 50315

Grand
4021 GRAND AVE 50312

Grand Colony
2824 GRAND AVE 50312

Grand Condominiums
3100 GRAND AVE 50312

Grand Prix
3205 GRAND AVE 50312

Grand Terrace
2917 GRAND AVE 50312

Hallett Apt
1305 LOCUST ST 50309

Hamilton
2825 GRAND AVE 50312

Hampton House
4200 GRAND AVE 50312

Harrington
677 16TH ST 50314

Haven Homes
3717 6TH AVE 50313

Heather Dawn
2020 PLEASANT ST 50312

Heather Hills
707 18TH ST 50314

Heather Manor
600 E 5TH ST 50309

Hemminger
2125 INDIANOLA AVE 50315

Hickman Place
6315 HICKMAN RD 50322

Highpoint
7631 HICKMAN RD 50322

Hillcrest
7201 SE 5TH ST 50315

Imperial
3407 GRAND AVE 50312

Ingersoll Court
4906 INGERSOLL AVE 50312

Ingersoll Towers
3662 INGERSOLL AVE 50312

Inntowner
1300 WOODLAND AVE 50309

Jefferson Apt
1519 GRAND AVE 50309

Jensen Manor
4201 62ND ST 50322

Kingston
1200 GRAND AVE 50309

Lakeview
8700 CAROLE CIR 50322

Landmark South
200 DICKMAN RD 50315

Laurel Village
1020 9TH ST 50314

Ligutti Tower
555 5TH AVE 50309

Logan Park
1731 CLEVELAND AVE 50316

Luther Park
2824 E 16TH ST 50316

Magnolia Manor
400 E PHILIP ST 50315

Mckinley Arms
5209 SW 9TH ST 50315

Mercy Park
212 MERCY PARK 50314

Northtown
3830 6TH AVE 50313

Nottingham Square
2420 CANTERBURY RD .. 50322

Oakridge
926 OAKRIDGE DR 50314

Oaks
2305 GRAND AVE 50312

Old Main
2321 UNIVERSITY AVE 50311

Park Fleur
3131 FLEUR DR 50321

Park Forest
2198 E VIRGINIA AVE 50320

Park Place
615 PARK ST 50309

Patricia Villa
3600 PATRICIA DR 50322

Peppertree
3816 106TH ST 50322

Plaza Condo
300 WALNUT ST 50309

Plaza Manor
3815 66TH ST 50322

Plaza View
6221 SE 5TH ST 50315

Pleasant Court Apts
708 16TH ST 50314

Pleasant Prop
603 ALLISON AVE 50314

Plumwood Terrace
4805 86TH ST 50322

Plymouth Place
4111 INGERSOLL AVE 50312

Reed
3323 INGERSOLL AVE 50312

River Heights
253 FRANKLIN AVE 50314

River Hills
700 E 5TH ST 50309

River Hills II
1002 E 6TH ST 50316

Riverview Oaks
1424 PENN AVE 50316

Riverwood
1805 ARLINGTON AVE 50314

Rocklyn Court
6820 HOLCOMB AVE 50322

Royal View Manor
1101 CROCKER ST 50309

Scottish Rite
2909 WOODLAND AVE 50312

Sherwood Glen
8817 HICKMAN RD 50322

Southern Manor
3722 SE 14TH ST 50320

Southern Park
810 PAYTON AVE 50315

Southlawn Villa
3716 SE 14TH ST 50320

Southridge Vlg
1200 CUMMINS RD 50315

Southridge Vlg II
1120 CUMMINS RD 50315

Southview Manor
2417 SW 9TH ST 50315

Stanley
2714 INGERSOLL AVE 50312

Summit House
2880 GRAND AVE 50312

Sydmore
1441 CAPITOL AVE 50316

Terrace Hill
2525 GRAND AVE 50312

The Fleur
2712 FLEUR DR 50321

Thirty Six Sixty
3660 GRAND AVE 50312

Three Thousand Grand
3000 GRAND AVE 50312

Tours Apartments
208 11TH ST 50309

University Terrace
3523 UNIVERSITY AVE 50311

Urban Green
7715 HICKMAN RD 50322

Village Green
1222 E SENECA AVE 50313

Wakonda Village
1800 WATROUS AVE 50315

Wakonda West
2221 STANTON AVE 50321

Walnut Place
1404 E WALNUT ST 50316

Watrous
1300 E WATROUS AVE 50315

Wesley Acres
3520 GRAND AVE 50312

Wesley Grand
3524 GRAND AVE 50312

West Grand Towers (office)
3663 GRAND AVE 50312

Westover
6430 URBANDALE AVE ... 50322

Westown Park
4200 PARK AVE 50321

Westview Woods
3201 86TH ST 50322

Windsor Chateau
1250 73RD ST 50311

Windsor Park Cooper Homes
6750 SCHOOL ST 50311

Windsor Ter
3333 GRAND AVE 50312

Windsor Woods
1235 66TH ST 50311

Woodstock
1415 CAPITOL AVE 50316

BUILDINGS

Capital Square
400 LOCUST ST 50309

Des Moines Building
405 6TH AVE 50309

East Grand Office Park
200 E GRAND AVE 50309

Employers Mutual
717 MULBERRY ST 50309

Equitable
604 LOCUST ST 50309

Financial Center
666 WALNUT ST 50309

First Interstate Bank Bld
317 6TH AVE 50309

Fleming
218 6TH AVE 50309

Flynn Building
319 7TH ST 50309

Hubbell Building
904 WALNUT ST 50309

Investment Building
424 10TH ST 50309

Jewett Building
914 GRAND AVE 50309

Liberty Building
418 6TH AVE 50309

Masonic Temple
1011 LOCUST ST 50309

Midland Financial Building
206 6TH AVE 50309

National Travelers Building
820 KEOSAUQUA WAY 50309

Principal Tower
801 GRAND AVE 50309

Register Building
715 LOCUST ST 50309

Shops
806 WALNUT ST 50309

Two Ruan Center
601 LOCUST ST 50309

GOVERNMENT

DSM Airport
6214 FLEUR DR 50321

Federal Building
210 WALNUT ST 50309

Polk County Admin Building
111 COURT AVE 50309

Polk County Court House
500 MULBERRY ST 50309

HOTELS

Randolph Hotel
202 4TH ST 50309

DUBUQUE

APARTMENTS

Julien Dubuque Apartments
2 JULIEN DUBUQUE DR . 52003

BUILDINGS

Bryant Building
120 BRYANT ST 52003

Clock Tower West
3343 Center Grove Dr 52003

Marion Hall
1050 CARMEL DR 52003

Plaza 20 Shopping Center
2600 DODGE ST 52003

Villa Rapheal
1235 Mount Loretta Ave 52003

Warren Plaza
3500 DODGE ST 52003

GOVERNMENT

Naval Reserve
10677 AIRPORT RD 52003

HOSPITALS

Inn Plaza
3430 DODGE ST 52003

HOTELS

Ace Trailer Ct
701 CEDAR CROSS RD .. 52003

Days Inn
1111 DODGE ST 52003

Heartland Inn
4025 DODGE ST 52003

Midway Motor Lodge
3100 DODGE ST 52003

Midway Trlr Ct
3100 BRUNSKILL RD 52003

Super 8 Motel
2730 DODGE ST 52003

Twin T Trlr Ct
1800 MANSON RD 52003

IOWA CITY

APARTMENTS

1st Ave Apt
921 S 1ST AVE 52245

A & H Apt
929 IOWA AVE 52240

Albrecht Apt
315 ELLIS AVE 52246

Altamont Apt
321 N JOHNSON ST 52245

Arena View Apt
34 LINCOLN AVE 52246

Aur Campus Apt
806 E COLLEGE ST 52240

Aur Downtown Apt
927 E COLLEGE ST 52240

Autumn Park Apt
3042 MUSCATINE AVE 52240

Baculis Apt
1012 N SUMMIT ST 52245

Ben Kay Apt
207 MYRTLE AVE 52246

Benton Manor Apt
814 BENTON DR 52246

Blacks Gaslight Village
426 BROWN ST 52245

Blackstone Apt
118 S DUBUQUE ST 52240

Bluffwood Manor Apt
640 STUART CT 52245

Bowery Apt
815 BOWERY ST 52240

Boyd Apt
515 E COLLEGE ST 52240

Bryce Ann Apt
2432 PETSEL PL 52246

Burkley Pl N Apt
130 E JEFFERSON ST 52245

Burlington Apt
232 S SUMMIT ST 52240

Cambridge Pl Apt
1851 MELROSE AVE 52246

Camelot Ct Apt
736 MICHAEL ST 52246

Capitol House Apt
320 S DUBUQUE ST 52240

Carriage Hill Apt
701 CARRIAGE HL 52246

Cedarwood Apt
2100 BROADWAY ST 52240

Cilek Apt
715 IOWA AVE 52240

College Hill Apt
714 E COLLEGE ST 52240

Commonwealth Apt
340 ELLIS AVE 52246

Court Hill Apt
3455 E COURT ST 52245

Crest Town House Condo
915 OAKCREST ST 52246

Crest Valley Apt
47 VALLEY AVE 52246

Dodge Apt
636 S DODGE ST 52240

Dodge Manor Apt
316 S DODGE ST 52240

Dor Len Apt
614 E JEFFERSON ST 52245

Duane Means Apt
501 N DUBUQUE ST 52245

Dubuque Apt
329 N DUBUQUE ST 52245

Ecumenical Tower Apt
320 E WASHINGTON ST .. 52240

Edon Apt
2430 MUSCATINE AVE 52240

Ellis Ave Apt
329 ELLIS AVE 52246

Emerald Ct
315 EMERALD ST 52240

Fountain Apt
218 S LUCAS ST 52240

Gatens Apt
612 S DODGE ST 52240

Harrison Apt
416 S LINN ST 52240

Harry Miller Apt
625 E BURLINGTON ST ... 52240

Hillsboro West Apt
1015 W BENTON ST 52246

Hoffman Apt
5 WOOLF AVE 52246

Hollywood Apt
1102 HOLLYWOOD BLVD 52240

Holub Apt
308 N LINN ST 52245

Iowa Manor Apt
505 IOWA AVE 52240

Jefferson Manor Apt
505 E JEFFERSON ST 52245

Keller Apt
725 E COLLEGE ST 52240

Kunel Apt
411 N DUBUQUE ST 52245

Lakeside Manor
2401 HIGHWAY 6 E 52240

Lakewood Apt
807 OAKCREST ST 52246

Larew Apt
308 N CLINTON ST 52245

Lincoln Ave Apt
41 LINCOLN AVE 52246

Mac/hill Manor Apt
615 N DUBUQUE ST 52245

Market Street Apt
712 E MARKET ST 52245

Martin Apt
119 RIVER ST 52246

Mc Namer Apt
516 E COLLEGE ST 52240

Melrose Apt
741 MELROSE AVE 52246

Melrose Lake Apt
155 WOODSIDE DR 52246

Messe Apt
624 N LINN ST 52245

Meyers Apt
23 S DUBUQUE ST 52240

Montclair Apt
201 N 1ST AVE 52245

Monticello Apt
922 E COLLEGE ST 52240

Norway Apt
808 OAKCREST ST 52246

Oak Terrace Apt
1108 OAKCREST ST 52246

Old Gold Court Apt
731 MICHAEL ST 52246

Park Hill Apt
706 E COLLEGE ST 52240

Parklawn Apt
447 N RIVERSIDE DR 52246

Penny House
422 S DUBUQUE ST 52240

Pentacrest Apt
12 E COURT ST 52240

Pheasant Ridge Apt
2401 BARTELT RD 52246

R & J Apt
902 NEWTON RD 52246

Redford Apt
1012 NEWTON RD 52246

Ritter Apt
310 N CLINTON ST 52245

Riverview Apt
720 N DUBUQUE ST 52245

Rochester Square Apt
2315 ROCHESTER AVE ... 52245

Senate Apts
411 E MARKET ST 52245

Seville Apt
900 W BENTON ST 52246

Sherry Beth Apt
815 OAKCREST ST 52246

Steckling Apt
717 IOWA AVE 52240

Summit Apt
228 S SUMMIT ST 52240

Terrance Apt
804 N DUBUQUE ST 52245

Thompson Apt
610 SUNSET ST 52246

Town & Country Apt
1100 ARTHUR ST 52240

Trojan Valley Apt
415 WOODSIDE DR 52246

Trojan Woods Apt
708 OAKCREST ST 52246

Valley Apt
35 VALLEY AVE 52246

Villa Apt
603 GREENWOOD DR 52246

Walden Place Apts
2423 WALDEN RD 52246

Westgate Villa Apt
600 WESTGATE ST 52246

Westside Apt
945 OAKCREST ST 52246

Willowridge Apt
724 WESTGATE ST 52246

Woodlawn Apt
20 EVANS ST 52245

Yoder Apt
803 E COLLEGE ST 52240

BUILDINGS

Arcade Building
128 E WASHINGTON ST .. 52240

Bremer Building
120 E WASHINGTON ST .. 52240

Brewery Square
123 N LINN ST 52245

Commerce Centre
325 E WASHINGTON ST .. 52240

Dey Building
105 IOWA AVE 52240

Eastdale Plaza
1700 S 1ST AVE 52240

Iowa State Bank Building
102 S CLINTON ST 52240

Paul Helen Building
209 E WASHINGTON ST .. 52240

Plaza Centre One
125 S DUBUQUE ST 52240

Savings & Loan Building
103 E COLLEGE ST 52240

Schneider Building
114 E COLLEGE ST 52240

Sycamore Mall
1600 SYCAMORE ST 52240

Wardway Mall
1101 S RIVERSIDE DR 52246

GOVERNMENT

Court House
417 S CLINTON ST 52240

Federal Building
400 S CLINTON ST 52240

Johnson Admin Building
913 S DUBUQUE ST 52240

HOSPITALS

University Hospital & Clinics
200 HAWKINS DR 52242

Univ Of Iowa Hosp & Clin
1 UNIVERSITY OF IOWA . 52242

HOTELS

Lakeside Manor
2401 HIGHWAY 6 E 52240

COLLEGES

University Of Iowa
1 UNIVERSITY OF IOWA . 52242

MORNINGSIDE

APARTMENTS

Maple Heights Apt
5300 STONE AVE 51106

Morning Hills Apt
2627 S RUSTIN ST 51106

Morningside Estates
1331 S MAPLE ST 51106

River Heights Apt
2201 GIBSON ST 51106

Shire Apt
4236 HICKORY LN 51106

Southview Apt
2728 S HELEN ST 51106

Sun Ridge Court
4701 STONE AVE 51106

COLLEGES

Morningside College
1501 Morningside Ave 51106

NORTH SIDE

APARTMENTS

Bellevue Apt
2110 SUMMIT ST 51104

Castle Apt
2121 NEBRASKA ST 51104

Clifton Apt
95 W CLIFTON AVE 51104

Glen Oaks Apt
3800 GLEN OAKS BLVD ... 51104

Ida Apt
1901 PIERCE ST 51104

Metz Apt
2009 SUMMIT ST 51104

Pheasant Acres Apt
3640 INDIAN HILLS DR 51104

Ridge Oaks
2300 INDIAN HILLS DR 51104

Stellart Apt
2117 NEBRASKA ST 51104

HOSPITALS

Marian Health Center
2101 COURT ST 51104

COLLEGES

Briar Cliff College
3303 REBECCA ST 51104

ORANGE

APARTMENTS

Colonial Manor
425 ALLEN ST 50701

Gaertnier Apts
302 COMMERCIAL ST 50701

Hillcrest
833 W 2ND ST 50701

BUILDINGS

Conway Civic Center
200 W 4TH ST 50701

Russell Lamson Apt Building
209 W 5TH ST 50701

Waterloo Building
531 COMMERCIAL ST 50701

SIOUX CITY

APARTMENTS

Alahambra Apt
801 8TH ST 51105

Bolstein Apt
1624 JACKSON ST 51105

Book Apt
921 JACKSON ST 51105

Centennial Manor
441 W 3RD ST 51103

Central Apt
613 11TH ST 51105

Century Apt
515 COURT ST 51101

Follis Apt
923 DOUGLAS ST 51101

Martin Tower Apt
410 PIERCE ST 51101

Murray Apt
821 JACKSON ST 51105

Sioux Apartments
217 19TH ST 51105

Smith Apts
1716 NEBRASKA ST 51105

Swanson Apt
1700 JACKSON ST 51105

Sydney Apt
1003 PIERCE ST 51105

Terrace Apt
1623 NEBRASKA ST 51105

War Eagle Village
2800 W 4TH ST 51103

Westpark Apt
615 W 3RD ST 51103

BUILDINGS

Badgerow
622 4TH ST 51101

Benson
705 DOUGLAS ST 51101

Call Terminal Building
1106 4TH ST 51101

Commerce
520 NEBRASKA ST 51101

Davidson
505 6TH ST 51101

Frances
505 5TH ST 51101

Insurance Centre
507 7TH ST 51101

Livestock Exchange
807 CUNNINGHAM DR 51107

Orpheum Electric
520 PIERCE ST 51101

Pioneer
701 PIERCE ST 51101

Security Bank
423 6TH ST 51101

Terra Centre
600 4TH ST 51101

Toy Bank
522 4TH ST 51101

United Federal
700 4TH ST 51101

GOVERNMENT

City Hall
401 6TH ST 51101

Federal Building
320 6TH ST 51101

Woodbury Co Court House
620 DOUGLAS ST 51101

HOTELS

Imperial 400
110 NEBRASKA ST 51101

Roadway Inn
130 NEBRASKA ST 51101

WATERLOO

APARTMENTS

Cedar River Tower
106 E 3RD ST 50703

Friendship Village
600 PARK LN 50702

Heritage House
610 E 4TH ST 50703

Parkview
200 PARKVIEW BLVD 50702

Walnut Court
315 WALNUT ST 50703

BUILDINGS

First National Building
607 SYCAMORE ST 50703

Kwwl Building
500 E 4TH ST 50703

Repass Building
604 MULBERRY ST 50703

GOVERNMENT

Court House
316 E 5TH ST 50703

HOSPITALS

Covenant Medical Center
3421 W 9TH ST 50702

WEST DES MOINES

APARTMENTS

Colonial Village
4220 VILLAGE LN 50266

Green Valley
3405 WOODLAND AVE 50266

Meadow Ridge
1301 49TH ST 50266

Noelcrest
4701 WOODLAND AVE 50266

Sun Prairie
5911 VISTA DR 50266

Valley West
1800 36TH ST 50266

Warren House
3000 UNIVERSITY AVE 50266

Warren Terrace
3050 UNIVERSITY AVE 50266

Washington Heights
4105 WOODLAND PLZ 50266

Washington Square
3863 WOODLAND AVE 50266

Western Hills Condo
4501 WOODLAND AVE 50266

Woodland Place
4957 WOODLAND AVE 50266

Woodland West
4401 WOODLAND AVE 50266

BUILDINGS

Agri Industries
2829 WESTOWN PKY 50266

Colony Park
3737 WOODLAND AVE 50266

Neptune
4401 WESTOWN PKY 50266

One Corporate Place
1501 42ND ST 50266

Regency West 3
4800 WESTOWN PKY 50266

Regency West 4
4700 WESTOWN PKY 50266

Regency West 5
4500 WESTOWN PKY 50266

Regency West 7
4400 WESTOWN PKY 50266

Regency West 8
4350 WESTOWN PKY 50266

Travelers Building
1452 29TH ST 50266

West Towers
1200 35TH ST 50266

West Winds
1454 30TH ST 50266

Westown Business Ctr
1601 48TH ST 50266

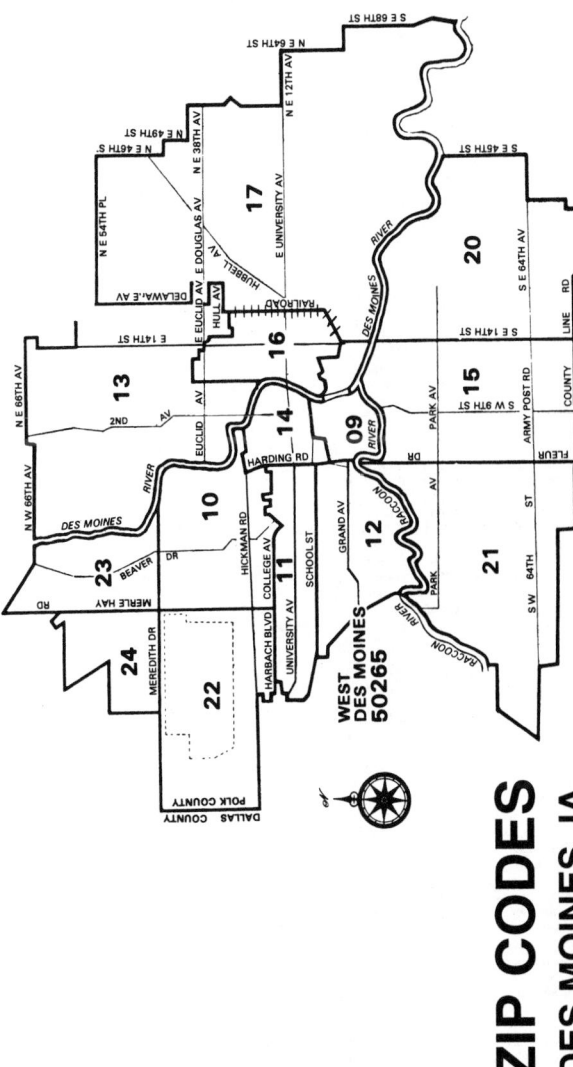

KANSAS
Abbreviation KS

Abbyville	67510
Abilene	67410
Ada	67414
Admire	66830
Agenda	66930
Agra	67621
Alamota (Dighton)	67839
Albert	67511
Alden	67512
Alexander	67513
Allen	66833
Alma	66401, 66501
Almena	67622
Alta Vista	66834
Altamont	67330
Alton	67623
Altoona	66710
Americus	66835
Ames	66931
Andale	67001
Andover	67002
Angola (Coffeyville)	67337
Antelope (Lincolnville)	66858
Anthony	67003
Antonino (Hays)	67601
Arcadia	66711
Argonia	67004
Arkansas City	67005
Arlington	67514
Arma	66712
Arnold	67515
Ashland	67831
Ashton (Geuda Springs)	67051
Assaria	67416
Atchison	66002
Atchison Topeka Santa Fe (Topeka)	66628
Athol	66932
Atlanta	67008
Attica	67009
Atwood	67730
Auburn	66402
Augusta	67010
Aurora	67417
Austin (Chanute)	66720
Axtell	66403
Badger (Galena)	66739
Baileyville	66404
Baldwin City	66006
Barber (Mulberry)	66756
Barnard	67418
Barnes	66933
Barnesville (Fulton)	66738
Bartlett	67332
Basehor	66007
Bassett (Iola)	66749
Batesville (Toronto)	66777
Bavaria (Salina)	67401
Baxter Springs	66713
Bazine	67516
Beattie	66406
Beaumont	67012
Beaver	67517
Beeler	67518
Bel Aire (Wichita)	67220
Bellaire (Lebanon)	66952
Belle Plaine	67013
Belleville	66935

Belmont (Kingman)	67068
Beloit	67420
Belpre	67519
Belvidere	67015
Belvue	66407
Bendena	66008
Benedict	66714
Bennington	67422
Bentley	67016
Benton	67017
Bern	66408
Berryton	66409
Beulah (Girard)	66743
Beverly	67423
Big Bow (Johnson)	67855
Big Elk (Baxter Springs)	66713
Bird City	67731
Bison	67520
Blaine (Westmoreland)	66549
Bloom (Minneola)	67865
Blue Cross (Topeka)	66629
Blue Mound	66010
Blue Rapids	66411
Bluff City	67018
Bogue	67625
Bonner Springs	66012
Brazilton (Girard)	66743
Bremen	66412
Brewster	67732
Bronson	66716
Brookville	67425
Brownell	67521
Bucklin	67834
Bucyrus	66013
Buffalo	66717
Buffville (Neodesha)	66757
Buhler	67522
Bunker Hill	67626
Burden	67019
Burdett	67523
Burdick	66838
Burlingame	66413
Burlington	66839
Burns	66840
Burr Oak	66936
Burrton	67020
Bushong (Allen)	66833
Bushton	67427
Buxton (Fredonia)	66736
Byers	67021
Caldwell	67022, 67032
Corbin	67022
Corbin	67032
Cambridge	67023
Caney	67333
Canton	67428
Capaldo (Pittsburg)	66762
Carbondale	66414
Carlton	67429
Carlyle (Iola)	66749
Carmean (Neosho Falls)	66758
Carona (Scammon)	66773
Cassoday	66842
Catharine	67627
Cato (Arcadia)	66711
Cawker City	67430
Cedar	67628
Cedar Point	66843
Cedar Vale	67024
Centerville	66014, 66740
Centralia	66415

Chanute	66720
Chapman	67431
Chase	67524
Chautauqua	67334
Cheney	67025
Cherokee	66724
Cherryvale	67335
Chetopa	67336
Cimarron	67835
Circleville	66416
Claflin	67525
Clay Center	67432
Clayton	67629
Clearview City	66019
Clearwater	67026
Clements (Cedar Point)	66843
Clifton	66937
Climax (Severy)	67137
Clyde	66938
Coalvale (Arcadia)	66711
Coats	67028
Cockerill (Mulberry)	66756
Codell	67630
Coffeyville	67337
Colby	67701
Coldwater	67029
Collyer	67631
Colony	66015
Columbus	66725
Colwich	67030
Comotara (Wichita)	67226
Concordia	66901
Conway (Mc Pherson)	67460
Conway Springs	67031
Coolidge	67836
Copeland	67837
Corbin (Caldwell)	67022, 67032
Corning	66417
Corwin (Hazelton)	67061
Cottonwood Falls	66845
Council Grove	66846, 66873
Dunlap	66846
Countryside (Shawnee Mission)	66202
Courtland	66939
Coyville	66727, 66736
Crestline	66728
Croweburg (Mulberry)	66756
Cuba	66940
Cullison (Pratt)	67124
Culver (Tescott)	67484
Cummings	66016
Cunningham	67035
Curranville (Mulberry)	66756
Damar	67632
Danville	67036
De Soto	66018-019
Dearing	67340
Deerfield	67838
Delavan (Herington)	67449
Delia	66418
Delphos	67436
Denison	66419
Dennis	67341
Densmore (Lenora)	67645
Denton	66017
Derby	67037
Devon (Fort Scott)	66701
Dexter	67038
Dighton	67839
Dodge City	67801

Dorrance	67634	
Douglass	67039	
Dover	66420	
Downs	67437	
Dresden	67635	
Drywood (Arcadia)	66711	
Duluth (Onaga)	66521	
Dundee (Great Bend)	67530	
Dunlap (Council Grove)	66846	
Duquoin (Harper)	67058	
Durand (Yates Center)	66783	
Durham	67438	
Dwight	66849	
Earlton (Chanute)	66720	
Eastborough	67206-207	
(Wichita)		
Easton	66020	
Edgerton	66021	
Edison (Girard)	66743	
Edmond	67636	
Edna	67342	
Edson	67733	
Effingham	66023	
El Dorado	67042	
Elbing	67041	
Elk City	67344	
Elk Falls	67345	
Elkhart	67950	
Ellinwood	67526	
Ellis	67637	
Ellsworth	67439	
Elmdale	66850	
Elsmore	66732	
Elwood	66024	
Emmett	66422	
Emporia	66801	
Englewood	67840	
Ensign	67841	
Erie	66733	
Esbon	66941	
Eskridge	66423	
Eudora	66025	
Eureka	67045	
Everest	66424	
Fairview	66425	
Fairway	66205	
(Shawnee Mission)		
Fall River	67047	
Falun	67442	
Farlington	66734	
Fellsburg (Lewis)	67552	
Florence	66851	
Fontana	66026	
Ford	67842	
Formoso	66942	
Fort Dodge	67843	
Fort Leavenworth	66027	
Fort Riley	66442	
Fort Scott	66701	
Fostoria	66426	
Fowler	67844	
Frankfort	66427	
Franklin	66735	
Fredonia	66736	
Freeport	67049	
Friend (Scott City)	67871	
Frontenac (Pittsburg)	66762-763	
Pittsburg	66763	
Fulton	66738	
Galatia (Olmitz)	67564-565	
Galena	66739	

Galesburg	66740	
Galva	67443	
Garden City	67846, 67868	
Garden Plain	67050	
Gardner	66030-031	
Garfield	67529	
Garland	66741	
Garnett	66032	
Gas	66742	
Gaylord	67638	
Gem	67734	
Geneseo	67444	
Geuda Springs	67051	
Girard	66743	
Glade	67639	
Glasco	67445	
Glen Elder	67446	
Goddard	67052	
Goessel	67053	
Goff	66428	
Goodland	67735	
Gorham	67640	
Gove	67736	
Grainfield	67737	
Grantville	66429	
Great Bend	67530	
Greeley	66033	
Green	67447	
Greenbush (Girard)	66743	
Greenleaf	66943	
Greensburg	67054	
Greenwich	67055	
Grenola	67346	
Gridley	66852	
Grinnell	67738	
Gross (Arcadia)	66711	
Guilford (Altoona)	66710	
Gypsum	67448	
Haddam	66944	
Hallowell (Columbus)	66725	
Halstead	67056	
Hamilton	66853	
Hanover	66945	
Hanston	67849	
Harding (Mapleton)	66754	
Hardtner	67057	
Harlan	67641	
Harper	67058	
Hartford	66854	
Harveyville	66431	
Havana	67347	
Haven	67543	
Havensville	66432	
Haviland	67059	
Hays	67601, 67667	
Antonino	67601	
Haysville	67060	
Hazelton	67061	
Healy	67850	
Heizer (Great Bend)	67530	
Hepler	66746	
Herington	67449	
Herkimer (Marysville)	66433	
Herndon	67739	
Hesston	67062	
Hewins (Cedar Vale)	67024	
Hiattville (Fort Scott)	66701	
Hiawatha	66434-435	
Reserve	66434	
Highland	66035	
Hilford (Neodesha)	66757	

Hill City	67642	
Hillsboro	67063	
Hillsdale	66036	
Hoisington	67544	
Holcomb	67851	
Hollenberg	66946	
Holton	66436	
Holyrood	67450	
Home	66438	
Hope	67451	
Horton	66439	
Howard	67349	
Hoxie	67740	
Hoyt	66440	
Hudson	67545	
Hugoton	67951	
Humboldt	66748	
Hunnewell (South Haven)	67140	
Hunter	67452	
Huron (Lancaster)	66041	
Hutchinson	67501-502	
	67504-505	
Medora	67502	
Independence	67301	
Ingalls	67853	
Inman	67546	
Iola	66749	
Ionia (Jewell)	66949	
Isabel	67065	
Iuka	67066	
Jamestown	66948	
Jennings	67643	
Jetmore	67854	
Jewell	66949	
Johnson	67855	
Junction City	66441-442	
Kalvesta	67856	
Kanopolis	67454	
Kanorado	67741	
Kansas City	66100-106	
	66109-113	
	66115, 66117-119	
	66160	
Lake Quivira	66106	
Kechi	67067	
Kelly (Seneca)	66538	
Kendall	67857	
Kensington	66951	
Kincaid	66039	
Kingman	67068	
Kingsdown	67858	
Kinsley	67547	
Kiowa	67070	
Kipp	67444	
Kismet	67859	
La Crosse	67548	
La Cygne	66040	
La Harpe	66751	
Labette (Oswego)	67356	
Lafontaine (Fredonia)	66736	
Lake City	67071	
Lake Quivira	66106	
(Kansas City)		
Lakin	67860	
Lamont	66855	
Lancaster	66041	
Lane	66042	
Langdon (Turon)	67583	
Lansing	66043	
Larned	67550	
Latham	67072	

171

Pomona	66076	
Porterville (Walnut)	66780	
Portis	67474	
Potter	66077	
Potwin	67123	
Powhattan	66527	
Prairie View	67664	
Prairie Village	66202	
	66204, 66206-208	
(Shawnee Mission)		
Prarie Village	66212	
(Shawnee Mission)		
Pratt	67124	
Prescott	66767	
Preston	67569	
Pretty Prairie	67570	
Princeton	66078	
Protection	67127	
Quaker (Columbus)	66725	
Quenemo	66528	
Quinter	67752	
Radium (Larned)	67550	
Radley (Pittsburg)	66762	
Rago	67128	
Ramona	67475	
Randall	66963	
Randolph	66554	
Ransom	67572	
Rantoul	66079	
Raymond	67573	
Reading	66868	
Redfield	66769	
Reece (Eureka)	67045	
Republic	66964	
Reserve (Hiawatha)	66434	
Rexford	67753	
Rice (Concordia)	66901	
Richfield	67953	
Richmond	66080	
Riley	66531	
Ringo (Girard)	66743	
Riverdale (Wellington)	67152	
Riverton	66770	
Robinson	66532	
Rock	67131	
Roeland Park	66202, 66205	
(Shawnee Mission)		
Rolla	67954	
Roper (Benedict)	66714	
Rosalia	67132	
Rose (Yates Center)	66783	
Rose Hill	67133	
Roseland (Scammon)	66773	
Rossville	66533	
Roxbury	67476	
Rozel	67574	
Rush Center	67575	
Russell	67665	
Russell Springs	67755	
Sabetha	66534	
Saint Francis	67756	
Saint George	66535	
Saint John	67576	
Saint Marys	66536	
Saint Paul	66771	
Salina	67401-402	
Bavaria	67401	
Satanta	67870	
Savonburg	66772	
Sawyer	67134	
Scammon	66773	

Scandia	66966	
Schoenchen	67667	
Schulte (Wichita)	67215	
Scott City	67871	
Scottsville (Beloit)	67420	
Scranton	66537	
Sedan	67361	
Sedgwick	67135	
Selden	67757	
Selkirk (Leoti)	67861	
Seneca	66538	
Severance (Troy)	66087	
Severy	67137	
Seward	67577	
Sharon	67138	
Sharon Springs	67758	
Shawnee Mission	66200-227	
	66250, 66262, 66267	
	66279, 66282, 66285	
Countryside	66202	
Fairway	66205	
Leawood	66206	
Leawood	66209	
Leawood	66211	
Leawood	66224	
Lenexa	66210	
Lenexa	66227	
Merriam	66202-66204	
Mission	66205	
Mission Hills	66208	
Mission Woods	66205	
Overland Park	66221	
Overland Park	66223-66224	
Prairie Village	66202	
Prairie Village	66204	
Prairie Village	66206-66208	
Prarie Village	66212	
Roeland Park	66202	
Roeland Park	66205	
Stanley	66221	
Stanley	66223-66224	
Westwood	66205	
Westwood Hills	66205	
Sherwin (Columbus)	66725	
Shields	67874	
Sieboldt (Oxford)	67119	
Silver Lake	66539	
Silverdale	67005	
(Arkansas City)		
Simpson	67478	
Sims (Baxter Springs)	66713	
Skidmore (Scammon)	66773	
Smith Center	66967	
Smolan	67479	
Soldier	66540	
Solomon	67480	
South Haven	67140	
South Hutchinson	67505	
Spearville	67876	
Spivey	67142	
Spring Grove (Galena)	66739	
Spring Hill	66083	
Stafford	67578	
Stanley	66221, 66223-224	
(Shawnee Mission)		
Stark	66775	
Sterling	67579	
Stilwell	66085	
Stippville (Columbus)	66725	
Stockton	67669	
Strauss (Mc Cune)	66753	

Strawn (Burlington)	66839	
Strong City	66869	
Stuttgart	67670	
Sublette	67877	
Summerfield	66541	
Sun City	67143	
Susank (Hoisington)	67544	
Sycamore	67363	
Sylvan Grove	67481	
Sylvia	67581	
Syracuse	67878	
Talmage	67482	
Tampa	67483	
Tecumseh	66542	
Tescott	67484	
Thayer	66776	
Timken	67582	
Tipton	67485	
Tonganoxie	66086	
Topeka	66600-601	
	66603-612, 66614-622	
	66624-629, 66634	
	66636-66638, 66642	
	66647, 66652-653	
	66658, 66667, 66675, 66683	
	66686, 66692, 66699	
Atchison Topeka		
Santa Fe	66628	
Blue Cross	66629	
Pauline	66619	
Toronto	66777	
Towanda	67144	
Treece	66778	
Tribune	67879	
Trousdale (Haviland)	67059	
Troy	66087	
Turon	67583, 67569	
Tyro	67364	
Udall	67146	
Ulysses	67880	
Uniontown	66779	
Utica	67584	
Valley Center	67147	
Valley Falls	66088	
Vassar	66543	
Vermillion	66544	
Vernon (Yates Center)	66783	
Victoria	67671	
Viola	67149	
Virgil	66870	
Vliets (Vermillion)	66544	
Wakarusa	66546	
Wakefield	67487	
Waldo	67673	
Waldron	67150	
Walker	67674	
Wallace	67761	
Walnut	66780	
Walton	67151	
Wamego	66547	
Washington	66968	
Waterville	66548	
Wathena	66090	
Waverly	66871	
Webber	66970	
Weir	66781	
Welda	66091	
Wellington	67152	
Wells	67488	
Wellsville	66092	
Weskan	67762	

KANSAS   IMPORTANT BUILDINGS

COUNTRYSIDE

GOVERNMENT

Johnson County Courthouse
6000 LAMAR AVE 66202

FAIRWAY

GOVERNMENT

Fairway City Hall
5252 BELINDER RD 66205

Westwood City Hall
4700 RAINBOW BLVD 66205

HUTCHINSON

BUILDINGS

First National Ctr
1 N MAIN ST 67501

Hutchinson Mall
1500 E 11TH AVE 67501

Wiley Building
100 N MAIN ST 67501

GOVERNMENT

Reno County Courthouse
206 W 1ST AVE 67501

KANSAS CITY

GOVERNMENT

City Hall
701 N 7TH ST 66101

Court House Building
710 N 7TH ST 66101

Federal Building
812 N 7TH ST 66101

LAWRENCE

BUILDINGS

Judicial Law Center
111 E 11TH ST 66044

GOVERNMENT

Douglas Cty Courthouse
1100 Massachusetts St 66044

Lawrence City Hall
6 E 6TH ST 66044

COLLEGES

Haskell Indian Jr College
155 INDIAN AVE 66046

LEAWOOD

GOVERNMENT

Leawood City Hall
9615 LEE BLVD 66206

LENEXA

GOVERNMENT

Lenexa City Hall
12350 W 87TH Street Pky   66215

HOSPITALS

Humana Medical Center
10500 QUIVIRA RD 66215

OLATHE

BUILDINGS

County Court House
100 N KANSAS AVE 66061

TOPEKA

APARTMENTS

Aldersgate Nursing Home
7220 SW ASBURY DR 66614

Brewster Pl Apts
1205 SW 29TH ST 66611

Carriage House Apts
1601 SW 37TH TER 66609

Cedar Ridge
3200 SW Eveningside Dr .. 66614

Chalet Apt
4140 SW 6TH AVE 66606

Christian Church Apts
3805 SW 18TH ST 66604

Crown Colony Apt
900 SW ROBINSON AVE . 66606

El Dorado Apt
4120 SW TWILIGHT DR ... 66614

Embassy Ii Apts
2940 SW GAGE BLVD 66614

Fairlawn Greens
5200 SW 20TH TER 66604

Glendale Apts
1209 SW GLENDALE DR . 66604

Hearthstone
3515 SW 6TH AVE 66606

Jackson Towers
1122 SW JACKSON ST 66612

Kansan Towers Apt
100 SE 9TH ST 66612

Knightsbridge Manor
501 SW FRANKLIN AVE ... 66606

La Casa Grande
2900 SW 31ST CT 66614

Landmark Plaza
1000 S KANSAS AVE 66612

Luther Place I
5000 SW HUNTOON ST ... 66604

Luther Place Ii
4900 SW HUNTOON ST ... 66604

Mission Towers Apts
2929 SE MINNESOTA AVE 66605

Oakbrook Apt
3201 SW TWILIGHT CT ... 66614

Park South Apts
3711 SW Park South CT ... 66609

Plaza West
5620 SW 22ND ST 66614

Polk Plaza
1312 SW POLK ST 66612

Raintree Apts
3704 SW 29TH ST 66614

Sterling Apts
705 SW POLK ST 66603

The Pines Apts
238 SW GAGE BLVD 66606

Townhouse Apts
635 SW HARRISON ST 66603

Tyler Towers
600 SW 14TH ST 66612

Warren House Apt
3500 SW 29TH ST 66614

White Lakes Plz Apts
3733 SW PLAZA DR 66609

Whitehall Apt
3930 SW TWILIGHT DR ... 66614

BUILDINGS

1 Townsite Plaza
534 S KANSAS AVE 66603

Bank Iv Tower
534 S KANSAS AVE 66603

Cap Fed Building
700 S KANSAS AVE 66603

Capital City Bank Plaza
3706 SW TOPEKA BLVD .. 66609

Capitol Tower
400 SW 8TH AVE 66603

Columbian Building
112 SW 6TH AVE 66603

Columbian Title Building
820 SE QUINCY ST 66612

Continental Medical Building
631 SW HORNE ST 66606

Garfield Med Plaza Building
901 SW GARFIELD AVE ... 66606

Hypermart
1501 SW Wanamaker Rd . 66604

Insurance Building
701 SW JACKSON ST 66603

Jayhawk Tower
700 SW JACKSON ST 66603

Kansas Expocentre
1 EXPOCENTRE DR 66612

Kpl Tower Office Building
818 S KANSAS AVE 66612

Liberty Plaza Building
214 SW 6TH AVE 66603

Medical Plz Building
1001 SW GARFIELD AVE . 66604

Merchant Towers
800 SW JACKSON ST 66612

Mills Building
109 SW 9TH ST 66612

Mulvane Medical Plaza
634 SW MULVANE ST 66606

New England Building
503 S KANSAS AVE 66603

Sw Plaza Office Building
3601 SW 29TH ST 66614

Townsite
200 SE 6TH AVE 66603

Townsite Plaza
120 SE 6TH AVE 66603

West Ridge Mall
1801 SW Wanamaker Rd . 66604

GOVERNMENT

City Hall
215 SE7TH ST 66603

Docking State Office Building
915 SW HARRISON ST 66612

Federal Building
444 SE QUINCY ST 66683

Ks Judicial Center
301 SW 10TH AVE 66612

Landon State Office Building
900 SW JACKSON ST 66612

Shawnee County Courthouse
200 SE 7TH ST 66603

State Capitol Building
300 SW 10TH AVE 66612

HOTELS

Best Western Meadow Acres
2950 SW TOPEKA BLVD ... 66611

Ramada Inn Downtown
420 SE 6TH AVE 66607

WICHITA

BUILDINGS

1st National Bank Building
106 W DOUGLAS AVE 67202

Bitting Building
107 N MARKET ST 67202

Broadway Plaza Building
105 S BROADWAY ST 67202

Centre City Plaza
151 N MAIN ST 67202

Century Plaza Building
111 W DOUGLAS AVE 67202

Colorado Derby Building
202 W 1ST ST N 67202

Commerce Plaza Building
401 E DOUGLAS AVE 67202

Douglas Building
104 S BROADWAY ST 67202

Epic Center
301 N MAIN ST 67202

Exchange Place
110 N MARKET ST 67202

Farmers And Bankers Building
200 E 1ST ST N 67202

Fourth Financial Ctr
100 N BROADWAY ST 67202

Ima Plaza
250 N WATER ST 67202

Kansas St Bank Building
125 N MARKET ST 67202

Kaufman Building
212 S MARKET ST 67202

Kress Energy Building
224 E DOUGLAS AVE 67202

Landmark Square
212 N MARKET ST 67202

O W Garvey Building
200 W DOUGLAS AVE 67202

One Main Place
100 N MAIN ST 67202

Page Court
220 W DOUGLAS AVE 67202

Petroleum Building
221 S BROADWAY ST 67202

R H Garvey Building
300 W DOUGLAS AVE 67202
Rule Building
321 E WILLIAM ST 67202

Sutton Pl
209 E WILLIAM ST 67202

Union Center Building
150 N MAIN ST 67202

GOVERNMENT

City Hall Building
455 N MAIN ST 67202

Federal Courthouse
401 N MARKET ST 67202

Sedgwick Cnty Courthouse
525 N MAIN ST 67203

MILITARY

Mc Connell Air Force Base
57837 COFFEYVILLE ST . 67221

KENTUCKY
Abbreviation KY

Aaron 42601
Abbott (Bedford) 40006
Abegall (Germantown) 41044
Aberdeen 42201
Absher (Columbia) 42728
Adairville 42202
Adams 41201
Addison (Hardinsburg) 40143
Adeline (Catlettsburg) 41129
Adolphus 42120
Aflex (Goody) 41529
Ages (Ages Brookside) 40801
Ages Brookside 40801
Ajax (Bulan) 41722
Akers (Cumberland) 40823
Akersville (Fountain Run) .. 42133
Albany 42602
Alcalde (Somerset) 42501
Alexandria 41001
Allegre 42203
Allen 41601
Allen Springs 42122, 42164
  (Alvaton)
Allendale (Summersville) .. 42782
Allensville 42204
Allock 41710
Almo 42020
Almo Heights (Almo) 42020
Alonzo (Adolphus) 42120
Alpha 42603
Alpine (Burnside) 42519
Alton (Lawrenceburg) 40342
Alva (Pathfork) 40863
Alvaton 42122
Amandaville (Bakerton) 42711
Amba (Harold) 41635
Amburgey 41801
Amos (Holland) 42153
Anchorage 40223, 40245
  (Louisville)
Anco (Sassafras) 41759
Anderson (Quality) 42268
Anna 42101, 42270
  (Bowling Green)
Annville 40402
Arch (Vertrees) 42785
Argillite 41121
Argo (Stopover) 41568
Argyle (Bethelridge) 42516
Arjay 40902
Ark (Ingram) 40955
Arlington 42021
Arrington Corner 42348
  (Hawesville)
Artemus 40903
Arthur (Brownsville) 42210
Ary 41712
Ashcamp 41512
Asher 40803
Ashland .. 41101-02, 41105, 41114
  Bellefonte 41101
  Cannonsburg 41101
  Cannonsburg 41105
  Ironville 41101
  Meads 41101
  Millseat 41101
  Naples 41101
  Naples 41105

Princess 41101
Rockdale 41101
Summit 41101
Summit 41105
Unity 41101
West Fairview 41101
Westwood 41101
Asphalt (Brownsville) 42210
Athertonville 42748
  (Hodgenville)
Athol 41307
Atwood (Morning View) 41063
Auburn 42206
Augusta 41002
Ault (Olive Hill) 41164
Aurora (Hardin) 42048
Austin 42123
Auxier 41602
Avawam 41713
Avondale (Paducah) 42001
Bagdad 40003
Bailey Creek (Evarts) 40828
Bailey Switch 40906
  (Barbourville)
Baileys Branch (Hestand) . 42151
Bainbridge (Cerulean) 42215
Bakerton 42711
Bald Hill (Flemingsburg) ... 41041
Baldrock (London) 40741
Balkan (Pineville) 40977
Ballardsville (Crestwood) .. 40014
Bandana 42022
Banner 41603
Banock (Morgantown) 42261
Barbourville 40906, 40911
  Bailey Switch 40906
  Baughman 40906
  Boone Heights 40906
  Carpenter 40906
  Crane Nest 40906
  Gausdale 40906
  Himyar 40906
  Jarvis 40906
  Kayjay 40906
  Sprule 40906
  Swan Lake 40906
  Swanpond 40906
  Tedders 40906
  Warren 40906
Bardstown 40004
Bardstown Junction 40165
  (Shepherdsville)
Bardwell 42023
Bark Camp (Corbin) 40701
Barlow 42024
Barnetts Creek 41256
  (Staffordsville)
Barnrock (Flatgap) 41219
Barnyard (Flat Lick) 40935
Barren River 42101
  (Bowling Green)
Barrier (Monticello) 42633
Basil (Gradyville) 42742
Baskett 42402
Bath (Mallie) 41836
Battle Run (Ewing) 41039
Battletown 40104
Baughman 40906, 40911
  (Barbourville)
  Barbourville 40911
Baxter 40806

Bayfork (Alvaton) 42122
Bays 41310
Bear Branch 41714
Bear Wallow (Cave City) ... 42127
Bearville (Emmalena) 41740
Beattyville 41311
Beaumont 42124, 42166
Beauty 41203
Beaver 41604
Beaver Bottom 41522
  (Elkhorn City)
Beaver Dam 42320
Beaverlick (Walton) 41094
Becks Store (Breeding) 42715
Beckton (Glasgow) 42141
Bedford 40006
Bee (Cub Run) 42729
Bee Spring 42207
Beech (Mary Alice) 40964
Beech Creek 42321
Beech Grove 40150, 42322
  (Lebanon Junction)
Beechburg (Wallingford) ... 41093
Beechland (Lewisburg) 42256
Beechmont 42323
Beechville (Edmonton) 42129
Beechy (South Shore) 41175
Belcher 41513
Belfry 41514, 41569
  Hatfield 41514
  Orinoco 41514
  Sharondale 41514
Bell City (Farmington) 42040
Bellefonte (Ashland) 41101
Belleview (Burlington) 41005
Bellevue (Newport) 41073
Bellwood (Bardstown) 40004
Belmont 40150, 41031
  (Lebanon Junction)
Belton 42324
Benham 40807
Benlo (Bowling Green) 42101
Bennettstown (Herndon) ... 42236
Benton 42025
Berea 40403-404
Berlin (Foster) 41043
Bernice (Fall Rock) 40932
Bernstadt (London) 40741
Berry 41003
Berrys Lick (Quality) 42268
Bethanna (Salyersville) 41465
Bethany 41313
Bethelridge 42516
Bethesda (Monticello) 42633
Bethlehem 40007
Betsey (Monticello) 42633
Betsy Layne 41605
Beulah (Dawson Springs) . 42408
Beulah Heights 42607
Beverly 40913
Bevinsville 41606
Big Branch (Elkhorn City) . 41522
Big Clifty 42712
Big Creek 40914
Big Fork (Yeaddiss) 41777
Big Laurel 40808
Big Ready (Roundhill) 42275
Big Rock (Yeaddiss) 41777
Big Sandy Junction 41129
  (Catlettsburg)
Big Spring 40106

Biggs (Fedscreek) 41524
Bighill 40405
Bimble 40915
Birk City (Owensboro) 42301
Black Gold (Sweeden) 42285
Black Mountain (Kenvir) ... 40847
Black Rock (Oak Grove) ... 42262
Blackey 41804
Blackford 42403
Blackjoe (Harlan) 40831
Bladeston (Brooksville) 41004
Blaine 41124
Blairs Mill 41472
   (West Liberty)
Blanche (Arjay) 40902
Blanchet (Corinth) 41010
Blandville 42026
Blaze (West Liberty) 41472
Bledsoe 40810
Blevins (Blaine) 41124
Blincoe (Loretto) 40037
Bliss (Columbia) 42728
Bloomfield 40008
Blowing Spring 42743
   (Greensburg)
Blowing Springs (Cub Run) 42729
Blue Bank (Flemingsburg) 41041
Blue Diamond (Bonnyman) 41719
Blue Level (Rockfield) 42274
Blue River 41607
Blue Spring (Cadiz) 42211
Bluehole 40917
Bluff Boom (Greensburg) .. 42743
Blythe (Hestand) 42151
Board Tree (Freeburn) 41528
Boaz 42027
Boiling Spring 42101
   (Bowling Green)
Boles (Tompkinsville) 42167
Bolyn (Garrett) 41630
Bonanza (Prestonsburg) .. 41653
Bonayer (Park City) 42160
Bondville (Salvisa) 40372
Bonnieville 42713
Bonnyman 41719
Boone Heights 40906
   (Barbourville)
Booneville 41314
Boons Camp 41204
Boston 40107, 42268
Botland (Bardstown) 40004
Bow 42714
Bowen 40309
Bowling Green 42101-104
   Anna 42101
   Barren River 42101
   Benlo 42101
   Boiling Spring 42101
   Bristow 42101
   Cassaday 42103
   Claypool 42103
   Crestmoor 42101
   Delafield 42101
   Eastland Park 42104
   Girkin 42101
   Glenmore 42101
   Gott 42103
   Greenhill 42103
   Greenwood 42104
   Guy 42101
   Indian Hills 42103

Lost River 42101
Matlock 42104
Memphis Junction 42101
Motley 42103
Mount Victor 42104
Nick 42101
Plano 42104
Plum Springs 42101
Rich Pond 42104
Riverside 42101
Rockland 42101
Sand Hill 42101
Shawnee Estates 42104
Springhill 42101
Sunnyside 42101
Three Springs 42104
Boxville (Morganfield) 42437
Boyce (Alvaton) 42122
Boyds Crossing 42782
   (Summersville)
Bracht (Crittenden) 41030
Bradford (Foster) 41043
Bradfordsville 40009
Bramlett (Greensburg) 42743
Brandenburg 40108
Breckinridge (Cynthiana) .. 41031
Breeding 42715
Bremen 42325
Bright Shade (Manchester) 40962
Brinegar (Olive Hill) 41164
Brinkley 41805
Bristow (Bowling Green) ... 42101
Britmark (Elkton) 42220
Broad Bottom (Pikeville) .. 41501
Broad Ford (Clarkson) 42726
Broadwell (Cynthiana) 41031
Brodhead 40409
Bromley 41016, 41086
   (Covington)
Bronston 42518
Brooklyn 42209
Brooks 40109
Brookside 40801
   (Ages Brookside)
Brooksville 41004
Browder 42326
Brownies Creek (Miracle) . 40856
Browning (Rockfield) 42274
Brownings Corner 41040
   (Falmouth)
Browningtown 40165
   (Shepherdsville)
Browns Crossroads 42602
   (Albany)
Browns Ford 42133
   (Fountain Run)
Browns Fork 41720
Brownsville 42210
Brownwood Manor 42301
   (Owensboro)
Bruin 41125
Brutus (Oneida) 40972
Bryan (Jamestown) 42629
Bryants Store 40921
Bryantsville 40410
Buckhorn 41721
Buckingham (Hi Hat) 41636
Buckner 40010
Buechel 40218, 40228
   (Louisville)
Buena Vista (Cynthiana) ... 41031

Buffalo (Gracey) 42232, 42716
   Mount Tabor 42716
   South Buffalo 42716
Bug (Albany) 42602
Bugtussle (Gamaliel) 42140
Bulan 41722
Bullittsville 41005
   (Burlington)
Buras (Custer) 40115
Burdine 41517
Burgin 40310
Burke (Sandy Hook) 41171
Burkesville 42717
Burkhart 41315
Burlington 41005
Burna 42028
Burnaugh (Catlettsburg) ... 41129
Burning Fork 41465
   (Salyersville)
Burnside 42519, 42555
   Alpine 42519
   Sloans Valley 42519
Burnwell 41518
Burton (Bypro) 41612
Burtonville (Tollesboro) 41189
Bush 40724
Bushong (Tompkinsville) .. 42167
Buskirk 41406, 41544
Busy 41723
Butchertown (Liberty) 42539
Butler 41006
Butterfly (Bonnyman) 41719
Bybee (Waco) 40385
Bypro 41612
Cadiz 42211
Cains Store (Nancy) 42544
Caledonia (Gracey) 42232
Calhoun 42327
California 41007
Callaway (Pineville) 40977
Calvary (Lebanon) 40033
Calvert City 42029
Calvin 40813
Camelia (West Paducah) .. 42086
Camp Dix 41127
Camp Ernest (Burlington) . 41005
Campbellsburg 40011
Campbellsville 42718-719
Campsprings (Melbourne) 41059
Campton 41301
Canada 41519
Cane Valley 42720
Caneyville 42721
Canmer 42722
Cannel City 41408
Cannon 40923
Cannonsburg 41101, 41105
   (Ashland)
Canoe (Jackson) 41339
Carbon Glow (Letcher) 41832
Carbondale 42408
   (Dawson Springs)
Carcassonne (Blackey) 41804
Carden (Glasgow) 42141
Cardinal (Hulen) 40845
Carl (Elkton) 42220
Carlisle 40311
Carntown (Butler) 41006
Carpenter (Barbourville) ... 40906
Carr Creek 41834, 41847
   (Littcarr)

Carrie 41725	Claymour (Elkton) 42220	Corydon 42406
Carrollton 41008, 41045	Claypool (Bowling Green) . 42103	Cottageville (Vanceburg) 41179
English 41008	Clear Creek (Pineville) 40977	Cottle 41412
Prestonville 41008	Clearfield 40313	Counts Cross Roads 41164
Carrs (Vanceburg) 41179	Cleaton 42332	(Olive Hill)
Carrsville (Smithland) 42081	Clementsville (Liberty) 42539	Covedale (Vanceburg) 41179
Carter 41128	Clermont 40110	Covington .. 41011-012, 41014-19
Carthage (California) 41007	Cliff (Prestonsburg) 41653	Bromley 41016
Cartwright (Albany) 42602	Clifford (Louisa) 41230	Crescent Park 41017
Carver 41409	Clifty 42216	Crestview Hills 41017
Cary (Pineville) 40977	Climax (Mount Vernon) 40456	Decoursey 41011
Casey (Morgantown) 42261	Clinton 42031	Dixie 41017
Casey Creek 42723	Clintonville (Paris) 40361	Edgewood 41017
Cash (Upton) 42784	Closplint 40927	Elsmere 41018
Cassaday (Bowling Green) .. 42103	Clover Bottom (Mc Kee) 40447	Erlanger 41018
Catalpa (Catlettsburg) 41129	Clover Darby (Closplint) 40927	Fort Mitchell 41017
Catherine (Windsor) 42565	Cloverport 40111	Fort Wright 41011
Catlettsburg 41129	Clovertown (Harlan) 40831	Kenton Hills 41011
Causey (Wooton) 41776	Cloyds Landing (Kettle) 42752	Kentonvale 41015
Cave City 42127	Coakley (Summersville) 42782	Lakeside Park 41017
Cave Ridge (Edmonton) 42129	Coalgood 40818	Latonia 41015
Cave Spring 42276	Coalton (Rush) 41168	Lookout Heights 41011
(Russellville)	Cobhill 40415	Ludlow 41016
Cave Springs (Olmstead) .. 42265	Coburg (Greensburg) 42743	Park Hills 41011
Cavehill (Rockfield) 42274	Coe (Tompkinsville) 42167	Rosedale 41015
Cawood 40815	Cofer (Edmonton) 42129	Rouse 41014
Cayce (Fulton) 42041	Cold Spring (Newport) 41076	Ryland 41015
Cecilia 42724	Coldiron 40819	South Fort Mitchell 41017
Cedar Flat (Edmonton) 42129	Coldwater (Murray) 42071	Taylor Mill 41015
Cedar Grove 42280	Coleman (Phelps) 41553	Villa Hills 41017
(Sharon Grove)	Coles Bend (Smiths Grove) 42171	Cowan (Ewing) 41039
Cedar Spring (Park City) 42160	Colesburg 40150	Coxs Creek 40013
Cedar Springs 42164	(Lebanon Junction)	Coxton (Harlan) 40831
(Scottsville)	Colfax (Hillsboro) 41049	Crab Orchard 40419
Cedarcrest (Faubush) 42532	Collista (Hagerhill) 41222	Crailhope (Center) 42214
Cedarville (Elkhorn City) 41522	Colly (Ermine) 41815	Craintown (Flemingsburg) . 41041
Center 42214	Columbia 42728	Crane Nest (Barbourville) . 40906
Center Point 42167	Columbus 42032	Cranks 40820
(Tompkinsville)	Colville (Cynthiana) 41031	Cravens (Bardstown) 40004
Centertown 42328	Combs 41729	Craycraft (Columbia) 42728
Central City 42330	Concord 41131	Crayne 42033
Cerulean 42215	Confederate (Eddyville) 42038	Craynor 41614
Chad (Cumberland) 40823	Confluence 41730	Creal (Mount Sherman) 42764
Chalybeate (Smiths Grove) 42171	Connersville (Cynthiana) ... 41031	Creekmore (Strunk) 42649
Chance (Columbia) 42728	Constance 41009	Creekville (Manchester) 40962
Chandlerville (Stambaugh) 41257	Constantine 40114	Creelsboro (Jamestown) 42629
Chapel Hill (Adolphus) 42120	Conway 40417	Crescent Park (Covington) 41017
Chaplin 40012	Cooktown (Austin) 42123	Crestmoor (Bowling Green) 42101
Chappell 40816	Cool Springs (Beaver Dam) 42320	Creston (Liberty) 42539
Charleston 42408	Cooperstown 42276	Crestview (Newport) 41076
(Dawson Springs)	(Russellville)	Crestview Hills 41017
Charters (Vanceburg) 41179	Coopersville 42611	(Covington)
Chatham (Augusta) 41002	Coral Hill (Glasgow) 42141	Crestwood 40014
Chavies 41727	Corbin 40701-702	Crittenden 41030
Chenoa (Pineville) 40977	Bark Camp 40701	Crockett 41413
Cherokee (Webbville) 41180	Cumberland Falls 40701	Crocus (Glens Fork) 42741
Chestnutburg (Manchester) 40962	Dortha 40701	Crofton 42217
Chevrolet (Harlan) 40831	Faber 40701	Croley (Clinton) 42031
Christine (Columbia) 42728	Lynncamp 40701	Cromona 41810
Cinda 41728	North Corbin 40701	Cromwell 42333
Cisco 41410	South Corbin 40701	Cropper (Pleasureville) 40057
Clarence (Eubank) 42567	Walden 40701	Cross Roads (Lewisburg) . 42256
Clark Hill (Olive Hill) 41164	Cordell (Blaine) 41124	Crown 41811
Clarksburg (Vanceburg) 41179	Corinth 41010, 42276	Crummies (Cawood) 40815
Clarkson 42726	Blanchet 41010	Crutchfield (Fulton) 42041
Claryville (Alexandria) 41001	Cork (Edmonton) 42129	Crystal 40420
Clay 42404	Corn Creek (Bedford) 40006	Cub Run 42729
Clay City 40312	Cornetts (Gordon) 41819	Cubage (Miracle) 40856
Clay Village 40065	Cornettsville 41731	Culver 41211
(Shelbyville)	Cornishville 40330	Cumberland 40823
Clayhole 41317	(Harrodsburg)	Cumberland City (Albany) . 42602

Fairplay	42735
Fairview	42210, 42221
(Brownsville)	
Fairview Hill (Hitchins)	41146
Falcon	41426
Fall Rock	40932
Falls Of Rough	40119
Fallsburg (Louisa)	41230
Falmouth	41040
Fancy Farm	42039
Fariston (London)	40741
Farler (Viper)	41774
Farmers	40319
Farmington	42040
Faubush	42532
Faxon (Murray)	42071
Fearisville (Vanceburg)	41179
Feathersburg	42723
(Casey Creek)	
Fedscreek	41524
Ferguson	42533
Fern Creek (Louisville)	40291
Ferrells Creek (Belcher)	41513
Field (Pineville)	40977
Fillmore	41323
Finchville	40022
Finley	42736
Finney (Glasgow)	42141
Firebrick	41137
Fisherville	40023
Fishtrap (Raccoon)	41557
Fiskburg (De Mossville)	41033
Fisty	41743
Fitch (Olive Hill)	41164
Flagg Spring (California)	41007
Flaherty (Vine Grove)	40175
Flanary (Mouthcard)	41548
Flat (Campton)	41301
Flat Fork	41427
Flat Lick	40935
Flat Rock	42261, 42653
(Morgantown)	
Flatgap	41219
Flatwoods	41139
Fleet (Gamaliel)	42140
Fleming (Neon)	41840
Fleming Neon (Neon)	41840
Flemingsburg	41041
Flener (Morgantown)	42261
Flingsville (Crittenden)	41030
Flippin (Tompkinsville)	42167
Florence	41022, 41042
Devon	41042
Hopeful Heights	41042
Floyd (Eubank)	42567
Fogertown	40936
Folsomdale (Hickory)	42051
Fonde (Frakes)	40940
Fonthill	42642
(Russell Springs)	
Foraker (Salyersville)	41465
Ford	40320, 40391
Fords Branch	41526
Fordsville	42343
Forest Hills	41527
Forkton (Tompkinsville)	42167
Fort Campbell	42223
Fort Knox	40121
Fort Mitchell (Covington)	41017
Fort Thomas (Newport)	41075
Fort Wright (Covington)	41011

Foster	41043
Fount (Woollum)	40999
Fountain Run	42133
Four Oaks (Falmouth)	41040
Fourmile	40939
Foxport (Wallingford)	41093
Frakes	40940
Frances (Marion)	42064
Francisville (Hebron)	41048
Frankfort	40601-604, 40618-622
Hattie	40601
Hatton	40601
Franklin	42134-135
Salmons	42134
Wallonia	42134
Franklinton	40057
(Pleasureville)	
Frazer	42618
Fredonia	42411
Fredville	41430
Freeburn	41528
Freedom	42157, 42629
(Mount Hermon)	
Freetown (Gamaliel)	42140
Fremont (Paducah)	42001
Frenchburg	40322
Frew (Wooton)	41776
Frisby (Monticello)	42633
Fritz (Salyersville)	41465
Frozen Creek (Jackson)	41339
Fruithill (Crofton)	42217
Fry (Greensburg)	42743
Fulgham (Clinton)	42031
Fullerton (South Shore)	41175
Fulton	42041
Fultz (Grayson)	41143
Fusonia (Viper)	41774
Gabbard (Ricetown)	41364
Gabe (Greensburg)	42743
Gadberry (Fairplay)	42735
Gage (La Center)	42056
Gainesville (Scottsville)	42164
Galveston	41629
Gamaliel	42140
Gap In Knob	40165
(Shepherdsville)	
Gapcreek (Alpha)	42603
Gapville	41433
Gardnersville	41033
(De Mossville)	
Garfield	40140
Garlin (Columbia)	42728
Garner (Rush)	41168, 41817
Larkslane	41817
Garrard	40941
Garrett	41630
Garrettsburg (Herndon)	42236
Garrison	41141
Garvin Ridge (Olive Hill)	41164
Gascon (Edmonton)	42129
Gaskill (Jenkins)	41537
Gasper (Auburn)	42206
Gassaway (Glasgow)	42141
Gausdale (Barbourville)	40906
Gays Creek	41745
Geneva (Corydon)	42406
Gentrys Mill (Columbia)	42728
Georgetown	40324
Germantown	41044
Gertrude (Brooksville)	41004
Gest (Pleasureville)	40057

Ghent	41045
Gilbertsville	42044
Gillem Branch (Flatgap)	41219
Gillmore	41327
Gilly (Gordon)	41819
Gilpin (Liberty)	42539
Gilreath (Pine Knot)	42635
Gilstrap (Morgantown)	42261
Gimlet (Olive Hill)	41164
Ginseng (Howardstown)	40028
Girdler	40943
Girkin (Bowling Green)	42101
Glasgow	42141-142
Beckton	42141
Carden	42141
Coral Hill	42141
Dry Fork	42141
Finney	42141
Gassaway	42141
Haywood	42141
Kino	42141
Lecta	42141
Oil City	42141
Pritchardsville	42141
Rocky Hill	42141
Roseville	42141
Slick Rock	42141
Temple Hill	42141
Gleanings (New Hope)	40052
Glen Dean	40119
(Falls Of Rough)	
Glen Springs (Vanceburg)	41179
Glencoe	41046
Glendale	42740
Glenmore	42101, 42270
(Bowling Green)	
Glens Fork	42741
Glenview	40025
Glo (Wayland)	41666
Globe (Olive Hill)	41164
Goddard (Wallingford)	41093
Goforth (Falmouth)	41040
Golden Ash (Harlan)	40831
Golden Pond (Cadiz)	42211
Goochtown (Eubank)	42567
Goodluck (Edmonton)	42129
Goodnight (Cave City)	42127
Goody	41529
Goose Rock	40944
Gordon	41819
Gordonsville	42276
(Russellville)	
Goshen	40026
Gott (Bowling Green)	42103
Grab (Greensburg)	42743
Grace (Manchester)	40962
Gracey	42232
Gradyville	42742
Graham	42344
Grahamville	42086
(West Paducah)	
Grahn	41142
Grancer	42261, 42287
(Morgantown)	
Grand Rivers	42045
Grandview (Tompkinsville)	42167
Grange City (Hillsboro)	41049
Grants Lick (Alexandria)	41001
Grassland (Brownsville)	42210
Grassy Creek	41332
(Hazel Green)	

Gravel Switch 40328
Gray 40734
Gray Hawk 40434
Grays Knob 40829
Grayson 41143
Grayson Springs 42726
  (Clarkson)
Greasy Creek (Shelbiana) 41562
Green Hall 41328
Green Road 40946
Greenbriar (Owensboro) .. 42301
Greencastle 42270
  (Richardsville)
Greenhill (Bowling Green) . 42103
Greenmount (London) 40741
Greensburg 42743
Greenup 41144
Greenville 42345
Greenwood 42104, 42634
  (Bowling Green)
Gregory (Monticello) 42633
Gresham (Greensburg) 42743
Grethel 41631
Griderville (Cave City) 42127
Grove Center 42437
  (Morganfield)
Guage (Jackson) 41339
Gubser Mill (California) 41007
Guerrant (Jackson) 41339
Guffey (Evarts) 40828
Gulnare (Pikeville) 41501
Gulston 40830
Gum Tree (Tompkinsville) . 42167
Gunlock 41632
Guston 40142
Guthrie 42234
Guy (Bowling Green) 42101
Haddix 41331
Hadensville (Guthrie) 42234
Hadley 42235
Hager (Salyersville) 41465
Hagerhill 41222
Halcom (Culver) 41211
Halcombs (Gordon) 41819
Haldeman 40329
Haleys Mill (Crofton) 42217
Halfway 42150
Halifax (Scottsville) 42164
Hall (Neon) 41840
Hallie 41821
Halo 41633
Hamilton (Union) 41091
Hamlin 42046
Hammackville (Trenton) ... 42286
Hammond (Flat Lick) 40935
Hammonville (Magnolia) ... 42757
Hampton 42047
Handshoe (Hueysville) 41640
Hannah (Blaine) 41124
Hansbrough (Cecilia) 42724
Hanson 42413
Happy 41746
Happy Acre 42642
  (Russell Springs)
Hardburly 41747
Hardin 42048
Hardin Springs 42712
  (Big Clifty)
Harding (Hardinsburg) 40143
Hardinsburg 40143
Hardshell (Lost Creek) 41348

Hardwick (Frazer) 42618
Hardy 41531, 41558
Hardyville 42746
Harlan 40831, 40840
  Blackjoe 40831
  Chevrolet 40831
  Clovertown 40831
  Coxton 40831
  Elcomb 40831
  Golden Ash 40831
  Helton 40831
  Kitts 40831
  Liggett 40831
  Saylor 40831
  Spruce Pine 40831
  Stanfill 40831
  Sunshine 40831
  Teetersville 40831
  Tway 40831
  Yancey 40831
Harlan Crossroads 42167
  (Tompkinsville)
Harned 40144
Harold 41635
Harper (Salyersville) 41465
Harrellsville (Lewisburg) .. 42256
Harrods Creek 40027
Harrodsburg 40330
Hartford 42347
Hartley (Virgie) 41572
Haskingsville 42743
  (Greensburg)
Hatfield (Belfry) 41514
Hattie (Frankfort) 40601
Hatton (Frankfort) 40601
Hawesville 42348
Hawkins (Cerulean) 42215
Hays (Smiths Grove) 42171
Haywood (Glasgow) 42141
Hazard 41701-702
  Darfork 41701
  Walkertown 41701
Hazel 42049
Hazel Green 41332
Hazel Patch 40729
  (East Bernstadt)
Heath (West Paducah) 42086
Hebron 41048
Hector (Manchester) 40962
Heekin (Williamstown) 41097
Heidelberg 41333
Heidrick 40949
Heiner (Bulan) 41722
Helechawa (Hazel Green) . 41332
Helena (Mays Lick) 41055
Hellier 41534
Helton (Harlan) ... 40831, 40840
  Harlan 40840
Henderson 42420
Hendron (Paducah) 42001
Henshaw (Morganfield) 42437
Hensleytown (Oak Grove) . 42262
Herd 40435
Herman (Guthrie) 42234
Herndon 42236
Heselton (Vanceburg) 41179
Hestand 42151
Hi Hat 41636
Hickman 42050
Hickory 42051
Higdon (Clarkson) 42726

High Bridge (Wilmore) 40390
High Point (West Paducah) 42086
High Top (London) 40741
Highgrove (Coxs Creek) ... 40013
Highland Heights 41076
  (Newport)
Highland Spring 42127
  (Cave City)
Highplains (Big Spring) 40106
Highsplint (Evarts) 40828
Highview (Louisville) 40228
Highway (Albany) 42602
Hillsboro 41049
Hilltop (Williamstown) 41097
Hima 40951
Himyar (Barbourville) 40906
Hindman 41822
Hinkle 40953
Hippo 41637
Hiram (Cumberland) 40823
Hiseville 42152
Hisle (Mc Kee) 40447
Hislope (Nancy) 42544
Hitchins 41146
Hite (Martin) 41649
Hode (Warfield) 41267
Hodgenville 42748
Hogue (Science Hill) 42553
Holbrook (Williamstown) ... 41097
Holland 42153
Hollow Bell (Lewisburg) ... 42256
Hollybush 41823
Hollyhill (Pine Knot) 42635
Holmes Mill 40843
Holy Cross (Loretto) 40037
Homer (Russellville) 42276
Honaker 41639
Honeybee (Parkers Lake) . 42634
Hooktown (Cynthiana) 41031
Hope 40334
Hopeful Heights 41042
  (Florence)
Hopkinsville 42240-241
Horntown (Clarkson) 42726
Horse Branch 42349
Horse Cave 42749
Horton (Beaver Dam) 42320
Hoskinston 40844
Hosman (Pineville) 40977
Hot Spot (Premium) 41845
Hovious (Casey Creek) 42723
Howardstown 40028
Howe Valley (Cecilia) 42724
Howel (Oak Grove) 42262
Hubbs (Bryants Store) 40921
Huddy 41535
Hudgins (Summersville) 42782
Hudson 40145
Hueysville 41640
Huff ....
42250
Hulen 40845
Hunter 41641
Hunters (Bardstown) 40004
Hustonville 40437
Hyden 41749, 41762
  Dryhill 41749
  Kaliopi 41749
  Sizerock 41749
Hydro (Smiths Grove) 42171
Iberia (Clarkson) 42726

(Simpsonville)
Lindseyville 42257
Linefork 41833
Linton (Cadiz) 42211
Linwood (Magnolia) 42757
Lionilli (Jenkins) 41537
Littcarr 41834
Little 41346
Little Barren 42743
(Greensburg)
Little Creek (Arjay) 40902
Little Muddy (Morgantown) . 42261
Little Sandy (Sandy Hook) . 41171
Livermore 42352
Livingston 40445, 40460
Lloyd 41156
Load (Greenup) 41144
Lockards Creek (Garrard) . 40941
Lockport 40036
Lockwood (Catlettsburg) .. 41129
Locust (Milton) 40045
Locust Grove (Falmouth) .. 41040
Locust Hill (Harned) 40144
Lodiburg (Irvington) 40146
Log Mountain (Pineville) .. 40977
Logansport (Morgantown) . 42261
Logville (Salyersville) 41465
Lola 42059
London 40741-743, 40745
Baldrock 40741
Bernstadt 40741
Fariston 40741
Greenmount 40741
High Top 40741
Mcwhorter 40741
Sasser 40741
Sublimity City 40741
Tuttle 40741
Lone 41347
Lone Oak (Paducah) 42001
Lone Star (Bonnieville) 42713
Lookout 41542
Lookout Heights 41011
(Covington)
Loretto 40037
Lost Creek 41348
Lost River 42101
(Bowling Green)
Louellen (Evarts) 40828
Louisa (Adams) 41201, 41230
Clifford 41230
Fallsburg 41230
Richardson 41230
Louisville . 40200-225, 40228-229
40231-233, 40241-243, 40245
.... 40250-253, 40255-259
.... 40261, 40266, 40268-270
40272, 40280, 40285, 40287
.... 40289, 40291-299
Anchorage 40223
Buechel 40218, 40228
Fern Creek 40291
General Electric Co 40225
Highview 40228
Jeffersontown .. 40269, 40299
Kentucky Lottery Corp . 40287
Kosmosdale 40272
Liberty National Bank . 40293
Liberty Natl Bank 40294
Liberty Natl Bank Accts
.... 40293

Lyndon 40222
Lyndon 40241-40242
Middletown 40243
National City Bank 40289
Okolona 40219, 40229
Pleasure Ridge Park
.... 40258, 40268
Saint Matthews 40257
Shively 40216
Standiford Field 40221
Univ Of Louisville 40292
Valley Station 40272
West Buechel 40218
Love (Morgantown) 42261
Lovelaceville 42060
Lovely 41231
Loving (Oakland) 42159
Lowes 42061
Lowgap (Breeding) 42715
Lowmansville 41232
Loyall 40854
Lucas 42156
Lucky Fork (Ricetown) 41364
Ludlow (Covington) 41016
Lynch 40855
Lyndon 40222, 40241-242
Lynn (Greenup) 41144
Lynn Grove (Murray) 42071
Lynncamp (Corbin) 40701
Lynnville 42063
Lytten (Sandy Hook) 41171
Macedonia (Crofton) 42217
Maceo 42355
Mackville 40040
Macon (Munfordville) 42765
Madisonville 42431
Maggard (Salyersville) 41465
Maggie (Cadiz) 42211
Magnolia 42757
Main Street (Pikeville) 41501
Majestic 41547
Mallie 41836
Malone 41451
Maloneton (South Shore) .. 41175
Mammoth Cave 42259
Manchester 40962
Manila (Oil Springs) 41238
Manitou 42436
Mannington (Clifty) 42216-217
Mannsville 42758
Manton (Loretto) 40037, 41649
Maple Grove (Cadiz) 42211
Maple Mount 42356
Marcum (Manchester) 40962
Mariba 40345
Marion 42064
Marrowbone 42759
Marshallville 41452
Marshes Siding 42631
Martha 41159
Martha Mills 41041
(Flemingsburg)
Martin 41649
Martinsville (Oakland) 42159
Mary (Campton) 41301
Mary Alice 40964
Marydell 40751
Mashfork (Salyersville) 41465
Mason 41054
Masonic Home 40041
Massac (Paducah) 42001

Matlock (Bowling Green) ... 42104
Matthew (West Liberty) 41472
Mattoon (Marion) 42064
Maud (Springfield) 40069
Maulden (Tyner) 40486
Mavity (Catlettsburg) 41129
Maxine (Sonora) 42776
May (Pine Top) 41843
Mayfield 42066
Mayking 41837
Maynard (Scottsville) 42164
Mays Lick 41055
Maysville 41056
Maytown (Campton) 41301
Mazie 41160
Mc Andrews 41543
Mc Carr 41544
Mc Daniels 40152
Mc Dowell 41647
Mc Henry 42354
Mc Kee 40447
Mc Kinney 40448
Mc Quady 40153
Mc Roberts 41835
Mc Veigh 41546
Mcgaha (Columbia) 42728
Mckinneysburg (Falmouth) 41040
Mcville (Burlington) 41005
Mcwhorter (London) 40741
Meador (Scottsville) 42164
Meadow Creek 40759
(Rockholds)
Meads (Ashland) 41101
Meally 41234
Means 40346
Meeting Creek (Eastview) . 42732
Melber 42069
Melbourne 41059
Mell (Greensburg) 42743
Melvin 41650
Memphis Junction 42101
(Bowling Green)
Mendola Village 41222
(Hagerhill)
Mentor (California) 41007
Merry Oaks (Smiths Grove) 42171
Meshack (Tompkinsville) ... 42167
Meta (Pikeville) 41501
Mexico (Marion) 42064
Mid (Gunlock) 41632
Middle Creek 42748
(Hodgenville)
Middleburg 42541
Middlesboro 40965
Middleton Heights 40065
(Shelbyville)
Middletown 40243, 42629
(Louisville)
Midway .. 40142, 40347, 42064
(Guston)
Milburn 42070
Milford 41061
Mill Creek (Mays Lick) 41055
Mill Springs 42632
Millard (Shelbiana) 41562
Millersburg 40348
Millerstown (Clarkson) 42726
Mills 40970
Millseat (Ashland) 41101
Millstone 41838
Milltown 42728, 42761

Gimlet	41164
Globe	41164
Ibex	41164
Lawton	41164
Limestone	41164
Prater	41164
Smoky Valley	41164
Stark	41164
Upper Tygart	41164
Wesleyville	41164
Wolf	41164
Olmstead	42265
Olympia	40358
Omaha (Pine Top)	41843
Oneida	40972
Ophir	41459
Orangeburg (Maysville)	41056
Orinoco (Belfry)	41514
Orkney (Mc Dowell)	41647
Orlando	40460
Osborn (Harold)	41635
Oscaloosa (Whitesburg)	41858
Ote (Greensburg)	42743
Otia (Tompkinsville)	42167
Oven Fork	40861
Overlook (Eddyville)	42038
Owensboro	42301-304
Birk City	42301
Brownwood Manor	42301
Dermont	42301
Ensor	42301
Greenbriar	42301
Moseleyville	42301
Newman	42301
Oak Ridge	42301
Owensby (Jamestown)	42629
Owenton	40359
Owingsville	40360
Ozark (Columbia)	42728
Paducah	42001-003
Avondale	42001
Fremont	42001
Hendron	42001
Lone Oak	42001
Massac	42001
Oakdale	42001
Reidland	42001
Saint Johns	42001
Woodlawn	42001
Paint Lick	40461
Paintsville	41240
Palma (Benton)	42025
Paris	40361-362
Clintonville	40361
Park (Horse Cave)	42749
Park City	42160
Park Hills (Covington)	41011
Parkers Lake	42634
Parksville	40464
Parnell (Monticello)	42633
Partridge	40862
Pascal (Hardyville)	42746
Pathfork	40863
Patsey (Stanton)	40380
Pauline (Russellville)	42276
Paw Paw	41551
Payne Gap (Jenkins)	41537
Payneville	40157
Pea Ridge (Elkton)	42220
Peabody (Big Creek)	40914
Peachgrove (Butler)	41006

Pearman (Clarkson)	42726
Pebworth (Booneville)	41314
Pecksridge (Flemingsburg)	41041
Peedee (Herndon)	42236
Pellville	42364
Pellyton (Columbia)	42728
Pembroke	42266
Penchem (Trenton)	42286
Pendleton	40055
Penrod	42365
Peonia (Clarkson)	42726
Peoples	40467
Perry Park	40363
Perrytown (Scottsville)	42164
Perryville	40468
Persimon (Tompkinsville)	42167
Petersburg	41080
Petersville (Vanceburg)	41179
Petra (Brooksville)	41004
Petroleum	42120, 42164
(Adolphus)	
Petros (Rockfield)	42274
Pewee Valley	40056
Phelps	41553
Phillipsburg (Finley)	42736
Philpot	42366
Phyllis	41554
Pickett (Milltown)	42761
Picnic (Breeding)	42715
Pierce (Greensburg)	42743
Pike View (Magnolia)	42757
Pikeville	41501-503
Broad Bottom	41501
Gulnare	41501
Main Street	41501
Meta	41501
Piso	41501
South Williamson	41501
Pilgrim	41250
Pine Grove	40402, 42566
(Annville)	
Pine Knob (Caneyville)	42721
Pine Knot	42635
Pine Mountain (Bledsoe)	40810
Pine Ridge	41360
Pine Top	41843
Piner (Morning View)	41063
Pineville	40977
Pinsonfork	41555
Pioneer Village (Fairdale)	40118
	40165, 40229
Pippa Passes	41844, 41861
Raven	41844
Piqua (Mount Olivet)	41064
Piso (Pikeville)	41501
Pittsburg	40755
Plainview (Louisville)	40224
Plank	40978
Plano (Bowling Green)	42104
Pleasant Hill	41006, 42273
(Butler)	
Pleasant View	40769
(Williamsburg)	
Pleasanthill	40330
(Harrodsburg)	
Pleasure Ridge Park	40258
	40268
(Louisville)	
Pleasureville	40057
Plum Springs	42101
(Bowling Green)	

Plummers Landing	41081
Plummers Mill	41081
(Plummers Landing)	
Plumville (Maysville)	41056
Poindexter (Cynthiana)	41031
Pointer (Nancy)	42544
Polkville (Oakland)	42159
Pomeroyton	40365
Pondsville (Smiths Grove)	42171
Poole	42444
Pope (Drake)	42128
Poplar Flat (Tollesboro)	41189
Poplar Plains	41041
(Flemingsburg)	
Poplarville (Somerset)	42501
Port Royal	40058
Portland	41033, 42761
(De Mossville)	
Post (Caneyville)	42721
Potters Fork (Jenkins)	41537
Pottsville (Hickory)	42051
Powderly	42367
Powersburg (Monticello)	42633
Powersville (Brooksville)	41004
Praise (Elkhorn City)	41522
Prater (Olive Hill)	41164
Premium	41845
Prentiss (Beaver Dam)	42320
Preston	40366
Prestonsburg	41653, 41668
Bonanza	41653
Cliff	41653
Dock	41653
Emma	41653
Lancer	41653
Sloan	41653
Watergap	41653
Woods	41653
Prestonville (Carrollton)	41008
Price (Hi Hat)	41636
Prices Mill (Adairville)	42202
Pricetown (Liberty)	42539
Priceville (Munfordville)	42765
Pride (Morganfield)	42437
Primrose	41362
Princess (Ashland)	41101
Princeton	42445
Printer	41655
Pritchardsville (Glasgow)	42141
Prospect	40059
Prosperity	42207, 42210
(Bee Spring)	
Providence	42450
Provo	42267
Pryse	40471
Public (Somerset)	42501
Pueblo (Monticello)	42633
Pulaski (Eubank)	42567
Puncheon (Kite)	41828
Purdy (Columbia)	42728
Putney	40865
Pyramid (Hippo)	41637
Pyrmid (Hippo)	41637
Pyrus (Gradyville)	42742
Quality	42268
Quicksand	41363
Quincy	41166
Quinton (Bronston)	42518
Rabbit Hash (Burlington)	41005
Raccoon	41557
Raceland (Russell)	41169

Radcliff 40159-160
Railton (Park City) 42160
Randolph (Edmonton) 42129
Ransom 41558
Raven 41844, 41861
 (Pippa Passes)
 Pippa Passes 41861
Ravenna 40472
Raymond (Webster) 40176
Raywick 40060
Ready (Caneyville) 42721
Rectorville (Maysville) 41056
Red Bird (Beverly) 40913
Red Cross (Park City) 42160
Red Hill (Drake) 42128
Red River (Adairville) 42202
Redbud (Evarts) 40828
Redbush (Flatgap) 41219
Redfox 41847
Redlick (Edmonton) 42129
Reed 42451
Reedyville 42210, 42275
 (Brownsville)
Regina 41559
Region (Roundhill) 42275
Reidland (Paducah) 42001
Relief (West Liberty) 41472
Rella (Arjay) 40902
Render (Beaver Dam) 42320
Renfro Valley 40473
Repton (Marion) 42064
Revelo 42638
Rex (Hardyville) 42746
Reynolds Station 42368
Rhoda (Brownsville) 42210
Rhodelia 40161
Ribbon (Jamestown) 42629
Ribolt (Tollesboro) 41189
Ricetown 41364
Riceville (Swamp Branch) . 41258
Rich Pond (Bowling Green) 42104
Richardson (Louisa) 41230
Richardsville 42270
Richelieu (Auburn) . 42206, 42261
Richmond 40475-476
Richwood (Walton) 41094
Rineyville 40162
Ringos Mills (Hillsboro) 41049
Risner (Martin) 41649
Ritner (Monticello) 42633
River 41254
Riverfront (Louisville) 40270
Riverside 42101, 42270
 (Bowling Green)
Riverton (Greenup) 41144
Roaring Spring (Cadiz) 42211
Roark 40979
Robards 42452
Robinson (Cynthiana) 41031
Robinson Creek 41560
Rochester 42273
Rock Creek (Clarkson) 42726
Rockbridge 42167
 (Tompkinsville)
Rockcastle (Cadiz) 42211
Rockdale (Ashland) 41101
Rockfield 42274
Rockholds 40759
Rockhouse 41364
Rockland (Bowling Green) 42101
Rockport 42369

Rocky Hill 42141, 42163
 (Glasgow)
Rockybranch 42640
Roff (Westview) 40178
Rogers 41365
Rollingburg (Greensburg) . 42743
Roseburg (Cub Run) 42729
Rosedale (Covington) 41015
Roseville (Glasgow) 42141
Rosine 42370
Ross (Melbourne) 41059
Rossland (Gray) 40734
Rosslyn (Stanton) 40380
Rosspoint (Baxter) 40806
Roundhill 42275
Rouse (Covington) 41014
Rousseau 41366
Rowdy 41367
Rowena (Jamestown) 42629
Rowletts 42772
Roxana 41848
Royal (Clarkson) 42726
Royalton 41464
Ruddels Mills (Cynthiana) . 41031
Rumsey 42371
Rush 41168
Russell 41169
Russell Springs 42642
Russellville 42276
Ruth (Somerset) 42501
Rutland (Cynthiana) 41031
Ryland (Covington) 41015
Sacramento 42372
Sadieville 40370
Sadler (Leitchfield) 42754
Saint Catharine 40061
Saint Charles 42453
Saint Elmo (Pembroke) 42266
Saint Francis 40062
Saint Helens 41368
Saint Johns (Paducah) 42001
Saint Joseph 42373
Saint Mary 40062-063
 (Saint Francis)
Saint Matthews 40206-207
 40257
 (Louisville)
Saint Paul 41170
Salem 42078, 42642
Salmons (Franklin) 42134
Salt Gum (Flat Lick) 40935
Salt Lick 40371
Salvisa 40372
Salyersville 41465
Sample (Hardinsburg) 40143
Samuels (Coxs Creek) 40013
Sand Hill (Bowling Green) . 42101
Sandcliff (Monticello) 42633
Sanders 41083
Sandgap 40481
Sandy City (Catlettsburg) .. 41129
Sandy Hook 41171
Sano (Columbia) 42728
Sarah (Culver) 41211
Sardis (Maysville) 41056
Sassafras 41759
Sasser (London) 40741
Saul 40981
Savage (Albany) 42602
Savage Branch 41129
 (Catlettsburg)

Savoyard (Horse Cave) 42749
Sawyer 42643
Saylor (Harlan) 40831
Scalf 40982
Schochoh (Adairville) 42202
Schultztown (Beaver Dam) 42320
Science Hill 42553
Scotts Station 40065
 (Shelbyville)
Scottsville 42164
Scranton (Frenchburg) 40322
Scuddy 41760
Se Ree 40164
Sebree 42455
Seco 41849
Sedalia 42079
Segal (Scottsville) .. 42164, 42210
Seitz 41466
Seminary (Albany) 42602
Senterville 41522
 (Elkhorn City)
Sergent (Whitesburg) 41858
Settle (Scottsville) 42164
Seventy Six (Albany) 42602
Sewell (Vancleve) 41385
Sewellton (Jamestown) 42629
Sextons Creek 40983
Seymour (Horse Cave) 42749
Shady Grove 42064, 42214
 (Marion)
Shadynook (Cynthiana) 41031
Shakertown (Harrodsburg) 40330
Shannon (Mays Lick) 41055
Sharer 42235, 42261
 (Hadley)
Sharkey (Hillsboro) 41049
Sharon (Augusta) 41002
Sharon Grove 42280
Sharondale (Belfry) 41514
Sharpe (Benton) 42025
Sharpsburg 40374
Shawhan (Cynthiana) 41031
Shawnee Estates 42104
 (Bowling Green)
Shelbiana 41562
Shelby Gap 41563
Shelbyville 40065-066
 Clay Village 40065
 Middleton Heights 40065
 Montclair 40065
 Olive Branch 40065
 Scotts Station 40065
 Snow Hill 40065
 Southville 40065
 Todds Point 40065
Shepherdsville 40165
Sherburne (Flemingsburg) 41041
Sheridan (Marion) 42064
Sherman (Dry Ridge) 41035
Shiloh (Murray) 42071
Shipley (Albany) 42602
Shively (Louisville) 40216
Shoal (Confluence) 41730
Shopville 42554
Short Creek (Caneyville) ... 42721
Shrewsbury (Caneyville) ... 42721
Sidney 41564
Siler 40763
Siloam (South Shore) 41175
Silver City (Morgantown) .. 42261
Silver Grove 41085

Silverhill	41467
Simpsonville	40067
Sims Fork (Arjay)	40902
Sitka	41255
Sizerock (Hyden) ... 41749, 41762	
Hyden	41762
Skyline (Hallie)	41821
Slade	40376
Slat (Monticello)	42633
Slaughters	42456
Slavans (Stearns)	42647
Slemp	41763
Slick Rock (Glasgow)	42141
Sligo (Pendleton)	40055
Sloan (Prestonsburg)	41653
Sloans Valley 42519, 42555	
(Burnside)	
Burnside	42555
Smilax	41764
Smith	40867
Smith Mills	42457
Smithfield	40068
Smithland	42081
Smiths Creek (Carter)	41128
Smiths Grove	42171
Smithview (Caneyville)	42721
Smoky Valley (Olive Hill)	41164
Snap (Clarkson)	42726
Snow (Albany)	42602
Snow Hill (Shelbyville)	40065
Soft Shell (Leburn)	41831
Soldier	41173
Solway (Big Clifty)	42712
Somerset 42501-502, 42564	
Alcalde	42501
Elihu	42501
Poplarville	42501
Public	42501
Ruth	42501
West Somerset	42564
Sonora	42776
South (Leitchfield)	42754
South Buffalo (Buffalo)	42716
South Carrollton	42374
South Corbin (Corbin)	40701
South Fort Mitchell	41017
(Covington)	
South Hill (Morgantown) ...	42261
South Newport (Newport) .	41071
South Portsmouth	41174
South Shore	41175
South Union	42283
South Williamson ... 41501, 41503	
(Pikeville)	
Pikeville	41503
Williamson	41503
Southdown (Ermine)	41815
Southgate (Newport)	41071
Southville (Shelbyville)	40065
Spa (Lewisburg)	42256
Sparta	41086
Speck (Casey Creek)	42723
Spence (Newport)	41071
Spider (Pine Top)	41843
Spottsville	42458
Spring Grove	42437
(Morganfield)	
Spring Lick	42779
Springdale (Maysville)	41056
Springfield	40069
Springhill (Clinton) . 42031, 42101	

Spruce Pine (Harlan)	40831
Sprule (Barbourville)	40906
Stacy Fork (West Liberty) ..	41472
Staffordsville	41256
Stambaugh	41257
Stamping Ground	40379
Standiford Field	40221
(Louisville)	
Stanfill (Harlan)	40831
Stanford	40484
Stanley	42375
Stanton	40380
Stanville	41659
Star Mills (Glendale)	42740
Stark (Olive Hill)	41164
Static (Albany)	42602
Stearns	42647
Steele	41566
Steff	42780
Stephens	41177
Stephensburg 42724, 42781	
(Cecilia)	
Stephensport	40170
Steubenville	42648
Stewartsville	41097
(Williamstown)	
Stiles (Howardstown)	40028
Stinnett	40868
Stockholm (Lindseyville) ...	42257
Stone	41567
Stonewall (Brooksville) ...	41004
Stoney Fork	40988
Stop (Monticello)	42633
Stopover	41568
Stovall (Park City)	42160
Straight Creek	40977
(Pineville)	
Stringtown 41048, 42220	
(Hebron)	
Strunk	42649
Sturgis	42459
Sublett (Salyersville)	41465
Sublimity City (London) ...	40741
Subtle (Edmonton)	42129
Sugar Grove (Morgantown)	42261
Sullivan	42460
Sulphur	40070
Sulphur Lick 42167, 42210	
(Tompkinsville)	
Sulphur Well (Edmonton) ..	42129
Summer Shade	42166
Summersville	42782
Summit	42783
Summitt (Ashland) . 41101, 41105	
Sunfish	42284
Sunny Lane (Morgantown)	42261
Sunnybrook (Monticello) ...	42633
Sunnyside (Bowling Green)	42101
Sunrise (Cynthiana)	41031
Sunshine (Harlan) .. 40831, 41175	
Susie (Monticello)	41064
Sutton 41041, 41562	
(Flemingsburg)	
Suwanee (Kuttawa)	42055
Swain (Pine Knot)	42635
Swamp Branch	41258
Swampton (Salyersville) ...	41465
Swan Lake (Barbourville) ..	40906
Swanpond (Barbourville) ...	40906
Sweeden	42285
Symbol (East Bernstadt) ...	40729

Symsonia	42082
Tabernacle (Elkton)	42220
Talbert	41377
Tallega	41378
Talley (Upton)	42784
Tanksley (Manchester)	40962
Tanner (Hodgenville)	42748
Tannery (Vanceburg)	41179
Tarkiln (Blaine)	41124
Tateville	42558
Taulbee (Vancleve)	41385
Tayeville (Taylorsville)	40071
Taylor Mill (Covington)	41015
Taylor Mines	42320
(Beaver Dam)	
Taylorsport (Hebron)	41048
Taylorsville	40071
Teaberry	41660
Tedders (Barbourville)	40906
Teddy (Liberty)	42539
Teetersville (Harlan)	40831
Teges (Oneida)	40972
Temple Hill (Glasgow)	42141
Thealka (Paintsville)	41240
Thelma	41260
Thornton	41855
Thousandsticks	41766
Three Point (Cawood)	40815
Three Springs 42104, 42746	
(Bowling Green)	
Threeforks 41261, 42159	
Threlkel (Roundhill)	42275
Thurlow (Greensburg)	42743
Tidalwave (Rockholds)	40759
Tilford (Delphia) 41735, 42721	
Tiline	42083
Tilton (Flemingsburg)	41041
Tina (Emmalena)	41740
Tinsley (Pineville)	40977
Tiny Town (Guthrie)	42234
Todds Point (Shelbyville) ...	40065
Toler	41569
Tollesboro	41189
Tolliver Town (Cromona) ...	41810
Tolu	
42084	
Tomahawk	41262
Tompkinsville	42167
Tonieville (Hodgenville) ...	42748
Toonerville (Mouthcard) ...	41548
Topmost	41862
Toria (Breeding)	42715
Totz	
40870	
Toulouse (Busy)	41723
Touristville (Monticello)	42633
Trace (Vanceburg)	41179
Tracy (Fountain Run)	42133
Tram	41663
Trammel (Scottsville)	42164
Trappist (New Haven)	40051
Trenton	42286
Tribbey (Bulan)	41722
Tribune (Marion)	42064
Trimble (Nancy)	42544
Trinity (Vanceburg)	41179
Trisler (Fordsville)	42343
Trosper	40995
Tuckertown (Oakland)	42159
Turkey (Booneville)	41314
Turkey Creek	41570

Turners Station	40075	Warren (Barbourville)	40906	Wilbur (Blaine)	41124
Tutor Key	41263	Warsaw	41095	Wildcat (Manchester)	40962
Tuttle (London)	40741	Washington	41096	Wilder (Newport)	41071
Tway (Harlan)	40831	Water Valley	42085	Wildie	40492
Twila (Wallins Creek)	40873	Watergap (Prestonsburg)	41653	Wilhurst (Vancleve)	41385
Tyewhoppety (Clifty)	42216	Waterview	42786	Willard	41181
Tyner	40486	Waverly	42462	Williamsburg	40769
Typo	41771	Wayland	41666	Williamson	41503
Ulvah (Cornettsville)	41731	Waynesburg	40489	(South Williamson)	
Ulysses	41264	Webb Mills (White Mills)	42788	Williamsport	41271
Union	41091	Webbs (Greensburg)	42743	Williamstown	41097
Union Star	40171	Webbs Cross Roads	42642	Willisburg	40078
Uniontown	42461	(Russell Springs)		Willow (Brooksville)	41004
Unity (Ashland)	41101	Webbville	41180	Willow Grove (Foster)	41043
University (Murray)	42071	Webster	40176	Wilmore	40390
Uno (Horse Cave)	42749	Wedonia (Mays Lick)	41055	Wilsonville (Fisherville)	40023
Upchurch (Albany)	42602	Weeksbury	41667	Wilton (Woodbine)	40771
Upper Tygart (Olive Hill)	41164	Welchs Creek	42287	Win (Oil Springs)	41238
Upton	42784	Wellington	40387	Winchester	40320, 40391-392
Urban (Manchester)	40962	Wellsburg (Foster)	41043	(Ford)	
Utica	42376	Wendover	41775	Wind Cave	40494
Vada (Beattyville)	41311	Wentz (Cornettsville)	41731	Windsor	42565
Valeria (Campton)	41301	Wesleyville (Olive Hill)	41164	Windy	42655
Valley Station	40272	West Buechel (Louisville)	40218	Windyville (Brownsville)	42210
(Louisville)		West Fairview (Ashland)	41101	Wingo	42088
Van (Whitesburg)	41858	West Garrett (Garrett)	41630	Winifred (Flatgap)	41219
Van Cleve (Murray)	42071	West Irvine (Irvine)	40336	Winslow Park (Marion)	42064
Van Lear	41265	West Liberty	41472, 41477	Winston	40495
Vance (Turners Station)	40075	Blairs Mill	41472	Wisdom (Edmonton)	42129
Vanceburg	41179	Blaze	41472	Wises Landing (Bedford)	40006
Vancleve	41385	Elamton	41472	Wittensville	41274
Vanzant (Falls Of Rough)	40119	Index	41472	Wolf (Olive Hill)	41164
Varney	41571	Matthew	41472	Wolf Coal (Jackson)	41339
Venters (Elkhorn City)	41522	Relief	41472	Wolf Creek (Battletown)	40104
Vento (Upton)	42784	Stacy Fork	41472	Wolf Lick (Lewisburg)	42256
Vernon (Hestand)	42151, 42167	Yocum	41472	Wolfpit (Elkhorn City)	41522
Verona	41092	West Louisville	42377	Wolverine (Jackson)	41339
Versailles	40383-384	West Paducah	42086	Wonnie (Salyersville)	41465
Vertrees	42785	West Point	40177	Woodbine	40771
Vest	41772	West Prestonsburg	41668	Woodburn	42170
Vester (Columbia)	42728	West Somerset (Somerset)	42564	Woodbury	42288
Vicco	41773	West Van Lear	41268	Woodlawn (Bardstown)	40004
Victory (East Bernstadt)	40729	West Viola (Hickory)	42051		41071, 42001
Villa Hills (Covington)	41017	Westbend (Clay City)	40312	Woodman	41574
Vincent	41386	Westfork (Scottsville)	42164	Woodrow (Garfield)	40140
Vine Grove	40175	Westport	40077	Woods (Evarts)	40828, 41653
Viola (Hickory)	42051	Westview	40178	Woodsonville (Horse Cave)	42749
Viper	41774	Westwood (Ashland)	41101	Woolcott (Brooksville)	41004
Virgie	41572	Wheatcroft	42463	Woollum	40999
Visalia (Morning View)	41063	Wheelersburg	41465	Wooton	41776
Volga	41266	(Salyersville)		Worthington	41183
Waco	40385	Wheelwright	41669	Worthville	41098
Waddy	40076	Whick	41390	Wrigley	41477
Walden (Corbin)	40701	Whickerville (Hardyville)	42746	Wurtland (Greenup)	41144
Waldo (Gunlock)	41632	Whippoorwill	42276	Yancey (Harlan)	40831
Wales (Virgie)	41572	(Russellville)		Yeaddiss	41777
Walker	40997	Whitaker (East Point)	41216	Yeaman (Fordsville)	42343
Walkertown (Hazard)	41701	White City (Hodgenville)	42748	Yellow Rock (Beattyville)	41311
Wallingford	41093	White Mills	42788	Yerkes	41778
Wallins (Wallins Creek)	40873	White Oak	41474	Yesse (Scottsville)	42164
Wallins Creek	40873	White Plains	42164, 42464	Yocum (West Liberty)	41472
Wallonia (Franklin)	42134	(Scottsville)		Yocum Creek (Evarts)	40828
Wallsend (Pineville)	40977	White Tower	41051	York (South Shore)	41175
Walnut Grove	42120, 42563	(Independence)		Yosemite	42566
(Adolphus)		Whitehouse	41269	Youngs Creek (Rockholds)	40759
Walnut Hill (Scottsville)	42164	Whitesburg	41858	Youngtown (Morgantown)	42261
Walton	41094	Whitesville	42378	Yuma (Elk Horn)	42733
Waneta	40488	Whitewood (Greensburg)	42743	Zachariah	41396
Warbranch	40874	Whitley City	42653	Zion (Guthrie)	42234
Warco (Langley)	41645	Wiborg (Whitley City)	42653	Zoe	41397
Warfield	41267	Wickliffe	42087	Zoneton (Shepherdsville)	40165

ANCHORAGE

BUILDINGS

Xerox Building
10001 LINN STATION RD . 40223

ANNA

BUILDINGS

Medical Center
720 E 2ND ST 42101

Old Courthouse Building
429 E 10TH ST 42101

Reservoir Park Prof Building
800 PARK ST 42101

GOVERNMENT

City Hall
1001 COLLEGE ST 42101

ASHLAND

GOVERNMENT

City Building
1700 GREENUP AVE 41101

Federal Building
1405 GREENUP AVE 41101

GOVERNMENT

US Postal Service
1140 CARTER AVE 41101

AVONDALE

GOVERNMENT

Federal Building
501 BROADWAY ST 42001

BIRK CITY

GOVERNMENT

Federal Building
423 FREDERICA ST 42301

BUECHEL

APARTMENTS

Stone Gate Apts
6600 OUTER LOOP 40228

BUILDINGS

Bashford Manor Mall
3600 BARDSTOWN RD ... 40218

Farmdale Adult Tower
6440 OUTER LOOP 40228

Watterson City East
1951 BISHOP LN 40218

Watterson City West
1941 BISHOP LN 40218

Watterson Towers Building
1930 BISHOP LN 40218

GOVERNMENT

Central Govt Center
7201 OUTER LOOP 40228

COVINGTON

BUILDINGS

Coppin Building
20 E 7TH ST 41011

Huntington Bank
540 MADISON AVE 41011

Kentucky National Bank
535 MADISON AVE 41011

FRANKFORT

GOVERNMENT

State Capitol Building
700 CAPITOL AVE 40601

JEFFERSONTOWN

APARTMENTS

Devex Apts
9912 TAYLORSVILLE RD . 40299

BUILDINGS

Embassy Sq Office Park
1900 Embassy Square Blvd 40299

Outlets Limited Mall
11501 BLUEGRASS PKY . 40299

LEXINGTON

BUILDINGS

Bakhaus Building
1500 LEESTOWN RD 40511

Commerce National Bank Plz
301 E MAIN ST 40507

First National Bank Building
167 W MAIN ST 40507

Kincaid Building
300 W VINE ST 40507

Lexington Civic Ctr
410 W VINE ST 40507

Lexington Financial Ctr
250 W MAIN ST 40507

Merrill Lynch Plz
100 E VINE ST 40507

Quality Place Plz
300 E MAIN ST 40507

Vine Center
333 W VINE ST 40507

GOVERNMENT

City Hall Annex
136 N MARTIN LUTHER KING
BLVD 40507

City Hall Annex
136 WALNUT ST 40507

Fayette Co Court House
215 W MAIN ST 40507

Federal Building
101 BARR ST 40507

Lexington Urban Co Gov
200 E MAIN ST 40507

US Post Office
1088 NANDINO 40511

COLLEGES

Transylvania University
300 N BROADWAY ST 40508

LOUISVILLE

APARTMENTS

800 Apts
800 S 4TH ST 40203

Baptist Towers
1014 S 2ND ST 40203

Medical Arts Building
1169 EASTERN PKY 40217

Medical Office Building
1170 E BROADWAY ST 40204

Medical Towers North
233 E GRAY ST 40202

Medical Towers South
234 E GRAY ST 40202

Mid City Mall
1250 BARDSTOWN RD ... 40204

Morrissey Building
304 W LIBERTY ST 40202

Nolan Building
2100 GARDINER LN 40205

Norwood Park #1
7400 New LaGrange Rd ... 40222

Norwood Park #2
7410 New LaGrange Rd ... 40222

Oxmoor Center/mall
7900 SHELBYVILLE RD ... 40222

Paragon Building
9100 SHELBYVILLE RD ... 40222

Paragon Centre 1
6060 DUTCHMANS LN 40205

Portland Federal Building
200 W BROADWAY ST 40202

Professional Towers Building
4010 DUPONT CIR 40207

R & S Building
834 E BROADWAY ST 40204

Republic Building
429 W Muhammad Ali Blvd 40202

Starks Building
455 S 4TH AVE 40202

The Mall Shopping Ctr
5000 SHELBYVILLE RD ... 40207

Vermont American Building
100 E LIBERTY ST 40202

GOVERNMENT

City Hall
601 W JEFFERSON ST 40202

Fiscal Court Building
531 COURT PL 40202

Hall Of Justice
600 W JEFFERSON ST 40202

Casa Bella Ct
3232 HIKES LN 40220

Churchill Park Apts
3091 Breckenridge Ln 40220

Dosker Manor East
415 E Muhammad Ali Blvd 40202

Dosker Manor North
413 E Muhammad Ali Blvd 40202

Dosker Manor West
409 E Muhammad Ali Blvd 40202

El Patio Pl
3228 HIKES LN 40220

Friendship House
960 S 4TH ST 40203

Hillebrand House
1235 S 3RD ST 40203

Kentucky Towers
430 W Muhammad Ali Blvd 40202

Puritan Apt
1244 S 4TH ST 40203

Shelby House Condo
8605 SHELBYVILLE RD ... 40222

Stonemill Village Apt
850 WASHBURN AVE 40222

Trinity Towers
537 S 3RD ST 40202

Whitehall Terrace
3218 HIKES LN 40220

BUILDINGS

1st National Tower
101 S 5TH ST 40202

515 Building
515 W MARKET ST 40202

Audubon Medical Plaza
3 AUDUBON PLAZA DR ... 40217

Bank Of Louisville Building
510 W BROADWAY ST 40202

Baptist East Drs Building
3950 KRESGE WAY 40207

Brown Williamson Tower
401 S 4TH AVE 40202

Child Evaluation Building
334 E BROADWAY ST 40202

Childrens Foundation Building
601 S FLOYD ST 40202

Civic Plaza Building
701 W JEFFERSON ST 40202

College Industrial Park
2300 S 4TH ST 40208

Commonwealth Building
680 S 4TH AVE 40202

Corporate Plaza
220 W MAIN ST 40202

Doctors Office Building
250 E LIBERTY ST 40202

Fincastle Building
305 W BROADWAY ST 40202

Heyburn Building
332 W BROADWAY ST 40202

Highland Professional Plz
801 BARRET AVE 40204

Highlands Doctors Building
850 BARRET AVE 40204

Humana Building
500 W MAIN ST 40202

Hurstbourne Park
9200 SHELBYVILLE RD ... 40222

Hurstbourne Place
9300 SHELBYVILLE RD ... 40222

Jefferson Mall
4801 OUTER LOOP 40219

Jefferson Trade Center
3600 CHAMBERLAIN LN . 40241

Kaden Towers
6100 DUTCHMANS LN 40205

Kendall Building
7321 New LaGrange Rd ... 40222

Ky Center For The Arts
5 RIVERFRONT PLZ 40202

Ky Home Life Building
239 S 5TH ST 40202

Legal Arts Building
200 S 7TH ST 40202

Lexington Square Off Park
12700 SHELBYVILLE RD . 40243

Liberty Centre I
1230 LIBERTY BANK LN .. 40222

Liberty Centre Ii
1230 S Hurstbourne Pky ... 40222

Marion E Taylor Building
312 S 4TH AVE 40202
Jeff County Courthouse
527 W JEFFERSON ST 40202

New Federal Building
600 DR MARTIN LUTHER KING
PL 40202

Us Gene Snyder Ct House
601 W BROADWAY ST 40202

OWENSBORO

GOVERNMENT

Daviess County Courthouse
212 SAINT ANN ST 42303

PADUCAH

GOVERNMENT

Mc Cracken Cnty Courthouse
301 S 6TH ST 42003

Paducah City Hall
300 S 5TH ST 42003

LOUISIANA
Abbreviation LA

Abbeville	70510-511
Cow Island	70510
Forked Island	70510
Intracoastal City	70510
Meaux	70510
Abita Springs	70420
Acme	71316
Addis	70710
Adner (Haughton)	71037
Afton (Tallulah)	71282
Aimwell	71401
Airview Terrace	71301
(Alexandria)	
Ajax (Marthaville)	71450
Akers	70421
Albany	70711
Alexandria	71301-303
	71306-307, 71309, 71315
Airview Terrace	71301
Anandale	71301
Camelia Gardens	71301
Camp Stafford	71301
Castle Village	71301
Castor Plunge	71301
Charles Park	71301
Cherokee Village	71301
De Selle	71301
Kolin	71301
Magda	71303
Martin Park	71301
Moreland	71301
Poland	71301
Roxana	71303
Samtown	71301
South Park	71301
Tanglewood	71301
Timber Trails	71301
Weil	71303
Westside	71301
Willow Glen	71302
Wilshire Park	71303
Woodside	71302
Alfalfa (Boyce)	71409
Algiers (New Orleans)	70114
Allemand (Houma)	70360
Allen (Robeline)	71469
Aloha (Colfax)	71417
Alto (Rayville)	71269
Ama	70031
Amelia	70340
Amite	70422
Anacoco	71403
Anandale (Alexandria)	71301
Angie	70426, 70467
Varnado	70467
Angola	70712
Ansley (Ruston)	71270
Antioch (Homer) 71040, 71275	
Antonia (Pollock)	71467
Arabi	70032
Arcadia	71001
Archibald	71218
Archie (Jonesville)	71343
Arcola (Roseland)	70456
Arizona (Homer)	71040
Armistead (Coushatta)	71019
Arnaudville	70512
Ashland	71002

Ashley (Tallulah)	71282
Athens	71003
Atkins (Elm Grove)	71051
Atlanta	71404
Avery Island	70513
Avondale (Westwego)	70094
Aycock (Homer)	71040
Azucena (Waterproof)	71375
Bagdad (Colfax)	71417
Bains	70775
(Saint Francisville)	
Baker	70704, 70714
Baldwin	70514
Ball (Pineville) 71360, 71405	
Balmoral (Newellton)	71357
Banks Springs (Columbia)	71418
Barataria	70036
Barnet Springs (Ruston) ... 71270	
Barron (Deville)	71328
Basile	70515
Baskin	71219
Bastrop	71220-221
Beekman	71220
Dewdrop	71220
Log Cabin	71220
Perryville	71220
Shelton	71220
Upland	71220
Wardville	71220
Batchelor	70715
Baton Rouge	70800-802
	70805-823, 70825-828
	70831, 70833, 70835-837
	70874, 70879, 70883-884
	70892-896, 70898
Cablevision	70883
Central	70818
Central	70837
Commerce Park	70884
Gateway	70835
Greenwood	70811
One American Place ...	70825
Scotlandville	70807
Scotlandville	70811
Scotlandville	70874
Southern	70813
University	70803
Zion City	70811
Bawcomville	71292
(West Monroe)	
Bayou Blue (Houma)	70360
Bayou Goula	70716
Bayou Petite Prairie	71345
(Lebeau)	
Bayou Rouge (Melville)	71353
Bayou Vista (Morgan City)	70380
Beachview (Kenner)	70062
Bear Creek (Bienville)	71008
Beaver (Oakdale)	71463
Bee Bayou (Rayville)	71269
Beekman (Bastrop)	71220
Belair (Braithwaite)	70040
Belcher	71004
Bell City	70630
Belle Chasse	70037
Belle Point (Reserve)	70084
Belle Rose	70341
Bellevue (Haughton)	71037
Bellview (Columbia)	71418
Bellwood (Provencal)	71468
Belmont	71406

Bennetts Bay	71430
(Forest Hill)	
Benson (Converse)	71419
Bentley	71407
Benton	71006
Bermuda (Natchez)	71456
Bernice	71222
Berwick	70342
Bethany	71007, 71450
Bethel (Marthaville)	71450
Bienville	71008
Big Bend	71318, 71355
Big Bend Road (Hamburg)	71339
Big Cane (Morrow) . 71356, 71362	
Big Island (Deville)	71328
Big Ridge (Columbia)	71418
Black Hawk (Vidalia)	71373
Blackburn (Haynesville)	71038
Blade (Jena)	71342
Blanchard	71009
Blanche (Glenmora)	71433
Blanks	70717
Blue Lake (Forest Hill)	71430
Bodcau (Haughton)	71037
Bodoc (Plaucheville)	71362
Bogalusa	70427, 70429
Lees Creek	70427
Mitch	70427
Mitchell City	70427
Plainview	70427
Rio	70427
Bohemia	70082
(Pointe A La Hache)	
Boline (Marthaville)	71450
Bond (Oakdale)	71463
Bonita	71223
Book (Jonesville)	71343
Boothville	70038
Bordelonville	71320
Borodino (Moreauville)	71355
Bosco (Monroe)	71201
Bossier City	71111-113
	71171-172
Bougere (Vidalia)	71373
Bourg	70343
Boutte	70039
Boyce	71409
Braithwaite	70040
Branch	70516
Breaux Bridge	70517
Breezy Hill (Pollock)	71467
Bridge City (Westwego)	70094
Brittany	70718
Broadmoor (New Orleans)	70125
Brookwood (Woodworth) ..	71485
Brouillette (Marksville)	71351
Broussard	70518
Brownsville (West Monroe)	71292
Brownville (Columbia)	71418
Bruly Saint Martin	70341
(Belle Rose)	
Brusly	70719
Bryceland	71014
Buckeye (Deville)	71328
Bucks Landing	71430
(Forest Hill)	
Bueche	70720
Bunkie	71322
Buras	70041
Burns Town (Lena)	71447
Burnside	70738

Burroughs (Columbia) 71418
Burnwood (Venice) 70091
Bush 70431
Bushes (Winnsboro) 71295
Butte Larose 70517
   (Breaux Bridge)
Bywater (New Orleans) 70117
Bywaters (New Orleans) 70117
Cablevision (Baton Rouge) 70883
Caddo (Oil City) 71061
Cade 70519
Cadeville (Eros) 71238
Calcasieu (Glenmora) 71433
Calcasieu Marine Tower 70629
   (Lake Charles)
Calhoun 71225
Calumet (Patterson) 70392
Calvin 71410
Camelia Gardens 71301
   (Alexandria)
Cameron 70631
Camp Beauregard 71360
   (Pineville)
Camp Claiborne 71430
   (Forest Hill)
Camp Stafford 71301
   (Alexandria)
Campground (Montgomery) 71454
Campti 71411
Cane River 71452, 71456
   (Melrose)
Cankton (Sunset) 70584
Carencro 70520
Carlisle 70042
Carlton (Calhoun) 71225
Carrollton (New Orleans) ... 70118
Cartwright (Choudrant) 71227
Carville 70721
Caspiana (Shreveport) 71115
Castle Village 71301
   (Alexandria)
Castor 71016
Castor Lane (Lena) 71447
Castor Plunge 71301, 71485
   (Alexandria)
Cecile (Shreveport) 71105
Cecilia 70521
Cedar Grove (Shreveport) .. 71106
Centenary (Shreveport) 71104
Center Point 71323
Centerville 70522, 71367
Central 70818, 70837
   (Baton Rouge)
Chalmette 70043-044
Chambers (Lecompte) 71346
Charenton 70523
Charles Park (Alexandria) . 71301
Chase 71324
Chataignier 70524
Chatham 71226
Chauvin 70344
Chef Menteur 70126
   (New Orleans)
Cheneyville 71325
Cheniere 71291-292
   (West Monroe)
Cherokee Village 71301
   (Alexandria)
Chestnut (Saline) 71070
Chickama (Lecompte) 71346
Chickasaw (Oak Grove) 71263

Chipola (Greensburg) 70441
Chopin 71447
Choudrant 71227
Choupique (Plaucheville) .. 71362
Church Point 70525
Claiborne 70433, 71291
   (Covington)
Clare (Florien) 71429, 71449
Clarence 71414
Clarks 71415
Clayton 71326
Clearwater (Cheneyville) .. 71325
Clifton (Mora) 71455
Clinton 70722
Cloutierville 71416
Cocodrie (Chauvin) 70344
Cocoville (Mansura) 71350
Colfax 71417
Colgrade (Winnfield) 71483
Collinston 71229
Colquitt (Haynesville) 71038
Columbia 71418
Columbus (Many) 71449
Commerce Park 70884
   (Baton Rouge)
Concord (Oak Grove) 71263
Concordia Lake (Ferriday) 71334
Consuella (Waterproof) 71375
Convent 70723
Converse 71419
Cooper Road (Shreveport) . 71107
Coopers (Leesville) 71446
Cooters Point 71375
   (Waterproof)
Copenhagen (Columbia) ... 71418
Corey (Monroe) 71201
Corinth (Dubach) 71235
Cotile (Boyce) 71409
Cotton Valley 71018
Cottonport 71327
Coushatta 71019
Covington 70433-435
   Claiborne 70433
   Riverwood 70433
   Saint Gertrude 70433
Cow Island (Abbeville) 70510
Crackville (Cottonport) 71327
Creole 70632
Crew Lake (Rayville) 71269
Crews (Montgomery) 71454
Crowley 70526-527
Crown Point (Marrero) 70072
Crowville 71230
Cullen 71021
Curry (Winnfield) 71483
Custom House 70116
   (New Orleans)
Cut Off 70345
Cypress 71291, 71433
   (West Monroe)
Cypress Gardens (Meraux) 70075
Danville (Bienville) 71008
Darrow 70725
Davant 70046
De Quincy (Dequincy) 70633
De Ridder (Deridder) 70634
De Selle (Alexandria) 71301
Dean Chapel (West Monroe)71291
Deer Park (Vidalia) 71373
Dehlco (Rayville) 71269
Delacroix (Saint Bernard) .. 70085

Delcambre 70528
Delhi 71232
Delta 71233
Delta Garden (Ferriday) 71334
Denham Springs 70726-727
   Port Vincent 70726
Dequincy 70633
Deridder 70634
Derry (Cloutierville) 71416
Des Allemands 70030
Destrehan 70047
Deville 71328
Dewdrop (Bastrop) 71220
Dixie (Shreveport) 71107
Dixie Gardens 71105
   (Shreveport)
Dodson 71422
Dogwood Terrace 71459
   (Leesville)
Dona (Grand Cane) 71032
Donaldsonville 70346
Donner 70352
Dora Bend (Cottonport) 71327
Doty Garden (Ferriday) 71334
Downsville 71234
Doyline 71023
Drew (West Monroe) 71291
Dry Creek 70637, 70662
Dry Prong 71423
Dubach 71235
Dubberly 71024
Dulac 70353
Dunbarton (Ferriday) 71334
Dunn (Delhi) 71232
Duplessis 70728
Dupont 71329
Duson 70529
Duty Ferry (Columbia) 71418
Dykesville (Haynesville) ... 71038
East Hodge (Hodge) 71247
East Point 71025
East Winnfield (Joyce) 71440
Eastside (Columbia) 71418
Ebarb (Noble) 71462
Echo 71330
Edgard 70049
Effie 71331
Egan 70531
Elam (Wisner) 71378
Elba (Melville) 71353
Elizabeth 70638
Elm Grove 71051
Elmer 71424
Elmwood (New Orleans) 70123
Elton 70532
Emmanuel (Chopin) 71412
Empire 70050
Englewood (Tallulah) 71282
Enterprise 71425
Eola (Bunkie) 71322
Epps 71237
Erath 70533
Eros 71238
Erwinville 70729
Esler (Pineville) 71360
Estherwood 70534
Esto (Many) 71449
Ethel 70730
Eunice 70535
Eureka (Downsville) 71234
Eva (Monterey) 71354

Jeanerette	70544
Jefferson (New Orleans)	70121
Jena	71342
Jennings	70546
Jigger	71249
Jones	71250
Jonesboro	71251
Jonesburg (Rayville)	71269
Jonesville	71343
Jordon Hill (Winnfield)	71483
Jowers (Montgomery)	71454
Joyce	71440
Junks (Clayton)	71326
Kadesh (Montgomery)	71454
Kaplan	70548
Keatchie	71046
Keithville	71047
Kelly	71441
Kellys (Ruston)	71270
Kemps Landing (Monterey)	71354
Kendricks Ferry (Gilbert)	71336
Kenilworth	70085
(Saint Bernard)	
Kenner	70062-065
Beachview	70062
Green Lawn Terrace	70062
Providence	70062
Kentwood	70444
Kickapoo (Gloster)	71030
Kilbourne	71253
Killian (Springfield)	70462
Killona	70066
Kinder	70648
Kingston (Grand Cane)	71032
Kingsville (Pineville)	71360
Kiroli Woods	71291
(West Monroe)	
Kisatchie (Provencal)	71468
Kolin (Alexandria) .. 71301, 71360
Koran (Haughton)	71037
Kraemer	70371
Krotz Springs	70750
Kurthwood	71443
La Chute (Shreveport)	71101
La Place	70068-069
Laplace	70068-069
Montz	70068
Labadieville	70372
Labarre	70751
Lacamp	71444
Lacassine	70650
Lacombe	70445
Lafayette	70501-509
	70593, 70598
Southside	70593
Lafitte	70067
Lake (Prairieville)	70769
Lake Arthur	70549
Lake Bruin 71357, 71366
(Newellton)	
Lake Charles	70601-602
	70605-606, 70609
	70611-612, 70715, 70616
	70629
Calcasieu Marine Twr .	70629
Lake Providence	71254
Lake St John (Ferriday)	71334
Lakeland	70752
Lakeshore (Monroe)	71203
Lakeside (Pineville)	71360
Lakeview 70124, 71107, 71456

(New Orleans)	
Lamkin (Monroe)	71201
Lamourie (Lecompte)	71346
Lapine (West Monroe)	71292
Laplace (La Place) 70068-069
Larose	70373-374
Larto (Jonesville)	71343
Latanier (Lecompte)	71346
Lawhon (Ringgold)	71068
Lawtell	70550
Le Blanc (Leblanc)	70651
Le Moyen (Morrow)	71356
Leander (Hineston)	71438
Lebeau	71345
Lecompte	71346
Lee Heights (Pineville)	71360
Lees Creek (Bogalusa)	70427
Leesville 71446, 71459, 71496
Coopers	71446
Dogwood Terrace	71459
Fort Polk	71459
Hawthorne	71446
Hicks	71446
Pickering	71446
Sandy Hill	71446
Tower Park	71446
Leeville (Golden Meadow)	70357
Leland (Sicily Island)	71368
Lemoine Town	71355
(Moreauville)	
Lena	71447
Leonville	70551
Lettsworth	70753
Levee Heights (Ferriday)	71334
Lewisburg (Mandeville)	70448
Liberty Hill (Bienville)	71008
Libuse	71348
Liddieville (Winnsboro)	71295
Lillie	71256
Linville (Marion)	71260
Lions (Reserve)	70084
Lisbon	71048
Lismore (Jonesville)	71343
Litroe (Marion)	71260
Little Caillou (Chauvin)	70344
Little Creek (Trout)	71371
Little Egypt	71450
(Marthaville)	
Livingston	70754
Livonia	70755
Lockhart (Spearsville)	71277
Lockport	70374
Locust Ridge	71366
(Saint Joseph)	
Log Cabin (Bastrop)	71220
Logansport	71049-050
Longstreet	71050
Loggy Bayou (Elm Grove) .	71051
Logtown (Monroe)	71202
Lonepine (Saint Landry)	71367
Longbridge (Cottonport)	71327
Longlake (Columbia)	71418
Longleaf	71448
Longstreet (Logansport)	71050
Longville	70652
Loranger	70446
Loreauville	70552
Lottie	70756
Loyds Bridge	71325
(Cheneyville)	
Lucas (Shreveport)	71105

Lucerne (Vidalia)	71373
Lucky (Bienville)	71008
Luling	70070
Luna (West Monroe)	71292
Lutcher	70071
Lydia	70569
Madison Park (Shreveport)	71105
Madisonville	70447
Magda (Alexandria)	71303
Magnolia	70341, 71456
(Belle Rose)	
Mamou	70554
Mandeville 70448, 70470-471
Hootenville	70448
Lewisburg	70448
Mangham	71259
Manifest (Jonesville)	71343
Mansfield	71052
Mansura	71350
Many	71449
Marco (Lena)	71447
Maringouin	70757
Marion	71260
Marksville	71351
Marrero	70072-073
Crown Point	70072
Mars Hill (Atlanta)	71404
Marthaville	71450
Martin Park (Alexandria)	71301
Mathews	70375
Maurepas	70449
Maurice	70555
Mayflower (Saint Joseph) .	71366
Mayna (Jonesville)	71343
Mccall (Donaldsonville)	70346
Mcdade (Elm Grove)	71051
Mcintyre (Minden)	71055
Mcnary (Glenmora)	71433
Mcneely (Colfax)	71417
Mcnutt (Boyce)	71409
Meadow Park Heights	71108
(Shreveport)	
Meaux (Abbeville)	70510
Meeker (Lecompte)	71346
Melder	71451
Melrose	71452
Melville	71353
Mer Rouge	71261
Meraux	70075
Mermentau	70556
Merryville	70653
Metairie	70001-006
	..... 70009-011, 70033, 70055
	70060
Michoud (New Orleans)	70129
Mid City (New Orleans)	70119
Midland (Morse)	70559
Midway	71071, 71430
(Sarepta)	
Mill Bayou (Hamburg)	71339
Mill Creek (Winnfield)	71483
Millerton (Haynesville)	71038
Millikin	71254
(Lake Providence)	
Milton	70558
Minden	71055, 71058
Gilark	71055
Mcintyre	71055
Pace	71055
Mineral Springs (Dubach) .	71235
Minorca (Ferriday)	71334

Mitch (Bogalusa) 70427
Mitchell (Converse) 71419
Mitchell City (Bogalusa) 70427
Mittie 70654
Modeste 70376
Moncla (Marksville) 71351
Monette Ferry (Lena) 71447
Monroe ... 71201-203, 71207-208
.... 71209-223
    Bosco 71201
    Corey 71201
    Fondale 71201
    Lakeshore 71203
    Lamkin 71201
    Logtown 71202
    Northeast 71201
    Pine Grove 71201
    Richwood 71202
Montcalm (Simsboro) 71275
Montecello (Waterproof) ... 71375
Montegut 70377
Monterey 71354
Montgomery 71454
Monticello 71254
    (Lake Providence)
Montpelier (Amite) 70422
Montrose 71452, 71457
    (Melrose)
Montz (La Place) 70068
Mooringsport 71060
Mora 71455
Moreauville 71355
Moreland (Alexandria) 71301
Morgan City 70380-381
    Bayou Vista 70380
Morganza 70759
Morrow 71356
Morse 70559
Morville (Vidalia) 71373
Mot (Plain Dealing) 71064
Mound (Tallulah) 71282
Mount Airy 70076
Mount Carmel (Florien) 71429
Mount Hermon 70450
Mount Lebanon (Gibsland) 71028
Mount Olive (Quitman) 71268
Mount Sinai (Haynesville) . 71038
Mount Union (Spearsville) . 71277
Mount Zion (Montgomery) . 71454
Mudville (Georgetown) 71432
Myrtle Grove 70083
    (Port Sulphur)
Nantatchie (Montgomery) . 71454
Napoleonville 70390
Natalbany 70451
Natchez 71456
Natchitoches .. 71457-458, 71497
    Hagewood 71457
    Irma 71457
    Montrose 71457
    Northwestern 71457
Nebo (Jena) 71342
Negreet 71460
New Belledeau (Hessmer) 71341
New Era (Acme) 71316, 71354
New Hope (Montgomery) .. 71454
New Iberia 70560, 70562
New Light (Mangham) 71259
New Orleans ... 70100, 70112-119
    .... 70121-131, 70139-143
    .... 70145-146, 70145-154

.... 70156-159, 70160-167
.... 70170, 70172, 70174-179
.... 70181-187, 70189-190
.... 70195
Algiers 70114
Broadmoor 70125
Bywater 70117
Bywaters 70117
Carrollton 70118
Chef Menteur 70126
Custom House 70116
Elmwood 70123
Gentilly 70122
Harahan 70123
Jefferson 70121
Lakeview 70124
Michoud 70129
Mid City 70119
North Orleans 70100
River Ridge 70123
Shrewsbury 70121
Vieux Carre 70112
Vieux Carre 70172
New Roads 70760
New Salem (Montgomery) 71454
New Sarpy 70047, 70078
    (Destrehan)
New Verda (Montgomery) . 71454
Newellton 71357
Newlight (Newellton) 71357
Newllano 71461
Noble 71462
Noles Landing (Sibley) 71073
Norco 70079
North (New Orleans) 70100
North Hodge (Hodge) 71247
North O (New Orleans) 70100
North Shore (Slidell) 70458
Northeast (Monroe) 71201
Northwestern 71457
    (Natchitoches)
Norwood 70761
Notnac (Newellton) 71357
Oak Grove 71263, 71275
    .... 71419, 71423
    Chickasaw 71263
    Concord 71263
    Goodwill 71263
    Terry 71263
Oak Ridge 71264, 71473
Oakdale 71463
Oakland (Marion) 71260
Oaks (Haynesville) 71038
Oberlin 70655
Odenburg (Simmesport) ... 71369
Odra (Montgomery) 71454
Oil City 71061
Okaloosa (Eros) 71238
Old Hwy 1 (Hamburg) 71339
Olinkraft 71291-292
    (West Monroe)
Olla 71465
Omega (Sondheimer) 71276
One American Place 70825
    (Baton Rouge)
Opelousas 70570-571
Ormond (Destrehan) 70047
Oscar 70762
Ostrica (Buras) 70041
Otis71466
Pace (Minden) 71055

Packton (Winnfield) 71483
Paincourtville 70391
Palmetto 71358
Panola (Ferriday) 71334
Paradis 70080
Paradise (Pineville) 71360
Parhams (Jonesville) 71343
Patch Leg (Montgomery) ... 71454
Patterson 70392
Paulina 70763
Pawnee (Glenmora) 71433
Pearl River 70452
Peason (Florien) 71429
Pecan Acres (Montgomery) 71454
Peck (Sicily Island) 71368
Pelican 71063
Pendleton (Many) 71449
Perry 70575
Perryville (Bastrop) 71220
Pickering (Leesville) 71446
Pierre Part 70339
Pilottown 70081
Pine Coupee (Flatwoods) . 71427
Pine Grove 70453, 71201
Pine Oak Terrace 71108
    (Shreveport)
Pine Prairie 70576
Pineville 71359-361
    Ball 71360
    Camp Beauregard 71360
    Esler 71360
    Green Gables 71360
    Kingsville 71360
    Kolin 71360
    Lakeside 71360
    Lee Heights 71360
    Paradise 71360
    Timber Trails 71360
    Wardville 71360
Pioneer 71266
Pitkin 70656
Plain Dealing 71064
Plainview (Bogalusa) 70427
Plaquemine 70764-765
Plattenville 70393
Plaucheville 71362
Pleasant Hill 71065
Pleasant Ridge (Olla) 71465
Point (Downsville) 71234
Point Clair (Carville) 70721
Pointe A La Hache 70082
Poland (Alexandria) 71301
Pollock 71467
Ponchatoula 70454
Poole (Elm Grove) 71051
Port Allen 70767
Port Barre 70577
Port Eads (Venice) 70091
Port Sulphur 70083
Port Vincent 70726
    (Denham Springs)
Porterville (Sarepta) 71071
Potash (Port Sulphur) 70083
Powhatan 71066
Poydras (Saint Bernard) ... 70085
Prairieville 70769
Pride 70770
Princeton 71067
Prospect 71407, 71423
    (Bentley)
Provencal 71468

Taft (Hahnville) 70057
Talisheek 70044
Talla Bena (Sondheimer) .. 71276
Tallulah 71282, 71284
 Afton 71282
 Ashley 71282
 Englewood 71282
 Mound 71282
 Quimby 71282
 Richmond 71282
 Thomastown 71282
Tangipahoa 70465
Tanglewood (Alexandria) .. 71301
Tannehill (Dodson) 71422
Taylor 71080
Taylor Hill (Lena) 71447
Taylortown (Elm Grove) 71051
Temple (Simpson) 71474
Tensas Bluff (Newellton) .. 71357
Terry (Oak Grove) 71263
Terrytown (Gretna) 70056
The Bluffs (Jackson) 70748
Theriot 70397
Thibodaux 70301-302, 70310
Thomas (Franklinton) 70438
Thomastown (Tallulah) 71282
Three Bridges 71454
 (Montgomery)
Tickfaw 70466
Timber Trails 71301, 71360
 (Alexandria)
Timberlake (Woodworth) ... 71485
Tioga 71477
Toca (Saint Bernard) 70085
Toledo (Many) 71449
Torbert 70781
Toro (Florien) 71429
Tower Park (Leesville) 71446
Transylvania 71286
Trees (Vivian) 71082
Trinity (Jonesville) 71343
Triumph (Buras) 70041
Trout 71371
Tullos 71479
Tunica 70782
Turkey Creek 70585
Turtle Lake (Ferriday) 71334
Uncle Sam 70792
Uneedus (Folsom) 70437
Union Church (Quitman) ... 71268
Union Grove (Montgomery) 71454
Union Hill 71433, 71454
 (Glenmora)
Union Springs (Converse) . 71419
Unionville (Dubach) 71235
University (Baton Rouge) .. 70803

Upland (Bastrop) 71220
Urania 71480
Utility (Jonesville) 71343
Vacherie 70090
Varnado (Angie) 70467
Venice 70091
Ventress 70783
Verda 71454, 71481
 (Montgomery)
Vernon (Ruston) 71270
Verret (Saint Bernard) 70085
Vick (Effie) 71331
Vidalia 71373
Vienna (Ruston) 71270
Vieux Carre 70112, 70172
 (New Orleans)
Ville Platte 70586
Vines Loop (Noble) 71462
Vinton 70668
Violet 70092
Vivian 71082
Vixen (Columbia) 71418
Voorhies (Moreauville) 71355
Vowells Mill (Robeline) 71469
Waggaman (Westwego) 70094
Wakefield 70784
Walker 70785
Wall Lake (West Monroe) .. 71291
Wallace (Edgard) 70049
Walters (Jonesville) 71343
Ward (Oakdale) 71463
Warden (Delhi) 71232
Wardville 71220, 71360
 (Bastrop)
Washington 70589
Waterford Spur (Killona) 70066
Waterproof 71375
Watson 70786
Waverly (Delhi) 71232
Wayside (Hamburg) 71339
Weil (Alexandria) 71303
Weldon (Bernice) 71222
Welsh 70591
West Monroe .. 71291-292, 71294
 Bawcomville 71292
 Brownsville 71292
 Cheniere 71291-71292
 Claiborne 71291
 Cypress 71291
 Dean Chapel 71291
 Drew 71291
 Forest Park 71291
 Highland Park 71291
 Kiroli Woods 71291
 Lapine 71292
 Luna 71292

 Olinkraft 71291-71292
 Siegle 71292
 Splane Place 71291
 Wall Lake 71291
Westdale (Shreveport) 71105
Westlake 70669
Weston (Jonesboro) 71251
Westside (Alexandria) 71301
Westwego 70094, 70096
 Avondale 70094
 Bridge City 70094
 South Kenner 70094
 Waggaman 70094
Westwood (Newellton) 71357
Weyanoke 70787
Whatley Landing (Trout) 71371
Wheeling (Montgomery) 71454
White Castle 70788
White Sulphur Springs 71371
 (Trout)
Whitehall (Bunkie) .. 71322, 71342
Whiteville (Bunkie) 71322
Wilda (Boyce) 71409
Wildsville 71377
Willhite (Downsville) 71234
Williams (Shreveport) 71105
Williana (Dry Prong) 71423
Willow Glen (Alexandria) ... 71302
Wilshire Park 71303
 (Alexandria)
Wilson 70789
Wilsona (Saint Joseph) 71366
Winnfield 71483
Winnsboro 71295
Wisner 71378
Womack (Chatham) 71226
Woodardville (Ringgold) 71068
Woodside 71302, 71353
 (Alexandria)
Woodville (Ruston) 71270
Woodworth 71485
Wyatt (Jonesboro) 71251
Youngsville 70592
Youree (Shreveport) 71105
Zachary 70791
Zenoria (Trout) 71371
Zimmer (Moreauville) 71355
Zion (Georgetown) 71432
Zion City (Baton Rouge) 70811
Zwolle 71486
Zylks (Rodessa) 71069

AIRVIEW TERRACE

BUILDINGS

Medical Arts Building
405 3RD ST 71301

Medical Terrace
301 4TH ST 71301

One Centre Court
1412 CENTRE CT 71301

GOVERNMENT

Louisiana State Offices
900 MURRAY ST 71301

Rapides Parish Courthouse
701 MURRAY ST 71301

HOSPITALS

Rapides Womens Hospital
501 Medical Center Dr 71301

ALEXANDRIA

BUILDINGS

Dunbar Plaza
3600 Jackson Street Ext ... 71303

Neilson Office Building
3700 Jackson Street Ext ... 71303

HOSPITALS

Veterans Administration
0 PO BOX 71306

ALLEMAND

BUILDINGS

1st National Bank
600 E MAIN ST 70360

American Bank
801 BARROW ST 70360

Terrebonne Bank Towers
720 E MAIN ST 70360

GOVERNMENT

Court House
400 E MAIN ST 70360

Federal
423 LAFAYETTE ST 70360

BATON ROUGE

BUILDINGS

Atrium
2900 WESTFORK DR 70827

Catfish Town
100 SAINT JAMES ST 70802

Commerce Building
333 LAUREL ST 70801

Guaranty Income Life Building
929 GOVERNMENT ST 70802

One Maritime Plaza
101 FRANCE ST 70802

Roumain Building
343 RIVERSIDE MALL 70801

Taylor Building
251 FLORIDA ST 70801

GOVERNMENT

Governmental Building
222 SAINT LOUIS ST 70802

Post Office Building
750 FLORIDA ST 70801

Us Crthouse And Fed Building
707 FLORIDA ST 70801

Us Post Office Building
750 FLORIDA ST 70801

BOSCO

BUILDINGS

1200 Building
1200 N 18TH ST 71201

141 Building
141 DESIARD ST 71201

Mid City Centre
909 N 18TH ST 71201

N 18th Professional Building
1205 N 18TH ST 71201

P And S Medical Complex
312 GRAMMONT ST 71201

Premier Bank Plaza
1900 N 18TH ST 71201

Premier Bank Building
130 DESIARD ST 71201

Washington Plaza
300 WASHINGTON ST 71201

Washington Square Building
211 N 3RD ST 71201

GOVERNMENT

Federal Building
201 JACKSON ST 71201

Ouachita Parish Courthous
300 SAINT JOHN ST 71201

State Office Building
122 SAINT JOHN ST 71201

BOSSIER CITY

BUILDINGS

Bossier City Office Park
3018 OLD MINDEN RD 71112

Professional Plaza
1007 GOULD DR 71111

CECILE

BUILDINGS

Knight Office Plaza
3000 KNIGHT ST 71105

One Bellemead Centre
6425 YOUREE DR 71105

Quadrangle Building
2001 E 70TH ST 71105

Shreve City Office Park
2920 KNIGHT ST 71105

Shreve City Office Park
2924 KNIGHT ST 71105

Shreve City Office Park
3004-020 KNIGHT ST 71105

South Pointe Plaza
3003 KNIGHT ST 71105

Southpointe Center
3007 KNIGHT ST 71105

Troy Plaza
2529 E 70TH ST 71105

CENTENARY

BUILDINGS

Celt Center Complex
2800 YOUREE DR 71104

Line Olive Building
745 OLIVE ST 71104

COOPER ROAD

BUILDINGS

D And W Business Center
1434 HAWN AVE 71107

Roberts Office Center
1500 N MARKET ST 71107

GREENWOOD PARK

BUILDINGS

Centrum Office Plaza
2835 HOLLYWOOD AVE ... 71108

GRETNA

BUILDINGS

Oakwood Shopping Center
197 WESTBANK EXPY 70053

LA CHUTE

BUILDINGS

1st Federal Plaza
505 TRAVIS ST 71101

820 Jordan Partnership
820 JORDAN ST 71101

American Tower
401 MARKET ST 71101

Arkla Gas Building
525 MILAM ST 71101

Beck Building
400 TRAVIS ST 71101

Buckner Square
1700 BUCKNER ST 71101

Commercial Center
333 TEXAS ST 71101

Doctors Building
865 MARGARET PL 71101

Hibernia Bank Building
509 MARKET ST 71101

Hutchinson Building
504 TEXAS ST 71101

Petroleum Building
619 MARKET ST 71101

Premier Bank Tower
400 TEXAS ST 71101

Ricou Brewster Building
425 MILAM ST 71101

Shepherd Blanchard Building
631 MILAM ST 71101

Spring Street Plaza
800 SPRING ST 71101

Transcontinental Tower
330 MARSHALL ST 71101

Travis Place
666 TRAVIS ST 71101

Ward Building
525 MARSHALL ST 71101

GOVERNMENT

Caddo Parish Courthouse
501 TEXAS ST 71101

City Hall
1234 TEXAS AVE 71101

City Hall Annex
1237 MURPHY ST 71101

Federal Courthouse
300 FANNIN ST 71101

LAFAYETTE

BUILDINGS

First Nat Bank Towers
600 JEFFERSON ST 70501

Whitney National Bank
911 LEE AVE 70501

GOVERNMENT

Federal Building
705 JEFFERSON ST 70501

Parish Courthouse
800 S BUCHANAN ST 70501

State Office Building
302 JEFFERSON ST 70501

LAKE CHARLES

BUILDINGS

LA Savings Building
901 LAKE SHORE DR 70601

Lakeside Plaza Building
125 W BROAD ST 70601

Lakeside Plaza Building
125 ONE LAKESIDE PLZ . 70601

Magnolia Life Building
1011 LAKE SHORE DR 70601

Weber Building
834 RYAN ST 70601

METAIRIE

BUILDINGS

AAA
3445 N CAUSEWAY BLVD 70002

Galleria One
1 GALLERIA BLVD 70001

Heritage Plaza
111 Veterans Memorial Blvd 70005

Honeywell Building
6620 RIVERSIDE DR 70003

Imperial Building
3301 N CAUSEWAY BLVD 70002

Jefferson Bank
3525 N CAUSEWAY BLVD 70002

Jefferson Medical Tower
4300 HOUMA BLVD 70006

LA Federal Building
3421 N CAUSEWAY BLVD 70002

One Lakeway Center
3900 N CAUSEWAY BLVD 70002

Riverside Life Ins Building
6660 RIVERSIDE DR 70003

Security Homestead
4900 Veterans Mem. Blvd . 70006

Two Lakeway Center
3850 N CAUSEWAY BLVD 70002

NORTH SHORE

BUILDINGS

Towers
520 OLD SPANISH 70458

Whitney National Bank
1338 GAUSE BLVD 70458

GOVERNMENT

LA State Building
2331 CAREY ST 70458

SHREVEPORT

BUILDINGS

Diagnostic And Surgical
2751 VIRGINIA AVE 71103

THIBODAUX

COLLEGES

Nicholls State University
4000 Nicholls State Univ ... 70310

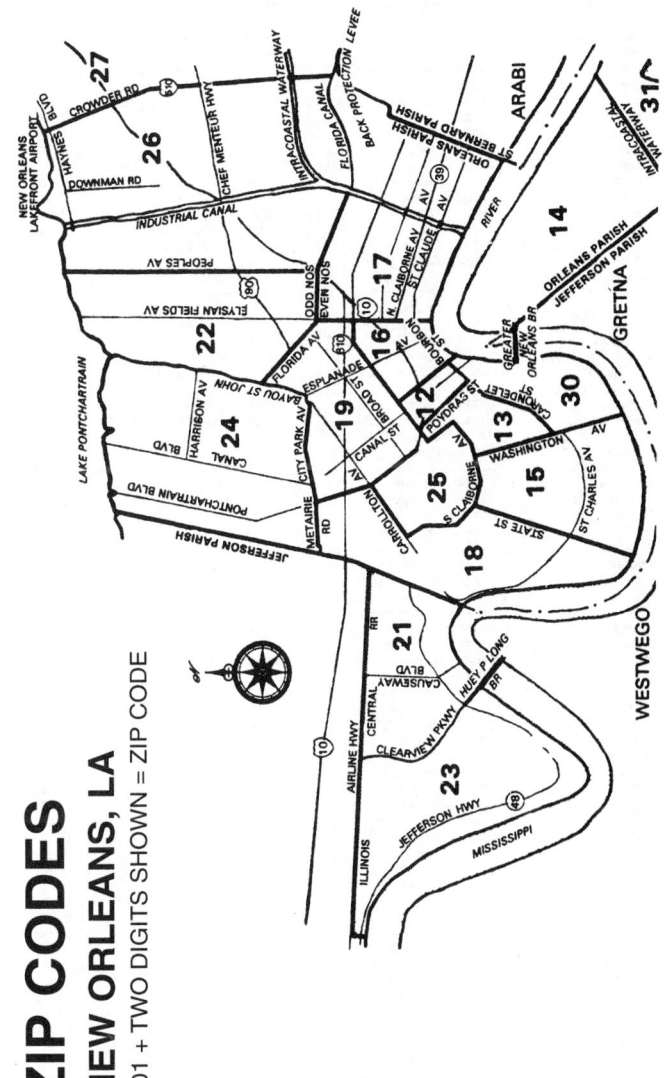

MAINE
Abbreviation ME

Abbot Village	04406
Acton	04001
Addison	04606
Albion	04910
Alfred	04002
Alna	04535
Andover	04216
Anson	04911
Ashland 04732, 04737, 04759	
Athens	04912
Atlantic	04608
Auburn	04210-212
Augusta 04330, 04332, 04336	
	04338
Togus	04330
Aurora	04408
Bailey Island	04003
Bangor	04401-402
Veazie	04401
Bar Harbor	04609
Bar Mills	04004
Bass Harbor	04653
Bath	04530
Bayville	04536
Beals	04611
Belfast	04915
Belgrade	04917
Belgrade Lakes	04918
Benedicta	04733
Bernard	04612
Berwick	03901
Bethel	04217
Biddeford	04005, 04007
Bingham	04920
Birch Harbor	04613
Birch Island (Brunswick)	04011
Blaine	04734
Blue Hill	04614
Blue Hill Falls	04615
Boothbay	04537, 04549
Boothbay Harbor	04536
	04538, 04570
(Bayville)	
Capitol Island	04538
Bowdoinham	04008
Bradford	04410
Bradley	04411
Brewer	04412
Bridgewater	04735
Bridgton	04009
Bristol	04539
Brooklin	04616
Brooks	04921
Brooksville	04617
Brookton	04413
Brownfield	04010
Brownville	04414, 04481
Brownville Junction	04415
Brunswick	04011, 04053
Birch Island	04011
Cundys Harbor	04011
Bryant Pond	04219
Buckfield	04220
Bucks Harbor	04618
Bucksport	04416
Burlington	04417
Burnham	04922
Bustins Island	04013

Calais	04619
Cambridge	04923
Camden	04843, 04847
Canaan	04924
Canton	04221
Cape Cottage	04107
(Cape Elizabeth)	
Cape Elizabeth	04107
Cape Neddick	03902
Cape Porpoise	04014
Capitol Island	04538
(Boothbay Harbor)	
Caratunk	04925
Cardville	04418
Caribou	04736
Carmel	04419
Casco	04015
Castine	04420, 04421
Center Lovell	04016
Chamberlain	04541
Charleston	04422
Chebeague Island	04017
Cherryfield	04622
China	04926
Clayton Lake	04737
Cliff Island	04019
Clinton	04927
Columbia Falls	04623
Coopers Mills	04341
Corea	04624
Corinna	04928
Cornish	04020
Costigan	04423
Cranberry Isles	04625
Crouseville	04738
Cumberland Center	04021
Cumberland Foreside	04110
Cundys Harbor (Brunswick)	04011
Cushing	04563
Cushing Island (Portland)	04109
Cutler	04626
Damariscotta	04543
Danforth	04424, 04492
Danville	04223
Deer Isle	04627
Denmark	04022
Dennysville	04628
Detroit	04929
Dexter	04930
Diamond Island (Portland)	04109
Dixfield	04224
Dixmont	04932
Dover Foxcroft	04426
Dresden	04342
Dryden	04225
Durham	04222
Eagle Lake	04739
East Andover	04226
East Baldwin	04024
East Blue Hill	04629
East Boothbay	04544
East Corinth	04427
East Dixfield	04227
East Eddington	04428
East Holden	04429
East Lebanon	04027
East Livermore	04228
East Machias	04630
East Millinocket	04430
East Newport	04933
East Orland	04431

East Parsonfield	04028
East Poland	04230
East Sebago	04029
East Stoneham	04231
East Vassalboro	04935
East Waterboro	04030
East Wilton	04234
East Winthrop	04343
Easton	04740
Eastport	04631
Edgecomb	04556
(North Edgecomb)	
Eliot	03903
Ellsworth	04605
Enfield	04433
Estcourt Station	04741
Etna	04434
Eustis	04936
Exeter	04435
Fairfield	04937
Falmouth	04105
Farmingdale	04344
Farmington	04938
Farmington Falls	04940
Fort Fairfield	04742
Fort Kent	04743
Fort Kent Mills	04744
Frankfort	04438
Franklin	04634
Freedom	04941
Freeport	04033, 04032
Frenchboro	04635
Frenchville	04745
Friendship	04547
Frye	04235
Fryeburg	04037
Gardiner	04344-346
(Farmingdale)	
Garland	04939
Georgetown	04548
Glen Cove	04846
Gorham	04038
Gouldsboro	04607
Grand Isle	04746
Grand Lake Stream	04637
Gray	04039
Great Diamond Island	04109
(Portland)	
Greene	04236
Greenville	04441, 04485
Greenville Junction	04442
Grove	04638
Guilford	04443, 04482
Hallowell	04347
Hampden	04444
Hancock	04640
Hanover	04237
Harbor Islands (Portland)	04109
Harborside	04642
Harmony	04942
Harrington	04643
Harrison	04040
Hartland	04943
Haynesville	04446
Hebron	04238
Hinckley	04944
Hiram	04041
Hollis Center	04042
Hope	04847
Houlton	04730, 04761
Howland	04448

Hudson	04449
Hulls Cove	04644
Island Falls	04747
Isle Au Haut	04645
Isle Of Springs	04549
Islesboro	04848
Islesford	04646
Jackman	04945
Jay	04239, 04262
Jefferson	04348
Jonesboro	04648
Jonesport	04649
Kenduskeag	04450
Kennebunk	04043
Kennebunkport	04014, 04046
(Cape Porpoise)	
Kents Hill	04349
Kezar Falls	04047
Kingfield	04947
Kingman	04451
Kittery	03904
Kittery Point	03905
Lagrange	04453
Lambert Lake	04454
Lee	04455
Leeds	04263
Levant	04456
Lewiston	04240-241, 04243
Liberty	04949
Lille	
04749	
Limerick	04048
Limestone	04750-751
Limington	04049
Lincoln	04457
Lincoln Center	04458
Lincolnville	04849
Lincolnville Center	04850
Lisbon (Durham)	04222, 04250
Lisbon Center	04251
Lisbon Falls	04252
Litchfield	04350
Little Deer Isle	04650
Little Diamond Island	04109
(Portland)	
Livermore	04253
Livermore Falls	04254
Locke Mills	04255
Long Island	04050
Lovell	04051
Lubec	04652
Mac Mahan (Georgetown)	04548
Machias	04654, 04606
Wesley	04686
Machiasport	04655
Madawaska	04756
Madison	04950
Manchester	04351
Manset	04656
Mapleton	04757
Maplewood	04095
(West Newfield)	
Mars Hill	04758
Masardis	04759
Matinicus	04851
Mattawamkeag	04459
Mechanic Falls	04256
Meddybemps	04657
Medomak	04551
Medway	04460
Merepoint	04053

Mexico	04257
Milbridge	04658
Milford	04461
Millinocket	04462
Milo	04463
Minot	04258
Minturn	04659
Monhegan	04852
Monmouth	04259
Monroe	04951
Monson	04464
Monticello	04760
Moody	04054
Morrill	04952
Mount Desert	04660
Mount Vernon	04352
Naples	04055
New Gloucester	04260
New Harbor	04554, 04558
New Limerick	04761
New Portland	04954
New Sharon	04955
New Sweden	04762
New Vineyard	04956
Newagen	04552
Newcastle	04553
Newfield	04056
Newport	04953
Newry	04261
Nobleboro	04555
Norridgewock	04957
North Amity (Orient)	04471
North Anson	04958
North Berwick	03906
North Bridgton	04057
North Brooklin	04661
North Fryeburg	04058
North Haven	04853
North Jay	04262
North Monmouth	04265
North New Portland	04961
North Sebago	04029
(East Sebago)	
North Shapleigh	04060
North Sullivan	04664
North Turner	04266
North Vassalboro	04962
North Waterboro	04061
North Waterford	04267
North Yarmouth	04097
Northeast Harbor	04662
Norway	04268
Oakfield	04763
Oakland	04963
Ocean Park	04063
Ogunquit	03907
Olamon	04467
Old Orchard Beach	04063-064
(Ocean Park)	
Old Town	04468
Oquossoc	04964
Orient	04471
Orland	04472
Orono	044069, 04473
Orrington	04474
Orrs Island	04066
Otter Creek	04665
Owls Head	04854
Oxbow	04764
Oxford	04270
Palermo	04354

Palmyra	04965
Paris	04271
Passadumkeag	04475
Patten	04765
Peaks Island	04108
Pejepscot	04067, 04086
Pemaquid	04558
Pembroke	04666
Penobscot	04476
Perham	04766
Perry	04667
Peru	04290
Phillips	04966
Phippsburg	04562, 04567
Pittsfield	04967
Plymouth	04969
Poland	04273
Poland Spring	04274
Pond Cove	04107
(Cape Elizabeth)	
Port Clyde	04855
Portage	04768
Porter	04068
Portland	04100-110
	04112, 04116, 04122-123
Cushing Island	04109
Diamond Island	04109
Great Diamond Island	04109
Harbor Islands	04109
Little Diamond Island	04109
Pownal	04069
Presque Isle	04769
Princeton	04637, 04668
(Grand Lake Stream)	
Prospect Harbor	04669
Quimby	04770
Randolph	04346
Rangeley	04970
Raymond	04071
Readfield	04355
Richmond	04357
Robbinston	04671
Rockland	04841
Rockport	04856
Rockwood	04478
Round Pond	04564
Roxbury	04275
Rumford	04276
Rumford Center	04278
Rumford Point	04279
Sabattus	04280
Saco	04072
Saint Agatha	04772
Saint Albans	04971
Saint David	04773
Saint Francis	04774
Saint George	04857
Salsbury Cove	04672
Sandy Point	04972
Sanford	04073
Sangerville	04479
Sargentville	04673
Scarborough	04070, 04074
West Scarborough	04070
Seal Cove	04674
Seal Harbor	04675
Searsmont	04973
Searsport	04974
Sebago Lake	04075
Sebasco Estates	04565
Sebec	04481

Sebec Lake	04482	Stonington	04645, 04681	West Boothbay Harbor	04575
Seboeis (Howland)	04448	(Isle Au Haut)		West Bowdoin	04287
Sedgwick	04676	Stratton	04982	West Buxton	04093
Shapleigh	04076	Strong	04983	West Enfield	04493
Shawmut	04975	Sunset	04683	West Farmington	04992
Sheridan	04775	Surry	04629, 04684	West Forks	04985
Sherman Mills	04776	(East Blue Hill)		West Kennebunk	04094
Sherman Station	04777	Swans Island	04685	West Lebanon	04027
Shirley Mills	04485	Temple	04984	(East Lebanon)	
Sinclair	04779	Tenants Harbor	04860	West Minot	04288
Skowhegan	04976	Thomaston	04861	West Newfield	04095
Small Point	04567	Thorndike	04986	West Paris	04289
Smithfield	04978	Togus (Augusta)	04330	West Peru (Peru)	04290
Smyrna Mills	04780	Topsfield	04490	West Poland	04291
Soldier Pond	04781	Topsham	04086	West Rockport	04865
Solon	04979	Trevett	04571	West Scarborough	04070
Sorrento	04677	Troy	04987	(Scarborough)	
South Berwick	03908	Turner	04282	West Southport	04576
South Bristol	04568	Turner Center	04283	West Sumner	04292
South Casco	04077	Union	04862	West Tremont	04690
South China	04358	Unity	04988	Westbrook	04092, 04098
South Freeport	04013, 04078	Upper Frenchville	04784	Westfield	04787
(Bustins Island)		Van Buren	04785	Whitefield	04353
South Gardiner	04359	Vanceboro	04491	Whiting	04691
South Harpswell	04079	Vassalboro	04989	Whitneyville	04692
South Paris	04281	Veazie (Bangor)	04401	Wilton	04294
South Portland	04106, 04116	Vienna	04360	Windham	04062, 04082
Portland	04106	Vinalhaven	04863	Windsor	04363
Portland	04116	Waite	04492	Winn	04495
South Thomaston	04858	Waldoboro	04572	Winslow (Waterville)	04901
South Waterford	04081	Walpole	04573	Winter Harbor	04693
South Windham	04082	Warren	04864	Winterport	04496
Southwest Harbor	04656, 04679	Washburn	04786	Winterville	04788
(Manset)		Washington	04574	Winthrop	04364
Springfield	04487	Waterboro	04087	Wiscasset	04578
Springvale	04083	Waterford	04088	Woodland	04694
Spruce Head	04859	Waterville	04901, 04903	Woolwich	04579
Squirrel Island	04570	Winslow	04901	Wytopitlock	04497
Stacyville	04782	Wayne	04284	Yarmouth	04096-097
Standish	04084	Weeks Mills	04361	York	03909
Steep Falls	04085	Weld	04285	York Beach	03910
Stetson	04488	Wellington (Harmony)	04942	York Harbor	03911
Steuben	04680	Wells	04090		
Stillwater	04489	Wesley (Machias)	04686		
Stockholm	04783	West Baldwin	04091		
Stockton Springs	04981	West Bethel	04286		

PORTLAND

GOVERNMENT

Cumberland Cty Courthouse
142 FEDERAL ST 04101

Federal Courthouse
156 FEDERAL ST 04101

Federal Courthouse
76 PEARL ST 04101

Portland City Hall
389 CONGRESS ST 04101

United States Customs
312 FORE ST 04101

United States Post Office
125 FOREST AVE 04101

HOSPITALS

Mercy Hospital
144 STATE ST 04101

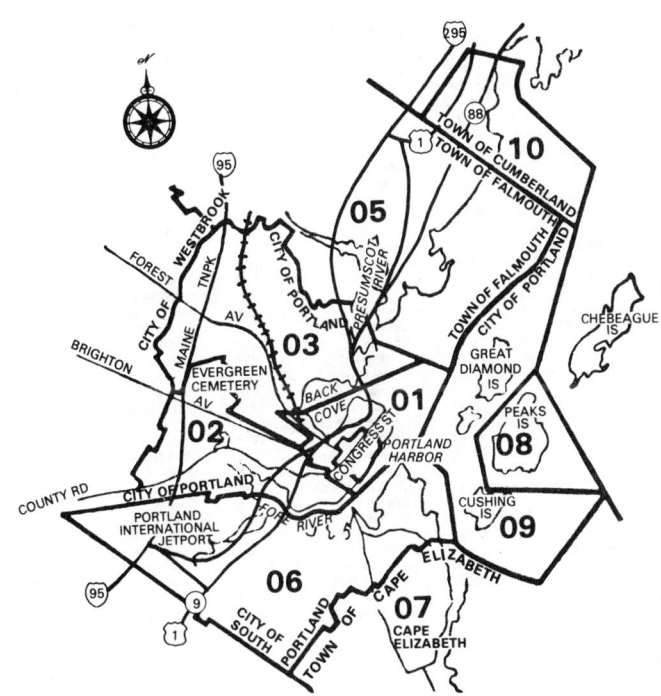

ZIP CODES
PORTLAND, ME
041 + TWO DIGITS SHOWN = ZIP CODE

Belgravia (Baltimore) 21206
Belmar (Baltimore) 21206
Beltsville 20704-705, 20797
Benedict 20612
Benevola (Boonsboro) 21713
Bengies (Baltimore) 21220
Benson 21018
Bentley Springs (Parkton) .. 21120
Berkley (Darlington) 21034
Berlin 21811
Berrett (Sykesville) 21784
Berwyn (College Park) 20740
Bethel (Chesapeake City) . 21915
Bethesda . 20813-817, 20824-825
     20827, 20899, 20892, 20897
     Chevy Chase 20813
     West Bethesda 20817
     West Bethesda 20827
Bethlehem 21609
Betterton 21610
Beverley Beach 21037
     (Edgewater)
Beverly Hills (Baltimore) 21214
Big Pool 21711
Big Spring (Clear Spring) .. 21722
Bishop (Bishopville) 21813
Bishophead (Toddville) .. 21672
Bishopville 21813
Bittinger 21522
Bivalve 21814
Bladensburg 20710, 20797
Bloomington 21523
Bloomsbury (Baltimore) .. 21228
Blue Mount (Monkton) 21111
Blue Mountain (Thurmont) 21788
Bolivar (Middletown) 21769
Bolton Hill (Baltimore) 21217
Bonnie Ridge (Baltimore) .. 21209
Boonsboro 21713
Borden Shaft (Frostburg) .. 21532
Boring 21020
Bowie 20715-721, 20797
     Mitchellville 20721
     West Bowie 20719
Bowling Green 21502
     (Cumberland)
Boyds 20841
Boyer Mill Heights 21774
     (New Market)
Bozman 21612
Braddock Heights 21714
Bradshaw 21021
Brandon Shores 21226
     (Baltimore)
Brandywine 20613
Breezewood (Odenton) 21113
Brentwood 20722
Bridgeport (Taneytown) 21787
Bridleshire (Baltimore) 21204
Brigadoon (Baltimore) 21207
Brighton (Baltimore) 21207
Brinklow 20862
Britinay (Baltimore) 21234
Broad Run (Burkittsville) 21718
Broadfield (Baltimore) 21228
Broadview (Baltimore) 21209
Brookeville 20833
Brooklandville 21022
Brooklyn (Baltimore) 21225
Brookview Farms 21286
     (Baltimore)

Brookwood (Baltimore) 21209
Broomes Island 20615
Brownsville 21715
Brunswick 21716
Bryans Road 20616, 20697
Bryantown 20617
Buckeystown 21717
Buffalo Run 21531
     (Friendsville)
Burkittsville 21718, 21755
     Arnoldtown 21718
     Broad Run 21718
Burns Corner (Aberdeen) .. 21001
Burtonsville 20866, 20897
Bushwood 20618
Butler 21023
Bynum (Forest Hill) 21050
Cabin John 20818
California 20619
Callaway 20620
Calvert (Rising Sun) 21911
Cambridge 21613
Camden Yards (Baltimore) 21230
Camp David (Thurmont) .. 21788
Camp Springs 20746, 20748
     (Suitland)
Campus Hills (Baltimore) .. 21286
Canton (Baltimore) 21224
Cape Loch Haven 21037
     (Edgewater)
Cape May Landing 21221
     (Baltimore)
Cape Saint Claire 21401
     (Annapolis)
Capital Heights 20731
     .... 20743, 20791
     Fairmont Heights 20743
     Seat Pleasant 20743
Cardiff 21024
Carlos (Frostburg) 21532
Carney (Baltimore) 21234
Carroll (Baltimore) 21229
Carrollton (Westminster) .. 21157
Carrolltowne (Sykesville) .. 21784
Carrollwood (Baltimore) .. 21220
Carsins Run (Aberdeen) .. 21001
Carvel Beach (Baltimore) .. 21226
Cascade 21719
Casselman (Grantsville) .. 21536
Castleton (Darlington) 21034
Catoctin View 21771
     (Mount Airy)
Catonsville (Baltimore) 21228
Catonsville Manor 21207
     (Baltimore)
Cavetown 21720
Cayots Corner 21915
     (Chesapeake City)
Cecilton 21913
Cedar Beach (Baltimore) .. 21221
Cedarcroft (Baltimore) 21212
Cedarmere (Owings Mills) . 21117
Cedarwood Estates 21208
     (Baltimore)
Cedonia (Baltimore) 21206
Centreville 21617
Chadwick Manor 21244
     (Baltimore)
Chance 21816, 21821
Chapelgate (Odenton) 21113
Chaptico 20621

Charles Village 21218
     (Baltimore)
Charlesmont (Baltimore) ... 21222
Charlestown 21228, 21914
     (Baltimore)
Charlotte Hall 20622
Chartley (Reisterstown) 21136
Chase 21027, 21220
Chattolanee 21117
     (Owings Mills)
Chelsea Beach (Pasadena) 21122
Cheltenham 20623
Cherry Hill 21225, 21921
     (Baltimore)
Chesaco Park (Baltimore) . 21237
Chesapeake Beach 20732
Chesapeake City 21915
Chesapeake Village 21220
     (Baltimore)
Chester 21619
Chesterfield (Pasadena) 21122
Chestertown 21620
Chestnut Grove 21756
     (Keedysville)
Chestnut Hill 21050
     (Forest Hill)
Chestnut Ridge 21136
     (Reisterstown)
Cheverly 20781, 20784-785
     (Hyattsville)
Chevy Chase 20814
     .... 20815, 20825
     (Bethesda)
     Somerset 20815
Chewsville 21721
Childs 21916
Chillum (Hyattsville) ... 20782-783
Church Creek 21622
Church Hill 21623, 21656
     Price 21656
Churchton 20733
Churchville 21028
Citicorp 21747-748
     (Hagerstown)
Claiborne 21624
Clarksburg 20871, 20897
Clarksville 21029
Clarysville (Frostburg) 21532
Clayton Manor (Joppa) 21085
Clear Spring 21722
Clear Water Beach 21226
     (Baltimore)
Clearview Village 21122
     (Pasadena)
Clements 20624
Clifton (Baltimore) 21213
Clifton East End 21205
     (Baltimore)
Clinton 20735, 20797
Cloisters (Baltimore) 21212
Cloverfield Manor 21234
     (Baltimore)
Cloverly (Silver Spring) 20904
Cobb Island 20625
Cockeysville 21030-031
     (Cockeysville Hunt Valley)
Cold Spring New Town 21209
     (Baltimore)
Coldstream (New Market) . 21774
Colesville 20904-905, 20914
     (Silver Spring)

Colgate (Baltimore) 21224
College (Westminster) 21157
College Estates 21702
　(Frederick)
College Hills (Baltimore) ... 21228
College Park .. 20740-742, 20797
　Berwyn 20740
　Berwyn Heights 20740
　North College Park 20740
　University Of MD 20742
Collmus (New Market) 21774
Colonial Gardens 21228
　(Baltimore)
Colonial Heights 21502
　(Cumberland)
Colonial Park (Baltimore) .. 21207
Colony Ridge (Odenton) 21113
Colora 21917
Coltons Point 20626
Columbia 21029, 21044-046
　(Clarksville)
Compton 20627
Comus (Dickerson) 20842
Conowingo 21918
Cooksville 21723
Coopersville (Butler) 21023
Coopstown (Forest Hill) 21050
Copper Hill (Baltimore) 21209
Copperville (Taneytown) 21787
Corbett (Monkton) 21111
Cordova 21625
Corriganville 21524
Cottage City (Brentwood) .. 20722
Country Ridge (Baltimore) 21221
Courtland Manor 21208
　(Baltimore)
Coventry (Baltimore) 21234
Cowentown (Elkton) 21921
Coxs Corner (Tyaskin) 21865
Crapo 21626
Creagerstown (Thurmont) . 21788
Crellin (Oakland) 21550
Cresaptown 21502, 21505
　(Cumberland)
Crisfield 21817
Crocheron 21627
Crofton 21114
Cromwood (Baltimore) 21234
Crownsville 21032
Crumpton 21628
Cub Hill (Baltimore) 21234
Cumberland 21501-505
　Bowling Green 21502
　Colonial Heights 21502
　Cresaptown 21502
　Cresaptown 21505
　Homewood 21502
　Lavale 21502
　Lavale 21504
　Locust Grove 21502
　Mapleside 21502
　Potomac Park 21502
　Upper Homewood 21502
Curtis Bay (Baltimore) 21226
Damascus 20872
Dameron 20628
Dames Quarter 21820
Daniels (Ellicott City) 21043
Darby Lux (New Market) ... 21774
Dares Beach 20678
　(Prince Frederick)

Dargan (Sharpsburg) 21782
Darlington 21034
Darnestown 20874, 20878
　(Germantown)
Dartmoor Woods 21227
　(Baltimore)
Davidsonville 21035
Daybreak Estates 21206
　(Baltimore)
Dayton 21036
Deal Island 21821
Deale 20751
Deep Creek Lake 21541
　(Mc Henry)
Deep Run Park (Baltimore) 21227
Deer Park (Oakland) 21550
Deerfield (Darlington) 21034
Delight (Reisterstown) 21136
Delmar 21875
Dembeigh Hill (Baltimore) . 21210
Dennings (New Windsor) .. 21776
Denton 21629
Derwood (Rockville) 20855
Detmold (Lonaconing) 21539
Detour 21725, 21757
Dickerson 20842
Dickey Woods (Baltimore) . 21228
Dickeyville (Baltimore) 21207
Discovery (Walkersville) 21793
District Heights 20747, 20753
　Forestville 20747
　Forestville 20753
Dixon Hill (Baltimore) 21209
Dogwood Flats (Barton) 21521
Doncaster Village 21234
　(Baltimore)
Donnybrook (Baltimore) 21286
Dorsey (Hanover) ... 21076, 21227
Dorseytown (Mount Airy) .. 21771
Doubs (Adamstown) 21710
Dowell 20629
Downsville (Williamsport) .. 21795
Drayden 20630
Drexel Woods (Baltimore) . 21228
Druid (Baltimore) 21217
Dublin (Darlington) . 21034, 21154
Dumbarton (Baltimore) 21208
Dunbrook (Pasadena) 21122
Dundalk (Baltimore) 21222
Dunkirk 20754
Eagle Nest (Baltimore) 21221
Eakles Mill (Keedysville) ... 21756
Earleville 21919
East Case (Baltimore) 21202
East End (Baltimore) 21205
East New Market 21631
Eastern Terrace 21221
　(Baltimore)
Eastfield (Baltimore) 21222
Easton 21601, 21606
Eastpoint (Baltimore) 21224
Eastport (Annapolis) 21403
Eastwood (Baltimore) 21224
Eckhart Mines 21528
Eden 21822
Eden Roc (Baltimore) 21208
Edgemere (Baltimore) 21222
Edgemont (Smithsburg) 21783
Edgewater 21037
Edgewood 21040
Edmondson Heights 21207

　(Baltimore)
Edmondson Village 21229
　(Baltimore)
Edmonston (Hyattsville) 20781
Elder Hill (Friendsville) 21531
Eldersburg (Sykesville) 21784
Elizabeth Landing 21122
　(Pasadena)
Elk Mills 21920
Elk Neck (Elkton) 21921
Elkridge (Baltimore) 21227
Elkton 21921-922
　Barksdale 21921
　Cherry Hill 21921
　Cowentown 21921
　Elk Neck 21921
　Fair Hill 21921
　Pleasant Hill 21921
Ellerslie 21529
Ellicott City 21041-043
　Daniels 21043
　Ilchester 21043
　Oella 21043
Elliott (Vienna) 21869
Elmwood (Baltimore) 21206
Emmitsburg 21727
Ernstville (Big Pool) 21711
Essex (Baltimore) 21221
Essexshire (Baltimore) 21221
Eudowood (Baltimore) 21204
Ewell 21824
Fair Brook (Baltimore) 21244
Fair Hill (Elkton) 21921
Fair Play 21733
Fairbrook Park 21244
　(Baltimore)
Fairmont Heights 20743
　(Capital Heights)
Fairmount 21867
　(Upper Fairmount)
Fairview Beach 21122
　(Pasadena)
Falls Gable (Baltimore) 21209
Fallston 21047
Farmington (Rising Sun) ... 21911
Faulkner 20632
Featherbed (Baltimore) 21207
Federalsburg 21632
Finksburg 21048
Finzel (Frostburg) 21532
Fishing Creek 21634
Fishtown (Baltimore) 21208
Flickersville 21756
　(Keedysville)
Flintstone 21530
Flohrville (Sykesville) 21784
Forest Heights 20745
　(Oxon Hill)
Forest Hill 21050
Foreston (Upperco) 21155
Forestville 20747, 20753
　(District Heights)
Forge Heights 21128
　(Perry Hall)
Fork 21051
Fort Detrick (Frederick) 21702
Fort George Meade 20755, 20797
　(Fort George G Meade)
Fort Howard 21052
Fort Mchenry (Baltimore) .. 21230
Fort Meade 20755

(Fort George G Meade)
Fort Ritchie (Cascade) 21719
Fort Washington 20744, 20749
Fountaindale (Middletown) .. 21769
Four Winds (Baltimore) 21204
Fowbelsburg (Upperco) 21155
Foxridge (Randallstown) 21133
Foxville (Smithsburg) 21783
Franklin 21223, 21562
(Baltimore)
Franklinville 21021, 21788
(Bradshaw)
Frederick ... 21701-705, 21709
College Estates 21702
Fort Detrick 21702
Harmony Grove 21701
Hood College 21701
Hopeland 21701
Lewistown 21701
Lime Kiln 21701
Oak Acres 21701
Pine Cliff 21701
Round Hill 21702
State Farm Ins Co 21709
Tulip Hill 21701
West Hills 21702
Frederick Village 21228
(Baltimore)
Fredericktown 21930
(Georgetown)
Freeland 21053, 21107
Friends Creek 21727
(Emmitsburg)
Friendship 20758
Friendsville 21531
Frizzelburg (Westminster) .. 21158
Frostburg 21532
Frostown (Middletown) 21769
Fruitland 21826
Fulton 20759
Funkstown 21734
Gaither 21735, 21784
Gaithersburg 20877-879
. 20882, 20854-86, 20897-99
Darnestown 20878
Germantown 20874
Laytonsville 20879, 20882
Montgomery Village
.... 20879, 20882, 20886
North Potomac 20878
Galena 21635, 21637
Galesville 20765
Gallagher Park 21212
(Baltimore)
Gambrills 21054
Gapland 21736
Garfield (Smithsburg) 21783
Garrett Park 20896
Garretts Mill (Knoxville) 21758
Garrison 21055, 21117
Garrison Farms 21208
(Baltimore)
Georgetown 21930
Germantown .. 20874-876, 20897
Darnestown 20874
Gibson Island 21056
Gilmore (Frostburg) 21532
Gilpintown (Flintstone) 21530
Gingerville (Edgewater) 21037
Girdletree 21829
Glade Town (Walkersville) . 21793

Glen Arden (Lanham) 20706
Glen Arm 21057
Glen Burnie 21060-062
Glen Cove (Darlington) 21034
Glen Cove Estates 21227
(Baltimore)
Glen Echo 20812
Glen Ellen (Baltimore) 21286
Glen Morris 21136
(Reisterstown)
Glenarden (Lanham) 20706
Glencoe (Sparks Glencoe) .. 21152
Glenelg 21737
Glenmar (Baltimore) 21208
Glenmont (Silver Spring) ... 20906
Glenn Dale 20769
Glenville (Darlington) 21034
Glenwood 21738
Glyndon 21071, 21136
Goldentree (Baltimore) 21221
Goldsboro 21636
Golts 21637
Goodnow Hill (Baltimore) .. 21206
Gortner (Oakland) 21550
Goucher Woods 21286
(Baltimore)
Govans (Baltimore) 21212
Govanstown (Baltimore) 21212
Graceham (Thurmont) 21788
Grahamtown (Frostburg) ... 21532
Granite (Woodstock) 21163
Grantsville 21536
Grasonville 21638
Gray Manor (Baltimore) 21222
Grays Level (Baltimore) 21228
Great Mills 20634
Green Haven (Pasadena) .. 21122
Green Meadow 20782
(Hyattsville)
Green Ridge (Bel Air) 21015
Green Spring Hills 21085
(Joppa)
Greenbelt
.... 20768, 20770-771, 20797
Greenbriar (Boonsboro) 21713
Greene Tree (Baltimore) ... 21208
Greengate (Baltimore) 21209
Greenland Beach 21226
(Baltimore)
Greenmount (Hampstead) .. 21074
Greensboro 21639
Greensburg (Smithsburg) .. 21783
Greenville (Taneytown) 21787
Grey Rock (Baltimore) 21208
Grimesdale (Baltimore) 21221
Guilford (Baltimore) 21218
Guilford Manor 21225
(Baltimore)
Gunpowder 21010
Gwynn Oak 21207, 21244
(Baltimore)
Gwynnbrook (Owings Mills) 21117
Hagerstown . 21740-42, 21746-49
Citicorp 21747-21749
MD Correctional Sys 21746
Northern 21742
Halcyon Gate (Baltimore) .. 21208
Halethorpe (Baltimore) 21227
Hamilton (Baltimore) 21214
Hampden (Baltimore) 21211
Hampstead 21074

Hampton (Baltimore) 21286
Hancock 21750
Hanover 21076-077, 21098
Dorsey 21076
Harmans 21076
Hanoverville (Hanover) 21076
Harbor Valley (Baltimore) .. 21225
Harborview (Baltimore) 21230
Harden Heights 21208
(Baltimore)
Harford Park (Baltimore) ... 21234
Harmans (Hanover) ... 21076-077
Hanover 21077
Harmony (Middletown) 21769
Harmony Grove (Frederick) 21701
Harney (Taneytown) 21787
Harperville (Lonaconing) ... 21539
Harrington Manor 21234
(Baltimore)
Harrisonville 21133
(Randallstown)
Harrisville ... 21771, 21911, 21917
(Mount Airy)
Hartland Run (Baltimore) .. 21221
Hartman (New Market) 21774
Harwood 20776
Harwood Park (Baltimore) . 21227
Havre de Grace 21078
Hawbottom (Middletown) ... 21769
Hawthorne (Baltimore) 21220
Haywood Heights 21207
(Baltimore)
Hebbville (Baltimore) 21244
Hebron 21830
Helen 20635
Helmsley Court 21208
(Baltimore)
Henderson 21640
Henryton 21080
Herald Harbor 21032
(Crownsville)
Heraldry Square 21244
(Baltimore)
Hereford (Monkton) 21111
Hew (Rockville) 20857
Hickory (Forest Hill) 21050
High Barbaree 21774
(New Market)
High Point (Pasadena) 21122
Highfield (Cascade) 21719
Highfields (Baltimore) 21228
Highland 20777
Highlandtown (Baltimore) .. 21224
Hillandale 20903
(Silver Spring)
Hillcrest (Baltimore) 21225
Hillcrest Heights 20748
(Temple Hills)
Hillendale (Baltimore) 21234
Hillsboro 21641
Hoffman (Frostburg) 21532
Holland Hills (Baltimore) ... 21206
Hollofield (Baltimore) 21244
Holly Hill Harbor 21037
(Edgewater)
Hollywood 20636
Homeland (Baltimore) 21212
Homewood (Cumberland) . 21502
Hoods Mill (Cooksville) 21723
Hoopersville 21634
(Fishing Creek)

Poplar Springs 21771
(Mount Airy)
Port Covington 21230
(Baltimore)
Port Deposit 21904
Port Herman 21915
(Chesapeake City)
Port Republic 20676
Port Tobacco 20677
Porterstown (Keedysville) . 21756
Potomac 20854, 20859
    Rockville 20854
    Rockville 20859
Potomac Park 21502
(Cumberland)
Powellville 21852
Powhatan Beach 21122
(Pasadena)
Powhattan Hill 21207
(Baltimore)
Preston 21655
Price (Church Hill) 21656
Prince Frederick ... 20678, 20697
Princess Anne 21853
Providence (Baltimore) 21286
Pumphrey (Baltimore) 21225
Putnam (Forest Hill) 21050
Pylesville 21132
Quail Ridge (Baltimore) 21227
Quantico 21856
Queen Anne 21657
Queenstown 21658
Rabbit Town (Vienna) 21869
Randalia 21915
(Chesapeake City)
Randallstown 21133
Raspeburg (Baltimore) 21206
Rawlings 21557
Rayville (Parkton) 21120
Reese (Westminster) 21157
Rehobeth 21857
Reisterstown 21136
Relay (Baltimore) 21227
Remington (Baltimore) 21211
Reservoir Hill 21217
(Baltimore)
Revere Park (Baltimore) ... 21234
Reynolds (Westernport) 21562
Rhodes Point (Ewell) 21824
Rhodesdale 21659
Richards Oak (Colora) 21917
Richardson Mews 21227
(Baltimore)
Ridervale (Baltimore) 21204
Riderwood 21139, 21204
Ridge 20680
Ridgeleigh (Baltimore) 21234
Ridgely 21660, 21681-688
Ridgeville (Mount Airy) 21757
Ringgold (Smithsburg) 21783
Ripplewood (Baltimore) 21244
Rising Sun 21911
Rison (Marbury) 20658
Riva 21140
Riverdale
    ..... 20737-738, 20797, 21146
Riverside (Belcamp) 21017
Riviera Beach (Pasadena) . 21122
Rock Hall 21661, 21790
Rock Hill Beach 21122
(Pasadena)

Rock Point 20682
Rock Springs (Rising Sun) . 21911
Rockdale (Baltimore) 21244
Rockland Run (Baltimore) . 21209
Rocks (Street) 21154
Rockview Beach 21122
(Pasadena)
Rockville . 20847-855, 20857-859
    20897
    Hew 20857
    North Bethesda 20852
Rockwell (Baltimore) 21228
Rocky Acres (Thurmont) ... 21788
Rocky Ridge 21778
Rogers Heights 20781
(Hyattsville)
Rognell Heights 21229
(Baltimore)
Rohrersville 21756, 21779
(Keedysville)
    Locust Grove 21779
Rosemont (Knoxville) 21758
Round Hill (Frederick) 21702
Royal Oak 21662
Rumbley (Westover) 21871
Rumsey Island (Joppa) 21085
Rush (Flintstone) 21530
Russellville (Lonaconing) .. 21539
Rutherford Green 21244
(Baltimore)
Ruxton (Baltimore) 21204
Sabillasville 21780
Saint Charles 20602-604
(Waldorf)
Saint Denis (Baltimore) 21227
Saint Helena (Baltimore) ... 21222
Saint Inigoes 20684
Saint James 21781
Saint Leonard 20685
Saint Marys 20686
(Saint Marys City)
Saint Michaels 21624
    .... 21647, 21663
(Claiborne)
    Michaels 21663
Salem (Vienna) 21869
Salisbury 21801-803
    South Salisbury 21801
Sanandrew (New Market) . 21774
Sand Spring 21531
(Friendsville)
Sandy Hook 21050, 21758
(Forest Hill)
Sandy Spring 20860
Sang Run (Mc Henry) 21541
Sanmar (Boonsboro) 21713
Savage 20763
Scotland 20687
Scotts Level (Baltimore) 21208
Seabrook 20703, 20706
(Lanham)
Seat Pleasant 20743
(Capital Heights)
Secretary 21664
Security Square 21244
(Baltimore)
Selbysport (Friendsville) ... 21531
Severn 21144
Severna Park 21146
Shady Oaks (Baltimore) ... 21220
Shady Side 20764

Shallmar (Kitzmiller) 21538
Shankville (Big Pool) 21711
Sharonville (Pasadena) 21122
Sharpsburg 21782
Sharptown 21861
Sherwood 21665
Sherwood Forest 21405
(Annapolis)
Showell 21862
Silver Hill (Suitland) 20746
Silver Manor (Baltimore) ... 21221
Silver Run (Westminster) ... 21158
Silver Spring 20900-908
    .... 20910-916, 20918, 20990
    20997
    Aspen Hill 20906, 20916
    Cloverly 20904
    Colesville 20914
    Glenmont 20906
    Hillandale 20903
    Leisure World 20906
    Norbeck 20906
    Suburb Maryland Fac . 20990
    Suburban Md Brmas ... 20997
    Takoma Park 20903
    Wheaton ... 20902, 20906, 915
    Woodmoor 20901
Simpsonville 21150
Smallwood (Westminster) .. 21157
Smithsburg 21783
Smoketown (Boonsboro) .. 21713
Snow Hill 21863
Snydersburg (Hampstead) . 21102
Sollers Point (Baltimore) ... 21222
Solomons 20688
Somerset (Chevy Chase) .. 20815
Sorrento (Baltimore) 21204
Sorrento Run (Baltimore) .. 21209
South Baltimore 21230
South Down Shores 21037
(Edgewater)
South River Park 21037
(Edgewater)
South Salisbury 21801
(Salisbury)
Southern Maryland Fac 20790
(Capital Heights)
Sparks Glencoe 21152
Sparrows Point 21219
(Baltimore)
Spencerville 20868
Spielman (Fair Play) 21733
Spoolsville (Middletown) ... 21769
Spready Oak (Rising Sun) . 21911
Spring Gap 21560
Spring Hill (Baltimore) 21234
Stafford (Darlington) 21034
Stanbrook (Baltimore) 21222
Stepney (Aberdeen) 21001
Stevens Wood (Baltimore) . 21244
Stevenson 21153, 21208
    Lystra Farms 21153
Stevensville 21666
Still Pond 21667
Stockton 21864
Stoneleigh (Baltimore) 21212
Street 21154
Sudbrook Park (Baltimore) 21208
Sudlersville 21668
Suitland 20746, 20752
    Camp Springs 20746

(Marriottsville)	Woolford 21677	Wynnewood (Baltimore) 21227
Granite 21163	Worton 21678	Yarrowsburg (Knoxville) 21758
Woodville (Mount Airy) 21771	Wrights Crossing 21532	Yeager (New Market) 21774
Woodwardville (Odenton) .. 21113	(Frostburg)	York Ridge (Baltimore) 21204
Woodwind (Baltimore) 21228	Wye Mills 21679	Zilman (Frostburg) 21532

IMPORTANT BUILDINGS

ACADEMY HEIGHTS

APARTMENTS

Caton House Apartments
734 EDMONDSON AVE 21228

Hill Mar Apartments
104 BEAUMONT AVE 21228

Milbert Apartments
105 EGGES LN 21228

Summit Park Apartments
10 STANLEY DR 21228

BUILDINGS

Caton Building
709 FREDERICK RD 21228

Catonsville Med Ctr Build
500 N ROLLING RD 21228

Catonsville Prof Center
405 FREDERICK RD 21228

Crismer Building
6100 Baltimore Natl. Pike . 21228

Edmondson Profess Buildin
6106 EDMONDSON AVE .. 21228

Maiden Choice Medical Ctr
716 MAIDEN CHOICE LN 21228

Medical Center W Building
6630 Baltimore Natl. Pike . 21228

One Mile West Sc
6600 Baltimore Natl. Pike . 21228

Pravia Medical Center Building
413 Commonwealth Ave ... 21228

Professional Arts Building
5550 Baltimore Natl. Pike . 21228

Suburbia Building
5602 Baltimore Natl. Pike . 21228

West Park Building
6400 Baltimore Natl. Pike . 21228

Wilken Beltway Plaza
817 MAIDEN CHOICE LN 21228

GOVERNMENT

Arbutus Catonsville Msc
900 WALKER AVE 21228

ADELPHI

APARTMENTS

Hampshire Towers
7333 New Hampshire Ave 20783

Hampshire Towers
7401 New Hampshire Ave 20783

Presidential Towers
1836 METZEROTT RD 20783

BUILDINGS

Crossroads Prof Building
7676 New Hampshire Ave 20783

Riggs Building
7411 RIGGS RD 20783

Sovran Bank Building
7950 NEW HAMPSHIRE AVE 20783

ANNAPOLIS

APARTMENTS

Admiral Apartments
219 HANOVER ST 21401

Anne Arundel Apartments
1000 MADISON ST 21403

Claiborne Pl Apartments
130 HEARNE RD 21401

College Pky Pl Apartments
570 BELLERIVE DR 21401

Constitution Apartments
9 CONSTITUTION AVE 21401

Fairfax Xing Condominiums
1900 FAIRFAX RD 21401

Glenwood Sr Citz Hi Rise
701 GLENWOOD ST 21401

Hanmore Apartments
191 PRINCE GEORGE ST 21401

Horn Pt Hbr Apartments
107 EASTERN AVE 21403

Murray Ave Apartments
5 MURRAY AVE 21401

Newport Condominiums
316 BURNSIDE ST 21403

Norwalk Apartments
20 SILOPANNA RD 21403

Severn 100 Condominium
100 SEVERN AVE 21403

Tecumseh Condominiums
312 SEVERN AVE 21403

Ten Oaks Manor Apartments
301 BURNSIDE ST 21403

Timothy House Apartments
29 W WASHINGTON ST ... 21401

BUILDINGS

Annapolis City Marina
410 SEVERN AVE 21403

Annapolis National Bank Building
2083 WEST ST 21401

Annapolis Office Plz I
170 JENNIFER RD 21401

Annapolis Professional
201 WEST ST 21401

Annapolis Science Center
120 Admiral Cochrane Dr .. 21401

Arundel Plaza Building
108 Old Solomons Island .. 21401

Bausum Rasin Building
1623 FOREST DR 21403

Bay Ridge Professional
1819 BAY RIDGE AVE 21403

Bestgate 900 Building
900 BESTGATE RD 21401

Bishop Office Building
37 Old Solomons Island Rd 21401

City Market Building
25 MARKET SPACE 21401

Clock Towers Shopping Ctr
1410 FOREST DR 21403

Colban Building
1419 FOREST DR 21403

College Pky Office Center
528 COLLEGE PKY 21401

Conte Annex Building
122 DEFENSE HWY 21401

Conte Building
116 DEFENSE HWY 21401

Courtyards Building
133 DEFENSE HWY 21401

Eastport Professional Bld
918 CHESAPEAKE AVE ... 21403

Executive Building
140 MAIN ST 21401

Farmers National W Buildi
111 Chinquapin Round Rd 21401

Generals Building
2086 GENERALS HWY 21401

Georgetown Plaza Building
914 BAY RIDGE RD 21403

Glenco Building
105 FORBES ST 21401

Gloucester Building
192 Duke Of Gloucester St 21401

Goodman Building
156 SOUTH ST 21401

Gottlieb Building
7 STATE CIR 21401

Green Holly Med Ctr Build
1277 GREEN HOLLY DR .. 21401

Gregory Building
2450 RIVA RD 21401

Harbor Square Mall
110 DOCK ST 21401

Hays Building
15 SCHOOL ST 21401

Hyatt Building
1919 WEST ST 21401

Katz Building
2060 WEST ST 21401

Lyons Professional Buildi
16 MURRAY AVE 21401

Market Square Mall
36 MARKET SPACE 21401

Maryland Ntl Bank Buildin
160 SOUTH ST 21401

Mason Building
929 WEST ST 21401

Mccrone Building
20 RIDGELY AVE 21401

Medical Building
121 CATHEDRAL ST 21401

Melridge Building
700 MELVIN AVE 21401

Melvin Ave Off Building
801 MELVIN AVE 21401

Nichols Center Building
177 DEFENSE HWY 21401

Parole Plz Off Building
2200 SOMERVILLE RD 21401

Parole Station Building
2049 WEST ST 21401

Pleasure Cove Yacht Club
2116 BAY FRONT TER 21401

Primedical Building
530 COLLEGE PKY 21401

Richards Professional Bld
1407 FOREST DR 21403

Riva 400 Office Pk Condo
2661 RIVA RD 21401

Riva Ii Building
175 Admiral Cochrane Dr .. 21401

Riva Road Building
2521 RIVA RD 21401

Riva Road Off Building
2568 RIVA RD 21401

Rowe Blvd Off Building
111 FORBES ST 21401

Sigma Business Center
45 Old Solomons Island Rd 21401

Signet Bank Building
2510 RIVA RD 21401

Sovran Bank Building
2530 RIVA RD 21401

Speer Building
3 CHURCH CIR 21401

The Livery Building
209 WEST ST 21401

Tilghman Building
42 STATE CIR 21401

Townsworth Building
150 SOUTH ST 21401

Weems Building
48 MARYLAND AVE 21401

Weems Creek Medical Ctr
600 RIDGELY AVE 21401

West Annapolis Profession
101 RIDGELY AVE 21401

West Court Building
2448 HOLLY AVE 21401

West Garrett Pl Building
275 WEST ST 21401

Westgate Building
80 WEST ST 21401

Woodbridge Ctr Building
2444 Solomons Island Rd . 21401

Yacht Haven Of Annapolis
326 1ST ST 21403

GOVERNMENT

AA Cty Courthouse Annex
101 SOUTH ST 21401

Anne Arundel Ct Courthous
7 CHURCH CIR 21401

Anne Arundel Cty Det Ctr
131 JENNIFER RD 21401

Arundel Center Building
44 CALVERT ST 21401

Jeffrey Building
16 FRANCIS ST 21401

Lowe House Office Buildin
84 COLLEGE AVE 21401

Maryland Court Of Appeals
361 ROWE BLVD 21401

Maryland Hall
801 CHASE ST 21401

Maryland Income Tax Build
110 CARROLL ST 21401

Maryland State House
100 STATE CIR 21401

Maryland Treasury Buildin
80 CALVERT ST 21401

Stanton Center
92 W WASHINGTON ST ... 21401

Tawes State Office Buildi
580 TAYLOR AVE 21401

William James Senate Off
110 COLLEGE AVE 21401

COLLEGES

USNA Administration Build
121 BLAKE RD 21402

USNA Alumni Hall
675 DECATUR RD 21402

USNA Chauvenet Hall
572 HOLLOWAY RD 21402

USNA Dahlgren Hall
103 FULLAM CT 21402

USNA Decatur Hall
117 DECATUR RD 21402

USNA Halligan Hall
181 WAINWRIGHT RD 21402

USNA Lejeune Hall
628 COOPER RD 21402

USNA Luce Hall
112 COOPER RD 21402

USNA Mahan Hall
106 MARYLAND AVE 21402

USNA Maury Hall
105 MARYLAND AVE 21402

USNA Michaelson Hall
572 HOLLOWAY RD 21402

USNA Mitscher Hall
101 COOPER RD 21402

USNA Nimitz Hall
589 MCNAIR RD 21402

USNA Preble Hall
118 MARYLAND AVE 21402

USNA Ricketts Hall
566 BROWNSON RD 21402

USNA Rickover Hall
590 HOLLOWAY RD 21402

USNA Sampson Hall
107 MARYLAND AVE 21402

USNA Ward Hall
290 BUCHANAN RD 21402

ANNESLIE

APARTMENTS

Crestwood Apartments
5001 MIDWOOD AVE 21212

Epiphany House Apartments
5610 YORK RD 21212

Govans Manor Apartments
5220 YORK RD 21212

New York Road Apartments
499 BEAUMONT AVE 21212

Oakland Apartments
5207 YORK RD 21212

Stoneleigh Apartments
6713 YORK RD 21212

Walker Mews Apartments
6225 YORK RD 21212

BUILDINGS

Armco Building
7215 YORK RD 21212

Belvedere Sq Market Build
529-40 E BELVEDERE Ave 21212

Belvedere Sq Office Build
540 E BELVEDERE AVE ... 21212

Bradford Federal Building
6900 YORK RD 21212

Charles Fountain Building
6301 N CHARLES ST 21212

Drumcastle Ctr Building
6305 YORK RD 21212

Homeland Center Building
5438 YORK RD 21212

ANTON WOODS

APARTMENTS

Ingram Manor Apartments
7301 PARK HEIGHTS AVE 21208

Marbrook Apartments
3623 7 MILE LN 21208

Marlene Apartments
3703 7 MILE LN 21208

N Oaks Retirement Commun
725 MOUNT WILSON LN . 21208

Park Newport Apartments
7219 PARK HEIGHTS AVE 21208

Pavilion In The Park Apar
4001 OLD COURT RD 21208

Pomona East Apartments
1 POMONA E 21208

Risteau Condominiums
2331 OLD COURT RD 21208

Seventy Two Eleven Apartm
7211 PARK HEIGHTS AVE 21208

Suburban Oaks Apartments
5 SLADE AVE 21208

Suburban Oaks Apartments
7 SLADE AVE 21208

BUILDINGS

Baltimore Inn Building
1726 Reisterstown Rd 21208

Bank Of Baltimore Buildin
1515 Reisterstown Rd 21208

Bedford Square Building
1314 BEDFORD AVE 21208

Beecham Square Building
3655 OLD COURT RD 21208

Commercentre Building
1777 Reisterstown Rd 21208

Dumbarton Sq Building
3723 OLD COURT RD 21208

Elko Building
15 WALKER AVE 21208

Greenwood Place Building
3 GREENWOOD PL 21208

Maryland National Bank Building
1414 Reisterstown Rd 21208

Naylors Court Building
4000 OLD COURT RD 21208

Old Court Exec Park Build
3701 OLD COURT RD 21208

Pikesville Med Ctr Buildi
1401 Reisterstown Rd 21208

Pikesville Plz Building
600 Reisterstown Rd 21208

Pomona Square Building
1700 Resiterstown Rd 21208

Rikir Place Building
1709 Reisterstown Rd 21208

Signet Bank Building
3635 OLD COURT RD 21208

Slade Prof Building
122 SLADE AVE 21208

Suburban Center Building
106 OLD COURT RD 21208

Sudbrook Station Building
115 SUDBROOK LN 21208

Walker Center Building
19 WALKER AVE 21208

Williamsburg Sq Building
17 WARREN RD 21208

ARBUTUS

APARTMENTS

Aladdin Trailer Village
7734 WASHINGTON BLVD 21227

Arbutus Apartments
5110 LEEDS AVE 21227

Beltway Trailers
2341 MONUMENTAL AVE 21227

Depaul House Apartments
3300 BENSON AVE 21227

Elkridge Mobile Home Park
6620 Washington Blvd 21227

Glenwood Village Trailer Park
4714 WASHINGTON BLVD 21227

Leeds Apartments
5112 LEEDS AVE 21227

M And M Trailer Park
6636 WASHINGTON BLVD 21227

BUILDINGS

Anderson Building
5820 Southwestern Blvd ... 21227

Beltway Professional Building
1900 Sulphur Spring Rd 21227

Benson Professional Building
3421 BENSON AVE 21227

Caton Dental Building
1901 Hammonds Ferry Rd 21227

Dorsey Business Ctr Building
6797 DORSEY RD 21227

East Dr Professional Ctr
5205 EAST DR 21227

Environmental Elem Buildi
3700 KOPPERS ST 21227

Hollins Ferry Professiona
4367 Hollins Ferry Rd 21227

Parkanna Med Ctr Building
4000 ANNAPOLIS RD 21227

ARLINGTON

APARTMENTS

Abundant Life Towers Apts
3915 CALLAWAY AVE 21215

Arlington Park Condos
6701 PARK HEIGHTS AVE 21215

Bel Park Tower Apartments
3800 W BELVEDERE AVE 21215

Blair House Apartments
6007 PARK HEIGHTS AVE 21215

Bristol House Apartments
4001 CLARKS LN 21215

Canterbury House Apartmen
6807 PARK HEIGHTS AVE 21215

Club House Condominium
6711 PARK HEIGHTS AVE 21215

Concord House Apartments
2500 W BELVEDERE AVE 21215

Diplomat Condominium
3737 CLARKS LN 21215

Dorchester House Apartmen
3600 GARRISON BLVD 21215

Elmont Towers Apartments
6317 PARK HEIGHTS AVE 21215

Embassy Apartments
3809 CLARKS LN 21215

Empress Apartments
6400 PARK HEIGHTS AVE 21215

Eton Hall Apartments
5906 PARK HEIGHTS AVE 21215

Forest Hill Apartments
3631 Liberty Heights Ave .. 21215

Greenhill North Apartment
2501 VIOLET AVE 21215

Greenhill South Apartment
2503 VIOLET AVE 21215

Groveland Hse Apartments
3901 GROVELAND AVE ... 21215

Hampshire House Apartment
6001 PARK HEIGHTS AVE 21215

Har Sinai House Apartment
3601 FORDS LN 21215

Imperial Condominium
3601 CLARKS LN 21215

Kennison Apartments
4310 BOWERS AVE 21215

London House Apartments
6101 PARK HEIGHTS AVE 21215

Manhattan Park Apartments
5715 PARK HEIGHTS AVE 21215

Marlene Apartments
3421 GLEN AVE 21215

Oxford House Apartments
6810 PARK HEIGHTS AVE 21215

Pall Mall Apartments
4410 PALL MALL RD 21215

Park Heights Apartments
5900 PARK HEIGHTS AVE 21215

Park Regent Condo
6414 PARK HEIGHTS AVE 21215

Park Towers E Apartments
7111 PARK HEIGHTS AVE 21215

Park Towers W Condominium
7121 PARK HEIGHTS AVE 21215

Park Towne Apartments
4639 PARK HEIGHTS AVE 21215

Robert Balter House Apart
3615 FORDS LN 21215

Sheffield House Apartment
6000 PARK HEIGHTS AVE 21215

Strathmore Towers Condo
6210 PARK HEIGHTS AVE 21215

Tioga Apartments
2800 Reisterstown Rd 21215

Wallis Apartments
3601 GARRISON BLVD 21215

Wildrose Manor Apartments
3703 FALLSTAFF RD 21215

Wilton Court Apartments
5209 Wilton heights Ave ... 21215

Windsor House Apartments
6503 PARK HEIGHTS AVE 21215

BUILDINGS

Fallstaff Medical Buildin
6821 Reisterstown Rd 21215

Hoffberger Profess Buildi
2435 W BELVEDERE AVE 21215

Metro Plaza Building
2301 Liberty Heights Ave .. 21215

Miden Building
5145 PARK HEIGHTS AVE 21215

Mondawmin Concourse Build
2301 Liberty Heights Ave .. 21215

Mondawmin Mall
2301 Liberty Heights Ave .. 21215

Park Circle Ctr Building
2901 DRUID PARK DR 21215

Park Rogers Med Ctr Build
3502 W ROGERS AVE 21215

Sinai Medical Building
2411 W BELVEDERE AVE   21215

United Federal Building
6609 Reisterstown Rd 21215

GOVERNMENT

Park West Multi Svc Ctr
3319 W BELVEDERE AVE 21215

ARMISTEAD GARDENS

APARTMENTS

JHU Med Res Hall Apartmen
1620 MCELDERRY ST 21205

Waters Towers Apartments
1400 E MADISON ST 21205

BUILDINGS

Broadway Medical Building
550 N BROADWAY 21205

Teamsters Assembly Hall
6000 ERDMAN AVE 21205

ASHLAR HILL

APARTMENTS

Linwood Court Apartments
2800 LINWOOD AVE 21234

BUILDINGS

Carney Professional Ctr
9403 HARFORD RD 21234

Carney Vlg Sc Building
9613 HARFORD RD 21234

Chesapeake Federal Buildi
2001 E JOPPA RD 21234

Foster Building
8700 OLD HARFORD RD . 21234

Harford Road Plz Building
9512 HARFORD RD 21234

Home Mutual Life Building
1740 E JOPPA RD 21234

Joppa Medical Center Building
2314 E JOPPA RD 21234

North Plaza Office Building
8813 Waltham Woods Rd . 21234

Nusinov Plaza Building
8714 SATYR HILL RD 21234

Oakleigh Professional Bld
1713 TAYLOR AVE 21234

Parkville Medical Center Building
8713 HARFORD RD 21234

ASPEN HILL

APARTMENTS

Homecrest House
14508 HOMECREST RD .. 20906

Homecrest House
14510 HOMECREST RD .. 20906

The Fairways South
3330 N Leisure World Blvd 20906

The Winexburg
2301 GLENALLAN AVE 20906

AUTUMN PARK

APARTMENTS

Arlington Baptist Apartme
7600 CLAYS LN 21244

Cedar Towers Apartments
3701 TWIN LAKES CT 21244

BUILDINGS

Grempler Building
7100 SECURITY BLVD 21244

Milford Mill Med Building
3610 MILFORD MILL RD .. 21244

One Rutherford Plz Buildi
7133 RUTHERFORD RD .. 21244

Security Square Mall
6901 SECURITY BLVD 21244

AVONDALE

BUILDINGS

Federal Center Building
6505 BELCREST RD 20782

Prince George Center
6525 BELCREST RD 20782

Prince Georges Plaza
3500 E WEST HWY 20782

GOVERNMENT

Prince Georges Library
6532 ADELPHI RD 20782

BACK RIVER HIGHLANDS

APARTMENTS

Alpine Apartments
1009 MACE AVE 21221

Essex Cooperative Apartme
1000 FRANKLIN AVE 21221

BUILDINGS

Country Rdg Professional
1528 Country Ridge Ln 21221

Essex Med Ctr Building
406 EASTERN BLVD 21221

Germania Federal Building
809 EASTERN BLVD 21221

Marlyn Med Ctr Building
901 OLD EASTERN AVE .. 21221

Riverwood Plz Building
101 Back River Neck Rd ... 21221

Stemmers Run Med Arts Bld
405 STEMMERS RUN RD 21221

GOVERNMENT

Essex Multi Purpose Ctr
439 EASTERN BLVD 21221

Essex Rosedale Msc
8914 KELSO DR 21221

BALTIMORE

APARTMENTS

Aisquith School Hse Apart
249 N AISQUITH ST 21202

Akropolis Apartments
3433 Old Frederick Rd 21229

Albert Spencer Gdns Apart
501 DOLPHIN ST 21217

Allegro Condominiums
6 W MOUNT VERNON PL 21201

Allendale Ct Apartments
3600 W FRANKLIN ST 21229

Allenhurst Apartments
1217 E PRESTON ST 21202

Allston Apartments
3111 N CHARLES ST 21218

Ambassador Apartments
3811 CANTERBURY RD .. 21218

Anchorage Marina
2501 BOSTON ST 21224

Anchorage Towers Apartmen
2601 BOSTON ST 21224

Anneslie Apartments
1203 N CHARLES ST 21201

Apostolic Towers Apartmen
201 N WASHINGTON ST . 21231

Ashley Apartments
1701 E NORTH AVE 21213

Augusta Arms Apartments
201 S AUGUSTA AVE 21229

Avalon Apartments
1701 LINDEN AVE 21217

Avon Apartments
6 E READ ST 21202

Balmoral Towers Apartment
6800 LIBERTY RD 21207

Baltimorean Apartments
2905 N CHARLES ST 21218

Barclay House Apartments
3401 OAKFIELD AVE 21207

Basilica Pl Apartments
124 W FRANKLIN ST 21201

Bateman Apartments
2700 ELSINORE AVE 21216

Beethoven Apartments
1518 PARK AVE 21217

Bellemore Apartments
5712 ROLAND AVE 21210

Belvedere Condominiums
1 E CHASE ST 21202

Belvedere Towers Apartmen
1190 W NORTHERN PKY   21210

Belvidere Pl Apartments
115 E EAGER ST 21202

Benton House Condominiums
3 W MOUNT VERNON PL 21201

Berea Apostolic Apartment
1401 N LAKEWOOD AVE . 21213

Berkeley Arms Apartments
102 W 39TH ST 21210

Bernard E Mason Apartment
2121 Windsor Garden Ln .. 21207

Berwyn Manor Apartments
3908 Liberty Heights Ave .. 21207

Beulah Villa Apartments
2230 GARRISON BLVD 21216

Blackstone Apartments
3215 N CHARLES ST 21218

Blessed Sacrament Apartme
4101 OLD YORK RD 21218

Bolton House Apartments
1100 BOLTON ST 21201

Bolton North Apartments
1600 W Mount Royal Ave.. 21217

Brad Lee Apartments
3304 Auchentoroly Ter 21217

Brentwood Apartments
401 E 25TH ST 21218

Brexton Apartments
868 PARK AVE 21201

Briarley Hall Apartments
3203 N CHARLES ST 21218

Broadview Apartments
116 W UNIVERSITY PKY . 21210

Broadway Towers Apartment
201 N BROADWAY 21231

Brooks Hall Apartments
901 CHAUNCEY AVE 21217

Brunswick Apartments
300 E 32ND ST 21218

Burford Apartments
3209 N CHARLES ST 21218

Calvert Court Apartments
3024 N CALVERT ST 21218

Calverton Apartments
119 E 25TH ST 21218

Canterbury Hall Apartment
100 W 39TH ST 21210

Canton Cove Condominiums
2901 BOSTON ST 21224

Carey Apartments
710 W 40TH ST 21211

Carlton Apartments
3507 N CHARLES ST 21218

Carlyle Apartments
500 W UNIVERSITY PKY . 21210

Caroletta Apartments
901 W UNIVERSITY PKY . 21210

Carpenters Trailer Park
3701 N POINT RD 21222

Carriage House Apartments
1739 EUTAW PL 21217

Carrollton Condominium
3601 GREENWAY 21218

Carver Hall Apartments
1411 DIVISION ST 21217

Cathedral Arms Apartments
703 CATHEDRAL ST 21201

Cathedral Ct Apartments
900 CATHEDRAL ST 21201

Center Place Apartments
101 W CENTER PL 21222

Centre Towers Apartments
111 W CENTRE ST 21201

Charles Apartments
3333 N CHARLES ST 21218

Charles Towers N Apartmen
8 CHARLES PLZ 21201

Charles Towers N Apartmen
10 CHARLES PLZ 21201

Charles Towers S Apartmen
15 CHARLES PLZ 21201

Chase House Apartments
1027 CATHEDRAL ST 21201

Chesapeake Commons Apartm
601 N EUTAW ST 21201

Cheshire Apartments
2643 KENNEDY AVE 21218

Chestnut Apartments
3543 CHESTNUT AVE 21211

Christ Church Hbr Apartme
600 LIGHT ST 21230

Churchill Place Condos
820 WILLIAM ST 21230

Claremont Towers Apartmen
4320 CLAREWAY 21213

Classic Apartments
401 W REDWOOD ST 21201

Clifton Park Apartments
1605 HOMESTEAD ST 21218

Cloverdale Apartments
2436 LINDEN AVE 21217

Coleman Mnr Apartments
2201 WALBROOK AVE 21216

College Apartments
2 AIGBURTH RD 21286

Colonnade Condominium
4 W UNIVERSITY PKY 21218

Consulate Condominium
529 N CHARLES ST 21201

Deer Ridge Condo
1040 DEER RIDGE DR 21210

Dell House Apartments
2850 N CHARLES ST 21218

Denison Park Apartments
700 DENISON ST 21229

Desoto Apartments
3409 GREENWAY 21218

Dolly Apartments
710 N CARROLLTON AVE 21217

Douglas Apartments
2800 N CALVERT ST 21218

Druid Apartments
2028 MOUNT ROYAL TER 21217

Dukeland Court Apartments
2131 N DUKELAND ST 21216

Dulaney Towers Condo
1 SMETON PL 21204

Dundee Arms Apartments
3902 CANTERBURY RD .. 21218

Dunleer Apartments
41 SHIPPING PL 21222

Earl Court Apartments
1301 SAINT PAUL ST 21202

Eden Hall Condominium
3401 GREENWAY 21218

Edenwald Apartments
800 SOUTHERLY RD 21286

Elgin Apartments
3308 ELGIN AVE 21216

Ellerslie Apartments
601 WYANOKE AVE 21218

Elmwood House Apartments
3900 GWYNN OAK AVE ... 21207

Elrino Apartments
1701 ELRINO ST 21224

Emersonian Apartments
2502 EUTAW PL 21217

Emory Court Apartments
1100 WHITELOCK ST 21217

Esplanade Apartments
2525 EUTAW PL 21217

Etna Apartments
2421 LAKEVIEW AVE 21217

Eudowood Towers Apartment
1000 E JOPPA RD 21286

Evelyn Court Apartments
3600 ELDORADO AVE 21207

Federal Hill Atrium Apart
723 S CHARLES ST 21230

Federal Park Apartments
327 WARREN AVE 21230

Franklin Center Apartment
410 W FRANKLIN ST 21201

Franklin Court Apartments
506 N PACA ST 21201

Franklin Square Apartment
229 N MOUNT ST 21223

Frederick Douglass Apartm
1645 N CALHOUN ST 21217

Fremont House Apartments
851 GEORGE ST 21201

Garden Apartments
230 STONY RUN LN 21210

Garrison Duvall Apartment
2905 GARRISON BLVD 21216

Garrisonian Apartments
3303 GARRISON BLVD 21216

Geneva Condominium
3405 GREENWAY 21218

Georgian Apartments
1701 BOLTON ST 21217

Gladwyn Manor Apartments
3201 N CHARLES ST 21218

Glenmont Tower Apartments
6920 DONACHIE RD 21239

Goodlow House Apartments
200 CROSS KEYS RD 21210

Greater New Hope Tower
2725 WALBROOK AVE 21216

Greenehouse Apartments
519 W PRATT ST 21201

Greenmount Apartments
3633 GREENMOUNT AVE 21218

Gregory Gardens Apartment
5526 GWYNN OAK AVE ... 21207

Grove Park Mnr Apartments
4300 N CHARLES ST 21218

Guilford Apartments
1820 GUILFORD AVE 21202

Guilford Homewood Apartme
300 E UNIVERSITY PKY .. 21218

Guilford Manor Apartments
2 W UNIVERSITY PKY 21218

Guilford Towers Apartment
14 W COLD SPRING LN .. 21210

Gwynn Apartments
2231 GARRISON BLVD 21216

Gwynns Falls W Apartments
3700 Gwynns Falls Pky 21216

Hamill Court Apartments
1 HAMILL CT 21210

Hamlyn Apartments
103 W 39TH ST 21210

Hammond Apartments
101 W 39TH ST 21210

Hampton Court Apartments
311 DOLPHIN ST 21217

Hampton House Apartments
204 E JOPPA RD 21286

Hampton Plaza Apartments
302 E JOPPA RD 21286

Hanover Square Apartments
1 W CONWAY ST 21201

Harbor Court Condos
10 E LEE ST 21202

Harbor Hill Apartments
301 WARREN AVE 21230

Harford Apartments
5103 HARFORD RD 21214

Harper House Condominiums
111 HAMLET HILL RD 21210

Harvey Johnson Towers Apt
1510 MOSHER ST 21217

Hendersons Wharf Apartmen
1000 FELL ST 21231

Henrietta Sq Apartments
911 S CHARLES ST 21230

Henry Apartments
1125 N Patterson Park Ave 21213

Heritage Court Apartments
103 W CENTER PL 21222

Highfield House Condo
4000 N CHARLES ST 21218

Highland Apartments
3401 E BALTIMORE ST 21224

Hilltop Trailer Park
8200 PULASKI HWY 21237

Hollander Ridge High Rise
2000 ODELL AVE 21237

Hollins House Apartments
1010 W BALTIMORE ST ... 21223

Homestead Apartments
3101 SAINT PAUL ST 21218

Homewood Apartments
3003 N CHARLES ST 21218

Hopkins Hall Apartments
2200 MARYLAND AVE 21218

Hopkins House Apartments
110 W 39TH ST 21210

Horizon House Apartments
1101 N CALVERT ST 21202

Hunter Square Apartments
1011 HUNTER ST 21202

Independence Apartments
2201 MARYLAND AVE 21218

Inner Harbor Marina
400 KEY HWY 21230

International Hse Apartme
101-3 E Mount Royal Ave . 21202

Jefferson House Apartment
4 E 32ND ST 21218

JHU Bradford Apartments
3301 SAINT PAUL ST 21218

JHU Mccoy Hall Apartments
3401 N CHARLES ST 21218

JHU Wolman Hall Apartment
3339 N CHARLES ST 21218

Johnston Square Apartment
501 E PRESTON ST 21202

Jones Trailer Court
400 WISE AVE 21222

Kenilworth Apartments
339 BLOOM ST 21217

Kennedy Apartments
2651 KENNEDY AVE 21218

Kilham Apartments
842 PARK AVE 21201

Kirkwood House Apartments
6401 LOCH RAVEN BLVD 21239

Kramer Apartments
5440 FREDERICK AVE 21229

Lafayette Court Apartment
1100 ORLEANS ST 21202

Lake Drive Apartments
903 LAKE DR 21217

Lakeside Apartments
901 LAKE DR 21217

Lambeth House Apartments
200 TOWSONTOWN CT .. 21204

Lanvale Towers Apartments
1300 E LANVALE ST 21213

Lemko House Apartments
603 S ANN ST 21231

Libbi Apartments
2637 SAINT PAUL ST 21218

Lincoln Apartments
3800 CANTERBURY RD .. 21218

Lincoln Trailer Park
2410 LINCOLN AVE 21219

Lombardy Apartments
220 STONEYFORD RD 21210

Louis Foxwell Sr Mem Apts
3700 GREENSPRING AVE 21211

Louiston Court Apartments
2228 MOUNT ROYAL TER 21217

Loyola Wynnewood Twrs Apt
100 W COLD SPRING LN 21210

Madison Apartments
817 SAINT PAUL ST 21202

Marble Residence Apartmen
1203 SAINT PAUL ST 21202

Marlboro Square Apartment
410 W LOMBARD ST 21201

Marlborough Apartments
1701 EUTAW PL 21217

Martin Deporres Ctr Apart
908 VALLEY ST 21202

Maryland Institute Dorm
120 MCMECHEN ST 21217

Marylander Apartments
3501 SAINT PAUL ST 21218

Mcculloh Apartments
1102 DRUID HILL AVE 21201

Medeso Manor Apartments
301 BLOOM ST 21217

Memorial Apartments
301 MCMECHEN ST 21217

Monterrey Apartments
2400 LINDEN AVE 21217

Monument East Apartments
633 N AISQUITH ST 21202

Monument Place Apartments
704 CATHEDRAL ST 21201

Monument Place Condos
305 W MONUMENT ST 21201

Morrell Park Housing
1820 SPENCE ST 21230

Mt Clare Overlook Apartme
833 W PRATT ST 21201

Navarre Apartments
1700 EUTAW PL 21217

Nelmar Apartments
2401 BROOKFIELD AVE .. 21217

Nine O Nine W Apartments
909 W UNIVERSITY PKY . 21210

Nm Carroll Mnr Apartments
701 N ARLINGTON AVE ... 21217

Normandie Apartments
2624 SAINT PAUL ST 21218

Northway Apartments
3700 N CHARLES ST 21218

Norwood Apartments
5009 NORWOOD AVE 21207

Oak Court Apartments
3212 WALBROOK AVE 21216

Oakland Apartments
3210 WALBROOK AVE 21216

Old Friends Apartments
1714 PARK AVE 21217

Olympian Apartments
2042 PARK AVE 21217

Overlook Apartments
1401 WELDON PL S 21211

Owosso Apartments
905 LAKE DR 21217

Park Center Apartments
511 PARK AVE 21201

Park Charles Apartments
218 N CHARLES ST 21201

Park Gardens Apartments
2300 EUTAW PL 21217

Park Lynn Apartments
4 UPLAND RD 21210

Park Madison Apartments
817 PARK AVE 21201

Park Terrace Apartments
3436 Auchentoroly Ter 21217

Parklay Apartments
1405 PARK AVE 21217

Peabody Apartments
205 E 30TH ST 21218

Peabody Dormitory
606 SAINT PAUL ST 21202

Penthouse Condominium
28 ALLEGHENY AVE 21204

Pill Hill Apartments
6000 IVYDENE TER 21209

Plaza Apartments
1631 PARK AVE 21217

Plymouth Hall Apartments
1701 MADISON AVE 21217

Poplar Court Apartments
2826 WINDSOR AVE 21216

Presbyterian Home Apartme
400 GEORGIA CT 21204

Preston Apartments
218 E PRESTON ST 21202

Primrose Place Apartments
820 S CATON AVE 21229

Queen Anne Belvedere
1214 N CHARLES ST 21201

Redwood Square Apartments
412 W REDWOOD ST 21201

Ridgely Condominium
205 E JOPPA RD 21286

Ridgemede Condominiums
221 RIDGEMEDE RD 21210

Ridgewood Condominiums
310 RIDGEMEDE RD 21210

Rochambeau Apartments
1 W FRANKLIN ST 21201

Rochester Ct Apartments
2513 LINDEN AVE 21217

Rogers Hall Apartments
3506 GREENWAY 21218

Roland House Apartments
4129 ROLAND AVE 21211

Roland Hts Condominiums
4401 ROLAND AVE 21210

Roland Oaks Apartments
4003 ROLAND AVE 21211

Roland Park Condo
6 UPLAND RD 21210

Roland Park Pl Apartments
830 W 40TH ST 21211

Roland View Twrs E Apartm
3939 ROLAND AVE 21211

Roland View Twrs W Apartm
3838 ROLAND AVE 21211

Rosemont Towers Apartment
740 POPLAR GROVE ST . 21216

Roslyn Apartments
2700 ROSLYN AVE 21216

Rugby Hall Apartments
526 W UNIVERSITY PKY . 21210

Ruscombe Gdns Apartments
4800 YELLOWWOOD AVE 21209

Ruxton Towers Apartments
8415 BELLONA LN 21204

Ruxton Township Apartment
1600 RUXTON RD 21204

Sagamore Apartments
2445 LAKEVIEW AVE 21217

Sail Cloth Factory Apartm
121 S FREMONT AVE 21201

Saint James Condos
3704 N CHARLES ST 21218

Saint James Ter Apartment
827 N ARLINGTON AVE ... 21217

Saint Paul At Chase Apart
1101 SAINT PAUL ST 21202

Saint Paul Ct Apartments
3120 SAINT PAUL ST 21218

Saint Paul Regency Apartm
1010 SAINT PAUL ST 21202

Saint Paul St Apartments
920 SAINT PAUL ST 21202

School House Apartments
2000 E NORTH AVE 21213

Seaview Apartments
202 WOODLAND AVE 21222

Seminole Apartments
2425 LAKEVIEW AVE 21217

Sharp Leadenhall Ct Apart
911 LEADENHALL ST 21230

Shipyard Apartments
2639 BOSTON ST 21224

Sotir Mews Condominiums
1414 WILLIAM ST 21230

Southern High Assoc Apart
201 WARREN AVE 21230

Spring House Apartments
5203 FALLS ROAD TER ... 21210

Stafford Apartments
716 N CHARLES ST 21201

Stephen Marc Apartments
4300 Liberty Heights Ave .. 21207

Sutton Place Apartments
1111 PARK AVE 21201

Sylcrest Apartments
600 WHITELOCK ST 21217

Tabco Towers Apartments
305 E JOPPA RD 21286

Talbot Court Apartments
2606 TALBOT RD 21216

Telephone Apartments
220 E 31ST ST 21218

Temple Garden Apartments
2601 MADISON AVE 21217

Terra Royal Apartments
2306 MOUNT ROYAL TER 21217

Thames Point Condo
1900 THAMES ST 21231

Thirty Nine Hundred Apart
3900 N CHARLES ST 21218

Tindeco Wharf Apartments
2809 BOSTON ST 21224

Tower Marina
3101 WATERVIEW AVE 21230

Towsontown Condominium
519 EPSOM RD 21286

Tsu Burkshire Apartments
10 W BURKE AVE 21204

Tsu Towson Run Apartments
205 Towsontown Blvd W ... 21204

Tudor Arms Apartments
501 W UNIVERSITY PKY . 21210

Tuscany Apartments
221 STONY RUN LN 21210

Umab Student Union Apartm
621 W LOMBARD ST 21201

University One Condos
1 E UNIVERSITY PKY 21218

Upshire Apartments
1504 UPSHIRE RD 21218

Upton Court Apartments
600 W LAFAYETTE AVE ... 21217

Victoria Apartments
3314 ELGIN AVE 21216

Virginia Towers Apartment
500 VIRGINIA AVE 21286

Warrington Apartments
3908 N CHARLES ST 21218

Washington Apartments
700 N CHARLES ST 21201

Waterplace Condominium
123 W BARRE ST 21201

Wentworth Arms Apartments
311 CATHEDRAL ST 21201

West Twenty Apartments
11 W 20TH ST 21218

West University Pky Apart
505 W UNIVERSITY PKY . 21210

Westminster Hse Apartment
524 N CHARLES ST 21201

Windsor Arms Apartments
4242 BONNER RD 21216

Windsor Court Apartments
2111 GARRISON BLVD 21216

Winona Apartments
700 PARK AVE 21201

Winthrop House Condo
4100 N CHARLES ST 21218

Woodcliff Mnr Apartments
108 W 39TH ST 21210

Woodhome Apartments
914 N CHARLES ST 21201

Woodrow Apartments
300 E 30TH ST 21218

Wyman House Apartments
123 W 29TH ST 21218

Wyman Park Apartments
3925 BEECH AVE 21211

Wyman Towers Apartments
3100 SAINT PAUL ST 21218

York Apartments
545 WYANOKE AVE 21218

Zion Towers Apartments
1100 PENNSYLVANIA AVE 21201

BUILDINGS

Acres Building
3 MIDDLE RIVER RD 21220

Adams Building
600 BALTIMORE AVE 21204

Alameda Building
5662 THE ALAMEDA 21239

Alecci Building
5718 HARFORD RD 21214

Alex Brown And Sons Build
102 W Pennsylvania Ave .. 21204

American Building
231 E BALTIMORE ST 21202

American National Buildin
204 N LIBERTY ST 21201

Applefeld Building
324 W BALTIMORE ST 21201

Armory Building
300 ARMORY PL 21201

Arundel Corp Ctr Building
110 WEST RD 21204

Atrium At Greenspring
2835 SMITH AVE 21209

Baltimore And Ohio Buildi
2 N CHARLES ST 21201

Baltimore Fed Finan Build
300 E LOMBARD ST 21202

Baltimore Life Building
901 N HOWARD ST 21201

Baltimore Port Truck Plz
5501 ODONNELL ST 21224

Baltimore Travel Plaza
5625 ODONNELL ST 21224

Bank Of Baltimore Buildin
120 E BALTIMORE ST 21202

Bates Building
2 MARKET PL 21222

Belair Market
500 FORREST ST 21202

Belair Market N Building
470 N GAY ST 21202

Belair Market S Building
471 N GAY ST 21202

Belevedere Mall
1023 N CHARLES ST 21201

Belle Grove Business Park
4700 BELLE GROVE RD .. 21225

Blakely Building
8817 BELAIR RD 21236

Blaustein Building
1 N CHARLES ST 21201

Bosley Building
210 ALLEGHENY AVE 21204

Bourse Building
406 WATER ST 21202

Brandon I Building
7609 ENERGY PKY 21226

Broadway Market Building
600 S BROADWAY 21231

Broadway Market N Buildin
1640 ALICEANNA ST 21231

Broadway Market S Buildin
1641 ALICEANNA ST 21231

Brokerage Tower Building
34 MARKET PL 21202

Browns Arcade Building
326 N CHARLES ST 21201

Builders Exchange Buildin
2301 N CHARLES ST 21218

Byron Station Building
8601 HONEYGO BLVD 21236

Campbell Building
100 W Pennsylvania Ave .. 21204

Candler Building
714 E PRATT ST 21202

Canton House Building
300 WATER ST 21202

Carl Building
7902 BELAIR RD 21236

Caruth Building
6737 DOGWOOD RD 21207

Catalyst Square Building
1501 SULGRAVE AVE 21209

Cathedral Place Building
300 CATHEDRAL ST 21201

Catholic Center Building
320 CATHEDRAL ST 21201

Charles Center S Building
36 S CHARLES ST 21201

Charles Towers N Building
8 CHARLES PLZ 21201

Charles Towers N Building
10 CHARLES PLZ 21201

Charles Towers S Building
15 CHARLES PLZ 21201

Charles Towson Building
1104 KENILWORTH DR 21204

Charleswood Building
8422 BELLONA LN 21204

Chesapeake Building
305 W Chesapeake Ave ... 21204

Chesapeake Ntl Bank Build
25 W CHESAPEAKE AVE . 21204

Civic Plaza Building
200 W BALTIMORE ST 21201

Commerce Exchange Buildin
17 COMMERCE ST 21202

Con Rail Produce Terminal
340 W NORTH AVE 21217

Constellation Plz Buildin
1 E PRATT ST 21202

Continental Building
17 W Pennsylvania Ave 21204

Convention Center Mall
100 S CHARLES ST 21201

Court Square Building
200 E LEXINGTON ST 21202

Court Towers Building
210 W Pennsylvania Ave .. 21204

Courthouse Commons Buildi
222 BOSLEY AVE 21204

Credit Union Building
401 E FAYETTE ST 21202

Cross Keys Vlg Sq Buildin
1 VILLAGE SQ 21210

Crown Industrial Park
4401 EASTERN AVE 21224

Curtis Bay Med Ctr Buildi
4710 PENNINGTON AVE . 21226

Daley Building
521 E JOPPA RD 21286

Domenick Crdt Union Build
8501 LA SALLE RD 21286

Dulaney Center Building
849 FAIRMOUNT AVE 21286

Dulaney Center Ii Buildin
901 Dulaney Valley Rd 21204

Dun And Bradstreet Buildi
7400 YORK RD 21204

Dundalk Med Ctr Building
7538 HOLABIRD AVE 21222

Eastpoint Med Ctr Buildin
1012 S NORTH POINT RD 21224

Eastpoint Office Sq Building
1107 N POINT BLVD 21224

Equitable Bank Center
100 S CHARLES ST 21201

Equitable Building
10 N CALVERT ST 21202

Eutaw Building
404 W BALTIMORE ST 21201

Evander Building
2326 N CHARLES ST 21218

Evans Profess Building
6304 KENWOOD AVE 21237

Executive Building
22 WEST RD 21204

Exeter Building
1001 EASTERN AVE 21202

Fairfax Building
101 E REDWOOD ST 21202

Fairmount Place Building
515 FAIRMOUNT AVE 21286

Falls Lane Med Ctr Buildi
4419 FALLS RD 21211

Fallsway Building
1501 GUILFORD AVE 21202

Federal Hill Atrium Build
723 S CHARLES ST 21230

Federal Hill Pl Building
814 LIGHT ST 21230

Fidelity Building
210 N CHARLES ST 21201

Financial Center Building
114 E LEXINGTON ST 21202

First American Building
210 E LOMBARD ST 21202

First Center One Building
110 S PACA ST 21201

First Maryland Building
25 S CHARLES ST 21201

Four Sixes Building
6666 SECURITY BLVD 21207

Franklin Sq Med Arts Building
9101 Franklin Square Dr ... 21237

Frederick Villa Professio
5411 OLD FREDERICK RD 21229

Fuller Med Ctr Building
6918 RIDGE RD 21237

Fullerton Plz Shop Center
7927 BELAIR RD 21236

Furness House Building
19 SOUTH ST 21202

Gallery At Harbor Place
200 E PRATT ST 21202

Garrett Building
233 E REDWOOD ST 21202

Garwyn Med Ctr Building
2300 GARRISON BLVD 21216

Gault Building
130 W HAMILTON ST 21201

Gayety Building
409 E BALTIMORE ST 21202

Golden Ring Mall
6400 ROSSVILLE BLVD ... 21237

Golden Ring Med Ctr Build
8552 PHILADELPHIA RD . 21237

Greater Dundalk Mc Building
2112 DUNDALK AVE 21222

Greenland Branch Building
430 Greenland Beach Rd . 21226

Hamilton Federal Building
5600 HARFORD RD 21214

Hammonds Ln Med Ctr Build
606 HAMMONDS LN 21225

Hampton House Building
204 E JOPPA RD 21286

Hampton Plaza Building
300 E JOPPA RD 21286

Harbor Ct Office Building
575 S CHARLES ST 21201

Harbor Light S Building
810 LIGHT ST 21230

Harbor Place Building
301 LIGHT ST 21202

Harbor Place Building
201 E PRATT ST 21202

Hawthorne Shopping Center
40 KINGSTON RD 21220

Herget Harbor Building
204 E LOMBARD ST 21202

Hillendale Sq Building
1045 TAYLOR AVE 21286

Ibm Tower Building
100 E PRATT ST 21202

Inner Harbor Ctr Building
400 E PRATT ST 21202

Investment Building
1 INVESTMENT PL 21204

IPC Building
4 E FRANKLIN ST 21202

ITC Building
405 E JOPPA RD 21286

Jackson Towers Building
1123 N EUTAW ST 21201

Jefferson Building
2 E FAYETTE ST 21202

Jefferson Building
105 W CHESAPEAKE AVE 21204

Jewelers Building
31 S CALVERT ST 21202

Johnston Profess Building
3333 N CALVERT ST 21218

Joppa Corners Sc
4136 E JOPPA RD 21236

K Mart Shopping Center
222 N POINT BLVD 21224

Katz Building
111 N CHARLES ST 21201

Kellner Building
3503 N CHARLES ST 21218

Kelly Foundation Building
650 W LOMBARD ST 21201

Kenilworth West Building
660 KENILWORTH DR 21204

Keyser Building
207 E REDWOOD ST 21202

Lafayette Building
40 W CHESAPEAKE AVE . 21204

Lafayette Market
1700 PENNSYLVANIA AVE 21217

Lake Falls Profess Buildi
6115 FALLS RD 21209

Lake Falls Vlg Building
6080 FALLS RD 21209

Latrobe Building
2 E READ ST 21202

Leeds Federal Building
1101 MAIDEN CHOICE LN 21229

Legg Mason Building
7 E REDWOOD ST 21202

Legg Mason Tower Building
111 S CALVERT ST 21202

Legg Mason Towson Buildin
600 WASHINGTON AVE ... 21204

Logan Medical Building
3401 DUNDALK AVE 21222

Looper Building
104 W MADISON ST 21201

Loyola Federal Building
22 W Pennsylvania Ave 21204

Madison Park Med Ctr Building
920 W NORTH AVE 21217

Maryland Bar Ctr Building
520 W FAYETTE ST 21201

Maryland Exec Park Building
8600 LA SALLE RD 21286

Maryland Indemn Building
10 S CALVERT ST 21202

Maryland Ntl Bank Buildin
10 LIGHT ST 21202

Maryland Trust Building
16 S CALVERT ST 21202

Medical Arts Building
101 W READ ST 21201

Medical Ctr Dundalk Build
1576 MERRITT BLVD 21222

Medical Professional Building
4200 EDMONDSON AVE .. 21229

Medical Services Building
3350 WILKENS AVE 21229

Mercantile Bank Building
2 HOPKINS PLZ 21201

Mercy Doctors Office Building
333 SAINT PAUL PL 21202

Mill Center Building
3000 CHESTNUT AVE 21211

Mitcherling Building
9652 BELAIR RD 21236

Mount Vernon Building
701 SAINT PAUL ST 21202

Munsey Building
7 N CALVERT ST 21202

Nationsbank Building
31 LIGHT ST 21202

New Banneker Building
12 E PLEASANT ST 21202

Northeast Professional
6600 BELAIR RD 21206

Northern Pky E Profession
1900 E NORTHERN PKY . 21239

Nottingham Centre Buildin
502 WASHINGTON AVE ... 21204

Ntl Marine Bank Building
33 S GAY ST 21202

Old Town Bank Building
321 FALLSWAY 21202

Olde Forge Office Buildin
8441 BELAIR RD 21236

Oldtown Med Ctr Building
1235 E MONUMENT ST ... 21202

One Calvert Plz Building
1 S CALVERT ST 21202

One Center Plz Building
120 W FAYETTE ST 21201

One Charles Ctr Building
100 N CHARLES ST 21201

One Market Centre Buildin
300 W LEXINGTON ST 21201

One West Pennsylvania Ave
1 W PENNSYLVANIA AVE 21204

Osler Med Ctr Building
7600 OSLER DR 21204

Pace Plaza Building
1724 WOODLAWN DR 21207

Park Charles Building
218 N CHARLES ST 21201

Park Liberty Building
111 PARK AVE 21201

Park Plz Professional Ctr
800 N CHARLES ST 21201

Patapsco Federal Building
1301 MERRITT BLVD 21222

Penn Dol Building
1133 PENNSYLVANIA AVE 21201

Perry Hall Professional
9712 BELAIR RD 21236

Physicians Pavillion Building
6565 N CHARLES ST 21204

Pine Heights Professional
1001 PINE HEIGHTS AVE 21229

Point Breeze Bus Ctr Building
2500 BROENING HWY 21224

Port Liberty Indust Ctr
1900 FRANKFURST AVE . 21226

Prestway Building
204 E PRESTON ST 21202

Professional Centre Build
120 SISTER PIERRE DR . 21204

Providence Building
920 PROVIDENCE RD 21286

Putty Hill Office Buildin
8019 BELAIR RD 21236

Quadrangle Building
2 HAMILL RD 21210

Raleigh Indust Ctr Build
1100 WICOMICO ST 21230

Ramsay Professional Ctr
1200 E JOPPA RD 21286

Rcm And D Building
555 FAIRMOUNT AVE 21286

Redwood Tower Building
217 E REDWOOD ST 21202

Riderwood Building
1107 KENILWORTH DR 21204

Roland Park Shop Ctr Building
4800 ROLAND AVE 21210

Rosedale Federal Building
6708 BELAIR RD 21206

Rotunda Building
711 W 40TH ST 21211

Saint Josephs Professiona
7401 OSLER DR 21204

Saint Paul Plz Building
200 SAINT PAUL PL 21202

Saint Paul Sq Building
326 SAINT PAUL PL 21202

Service Centers Building
21 FONTANA LN 21237

Seven Courts Office Build
4111 E JOPPA RD 21236

Seven O Seven Building
707 N CALVERT ST 21202

Severn Building
701 CATHEDRAL ST 21201

Shell Building
200 E JOPPA RD 21286

Signet Tower Building
7 SAINT PAUL ST 21202

Slagle West Office Buildi
2126 MARYLAND AVE 21218

Stanbalt Building
501 SAINT PAUL PL 21202

Sun Life Building
20 S CHARLES ST 21201

Supplee Building
11 E LEXINGTON ST 21202

Susquehanna Building
29 W Susquehanna Ave ... 21204

The Exchange Building
1122 KENILWORTH DR 21204

Totman Building
210 E REDWOOD ST 21202

Tower Suites Building
118 N HOWARD ST 21201

Towne Building
11 E MOUNT ROYAL AVE . 21202

Towson Equitable Building
401 WASHINGTON AVE ... 21204

Towson Mercantile Buildin
409 WASHINGTON AVE ... 21204

Towson Town Ctr Building
825 Dulaney Valley Rd 21204

Trailways Building
210 W FAYETTE ST 21201

Tremont Plaza Building
222 SAINT PAUL ST 21202

United Way Building
22 LIGHT ST 21202

Uofm Professional Buildin
419 W REDWOOD ST 21201

Usf And G Tower Building
100 LIGHT ST 21202

Vansant Building
210 E LEXINGTON ST 21202

Vickers Building
225 E REDWOOD ST 21202

Walbert Building
1800 N CHARLES ST 21201

War Memorial Building
105 N GAY ST 21202

West Cold Spring Building
200 W COLD SPRING LN 21210

Whitaker Building
222 E SARATOGA ST 21202

White Marsh Busin Ctr I
5020 CAMPBELL BLVD 21236

White Marsh Busin Ctr Ii
5022 CAMPBELL BLVD 21236

White Marsh Busin Ctr Iii
5024 CAMPBELL BLVD 21236

White Marsh Busin Ctr Iv
5026 CAMPBELL BLVD 21236

White Marsh Health Ctr
8114 SANDPIPER CIR 21236

White Marsh Mall
8200 PERRY HALL BLVD . 21236

White Marsh Professional
7939 HONEYGO BLVD 21236

Whitesquare Professional
9105 Franklin Square Dr ... 21237

Windsor Court Building
8320 BELLONA AVE 21204

Windy Brae Building
6525 N CHARLES ST 21204

Wolfe Building
110 E LEXINGTON ST 21202

Woodlawn Building
1508 WOODLAWN DR 21207

World Trade Ctr Building
401 E PRATT ST 21202

Wr Grace Building
10 E BALTIMORE ST 21202

Wyndhurst Building
600 WYNDHURST AVE 21210

York At Terracedale Build
7801 YORK RD 21204

York Building
724 YORK RD 21204

York Stevenson Building
7300 YORK RD 21204

Zullo Medical Building
1665 MERRITT BLVD 21222

GOVERNMENT

Baltimore Arena
201 W BALTIMORE ST 21201

Baltimore City Hall
100 HOLLIDAY ST 21202

Baltimore County Off Building
111 W CHESAPEAKE AVE 21204

Baltimore Ct House East
111 N CALVERT ST 21202

Baltimore Cty Court House
400 WASHINGTON AVE ... 21204

Baltimore Cty Cts Buildin
401 BOSLEY AVE 21204

Baltimore Cty Pub Safety
700 E JOPPA RD 21286

Charles L Benton Jr Build
417 E FAYETTE ST 21202

Dundalk Health Center
7700 DUNMANWAY 21222

Eastern Regional Hlth Ctr
9100 Franklin Square Dr ... 21237

Fallon Federal Building
31 HOPKINS PLZ 21201

Federal Depot
2800 EASTERN BLVD 21220

Festival Hall
200 W CAMDEN ST 21201

Garmatz Federal Building
101 W LOMBARD ST 21201

Glenn L Martin Airport
701 WILSON POINT RD ... 21220

Maryland Employment Secur
1100 EUTAW PL 21201

Maryland Employment Secur
1100 N EUTAW ST 21201

Maryland State Office Bld
301 W PRESTON ST 21201

Maryland State Offices
2100 GUILFORD AVE 21218

Merritt Center Building
7701 DUNMANWAY 21222

Mitchell Court House
101 SAINT PAUL ST 21202

Municipal Building
200 HOLLIDAY ST 21202

Oconnor State Off Buildin
201 W PRESTON ST 21201

Post Office Building
101 W CHESAPEAKE AVE 21204

US Custom House
40 S GAY ST 21202

HOSPITALS

Church Home Nursing Ctr
101 N BOND ST 21231

Maryland Institute Ems
636 W LOMBARD ST 21201

UOFM Hosp Hth Sci Library
111 S GREENE ST 21201

UOFM Hosp Inst Pyschiatry
645 W REDWOOD ST 21201

UOFM Hospital Medical Ctr
120 S GREENE ST 21201

MILITARY

Dundalk Armory
2101 DUNDALK AVE 21222

COLLEGES

UMAB Administration Build
737 W LOMBARD ST 21201

UMAB Allied Health Buildi
100 PENN ST 21201

UMAB Bressler Research Bl
655 W BALTIMORE ST 21201

UMAB Clinical Law Center
510 W BALTIMORE ST 21201

UMAB Davidge Hall
522 W LOMBARD ST 21201

UMAB East Hall Gray Lab
520 W LOMBARD ST 21201

UMAB Environmental Health
714 W LOMBARD ST 21201

UMAB Hayden Harris Hall
666 W BALTIMORE ST 21201

UMAB Howard Hall
660 W REDWOOD ST 21201

UMAB Law School
500 W BALTIMORE ST 21201

UMAB Lombard Building
511 W LOMBARD ST 21201

UMAB Marshall Library
500 W BALTIMORE ST 21201

UMAB Mstf
10 S PINE ST 21201

UMAB Newman Center
712 W LOMBARD ST 21201

UMAB Parsons Hall
622 W LOMBARD ST 21201

UMAB Pharmacy Hall
20 N PINE ST 21201

UMAB Pine Street Station
214 N PINE ST 21201

UMAB Redwood Hall
721 W REDWOOD ST 21201

UMAB School Of Nursing
655 W LOMBARD ST 21201

UMAB School Of Social Wor
525 W REDWOOD ST 21201

UMAB Whitehurst Hall
624 W LOMBARD ST 21201

BEL AIR

APARTMENTS

Allendale Condominium
107 E BROADWAY 21014

Bel Air Apartments
600 N HICKORY AVE 21014

Bright Oaks Apartments
50 BRIGHT OAKS DR 21015

Broadway Apartments
83 E BROADWAY 21014

Garfield Apartments
411 KENMORE AVE 21014

Harford Senior Housing
300 SUNFLOWER DR 21014

Hickory Court Apartments
126 N HICKORY AVE 21014

Lee Apartments
142 WILLIAMS ST 21014

Oak Court Apartments
745 N HICKORY AVE 21014

Reckord Apartments
162 WILLIAMS ST 21014

Richardson Apartments
816 S MAIN ST 21014

Tommy Lynn Apartments
30 E BROADWAY 21014

BUILDINGS

Archer Building
17 W COURTLAND ST 21014

Bel Air Commercial Park
728 BALTIMORE PIKE 21014

Bel Air Lee Med Ctr Build
715 S SHAMROCK RD 21014

Bel Air Square Building
260 GATEWAY DR 21014

Bob Turley Building
800 BALTIMORE PIKE 21014

Bond Street Centre Building
212 S BOND ST 21014

Broadway Prof Building
10 W BROADWAY 21014

Business Ctr Harford Mall
227 GATEWAY DR 21014

Courtland Square Building
101 S MAIN ST 21014

Cross Roads Village
2208 Old Emmorton Rd 21015

Del Plaza Shopping Center
804 CONOWINGO RD 21014

Emmorton Crossroads Building
2105 LAUREL BUSH RD .. 21015

Emmorton Professional Bld
2107 LAUREL BUSH RD .. 21015

Fallston Commercial Park
1226 BALTIMORE PIKE ... 21014

Family Care Center
2103 LAUREL BUSH RD .. 21015

Foard Building
100 N MAIN ST 21014

Fountain Green Plz Buildi
1301 CHURCHVILLE RD . 21014

Franklin Sq At Bel Air
206 S HAYS ST 21014

Getz Building
45 N MAIN ST 21014

Harford Mall
600 BEL AIR RD 21014

Holden Building
25 W COURTLAND ST 21014

Hopkins House Building
141 N MAIN ST 21014

Legg Mason Building
34 S MAIN ST 21014

Loyola Federal Building
221 S MAIN ST 21014

Main St Center Building
321 S MAIN ST 21014

Main St North Building
52 N MAIN ST 21014

Maryland Ntl Bank Buildin
307 S TOLLGATE RD 21014

Metzler Building
1212 CHURCHVILLE RD . 21014

One N Main Professional
1 N MAIN ST 21014

Parris Castoro Profession
620 BOULTON ST 21014

Plumtree Professional Ctr
104 PLUMTREE RD 21015

Sparr Building
105 S HICKORY AVE 21014

Stephen Building
1208 CHURCHVILLE RD . 21014

Temple Hills Corpor Ctr
108 E WHEEL RD 21015

Terlyn Sq I Condominium
15 CHURCHVILLE RD 21014

The Festival At Bel Air
5 BEL AIR SOUTH PKY 21015

Tollgate Towne Ctr Buildi
615 BEL AIR RD 21014

Ward Building
23 N MAIN ST 21014

Winters Run Professional
1131 BALTIMORE PIKE 21014

GOVERNMENT

Harford Cty Court House
20 W COURTLAND ST 21014

Harford Cty Govt Adm Building
220 S MAIN ST 21014

Harford Cty Office Buildi
45 S MAIN ST 21014

Risteau District Court
2 S BOND ST 21014

Risteau Multi Service Ctr
2 S BOND ST 21014

BETHESDA

APARTMENTS

Chelsea Towers
7401 WESTLAKE TER 20817

Classic Residence By Hyat
8100 CONNECTICUT AVE 20815

Highland House
5480 WISCONSIN AVE 20815

Highland House West
4450 S PARK AVE 20815

Kenwood House
5100 DORSET AVE 20815

Kenwood Place
5301 WESTBARD CIR 20816

Lakeview House Apts
10250 WESTLAKE DR 20817

Linden Hill
5400 POOKS HILL RD 20814

Madison Park
5000 BATTERY LN 20814

North Park Apts
4615-620 N PARK AVE 20815

Phoenix Of Bethesda
4925 BATTERY LN 20814

Pooks Hill Apts
3 POOKS HILL RD 20814

Seasons Apts
4710 BETHESDA AVE 20814

Somerset House
5600 WISCONSIN AVE 20815

The Carleton
4550 N PARK AVE 20815

The Elizabeth Apts
4601 N PARK AVE 20815

The Irene Apts
4701 WILLARD AVE 20815

The Kenwood
5101 RIVER RD 20816

The Promenade Apts
5225 POOKS HILL RD 20814

The Riviera
4242 E WEST HWY 20815

The Willoughby
5500 FRIENDSHIP BLVD . 20815

The Willoughby
4515 WILLARD AVE 20815

Topaz House
4400 E WEST HWY 20814

Triangle Towers
4853 CORDELL AVE 20814

Waverly House
4521 E WEST HWY 20814

Westlake Towers
7420 WESTLAKE TER 20817

Westwood Towers Apts
5401 WESTBARD AVE 20816

BUILDINGS

Air Rights Building
7315 WISCONSIN AVE 20814

Air Rights Building N Wing
4550 MONTGOMERY AVE 20814

Artery Plaza
7200 WISCONSIN AVE 20814

Barlow Building
5454 WISCONSIN AVE 20815

Bedford Building
6500 ROCK SPRING DR .. 20817

Bethesda Bradley Building
6900 WISCONSIN AVE 20815

Bethesda Gateway Building
7201 WISCONSIN AVE 20814

Bethesda Office Center
4520 E WEST HWY 20814

Blackwell Building
7758 WISCONSIN AVE 20814

Camalier Building
10215 FERNWOOD RD ... 20817

Champlain Building
6410 ROCKLEDGE DR 20817

Chevy Chase Building
5530 WISCONSIN AVE 20815

Chevy Chase Lake Building
8401 CONNECTICUT AVE 20815

Chevy Chase Metro Building
2 WISCONSIN CIR 20815

Clark Building
7500 Old Georgetown Rd . 20814

Del Ray Building
4905 DEL RAY AVE 20814

Democracy Plaza
6701 DEMOCRACY BLVD 20817

East West Towers
4330 E WEST HWY 20814

East West Towers
4340 E WEST HWY 20814

East West Towers
4350 E WEST HWY 20814

Federal Building
7550 WISCONSIN AVE 20814

Hampden Square
4800 MONTGOMERY LN . 20814

Kenwood Professional Building
5272 RIVER RD 20816

Lee Building
6935 WISCONSIN AVE 20815

Little Falls Mall
4701 SANGAMORE RD ... 20816

Lorenz Building
2 Bethesda Metro Ctr 20814

MD National Bank Building
7735 Old Georgetown Rd . 20814

Montgomery Building
4720 MONTGOMERY LN . 20814

Montgomery Mall
7101 DEMOCRACY BLVD 20817

NIH
5333 WESTBARD AVE 20816

One Democracy Center
6901 ROCKLEDGE DR 20817

One Rockledge Centre
6705 ROCKLEDGE DR 20817

Phillips Building
4915 SAINT ELMO AVE 20814

Sovran Bank Building
4700 HAMPDEN LN 20814

Two Democracy Center
6903 ROCKLEDGE DR 20817

Two Rockledge Centre
6701 ROCKLEDGE DR 20817

GOVERNMENT

Bethesda Library
7400 ARLINGTON RD 20814

HOTELS

Bethesda Motel Manor Inn
7740 WISCONSIN AVE 20814

Bethesda Residence Inn
7335 WISCONSIN AVE 20814

Holiday Inn
5520 WISCONSIN AVE 20815

Hyatt Regency Hotel
1 Bethesda Metro Ctr 20814

Ramada Inn
8400 WISCONSIN AVE 20814

BOWIE

APARTMENTS

Collington Episcopal Cent
10450 LOTTSFORD RD ... 20721

Lake Arbor Towers
11411 LAKE ARBOR WAY 20721

BUILDINGS

Belair Prof Building
3231 SUPERIOR LN 20715

Bowie Prof Building
3327 SUPERIOR LN 20715

Free State Mall
15500 ANNAPOLIS RD 20715

Whitehall Prof Building
6911 LAUREL BOWIE RD 20715

BOWLING GREEN

APARTMENTS

Tradewinds Mobile Home Pk
14201 Winchester Rd SW . 21502

Woodside Mobile Home Park
13301 Winchester Rd SW . 21502

CARROLLTON

APARTMENTS

Bank Apartments
35 W MAIN ST 21157

Brooks Apartments
88 W MAIN ST 21157

Chase Apartments
7 CHASE ST 21157

Church Street Apartments
66 S CHURCH ST 21157

Davis Apartments
37 W MAIN ST 21157

Graceland Apartments
154 E GREEN ST 21157

Green Gable Apartments
4 BOND ST 21157

Haines Apartments
172 E MAIN ST 21157

Hickory Hill Trailer Park
1001 STATE ROUTE 140 .. 21157

Hoff Brothers Apartments
257 E MAIN ST 21157

Hub Apartments
39 E MAIN ST 21157

Humbert Apartments
198 E GREEN ST 21157

Locust House Apartments
30 LOCUST ST 21157

Rosenstock Apartments
27 E MAIN ST 21157

Sullivan Apartments
174 PENNSYLVANIA AVE . 21157

Warner Apartments
110 E MAIN ST 21157

Ziles Trailer Court
3515 RIDGE RD 21157

BUILDINGS

Albaugh Babylon Building
10 E MAIN ST 21157

Ashburton Building
1 E MAIN ST 21157

Barrell House Building
10 DISTILLERY RD 21157

Billingslea Medical Build
542 WASHINGTON RD 21157

Carroll Theatre Building
91 W MAIN ST 21157

Charles Carroll Building
117 E MAIN ST 21157

Court St Professional Ctr
125 N COURT ST 21157

Cranberry Mall Building
400 N CENTER ST 21157

Crossroad Sq Shop Ctr
625 BALTIMORE BLVD 21157

East Main St Building
133 E MAIN ST 21157

Firemans Building
66 E MAIN ST 21157

Gateway West Building
125 AIRPORT DR 21157

Main Court Building
201 E MAIN ST 21157

Main St Exchange Building
412 MALCOLM DR 21157

Ridge Medical Ctr Buildin
19 RIDGE RD 21157

Times Building
61 E MAIN ST 21157

Union National Bank Build
115 E MAIN ST 21157

Westminster Professional
532 BALTIMORE BLVD 21157

Westminster Trade Ctr I
150 AIRPORT DR 21157

GOVERNMENT

Carroll Cty Court House
43 N COURT ST 21157

Carroll Cty Office Annex
55 N COURT ST 21157

District Court
100 N COURT ST 21157

Senior Citizens Center
7 SCHOOL HOUSE AVE ... 21157

Westminster City Hall
100 LONGWELL AVE 21157

CHEVERLY

BUILDINGS

Capital Plaza
6200 ANNAPOLIS RD 20784

Cheverly Prof Building East
6005 LANDOVER RD 20785

Cheverly Prof Building West
6001 LANDOVER RD 20785

Landover Mall East Off Bl
2103 BRIGHTSEAT RD 20785

CLOVERLY

APARTMENTS

Columbia Towers
12001 Old Columbia Pike . 20904

Montgomery White Oak Apts
11550 STEWART LN 20904

The Renaissance Plaza
14000 CASTLE BLVD 20904

White Oak Towers
11700 Old Columbia Pike . 20904

BUILDINGS

C & P Telephone Building
13101 COLUMBIA PIKE ... 20904

C & P Telephone Fairland
13100 COLUMBIA PIKE ... 20904

Colorfax Building
11961 TECH RD 20904

Katz Office Building
11911 TECH RD 20904

White Oak Prof Building
11161 NEW HAMPSHIRE AVE20904

COCKEYSVILLE

APARTMENTS

Broadmead Apartments
13801 YORK RD 21030

BUILDINGS

Aspen Mill Professional
54 SCOTT ADAM RD 21030

Center Pointe Building
200 INTERNATIONAL CIR 21030

Church Lane Building
117 CHURCH LN 21030

Cockeysville Rd Building
120 COCKEYSVILLE RD . 21030

Cranbrook Building
10400 RIDGELAND RD 21030

Cranbrook Med Ctr Buildin
10402 RIDGELAND RD 21030

Executive Plaza
11350 MCCORMICK RD ... 21031

Executive Plaza Ii
11350 MCCORMICK RD ... 21031

Executive Plaza Iii
11350 MCCORMICK RD ... 21031

Executive Plaza Iv
11350 MCCORMICK RD ... 21031

Gatehouse At North Park
1 N PARK DR 21030

Holly Gate Off Complex
12 GALLOWAY AVE 21030

Honeywell Building
217 INTERNATIONAL CIR 21030

Hunt Valley Mall
118 SHAWAN RD 21030

Hunt Valley Med Ctr Build
10 WARREN RD 21030

Hunt Valley Professional
9 SCHILLING RD 21031

Mackenzie Building
50 SCOTT ADAM RD 21030

Medstat Building
113 OLD PADONIA RD 21030

Park Center At North Park
6 N PARK DR 21030

Schilling Plz N Building
226 SCHILLING CIR 21031

Schilling Plz S Building
230 SCHILLING CIR 21031

Scotts Corner Sc Building
10245 YORK RD 21030

Shawan Center Building
201 INTERNATIONAL CIR 21030

Valley Place Building
10616 BEAVER DAM RD . 21030

Yorkridge Ctr N Building
10626 YORK RD 21030

COLLEGE ESTATES

APARTMENTS

Applegate Apartments
1418 TANEY AVE 21702

Country Hill Apartments
1000 HEATHER RIDGE DR21702

Taney Village Apartments
1421 TANEY AVE 21702

Willowcrest Apartments
160 WILLOWDALE DR 21702

BUILDINGS

Amber Mdws Professional
198 THOMAS JOHNSON DR21702

Frederick Cty Sq Building
1003 W PATRICK ST 21702

Frederick Shopping Center
1301 W 7TH ST 21702

Fredericktown Mall
1301 W PATRICK ST 21702

COLUMBIA

APARTMENTS

Abbott House Apartments
5495 CEDAR LN 21044

Concord House Condominium
10850 GREEN MOUNTAIN CIR ..
.... 21044

Harmony Hall Apartments
6336 CEDAR LN 21044

Hickory Ridge Pl Apartmen
10799 Hickory Ridge Rd ... 21044

Kings Gate Apartments
7317 EDENBROOK 21046

Longwood Apartments
6150 FORELAND GARTH 21045

Merion Clarys Frst Condos
12290 Green Meadow Dr . 21044

Tor High Rise Apartments
5764 Stevens Forest Rd .. 21045

Vantage House Condominium
5400 VANTAGE POINT RD 21044

Watermark Condominiums
10001 WINDSTREAM DR 21044

BUILDINGS

American City Building
10227 WINCOPIN CIR 21044

Ao Building
9110 RED BRANCH RD ... 21045

Banneker Building
5829 BANNEKER RD 21044

Broken Land S Building
9821 BROKEN LAND PKY 21046

Chesapeake Building
9017 RED BRANCH RD ... 21045

Chesapeake Center Iii Bld
9220 RUMSEY RD 21045

Clark Building
5565 STERRETT PL 21044

Columbia Business Center
6490 DOBBIN RD 21045

Columbia Corp Park I
8850 STANFORD BLVD ... 21045

Columbia Corp Park Ii
8840 STANFORD BLVD 21045

Columbia Mall
10300 Little Patuxent Pky 21044

Columbia Market Pl Buildi
9400 Snowden River Pky . 21045

Columbia Medical Building
11055 Little Patuxent Pky . 21044

Columbia Professional Bld
10840 Little Patuxent Pky 21044

Dobbin Center Building
6435 DOBBIN RD 21045

Dobbin Square Building
6476 Dobbin Center Way21045

Dorsey Building
9033 RED BRANCH RD ... 21045

Entre Executive Suites
9101 GUILFORD RD 21046

Equitable Bank Ctr Buildi
10320 Little Patuxent Pky 21044

Exhibit Building
10215 WINCOPIN CIR 21044

Gorman Plaza Building
8950 STATE ROUTE 108 . 21045

Grempler Building
10741 Little Patuxent Pky 21044

Grosvenor Century Plz 1000
10630 Little Patuxent Pky 21044

Guilford Industrial Park
9520 GERWIG LN 21046

Harpers Farm Office Ctr
5999 HARPERS FARM RD 21044

Hawthorne Exec Ctr Buildi
10705 CHARTER DR 21044

Heathrow Busin Ctr Buildi
9176 RED BRANCH RD ... 21045

Hickory Ridge Office Building
10805 Hickory Ridge Rd ... 21044

Hillcroft Office Building
6310 Stevens Forest Rd .. 21044

Howard Comm Professional
5560 STERRETT PL 21044

Joseph Square Building
5485 HARPERS FARM RD 21044

Kahler Hall
5440 OLD TUCKER ROW 21044

Kelly Building
9009 MENDENHALL CT ... 21045

Kings Contrivance Vlg Ctr
8640 STATE ROUTE 32 ... 21046

Lakefront North Building
5550 STERRETT PL 21044

Long Reach Village Center
8775 CLOUDLEAP CT 21045

Lovell Building
9030 RED BRANCH RD ... 21045

Loyola College Busin Ctr
7135 MINSTREL WAY 21045

Medical Arts Building
11085 Little Patuxent Pky . 21044

Merrill Lynch Building
5840 BANNEKER RD 21044

Oakland Building
9052 STATE ROUTE 108 . 21045

Oakland Mills Off Buildin
5865 Robert Oliver Pl 21045

Oakland Mills Vlg Ctr Bld
5851 Robert Oliver Pl 21045

Oakwood Business Ctr Building
7060 OAKLAND MILLS RD21044

One Centre Park Building
8808 CENTER PARK DR .. 21045

One Knoll North Building
5450 KNOLL NORTH DR . 21045

One Mall North Building
10025 Governor Warfield
Pky 21044

One Oakwood Ctr Building
7050 Oakland Mills Rd 21046

Overlook Center Building
5457 TWIN KNOLLS RD .. 21045

Parkside Building
10500 Little Patuxent Pky 21044

Parkview Office Building
10480 LITTLE PATUXENT PKY ..
.... 21044

Quarry Park Pl Building
9175 STATE ROUTE 32 ... 21046

Red Branch Busin Ctr Building
9198 RED BRANCH RD ... 21045

Ridgely Building
5575 STERRETT PL 21044

Rumsey Center Building
9150 RUMSEY RD 21045

Ryland Group Building
10221 WINCOPIN CIR 21044

Sam Shoemaker Building
11065 Little Patuxent Pky . 21044

Snowden Ctr Retail Buildi
6955 OAKLAND MILLS RD 21045

Standard Court Building
9160 RED BRANCH RD ... 21045

Sterrett Building
5585 STERRETT PL 21044

Stevens Forest Prof Ctr
9650 SANTIAGO RD 21045

Symphony Woods Office Ctr
5950 Symphony Woods ... 21044

Tapo Building
6851 OAK HALL LN 21045

Ten Columbia Corp Center
10400 Little Patuxent Pky 21044

The Clusters Building
5397 TWIN KNOLLS RD .. 21045

Thirty Columbia Corp Ctr
10440 Little Patuxent Pky 21044

Three Centre Park Buildin
8815 CENTER PARK DR .. 21045

Three Lakefront N Buildin
5570 STERRETT PL 21044

Toyota Building
9050 RED BRANCH RD ... 21045

Trellis Center Building
10750 Hickory Ridge Rd ... 21044

Twenty Columbia Corp Ctr
10420 Little Patuxent Pky 21044

Two Centre Park Building
8818 CENTER PARK DR .. 21045

Two Knoll North Building
5500 KNOLL NORTH DR . 21045

Waterview Off Ctr Buildin
7130 MINSTREL WAY 21045

Wilde Lake Vlg Gm Buildi
10451 TWIN RIVERS RD . 21044

Woodmere Ii Building
9891 BROKEN LAND PKY 21046

Woodside Exec Ctr Buildin
6325 WOODSIDE CT 21046

GOVERNMENT

Faulkner Ridge Center
10598 MARBLE FAUN LN 21044

DANIELS

APARTMENTS

Heartlands Apartments
3004 N RIDGE RD 21043

Lauperts Apartments
6209 WATERLOO RD 21043

BUILDINGS

Court Hill Building
8370 COURT AVE 21043

Court House Sq. Bldg.
3505 ELLICOTT MILLS 21043

Executive Center I Buildi
3300 N RIDGE RD 21043

Golden Triangle Shop Ctr
8801 Baltimore Natl. Pike . 21043

Great Oaks Plz Building
8455 Baltimore Natl. Pike . 21043

Knollview Plaza Building
4900 WATERLOO RD 21043

Normandy Shopping Ctr Bld
8450 Baltimore Natl. Pike . 21043

Professional Building
3716 COURT PL 21043

Rockland Arts Ctr Buildin
8510 HIGH RIDGE RD 21043

Rogers Building
3696 PARK AVE 21043

Rogers Center Building
8525 Baltimore Natl. Pike . 21043

Tiber Place Building
8307 MAIN ST 21043

GOVERNMENT

Edwin Warfield Building
3410 COURT HOUSE DR . 21043

George Howard Building
3430 COURT HOUSE DR . 21043

Howard Cty Courthouse
8360 COURT AVE 21043

John Lee Carroll Building
3450 COURT HOUSE DR . 21043

Multi Service Ctr Buildin
3451 COURT HOUSE DR . 21043

DARNESTOWN

APARTMENTS

The Chase
9890 Washington Blvd 20878

Washingtonian Towers
9701 FIELDS RD 20878

BUILDINGS

Mont Professional Building
656 Quince Orchard Rd 20878

HOTELS

Red Roof Inn
497 Quince Orchard Rd 20878

DISTRICT HEIGHTS

APARTMENTS

Oakcrest Towers Apts
2020 BROOKS DR 20747

ELLICOTT CITY

BUILDINGS

Awalt Building
9051 Baltimore Natl. Pike . 21042

Bethany 40 Center Buildin
10176 Baltimore Natl. Pike 21042

Chatham Mall Building
9200 Baltimore Natl. Pike . 21042

Dorsey Search Med Buildin
9501 Old Annapolis Rd 21042

Dorsey Search Office Building
4785 Dorsey Hall Dr 21042

Ellicott Plaza Building
9235 Baltimore Natl. Pike . 21042

Frederick Crossing Building
3570 SAINT JOHNS LN 21042

Howard Cty Doctors Buildi
9380 Baltimore Natl. Pike . 21042

Howard Cty Med Building Ii
3459 SAINT JOHNS LN 21042

Howard Cty Med Ctr Buildi
9055 CHEVROLET DR 21042

Malabar Plaza Building
9275 Baltimore Natl. Pike . 21042

Mcalpine Professional Ctr
9141 Baltimore Natl. Pike . 21042

Saint Johns Plz Building
9150 Baltimore Natl. Pike . 21042

Vallymede Plaza Building
9469 Baltimore Natl. Pike . 21042

Victoria Plaza Building
9339 Baltimore Natl. Pike . 21042

Village Grn Shopping Ctr
9338 Baltimore Natl. Pike . 21042

FOREST HEIGHTS

BUILDINGS

Enterprise Building
6192 OXON HILL RD 20745

Five Star Building
6178 OXON HILL RD 20745

Lucente Building
6188 OXON HILL RD 20745

United Bank Building
5620 Saint Barnabas Rd .. 20745

FRANKLIN

APARTMENTS

Hammond Hgts Apartments
421 HAMMOND ST 21562

FREDERICK

APARTMENTS

Brooklawn Apartments
1001 CARROLL PKY 21701

Carver Apartments
101 MADISON ST 21701

Catoctin View Apartments
800 MOTTER AVE 21701

Eighth St Court Apartment
123 E 8TH ST 21701

Hillside Apartments
25 WATER ST 21701

John Hanson Apartments
500 N BENTZ ST 21701

Lincoln Apartments
33 S BENTZ ST 21701

Parkview Apartments
750 CARROLL PKY 21701

Prospect Plaza Apartments
501 PROSPECT BLVD 21701

Stewart Manor Apartments
1300 MOTTER AVE 21701

Taney Apartments
600 N BENTZ ST 21701

Wayside Apartments
423 E PATRICK ST 21701

BUILDINGS

Francis Scott Key Mall
5500 Buckeystown Pike ... 21701

Frederick Po Building
201 E PATRICK ST 21701

Park Ave Med Ctr Building
335 PARK AVE 21701

Patrick St Shopping Ctr
467 W PATRICK ST 21701

Professional Building
228 N MARKET ST 21701

Westview Off Ct Building
5300 WESTVIEW DR 21701

GOVERNMENT

Frederick Cty Court House
100 W PATRICK ST 21701

GAITHERSBURG

APARTMENTS

Asbury Towers
211 RUSSELL AVE 20877

Forest Oak Towers
101 ODENDHAL AVE 20877

Village House
19310 CLUB HOUSE RD . 20879

Walker House
18700 Walkers Choice Rd 20879

BUILDINGS

Lake Forest Office Building
702 RUSSELL AVE 20877

Lakeforest Building
444 N FREDERICK AVE ... 20877

Lakeforest Mall
701 RUSSELL AVE 20877

Montgomery Executive Cent
6 Montgomery Village Ave 20879

Shady Grove Profes Building
16220 S FREDERICK AVE 20877

Standard Federal Building
481 N FREDERICK AVE ... 20877

GOVERNMENT

Gaithersburg Library
18330 Montgomery Village 20879

HOSPITALS

Asbury Health Care Center
301 RUSSELL AVE 20877

HOTELS

Comfort Inn
16216 S FREDERICK AVE 20877

Marriott
805 RUSSELL AVE 20879

Marriott Hotel
620 PERRY PKY 20877

GERMANTOWN

COLLEGES

Montgomery College
20200 OBSERVATION DR 20876

GLEN BURNIE

APARTMENTS

Glen Sq Apartments
102 CRAIN HWY N 21061

Pinewood Apartments
7885 GORDON CT 21060

Pinewood Ii Apartments
7900 BENESCH CIR 21060

BUILDINGS

Aquahart Plaza Building
13 AQUAHART RD 21061

Azar Building
103 ROESLER RD 21060

Boulevard Professional
7422 BALTIMORE ANNAPOLIS
BLVD 21061

Brantley Building
8 CRAIN HWY N 21061

Brewster Building
1410 CRAIN HWY N 21061

Burwood Plz Professional
6413 BURWOOD PLZ 21061

Crain Center Building
550 CRAIN HWY N 21061

Crain Mayo Medical Ctr
1720 CRAIN HWY S 21061

Crain Professional Buildi
7935 CRAIN HWY S 21061

Crain South Plz Building
1404 CRAIN HWY S 21061

Crain Towers Building
1600 CRAIN HWY S 21061

Dartmouth Building
1412 CRAIN HWY N 21061

Eastham Building
1414 CRAIN HWY N 21061

Empire Medical Building
200 HOSPITAL DR 21061

Empire Towers Building
7310 RITCHIE HWY 21061

Glen Burnie Mall
6711 RITCHIE HWY 21061

Glen Burnie Town Ctr Building
7477 BALTIMORE ANNAPOLIS
BLVD 21061

Glen Burnie Vlg Sc
7534 RITCHIE HWY 21061

Glen Plz Shopping Center
7602 BALTIMORE ANNAPOLIS
BLVD 21060

Glenn Prof Ctr Building
408 CRAIN HWY S 21061

Harundale Mall
7700 RITCHIE HWY 21061

Irvington Fed Building
7711 QUARTERFIELD RD 21061

Kline Building
423 CRAIN HWY S 21061

La Fontaine Blue Bridal
7514 RITCHIE HWY 21061

Marley Station Mall
7900 RITCHIE HWY 21061

Medco Med Ctr Building
7445 E Furnace Branch Rd 21060

Medix Building
1406 CRAIN HWY S 21061

Mewshaw Building
2 CRAIN HWY N 21061

N Arundel Exec Building
300 HOSPITAL DR 21061

North Arundel Medical Bld
7300 RITCHIE HWY 21061

North Arundel Physic Ctr
203 HOSPITAL DR 21061

Oakwood Professional
7845 OAKWOOD RD 21061

Pavan Professional Center
420 CRAIN HWY S 21061

Pyramid Building
1404 CRAIN HWY S 21061

Regester Building
302 CRAIN HWY S 21061

Severn Sq Professional Bl
456 OLD Quarterfield Rd .. 21061

Southgate Marketplace
337 HOSPITAL DR 21061

Southgate Professional
325 HOSPITAL DR 21061

Steffey Building
407 CRAIN HWY S 21061

Sun Vly Shopping Center
7931 BALTIMORE ANNAPOLIS
BLVD 21060

Town Center Sc
7400 RITCHIE HWY 21061

Wellham Med Ctr Building
14 WELLHAM AVE NW 21061

Wilson Building
7450 BALTIMORE ANNAPOLIS
BLVD 21061

GOVERNMENT

Arundel Ctr N Building
101 CRAIN HWY N 21061

District Court Building
7500 RITCHIE HWY 21061

Pascal Sr Citizens Center
125 DORSEY RD 21061

HAGERSTOWN

APARTMENTS

Alexander House Apartment
7 E WASHINGTON ST 21740

Avalon Apartments
156 S POTOMAC ST 21740

Beverly Ter Apartments
42 EAST AVE 21740

Bilt Well Apartments
911 GUILFORD AVE 21740

Bowman Apartments
453 W ANTIETAM ST 21740

Broadway Apartments
136 BROADWAY 21740

Burhans Apartments
436 W WASHINGTON ST . 21740

Burton Apartments
60 E WASHINGTON ST 21740

Calvert Apartments
140 W ANTIETAM ST 21740

Carolyn Apartments
908 HAMILTON BLVD 21742

Cearfoss Apartments
216 N LOCUST ST 21740

Coble Apartments
655 S POTOMAC ST 21740

Colonial Apartments
55 S POTOMAC ST 21740

Crestview Apartments
479 N POTOMAC ST 21740

Devonshire Apartments
50 W HILLCREST RD 21742

Edison Apartments
15 S POTOMAC ST 21740

El Claire Apartments
401 S POTOMAC ST 21740

Elizabeth Ct Apartments
55 E WASHINGTON ST 21740

Franklin Apartments
25 W FRANKLIN ST 21740

Garden Apartments
232 BRYAN PL 21740

Gilmore Apartments
15 W ANTIETAM ST 21740

Gorman Apartments
34 N LOCUST ST 21740

Graceland Apartments
36 BROADWAY 21740

Grey Gables Apartments
602 POTOMAC AVE 21740

Hamilton Apartments
920 HAMILTON BLVD 21742

Herings Apartments
346 S POTOMAC ST 21742

Hillcrest Apartments
934 HAMILTON BLVD 21742

Homestead Apartments
27 E WASHINGTON ST 21740

Joes Apartments
23 E WASHINGTON ST 21740

Jones Apartments
310 N POTOMAC ST 21740

Keller Apartments
554 FREDERICK ST 21740

Kneisley Apartments
457 W WASHINGTON ST . 21740

Lambert Apartments
31 E FRANKLIN ST 21740

Long Meadows Apartments
300 W NORTHERN AVE ... 21742

Lynley Apartments
4 E ANTIETAM ST 21740

Lynn Haven Apartments
331 S POTOMAC ST 21740

Midcity Apartments
40 E WASHINGTON ST 21740

Mitchell Apartments
400 MITCHELL AVE 21740

Moller Apartments
101 SURREY AVE 21740

Mount Royal Apartments
673 OAK HILL AVE 21740

MountVernon Apartments
21 W ANTIETAM ST 21740

Mulberry Apartments
17 N MULBERRY ST 21740

Nee Apartments
201 E FRANKLIN ST 21740

North Avenue Apartments
30 E NORTH AVE 21740

Oakleigh Apartments
1106 OAK HILL AVE 21742

Oliver Apartments
478 PANGBORN BLVD 21742

Potomac Hill Apartments
1006 POTOMAC AVE 21742

Potomac Towers Apartments
11 W BALTIMORE ST 21740

Reid Apartments
1056 DUAL PL 21740

Shilling Apartments
912 HAMILTON BLVD 21742

Shirley Jean Apartments
111 E BALTIMORE ST 21740

Spessard Apartments
216 N CANNON AVE 21740

Statler Apartments
155 SUMMIT AVE 21740

SummitView Apartments
165 SUMMIT AVE 21740

Surrey Apartments
610 SUMMIT AVE 21740

Sutterlyn Arms Apartments
1205 POTOMAC AVE 21742

Terrace Court Apartments
629 OAK HILL AVE 21740

Wareham Apartments
134 W WASHINGTON ST . 21740

Wentworth Apartments
118 BROADWAY 21740

Young Apartments
31 E WASHINGTON ST 21740

Zeller Apartments
866 DEWEY AVE 21742

BUILDINGS

Antietam Professional Ctr
138 E ANTIETAM ST 21740

Columbia First Building
100 W WASHINGTON ST . 21740

County Market
835 W HILLCREST RD 21742

East Building
201 S CLEVELAND AVE ... 21740

Foxshire Plaza Building
1423 DUAL HWY 21740

Lavonne Apartments
245 N POTOMAC ST 21740

Professional Arts Buildin
5 PUBLIC SQ 21740

Snyder Building
24 N JONATHAN ST 21740

Valley Mall
17301 VALLEY MALL RD . 21740

GOVERNMENT

Court House Annex
24 SUMMIT AVE 21740

Hagerstown City Hall
54 N POTOMAC ST 21740

Washington Cty Annex
33 W WASHINGTON ST ... 21740

Washington Cty Court Hous
95 W WASHINGTON ST ... 21740

HILLANDALE

BUILDINGS

Medical Building
831 UNIVERSITY BLVD E 20903

LAUREL

APARTMENTS

Steward Towers
200 FORT MEADE RD 20707

BUILDINGS

Montpelier Professional B
9811 MALLARD DR 20708

Professional Building
3450 FORT MEADE RD ... 20724

GOVERNMENT

Johns Hopkins
11100 Johns Hopkins Rd .. 20723

HOTELS

Econo Lodge
9750 Washington Blvd N .. 20723

Red Roof Inn
12525 Laurel Bowie Rd 20708

Valencia Motel
10131 Washington Blvd N 20723

NORTH BETHESDA

APARTMENTS

Betheny House Apts
199 ROLLINS AVE 20852

Forum Apt
11801 ROCKVILLE PIKE . 20852

Grosvenor House
10101 GROSVENOR PL .. 20852

Grosvenor Park Apts
10201 GROSVENOR PL .. 20852

Grosvenor Park Apts
10401 GROSVENOR PL .. 20852

Grosvenor Tower
10301 GROSVENOR PL .. 20852

Old Georgetown Village
11400 STRAND DR 20852

Revitz House Hebrew Home
6111 MONTROSE RD 20852

The Fallswood
5800 NICHOLSON LN 20852

The Fallswood
5802 NICHOLSON LN 20852

The Pavilion Apts
5901 MONTROSE RD 20852

The Wisconsin
5809 NICHOLSON LN 20852

Woodmont Park
1001 ROCKVILLE PIKE ... 20852

BUILDINGS

1776 Plaza
1776 E JEFFERSON ST .. 20852

Beltway View Building
6110 EXECUTIVE BLVD ... 20852

Energy Building
6011 EXECUTIVE BLVD ... 20852

Executive Plaza
6120 EXECUTIVE BLVD ... 20852

Executive Plaza
6130 EXECUTIVE BLVD ... 20852

Jefferson Plaza
600 E JEFFERSON ST 20852

Nebel Office Center
11600 NEBEL ST 20852

One Central Plaza
11300 ROCKVILLE PIKE . 20852

One Montrose Metro
11921 ROCKVILLE PIKE . 20852

One White Flint North
11555 ROCKVILLE PIKE . 20852

Rock-wall Ii
5515 SECURITY LN 20852

Tenley Building
50 W EDMONSTON DR ... 20852

The Atrium Building
6101 EXECUTIVE BLVD ... 20852

Twinbrook Metro Center
12300 TWINBROOK PKY 20852

Willco Building
6000 EXECUTIVE BLVD ... 20852

HOTELS

Days Inn
1775 ROCKVILLE PIKE ... 20852

ROCKVILLE

APARTMENTS

Americana Center Apts
118 MONROE ST 20850

Hamilton House
4 MONROE ST 20850

Heritage House
95 DAWSON AVE 20850

BUILDINGS

General Electric Building
401 N WASHINGTON ST .. 20850

Jefferson Building
22 W JEFFERSON ST 20850

North Washington Center
110 N WASHINGTON ST .. 20850

One Metro Square
51 MONROE ST 20850

Rockville Metro Center
250 HUNGERFORD DR ... 20850

GOVERNMENT

M C Executive Office Building
101 MONROE ST 20850

M C Judicial Center
50 COURTHOUSE SQ 20850

Montgomery Cty Courthouse
27 COURTHOUSE SQ 20850

HOTELS

Courtyard By Marriott
2500 RESEARCH BLVD ... 20850

Days Inn
16001 SHADY GROVE RD 20850

Sheraton Inn Potomac
3 RESEARCH CT 20850

Woodfin Suites Hotel
1380 PICCARD DR 20850

SILVER SPRING

APARTMENTS

Americana Fenmark
9900 GEORGIA AVE 20902

Arcola Towers
1135 University Blvd W 20902

Belford Towers
6731 New Hampshire Ave 20912

Blair East
1220 E WEST HWY 20910

Blair House
8201 16TH ST 20910

Blair Plaza
1401 BLAIR MILL RD 20910

Blair Towers
8101 EASTERN AVE 20910

Charter House
1316 FENWICK LN 20910

Claridge House
2445 LYTTONSVILLE RD . 20910

Cole Spring Plaza
1001 SPRING ST 20910

Dalton House
733 SLIGO AVE 20910

Edinburgh House
7513 MAPLE AVE 20912

Elizabeth House
1400 FENWICK LN 20910

Franklin Apts
7620 MAPLE AVE 20912

Georgian Towers
8715 1ST AVE 20910

Georgian West
8708 1ST AVE 20910

Hillbrook Towers
515 THAYER AVE 20910

Inwood House
10921 INWOOD AVE 20902

Kenwood House
95 E WAYNE AVE 20901

Leafy House
10000 BRUNSWICK AVE . 20910

Manchester Arms
8401 MANCHESTER RD .. 20901

Manchester House
25 E WAYNE AVE 20901

Maple Towers
7610 MAPLE AVE 20912

Mapleview Apts
7710 MAPLE AVE 20912

Montgomery Towers
415 SILVER SPRING AVE 20910

Park Bradford
8601 MANCHESTER RD .. 20901

Park Maple
7777 MAPLE AVE 20912

Park Sutton Apts
1900 LYTTONSVILLE RD . 20910

Parkside Plaza
9039 SLIGO CREEK PKY 20901

Parkview Towers
7667 MAPLE AVE 20912

Pickwick Towers
710 ROEDER RD 20910

Silver Spring House
555 THAYER AVE 20910

Sligo House
603 SLIGO AVE 20910

Springwood Apts
1220 BLAIR MILL RD 20910

Suburban Apts
8600 16TH ST 20910

Sudbury House
2100 WASHINGTON AVE . 20910

Summit Hills Apts
8500 16TH ST 20910

Summit Hills Apts
1701 E WEST HWY 20910

Summit Hills Apts
1703 E WEST HWY 20910

Summit Hills Apts
1705 E WEST HWY 20910

Summit House
8484 16TH ST 20910

Takoma Towers
7051 CARROLL AVE 20912

Thayer Ter Apts
525 THAYER AVE 20910

Thayer Towers
575 THAYER AVE 20910

The 7611 Maple
7611 MAPLE AVE 20912

The Barbazon
735 SLIGO AVE 20910

The Carolyn
614 SLIGO AVE 20910

The Deauville
7520 MAPLE AVE 20912

The Oaks
321 UNIVERSITY BLVD W 20901

The Point
11200 LOCKWOOD DR ... 20901

The Warwick
1131 University Blvd W 20902

Twin Towers
1110 FIDLER LN 20910

University Towers
1111 University Blvd W 20902

Wayne House
75 E WAYNE AVE 20901

BUILDINGS

1100 Wayne Building
1100 WAYNE AVE 20910

8484 Georgia Ave Building
8484 GEORGIA AVE 20910

American Finance Building
1320 FENWICK LN 20910

American Nat Bank Building
8701 GEORGIA AVE 20910

Burkeland Med Ctr
10313 GEORGIA AVE 20902

Computer Building
11141 GEORGIA AVE 20902

Computer Building
962 WAYNE AVE 20910

Continental Building
818 ROEDER RD 20910

Doctors Medical Park East
2101 MEDICAL PARK DR 20902

Doctors Medical Park West
10301 GEORGIA AVE 20902

Equitable Federal Building
11501 GEORGIA AVE 20902

Fairview Building
8905 FAIRVIEW RD 20910

Forest Glen Medical Ctr
9801 GEORGIA AVE 20902

Guardian Federal Building
8605 CAMERON ST 20910

Lee Plaza
8601 GEORGIA AVE 20910

Metropolitan Building
8720 GEORGIA AVE 20910

Montgomery Professional B
911 SILVER SPRING AVE 20910

Nations Bank Building
8252 GEORGIA AVE 20910

Perpetual Building
8700 GEORGIA AVE 20910

Professional Building
1109 SPRING ST 20910

Signet Building
850 SLIGO AVE 20910

Silver Spring Med Building
10620 GEORGIA AVE 20902

Spring St Office Building
1111 SPRING ST 20910

Summit Building
8555 16TH ST 20910

The Adventist Building
7610 CARROLL AVE 20912

The World Building
8121 GEORGIA AVE 20910

Wheaton Plz N Office Building
2730 University Blvd W 20902

Wheaton Plz Shopping Ctr
11160 VEIRS MILL RD 20902

HOSPITALS

Holy Cross Hospital
1500 FOREST GLEN RD . 20910

Washington Adventist Hosp
7600 CARROLL AVE 20912

HOTELS

Quality Cts
8040 13TH ST 20910

COLLEGES

Montgomery College
7600 TAKOMA AVE 20912

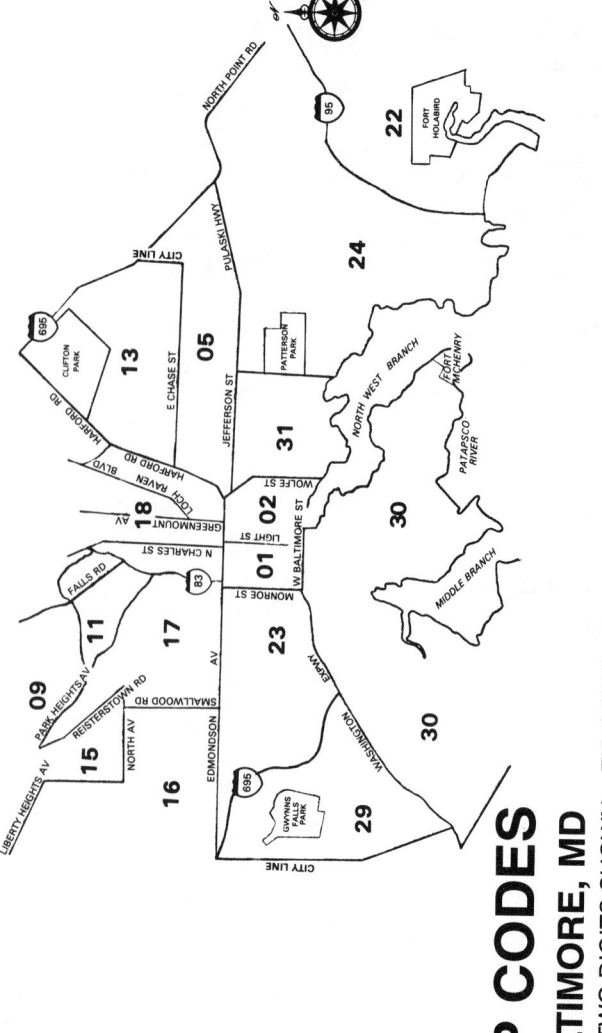

ZIP CODES
BALTIMORE, MD
212 + TWO DIGITS SHOWN = ZIP CODE

MASSACHUSETTS
Abbreviation MA

Abington 02351
Accord 02018
Acton 01718-720
(Village Of Nagog Woods)
Alton 01720
Davis 01720
East Acton 01720
North Acton 01720
South Acton 01720
West Acton 01720
Acushnet 02743
Adams 01220
Agawam 01001
Alford 01230, 01266
(Great Barrington)
Allendale (Pittsfield) 01201
Allston 02134
Alton (Acton) 01720
Amesbury 01913
Amherst 01002-004, 01059
Cushman 01002
Pelham 01002
South Amherst 01002
West Pelham 01002
Andover 01810, 01812, 01899
.... 05501, 05544
Bar Coded I R South .. 01899
IRS 01812
IRS Service Center 05501
IRS Service Center 05544
Arlington 02174
Arlington Heights 02175
Ashburnham 01430, 01466
Lane Village 01430
North Ashburnham 01430
Pages Beach 01430
South Ashburnham 01466
Wellville 01430
Ashby 01431
Ashfield 01330
Ashland 01721
Ashley Falls 01222
Assinippi (Hanover) 02339
Assonet 02702
Athol 01331, 01368
New Salem 01331
Phillipston 01331
South Royalston 01331
Attleboro 02703
Attleboro Falls 02763
(North Attleboro)
Auburn 01501
Auburndale 02166
Avon 02322
Ayer 01432-433
Babson Park 02157
Bakers Grove 01473
(Westminster)
Baldwinville 01436
Barnstable 02630, 02668
Barre 01005
Bass River 02664
(South Yarmouth)
Bay Banks (Woburn) 01815
Bay State (Northampton) .. 01060
Beachmont (Revere) 02151
Beachwood (Stockbridge) . 01262
Becket 01223

Becket Center (Chester) 01011
Bedford 01730-731
Belchertown 01007
Bellingham 02019
Belmont 02178
Berkley 02779
Berkshire 01224
Berkshire Heights 01230
(Great Barrington)
Berlin 01503, 01549
South Berlin 01549
West Berlin 01503
Bernardston 01337
Beverly 01915
Big Pond (East Otis) 01029
Billerica 01821-822, 01862
Blackstone 01504
Blandford 01008
Blissville (Orange) 01364
Bolton 01740
Bondsville 01009
Boston 02100-137, 02154
.... 02163, 02196, 02199
.... 02201-212, 02215-217
02222, 02241, 02266, 02272
.... 02293, 02295, 02297
Bank Of Boston 02241
Cambridge 02163
Cash Management 02297
East Boston 02128
Fidelity Service Co 02293
John Hancock Ins 02295
Kenmore 02215
Massachusetts Tax 02204
National Shawmut Bk .. 02211
Shared Firm Zip 02196
Soldiers Field 02163
South Boston 02127
NYNEX 02207
Bourne 02532, 02559
(Buzzards Bay)
Bourndale (Buzzards Bay) 02532
Boxboro 01719
Boxford 01921
Boylston 01505
Bradford (Haverhill) 01835
Bradstreet (Hatfield) 01038
Braggville (Holliston) 01746
Braintree 02184
Bramanville (Millbury) 01527
Brant Rock 02020
Brewster 02631, 02645
East Brewster 02631
West Brewster 02631
Bridgewater 02324-325
Brighton 02135, 02146
Boston 02135
Brightwood (Springfield) ... 01107
Brimfield 01010
Brockton 02401-405, 02411
.... 02325
Brookfield 01506
Brookline 02146, 02167
Brighton 02146
Brookline Village 02147
Brooks Village 01468
(Templeton)
Bryantville 02327
Buckland 01338
Buffumville (Oxford) 01540
Bullardville (Winchendon) . 01475

Burlington 01803, 01805
Buzzards Bay 02532, 02542
Bourne 02532
Bournedale 02532
Camp Edwards 02542
Main Street 02532
Mashnee Island 02532
Onset 02532
Byfield 01922
Cambridge 02138-142
.... 02163, 02238-239
East Cambridge 02141
Harvard Square 02238
Inman Square 02139
Kendall Square 02142
North Cambridge 02140
Porter Square 02140
Camp Edwards 02542
(Buzzards Bay)
Canton 02021
Capertown (West Upton) ... 01568
Carlisle 01741
Carver 02330
Cataumet 02534
Cedarville (Plymouth) 02360
Centerville .. 02632, 02634, 02636
Craigville 02636
Central Village 02790
(Westport)
Chaffin (Holden) 01520
Chappaquiddick Island 02539
(Edgartown)
Chappaquoit 02574
(West Falmouth)
Charlemont 01339, 01346
Hawley 01339
West Hawley 01339
Charleston (Charlton) 01507
Charlestown 02129
Charlton 01507
Charlton City 01508
Chartley 02712
Chaseville (Webster) 01570
Chatham 02633
Chatham Port 02650
(North Chatham)
Chelmsford 01824
Chelsea 02150
Cherry Brook (Weston) 02193
Cherry Valley (Worcester) . 01611
Cherryfield (Framingham) . 01701
Cheshire 01225
Chester 01011
Chesterfield 01012
Chestnut Hill 02167
Chicopee 01013-014
.... 01020-022
Chilmark 02535
Clarksburg (North Adams) . 01247
Clevelandtown (Edgartown) 02539
Clinton 01510
Clover Hill (Marlborough) . 01752
Cochituate (Wayland) 01778
Cohasset 02025
Cold Spring (Otis) 01253
Colonial Park (Webster) 01570
Colrain 01340
Cominsville (Rochdale) 01542
Concord 01742
Conway 01341
Cooleyville (New Salem) ... 01355

Holden 01520
Holland 01521, 01550
   Fiskdale 01521
Holliston 01746
Holyoke 01040-041
Hoosac Tunnel (Rowe) 01367
Hopedale 01747
Hopkinton 01748
Horseneck Beach 02790
   (Westport)
Houghs Neck (Quincy) 02169
Housatonic 01236
Hoveys Corner (Pepperell) 01463
Hubbardston 01452
Hudson 01749
Hull02045
Humarock 02047
Huntington 01050
Hyannis 02601
Hyannis Port 02647
Hyde Park 02136-137
   Boston 02136
Indian Orchard 01151
Inman Square (Cambridge) 02139
Interlaken 01266
   (West Stockbridge)
Ipswich 01938
Islington (Westwood) 02090
Jamaica Plain 02130
Jefferson 01522
Kendal Green (Weston) 02193
Kendall Square 02142
   (Cambridge)
Kenmore (Boston) 02215
Kingsbury Beach 02642
   (Eastham)
Kingston 02364
Knightville (Huntington) 01050
Konkapot (Mill River) 01244
Lake Boone (Stow) 01775
Lake Mattawa (Orange) 01364
Lake Pleasant 01347
Lakeville 02347
Lakewood Park 01473
   (Westminster)
Lambs Grove (Spencer) 01562
Lancaster 01523
Lane Village (Ashburnham) 01430
Lanesboro 01237
Larrywaug (Stockbridge) ... 01262
Laurel Park (Northampton) 01060
Lawrence 01840-843
   South Lawrence 01843
Lee 01238, 01264
   East Lee 01238
   West Becket 01238
Leeds 01053
Leicester 01524
Leino Park (Westminster) .. 01473
Lenox 01240
Lenox Dale 01242
Leominster 01453
Leverett 01054
Lexington 02173
Leyden 01301, 01337
   (Greenfield)
Lincoln 01773
Lindenwood (Stoneham) .. 02180
Linwood 01525
Lithia (Goshen) 01032
Little River (Westfield) 01085

Littleton 01460
Lockerville (Natick) 01760
Locks Village 01072
   (Shutesbury)
Longmeadow 01106, 01116
   East Longmeadow 01116
Loudville (Easthampton) ... 01027
Lowell 01850-854
Ludlow 01056
Lunds Corner 02745
   (New Bedford)
Lunenburg 01462
Lynn 01901-906, 01910
   East Lynn 01904
   West Lynn 01905
Lynnfield 01940
Lyonsville (Colrain) 01340
Magnolia (Gloucester) 01930
Mahkeenac Heights 01240
   (Lenox)
Main Street 02532
   (Buzzards Bay)
Malden 02148
Manchaug 01526
Manchester 01944
Manomet 02345
Mansfield 02048
Maplewood (Malden) 02148
Marblehead 01945, 01947
Marina Bay (Quincy) 02171
Marion 02738
Marlborough 01752
Marshfield 02050-051, 02065
   Ocean Bluff 02065
Marstons Mills 02648
Mashnee Island 02532
   (Buzzards Bay)
Mashpee 02649
Mattapan 02126
Mattapoisett 02739
Maynard 01754
Mayo Beach (Wellfleet) 02667
Medfield 02052
Medford 02153, 02155
   Stewartville 02155
   West Medford 02155
Medway 02053
Megansett 02556
   (North Falmouth)
Melrose 02176-177
Mendon 01756
Menemsha 02552
Merrimac 01860
Methuen 01844
Middleboro
   .... 02344, 02346, 02348-349
   Aetna Life & Casualty Co .....
      02344
   Ocean Spray 02349
   Talbots 02348
Middlefield 01243
Middleton 01949
Milford 01757
Mill River 01244
Millbury 01527, 01586
   Bramanville 01527
   Dorothy Manor 01527
   East Millbury 01527
   West Millbury 01586
Millers Falls 01349
   (Turners Falls)

Millerville (Blackstone) 01504
Millis 02054
Millville 01529
Milton 02186
Milton Village 02187
Minot 02055
Monponsett 02350
Monroe (Monroe Bridge) .. 01350
Monroe Bridge 01350
Monson 01057
Montague 01351
Montague City 01376
   (Turners Falls)
Monterey 01245
Montgomery (Westfield) 01085
Montwait (Framingham) 01701
Monument Beach 02553
Moody Corner 01075
   (South Hadley)
Moores Corner (Leverett) .. 01054
Morningdale (Boylston) 01505
Morseville 01508, 01760
   (Charlton City)
Mount Hermon 01354
Mount Holyoke 01075
   (South Hadley)
Mount Tom (Easthampton) 01027
Mount Washington 01258
   (South Egremont)
Mystic Grove (Charlton) 01507
Nabnasset (Westford) 01886
Nahant 01908
Nantasket Beach (Hull) 02045
Nantucket ... 02554, 02564, 02584
Natick 01760
Nauset Heights 02643
   (East Orleans)
Needham 02194
New Ashford (Lanesboro) . 01237
New Bedford 02740-746
   Lunds Corner 02745
   North 02746
   Orchard Street 02744
New Braintree 01531
New Marlboro 01230
   (Great Barrington)
New Salem 01331
   .... 01355, 01364
   (Athol)
   Cooleyville 01355
   Orange 01355
New Seabury (Mashpee) .. 02649
New Town (Newton) 02258
New Village 01588
   (Whitinsville)
Newbury 01951
Newburyport 01950
Newton 02158-162
   .... 02164-168, 02195, 02258
   New Town 02258
   Nonantum 02195
   Riverside 02158
   West Newton 02165
Nipmuck (Mendon) 01756
Nobscot (Framingham) 01701
Nonantum (Newton) 02195
Noquochoke (Westport) 02790
Norfolk 02056
Norfolk Downs (Quincy) 02171
North (New Bedford) 02746
North Abington (Abington) . 02351

North Acton (Acton) 01720
North Adams 01247
North Amherst 01059
North Andover 01845
North Ashburnham 01430
  (Ashburnham)
North Attleboro 02760-763
  Attleboro Falls 02763
North Billerica 01862
North Blandford 01008
  (Blandford)
North Brookfield 01535
North Cambridge 02140
  (Cambridge)
North Carver 02355
North Chatham 02650
North Chelmsford 01863
North Chester 01050
  (Huntington)
North Dartmouth 02747
North Dighton 02764, 02754
North Eastham 02651
North Easton 02356-357
North Egremont 01252
North Falmouth 02556, 02565
  Megansett 02556
  Old Silver Beach 02556
  Silver Beach 02565
North Farms (Northampton) 01060
North Grafton 01536
North Hadley (Hadley) 01035
North Harwich (Harwich) ... 02645
North Hatfield 01066
North Lancaster 01523
  (Lancaster)
North Leominster 01453
  (Leominster)
North Leverett (Leverett) ... 01054
North Littleton 01460
  (Littleton)
North Marshfield 02059
North Milford (Milford) 01757
North Natick (Natick) 01760
North New Salem (Orange) 01364
North Orange (Orange) 01364
North Otis (Otis) 01253
North Oxford 01537
North Pembroke 02358
North Pepperell 01463
  (Pepperell)
North Plymouth (Plymouth) 02360
North Quincy (Quincy) 02171
North Reading 01864,01889
North Rutland (Rutland) ... 01543
North Scituate 02060
North Seekonk (Seekonk) . 02771
North Sudbury (Sudbury) .. 01776
North Swansea (Swansea) 02777
North Tisbury 02568
  (Vineyard Haven)
North Truro 02652
North Uxbridge 01538
North Waltham (Waltham) . 02154
North Westport (Westport) 02790
North Weymouth 02191
  (Weymouth)
Northampton 01060-061
  Bay State 01060
  Florence 01060
  Laurel Park 01060
  North Farms 01060

Pine Grove 01060
  West Farms 01060
Northborough 01532
Northbridge 01534
Northfield 01354, 01360
  (Mount Hermon)
  East Northfield 01360
Northside (Charlton City) .. 01508
Norton 02766
Norwell 02061
Norwood 02062
Nutting Lake 01865
Oak Bluffs 02557
Oak Grove (Malden) 02148
Oakdale 01539
Oakham 01068
Ocean Bluff (Marshfield) .. 02065
Ocean Spray (Middleboro) 02349
Old City (Townsend) 01474
Old Furnace 01031
  (Gilbertville)
Old Silver Beach 02556
  (North Falmouth)
Oldsfield (Sherborn) 01770
Onset 02532, 02558
  (Buzzards Bay)
Orange (New Salem)
  01355, 01364, 01378
  Blissville 01364
  Eagleville 01364
  Lake Mattawa 01364
  New Salem 01364
  North New Salem 01364
  North Orange 01364
  Warwick 01364
Orchard Street 02744
  (New Bedford)
Ordway (Hudson) 01749
Orleans 02653
Osceola (Richmond) 01254
Osterville 02655
Otis01253
Otter River 01436
  (Baldwinville)
Oxford 01540
Oyster Harbors 02655
  (Osterville)
Padanaram Village 02748
  (South Dartmouth)
Pages Beach 01430
  (Ashburnham)
Pakachoag (Auburn) 01501
Palmer 01069
Parkwood Bch (Wareham) 02571
Patuisset (Pocasset) 02559
Paxton (Worcester) 01612
Peabody 01960-961, 01964
  West Peabody 01960
Pelham (Amherst) 01002
Pembroke 02359
Pepperell 01463
Peru (Hinsdale) 01235
Petersham 01366
Phillipston (Athol) 01331
Pierceville 02576
  (West Wareham)
Pigeon Cove (Rockport) 01966
Pine Grove (Northampton) 01060
Pine Lake (Sudbury) 01776
Pinehurst 01866
Pinehurst Beach 02571

  (Wareham)
Pingryville (Littleton) 01460
Pitcherville 01452
  (Hubbardston)
Pittsfield 01201-203
  Allendale 01201
Plainfield 01070
Plainville 02762
Pleasant Lake (Harwich) ... 02645
Plum Island 01950-951
  (Newburyport)
Plummer Corner 01588
  (Whitinsville)
Plymouth 02360-363
  Cedarville 02360
  North Plymouth 02360
Plympton 02367
Pocasset 02559
Podunk (East Brookfield) .. 01515
Point Of Pines (Revere) 02151
Point Pleasant (Webster) .. 01570
Point Shirley (Winthrop) ... 02152
Pomeroy Corner 01075
  (South Hadley)
Ponakin Mill (Lancaster) ... 01523
Pondville (Auburn) 01501
Porter Square (Cambridge) 02140
Prentice Gardens 01588
  (Whitinsville)
Prides Crossing 01965
Princess House 02754
  (North Dighton)
Princeton 01541
Princeton Station 01452
  (Hubbardston)
Priscilla Beach 02381
  (White Horse Beach)
Providencetown 02657
  (Provincetown)
Provincetown 02657
Quincy 02169-171, 02269
  Houghs Neck 02169
  Marina Bay 02171
  Norfolk Downs 02171
  North Quincy 02171
  South Quincy 02169
  Squantum 02171
  West Quincy 02169
  Wollaston 02170
Quissett (Falmouth) 02540
Randolph 02368
Raynham 02767-768
Reading 01867
Readville 02137
Rehoboth 02769
Revere 02151
Richardson Corners 01508
  (Charlton City)
Richmond 01254
Risingdale 01230
  (Great Barrington)
Riverdale 01534, 01930
  (Northbridge)
Riverside 01267, 01376, 02158
  (Williamstown)
Rochdale 01542
Rochester 02770
Rockland 02370
Rockport 01966
Rocky Nook (Kingston) 02364
Roslindale 02131

Rowe 01367
Rowley 01969
Roxbury 02118-120
  Boston 02118-120
Royalston 01368
Russell 01071
Russell'ville (Westfield) 01085
Rutland 01543
Saconesset Hills 02540
  (Falmouth)
Sagamore 02561
Sagamore Beach 02562
Salem 01970-971
Salisbury 01952
Sandersdale (Southbridge) 01550
Sandisfield 01255
Sandwich 02563
Santuit (Cotuit) 02635
Saugus 01906
Saundersville 01560
  (South Grafton)
Savoy 01256
Saxonville (Framingham) .. 01701
Scituate 02066
Seekonk 02771
Segreganset (Dighton) 02715
Shaker Village (Harvard) .. 01451
Sharon 02067
Shattuckville 01369
Sheffield 01257
Shelburne 01370
  (Shelburne Falls)
Sheldonville 02070
Sherborn 01770
Sherwood Forest (Becket) 01223
Shirley 01464
Shrewsbury 01545-546
Shutesbury 01072
Siasconset 02564
Silver Beach 02565
  (North Falmouth)
Silver Hill (Weston) 02193
Silver Lake (Kingston) 02364
Sippewisset (Falmouth) 02540
Snug Harbor (Duxbury) 02331
Soldiers Field (Boston) 02163
Somerset 02725-726
  Fall River 02725-726
Somerville 02143-145
  East Somerville 02143
  West Somerville 02144
  Winter Hill 02145
South Acton (Acton) 01720
South Amherst (Amherst) .. 01002
South Ashburnham 01466
  (Ashburnham)
South Ashfield (Ashfield) ... 01330
South Attleboro 02703
  (Attleboro)
South Barre 01074
South Berlin (Berlin) 01549
South Bolton (Bolton) 01740
South Boston (Boston) 02127
South Braintree 02184
  (Braintree)
South Carver 02366
South Charlton (Charlton) . 01507
South Chatham 02633, 02659
  (Chatham)
South Chelmsford 01824
  (Chelmsford)

South Dartmouth 02748
South Deerfield 01373
South Dennis 02660
South Easton 02375
South Egremont 01252, 01258
  (North Egremont)
  Mount Washington 01258
South Framingham 01701
  (Framingham)
South Gardner (Gardner) .. 01440
South Grafton 01560
South Hadley 01075
South Hamilton 01982
South Harwich 02661
South Hyannis (Hyannis) .. 02601
South Lancaster 01561
South Lawrence 01843
  (Lawrence)
South Lee 01260
South Lincoln (Lincoln) 01773
South Lynnfield 01940
  (Lynnfield)
South Mashpee (Mashpee) 02649
South Milford (Hopedale) .. 01747
South Natick (Natick) 01760
South Orleans 02662
South Quincy (Quincy) 02169
South Royalston (Athol) ... 01331
South Sandisfield 01255
  (Sandisfield)
South Spencer (Spencer) . 01562
South Sutton 01516
  (East Douglas)
South Swansea (Swansea) 02777
South Truro (Truro) 02666
South Uxbridge (Uxbridge) 01569
South Village (Ashby) 01431
South Walpole 02071
South Waltham (Waltham) 02154
South Wareham 02571
  (Wareham)
South Wellfleet 02663
South Weymouth 02190
  (Weymouth)
South Williamstown 01267
  (Williamstown)
South Worthington 01050
  (Huntington)
South Yarmouth 02664, 02673
  Bass River 02664
Southampton 01073
Southborough 01745, 01772
  Cordaville 01772
  Fayville 01745
  Southville 01772
  Trenton 01772
Southbridge 01550
Southfield 01259
Southville (Southborough) 01772
Southwick 01077
Spencer 01562
Spindleville (Hopedale) 01747
Springfield 01101-05, 01107-09
      01111, 01114-115, 01118-119
    .. 01128-29, 01133, 01138-39
    ..... 01144, 01151-152, 01199
  Brightwood 01107
  Highland 01109, 01119, 01129
Squantum (Quincy) 02171
Sterling 01564
Stewartville (Medford) 02155

Still River 01467
Stockbridge 01262-263
Stoneham 02180
Stoneville (Erving) .. 01344, 01501
Stony Brook (Weston) 02193
Stoughton 02072
Stow 01775
Sturbridge 01566
Sudbury 01776
Sunderland 01375
Sunnyside (Webster) 01570
Sutton 01590
Swampscott 01907
Swansea 02777
Sweets Corner 01267
  (Williamstown)
Swift River (Cummington) . 01026
Swifts Beach (Wareham) .. 02571
Tafts Corner (Spencer) 01562
Talbots (Middleboro) 02348
Taunton 02718, 02779-780
  (East Taunton)
Teaticket (East Falmouth) . 02536
Templeton 01468
Tewksbury 01876
Texas (North Oxford) 01537
Thorndike 01079
Three Rivers 01080
Thumperton Beach 02651
  (North Eastham)
Tisbury (Vineyard Haven) . 02568
Tobeys Island 02553
  (Monument Beach)
Tolland (Granville) 01034
Topsfield 01983
Townsend 01469, 01474
  Old City 01474
  West Townsend 01474
Trenton (Southborough) ... 01772
Truro 02666
Turners Falls 01349, 01376
  Gill 01376
  Millers Falls 01349
  Montague City 01376
  Riverside 01376
Tyngsboro 01879
Tyringham 01264
Union Point (Webster) 01570
Uphams Corner 02125
  (Dorchester)
Upton (West Upton) 01568
Uxbridge 01569
Van Deusenville 01230
  (Great Barrington)
Vineyard Haven 02568, 02573
  North Tisbury 02568
  Tisbury 02568
  West Chop 02573
Waban 02168
Wakefield 01880
Wales 01081
Walpole 02081
Waltham 02154, 02254
  Boston 02154
  North Waltham 02154
  South Waltham 02154
Waquoit (East Falmouth) .. 02536
Ward Hill (Haverhill) 01835
Ware 01082
Wareham 02571
Warren 01083, 01092

IMPORTANT BUILDINGS   MASSACHUSETTS

ALLSTON

HOTELS

Guest Quarters Hotel
400 SOLDIERS FIELD RD   02134

AMHERST

COLLEGES

Amherst College
0 COLLEGE ST 01002

Hampshire College
893 WEST ST 01002

Univ Of Massachusetts
0 MASSACHUSETTS AVE   01003

BOSTON

BUILDINGS

1 Financial Center
1 FINANCIAL CTR 02111

Boston Garden
150 CAUSEWAY ST 02114

Christian Science Center
1 NORWAY ST 02115

Copley Place
1 COPLEY PL 02116

Custom House
2 INDIA ST 02109

International Place
1 INTERNATIONAL PL 02110

John Hancock Towers
200 CLARENDON ST 02116

Park Sq Building
31 SAINT JAMES AVE 02116

Prudential Tower
800 BOYLSTON ST 02199

Registry Motor Vehicles
100 NASHUA ST 02114

State St Bank Building
225 FRANKLIN ST 02110

GOVERNMENT

Charles F Hurley Building
19 STANIFORD ST 02114

John F Kennedy Fed Building
15 NEW SUDBURY ST 02203

State House
24 BEACON ST 02133

Thomas P Oneil Fed Building
10 CAUSEWAY ST 02222

Transportation Building
10 PARK PLZ 02116

HOSPITALS

Arbour Hospital
49 ROBINWOOD AVE 02130

Beth Israel Hospital
330 BROOKLINE AVE 02215

Boston City Hospital
751 ALBANY ST 02118

Brigham And Womens Hosp
75 FRANCIS ST 02115

Brigham And Womens Hospit
721 HUNTINGTON AVE 02115

Childrens Hospital
300 LONGWOOD AVE 02115

Faulkner Hospital
1153 CENTRE ST 02130

Joslin Clinic
1 JOSLIN PL 02215

Lemuel Shattuck Hospital
170 MORTON ST 02130

Mass General Hospital
14 FRUIT ST 02114

New England Deaconess
185 PILGRIM RD 02215

New England Medical Ctr
750 WASHINGTON ST 02111

Spaulding Rehab Hospital
125 NASHUA ST 02114

Waltham Hospital
20 HOPE AVE 02154

HOTELS

Back Bay Hilton Hotel
40 BELVIDERE ST 02115

Colonnade Hotel
120 HUNTINGTON AVE 02116

Copley Plaza Hotel
138 SAINT JAMES AVE 02116

Guest Quarters Suite Hotl
550 WINTER ST 02154

Hotel Meridian
250 FRANKLIN ST 02110

Lafayette Hotel
1 Avenue De Lafayette 02111

Marriott Long Wharf Hotel
296 STATE ST 02109

Waltham Vista Hotel
70 3RD AVE 02154

Weston Hotel
10 HUNTINGTON AVE 02116

COLLEGES

Boston University
755 Commonwealth Ave ... 02215

Emanuel College
400 FENWAY 02115

Emerson College
150 BEACON ST 02116

Harvard Dental School
188 LONGWOOD AVE 02115

Northeastern University
360 HUNTINGTON AVE 02115

Simmons College
300 FENWAY 02115

Suffolk University
8 ASHBURTON PL 02108

Suffolk University
20 DERNE ST 02114

Tufts Dental
136 HARRISON AVE 02111

Univ Of Mass
100 WILLIAM T MORRISSEY
BLVD 02125

Wentworth Institute
550 HUNTINGTON AVE 02115

BRAINTREE

HOSPITALS

Mass Respiratory Hospital
2001 WASHINGTON ST ... 02184

BRIGHTON

HOSPITALS

St Johns Hospital
296 ALLSTON ST 02146

BRIGHTWOOD

HOSPITALS

Bay State Medical
759 CHESTNUT ST 01107

BROCKTON

HOSPITALS

Veterans Hospital
940 Belmont Street 02401

CAMBRIDGE

HOSPITALS

Cambridge Hospital
1493 CAMBRIDGE ST 02139

Sancta Maria Hospital
799 CONCORD AVE 02138

HOTELS

Charles Hotel
1 BENNETT ST 02138

Howard Johnson Motel
777 MEMORIAL DR 02139

Hyatt Regency
575 MEMORIAL DR 02139

Royal Sonesta Hotel
5 CAMBRIDGE PKY 02142

Sheraton Commander Hotel
16 GARDEN ST 02138

COLLEGES

Harvard University
1 HARVARD YARD 02138

Lesley College
29 EVERETT ST 02138

M I T
77 Massachusetts Ave 02139

EAST MILTON

HOSPITALS

Milton Hospital
92 HIGHLAND ST 02186

COLLEGES

Curry College
1071 BLUE HILL AVE 02186

FALMOUTH

APARTMENTS

Admiralty Apts
135 SCRANTON AVE 02540

Greengate Apts
35 GREENGATE RD 02540

Harbor View Apts
115 SCRANTON AVE 02540

HIGHLAND

BUILDINGS

Eastfield Mall Building
1655 BOSTON RD 01129

HOUGHS NECK

HOSPITALS

Quincy Hospital
114 WHITWELL ST 02169

LEXINGTON

HOTELS

Sheraton Lexington Hotel
727 MARRETT RD 02173

NEW BEDFORD

GOVERNMENT

City Hall
133 WILLIAM ST 02740

Federal Building
53 N 6TH ST 02740

NEWTON

HOSPITALS

Newton Wellesley Hospital
2014 WASHINGTON ST ... 02162

NORTH WALTHAM

HOTELS

Best Western Hotel
477 Totten Pond Road 02154

COLLEGES

Bentley College
485 Beaver Street 02154

Brandeis University
415 South Street 02154

SOUTH WEYMOUTH

HOSPITALS

South Shore Hospital
55 FOGG RD 02190

MILITARY

US Naval Air Station
1134 MAIN ST 02190

SPRINGFIELD

BUILDINGS

Basketball Hall Of Fame
1150 Columbus Street 01105

City Hall
36 COURT ST 01103

Federal Building
1550 MAIN ST 01103

WELLESLEY

COLLEGES

Wellesley College
106 CENTRAL ST 02181

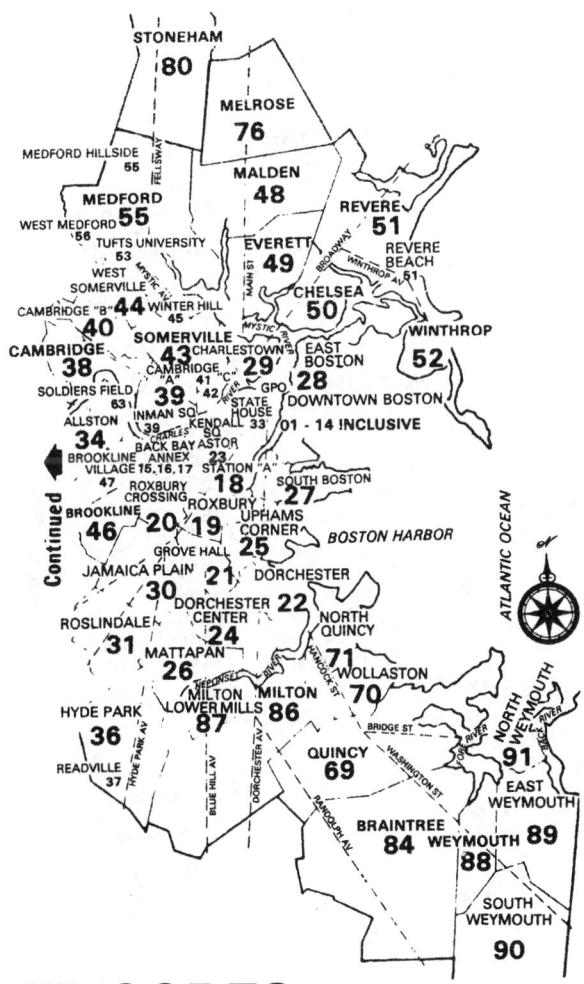

ZIP CODES

BOSTON, MA

021 + TWO DIGITS SHOWN = ZIP CODE

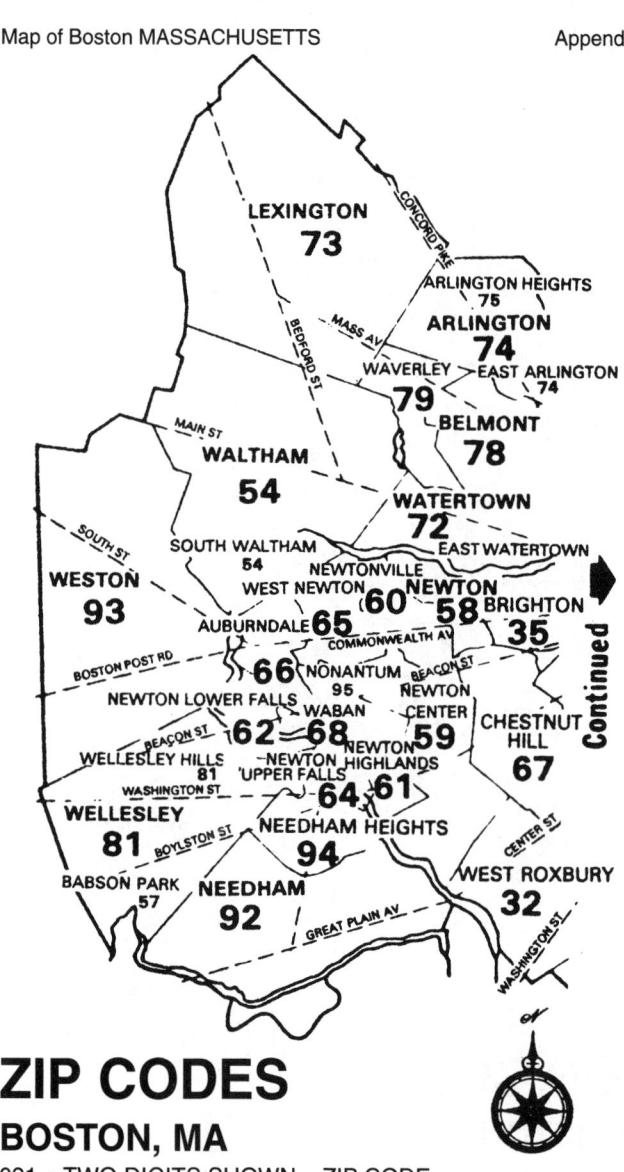

ZIP CODES
BOSTON, MA
021 + TWO DIGITS SHOWN = ZIP CODE

**AREA MAP
OF COMMUNITIES
COVERED IN THE
METRO BOSTON
STREET LISTING**

COMMUNITY ABBREVIATIONS

ALL -	Allston	**NQ** -	North Quincy
ARL -	Arlington	**NUF** -	Newton Upper Falls
AUB -	Auburndale	**NWH** -	Newton Heights
BEL -	Belmont	**NWV** -	Newtonville
BRA -	Braintree	**NWY** -	North Weymoth
BRI -	Brighton	**QUI** -	Quincy
BRO -	Brookline	**REV** -	Revere
CAM -	Cambridge	**ROS** -	Roslindale
CHA -	Charlestown	**ROX** -	Roxbury
CHE -	Chelsea	**RXC** -	Roxbury Crossing
CHH -	Chestnut Hill	**SB** -	South Boston
DOR -	Dorchester	**SF** -	Soldiers Field
EB -	East Boston	**SOM** -	Somerville
EV -	Everett	**STO** -	Stoneham
EWY -	East Weymouth	**SWY** -	South Weymouth
HP -	Hyde Park	**WAB** -	Waban
JP -	Jamaica Plain	**WAL** -	Walmant
LEX -	Lexington	**WAT** -	Watertown
MAL -	Malden	**WAV** -	Waverly
MAT -	Mattapan	**WEL** -	Wellesley
MED -	Medford	**WES** -	Weston
MEL -	Melrose	**WH** -	Wellsley Hills
MIL -	Milton	**WIN** -	Winthrop
N -	Needham	**WN** -	West Newton
NCE -	Newton Center	**WOL** -	Wollaston
NEW -	Newton	**WRX** -	West Roxbury
NH -	Needham Heights	**WS** -	West Somerville
NLF -	Newton Lower Falls	**WY** -	Weymouth

MICHIGAN
Abbreviation MI

Acme 49610
Ada 49301, 49355-357
    Amway Corp ... 49355-49357
Addison 49220
Addison Township 48367
    (Leonard)
Adrian 49221
Afton 49705
Ahmeek 49901
Akron 48701
Alanson 49706
Alaska (Alto) 49302
Alba 49611
Albion 49224
Alden 49612
Alger 48610
Algonac 48001
Allegan 49010
Allen 49227
Allen Park 48101
Allendale 49401
Allens Cove (Luna Pier) 48157
Allenton 48002
Allouez 49805
Alma 48801
Almont 48003
Alpena 49707
Alpha 49902
Alto 49302
Amasa 49903
Anchorville 48004
Ann Arbor 48103-109, 48113
    Barton Hills 48105
    Delhi 48103
    Dixboro 48105
    Loch Alpine 48103
    Pittsfield Township 48104
    Scio Township 48103
    Superior Township
    48104-105
Antrim (Byron) 48418
Applegate 48401
Arcadia 49613
Argyle 48410
Armada 48005
Arnold 49819
Ashley 48806
Athens 49011
Atlanta 49709
Atlantic Mine 49905
Atlas 48411
Attica 48412
Au Gres 48703
Au Sable (Oscoda) 48750
Au Train 49806
Auburn 48611
Auburn Hills 48321, 48326
    Lake Angelus 48326
Augusta 49012
Avalon Beach (Monroe) 48161
Avoca 48006
Azalia 48110
Bad Axe 48413
Bailey 49303
Baldwin 49304
Bancroft 48414
Bangor 49013
Bannister 48807

Baraga 49908
Barbeau 49710
Bark River 49807
Baroda 49101
Barryton 49305
Barton City 48705
Barton Hills (Ann Arbor) ... 48105
Bass Lake (Pentwater) 49449
Bath 48808
Battle Creek 49015-018
    Springfield 49015
Bay City 48706-708, 48710
Bay Crest (Monroe) 48161
Bay Port 48720
Bay View (Petoskey) 49770
Bear Lake 49614
Beaver Grove (Marquette) .. 49855
Beaverton 48612
Bedford 49020
Beecher (Flint) 48505
Beechwood 49909
Belding 48809, 48887
Bellaire 49615
Belleville 48111-112
    Roulo 48111
    Sumpter Township 48111
    Van Buren Township 48111
Bellevue 49021
Belmont 49306
Bentley 48613
Benton Harbor 49022-023
Benzonia 49616
Bergland 49910
Berkley 48072
Berlin (Allenton) 48002
Berrien Center 49102
Berrien Springs 49103-104
Berville (Allenton) 48002
Bessemer 49911
Beulah 49617
Beverly Hills (Franklin) 48025
Big Bay 49808
Big Rapids 49307
Bingham Farms 48025, 48034
    (Franklin)
Birch Run 48415
Birmingham 48009, 48012
Bitely 49309
Black River 48721
Blanchard 49310
Blissfield 49228
Bloomfield Hills 48301-304
Bloomingdale 49026
Bolles Harbor (Monroe) 48161
Boon 49618
Borculo (Zeeland) 49464
Boyne City 49712
Boyne Falls 49713
Bradley 49311
Brampton (Gladstone) 49837
Branch 49402
Brandon (Ortonville) 48462
Brant 48614
Breckenridge 48615
Breedsville 49027
Brethren 49619
Bridgeport 48722
Bridgeton (Grant) 49327
Bridgewater 48115
Bridgman 49106
Brimley 49715, 49778

Raco 49715
Raco 49778
Britton 49229
Brohman 49312
Bronson 49028
Brooklyn 49230
Brown City 48416
Bruce Crossing 49912
Bruce Xing 49912
    (Bruce Crossing)
Brunswick 49313
Brutus 49716
Buchanan 49107
Buckley 49620
Burlington 49029
Burnips 49314
Burns (Byron) 48418
Burnside (Brown City) 48416
Burr Oak 49030
Burt 48417
Burt Lake 49717
Burton 48509, 48519, 48529
    Flint 48509, 48519, 48529
    Northeast 48509
    Southeast 48519, 48529
Byron 48418
Byron Center 49315
Cadillac 49601
Cadmus 49231
Caledonia 49316
Calumet 49913, 49918, 49942
    Centennial Heights 49913
    Laurium 49913
Camden 49232
Camp Grayling (Grayling) . 49739
Cannonsburg 49317
Capac 48014
Carland (Elsie) 48831
Carleton 48117
Carney 49812
Caro 48723
Carp Lake 49718
Carrollton 48724
Carson City 48811
Carsonville 48419
Cascade (Grand Rapids) .. 49506
Caseville 48725
Casnovia 49318
Caspian 49915
Cass City 48726
Cassopolis 49031
Cedar 49621
Cedar Lake 48812
Cedar River 49813
Cedar Springs 49319
Cedarville 49719
Cement City 49233
Centennial Heights 49913
    (Calumet)
Center Line 48015
Central Lake 49622
Centreville 49032
Ceresco 49033
Champion 49814
Channing 49815
Charlevoix 49711, 49720
    (Bayshore)
Charlotte 48813
Chase 49623
Chassell 49916
Chatham 49816

Fraser 48026
Frederic 49733
Free Soil 49411
Freedom Township 48118
    (Chelsea)
Freeland 48623
Freeport 49325
Fremont 48787, 49412
Frenchtown (Monroe) 48161
Frontier 49239
Fruitport 49415
Fulton 49052
Gaastra 49927
Gagetown 48735
Gaines 48436
Galesburg 49053
Galien 49113
Garden 49835
Garden City 48135-136
Gay (Lake Linden) 49945
Gaylord 49735
Genesee 48437
Genoa Township (Brighton) 48116
Germfask 49836
Gibraltar (Rockwood) 48173
Gilford 48736
Gladstone 49837
Gladwin 48624
Glen Arbor 49636
Glenn 49416
Glennie 48737
Gobles 49055
Goetzville 49736
Good Hart 49737
Goodells 48027
Goodison (Rochester) 48306
Goodland (Imlay City) 48444
Goodrich 48438
Gould City 49838
Gowen 49326
Grand Beach (New Buffalo) 49117
Grand Blanc 48439
Grand Haven 49417
Grand Junction 49056
Grand Ledge 48837
Grand Marais 49839
Grand Rapids . 49500-510, 49512
    49514, 49516, 49518, 49523
    49530, 49546, 49548, 49550
    49555, 49560, 49588, 49599
    Business Reply Mail 49502
    Cascade 49506
    Cutlerville 49508, 49548
    East Grand Rapids 49506
    Forest Hills 49506
    Kentwood 49506 49508
    49512, 49518, 49546, 49548
    Michigan Bulb Co 49550
    Radio Bible Class 49555
    Standale 49504
    Walker 49504, 49514
    Wyoming 49548
    Zondervan Corp 49530
Grandview Beach 48145
    (La Salle)
Grandville 49418, 49468
Grant 49327
Grant Township (Jeddo) 48032
Grape (Monroe) 48161
Grass Lake 49240
Grawn 49637

Grayling 49738-739
Great Lake Beach 48450
    (Lexington)
Green Oak Township 48116
    (Brighton)
Greenbush 48738
Greenland 49929
Greenville 48838
Greenwood (Avoca) 48006
Gregory 48137
Grindstone City 48467
    (Port Austin)
Grosse Ile 48138
Grosse Pointe 48230, 48236
    Detroit 48230
    Detroit 48236
Gulliver 49840
Gwinn 49841, 49843
    Princeton 49841
Hadley 48440
Hagar Shores 49039
Hale 48739
Hamburg 48139
Hamilton 49419
Hamtramck (Detroit) 48212
Hancock 49930
Hanover 49241
Harbert 49115
Harbor Beach 48441
Harbor Springs 49737, 49740
    (Good Hart)
    Wequetonsing 49740
Hardwood (Bark River) 49740
Harper Woods 48225
Harrietta 49638
Harris 49845
Harrison 48625
Harrison Township 48045
Harrisville 48740
Harsens Island 48028
Hart 49420
Hartford 49057
Hartland 48353
Hartland Township 48116
    (Brighton)
Harvey (Marquette) 49855
Haslett 48840
Hastings 49058
Hawks 49743
Hazel Park 48030
Hell (Pinckney) 48169
Hemlock 48626
Henderson 48841
Hermansville 49847
Herron 49744
Hersey 49639
Hesperia 49421
Hessel 49745
Hickory Corners 49060
Hickory Island 48138
    (Grosse Ile)
Higgins Lake 48627
Highland 48356-357
Highland Park (Detroit) 48203
Hillcrest Orchard 48145
    (La Salle)
Hilliards (Hopkins) 49328
Hillman 49746
Hillsdale 49242
Holland 49422-424
Holly 48442

Holt 48842
Holton 49425
Homer 49245
Honor 49640
Hope 48628
Hopkins 49328
Horton 49246
Houghton 49921, 49931
    (Dodgeville)
Houghton Lake 48629
Houghton Lake Heights 48630
Howard City 49329
Howell 48843-844, 48863
Hubbard Lake 49747
Hubbardston 48845
Hubbell 49934
Hudson 49247
Hudson Mills (Dexter) 48130
Hudsonville 49426
Hulbert 49748
Hunters Creek (Lapeer) 48446
Huntington Woods 48070
Huron City (Port Austin) 48467
Huron Township 48164
    (New Boston)
Ida 48140
Idlewild 49642
Imlay (Imlay City) 48444
Imlay City 48444
Independence 48346, 48348
    (Clarkston)
Indian River 49749
Ingalls 49848
Inkster 48141
Interlochen 49643
Ionia 48846
Ira (Fair Haven) 48023
Iron Mountain 49801-802
    East Kingsford 49801
    Kingsford 49801-802
Iron River 49909, 49935
    (Beechwood)
Irons 49644
Ironwood 49938
Ishpeming 49849, 49865
    North Lake 49849
Ithaca 48847
Jackson 49201-204
Jamestown 49427
Jasper 49248
Jeddo 48032
Jenison 49428-429
Jerome 49249
Johannesburg 49751
Jones 49061
Jonesville 49250
Kalamazoo 49001-009, 49019
    Kazoo 49004
    Parchment 49004
    Portage 49008-009
Kaleva 49645
Kalkaska 49646
Kawkawlin 48631
Kazoo (Kalamazoo) 49004
Kearsarge 49942
Keego Harbor 48320
Kendall 49062
Kenockee (Avoca) 48006
Kent City 49330
Kenton 49943
Kentwood ... 49506, 49508, 49512

.... 49518, 49546, 49548	
(Grand Rapids)	
Kewadin 49648	
Keweenaw Bay (Baraga) .. 49908	
Kimball (Smiths Creek) 48074	
Kincheloe 49788	
Kinde 48445	
Kingsford 49801-802	
(Iron Mountain)	
Kingsley 49649	
Kingston 48741	
Kinross 49752	
L Anse (Lanse) 49946	
La Salle 48145	
Lachine 49753	
Lacota 49063	
Laing (Snover) 48472	
Laingsburg 48848	
Lake 48632	
Lake Angelus 48326	
(Auburn Hills)	
Lake Ann 49650	
Lake City 49651	
Lake Fenton (Fenton) 48430	
Lake George 48633	
Lake Leelanau 49653	
Lake Linden 49945	
Lake Nepessing (Lapeer) .. 48446	
Lake Odessa 48849	
Lake Orion 48359-362	
Orion 48362	
Lakeland 48143	
Lakeport (Fort Gratiot) 48059	
Lakeside 49116	
Lakeview 48850	
Lakeville 48366	
Lakewood (Luna Pier) 48157	
Lambertville 48144	
Lamont 49430	
Lanse 49946	
Lansing ... 48900-901, 48906-913	
.... 48915-919, 48921-922	
.... 48924, 48929-930, 48933	
48937, 48950, 48956, 48980	
Lucky Losers (Lansing) 48916	
Oldsmobile 48921	
Lapeer 48446	
Lathrup Village 48076	
(Southfield)	
Laurium (Calumet) 49913	
Lawrence 49064	
Lawton 49065	
Le Roy (Leroy) 49655	
Leland 49654	
Lennon 48449	
Lenox 48048, 48050	
(New Haven)	
Leonard 48367	
Leonidas 49066	
Leroy 49655	
Leslie 49251	
Levering 49755	
Lewiston 49756	
Lexington 48450	
Lima Center 48118, 48130	
(Chelsea)	
Limestone (Chatham) 49816	
Lincoln 48742	
Lincoln Park 48146	
Linden 48451	
Linwood 48634	

Litchfield 49252	
Little Lake 49833	
Livonia 48150-154	
Loch Alpine (Ann Arbor) 48103	
London (Maybee) 48159	
London Township (Milan) .. 48160	
Long Lake 48743	
Loretto 49852	
Lowell 49331	
Luce Township (Chelsea) .. 48118	
Lucky Losers (Lansing) 48916	
Ludington 49431	
Lum (Attica) 48412	
Luna Pier 48157	
Lupton 48635	
Luther 49656	
Luzerne 48636	
Lyndon Township 48118	
(Chelsea)	
Lynn (Yale) 48097	
Lyons 48851	
Macatawa 49434	
Mackinac Island 49757	
Mackinaw City 49701	
Macomb 48042, 48044	
Madison Heights 48071	
Mancelona 49659	
Manchester 48158	
Manistee 49660	
Manistique 49854	
Manitou Beach 49253	
Manton 49663	
Maple City 49664	
Maple Rapids 48853	
Marcellus 49067	
Marenisco 49947	
Marine City 48039	
Marion 49665	
Marlette 48453	
Marne 49435	
Marquette 49855	
Marshall 49068-068	
Martin 49070	
Marysville 48040	
Mason 48854	
Mass City 49948	
Mattawan 49071	
Maybee 48159	
Mayfield 49666	
Mayville 48744	
Mc Bain 49657	
Mc Millan 49853	
Mcbrides 48852	
Mears 49436	
Mecosta 49332	
Melvin 48454	
Melvindale 48122	
Memphis 48041	
Mendon 49072	
Menominee 49858	
Merrill 48637	
Merritt 49667	
Mesick 49668	
Metamora 48455	
Michcon (Detroit) 48268	
Michiana (New Buffalo) 49117	
Michigamme 49861	
Middleton 48856	
Middleville 49333	
Middlevle (Middleville) 49333	
Midland 48640-642, 480667	

.... 48670, 48674, 48686	
Mikado 48745	
Milan 48160	
Milford 48380-382	
Millbrook 49334	
Millersburg 49759	
Millington 48746	
Millville (Lapeer) 48446	
Minden City 48456, 48465	
Mio 48647	
Mohawk 49950	
Moline 49335	
Monroe 48159, 48161	
(Maybee)	
Avalon Beach 48161	
Bay Crest 48161	
Bolles Harbor 48161	
Erie Shores 48161	
Frenchtown 48161	
Grape 48161	
Raisinville Township ... 48161	
Stony Point 48161	
Woodland Beach 48161	
Montague 49437	
Montgomery 49255	
Montrose 48457	
Moorestown (Lake City) 49651	
Mooreville (Milan) 48160	
Moran 49760	
Morenci 49256	
Morley 49336	
Morrice 48857	
Moscow 49257	
Mosherville 49258	
Mott Park (Flint) 48504	
Mount Clemens 48043, 48046	
Mount Morris 48458	
Mount Pleasant .. 48804, 48858-9	
Muir 48860	
Mullett Lake 49761	
Mulliken 48861	
Munger 48747	
Munising 49862	
Munith 49259	
Muskegon 49440-445	
Dalton 49445	
North Muskegon 49445	
Norton Shores 49441	
Roosevelt Park 49441	
Mussey (Capac) 48014	
Nadeau 49863	
Nahma 49864	
Napoleon 49261	
Nashville 49073	
National City 48748	
National Mine 49865	
Naubinway 49762	
Nazareth 49074	
Negaunee 49866	
New Baltimore 48047, 48051	
Chesterfield 48047	
Chesterfield 48051	
New Boston 48164	
New Buffalo 49117	
New Era 49446	
New Haven 48048, 48050	
Chesterfield 48050	
Lenox 48048	
Lenox 48050	
New Hudson 48165	
New Lothrop 48460	

New Port (Newport) 48166
New Troy 49119
Newaygo 49337
Newberry 49868
Newport 48166
Niles 49120-121
Nisula 49952
North Adams 49262
North Branch 48461
North Dorr (Dorr) 49323
North Lake (Ishpeming) 49849
North Manitou (Leland) 49654
North Muskegon 49445
  (Muskegon)
North Shores (La Salle) 48145
North Star 48862
North Street 48049
Northeast (Flint) 48506, 48509
Northfield Township 48189
  (Whitmore Lake)
Northland 49869
Northport 49670
Northport Point 49670
  (Northport)
Northville 48167
Northwest 48504, 48531-532
  (Flint)
Norton Shores (Muskegon) 49441
Norvell 49263
Norway 49870
Nottawa 49075
Novi 48374-377
Nunica 49448
Oak Grove 48863
Oak Park 48237
Oakland 48306, 48363
  (Rochester)
Oakley 48649
Oakville (Milan) 48160
Oden 49764
Okemos 48805, 48864
Old Mission 49673
Oldsmobile (Lansing) 48921
Olivet 49076
Omena 49674
Omer 48749
Onaway 49765
Onekama 49675
Onondaga 49264
Onsted 49265
Ontonagon 49953
Orchard Lake 48323-324
  (West Bloomfield)
Orion 48359-360, 48362
  (Lake Orion)
Orleans 48865
Ortonville 48462
Oscoda 48750, 48753
  Au Sable 48750
Oshtemo 49077
Osseo 49266
Ossineke 49766
Otisville 48463
Otsego 49078
Ottawa Lake 49267
Otter Lake 48464
Otterburn (Swartz Creek) .. 48473
Ovid 48866
Owasippe (Twin Lake) 49457
Owendale 48754
Owosso 48867

Oxford 48370-371
Painesdale 49955
Palmer 49871
Palms 48465
Palmyra 49268
Palo 48870
Paradise 49768
Parchment (Kalamazoo) ... 49004
Paris 49338
Parisville (Ruth) 48470
Parma 49269
Parshallville (Fenton) 48430
Paw Paw 49079
Pearl Beach (Algonac) 48001
Peck 48466
Pelkie 49958
Pellston 49769
Pentwater 49449
Perkins 49872
Perrinton 48871
Perronville 49873
Perry 48872
Petersburg 49270
Petoskey 49770
Pewamo 48873
Pickford 49774
Pierson 49339
Pigeon 48755
Pinckney 48169
Pinconning 48650
Pittsfield Township 48104
  (Ann Arbor)
Pittsford 49271
Plainfield (Gregory) 48137
Plainwell 49080
Pleasant Lake 48158, 49272
  (Manchester)
Pleasant Ridge 48069
Plymouth 48170
Podunk (Manchester) 48158
Pointe Aux Barques 48467
  (Port Austin)
Pointe Aux Peaux 48166
  (Newport)
Pointe Aux Pins 49775
Pompeii 48874
Pontiac 48340-343, 48347
Port Austin 48467
Port Hope 48468
Port Huron 48060-061
Port Sanilac 48469
Port Sheldon (West Olive) . 49460
Portage 49001-002
.... 49008-009, 49081
  (Kalamazoo)
Portland 48875
Posen 49776
Potters Lake (Lapeer) 48446
Potterville 48876
Powers 49874
Prattville 49273
Prescott 48756
Presque Isle 49777
Princeton (Gwinn) 49641
Prudenville 48651
Pullman 49450
Putnam Township 48169
  (Pinckney)
Quincy 49082
Quinnesec 49876
Raco (Brimley) 49715, 49778

Raisinville Township 48161
  (Monroe)
Ralph 49877
Ramsay 49959
Rankin (Swartz Creek) 48473
Rapid City 49676
Rapid River 49878
Ravenna 49451
Rawsonville (Ypsilanti) 48197
Ray48096
Rea (Dundee) 48131
Reading 49274
Redford 48239-240
  Detroit 48239-240
Reed City 49677
Reese 48757
Remus 49340
Republic 49879
Rhodes 48652
Richland 49083
Richmond 48062
Richville 48758
Ridgeway 49275
Riga 49276
Riley (Memphis) 48041
Ripley (Hancock) 49930
River Rouge 48218
Riverdale 48877
Riverside 49084
Riverview (Wyandotte) 48192
Rives Junction 49277
Rochester 48306-309
  Goodison 48306
  Oakland 48306
Rock 49880
Rockford 49341, 49351
Rockland 49960
Rockwood 48173
Rodney 49342
Rogers City 49779
Rollin 49278
Romeo 48065
Romulus 48174
Roosevelt Park 49441
  (Muskegon)
Roscommon 48653
Rose (Holly) 48442
Rose Center (Fenton) 48430
Rose City 48654
Rosebush 48878
Roseville 48066
Rothbury 49452
Roulo (Belleville) 48111
Royal Oak 48067-068
.... 48071, 48073
Royal Oak Township 48220
  (Ferndale)
Ruby (North Street) 48049
Rudyard 49780
Rumely 49826
Russell Island (Algonac) ... 48001
Ruth 48470
Saginaw 48601-609, 48663
Sagola 49881
Saint Charles 48655
Saint Clair 48079
Saint Clair Shores 48080-082
Saint Helen 48656
Saint Ignace 49781
Saint James 49782
Saint Johns 48879

Saint Joseph	49085
Saint Louis	48880
Salem	48175
Saline	48176
Samaria	48177
Sand Beach	48441
(Harbor Beach)	
Sand Creek	49279
Sand Lake	49343
Sandusky	48471
Sanford	48657
Sang (Harrison Township)	48045
Saranac	48881
Saugatuck	49453
Sault Sainte Marie	49783-6,49788
Sawyer	49125
Schaffer (Bark River)	49807
Schoolcraft	49087
Scio (Dexter)	48130
Scio Township (Ann Arbor)	48103
Scofield (Maybee)	48159
Scotts	49088
Scottville	49454
Sears	49679
Sebewaing	48759
Seneca	49280
Seney	49883
Shaftsburg	48882
Sharon (Manchester)	48158
Shelby	49455
Shelby Township	48315-318
(Utica)	
Shelbyville	49344
Shepherd	48883
Sheridan	48884
Sherwood	49089
Shingleton	49884
Sidnaw	49961
Sidney	48885
Sigel (Harbor Beach)	48441
Silverwood	48760
Simplicity Pattern	49121
(Niles)	
Six Lakes	48886
Skandia	49885
Skanee	49962
Skidway Lake	48756
Smiths Creek	48074
Smyrna	48887
Snover	48472
Sodus	49126
Somerset	49281
Somerset Center	49282
South Boardman	49680
South Branch	48761
South Haven	49090
South Lyon	48178
South Manitou (Leland)	49654
South Range	49963
South Rockwood	48179
Southeast	48519, 48529
(Burton)	
Southfield	48034, 48037
	48075-076, 48086
Bingham Farms	48034
Lathrup Village	48076
Southfield Township	48025
(Franklin)	
Southgate	48195
Spalding	49886
Sparta	49345

Spring Arbor	49283
Spring Lake	49456
Springfield	48350, 49015
(Davisburg)	
Springport	49284
Spruce	48762
Stalwart	49789
Stambaugh	49964
Standale (Grand Rapids)	49504
Standish	48658
Stanton	48888
Stanwood	49346
Stephenson	49813, 49887
(Cedar River)	
Sterling	48659
Sterling Heights	48310-314
Stevensville	49127
Stockbridge	49285
Stony Creek (Milan)	48160
Stony Point (Monroe)	48161
Stronach (Manistee)	49660
Strongs	49790
Sturgis	49091
Sumner	48889
Sumpter Township	48111
(Belleville)	
Sunfield	48890
Superior Township	48104-105
	48197
(Ann Arbor)	
Suttons Bay	49682
Swartz Creek	48473
Sylvan Lake	48320
(Keego Harbor)	
Sylvan Township (Chelsea)	48118
Tawas City	48763-764
East Tawas	48763
Taylor	48180
Taymouth (Montrose)	48457
Tecumseh	49286
Tekonsha	49092
Temperance	48182
Thetford (Clio)	48420
Thompson (Manistique)	49854
Thompsonville	49683
Three Oaks	49128
Three Rivers	49093
Tipton	49287
Toivola	49965
Topinabee	49791
Total Petroleum (Alma)	48802
Tower	49792
Traunik	49890
Traverse City	49684-686
Trenary	49891
Trenton	48183
Trout Creek	49943, 49967
(Kenton)	
Trout Lake	49793
Troy	48007
	48083-084, 48098-099
Trufant	49347
Turner	48765
Tuscola	48769
Tustin	49688
Twin Lake	49457
Twining	48766
Ubly	48475
Unadilla (Gregory)	48137
Union	49130
Union City	49094

Union Lake	48387
Union Pier	49129
Unionville	48767
Utica	48315-318
Shelby Township	48315-318
Van Buren Township	48111
(Belleville)	
Vandalia	49095
Vanderbilt	49795
Vassar	48768
Vermontville	49096
Vernon	48476
Vestaburg	48891
Vicksburg	49097
Vulcan (Loretto)	49852, 49892
Wabaningo	49461, 49463
(Whitehall)	
Whitehall	49463
Wakefield	49968
Waldron	49288
Walhalla	49458
Walker	49504, 49514
(Grand Rapids)	
Walkerville	49459
Wallace	49893
Walled Lake	48390-391
Commerce	48390
Wolverine Lake	48390
Walloon Lake	49796
Waltz (New Boston)	48164
Warren	48089-093, 48097
Washington	48094-095
Waterford	48327-329
Waters	49797
Watersmeet	49969
Watervliet	49098
Watton	49970
Wayland	49348
Wayne	48184
Webberville	48892
Webster (Dexter)	48130
Weidman	48893
Wells	49894
Wellston	49689
Wequetonsing	49740
(Harbor Springs)	
West Bloomfield	48322-325
Orchard Lake	48323-324
West Branch	48661
West Millbrook	49310
(Blanchard)	
West Olive	49460
Westland	48185
Weston	49289
Westphalia	48894
Wetmore	49895
Wheeler	48662
White Cloud	49349
White Lake	48383, 48386
White Pigeon	49099
White Pine	49971
Whitehall	49461, 49463
Wabaningo	49461
Whitmore Lake	48189
Whittaker	48190
Whittemore	48770
Williamsburg	49690
Williamston	48895
Williamsville (Gregory)	48137
Willis	48191
Willow (New Boston)	48164

ANN ARBOR

APARTMENTS

Charlton
2043 CHARLTON ST 48103

Hidden Valley Club Apt
605 Hidden Valley Club Dr 48104

Huron Towers
2200 FULLER RD 48105

Ivanhoe Apt
1533 PINE VALLEY BLVD 48104

Manchester Manor
2016 MEDFORD RD 48104

Mary Markley Hall
1503 WASHINGTON HTS 48109

Maynard House
400 MAYNARD ST 48104

Medical Center Ct
1005 MAIDEN LN 48105

Mulberry Row
2716 PACKARD ST 48108

Nature Cove Condo
2115 NATURE COVE CT .. 48104

Pine Valley
1521 PINE VALLEY BLVD 48104

Shoreview
420 KELLOGG ST 48105

Spruce Knob
2960 BIRCH HOLLOW DR 48108

Strawberry Hills
2756 GOLFSIDE DR 48108

Tower Plaza
555 E WILLIAM ST 48104

Town And Country
2572 CARPENTER RD 48108

Traver Knoll
1023 BARTON DR 48105

University Towers
536 S FOREST AVE 48104

BUILDINGS

Administrative Services
1009 GREENE ST 48109

Alice Lloyd Hall
100 OBSERVATORY ST ... 48109

Alumni Center
200 FLETCHER CT 48109

Alumni Memorial Hall
525 S STATE ST 48109

Angell Hall
435 S STATE ST 48109

Arborland Mall
3693 WASHTENAW AVE .. 48104

Art And Architecture Building
2000 BONISTEEL DR 48109

Automotive Lab
2320 HERBERT AVE 48109

Bentley Historical Librar
1150 BEAL AVE 48109

Betsy Barbour Hall
420 S STATE ST 48109

Bursley Hall
1931 DUFFIELD ST 48109

Burton Memorial Tower
230 S INGALLS ST 48109

Business Administration
904 MONROE ST 48109

Chrysler Center
2121 BONISTEEL DR 48109

City Center Building

220 E HURON ST 48104

Clements Library
909 S UNIVERSITY AVE .. 48109

Clerence Cook Little Building
425 E UNIVERSITY AVE .. 48109

College Pharmacy Building
428 CHURCH ST 48109

Communications Services
412 MAYNARD ST 48109

Computing Center
1075 BEAL AVE 48109

Couzins Hall
1200 E ANN ST 48109

Dennison
501 E UNIVERSITY AVE .. 48109

Dental Building
1011 N UNIVERSITY AVE 48109

Dow
2300 HAYWARD ST 48109

East Engineering Building
525 E UNIVERSITY AVE .. 48109

East Liberty Plaza
255 E LIBERTY ST 48104

East Quad Dorm
701 E UNIVERSITY AVE .. 48109

Eng Student Serv
2360 BONISTEEL DR 48109

Engineering
1301 BEAL AVE 48109

First National
201 S MAIN ST 48104

Fleming Administration
503 THOMPSON ST 48109

Frieze Building
105 S STATE ST 48109

Gerald R Ford Library
1000 BEAL AVE 48109

Haven Hall
505 S STATE ST 48109

Helen Newberry Hall
432 S STATE ST 48109

Human Resources And Dev
1111 KIPKE DR 48109

Hutchins Hall
625 S STATE ST 48109

Industrial Operation Engr
1205 BEAL AVE 48109

Inst Of Legal Education
1020 GREENE ST 48109

Institute Of Science
2200 BONISTEEL DR 48109

International Center
603 E MADISON ST 48109

Kelsey Museum
434 S STATE ST 48109

Lane Hall
204 S STATE ST 48109

Law Quad
551 S STATE ST 48109

Legal Research Building
801 MONROE ST 48109

LSA
500 S STATE ST 48109

Martha Cook Dorm
906 S UNIVERSITY AVE .. 48109

Mason Hall
419 S STATE ST 48109

Michigan League
227 S INGALLS ST 48109

Michigan Union
530 S STATE ST 48109

Modern Languages Building
812 E WASHINGTON ST .. 48109

Mortimar E Cooley Buildin
2355 BONISTEEL DR 48109

Mosher Hall
200 OBSERVATORY ST ... 48109

Museums
1109 GEDDES AVE 48109

Natural Science Building
830 N UNIVERSITY AVE .. 48109

Naval Arch And Marine Eng
2600 DRAPER DR 48109

North Campus Commons
2101 BONISTEEL DR 48109

North Campus Housing
3261 BAXTER RD 48109

North Hall
1105 N UNIVERSITY AVE 48109

North Ingalls Building
300 N INGALLS ST 48109

North University Building
1205 N UNIVERSITY AVE 48109

Observatory
1398 E ANN ST 48109

Phoenix Lab Ford Reactor
2301 BONISTEEL DR 48109

Plymouth
2929 PLYMOUTH RD 48105

Power Center Arts
121 FLETCHER CT 48109

Professional Building
2350 WASHTENAW AVE .. 48104

Property Control
3241 BAXTER RD 48109

Rackham
915 E WASHINGTON ST .. 48109

Randall
500 E UNIVERSITY AVE .. 48109

Research Activities Building
2450 HAYWARD ST 48109

Samuel Trask Dana Natural
430 E UNIVERSITY AVE .. 48109

School Of Education Building
610 E UNIVERSITY AVE .. 48109

School Of Music
1100 BAITS DR 48109

School Of Public Health
109 OBSERVATORY ST ... 48109

Simpson Memorial Insititu
102 OBSERVATORY ST ... 48109

South Quad Dorm
600 E MADISON ST 48109

Space Research Laboratory
2455 HAYWARD ST 48109

Stearns
2005 BAITS DR 48109

Stockwell Dorm
324 OBSERVATORY ST ... 48109

Student Activities Building
515 E JEFFERSON ST 48109

Tappan Hall
519 S STATE ST 48109

Tower Professional Center
3250 PLYMOUTH RD 48105

Transporation Services
1213 KIPKE DR 48109

University Of Michigan Laundry
1665 DEAN RD 48109

UM Trans Research Inst
2901 BAXTER RD 48109

Undergraduate Library
919 S UNIVERSITY AVE .. 48109

Utilities Department
326 E HOOVER AVE 48109

Vera Baits #1
1230 HUBBARD ST 48109

Vera Baits #2
1440 HUBBARD ST 48109

Victor Vaughn Building
1111 CATHERINE ST 48109

Washington Square
202 E WASHINGTON ST .. 48104

West Engineering Building
550 E UNIVERSITY AVE .. 48109

West Quad
541 THOMPSON ST 48109

West Quad Annex
580 UNION DR 48109

Wolverine Towers
3001 S STATE ST 48108

HOSPITALS

Veterans Hosp Ann Arbor
2215 FULLER RD 48105

AUBURN HILLS

APARTMENTS

Westbury
201 N SQUIRREL RD 48326

AVALON BEACH

APARTMENTS

Briarwyck Arms
927 N MACOMB ST 48161

Chestnut Hills
2840 N MONROE ST 48161

Countryside/carriage Mano
1513 STEWART RD 48161

Frenchtown Place
1201 N MACOMB ST 48161

Mable H Kehres
15275 S DIXIE HWY 48161

Village Green
1600 PARK CT 48161

Washington Arms
725 WASHINGTON ST 48161

Woodcraft Sq
800 W 7TH ST 48161

BUILDINGS

Macomb Professional Cente
721 N MACOMB ST 48161

Medical Arts Pl
750 STEWART RD 48161

GOVERNMENT

Monroe Courthouse
106 E 1ST ST 48161

BATTLE CREEK

APARTMENTS

Brookside Rental Office
4201 W DICKMAN RD 49015

Fairlane Apt
701 AVENUE A 49015

BUILDINGS

Comerica Bank Building
25 MICHIGAN AVE W 49017

Great Lakes Fed Building
15 CAPITAL AVE NE 49017

Michigan Bank Building
1 MICHIGAN AVE W 49017

GOVERNMENT

Brown Building
1346 COLUMBIA AVE W .. 49015

Old Kent Bank Building
67 MICHIGAN AVE W 49017

BAY CITY

APARTMENTS

Bay Manor
3465 KIESEL RD 48706

Maloney Manor
210 FITZHUGH ST 48708

BUILDINGS

Allen Medical Building
200 S WENONA ST 48706

Bay City Bank Building
213 CENTER AVE 48708

Davison Building
916 WASHINGTON AVE ... 48708

East Medical Building
2110 16TH ST 48708

Executive Center
1600 CENTER AVE 48708

Phoenix Building
723 WASHINGTON AVE ... 48708

Shearer Building
311 CENTER AVE 48708

GOVERNMENT

Euclid Plaza
503 N EUCLID AVE 48706

BERKLEY

APARTMENTS

Oxford Park Towers
2345 OXFORD RD 48072

BEVERLY HILLS

BUILDINGS

Bingham Center
30100-800 Telegraph Rd .. 48025

BINGHAM FARMS

APARTMENTS

Claymoor
29260 FRANKLIN RD 48034

Franklin Park Towers
27000-600 FRANKLIN RD   48034

Heatherwood
22800 CIVIC CENTER DR 48034

Leslie Towers
25701 W 12 MILE RD 48034

Mc Donnell Towers
24300 CIVIC CENTER DR 48034

Mc Donnell Towers
24400 CIVIC CENTER DR 48034

Southfield Towers East
20855 LAHSER RD 48034

Southfield Towers North
20965 LAHSER RD 48034

Southfield Towers West
20925 LAHSER RD 48034

Willow Park
28675 FRANKLIN RD 48034

BUILDINGS

American Center Building
27777 FRANKLIN RD 48034

Claymoor
29260 FRANKLIN RD 48034

Essex Centre
28400 Northwestern Hwy .. 48034

Farmbrook Medical Two
29877 TELEGRAPH RD ... 48034

First Center Complex
26911-957 Northwestern
Hwy 48034

Franklin Center
29100 Northwestern Hwy .. 48034

Galleria Officentre
200-400 Galleria Officentre 48034

Galleria Officentre
27800 Northwestern Hwy .. 48034

Galleria Officentre
100 Galleria Officentre 48034

Giffels
25200 TELEGRAPH RD ... 48034

La Mirage Shoppes
29555 Northwestern Hwy .. 48034

Lahser Center
26400 LAHSER RD 48034

Manufacturers Southfield
29201 TELEGRAPH RD ... 48034

Michigan Life
28333 TELEGRAPH RD ... 48034

Omni Officentre
26877 Northwestern Hwy .. 48034

One Northwestern Plaza
28411 Northwestern Hwy .. 48034

Onyx Plaza
29777 TELEGRAPH RD ... 48034

Raleigh Officentre
25330 TELEGRAPH RD ... 48034

Silver Triangle
25505 W 12 MILE RD 48034

Solomon
28588 Northwestern Hwy .. 48034

Victor Center
27400 Northwestern Hwy .. 48034

Westview Park
26100 AMERICAN DR 48034

Westview Park
26200 AMERICAN DR 48034

BLOOMFIELD HILLS

APARTMENTS

Four Seasons
2945 S WOODWARD AVE 48304

Whethersfield
5720-780 Whethersfield Ln 48301

Willoway
801 W LONG LAKE RD 48302

BUILDINGS

Bloomfield Medical Center
1575 S WOODWARD AVE 48302

Bloomfield Medical Vlg
6405 TELEGRAPH RD 48301

Mail Boxes Etc
6632 TELEGRAPH RD 48301

CANTON

APARTMENTS

Fairway Club
40472 TAMARACK DR 48188

CHESTERFIELD

APARTMENTS

New Baltimore Towers
51140 HOOKER ST 48047

Presbyterian Village
33875 KIELY DR 48047

COMMERCE

APARTMENTS

Walled Lake Villa
1035 Walled Lake Villa Dr . 48390

DEARBORN

APARTMENTS

Dearborn Towers
22700 GARRISON ST 48124

Hubbard Manor East
5500 CALHOUN ST 48126

Kennedy Plaza
5111 BINGHAM STREET .. 48126

Morley Manor
21800 MORLEY AVE 48124

Sisson Manor
1515 MASON ST 48124

BUILDINGS

Budny
4917 SCHAEFER RD 48126

Fairlane Towncenter
18900 MICHIGAN AVE 48126

Garrison Place E
19855 OUTER DR 48124

Garrison Place W
19855 OUTER DR 48124

Park Lane Towers
4 PARKLANE BLVD 48126

Parklane Office Center
6 PARKLANE BLVD 48126

Parklane Tower East
1 PARKLANE BLVD 48126

Parklane Tower West
3 PARKLANE BLVD 48126

Village Plaza
23400 MICHIGAN AVE 48124

HOTELS

The Ritz Carlton Hotel
300 TOWN CENTER DR .. 48126

DETROIT

APARTMENTS

1300 Lafayette
1300 E LAFAYETTE ST 48207

Chateau Frontenac
10410 E JEFFERSON AVE 48214

Jeffersonian
9000 E JEFFERSON AVE . 48214

Lafayette Townhouses
1321 NICOLET PL 48207

Leland House
400 BAGLEY ST 48226

Millender Center
555 BRUSH ST 48226

Riverfront Park Tower
300 RIVERFRONT DR 48226

Townhouse
1511 1ST ST 48226

Trolley Plaza
1431 WASHINGTON BLVD 48226

Whittier Towers
415 BURNS DR 48214

BUILDINGS

Book
1249 WASHINGTON BLVD 48226

Buhl
535 GRISWOLD ST 48226

Cadillac Square
111 CADILLAC SQ. 48226

Cadillac Tower
65 CADILLAC SQ 48226

City County Building
2 WOODWARD AVE 48226

Comerica Bank Building
211 W FORT ST 48226
David Stott
1150 GRISWOLD ST 48226

David Whitney
1553 WOODWARD AVE ... 48226

Federal
231 W LAFAYETTE BLVD . 48226

First Federal
1001 WOODWARD AVE ... 48226

First National Building
660 WOODWARD AVE 48226

Ford Building
615 GRISWOLD ST 48226

Free Press
321 W LAFAYETTE BLVD . 48226

General Motors Building
3044 W GRAND BLVD 48202

Guardian
500 GRISWOLD ST 48226

John Maden
150 JEFFERSON ST. 48226

Lafayette
149 MICHIGAN AVE 48226

Mcnamara Building
477 MICHIGAN AVE 48226

Metropolitan
33 JOHN R ST 48226

Michigan
220 BAGLEY ST 48226

Michigan Mutual
28 W ADAMS AVE 48226

Michigan Plaza
1200 6TH ST 48226

Murphy Building
155 W CONGRESS ST 48226

New Center
7430 2ND AVE 48202

New Center One Building
3031 W GRAND BLVD 48202

One Kennedy Square
719 GRISWOLD ST 48226

Penobscot Building
645 GRISWOLD ST 48226

Renaissance Tower 100
404 E JEFFERSON AVE ... 48243

Renaissance Tower 200
434 E JEFFERSON AVE ... 48243

Renaissance Tower 300
424 E JEFFERSON AVE ... 48243

Renaissance Tower 400
414 E JEFFERSON AVE ... 48243

State Of Michigan
7310 WOODWARD AVE ... 48202

Veterans Memorial
151 W JEFFERSON AVE .. 48226

Water Board Building
735 RANDOLPH ST 48226

Wayne County
600 RANDOLPH ST 48226

HOTELS

Holiday Inn
5801 SOUTHFIELD FWY . 48228

Hotel Pontchartrain
2 WASHINGTON BLVD 48226

Residence Inn
5777 SOUTHFIELD ST. 48228

ELOISE

APARTMENTS

Bonnie-venoy
7005 BONNIE DR 48185

Capri Terrace Apt
31471 CAPRI TER 48185

Scotsdale Circle
37650 DALE DR 48185

The Landings
7051 LAKEVIEW BLVD 48185

Waynewood
6737 N WAYNE RD 48185

Western Hills
320 HICKORY LN 48185

Westland Towers
6501 YALE ST 48185

Woodland Villa
7310 DREW CIR 48185

BUILDINGS

Westland Shopping Center
35000 WARREN RD 48185

FARMINGTON

APARTMENTS

Cardinal Retirement Vlg
36550 GRAND RIVER AVE 48335

Carrington Place Apt
35250 FREEDOM RD 48335

Farmington Oaks Apt
21900 FARMINGTON RD . 48336

Farmington Place
32900 GRAND RIVER AVE 48336

Fox Point Townhouse
26375 HALSTED RD 48331

Halsted Place
29451 HALSTED RD 48331

BUILDINGS

Farmington Square Prof
32910 W 13 MILE RD 48334

North Valley Office Ctr
30600 Northwestern Hwy .. 48334

North Valley Office Ctr
30500 Northwestern Hwy .. 48334

Quakertown Medical Arts
32905 W 12 MILE RD 48334

FLINT

BUILDINGS

Ametech Building
352 S SAGINAW ST 48502

Atwood Building
436 S SAGINAW ST 48502

Citizens Banking Ctr
328 S SAGINAW ST 48502

Dryden Building
601 S SAGINAW ST 48502

Genesee Towers
120 E 1ST ST 48502

Mott Foundation Building
503 S SAGINAW ST 48502

North Bank Center Annex
416 N SAGINAW ST 48502

North Bank Center North
432 N SAGINAW ST 48502

North Bank Center South
400 N SAGINAW ST 48502

Paterson Building
653 S SAGINAW ST 48502

Phoenix Building
801 S SAGINAW ST 48502

GOVERNMENT

City Hall
1101 S SAGINAW ST 48502

County Admin Building
1101 BEACH ST 48502

Court House
900 S SAGINAW ST 48502

Federal Building
600 CHURCH ST 48502

Floyd Mccree Human Svcs
630 S SAGINAW ST 48502

Mcavinchey Building
919 BEACH ST 48502

GRAND RAPIDS

APARTMENTS

Morton House
55 IONIA AVE NW 49503

Oakwood Manor
547 CHERRY ST SE 49503

Olds Manor
201 MICHIGAN ST NW 49503

BUILDINGS

50 Monroe Place
50 MONROE AVE NW 49503

Blvd Professional Center
26 SHELDON BLVD SE 49503

Calder Plaza Building
250 MONROE AVE NW 49503

Campau Sq Pz Bd
99 MONROE AVE NW 49503

College Medical Building
50 COLLEGE AVE SE 49503

Commerce Building
5 LYON ST NW 49503

Federal Square Building
29 PEARL ST NW 49503

Frey Building
300 OTTAWA AVE NW 49503

Furniture Co Building
82 IONIA AVE NW 49503

Grand Center
245 MONROE AVE NW 49503

Grand Plaza Place
220 LYON ST NW 49503

Ledyard Building
125 OTTAWA AVE NW 49503

Loraine Building
124 E FULTON ST 49503

Mckay Tower
146 Monroe Center St NW 49503

Metrobanc Building
201 MONROE AVE NW 49503

Michigan Con Gas Co Building
200 MONROE AVE NW 49503

Michigan National Bank Building
77 MONROE CENTER ST NW ...
.... 49503

Michigan St Centre
426 MICHIGAN ST NE 49503

Mutual Home Building
171 MONROE AVE NW 49503

NBD Building
200 OTTAWA AVE NW 49503

OKB Building
111 LYON ST NW 49503

Old Town River Front Building
248 LOUIS CAMPAU PROMENADE
NW 49503

Peoples Building
60 Monroe Center St NW .. 49503

Riverfront Plaza Building
55 CAMPAU AVE NW 49503

Riverview Center Towers
678 FRONT AVE NW 49504

St Marys Medical Building
260 JEFFERSON AVE SE   49503

The Trade Center
50 LOUIS ST NW 49503

Towers Medical Building
21 MICHIGAN ST NE 49503

Trust Building
40 PEARL ST NW 49503

Two Fountain Place
2 FOUNTAIN ST NE 49503

Waters Building
161 OTTAWA AVE NW 49503

GOVERNMENT

City County Building
300 MONROE AVE NW 49503

Federal Building
110 MICHIGAN ST NW 49503

Hall Of Justice Building
333 MONROE AVE NW 49503

State Office Building
350 OTTAWA AVE NW 49503

HOSPITALS

Kent Oaks Hospital
1330 BRADFORD ST NE . 49503

Mary Free Bed Hospital
235 WEALTHY ST SE 49503

Michigan Vets Facility
3000 MONROE AVE NE ... 49505

HARRISON TOWNSHIP

APARTMENTS

Harbor Club
36000 JEFFERSON AVE .. 48045

Metro Tower
26450 CROCKER BLVD ... 48045

Saint George Tower
42250 HAYES RD 48038

HOLLAND

APARTMENTS

Greenbriar Apt
121 S WAVERLY RD 49423

Stonegate Apt
791 E 16TH ST 49423

Wildwood Creek Manor
431 DIEKEMA AVE 49423

HOWELL

GOVERNMENT

County Court House
200 E GRAND RIVER AVE 48843

JACKSON

BUILDINGS

Jackson County Tower
120 W MICHIGAN AVE 49201

GOVERNMENT

County
312 S JACKSON ST 49201

Federal Building
200 OTSEGO AVE 49201

Jackson State Office
301 E LOUIS GLICK HWY   49201

KALAMAZOO

APARTMENTS

Alpine Apt
4307 DUKE ST 49008

Crosstown Pky Apt
550 W CROSSTOWN PKY 49008

Kilgore Downs Apt
722 W KILGORE RD 49008

Milwood Apt
1401 BANBURY RD 49001

Pepper Tree Apt
1842 S 11TH ST 49009

Regency Sq Apt
611 REGENCY SQ 49008

Seville Apt
5050 BECKLEY DR 49009

Sprucetree Apt
5419 MEREDITH DR 49002

Willow Creek Apt
3721 GREENLEAF CIR 49008

BUILDINGS

Crossroads Mall
6650 S WESTNEDGE AVE 49002

North Professional Building
1717 SHAFFER ST 49001

South Professional Building
1631 GULL RD 49001

GOVERNMENT

Federal Building
410 W MICHIGAN AVE 49007

Comerica Building
151 S ROSE ST 49007

Kalamazoo Building
107 W MICHIGAN AVE 49007

Kalamazoo Center
100 W MICHIGAN AVE 49007

Market Square
309 WASHINGTON SQ N . 48933

Medical Arts
1322 E MICHIGAN AVE 48912

Medical Center West
701 N LOGAN ST 48915

Medical Dental Building
2909 E Grand River Ave ... 48912

Michigan Dental
230 WASHINGTON SQ N . 48933

Michigan National Tower
124 W ALLEGAN ST 48933

One Michigan Ave
120 WASHINGTON SQ N . 48933

State Emp Credit Union
501 S CAPITOL AVE 48933

GOVERNMENT

City Hall
124 W MICHIGAN AVE 48933

City Hall Annex
119 WASHINGTON SQ N . 48933

County Building
303 W KALAMAZOO ST ... 48933

Federal Building
315 W ALLEGAN ST 48933

HOTELS

Holiday Inn
7501 W SAGINAW HWY .. 48917

LATHRUP VILLAGE

BUILDINGS

Congress Building
30555 SOUTHFIELD RD .. 48076

Travelers Tower I
26555 EVERGREEN RD .. 48076

Travelers Tower Ii
26533 EVERGREEN RD .. 48076

LIVONIA

APARTMENTS

Franklin Square
28940 LANCASTER ST 48154

BUILDINGS

Brashear Towers
17841 N Laurel Park Dr 48152

Brentwood Medical Center
28711 8 MILE RD 48152

Cadillac Motor
12000 MIDDLEBELT RD .. 48150

Chevrolet Motor
13000 ECKLES RD 48150

Ford Motor
29500 PLYMOUTH RD 48150

Livonia Pavilion East
29200 VASSAR ST 48152

Wonderland Mall
29859 PLYMOUTH RD 48150

HOSPITALS

Oakcreek Medical
29200 Schoolcraft Rd 48150

MADISON HEIGHTS

APARTMENTS

Concord Towers
32600 CONCORD DR 48071

Madison Heights Co-op
500 E IRVING AVE 48071

Madison Towers
27777 DEQUINDRE RD ... 48071

Solberg Towers
27787 DEQUINDRE RD ... 48071

MIDLAND

APARTMENTS

Tek Circle Apts
2801 RONAN ST 48642

Woodland Place Apt
4512 N SAGINAW RD 48640

GOVERNMENT

City Hall
333 W ELLSWORTH ST ... 48640

County Building
220 W ELLSWORTH ST ... 48640

MOUNT CLEMENS

APARTMENTS

Clemens Tower
50 CHURCH ST 48043

Park Place Towers
34 PARK ST 48043

BUILDINGS

Macomb Daily Building
67 CASS AVE 48043

Town Square
10 S GRATIOT AVE 48043

GOVERNMENT

City Of Mt Clemens
1 CROCKER BLVD 48043

County Of Macomb
10 N GRATIOT AVE 48043

MUSKEGON

APARTMENTS

Bayview Towers
864 SPRING ST 49442

Columbia Court
65 E COLUMBIA AVE 49444

Hartford Terrace
1080 TERRACE ST 49442

Jefferson Towers
1077 JEFFERSON ST 49440

Pine Grove Manor
1764 E APPLE AVE 49442

BUILDINGS

Comerica Bank Building
161 MUSKEGON MALL 49440

Federal Savings & Loan
880 1ST ST 49440

Frauenthal Building
425 W WESTERN AVE 49440

Lumbermans Bank
221 W WEBSTER AVE 49440

Medical Arts Center
315 W CLAY AVE 49440

Michigan Theatre
425 W WESTERN AVE 49440

Mid Town
1095 3RD ST 49441

Terrace Plaza
250 MORRIS AVE 49440

GOVERNMENT

County Building
990 TERRACE ST 49442

Federal Building
800 1ST ST 49440

ORCHARD LAKE

BUILDINGS

Croswinds Mall
4301 ORCHARD LAKE RD 48323

PONTIAC

APARTMENTS

Carriage Circle Apt
255 Carriage Circle Dr 48342

Fox Point
900 MARTIN LUTHER KING JR
BLVD S 48341

Lakehaven Manor
1915 BALDWIN AVE 48340

Phoenix Center
351 WIDE TRACK DR E ... 48342

Presbyterian Village
420 S OPDYKE RD 48341

Woodland Heights
120 N EDITH ST 48342

BUILDINGS

NBD
28 N SAGINAW ST 48342

Pontiac Place
140 S SAGINAW ST 48342

Riker Building
35 W HURON ST 48342

St Joseph Mercy Medical
888 WOODWARD AVE 48341

GOVERNMENT

Childrens Village
1200 N TELEGRAPH RD . 48341

County Executive Admin
1200 N TELEGRAPH RD . 48341

O C Board Of Commisioners
1200 N TELEGRAPH RD . 48341

O C Central Services Admn
1200 N TELEGRAPH RD . 48341

O C Friend Of The Court
1200 N TELEGRAPH RD . 48341

O C Register Of Deeds
1200 N TELEGRAPH RD . 48341

Oak County Circuit Court
1200 N TELEGRAPH RD . 48341

Oak County Jury Commission
1200 N TELEGRAPH RD . 48341

Oak County Probation Dept
1200 N TELEGRAPH RD . 48341

Oakland County Court Admin
1200 N TELEGRAPH RD . 48341

Oakland County Public Svcs
1200 N TELEGRAPH RD . 48341

Oakland County Clerk
1200 N TELEGRAPH RD . 48341

Oakland County Executive
1200 N TELEGRAPH RD . 48341

Oakland County Probate Ct
1200 N TELEGRAPH RD . 48341

Oakland County Treasurer
1200 N TELEGRAPH RD . 48341

Oakland Cty Auditing Dept
1200 N TELEGRAPH RD . 48341

Oakland Cty Computer Svcs
1200 N TELEGRAPH RD . 48341

Veteran Services
1200 N TELEGRAPH RD . 48341

PORT HURON

APARTMENTS

Grandview Towers
1016 7TH ST 48060

Port Haven Manor
3900 ASPEN DR 48060

BUILDINGS

Court Of Flags Mall
2887 KRAFFT RD 48060

Mich National Bank
800 MILITARY ST 48060

GOVERNMENT

City Of Port Huron
100 MCMORRAN BLVD ... 48060

County Of St Clair
201 MCMORRAN BLVD ... 48060

RAWSONVILLE

APARTMENTS

Belmont American
311 JARVIS ST 48197

Camelot
2982 WASHTENAW RD ... 48197

Chateau Vert East
1459 E Chateau Vert St 48197

Chidester Pl
330 CHIDESTER ST 48197

Golfside
2705 GOLFSIDE DR 48197

Hunt Club
4403 HUNT CLUB DR 48197

Huron River Dr
1419 GREGORY ST 48197

Schooner Cove
5050 BOSUNS WAY 48197

Shorebridge Tower
5900 BRIDGE RD 48197

Town Center Place
401 W MICHIGAN AVE 48197

Triangle West
1926 WASHTENAW RD ... 48197

BUILDINGS

Barron
4870 W CLARK RD 48197

Medical Arts Washtenaw
3075 W CLARK RD 48197

Ypsilanti City Hall
1 S HURON ST 48197

HOSPITALS

St Joseph Mercy Hospital
5301 E HURON RIVER DR 48197

RIVERVIEW

APARTMENTS

Edinger
114 OAK ST 48192

Green Trees
19620 FORT ST 48192

Huntington House S
17400 FORT ST 48192

Islandview Manor
12621 HALE ST 48192

King Forest
19300 FORT ST 48192

Riverview Co Op
13333 Pennsylvania Ave ... 48192

Towers
20 CHESTNUT ST 48192

Wyandotte Co Op
2455 BIDDLE ST 48192

GOVERNMENT

Wyandotte City Hall
3131 BIDDLE ST 48192

ROCHESTER

APARTMENTS

Avon Towers
435 S LIVERNOIS RD 48307

Danish Village
2566 WALTON BLVD 48309

Waltonwood Apt
3250 WALTON BLVD 48309

ROYAL OAK

APARTMENTS

Barton Towers Co-op
333 N TROY ST 48067

Royal Oak Manor
606 S WILLIAMS ST 48067

BUILDINGS

4th Street Office Plaza
301 W 4TH ST 48067

First Of America
3101 N WOODWARD AVE 48073

Washington Square Plaza
306 S WASHINGTON AVE 48067

Wm Beaumont Medical
3535 W 13 MILE RD 48073

SAGINAW

APARTMENTS

Bancroft Apartments
107 S WASHINGTON AVE 48607

Bay Pointe Apartments
3051 Shattuck Arms Blvd .. 48603

Cabaret Apts
3835-985 Cabaret Trl W 48603

Castle Way Apts
5875 WEISS ST 48603

Davenport Manor
2811 DAVENPORT AVE 48602

Elmwood Manor
2814 E GENESEE AVE 48601

Fontaine Apts
4891 FONTAINE BLVD 48603

Fox Glen Apartments
6160 FOX GLEN DR 48603

Green Acres Apt
4520 COLONIAL DR 48603

Hidden Hollow Apts
1800 BEACON DR 48602

Jefferson Apartments
505 MILLARD ST 48607

Liberty Square
280 N COLONY DR 48603

Maplewood Manor
535 S WARREN AVE 48607

New Amadore Apartments
518 THOMPSON ST 48607

Pinewood Manor
2715 S JEFFERSON AVE . 48601

Poplars
4444 STATE ST 48603

Rolling Green Apts
2127 N CENTER RD 48603

Rosien Towers
310 S HARRISON ST 48602

Waterside Apts
4180 Harbour Towne Dr 48603

Westchester Village
4055 W MICHIGAN AVE ... 48603

BUILDINGS

Commerce Center
301 E GENESEE AVE 48607

International Mall
310 JOHNSON ST 48607

Medical Arts One
4705 Towne Centre Rd 48604

Plaza North
4800 Fashion Square Blvd .. 48604

Professional Art Building A
5090 STATE ST 48603

Second National Bank Building
101 N WASHINGTON AVE 48607

GOVERNMENT

Federal Building
100 S WARREN AVE 48607

State Office Building
411 E GENESEE AVE 48607

SAINT CLAIR

APARTMENTS

Senior Citizens Complex
400 S 3RD ST 48079

SHELBY TOWNSHIP

APARTMENTS

Spring Hill
4200 W UTICA RD 48317

SOUTHFIELD

APARTMENTS

5000 Prudential Town Ctr
5000 TOWN CTR 48075

Carlyle Towers
23300 PROVIDENCE DR . 48075

Charter House
16300 W 9 MILE RD 48075

Embassy Towers
15800 PROVIDENCE DR . 48075

Highland Towers
25225 GREENFIELD RD .. 48075

Meadowcrest Apt
24200 LATHRUP BLVD 48075

North Park Place
16400 N PARK DR 48075

North Park Tower
16500 N PARK DR 48075

BUILDINGS

2000 Prudential Town Ctr
2000 TOWN CTR 48075

3000 Prudential Town Ctr
3000 TOWN CTR 48075

4000 Prudential Town Ctr
4000 TOWN CTR 48075

Advance Building
23077 GREENFIELD RD .. 48075

American Office Park
19675 W 10 MILE RD 48075

American Office Park
24700 Northwestern Hwy .. 48075

American Office Park
24800 Northwestern Hwy .. 48075

Clausen
16000 W 9 MILE RD 48075

Clausen
23100 PROVIDENCE DR . 48075

Honeywell Center
17515 W 9 MILE RD 48075

Horizon Heritage Plaza
24901 Northwestern Hwy .. 48075

Mt Vernon Quadrangle
23777 GREENFIELD RD .. 48075

North Park Plaza
17117 W 9 MILE RD 48075

Northland Center
21500 Northwestern Hwy .. 48075

Northland Medical
20905 GREENFIELD RD .. 48075

Northland Towers East
15565 NORTHLAND DR E 48075

Northland Towers West
15565 Northland Dr W 48075

One Northland Dr
16900 W 8 MILE RD 48075

One Northland Plaza
20755 GREENFIELD RD .. 48075

Pinewood Plaza
22255 GREENFIELD RD .. 48075

Providence Medical
22250 PROVIDENCE DR . 48075

Southfield Medical
15901 W 9 MILE RD 48075

Tower 14
21700 Northwestern Hwy .. 48075

Town Center
1000 TOWN CTR 48075

Trowell
24681 Northwestern Hwy .. 48075

SOUTHGATE

APARTMENTS

Overbrook
14905 OVERBROOK DR .. 48195

Southgate Seniors
11255 ALLEN RD 48195

STERLING HEIGHTS

APARTMENTS

American House Sr Citizen
11255 15 MILE RD 48312

Birchcrest Manor Apt
41255 POND VIEW DR 48314

Cambridge House Apt
8301 16 1/2 MILE RD 48312

Schoenherr Towers
37500 SCHOENHERR RD 48312

Shore Haven Manor
14560 LAKESIDE CIR 48313

Shoreline
15000 SHORELINE DR 48313

Sterling Meadows Apt
33433 SCHOENHERR RD 48312

BUILDINGS

Sterling Town Center
12900 HALL RD 48313

TROY

APARTMENTS

Oakland Park Towers
920 JOHN R RD 48083

Oakland Park Towers
930 JOHN R RD 48083

BUILDINGS

Ameritech Publishing
100 E BIG BEAVER RD 48083

Beaumont Medical
44199 DEQUINDRE RD ... 48098

City Center
888 W BIG BEAVER RD ... 48084

Continental Plaza
2701 TROY CENTER DR . 48084

Drummer
2075 W BIG BEAVER RD . 48084

Huntington Bank Building
801 W BIG BEAVER RD ... 48084

Liberty Center
50 W BIG BEAVER RD 48084

Liberty Center
100 W BIG BEAVER RD ... 48084

Northfield Financial Building
900 TOWER DR 48098

Troy Place
3001 W BIG BEAVER RD . 48084

Two Northfield Plaza
5700 CROOKS RD 48098

Wilshire Plaza
901 WILSHIRE DR 48084

WARREN

APARTMENTS

Centerline Gardens
28490 MOUND RD 48092

Parkview Towers
27200 PARKVIEW BLVD .. 48092

Stillwell Manor
26600 BURG RD 48089

Ukranian Retirement Villa
26377 RYAN RD 48091

BUILDINGS

Comerica
30500 VAN DYKE AVE 48093

GOVERNMENT

City Of Warren
29500 VAN DYKE AVE 48093

Macomb County Sw Center
29600 S Civic Center Blvd 48093

HOTELS

Homewood Suite Hotel
30180 N Civic Center Blvd 48093

Residence Inn
30120 N Civic Center Blvd 48093

WATERFORD

APARTMENTS

American Heritage Apt
3295 WATKINS LAKE RD . 48328

Lakeland Place
2700 Elizabeth Lake Rd 48328

BUILDINGS

Summit Place Mall
315 N TELEGRAPH RD ... 48328

WAYNE

APARTMENTS

Parkview Terrace
34420 SIMS ST 48184

Wayne Towers
35200 SIMS ST 48184

Westchester Tower
35700 MICHIGAN ST. 48184

HOTELS

Cadillac
32561 MICHIGAN AVE 48184

WEST BLOOMFIELD

APARTMENTS

Fleishman Residence
6710 W MAPLE RD 48322

WILLOW RUN

APARTMENTS

Clark East Towers
1550 E CLARK RD 48198

Cliffs On The Point
812 CLIFFS DR 48198

Green Terrace
772 GREEN RD 48198

Huron View West
831 GREEN RD 48198

Lake In The Woods
2500 Lake In The Woods .. 48198

Sunnyside
1425 LEFORGE RD 48198

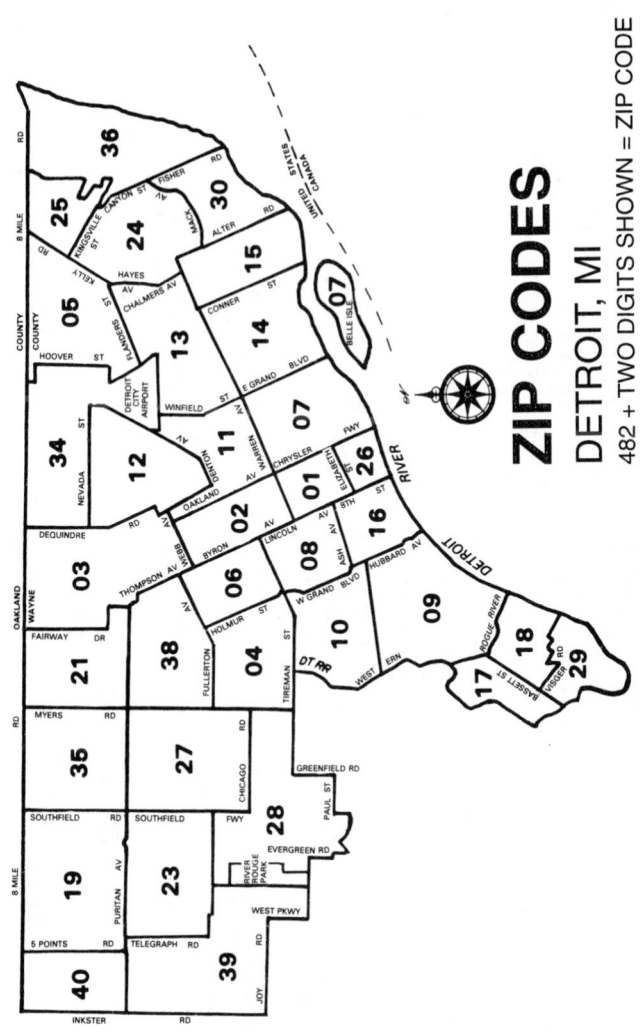

MINNESOTA
Abbreviation MN

Abmps (Minneapolis) 55472
Ada 56510
Adams 55909
Adolph 55701
Adrian 56110
Afton 55001
Agder (Blackduck) 56663
Agram (Pierz) 56364
Ah Gwah Ching 56430
Aitkin 56431
Akeley 56433
Alango (Angora) 55703
Alaska (Puposky) 56667
Albany 56307
Albert Lea 56007
Alberta 56207
Albertville 55301
Alborn 55702
Alden 56009
Aldrich 56434
Alexandria 56308
Alida (Shevlin) 56676
Almelund 55002
Almora (Henning) 56551
Alpha 56111
Altura 55910
Alvarado 56710
Alvwood (Blackduck) 56630
Amboy 56010
Amiret 56112
Amor (Battle Lake) 56515
Andover (Anoka) 55304
Andyville (Austin) 55912
Angle Inlet 56711
Angora 55703
Angus 56712
Ann Lake (Ogilvie) 56358
Annandale 55302
Anoka 55303-304
   Andover 55304
   Ham Lake 55304
   Ramsey 55303
   Soderville 55304
Ansel (Brainerd) 56401
Antlers Park (Lakeville) 55044
Apple Valley (Saint Paul) ... 55124
Appleton 56208
Arago (Park Rapids) 56470
Arco 56113
Arcturus (Taconite) 55786
Arden Hills (Saint Paul) 55112
Ardenhurst (Northome) 56661
Arendahl (Peterson) 55962
Argonne (Lakeville) 55044
Argyle 56713
Arlington 55307
Arnesen (Roosevelt) 56673
Arrowhead (Brookston) 55711
Ash Lake (Orr) 55771
Ashby 56309
Ashley (Sauk Centre) 56378
Askov 55704
Aslo (Askov) 55704
Atkinson (Carlton) 55718
Atwater 56209
Audubon 56511
Ault (Brimson) 55602
Aure (Pinewood) 56664

Aurora 55705, 55917
   Palo 55705
   Pineville 55705
   White 55705
Austin 55912
Automba (Kettle River) 55757
Averill (Glyndon) 56547
Avoca 56114
Avon 56310
Babbitt 55706
Backus 56435
Badger 56714
Badoura (Akeley) 56433
Bagley 56621
Baker 56513
Balaton 56115
Balkan (Chisholm) 55719
Ball Bluff (Jacobson) 55752
Balsam (Tamarack) 55787
Bangor (Sedan) 56380
Bar Code (Saint Paul) 55172
Barclay (Pine River) 56474
Barnesville 56514
Barnum 55707
Barrett 56311
Barrows (Brainerd) 56401
Barry 56210
Barsness (Starbuck) 56381
Bartlett (Hewitt) 56453
Bass Brook (Cohasset) 55721
Bassett (Brimson) 55602
Basswood (Richville) 56576
Battle (Saum) 56674
Battle Lake 56515
Battle River (Blackduck) 56630
Baudette 56623
Baxter 56401, 56425
   (Brainerd)
   Brainerd 56425
Bay Lake (Deerwood) 56444
Bayport 55003
Baytown (Bayport) 55003
Bayview (Onamia) 56359
Bear Creek (Shevlin) 56676
Bear River (Cook) 55723
Beardsley 56211
Bearville (Togo) 55788
Beaulieu (Mahnomen) 56557
Beaver Bay 55601
Beaver Creek 56116
Becida (Solway) 56678
Becker 55308
Bejou 56516
Belgrade 56312
Belle Plaine 56011
Bellevue (Royalton) 56373
Bellingham 56212
Beltrami 56517
Belview 56214
Bemidji 56601, 56619
   Grant Valley 56601
   Jones 56601
   Northern 56601
   Nymore 56601
   Port Hope 56601
   Sugar Bush 56601
   Ten Lake 56601
   Turtle River 56601
Bena 56626, 56641
Benedict 56436
Bennettville (Aitkin) 56431

Bennington 55936
   (Grand Meadow)
Benson 56215
Bergville (Northome) 56661
Berne (West Concord) 55985
Berner (Gonvick) 56644
Beroun 55004, 55063
Bertha 56437
Beseman (Wright) 55798
Bethany (Altura) 55910
Bethel 55005
Beulah (Outing) 56662
Big Falls 56627
Big Lake 55309
Bigelow 56117
Bigfork 56628
Bingham Lake 56118
Birch (Blackduck) 56630
Birch Beach (Williams) 56686
Birch Lake (Hackensack) .. 56452
Birchdale 56336, 56629
   (Grey Eagle)
   Indus 56629
   Manitou 56629
Birchwood (Saint Paul) 55110
Bird Island 55310
Biwabik 55708
Bixby (Blooming Prairie) ... 55917
Black River (Loman) 56654
Blackberry (Grand Rapids) 55744
Blackduck 56630, 56663
   Agder 56663
   Alvwood 56630
   Battle River 56630
   Birch 56630
   Cormant 56630
   Funkley 56630
   Hornet 56630
   Langor 56630
   Moose Park 56630
   Pennington 56663
   Quiring 56630
   Summit 56630
Blackhoof (Carlton) 55718
Blaine 55014, 55434, 55449
   (Circle Pines)
Blind Lake (Pine River) 56474
Blomkest 56216
Blooming Prairie 55917
Bloomington 55420, 55425
   .... 55431, 55435, 55437-439
   (Minneapolis)
Blue Earth 56013
Blue Grass (Sebeka) 56477
Blue Mounds (Starbuck) ... 56381
Blueberry (Menahga) 56464
Bluffton 56518
Bock 56313
Bogus Brook (Pease) 56363
Bombay (Kenyon) 55946
Bonnie Glen 55013
   (Chisago City)
Boray (Bovey) 55709
Border (Baudette) 56623
Borup 56519
Bovey 55709
Bowlus 56314
Bowstring 56631
Boy Lake (Longville) 56655
Boy River 56632
Boyd 56218

Bradbury (Onamia) 56359
Braham 55006
Brainerd 56401
.... 56425, 56456
  Ansel 56401
  Barrows 56401
  Baxter 56401
  Bull Moose 56401
  Bungo 56401
  Crow Wing 56401
  Daggett Brook 56401
  East Gull Lake 56401
  Fairview 56401
  Home Brook 56401
  Lake Shore 56401
  Long Lake 56401
  Nokay Lake 56401
  Pine Center 56401
  Platte Lake 56401
  Poplar 56401
Branch (North Branch) 55056
Brandon 56315
Bratsberg (Rushford) 55971
Breckenridge 56520
Breezy Point 56472
  (Pequot Lakes)
Breitung (Tower) 55790
Bremen (Finlayson) 55735
Brennyville (Foley) 56329
Brevator (Saginaw) 55779
Brevik (Longville) 56655
Brewster 56119
Bricelyn 56014
Brimson 55602
Britt55710
Brook Park 55007
Brooklyn (Hibbing) 55746
Brooklyn Center 55428-430
.... 55443-444
  (Minneapolis)
Brooklyn Park 55445
  (Minneapolis)
Brooks 56715
Brookston 55711
Brooten 56316
Browerville 56438
Browns Valley 56219
Brownsdale 55918
Brownsville 55919
Brownton 55312
Bruce (Swanville) 56382
Bruno 55712
Brunswick (Mora) 55051
Brushvale (Breckenridge) . 56520
Buckman 56317
Buffalo 55313
Buffalo Lake 55314
Buh (Pierz) 56364
Buhl 55713
Bull Moose (Brainerd) 56401
Bungo (Brainerd) 56401
Burnett (Culver) 55727
Burnsville 55306, 55337
  Savage 55306
Burtrum 56318
Butler (New York Mills) ... 56567
Butterfield 56120
Buyck (Orr) 55771
Byron 55920
Caledonia 55921
Callaway 56521

Calumet 55716
Cambridge 55008
Campbell 56522
Canby 56220
Canisteo (Kasson) 55944
Cannon Falls 55009
Canton 55922
Canyon 55717, 55724
  Lake Nichols 55717
  Northland 55717
  Shaw 55717
Carimona (Preston) 55965
Carlisle (Fergus Falls) 56537
Carlos 56319
Carlton 55718
Carp (Baudette) 56623
Carpenter (Togo) 55788
Carver 55315
Cass Lake 56633
Castle Danger 55616
  (Two Harbors)
Castle Rock 55010
Cedar 55011
Cedar East Bethel (Cedar) . 55011
Cedar Mills (Hutchinson) ... 55350
Cedar Valley (Floodwood) . 55736
Celina (Togo) 55788
Center City 55002, 55012
  (Almelund)
  Chisago Lake 55012
Centerville (Hugo) 55038
Central Lakes (Eveleth) ... 55734
Ceylon 56121
Champlin 55316
Chandler 56122
Chanhassen 55317
Charles (Saint Charles) ... 55972
Charlesville (Tintah) 56583
Chaska 55318
Chatfield 55923
Chengwatana (Pine City) .. 55063
Cherry Grove 55975
  (Spring Valley)
Chester (Trail) 56684
Chicago Bay (Hovland) 55606
Chisago City 55013
Chisago Lake 55012
  (Center City)
Chisholm 55719
Chokio 56221
Circle Pines 55014
Clara City 56222
Claremont 55924
Clarissa 56440
Clark (Tamarack) 55787
Clarkfield 56223
Clarks Grove 56016
Clear Lake 55319
Clearbrook 56634
Clearwater 55320
Clements 56224
Clementson (Baudette) 56623
Cleveland 56017
Climax 56523
Clinton 56225
Clitherall 56524
Clontarf 56226
Cloquet 55720
Clough (Randall) 56475
Clover 56458, 56652
  (Lake George)

Cohasset 55721
Cokato 55321
Colby (Hoyt Lakes) 55750
Cold Spring 56320
Coleraine 55722
Collegeville 56321
Cologne 55322
Columbia Heights 55421
  (Minneapolis)
Columbus (Cedar) 55011
Colvin (Makinen) 55763
Comfort (Grasston) 55030
Comfrey 56019
Comstock 56525
Concord (West Concord) .. 55985
Conger 56020
Cook 55723, 55788
  Bear River 55723
  Field 55723
  Linden Grove 55723
  Morcom 55723
  Owens 55723
  Togo 55723
Cooley (Nashwauk) 55769
Coon Lake Beach 55092
  (Wyoming)
Coon Rapids 55433, 55448
  (Minneapolis)
Copas (Scandia) 55073
Copley (Bagley) 56621
Corcoran 55311, 55340
.... 55357, 55374
  (Osseo)
Cormant (Blackduck) 56630
Cormorant 56572
  (Pelican Rapids)
Cornish (Jacobson) 55752
Correll 56227
Cosmos 56228
Cottage Grove 55016
Cotton 55724
Cottonwood 56229
Courtland 56021
Cove (Onamia) 56359
Craigville (Effie) 56639
Crane Lake 55725
Croftville (Grand Marais) ... 55604
Cromwell 55726
Crooked Lake (Outing) 56662
Crookston 56716
Crosby 56441
Crosby Beach (Deerwood) . 56444
Crosslake 56442
Crow Wing (Brainerd) 56401
Crystal 55422, 55427-428
  (Minneapolis)
Crystal Bay 55323, 55614
  Orono 55323
Culdrum (Flensburg) 56328
Culver 55727
Cummingsville (Chatfield) . 55923
Currie 56123
Cushing 56443
Cusson (Orr) 55771
Cuyuna (Deerwood) 56444
Cyrus 56323
Daggett Brook (Brainerd) .. 56401
Dailey (Onamia) 56359
Dakota 55925
Dalbo 55017
Dale (Hawley) 56549

Garvin	56132
Gary	56545
Gatzke	56724
Gaylord	55334
Gem Lake (Saint Paul)	55110
Gemmell (Mizpah)	56660
Geneva	56035
Genoa (Eveleth)	55734
Georgetown	56546
Germania (Eagle Bend)	56446
Getty (Sauk Centre)	56378
Gheen	55740
Ghent	56239
Gibbon	55335
Giese (Finlayson)	55735
Gilbert	55741
Gilchrist (Sedan)	56380
Gilman	56333
Gilmanton (Foley)	56329
Glen (Aitkin)	56431
Glencoe	55336
Glendale (Orr)	55771
Glenville	56036
Glenwood	56334
Glory (Aitkin)	56431
Glyndon	56547
Golden Valley	55416
	55422, 55426-427
(Minneapolis)	
Gonvick	56644
Good Hope (Squaw Lake)	56681
Good Thunder	56037
Goodhue	55027
Goodland	55742
Goodridge	56725
Goodview (Winona)	55987
Graceville	56240
Graham (Foley)	56329
Granada	56039
Grand Falls (Big Falls)	56627
Grand Lake (Saginaw)	55779
Grand Marais	55604
Grand Meadow	55936
Grand Portage	55605
Grand Rapids . 55730, 55744-755	
Blackberry	55744
Frohn	55744
Harris	55744
La Prairie	55744
Spang	55744
Trout Lake	55744
Wabana	55744
Grandy	55029
Granger	55937
Granite Falls	56241
Granite Ledge (Foley)	56329
Grant Township	55115
(Saint Paul)	
Grant Valley (Bemidji)	56601
Grass Lake	55006, 55030
(Braham)	
Grasston	55030, 55036
Comfort	55030
Grass Lake	55030
Grattan (Northome)	56661
Greaney (Gheen)	55740
Great Scott (Buhl)	55713
Green Isle	55338
Greenbush	56726
Greenfield	55357, 55373
(Loretto)	

Greenleafton (Preston)	55965
Greenwald	56335
Greenway (Marble)	55764
Greenwood	55331, 56634
(Excelsior)	
Grey Cloud Island	55071
(Saint Paul Park)	
Grey Eagle	56336
Groningen (Sandstone)	55072
Grove (Greenwald)	56335
Grove City	56243
Grove Lake (Glenwood)	56334
Grygla	56727
Gully	56646
Guthrie (Laporte)	56461
Hackensack	56452
Hackett (Baudette)	56623
Hadley	56133
Hagali (Hines)	56647
Halden (Floodwood)	55736
Hallock	56728
Halma	56729
Halstad	56548
Ham Lake (Anoka)	55304
Hamburg	55339
Hamel	55340
Hammond (Zumbro Falls)	55991
Hampton	55031
Hancock	56244
Hangaard (Gonvick)	56644
Hanley Falls	56245
Hanover	55341
Hanska	56041
Happyland (Littlefork)	56653
Harding (Pierz)	56364
Hardwick	56134
Harmony	55939
Harnell Park (Saginaw)	55779
Harris	55032, 55744
Fish Lake	55032
Stark	55032
Sunrise	55032
Hart (Rushford)	55971
Hartford (Browerville)	56438
Hartland	56042
Hassan (Rogers)	55374
Hassman (Aitkin)	56431
Hastings	55033
Hatfield (Pipestone)	56164
Haugen (Tamarack)	55787
Havana (Owatonna)	55060
Hawick	56246
Hawley	56549
Hay Brook (Isle)	56342
Hayfield	55940
Haypoint (Hill City)	55748
Hayward	56043
Hazel Run	56247
Hazelton (Aitkin)	56431
Hector	55342
Henderson	56044
Hendricks	56136
Hendrickson (Laporte)	56461
Hendrum	56550
Henning	56551
Henriette	55036
Herman	56248
Hermantown (Duluth)	55810-811
Heron Lake	56137
Hewitt	56453
Hibbing	55746-747, 55754

Brooklyn	55746
Kelly Lake	55754
Kitzville	55746
Lavinia	55746
Leetonia	55746
Little Swan	55746
Lynwood	55746
North Hibbing	55746
Ruby Junction	55746
Silica	55746
Stuntz	55746
Wilpen	55746
High Forest	55976
(Stewartville)	
Highland	55616, 55986
(Two Harbors)	
Hill City	55748
Hillman	56338
Hills	56138
Hilltop (Minneapolis)	55421
Hillview (Sebeka)	56477
Hinckley	55037
Hines	56647
Hiram (Hackensack)	56452
Hitterdal	56552
Hoff (Cyrus)	56323
Hoffman	56339
Hokah	55941
Holdingford	56340
Holland	56139
Hollandale	56045
Holloway	56249
Holman (Taconite)	55786
Holmes City	56341
Holst (Leonard)	56652
Holt (Newfolden)	56738
Holyoke	55749, 55797
Wrenshall	55749
Home Brook (Brainerd)	56401
Homer	55942
Hope	56046
Hopkins	55305, 55343, 55345
Eden Prairie	55343
Edina	55343
Minnetonka	55305
Minnetonka	55343
Minnetonka	55345
Hornet (Blackduck)	56630
Houston	55943
Hovland	55606
Howard Lake	55349
	55393, 55575
Hoyt Lakes	55750
Hubbard (Park Rapids)	56470
Hugo	55038
Humboldt	56731
Huntersville (Menahga)	56464
Huntley	56047
Hutchinson	55350
Ida (Garfield)	56332
Ideal Corners	56472
(Pequot Lakes)	
Idington (Angora)	55703
Ihlen	56140
Independence (Delano)	55328
	55357, 55359, 55373
Indus (Birchdale)	56629
Industrial (Saginaw)	55779
Inger (Deer River)	56636
Inguadona (Longville)	56655
International Falls	56649

Manitou (Birchdale)	56629
Mankato	56001-003
North Mankato	56003
Mantorville	55955
Mantrap (Nevis)	56467
Maple (Pequot Lakes)	56472
Maple Grove (Osseo)	55311
	55369, 55569, 56450
Osseo	55569
Maple Hill (Grand Marais)	55604
Maple Lake	55358
Maple Plain	55348, 55359
	55393, 55570-572, 55574
	55576-579, 55592-593
Howard Lake	55393
Independence	55359
Medina	55359
Minnetrista	55359
Orono	55359
Maple Ridge (Puposky)	56667
Mapleton	56065
Maplewood (Saint Paul)	55109
	55117, 55119
Marble	55764
Marcell	56657
Margie	56658
Marietta	56257
Marine On Saint Croix	55047
Markham (Makinen)	55763
Markville (Sandstone)	55072
Marshall (Lyle)	55953, 56258
Martin Lake (Stacy)	55079
Max	56659
May	55047, 56466
(Marine On Saint Croix)	
Mayer	55360
Maynard	56260
Mayo Clinic (Rochester)	55905
Maywood (Foley)	56329
Mazeppa	55956
Mc Grath	56350
Mc Gregor	55745, 55760
Mc Kinley	55761
Mcdavitt (Iron)	55751
Mcintosh	56556
Meadow (Sebeka)	56477
Meadowlands	55765, 55789
Elmer	55765
Ness	55765
Payne	55765
Toivola	55789
Medford	55049
Medicine Lake	55441
(Minneapolis)	
Medina (Hamel)	55340
	55356-357, 55359, 55391
Melby (Evansville)	56326
Melrose	56352
Melrude (Cotton)	55724, 55766
Ellsburg	55766
Whiteface	55766
Menahga	56464
Mendota	55150
Mendota Heights	55118, 55120
(Saint Paul)	
Mentor	56736
Meriden	56067
Merrifield	56465
Mesaba (Hoyt Lakes)	55750
Middle River	56737
Midway (Virginia)	55792, 56464

Miesville (Cannon Falls)	55009
Milaca	56353
Milan	56262
Millville	55957
Milo (Foreston)	56330
Milroy	56263
Milton (West Concord)	55985
Miltona	56354
Minerva (Bagley)	56621
Minneapolis	55400-450
	55454-455, 55458-460, 55468
	55470, 55472, 55478-480
	55483-488
Abmps	55472
Blaine	55434, 55449
Bloomington	55420, 55425
	55431, 55435, 55437-55439
Brooklyn Ctr	55443-55444
Brooklyn Park	55443-55445
Columbia Heights	55421
Coon Rapids	55433, 55448
Crystal	55422, 55427-55428
Damark	55468
Daytons Dept Stores	55478
Edina	55410, 55416, 55424
Edina	55439
First National Bank	55486
Fridley	55421
Fridley	55432
Golden Valley	
	55416, 55422, 55426-55427
Hennepin County Govt Jtn	
	55487
Hilltop	55421
Medicine Lake	55441
New Hope	55427-55428
North W Bell Tele	55483
Northern States Power	55484
Norwest Bank	55479, 55485
Plymouth	55446-55447
Richfield	55423
Robbinsdale	55422
Saint Anthony	55418, 55421
Saint Anthony Village	55418
Saint Anthony Village	55421
Saint Louis Park	
	55416, 55424, 55426, 55436
Spring Lake Park	55432
Minneiska (Altura)	55910
Minneota	56264
Minnesota City	55959
Minnesota Lake	56068
Minnetonka (Hopkins)	55305
	55343, 55345
Minnetonka Beach	55361
Minnetrista (Maple Plain)	55359
	55364, 55387
Minnewana (Mc Gregor)	55760
Minnewaska (Clearbrook)	56634
Mission (Crosby)	56441
Mizpah	56660
Moland (Kenyon)	55946
Montevideo	56265
Montgomery	56069
Monticello	55362, 55365
	55561, 55563, 55565
	55580-582, 55584-591
Otsego	56362
Montrose	55363
Moorhead	56560-563
Kragnes	56560

Moose Creek (Shevlin)	56676
Moose Lake	55767
Moose Park (Blackduck)	56630
Mora	55051
Moran (Staples)	56479
Morcom (Cook)	55723
Morgan	56266
Morgan Park (Duluth)	55808
Morrill (Foley)	56329
Morris	56267
Morrison (Palisade)	56469
Morristown	55052
Morse (Ely)	55731, 56636
Morton	56270
Motley	56466
Mound	55364
Mounds View (Saint Paul)	55112
Mount Morris (Hillman)	56338
Mountain Iron	55768
Mountain Lake	56159
Mozeppa (Mizpah)	56660
Mudgett (Onamia)	56359
Munson (Richmond)	56368
Murdock	56271
Murphy City (Finland)	55603
Myrtle	56070
Nashua	56565
Nashville (Truman)	56088
Nashwauk	55769
Nassau	56272
Navarre	55392
Naytahwaush	56566
Nebish (Nevis)	56467, 56667
Nelson	56355
Nerstrand	55053
Ness (Meadowlands)	55765
Nett Lake	55772
Nett River (Big Falls)	56627
Nevada (Lyle)	55953
Nevis	56467
New Auburn	55366
New Brighton (Saint Paul)	55112
New Brighton Boxes	55190-191
(Saint Paul)	
New Germany	55367
New Hartford (Dakota)	55925
New Hope	55427-428
(Minneapolis)	
New London	56273
New Market	55054
New Munich	56356
New Prague	56071
New Prairie (Cyrus)	56323
New Richland	56072
New Scandia	55047, 55073
(Marine On Saint Croix)	
New Trier (Hampton)	55031
New Ulm	56073
New York Mills	56567
Newfolden	56738
Newport	55055
Newry (Blooming Prairie)	55917
Nichols (Mountain Iron)	55768
Nickerson (Wrenshall)	55797
Nicollet	56074
Nicolville (Austin)	55912
Nielsville	56568
Nimrod	56478
Nisswa	56468
Nodine (Dakota)	55925
Nokay Lake (Brainerd)	56401

Ronneby (Foley)	56329
Roosevelt	56673, 56682
Arnesen	56673
Laona	56673
Roscoe	55983, 56371
(Wanamingo)	
Zion	56371
Rose City (Eagle Bend)	56446
Rose Creek	55970
Roseau	56751
Rosemount	55068
Roseville	55112-113, 55126
(Saint Paul)	
Roseville Boxes	55182
(Saint Paul)	
Rosewood	56701
(Thief River Falls)	
Rosing (Motley)	56466
Ross (Roseau)	56751
Rossburg (Aitkin)	56431
Rothsay	56579
Round Lake	56167
Royalton	56373
Ruby Junction (Hibbing)	55746
Runeberg (Menahga)	56464
Rush City	55067, 55069
(Rock Creek)	
Rushford	55971
Rushmore	56168
Russell	56169
Ruthton	56170
Rutledge	55778
Sabin	56580
Sacred Heart	56285
Saginaw	55779
Sago (Swan River)	55784
Saint Anthony	55418, 55421
(Minneapolis)	
Saint Bonifacius	55375
Saint Charles	55972
Saint Clair	56080
Saint Cloud	56301-304, 56372
	56393, 56395-398
Fingerhut	
	56393, 56395, 56396, 56372
Saint Croix	55047
(Marine On Saint Croix)	
Saint Francis	55070, 56331
Saint George (Foley)	56329
Saint Hilaire	56754
Saint James	56081
Saint Joseph	56374-375
Saint Leo	56286
Saint Louis Park	55416
	55424, 55426, 55436
(Minneapolis)	
Saint Martin	56376
Saint Mathias	56449
(Fort Ripley)	
Saint Michael	55376
Saint Olaf (Dalton)	56324
Saint Paul	55100-128, 55133
	55144-46, 55150, 55155
	55161, 55164-166
	55168-172, 55175
	55177, 55182, 55189-191
3 M	55144
Apple Valley	55124
Arden Hills	55112
Birchwood	55110
Dellwood	55110

Eagan	55120-55123
Falcon Heights	55108, 55113
First Bank St Paul	55170
First Bank Visa	55171
Fort Snelling	55111
Gem Lake	55110
Grant Township	55115
Landfall Village	55128
Lauderdale	55108, 55113
Lilydale	55118
Lino Lakes	55110, 55126
Little Canada	55109, 55117
Mahtomedi	55115
Maplewood	55109, 55117
	55119,55144
Mendota Heights	55118, 120
Minn Mining Boxes	55133
Mounds View	55112
New Brighton	55112
North Oaks	55127
North Saint Paul	55109
Oakdale	55128
Pine Springs	55115, 55128
Roseville	55126
Roseville Boxes	55182
Shoreview	55126
Spotts Inc	55177
State Farm Ins	55161
State Offices	55155
State Tax Dept	55145-55146
Sunfish Lake	55118
Twin Cities Amf	55111
USPS Fac Area Office	55169
V A	55168
Vadnais Heights	55110, 127
West Saint Paul	55107, 118
White Bear Lake	55110, 115
White Bear Township	55110
Woodbury	55125
Saint Peter	56082
Saint Rosa (Freeport)	56331
Saint Stephen	56375
Saint Vincent	56755
Salem (Boy River)	56632
Salo (Mc Gregor)	55760
Salol	56756
Sanborn	56083
Sand Lake (Spring Lake)	56680
Sandstone	55072
Sandy (Britt)	55710
Santiago	55377
Saratoga (Saint Charles)	55972
Sargeant	55973
Sartell	56377
Sauk Centre	56378, 56389
Ashley	56378
Getty	56378
Kandota	56378
Padua	56378
West Union	56378
Sauk Rapids	56379
Saum	56674
Savage	55306, 55378
(Burnsville)	
Savannah (Taconite)	55786
Sawyer	55780
Scandia	55073
Scanlon (Cloquet)	55720
Schley (Cass Lake)	56633
Schoolcraft (Lake George)	56458
Schroeder	55613

Seaforth	56287
Searles	56084
Sebeka	56477
Sedan	56380
Selicka (Sebeka)	56477
Shafer	55074, 55084
Franconia	55074
Shakopee	55379
Shamrock (Mc Gregor)	55760
Shaw (Canyon)	55717
Shell River (Menahga)	56464
Shelly	56581
Sherburn	56171
Sheshebee (Mc Gregor)	55760
Shevlin	56676
Shingobee (Walker)	56484
Shooks (Northome)	56661
Shoreview (Saint Paul)	55126
Shorewood	55331, 55364
(Excelsior)	
Shotley (Kelliher)	56650
Shovel Lake (Swatara)	55785
Sibley (Pequot Lakes)	56472
Side Lake	55781
Silica (Hibbing)	55746
Silver (Kettle River)	55757
Silver Bay	55614
Silver Brook (Carlton)	55718
Silver Creek	55380, 55616
Silver Lake	55381
Silverdale (Gheen)	55740
Sinclair (Leonard)	56652
Skelton (Barnum)	55707
Skibo (Hoyt Lakes)	55750
Skyburg (Kenyon)	55946
Slater (Remer)	56672
Slayton	56172
Sleepy Eye	56085
Smoky Hollow (Remer)	56672
Snellman (Osage)	56570
Soderville (Anoka)	55304
Solem (Kensington)	56343
Solway	56678
Soudan	55782
South Fork (Ogilvie)	56358
South Harbor (Onamia)	56359
South Haven	55382
South International Falls	56679
South Rushford (Rushford)	55971
South Saint Paul	55075-077
Spalding (Mc Gregor)	55760
Spang (Grand Rapids)	55744
Spectacle Lake	55008
(Cambridge)	
Spicer	56288
Split Rock (Kettle River)	55757
Spooner (Baudette)	56623
Spring Grove	55974
Spring Lake	56680
Spring Lake Park	55432
(Minneapolis)	
Spring Park	55384
Spring Valley	55975
Springfield	56087
Spruce Center (Miltona)	56354
Squaw Lake	56681
Stacy	55078-079
Lent	55079
Martin Lake	55079
Stanchfield	55080
Stanford (Stanchfield)	55080

Stanton (Dennison) 55018
Staples 56479
Starbuck 56381
Stark (Harris) 55032
Steen 56173
Stephen 56757
Stewart 55385, 55616
Stewartville 55976
Stillwater 55082-083
   Oak Park Heights 55082
   West Lakeland 55082
Stockton 55988
Stokes (Bigfork) 56628
Stoney Brook (Brookston) .. 55711
Storden 56174
Stowe Prairie (Hewitt) 56453
Strandquist 56758
Strathcona 56759
Stuntz (Hibbing) 55746
Sturgeon (Angora) 55703
Sturgeon Lake 55783
Sugar Bush (Bemidji) 56601
Summit 55917, 56630
   (Blooming Prairie)
Sunburg 56289
Sunfish Lake 55077, 55118
   (Inver Grove Heights)
Sunrise (Harris) 55032, 55056
Svea (Blomkest) 56216
Swan River 55784
Swanburg (Pine River) 56474
Swanville 56382
Swatara (Hill City) .. 55748, 55785
   Macville 55785
   Shovel Lake 55785
Swift 56682
Sylvan (Pillager) 56473
Syre (Twin Valley) 56584
Tabor (Angus) 56712
Taconite 55786
Talmoon 56637
Tamarack 55787
Taopi 55977
Taunton 56291
Taylors Falls 55084
Ten Lake (Bemidji) 56601
Tenney (Tintah) 56583
Tenstrike 56683
Theilman 55978
Thief River Falls 56701
Thomastown (Verndale) 56481
Thomson (Carlton) 55718
Thor (Aitkin) 56431
Thorpe (Akeley) 56433
Thunder Lake (Remer) 56672
Timothy (Manhattan Beach) 56463
Tintah 56583
Todd (Park Rapids) 56470
Tofte 55615
Togo (Cook) 55723, 55788
   Bearville 55788
   Carpenter 55788
   Celina 55788
   Cook 55788
Toimi (Brimson) 55602
Toivola (Meadowlands) 55789
Tonka Bay (Excelsior) 55331
Torrey (Boy River) 56632
Tower 55790
Tracy 56175
Trail 56684

Trelipe (Outing) 56662
Trimont 56176
Trommald (Crosby) 56441
Trosky 56177
Trout Lake (Grand Rapids) 55744
Troy (Saint Charles) 55972
Truman 56088
Tumuli (Dalton) 56324
Turner (Mc Gregor) 55760
Turtle Creek 56438
   (Browerville)
Turtle Lake 56484, 56667
   (Walker)
Turtle River (Bemidji) 56601
Twig 55791
Twin Lakes 55718, 56089
   (Carlton)
Twin Valley 56584
Two Harbors 55616
Tyler 56178
Ulen 56585
Underwood 56586
Upsala 56384
Urbank (Parkers Prairie) ... 56361
Urness (Evansville) 56326
Utica 55979
Vadnais Heights 55110, 55127
   (Saint Paul)
Van Buren (Floodwood) 55736
Vasa (Welch) 55089
Verdi 56179
Verdon (Palisade) 56469
Vergas 56587
Vermilion Dam (Orr) 55771
Vermillion 55085
Verndale 56481
Vernon Center 56090
Veseli (Lonsdale) 55046
Vesta 56292
Victoria 55386
Viking 56760
Villard 56385
Vineland (Onamia) 56359
Vining 56588
Viola (Eyota) 55934
Virginia 55777, 55792
   Florenton 55792
   Franklin 55792
   Midway 55792
   West Virginia 55792
   Wouri 55792
Waasa (Embarrass) 55732
Wabana (Grand Rapids) ... 55744
Wabasha 55101, 55981
   (Saint Paul)
   Dumfries 55981
Wabasso 56293
Wabedo (Longville) 56655
Waconia 55387
Wadena 56482
Wagner (Finlayson) 55735
Wahkon 56386
Wahnena (Boy River) 56632
Waite Park 56387
Walden (Cyrus) 56323, 56474
Waldo (Two Harbors) 55616
Waldorf 56091
Wales (Two Harbors) 55616
Walker 56484
Walnut Grove 56180
Walters 56092

Waltham 55982
Wanamingo 55983
Wanda 56294
Wannaska 56761
Warba 55793
Ward (Browerville) 56438
Ward Springs (Grey Eagle) 56336
Warman (Mora) 55051
Warren 56762
Warroad 56763
Warsaw 55087
Waseca 56093
Wasioja (Dodge Center) 55927
Waskish 56685
Wastedo (Cannon Falls) 55009
Waterford (Northfield) 55057
Watertown 55388
Waterville 56096
Watkins 55389
Watson 56295
Waubun 56589
Waukenabo (Palisade) 56469
Waverly 55390
Wawina 55794
Wayzata 55391
Wealthwood (Aitkin) 56431
Weaver (Altura) 55910
Weber (North Branch) 55056
Webster 55088
Welch (Hastings) .. 55033, 55089
   Etter 55089
   Vasa 55089
Welcome 56181
Wells 56097
Wendell 56590
West Concord 55985
West Duluth (Duluth) 55807
West Lakeland 55082
   (Stillwater)
West Rock (Pine City) 55063
West Saint Paul 55107, 55118
   (Saint Paul)
West Union 56378, 56389
   (Sauk Centre)
   Sauk Centre 56389
West Virginia (Virginia) 55792
Westbrook 56183
Westport (Villard) 56385
Whalan 55986
Wheaton 56296
Wheeling (Nerstrand) 55053
Whipholt 56485
White (Aurora) 55705
White Bear Lake 55110, 55115
   (Saint Paul)
White Earth 56591
White Oak (Akeley) 56433
White Rock (Cannon Falls) 55009
Whiteface (Melrude) 55766
Whyte (Two Harbors) 55616
Wig Wam Bay (Onamia) ... 56359
Wilder (Windom) 56101
Wildwood (Northome) 56661
Wilkinson 55090, 56633
   (Willernie)
Willernie 55090
Williams 56686
Willmar 56201
Willow River 55795
Willow Valley (Gheen) 55740
Wilmont 56185

ANOKA

GOVERNMENT

Anoka County Courthouse
325 E MAIN ST 55303

BEMIDJI

GOVERNMENT

State Office Building
1819 BEMIDJI AVE N 56601

BLOOMINGTON

BUILDINGS

1 Appletree Square
8009 34TH AVE S 55425

2 Appletree Square
8011 34TH AVE S 55425

International Plaza
7900 International Dr 55425

Southgate Office Plaza
5001 W 80TH ST 55437

BURNSVILLE

BUILDINGS

Northridge Office Center
200 HIGHWAY 13 W 55337

DULUTH

APARTMENTS

Chateau De Ville
3820 LONDON RD 55804

Chateau Du Lac
3800 LONDON RD 55804

Chateau Du Luth
3780 LONDON RD 55804

Faithaven Apt
4901 GRAND AVE 55807

Gateway Towers
612 W SUPERIOR ST 55802

Grandview Apt
301 E 2ND ST 55805

Greysolon Plaza
231 E SUPERIOR ST 55802

Lenox Place
701 W SUPERIOR ST 55802

Midtowne Manor I
2021 W 2ND ST 55806

Midtowne Manor II
2011 W 2ND ST 55806

Mt Royal Manor
100 ELIZABETH ST 55803

Ramsey Manor
400 N 53RD AVE W 55807

S-elect Homes
801 E 2ND ST 55805

St Anns Home
330 E 3RD ST 55805

BUILDINGS

Alworth Building
306 W SUPERIOR ST 55802

Arrowhead Plaza
205 W 2ND ST 55802

Beal Building
5 N 3RD AVE W 55802

Board Of Trade Building
301 W 1ST ST 55802

First Bank Place
130 W SUPERIOR ST 55802

Lake Superior Plaza
8 W SUPERIOR ST 55802

Lonsdale Building
302 W SUPERIOR ST 55802

Medical Arts Building
324 W SUPERIOR ST 55802

Meierhoff Building
325 S LAKE AVE 55802

Miller Hill Mall
1600 Miller Trunk Hwy 55811

Missabe Building
227 W 1ST ST 55802

Norwest Center
230 W SUPERIOR ST 55802

Ordean Building
424 W SUPERIOR ST 55802

Phoenix Building
333 W SUPERIOR ST 55802

Sellwood Building
202 W SUPERIOR ST 55802

Torrey Building
314 W SUPERIOR ST 55802

Waterfront Plaza
325 S LAKE AVE 55802

YWCA
202 W 2ND ST 55802

GOVERNMENT

City Hall
411 W 1ST ST 55802

County Court House
100 N 5TH AVE W 55802

Federal Building
515 W 1ST ST 55802

Government Service Center
320 W 2ND ST 55802

EDINA

BUILDINGS

Colanade Building
5500 HIGHWAY 12 55416

FORT SNELLING

BUILDINGS

Twin Cities Intl Airport
0 MPLS Stp Intl. Airport 55111

GOVERNMENT

Bishop Henry Whipple
0 FORT SNELLING 55111

GOLDEN VALLEY

BUILDINGS

Interchange South
400 COUNTY ROAD 18 S 55426

Interchange Towers
600 COUNTY ROAD 18 S 55426

MINNEAPOLIS

BUILDINGS

100 Washington Square
100 WASHINGTON AVE S 55401

Baker Building
706 2ND AVE S 55402

Bridge Place
220 S 2ND ST 55401

Butler Square
100 N 6TH ST 55403

Cargill Building
110 S 7TH ST 55402

Ceresota Building
155 5TH AVE S 55401

Chamber Of Commerce Building
15 S 5TH ST 55402

Childrens Health Center
2545 CHICAGO AVE 55404

City Place
730 HENNEPIN AVE 55403

Crown Roller Mill
105 5TH AVE S 55401

Doctors Building
90 S 9TH ST 55402

First Bank Place West
120 S 6TH ST 55402

First Ntl Bank Building
120 S 6TH ST 55402

Foshay Tower
821 MARQUETTE AVE 55402

Grain Exchange
400 S 4TH ST 55415

Hyatt Merchandise Mart
1300 NICOLLET MALL 55403

Ids Center
80 S 8TH ST 55402

International Centre
900 2ND AVE S 55402

Lumber Exchange
10 S 5TH ST 55402

Marquette Bank Building
90 S 6TH ST 55402

Marquette Building
607 MARQUETTE AVE 55402

Medical Arts Building
825 NICOLLET AVE 55402

Metropolitan Medical Building
825 S 8TH ST 55404

Midland Bank Building
401 2ND AVE S 55401

Midwest Plaza East
800 MARQUETTE AVE 55402

Midwest Plaza West
801 NICOLLET MALL 55402

Multifoods
733 MARQUETTE AVE 55402

Multifoods Tower
33 S 6TH ST 55402

National City Bank
75 S 5TH ST 55402

National City Bank
510 MARQUETTE AVE 55402

Nicollet Mall Building
512 NICOLLET AVE 55402

Northstar East
608 2ND AVE S 55402

Northstar West
110 S 7TH ST 55402

Peavey Building
730 2ND AVE S 55402

Pillsbury Center
200 S 6TH ST 55402

Piper Jaffray Towers
222 S 9TH ST 55402

Plymouth Building
12 S 6TH ST 55402

Professional Building
822 MARQUETTE AVE 55402

Roanoke Building
109 S 7TH ST 55402

Sexton Building
529 S 7TH ST 55415

Soo Line Building
507 MARQUETTE AVE 55402

Summit Bank Building
310 4TH AVE S 55415

Title Ins Building
400 2ND AVE S 55401

Towle Building
330 2ND AVE S 55401

Twin City Federal Tower
121 S 8TH ST 55402

Wcco Building
625 2ND AVE S 55402

GOVERNMENT

Main Post Office
100 S 1ST ST 55401

ROCHESTER

APARTMENTS

Central Towers
200 1ST AVE NW 55901

Kahler Hotel
20 2ND AVE SW 55902

Madonna Towers
4001 19TH AVE NW 55901

North Gate Plaza
902 11TH AVE NW 55901

Rochester Towers
207 5TH AVE SW 55902

SAINT CLOUD

APARTMENTS

Carter Place
501 1ST ST N 56303

Cedar Square East Apt
1500 E Saint Germain St .. 56304

BUILDINGS

Metropolitan Federal
1010 SAINT GERMAIN ST. 56301

Norwest Center
400 1ST ST S 56301

Zapp Bank Building
1015 W Saint Germain St . 56301

SAINT PAUL

BUILDINGS

1 Capital Centre Plaza
386 WABASHA ST N 55102

1st Natl Bank Building
332 MINNESOTA ST 55101

1st Trust Center
180 5TH ST E 55101

Allen Building
287 6TH ST E 55101

American Center
150 KELLOGG BLVD E 55101

American Natl Bank Building
101 5TH ST E 55101

Capital Square
550 CEDAR ST 55101

Central Medical
393 DUNLAP ST N 55104

City Hall Annex
25 4TH ST W 55102

Control Data Annex
261 5TH ST E 55101

Court International Building
2550 UNIVERSITY AVE W 55114

Degree Of Honor
325 CEDAR ST 55101

Doctors Professional
280 SMITH AVE N 55102

Empire
360 ROBERT ST N 55101

Endicott On 4th
141 4TH ST E 55101

Endicott On Robert
350 ROBERT ST N 55101

Farm Credit Building
375 JACKSON ST 55101

Gallery Profesional
17 EXCHANGE ST W 55102

Galtier Plaza
175 5TH ST E 55101

Gilbert
413 WACOUTA ST 55101

Hamm Building
408 SAINT PETER ST 55102

Hanover
480 CEDAR ST 55101

Hemar
85 7TH PL E 55101

Kellogg Square
111 KELLOGG BLVD E 55101

Landmark Center
75 5TH ST W 55102

Landmark Towers
345 SAINT PETER ST 55102

Lowertown Business Center
245 6TH ST E 55101

Lowry Sq
345 WABASHA ST N 55102

Lowry Square
7 7TH PL W 55102

Mc Call
366 JACKSON ST 55101

Mears Park Pl
405 SIBLEY ST 55101

Meritor Tower
444 CEDAR ST 55101

Metro Square
121 7TH PL E 55101

Metropolitan Federal Building
419 ROBERT ST N 55101

Midwest Federal Building
50 5TH ST E 55101

Minnesota Building Annex
310 CEDAR ST 55101

Minn Mutual Life Building
400 ROBERT ST N 55101

Minnesota Building
46 4TH ST E 55101

Nalpak
333 SIBLEY ST 55101

North Central Towers
445 MINNESOTA ST 55101

Northwestern
275 4TH ST E 55101

Norwest Center
55 5TH ST E 55101

Park Square Court
400 SIBLEY ST 55101

Pioneer
336 ROBERT ST N 55101

Pioneer Press Dispatch
345 CEDAR ST 55101

Rossmor
127 9TH ST E 55101

Rossmor
500 ROBERT ST N 55101

Saint Paul Center
444 CEDAR ST 55101

St Paul Building
6 5TH ST W 55102

Union Depot Place
214 4TH ST E 55101

World Trade Center
30 7TH ST E 55101

GOVERNMENT

Court House
15 KELLOGG BLVD W 55102

Federal Building
316 ROBERT ST N 55101

St Paul Post Office Building
180 KELLOGG BLVD E 55101

SOUTH SAINT PAUL

GOVERNMENT

South St Paul City Hall
125 3RD AVE N 55075

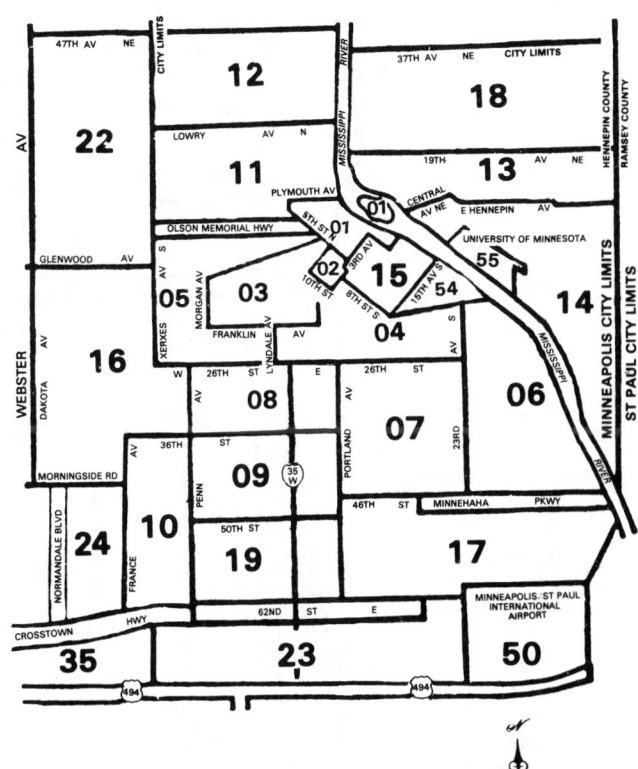

ZIP CODES

MINNEAPOLIS, MN

554 + TWO DIGITS SHOWN = ZIP CODE

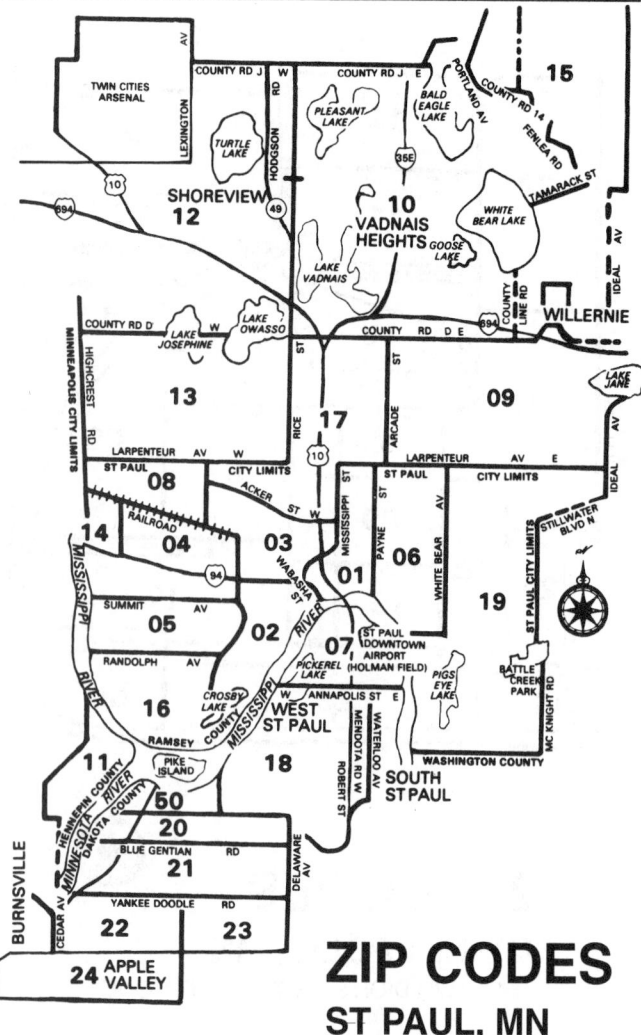

ZIP CODES

ST PAUL, MN

551 + TWO DIGITS
SHOWN = ZIP CODE

MISSISSIPPI
Abbreviation MS

Abbeville	38601
Abbott (West Point)	39773
Aberdeen	39730
Ackerman	39735
Adaton (Starkville)	39759
Agricola (Lucedale)	39452
Airey (Saucier)	39574
Albin (Webb)	38966
Algoma	38820
Alligator	38720
Alma (Guntown)	38849
Alpine (Blue Springs)	38828
Altitude (Booneville)	38829
Alva (Duck Hill)	38925
Amistead (Friars Point)	38631
Amory	38821
Anchor (Woodland)	39776
Anguilla	38721
Ansley (Lakeshore)	39558
Antioch (Laurel)	39440
Anvil (Tiplersville)	38674
Arcola	38722
Ariel (Gloster)	39638
Arkabutla	38602
Arlington (Bogue Chitto)	39629
Arm (Silver Creek)	39663
Arnold Line (Hattiesburg)	39401
Artesia	39736
Ashland	38603
Ashwood (Woodville)	39669
Askew (Crenshaw)	38621
Atlanta (Woodland)	39776
Auburn (Smithdale)	39664
Austin (Tunica)	38676
Avalon	38912
Avent (Mc Lain)	39456
Avon	38723
Bacots (Mc Comb)	39648
Bailey	39320
Baird (Indianola)	38751
Baldwyn	38824
Ballardsville (Tupelo)	38801
Ballentine (Crenshaw)	38621
Baltzer (Clarksdale)	38614
Banks (Robinsonville)	38664
Bankston (Weir)	39772
Banner	38913
Barr (Senatobia)	38668
Barrontown (Hattiesburg)	39401
Bartahatchie (Caledonia)	39740
Barth (Poplarville)	39470
Barto (Mc Comb)	39648
Basin (Lucedale)	39452
Bassfield	39421
Batesville	38606
Batson (Hattiesburg)	39401
Baugh (Clarksdale)	38669
Baxterville (Lumberton)	39455
Bay Saint Louis	39520-522
	39525, 39529
Bayside Park	39520
Diamondhead	39520
Saint Louis	39520
Bayside Park	39520
(Bay Saint Louis)	
Bear Garden (Hollandale)	38748
Bear Town (Mc Comb)	39648
Beasley (Pheba)	39755

Beaumont	39423
Becker	38825
Beechwood (Liberty)	39645
Beelake (Tchula)	39169
Belden	38826
Belen	38609
Belle Isle (Pearlington)	39572
Bellefontaine	39737
Belleville (New Augusta)	39462
Bellewood (Isola)	38754
Belmont	38827
Belzoni	39038
Benndale (Mc Lain)	39456
Benoit	38725
Bentley (Mantee)	39751
Benton	39039
Bentonia	39040
Benwood (Coffeeville)	38922
Berclair (Itta Bena)	38941
Berwick (Liberty)	39645
Bethany (Baldwyn)	38824
Bethlehem (Potts Camp)	38659
Beulah	38726
Bewelcome (Gloster)	39638
Big Creek	38914
Big Level (Perkinston)	39573
Bigbee (Amory)	38821
Bigbee Valley	39738
Biggersville (Corinth)	38834
Bigpoint (Pascagoula)	39567
Biloxi	39530-535
Diberville	39532
Keesler Field	39534
North Bay	39532
Triangle	39534
West Biloxi	39531
Binford (Aberdeen)	39730
Birdie (Coahoma)	38617
Bissell (Tupelo)	38801
Black Hawk (Coila)	38923
Blackjack (Starkville)	39759
Blackland (Booneville)	38829
Blackwater (Waterford)	38685
Blair (Guntown)	38849
Blodgett (Ovett)	39464
Bloody Springs (Belmont)	38827
Blue Lake (Drew)	38737
Blue Mountain	38610
Blue Springs	38828
Bluff (Blue Mountain)	38610
Bobo (Clarksdale)	38614
Boggan Bend (Guntown)	38849
Bogue Chitto	39629
Bolivar (Benoit)	38725
Bolton	39041
Bon Homme (Hattiesburg)	39401
Booneville	38829
Bowdre (Robinsonville)	38664
Bowman (Coldwater)	38618
Boyer (Indianola)	38751
Boyle	38730
Bradley (Starkville)	39759
Brandon	39042-043, 39047
Branyan (Blue Springs)	38828
Braxton	39044
Brazil (Tutwiler)	38963
Brewer (Shannon)	38868, 39476
Bristers Store (Jayess)	39641
Brookhaven	39601
Brooklyn	39425
Brooks (Drew)	38737

Brooksville	39739
Brownfield (Walnut)	38683
Bruce	38915
Bryant (Coffeeville)	38922
Buckatunna	39322
Buckhorn (Randolph)	38864
Bude	39630
Buena Vista	38663, 38851
(Ripley)	
Bunkley (Meadville)	39653
Burns (Raleigh)	39153
Burnsville	38833
Burrow (Tiplersville)	38674
Burtons (Booneville)	38829
Busy Corner (Liberty)	39645
Buxton (Sarah)	38665
Byhalia	38611
Cadamy (Tremont)	38876
Cadaretta (Gore Springs)	38929
Caesar (Picayune)	39466
Caile (Isola)	38754
Caledonia	39740
Calhoun (Laurel)	39440
Calhoun City	38916, 38955
Camden	39045
Campbell (Ripley)	38663
Camphill (Walnut)	38683
Cannon (Ashland)	38603
Canton	39046
Cardsville (Nettleton)	38858
Carlisle	39049
Carmichael (Beaumont)	39423
Carnes (Lumberton)	39455
Carolina (Nettleton)	38858
Carpenter (Hermanville)	39086
Carriere	39426
Carrollton	38917
Carson	39427
Carterville (Hattiesburg)	39401
Carthage	39051
Cary	39054
Cascilla	38920
Cassels (Gloster)	39638
Cedar Hill (Duck Hill)	38925
Cedarbluff	39741
Center (Blue Springs)	38828
Centralgrove (Aberdeen)	39730
Centreville	39631
Chalybeate (Walnut)	38683
Charleston	38921, 38958
Cowart	38921
Effie	38921
Sharkey	38921
Chatawa	39632
Chatham	38731
Cheraw (Foxworth)	39483
Cherrycreek	38828
(Blue Springs)	
Chester (Ackerman)	39735
Chesterville (Tupelo)	38801
Chiwapa (Pontotoc)	38863
Choctaw (Shaw)	38773, 39440
Chunky	39323
Clack (Robinsonville)	38664
Clara	39324
Clarksdale	38614, 38669
Baltzer	38614
Baugh	38669
Bobo	38614
Riverton	38614
Roundaway	38614

Sherard 38669
Stovall 38614
Clarkson (Mathiston) 39752
Clayton (Dundee) 38626
Clayton Village 39759
(Starkville)
Cleo (Laurel) 39440
Cleveland 38732-733
Zumbro 38732
Cliftonville 39739
(Brooksville)
Clinton 39056, 39058, 39060
Clove Hill (Lyon) 38645
Coahoma 38617
Cobbs (Brookhaven) 39601
Coffeeville 38922
Coila 38923
Coldwater 38618
Coles (Crosby) 39633
Coles Creek (Big Creek) 38914
Collins 39428
Collinsville 39325
Colony Town (Itta Bena) 38941
Colsub (Amory) 38821
Columbia 39429
Columbus 39701-705
Fairlane 39701
Mccrary 39701
New Hope 39701
Commerce (Robinsonville) 38664
Como 38619
Conehatta 39057
Corinth 38834
Cornersville (Potts Camp) . 38659
Corrona (Guntown) 38849
Cotton Plant 38610
(Blue Mountain)
Cottonville (Coldwater) 38618
Courtland 38620
Cowart (Charleston) 38921
Craig Springs (Sturgis) 39769
Crane Creek (Perkinston) . 39573
Cranfield (Roxie) 39661
Crawford 39743
Crenshaw 38621
Crockett (Senatobia) 38668
Crosby 39633
Crossroads 38701, 39470
(Greenville)
Crotts (Ellisville) 39437
Crowder 38622
Cruger 38924
Crystal Springs 39059
Cuevas (Pass Christian) ... 39571
Cumberland (Maben) 39750
Curtis Station 38606
(Batesville)
Cybur (Picayune) 39466
D Lo 39062
Dahomey (Benoit) 38725
Daisy Vestry (Perkinston) .. 39573
Daleville 39326
Dancy (Mantee) 39751
Darbun (Kokomo) 39643
Darling 38623
Darlove (Hollandale) 38748
Darracott (Aberdeen) 39730
Darrington (Crosby) 39633
Days (Lake Cormorant) 38641
De Kalb 39328
Decatur 39327

Deerbrook (Brooksville) 39739
Deeson (Duncan) 38740
Delta (Crenshaw) 38621
Delta City 39061
Dennis 38838
Dennis Landing (Gunnison) 38746
Dentontown (Slate Spring) 38955
Derby (Poplarville) 39470
Derma 38839
Dexter (Tylertown) 39667
Diamondhead 39520, 39525
(Bay Saint Louis)
Bay Saint Louis 39525
Diberville (Biloxi) 39532
Dixie (Hattiesburg) 39401
Doddsville 38736
Doloroso (Woodville) 39669
Donegal (Woodville) 39669
Dorsey (Fulton) 38843
Doskie (Burnsville) 38833
Drew 38737-738
Blue Lake 38737
Brooks 38737
Dwiggins 38737
Fitzhugh 38737
Goldfield 38737
Parchman 38738
Wade 38737
Whitney 38737
Dry Creek (Collins) 39428
Dubard (Grenada) 38901
Dubbs (Dundee) 38626
Dublin 38739
Duck Hill 38925
Dumas 38625
Duncan 38740
Dundee 38626
Dunleith (Leland) 38756
Durant 39063
Dwiggins (Drew) 38737
Dwyer (Sunflower) 38778
Earlygrove (Lamar) 38642
East Aberdeen (Aberdeen) 39730
East Lincoln (Brookhaven) 39601
East Moss Point 39563
(Moss Point)
East Side (Richton) 39476
Eastabuchie 39436
Eastfork (Smithdale) 39664
Eastlawn (Pascagoula) 39567
Eastport (Iuka) 38852
Eastside (Moss Point) 39563
Eatonville (Hattiesburg) 39401
Ecru 38841
Eddiceton (Mc Call Creek) 39647
Edinburg (Carthage) 39051
Edwards 39066
Effie (Charleston) 38921
Eggville (Saltillo) 38866
Egypt (Okolona) 38860
Electric Mills (Scooba) 39358
Elizabeth (Leland) 38756
Ellard (Bruce) 38915
Elliott 38926
Ellistown (Dennis) 38838
Ellisville 39437
Elsie (Vardaman) 38878
Eminence (Seminary) 39479
Endville (Blue Springs) 38828
Enid 38927
Enon (Jayess) 39641

Enterprise .. 39330, 39629, 39645
Errata (Laurel) 39440
Erwin (Chatham) 38731
Escatawpa 39552
Eskridge (Winona) 38967
Estill (Hollandale) 38748
Ethel 39067
Etta38627
Eunice (Gloster) 39638
Eupora 39744
Eutaw (Benoit) 38725
Evansville 38618, 38676
(Coldwater)
Fair River (Brookhaven) 39601
Fairfield (Blue Springs) 38828
Fairlane (Columbus) 39701
Fairview 38751, 38847
(Indianola)
Falcon 38628
Falkner 38629
Fame (Eupora) 39744
Farmhaven (Canton) 39046
Farmington (Corinth) 38834
Farrell 38630
Fayette 39069, 39081
Fentress (Ackerman) 39735
Fernwood 39635
Fitler 39070
Fitzhugh (Drew) 38737
Flora 39071
Florence 39073
Flowood (Jackson) 39208
Fontainebleau 39564
(Ocean Springs)
Foote (Hollandale) 38748
Fords Creek (Poplarville) .. 39470
Forest 39074
Fort Adams (Woodville) 39669
Foxworth 39483
Francis (Duncan) 38740
French Camp 39745
Friars Point 38631
Friendship (Ecru) ... 38841, 39601
Fruitland Park (Wiggins) 39577
Fulton 38843
Furrs (Pontotoc) 38863
Futheyville (Grenada) 38901
Gallman 39077
Gandsi (Seminary) 39479
Garden City (Roxie) 39661
Gatewood (Coffeeville) 38922
Gattman 38844
Gautier 39553
Geeslin Corner (Grenada) 38901
Geeville (Baldwyn) 38824
Georgetown 39078
Gibson (Aberdeen) 39730
Gillsburg (Osyka) 39657
Glade (Laurel) 39440
Glen 38846
Glen Allan 38744
Glendale (Hattiesburg) 39401
Glendora 38928
Gloster 39638
Glover (Walls) 38680
Gluckstadt (Madison) 39110
Golden 38847
Goldfield (Drew) 38737
Good Hope (Richton) 39476
Goodfood (Pontotoc) 38863
Goodman 39079

Goodyear (Picayune) 39466
Gore Springs 38929
Grace 38745
Grady (Eupora) 39744
Graham (Baldwyn) 38824
Grapeland (Benoit) 38725
Gravel Siding (Iuka) 38852
Gravestown (Ripley) 38663
Greenbrier Park 39466
   (Picayune)
Greenville 38701-704
.... 38731, 38755
   Crossroads 38701
   Refuge 38701
   Swiftwater 38701
Greenwood 38930, 38935
   Shellmound 38930
Greenwood Springs 38848
Grenada 38901-902, 38960
   Dubard 38901
   Futheyville 38901
   Geeslin Corner 38901
   Hardy 38901
   Sunnycrest 38901
Griffith (Cedarbluff) 39741
Gulf Hills 39564
   (Ocean Springs)
Gulfport 39501-503
.... 39505-507
   Orange Grove 39503
Gums (Coffeeville) 38922
Gunnison 38746
Guntown 38849
Hamburg (Roxie) 39661
Hamilton 39746
Hampton (Glen Allan) 38744
Hardy (Grenada) 38901
Harleston (Lucedale) 39452
Harmontown (Como) 38619
Harperville 39080
Harriston 39081
Harrisville 39082
Harvey (Petal) 39465
Hatley (Amory) 38821
Hattiesburg 39401-404
.... 39406-407
   Arnold Line 39401
   Barrontown 39401
   Batson 39401
   Bon Homme 39401
   Carterville 39401
   Dixie 39401
   Eatonville 39401
   Glendale 39401
   Indian Springs 39401
   Lamar Park 39401
   Leeville 39401
   Lux 39401
   Macedonia 39401
   Maybank 39401
   Mccallum 39401
   Meyers 39401
   Morriston 39401
   Oak Grove 39401
   Palmers Crossing 39401
   Pine Grove 39401
   Rawls Springs 39401
   Runnelstown 39401
   Southern 39401
   Sunrise 39401
Hazlehurst 39083

Heads (Leland) 38756
Heathman (Indianola) 38751
Heidelberg 39439
Helena (Pascagoula) 39567
Helm (Leland) 38756
Hendrix (Kilmichael) 39747
Henleyfield (Carriere) 39426
Hermanville 39086
Hernando 38632
Heucks (Brookhaven) 39601
Hickory 39332
Hickory Flat 38633
Hickory Grove 39759
   (Starkville)
Higgins (Sumrall) 39482
Highlandale (Minter City) .. 38944
Highway Village 39669
   (Woodville)
Hillhouse (Alligator) 38720
Hillman (Leakesville) 39451
Hillsboro 39087
Hillsdale (Poplarville) 39470
Hinchcliff (Marks) 38646
Hinkle (Rienzi) 38865
Hintonville (New Augusta) . 39462
Hobo Station (Booneville) . 38829
Hohenlinden (Mantee) 39751
Holcomb 38940
Holcut (Iuka) 38852
Hollandale 38748
Hollis (Vardaman) 38878
Holly Bluff 39088
Holly Grove (Sidon) 38954
Holly Ridge 38749
Holly Springs 38634-635, 38649
Hollywood (Tunica) 38676
Holmesville (Mc Comb) 39648
Holts (Burnsville) 38833
Homochitto (Gloster) 39638
Horn Lake 38637
Hot Coffee (Collins) 39428
Houlka 38850
Houston 38851
Howison (Saucier) 39574
Hoy (Laurel) 39440
Hurley 39555
Hurricane (Thaxton) 38871
Hushpuckena (Shelby) 38774
Inda (Perkinston) 39573
Independence 38638
Indian Springs 38846, 39401
   (Glen)
Indianola 38749, 38751
   (Holly Ridge)
   Baird 38751
   Boyer 38751
   Fairview 38751
   Heathman 38751
   Kinlock 38751
   Marie 38751
   Pollock 38751
   Saints Rest 38751
   Woodburn 38751
Industrial (Picayune) 39466
Ingomar (New Albany) 38652
Inverness 38753
Iowana (Gautier) 39553
Ireland (Woodville) 39669
Irene (Summit) 39666
Isola 38754
Itta Bena 38941

Iuka 38852
Jacinto (Rienzi) 38865
Jackson ... 39201-213, 39215-218
   .... 39225, 39232, 39235-236
   .... 39250, 39269, 39271-272
   .... 39282-284, 39286
   .... 39288-289, 39296, 39298
   Flowood 39208
   Pearl 39208
   Pearl 39288
   Richland 39218
   Visa 39271
Jago (Horn Lake) 38637
James (Hollandale) 38748
Jamestown (Foxworth) 39483
Jayess 39641
Jefferson (Carrollton) 38917
Jeffries (Dundee) 38626
Jennings (Magnolia) 39652
Jericho (Baldwyn) 38824
Johnson (Ellisville) 39437
Johnston (Summit) 39666
Jonathan (Leakesville) 39451
Jonestown 38639
Jug Fork (Blue Springs) 38828
Jumpertown (Booneville) .. 38829
Keesler Field (Biloxi) 39534
Kendrick (Corinth) 38834
Keownville (New Albany) . 38652
Kerin (Cruger) 38924
Kilmichael 39747
Kiln 39556
Kinlock (Indianola) 38751
Kirby (Roxie) 39661
Kirkville (Baldwyn) 38824
Knoxo (Tylertown) 39667
Knoxville (Roxie) 39661
Kokomo 39643
Kola (Collins) 39428
Kolola Springs 39740
   (Caledonia)
Kosciusko 39090
Kossuth (Corinth) 38834
Kreole (Moss Point) 39563
Lackey (Aberdeen) 39730
Lafayette (Oxford) 38655
Lake 39092
Lake Cormorant 38641
Lake View (Walls) 38680
Lakeshore 39558
Lamar 38642
Lamar Park (Hattiesburg) .. 39401
Lambert 38643
Lamont 38755
Laneheart (Woodville) 39669
Lantrip (Bruce) 38915
Larue (Ocean Springs) 39564
Latimer (Ocean Springs) .. 39564
Latonia (Lucedale) 39452
Lauderdale 39335
Laurel 39440-442
   Antioch 39440
   Calhoun 39440
   Choctaw 39440
   Cleo 39440
   Errata 39440
   Glade 39440
   Hoy 39440
   Lightsey 39440
   Limbert 39440
   Mill Creek 39440

Old Cairo (Booneville)	38829
Old Hamilton (Hamilton)	39746
Old Houlka (Houlka)	38850
Old Union (Shannon)	38868
Oldenburg (Roxie)	39661
Oldham (Iuka)	38852
Olive Branch	38654
Oloh (Sumrall)	39482
Oma (Monticello)	39654
Ora (Collins)	39428
Orange Grove	39503, 39567
(Gulfport)	
Osborn (Starkville)	39759
Osborne Creek	38829
(Booneville)	
Osyka	39657
Ouetti (Ovett)	39464
Ovett	39464
Oxberry (Holcomb)	38940
Oxford	38655, 39638
Lafayette	38655
Ozona (Carriere)	39426
Pace	38764
Pachuta	39347
Paden (Tishomingo)	38873
Palmers Crossing	39401
(Hattiesburg)	
Panther Burn	38765
Parchman (Drew)	38738
Parham	38848
(Greenwood Springs)	
Paris (Water Valley)	38949
Pascagoula	39563
	39567-569, 39581
(Moss Point)	
Bigpoint	39567
Eastlawn	39567
Helena	39567
Orange Grove	39567
Pasgoula	39567
Pecan	39567
Three Rivers	39567
Wade	39567
Pasgoula (Pascagoula)	39567
Pass Christian	39571
Patrick (Starkville)	39759
Pattison	39144
Paul (Cascilla)	38920
Paulding	39348
Paynes (Cascilla)	38920
Pearl (Jackson)	39208, 39288
Pearlhaven (Brookhaven)	39601
Pearlington	39572
Pecan (Pascagoula)	39567
Pecan Grove (Ellisville)	39437
Pelahatchie	39145
Pendorff (Laurel)	39440
Penns (Crawford)	39743
Penton (Robinsonville)	38664
Peoples (Ripley)	38663
Peoria (Liberty)	39645
Percy (Hollandale)	38748
Perkinston	39573
Perrytown (Crosby)	39633
Perthshire (Gunnison)	38746
Petal	39465
Pheba	39755
Philadelphia	39350
Phillipstown (Sidon)	38954
Piave (Richton)	39476
Picayune	39466

Pickens	39146, 39179
Vaughan	39179
Pickwick (Foxworth)	39483
Pinckneyville (Woodville)	39669
Pine Flat (Water Valley)	38965
Pine Grove (Booneville)	38829
	38868, 39401
Pine Ridge (Purvis)	39475
Pine Valley	38965
(Water Valley)	
Pinebluff (Mantee)	39751
Pinedale (Etta)	38627
Pinegrove (Hickory Flat)	38633
Pineview (Laurel)	39440
Piney Woods	39148
Pinola	39149
Pisgah (Rienzi)	38865
Pistol Ridge (Lumberton)	39455
Pittman (Foxworth)	39483
Pittsboro	38951
Plantersville	38862
Pleasant Grove	38657
Pleasant Hill (Nesbit)	38651-652
	39668
Pleasant Ridge (Dumas)	38625
Plymouth (Pontotoc)	38863
Poagville (Coldwater)	38618
Pocahontas	39072
Polfry (Ocean Springs)	39564
Pollock (Indianola)	38751
Pontotoc	38863
Pope	38658
Poplar Corners (Walls)	38680
Poplar Creek (Kilmichael)	39747
Poplarville	39470
Port Gibson	39150
Porterville	39352
Possum Trot (Pontotoc)	38863
Possumneck (West)	39192
Potts Camp	38659
Powell (Dundee)	38626
Powers (Laurel)	39440
Prairie	39756
Prentiss	39474
Preston	39354
Pricedale (Summit)	39666
Prichard (Tunica)	38676
Progress (Mc Comb)	39648
Puckett	39151
Pulaski	39152
Pumpkin Center	38652
(New Albany)	
Purvis	39475
Pyland (Houston)	38851
Quentin (Mc Call Creek)	39647
Quincy	38848
(Greenwood Springs)	
Quitman	39355
Quito (Itta Bena)	38941
Rainey (Moselle)	39459
Raleigh	39153
Randolph	38864
Ratliff (Guntown)	38849
Rawls Springs	39401
(Hattiesburg)	
Raymond	39154
Red Banks	38661
Redstar (Brookhaven)	39601
Redwood	39156
Refuge (Greenville)	38701
Reid (Vardaman)	38878

Rena Lara	38767
Rexburg (Leland)	38756
Rhodes (Richton)	39476
Riceville (Perkinston)	39573
Richardson (Picayune)	39466
Richland (Jackson)	39218
Richmond (Plantersville)	38862
Richton	39476
Ridgeland	39157-158
Rienzi	38865
Ripley	38663
Rising Sun (Sidon)	38954
Riverton (Clarksdale)	38614
Robinsonville	38664
Robinwood (Monticello)	39654
Rochdale (Duncan)	38740
Rock Hill (Purvis)	39475
Rocky Hill (Starkville)	39759
Roebuck (Sidon)	38954
Rogerslacy (Sandersville)	39477
Rolling Fork	39159
Rome	38768
Rose Hill	39356
Rosebloom (Cascilla)	38920
Rosedale	38769
Rosella (Monticello)	39654
Rosetta (Crosby)	39633
Rough Edge (Pontotoc)	38863
Roundaway (Clarksdale)	38614
Roundlake (Duncan)	38740
Roxie	39661
Rudyard (Coahoma)	38617
Ruleville	38771
Runnelstown (Hattiesburg)	39401
Ruth	39662
Sabino (Marks)	38646
Sabougla (Slate Spring)	38955
Saint Louis	39520
(Bay Saint Louis)	
Saints Rest (Indianola)	38751
Salem (Tylertown)	39667
Sallis	39160
Saltillo	38866
Sanatorium	39112
Sand Hill	39437, 39476
(Ellisville)	
Sandersville	39477
Sandhill	39161
Sandy Hook	39478
Sanford (Seminary)	39479
Sanitorium (Sanatorium)	39112
Sapa (Eupora)	39744
Sarah	38665
Sardis	38666
Sarepta (Randolph)	38864
Sartinsville (Jayess)	39641
Satartia	39162
Saucier	39574
Saukum (Crosby)	39633
Sauls (Ruth)	39662
Savage (Sarah)	38665
Savannah (Poplarville)	39470
Schlater	38952
Scobey	38953
Scooba	39358
Scott	38772
Sebastopol	39359
Sellers (Perkinston)	39573
Seminary	39479
Senatobia	38668
Seneca (Lumberton)	39455

Sessums (Starkville) 39759
Shady Grove (Laurel) 39440
Shannon 38868
Sharkey (Charleston) 38921
Sharon 39163, 39640
Shaw 38773
Shelby 38774
Shellmound (Greenwood) . 38930
Shepherd (Bruce) 38915
Sherard (Clarksdale) 38669
Sherman 38869
Sherwood (Mathiston) 39752
Shipman (Lucedale) 39452
Shivers (Pinola) 39149
Shubuta 39360
Shuqualak 39361
Sibleton (Kilmichael) 39747
Sibley 39165
Sidon 38954
Silver City 39166
Silver Creek 39663
Silver Run (Perkinston) 39573
Skene 38775
Skuna (Bruce) 38915
Slate Spring 38855
Slayden (Lamar) 38642
Sledge 38670
Smith (Collins) 39428
Smithdale 39664
Smithville 38870
Snow Lake Shores 38603
  (Ashland)
Society Hill (Oak Vale) 39656
Somerville (Minter City) 38944
Sonora (Houston) 38851
Sontag 39665
Soso 39480
South Amory (Amory) 38821
South Mccomb (Mc Comb) 39648
Southaven 38671
Southern (Hattiesburg) 39401
Sparta (Woodland) 39776
Splunge 38848
  (Greenwood Springs)
Spring Hill 38647, 38874
  (Michigan City)
Springdale (Water Valley) . 38965
Springville (Pontotoc) 38863
Stafford Springs 39439
  (Heidelberg)
Star 39167
Starkville 39759
Steens 39766
Steiner (Shaw) 38773
Stewart 39767
Stoneville 38776
Stonewall 39363
Stovall (Clarksdale) 38614
Straight Bayou (Anguilla) .. 38721
Strayhorn (Sarah) 38665
Strengthford (Laurel) 39440
Stringer 39481
Strongs (Aberdeen) 39730
Sturgis 39769
Success (Saucier) 39574
Summit 39666
Sumner 38957
Sumrall 39482
Sunflower 38778
Sunnycrest (Grenada) 38901
Sunnyside (Minter City) 38944

Sunrise (Hattiesburg) 39401
Swan Lake 38958
Sweatman (Duck Hill) 38925
Swiftown 38959
Swiftwater (Greenville) 38701
Sylvarena (Raleigh) 39153
Symonds (Rosedale) 38769
Talowah (Lumberton) 39455
Taska (Red Banks) 38661
Tatum (Gloster) 39638
Taylor 38673
Taylorsville 39168
Tchula 39169
Teasdale (Enid) 38927
Ten Mile (Perkinston) 39573
Terrell (Prentiss) 39474
Terry 39170
Terza (Batesville) 38606
Thaxton 38871
Thomastown 39171
Thompson (Smithdale) 39664
Thorn (Houston) 38851
Thornton 39172
Thrashers (Booneville) 38829
Three Rivers (Pascagoula) 39567
Thyatira (Senatobia) 38668
Tibbee (West Point) 39773
Tibbs (Sledge) 38670
Tie Plant 38960
Tillatoba 38961
Tilton (Monticello) 39654
Tinsley 39173
Tiplersville 38674
Tippo 38962
Tishomingo 38873
Toccopola 38874
Tomnolen (Eupora) 39744
Toomsuba 39364
Topeka (Jayess) 39641
Topisaw (Summit) 39666
Tougaloo 39174
Trebloc 38875
Tremont 38876
Triangle (Biloxi) 39534
Tribbett 38779
Trinity (Crawford) 39743
Troy (Pontotoc) 38863
Tuckers Crossing (Laurel) . 39440
Tula 38675
Tunica 38676
Tupelo 38801-803
  Ballardsville 38801
  Bissell 38801
  Chesterville 38801
  Mount Vernon 38801
Turnbull (Woodville) 39669
Turon (Smithville) 38870
Tutwiler 38963
Tylertown 39667
Tyro (Senatobia) 38668
Tyson (Coffeeville) 38922
Union (Plantersville) 38862
  .... 39365, 39437
Union Hall (Brookhaven) ... 39601
University 38677
Utica 39175
Vaiden 39176
Valewood (Glen Allan) 38744
Valley Hill (Carrollton) 38917
Valley Park 39177
Van Buren (Nettleton) 38858

Van Cleave 39564
  (Ocean Springs)
Van Vleet 38877
Vance 38964
Vancleave (Ocean Springs) 39564
Vardaman 38878
Varden (Vardaman) 38878
Vaughn (Brookhaven) 39601
Velma (Water Valley) 38965
Vernal (Lucedale) 39452
Verona 38879
Vicksburg 39180-182
Victoria 38679
Villa Ridge (Lumberton) 39455
Visa (Jackson) 39271
Vossburg 39366
Waco (Inverness) 38753
Waddell (Cedarbluff) 39741
Wade (Drew) 38737, 39567
Wakefield (Coldwater) 38618
Wallerville (New Albany) ... 38652
Wallhill (Coldwater) 38618
Walls 38680
Walnut 38683, 38964
  Brownfield 38683
  Camphill 38683
  Chalybeate 38683
Walnut Grove 39189
Walters (Ellisville) 39437
Walthall 39771
Vanilla (Monticello) 39654
Wardwell (Vardaman) 38878
Washington 39190
Water Valley 38949, 38965
  Paris 38949
  Pine Flat 38965
  Pine Valley 38965
  Springdale 38965
  Velma 38965
Waterford 38685
Waveland 39576
Waxhaw (Gunnison) 38746
Way (Canton) 39046
Waynesboro 39367
Wayside 38780
Webb 38966
Weir 39772
Wells Town (Lumberton) ... 39455
Wenasoga (Corinth) 38834
Wesson 39191
West 39192
West Biloxi (Biloxi) 39531
West Days 38641
  (Lake Cormorant)
West Lincoln (Brookhaven) 39601
West Point 39773
West Poplarville 39470
  (Poplarville)
Wheeler 38880
White Apple (Roxie) 39661
White Cap (Gloster) 39638
White Sand (Caledonia) 39740
Whitebluff (Foxworth) 39483
Whitehead (Glendora) 38928
Whites (West Point) 39773
Whites Crossing (Wiggins) 39577
Whitfield 39193, 39464
Whitney (Drew) 38737
Wiggins 39577
Wilkinson (Woodville) 39669
Willet (Hollandale) 38748

IMPORTANT BUILDINGS   MISSISSIPPI

BILOXI

GOVERNMENT

Federal Court House
725 WASHINGTON LOOP 39530

FLOWOOD

BUILDINGS

Mirror Lake Plaza
2829 LAKELAND DR 39208

GULFPORT

BUILDINGS

One Government Plz Building
2909 13TH ST 39501

GOVERNMENT

U S Naval Home
1800 BEACH DR 39507

HATTIESBURG

COLLEGES

University Of Southern MS
2901 HARDY ST 39406

JACKSON

BUILDINGS

Barnett Building
200 S PRESIDENT ST 39201

Capital Towers Building
125 S CONGRESS ST 39201

Deposit Guaranty Bk Building
200 E CAPITOL ST 39201

Deposit Guaranty Plz Building
210 E CAPITOL ST 39201

Hinds Professional Building
1815 HOSPITAL DR 39204

Lamar Life Building
317 E CAPITOL ST 39201

Lefleurs Bluff Tower
4780 I 55 N 39211

Magnolia Fed Bank Building
202 N CONGRESS ST 39201

Medical Arts Building East
1190 N STATE ST 39202

Medical Arts Building West
1151 N STATE ST 39202

One Jackson Place
188 E CAPITOL ST 39201

Saint Dominic Med Mall
971 LAKELAND DR 39216

Security Centre
200 S LAMAR ST 39201

Stadium Tower
440 E Woodrow Wilson Av 39216

Standard Life Building
127 S ROACH ST 39201

Trustmark Natl Bank Building
248 E CAPITOL ST 39201

University Plaza
500 E Woodrow Wilson Av 39216

University Plaza
514 E Woodrow Wilson Av 39216

GOVERNMENT

A H Mccoy Federal Building
100 W CAPITOL ST 39269

Capitol Building
400 HIGH ST 39201

Carroll Gartin Building
450 HIGH ST 39201

City Hall
219 S PRESIDENT ST 39201

County Chancery Court Bld
316 S PRESIDENT ST 39201

Heber Ladner Building
401 MISSISSIPPI ST 39201

Hinds Count Court Building
327 E PASCAGOULA ST .. 39201

James O Eastland Building
245 E CAPITOL ST 39201

Municipal Court Building
327 E PASCAGOULA ST .. 39201

Public Empl Ret Syst Building
429 MISSISSIPPI ST 39201

Walter Sillers Building
550 HIGH ST 39201

Woolfolk State Office
501 N WEST ST 39201

MEEHAM

GOVERNMENT

City Hall
601 24TH AVE 39301

Federal Building
2100 9TH ST 39301

Lauderdale Co Court House
500 CONSTITUTION AVE 39301

MISSOURI
Abbreviation MO

Acornridge (Puxico) 63960
Adair (Brashear) 63533
Adrian 64720
Advance 63730
Affton (Saint Louis) 63123
Agency 64401
Alba 64830
Albany 64402
Aldrich 65601
Alexandria 63430
Allbright (Marquand) 63655
Allendale 64420
Allenton 63001
Allenville (Chaffee) 63740
Alley Springs (Eminence) .. 65466
Alma 64001
Altamont 64620
Altenburg 63732
Alton 65606
Amazonia 64421
Americus (Rhineland) 65069
Amity 64422
Amoret 64722
Amsterdam 64723
Anabel 63431
Anderson 64831
Annada 63330
Annapolis 63620
Anniston 63820
Antonia (Barnhart) .. 63012, 63052
Anutt (Lecoma) 65540
Apple Creek (Oak Ridge) .. 63769
Appleton City 64724
Arab 63733
Arbela 63432, 63442
Arbor (Chaffee) 63740
Arbyrd 63821
Arcadia 63621
Archie 64725
Arcola 65603
Ardmore (Excello) 65247
Argyle 65001
Armstrong 65230
Arnold 63010
Aroma (Granby) 64844
Arrow Rock 65320
Asbury 64832
Ash (Madison) 65263
Ash Grove 65604
Ashburn 63433
Asherville (Puxico) 63960
Ashland 65010
Ashton (Luray) 63453
Athens (Revere) 63465
Atlanta 63530
Att (Kansas City) 64184
Auburn (Elsberry) 63343
Augusta 63332
Aullville (Higginsville) 64037
Aurora 65605
Aurora Springs (Eldon) 65026
Auxvasse 65231
Ava 65608
Avalon 64621
Avilla 64833
Avondale (Kansas City) 64117
Babbtown (Meta) ... 65058, 65085
Bachelor (Auxvasse) 65231

Baden (Saint Louis) 63147
Bagnell (Eldon) 65026
Bahner (Smithton) 65350
Bairdtown (Milan) 63556
Bakersfield 65609
Ballwin 63011, 63021-022
  Ellisville 63011
  Ellisville 63021
  Manchester 63011
  Manchester 63021
  Sherman 63021
  Town And Country 63011
  Twin Oaks 63021
  Winchester 63011
  Winchester 63021
Baring 63531
Barnard 64423
Barnesville (Atlanta) 63530
Barnett 65011
Barnhart 63012
Bates City 64011
Battlefield 65619
  (Brookline Station)
Bay (Hermann) 65041
Beaman (Smithton) 65350
Beaufort 63013
Bel Nor (Saint Louis) 63121
Bel Ridge (Saint Louis) 63121
Belgrade 63622
Bell City 63735
Bella Villa (Saint Louis) 63125
Bellair (Bunceton) 65237
Belle 65013
Belle Center (Joplin) 64801
Bellerive (Saint Louis) 63121
Belleview 63623
Bellflower 63333
Belton 64012
Bem (Owensville) 65066
Bendavis 65433
Bennett (Briar) 63931
Benton 63736
Benton City 65232
Berger 63014
Berkeley (Saint Louis) 63134
.... 63140
Bernie 63822
Berryman (Steelville) 65565
Bertrand 63823
Berwick (Pierce City) 65723
Bethany 64424
Bethel 63434
Beulah 65436
Beverly Hills 63121
  (Saint Louis)
Bevier 63532
Bible Grove (Baring) 63531
Biehle (Perryville) 63775
Big Creek (Marquand) 63655
Big Piney (Newburg) 65550
Big Springs 63363
  (New Florence)
Bigelow (Craig) 64437
Billings 65610
Billingsville (Boonville) 65233
Birch Tree 65438
Birmingham (Kansas City) . 64161
Bismarck 63624
Bixby 65439
Black 63625
Black Jack (Florissant) 63033

Black Walnut 63301
  (Saint Charles)
Blackburn 65321
Blackwater 65322
Blackwell 63626
Blairstown 64726
Bland 65014, 65062
  Canaan 65014
  Cleavesville 65014
  Cooper Hill 65014
  Old Woolam 65014
  Red Bird 65014
Blodgett 63824
Bloomfield 63825
Bloomington (Bevier) 63532
Bloomsdale 63627
Blue Eye 65611
Blue Springs 64013-015
  Lake Tapawingo 64015
Bluffton (Rhineland) 65069
Blythedale 64426
Boekerton (Portageville) ... 63873
Bogard 64622
Bolckow 64427
Bolivar 65613, 65727
  Slagle 65613
Bonne Terre 63628
Bonnots Mill 65016
Boonesboro (Franklin) 65250
Boonville 65233
Boss 65440
Bosworth 64623
Boulder City (Granby) 64844
Bourbon 65441
Bowen (Windsor) 65360
Bowling Green 63334
Boynton (Milan) 63556
Bradleyville 65614
Bragg City 63827
Braggadocio 63826
Branch (Macks Creek) 65786
Brandsville 65688
Branson 65616
Branson West 65737
  (Reeds Spring)
Brashear 63533
Braymer 64624
Brazeau 63737
Brazito (Jefferson City) 65109
Breckenridge 64625
Breckenridge Hills 63114
  (Saint Louis)
Brentwood (Saint Louis) 63144
Brewer (Perryville) 63775
Briar 63931
Bridgeton 63044-045
  Hazelwood 63044
Brighton 65617
Brimson (Gilman City) 64642
Brinktown 65443
Briscoe (Troy) 63379
Brixey 65618
Bronaugh 64728
Brookfield 64628
Brookline Station 65619
Brooklyn Heights 64836
  (Carthage)
Broseley 63932
Browning 64630
Browns Spring (Billings) 65610
Browns Station (Columbia) 65202

Brownwood	63738	Cedar Gap (Seymour)	65746	Colony (Baring) 63531, 63563
Brumley	65017	Cedar Hill	63016	Columbia 65201-203, 65205
Bruner	65620	Cedar Ridge (Long Lane)	65590	.... 65211-12, 65216-18
Brunswick	65236	Cedarcreek	65627	Browns Station	65202
Brush Creek (Owensville)	65066	Cedron (Jamestown)	65046	Deer Park	65201
Buckhorn (Marquand)	63655	Census Bureau	64189	Easley	65203
	65583	(Kansas City)		Elkhurst	65201
Bucklin	64631	Center	63436	Harg	65201
Buckner	64016	Centertown	65023	Hinton	65202
Bucyrus	65444	Centerview	64019	Huntsdale	65203
Buell (Montgomery City)	63361	Centerville	63633	Lindbergh	65202
Buffalo	65622	Central City (Joplin)	64801	Mcbaine	65203
Bunceton	65237	Centralia	65240	Midway	65202
Bunker	63629	Chadwick	65629	Murry	65202
Burfordville	63739	Chaffee	63740	Pierpont	65201
Burke City (Saint Louis)	63135	Chain Of Rocks	63369	Prathersville	65202
Burlington Junction	64428	(Old Monroe)		Sapp	65203
Bute (Milan)	63556	Chamois	65024	Shaw	65202
Butler	64730	Chariton (Coatsville)	63535	Stephens	65202
Butterfield	65623	Charlack (Saint Louis)	63114	Commerce	63742
Bynumville (Salisbury)	65281	Charleston	63834	Conception	64433
Byron (Belle)	65013	Cherry Box (Clarence)	63437	Conception Junction	64434
Cabool	65689		63451	Concordia	64020
Cadet	63630	Cherryville	65446	Connelsville (Novinger)	63559
Cainsville	64632	Chesterfield 63005-006, 63017		Conran	63838
Cairo	65239	Clarkson Valley	63005	Conway	65632
Caledonia	63631	Clarkson Valley	63017	Cook Station	65449
Calhoun	65323	Gumbo	63017	Cooper Hill (Bland)	65014
California 65018, 65042		Town And Country	63017	Cooter	63839
Kliever	65018	Chestnutridge	65630	Cora (Milan)	63556
Callao	63534	Chicopee (Van Buren)	63965	Corder	64021
Calverton Park	63135	Chilhowee	64733	Corning	64435
(Saint Louis)		Chillicothe	64601	Corridon (Centerville)	63633
Calwood (Fulton)	65251	Chula	64635	Corso (Silex)	63377
Cambridge (Gilliam)	65330	Clara (Houston)	65483	Cosby	64436
Camden	64017	Clarence	63437	Cottleville	63338
Camden Point	64018	Clark	65243	Cotton (Bunceton)	65237
Camdenton	65020	Clarks Fork (Boonville)	65233	Cottonwood Point	63830
Cameron	64429	Clarksburg	65025	(Caruthersville)	
Camp Branch (Warrenton)	63383	Clarksdale	64430	Couch	65690
Camp Clark (Nevada)	64772	Clarkson Valley 63005, 63017		Courtois (Steelville)	65565
Campbell	63933	(Chesterfield)		Cowgill	64637
Campbellton (New Haven)	63068	Clarksville	63336	Craig	64437
	63090	Clarkton	63837	Crane	65633
Canaan (Bland)	65014	Clay (Hannibal)	63401	Creighton	64739
Canalou	63828	Clayton (Saint Louis)	63105	Crescent (Eureka)	63025
Canton	63435		63124	Crestwood (Saint Louis)	63126
Cape Fair	65624	Clearmont	64431	Cretcher (Sweet Springs)	65351
Cape Girardeau 63701-703,		Clearwater	63670	Creve Coeur (Saint Louis)	63141
	63705	(Sainte Genevieve)		Crocker	65452
Caplinger Mills	65607	Cleavesville (Bland)	65014	Cross Timbers	65634
Cappeln (Foristell)	63348	Cleveland	64734	Crosstown (Perryville)	63775
Capps Creek (Miller)	65707	Clever	65631	Crystal City	63019
Cardwell	63829	Clifton Hill	65244	Crystal Lake Park	63131
Carl Junction	64834	Climax Springs	65324	(Saint Louis)	
Carrington (Fulton)	65251	Clinton	64735	Cuba	65453
Carrollton	64633	Cliquot (Dunnegan)	65640	Curryville	63339
Carterville	64835	Clover Bottom	63090	Cyrene (Bowling Green)	63334
Carthage	64836	(Washington)		Dadeville	65635
Caruth (Kennett)	63857	Clubb	63934	Daisy	63743
Caruthersville	63830	Clyde	64432	Dalton	65246
Carytown (Carthage)	64836	Coatsville	63535	Damascus (Osceola)	64776
Cascade	63632	Cobalt City	63645	Danville	63361
Case (Hermann)	65041	(Fredericktown)		(Montgomery City)	
Cass (Elk Creek)	65464	Coffey	64636	Dardenne (O Fallon)	63366
Cassville (Butterfield)	65623	Coffman	63670	Darksville (Huntsville)	65259
	65625	(Sainte Genevieve)		Darlington	64438
Catawissa	63015	Coldwater (Silva)	63964	Davis (Troy)	63379
Catron	63833	Cole Camp	65325	Davisville	65456
Caulfield	65626	College Mound (Excello)	65247	Dawn	64638
Cedar City	65022	Collins	64738	De Kalb	64440

De Soto 63020
De Witt 64639
Dearborn 64439
Deepwater 64740
Deer Park (Columbia) 65201
Deer Ridge (La Belle) 63447
Deerfield 64741
Deering 63840
Defiance 63341
Dellwood 63135-136
(Saint Louis)
Delta 63744
Denver 64441
Des Arc 63636
Des Peres (Saint Louis) ... 63122
.... 63131
Desloge (Flat River) 63601
.... 63624
Desoto (De Soto) 63020
Detmold (New Haven) 63068
Devils Elbow 65457
Dexter 63841
Diamond 64840
Diehlstadt (Charleston) 63834
Diggins 65636
Dissen (New Haven) 63068
Dittmer 63023
Dixie (New Bloomfield) 65063
Dixon 65459
Doe Run 63637
Doniphan 63935
Doolittle (Rolla) 65401
Dora 65637
Doss (Salem) 65560
Dover 64022
Downing 63536
Drake (Owensville) 65066
Dresden (Sedalia) .. 65301, 65337
Drexel 64742
Drury 65638
Dudley 63936
Duenweg 64841
Dugginsville (Theodosia) .. 65761
Duke 65461
Duncans Bridge (Clarence) 63437
Dunksburg (Sweet Springs) 65351
Dunnegan 65640
Duquesne (Joplin) 64801
Durham 63438
Dutchtown 63745
Dutzow 63342
Eagle Rock 65641
Eagleville 64442
Earth City 63045
Easley (Columbia) 65203
East Lynne 64743
East Prairie 63845
Easton 64443
Eastwood (Van Buren) 63965
Economy (Atlanta) 63530
Edgar Springs 65462
Edgerton 64444
Edina 63537
Edmundson (Saint Louis) .. 63134
Edwards 65326
El Dorado Springs 64744
Eldon 65026, 65072
Aurora Springs 65026
Bagnell 65026
Eldridge 65463
Elk Creek 65464

Elkhead (Sparta) 65753
Elkhorn (Warrenton) 63383
Elkhurst (Columbia) 65201
Elkland 65644
Ellington 63638
Ellis Prairie (Bucyrus) 65444
Ellisville (Ballwin) ... 63011, 63021
Ellsinore 63937
Elmer 63538
Elmo 64445
Elmwood (Blackburn) 65321
Elsberry 63343
Elston (Jefferson City) 65109
Elvins (Flat River) 63601
Ely (Palmyra) 63461
Emden 63439
Eminence 65466
Emma 65327
Englewood (Ashland) 65010
Enon (Russellville) 65074
Eolia 63344
Equality (Tuscumbia) 65082
Ernestville (Concordia) 64020
Essex 63846
Esther (Flat River) 63601
Estill (New Franklin) 65274
Ethel 63539
Ethlyn (Old Monroe) 63369
Etlah (Berger) 63014
Etterville 65031
Eudora 65645
Eugene 65032
Eunice 65468
Eureka 63025
Evansville (Moberly) 65270
Evening Shade (Plato) 65552
Everton 65646
Ewing 63440
Excello 65247
Excelsior Springs 64024
Exeter 65647
Fagus 63938
Fair Grove 65648
Fair Play 65649
Fairdealing 63939
Fairfax 64446
Fairmont (Wyaconda) 63474
Fairport 64447
Fairview 64842
Falcon 65470
Farber 63345
Farley 64028
Farmington 63640
Farrar 63746
Faucett 64448
Fayette 65248
Femme Osage (Augusta) .. 63332
Fenton 63026, 63099
Ferguson 63135-136, 63145
(Saint Louis)
Ferrelview (Kansas City) ... 64163
Festus 63028
Fidelity (Carthage) 64836
Fillmore 64449
Finley (Ozark) 65721
Fisk 63940
Flat River ... 63601, 63644, 63653
Desloge 63601
Elvins 63601
Esther 63601
Leadington 63601

Rivermines 63601
Flemington 65650
Fletcher 63030
Flinthill 63346
Flor (Florissant) 63031
Flordell Hills 63136
(Saint Louis)
Florence 65329
Florida (Stoutsville) 65283
Florissant 63031-034
Black Jack 63033
Flor 63031
Foley 63347
Folk (Westphalia) 65085
Fordland 65652
Forest City 64451
Forest Green (Salisbury) ... 65281
Forest Springs 63446
(Knox City)
Foristell 63348
Forsyth 65653
Fort Leonard Wood 65473
Fort Lyon (Windsor) 65360
Fort Osage (Sibley) 64088
Fortescue 64452
Fortuna 65034
Foster 64745
Four Seasons 65049
(Lake Ozark)
Frankclay 63644
Frankenstein 65016
(Bonnots Mill)
Frankford 63441
Franklin 65250
Fredericksburg (Morrison) . 65061
Fredericktown 63645
Freeborn (Clarkton) 63837
Freeburg 65035
Freedom (Chamois) 65024
Freeman 64746
Freistatt 65654
Fremont 63941
French Village 63036
Friedheim 63747
Fristoe (Warsaw) 65355
Frohna 63748
Frontenac (Saint Louis) 63131
Fulton 65251
Gainesville 65655
Howards Ridge 65655
Galena 65656
Gallatin 64640
Galmey (Wheatland) 65779
Galt 64641
Gamma (Bellflower) 63333
Garden City 64747
Garrison 65657
Garwood (Van Buren) 63965
Gasconade 65036
Gatewood 63942
Gentry 64453
Gentryville (Albany) 64402
Georgetown (Sedalia) 65301
Gerald 63037
Gibbs 63540
Gibson 63847
Gideon 63848
Gilliam 65330
Gilman City 64642
Gilmore (Wentzville) 63385
Gipsy 63750

Gladden (Salem)	65560
Gladstone (Kansas City)	64118
Glasgow	65254
Glasgow Village	63137
(Saint Louis)	
Glenallen	63751
Glencoe	63038
Glendale (Saint Louis)	63122
Glensted (Versailles)	65084
Glenwood	63541
Glover	63646
Gobler	63849
Goldberry (Ethel)	63539
Golden	65658
Golden City	64748
Goldsberry (Ethel)	63539
Gooch Mill (Boonville)	65233
Goodfellow Terrace	63120
(Saint Louis)	
Goodland (Belleview)	63623
Goodman	64843
Goodson	65659
Gordonville	63752
Gorin	63543
Goss (Paris)	65275
Gouch Mill (Prairie Home)	65068
Gower	64454
Graff	65660
Graham	64455
Grain Valley	64029
Granby	64844
Grand Falls (Joplin)	64801
Grand Pass (Malta Bend)	65339
Grandin	63943
Grandview	64030
Granger	63442
Grant City	64456
Granville (Paris)	65275
Grassy	63753
Gravelton (Marquand)	63655
Gravois Mills	65037-038
Gray Summit	63039
Grayridge	63850
Grays Point (Miller)	65707
Graysville (Livonia)	63551
	63565
Green Castle	63544
Green City	63545
Green Lawn (Perry)	63462
Green Ridge	65332
Greenbrier (Advance)	63730
Greendale (Saint Louis)	63133
Greenfield	65661
Greensburg (Baring)	63531
Greentop	63546
Greenview (Camdenton)	65020
Greenville	63944
Greenwood	64034
Gretna (Branson)	65616
Grogan (Elk Creek)	65464
Grover	63040
Grovespring	65662
Grubville	63041
Guilford	64457
Gumbo (Chesterfield)	63017
Gunn City (Latour)	64760
Guthrie (New Bloomfield)	65063
Hagars Grove (Clarence)	63437
Hahatonka (Camdenton)	65020
Hale	64643
Half Way	65663

Hallsville	65255
Halltown	65664
Hamilton	64644
Hams Prairie (Fulton)	65251
Hanley Hills	63133
(Saint Louis)	
Hannibal	63401
Hardenville	65666
Hardin	64035
Harg (Columbia)	65201
Harris	64645
Harrisburg	65256
Harrisonville	64701
Hart (Seneca)	64865
Hartford (New Hartford)	63364
Hartsburg	65039
Hartshorn	65479
Hartville	65667
Hartwell (Urich)	64788
Harvester (Saint Charles)	63303
Harviell	63945
Harwood	64750
Hassard (Monroe City)	63456
Hastain (Edwards)	65326
Hatfield	64458
Hatton (Auxvasse)	65231
Hawk Point	63349
Hayden (Dixon)	65459
Hayti	63851
Hayti Heights (Hayti)	63851
Hayward (Portageville)	63873
Haywood City (Benton)	63736
	63771
Hazelwood	63042-045
Robertson	63042
Vigus	63042
Helena	64459
Hematite	63047
Hemple (Stewartsville)	64490
Henley	65040
Henrietta	64036
Herculaneum	63048
Hermann	65041, 65056
Bay	65041
Case	65041
Swiss	65041
Hermitage	65668
Hickory Hill (Henley)	65040
Higbee	65257
Higginsville	64037
High Gate (Saint James)	65559
High Hill	63350
High Point	65042
High Ridge	63049
Highland (Perryville)	63775
Highlandville	65669
Hillsboro	63050
Hinton (Columbia)	65202
Hiram	63947
Hoberg (Mount Vernon)	65712
Hoene Spring (Eureka)	63025
Holcomb	63852
Holden	64040
Holland	63853
Holliday	65258
Hollister	65672
Holt	64048
Holts Summit	65043
Homestown (Wardell)	63879
Honey Creek	65101
(Jefferson City)	

Hope (Morrison)	65061
Hopewell (Mineral Point)	63660
Hopkins	64461
Horine (Pevely)	63070
Hornersville	63855
Hornet (Seneca)	64865
Horton	64751
House Creek (Van Buren)	63965
House Springs	63051
Houston	65483
Houstonia	65333
Howards Ridge	65655
(Gainesville)	
Howardville (New Madrid)	63869
Huggins	65484
Hughesville	65334
Hugo (Linn Creek)	65052
Humansville	65674
Hume	64752
Humphreys	64646
Hunnewell	63443
Huntington (Hannibal)	63401
Huntleigh (Saint Louis)	63131
Huntsdale (Columbia)	65203
Huntsville	65259
Hurdland	63547
Hurley	65675
Iantha (Lamar)	64759
Iberia	65486
Ilasco (Hannibal)	63401
Imperial	63052-053
Antonia	63052
Otto	63052
Independence	64050-058
Sugar Creek	64054
Indian Creek	63456
(Monroe City)	
Indian Grove (Brunswick)	65236
Ink (Eminence)	65466
Ionia	65335
Iron Gates (Joplin)	64801
Iron Mountain (Ironton)	63650
Iron Mountain Lake	63624
(Bismarck)	
Irondale	63648
Ironton	63650
Irwin (Lamar)	64759
Isabella	65676
Jackson	63755
Jacksonville	65260
Jadwin	65501
Jameson	64647
Jamesport	64648
Jamestown	65046
Jane (Pineville)	64856
Japan (Sullivan)	63080
Jasper	64755
Jefferson City	65101-110
Brazito	65109
Elston	65109
Honey Creek	65101
Osage City	65101
Saint Martins	65109
Schubert	65101
Taos	65101
Wardsville	65101
Jenkins (Aurora)	65605
Jennings (Saint Louis)	63136
Jerico Springs	64756
Jerome	65529
Jonesburg	63351

Marion (Centertown)	65023	
Marionville	65705	
Maritz Inc (Fenton)	63099	
Marquand	63655	
Marshall	65340	
Marshfield	65706	
Marston	63866	
Marthasville	63357	
Martin City (Kansas City)	64147	
Martinsburg	65264	
Martinstown (Novinger)	63559	
	63565	
Martinsville	64467	
Marvin (Versailles)	65084	
Maryknoll (Old Monroe)	63369	
Maryland Heights	63043	
Marys Home (Eugene)	65032	
Maryville	64468	
Matson (Defiance)	63341	
Matthews	63867	
Maud (Clarence)	63437	
Maxville (Arnold)	63010	
Maysville	64469	
Mayview	64071	
Maywood	63454	
Mc Bride	63776	
Mc Clurg	65701	
Mc Fall	64657	
Mc Gee	63763	
Mc Girk	65055	
Mcbaine (Columbia)	65203	
Mckittrick	65056	
Meadville	64659	
Medill (Kahoka)	63445	
Mehlville (Saint Louis)	63129	
Memphis	63555	
Mendon	64660	
Mendota (Unionville)	63565	
Menfro	63765	
Mercer	64661	
Mercyville (Elmer)	63538	
Meta	65058	
Metz	64765	
Mexico	65265	
Miami	65344	
Middle Brook	63656	
Middle Grove (Madison)	65263	
Middletown	63359	
Midland (Novinger)	63559	
Midway (Columbia)	65202	
Milan	63556	
Mildred (Kirbyville)	65679	
Milford	64766	
Mill Spring	63952	
Millard (Kirksville)	63501	
Millcreek (Fredericktown)	63645	
Miller	65707	
Millersburg (Fulton)	65251	
Millersville	63766	
Millwood (Silex)	63377	
Milo	64767	
Mincy (Kirbyville)	65679	
Mindenmines	64769	
Mine La Motte	63645	
(Fredericktown)		
Mineral Point	63660	
Mint Hill (Chamois)	65024	
Mirabile (Polo)	64071	
Missouri City	64072	
Moberly	65270	
Mokane	65059	

Moline Acres	63136	
(Saint Louis)		
Monett	65708	
Monkey Run (Hannibal)	63401	
Monroe City	63456	
Monsanto (Saint Louis)	63167	
	63198	
Montgomery City	63361	
Monticello	63457	
Montier	65546	
Montreal	65591	
Montrose	64770	
Montserrat (Knob Noster)	65336	
Moody	65777	
Mooresville	64664	
Mora	65345	
Morehouse	63868	
Morgan Heights (Carthage)	64836	
Morley	63767	
Morrison (Gasconade)	65036	
	65061	
Fredericksburg	65061	
Hope	65061	
Pershing	65061	
Morrisville (Eudora)	65645	
	65710	
Morse Mill	63066	
Mosby	64073	
Moscow Mills	63362	
Moselle (Union)	63084	
Mound City	64470	
Moundville	64771	
Mount Hulda (Cole Camp)	65325	
Mount Leonard	65339	
(Malta Bend)		
Mount Moriah	64665	
Mount Sterling	65062	
Mount Vernon	65712	
Mountain Grove	65711	
Mountain View	65548	
Murphy (Fenton)	63026	
Murry (Columbia)	65202	
Musselfork (Keytesville)	65261	
Myrtle	65778	
Mystic (Green City)	63545	
Napoleon	64074	
Napton (Marshall)	65340	
Naylor	63953	
Nebo (Falcon)	65470	
Neck City	64849	
Neelyville	63954	
Nelson	65347	
Neosho	64850, 64853	
Nevada	64772	
New Bloomfield	65063	
New Boston	63557	
New Cambria	63558	
New Florence	63363	
New Franklin	65274	
New Hamburg (Benton)	63736	
New Hampton	64471	
New Hartford	63364	
New Haven	63068	
New Hope (Elsberry)	63343	
New London	63459	
New Madrid	63869	
New Melle	63365	
New Offenburg	63661	
New Point (Oregon)	64473	
New Truxton (Truxton)	63381	
New Wells (Altenburg)	63732	

Newark	63458	
Newburg	65550	
Newtonia	64853	
Newtown	64667	
Niangua	65713	
Nind (Kirksville)	63501	
Nixa	65714	
Noble	65715	
Noel	64854	
Norborne	64668	
Normandy (Saint Louis)	63121	
North County	63137-138	
(Saint Louis)		
North Kansas City	64116	
(Kansas City)		
North Lilbourn (Lilbourn)	63862	
North Salem (Winigan)	63566	
Northwoods (Saint Louis)	63121	
Norwood	65717	
Nottinghill (Thornfield)	65762	
Novelty	63460	
Novinger	63559	
Number Eight (Bevier)	63532	
O Fallon	63366-367	
Dardenne	63366	
Saint Paul	63366	
Oak Grove	64075	
Oak Ridge	63769	
Oakland (Saint Louis)	63122	
Oakville (Saint Louis)	63129	
Oakwood (Hannibal)	63401	
Oates (Black)	63625	
Ocie (Theodosia)	65761	
Odessa	64076	
Old Alexandria (Troy)	63379	
Old Appleton	63770	
Old Fredonia (Warsaw)	65355	
Old Mines (Cadet)	63630	
Old Monroe	63369	
Old Woolam (Bland)	65014	
Old Woollam (Owensville)	65066	
Oldfield	65720	
Olean	65064	
Olivette (Saint Louis)	63132	
Olney	63370	
Olympian Village	63020	
(De Soto)		
Oran	63771	
Orchard Farm	63301	
(Saint Charles)		
Oregon	64473	
Oronogo	64855	
Orrick	64077	
Osage Beach	65065	
Osage City	65101	
(Jefferson City)		
Osborn	64474	
Osceola	64776	
Otterville	65348	
Otto (Imperial)	63052	
Overland (Saint Louis)	63114	
Overton (Boonville)	65233	
Owasco (Milan)	63556	
Owensville	65066	
Owls Bend (Eminence)	65466	
Oxly	63955	
Ozark	65721	
Pacific	63069	
Pagedale (Saint Louis)	63133	
Painton	63772	
Palace (Plato)	65552	

Bel Nor	63121	
Bel Ridge	63121	
Bella Villa	63125	
Bellerive	63121	
Berkeley	63134	
Berkeley	63140	
Beverly Hills	63121	
Breckenridge Hills	63114	
Brentwood	63144	
Burke City	63135	
Calverton Park	63135	
Charlack	63114	
Clayton	63105	
Clayton	63124	
Crestwood	63126	
Creve Coeur	63141	
Crystal Lake Park	63131	
Dellwood	63135-136	
Des Peres	63122	
Des Peres	63131	
Edmundson	63134	
Ferguson	63145	
Flordell Hills	63136	
Frontenac	63131	
Glasgow Village	63137	
Glendale	63122	
Goodfellow Terrace	63120	
Greendale	63133	
Hanley Hills	63133	
Huntleigh	63131	
Jennings	63136	
Kinloch	63140	
Kirkwood	63122	
Ladue	63124	
Lemay	63125	
Maplewood	63143	
Mehlville	63129	
Moline Acres	63136	
Monsanto	63167	
Monsanto	63198	
Normandy	63121	
North County	63137-138	
Northwoods	63121	
Oakland	63122	
Oakville	63129	
Olivette	63132	
Overland	63114	
Pagedale	63133	
Pasadena Hills	63121	
Pine Lawn	63120	
Ralston Purina	63164	
Richmond Heights	63117	
Riverview	63137	
Rock Hill	63119	
Saint John	63114	
Sappington	63126-128	
Shrewsbury	63119	
South County	63129	
Spanish Lake	63138	
Sunset Hills	63127	
Town And Country	63131	
University City	63124	
University City	63130	
Velda Village	63121	
Vinita Park	63114	
Warson Woods	63122	
Webster Groves	63119	
Wellston	63112	
Wellston	63133	
West County	63146	
Woodson Terrace	63134	

Saint Martins	65109	
(Jefferson City)		
Saint Mary	63673	
Saint Marys (Saint Mary)	63673	
Saint Patrick	63466	
Saint Paul (O Fallon)	63366	
Saint Peters	63376	
Saint Robert	65583	
(Waynesville)		
Saint Thomas	65076	
Sainte Genevieve	63670	
Salem	65560	
Saline City (Slater)	65349	
Salisbury	65281	
Salt Pond (Sweet Springs)	65351	
Salt River (Perry)	63462	
Sand Hill (Rutledge)	63563	
Sandy Hook (Jamestown)	65046	
Santa Fe	65282	
Santiago (Windsor)	65360	
Sapp (Columbia)	65203	
Sappington	63126-128	
(Saint Louis)		
Sarcoxie	64862	
Savannah	64485	
Saverton	63467	
Schell City	64783	
Schluersburg (Augusta)	63332	
Schubert (Jefferson City)	65101	
Scopus (Marble Hill)	63764	
Scotland (Carthage)	64836	
Scott City	63780	
Sedalia	65301-302	
Dresden	65301	
Georgetown	65301	
Longwood	65301	
Springfork	65301	
Sedgewickville	63781	
Seligman	65745	
Senath	63876	
Seneca	64865	
Sereno (Perryville)	63775	
Seymour	65746	
Shannondale (Salem)	65560	
Sharon (Slater)	65349	
Shaw (Columbia)	65202	
Shelbina	63468	
Shelbyville	63469	
Sheldon	64784	
Shell Knob	65747	
Sheridan	64486	
Sherman (Ballwin)	63021	
Shibleys Point (Novinger)	63559	
Shook	63963	
Shrewsbury (Saint Louis)	63119	
Sibley	64088	
Sidney (Green Castle)	63544	
Sikeston	63801	
Silex	63377	
Siloam Springs	65775	
(West Plains)		
Silva (Clubb)	63934, 63964	
Coldwater	63964	
Silver Lake (Perryville)	63775	
Simmons (Houston)	65483	
Skidmore	64487	
Slagle (Bolivar)	65613	
Slater	65349	
Sligo (Salem)	65560	
Smithfield	64834	
(Carl Junction)		

Smithton	65350	
Smithville	64089	
Snyder (Triplett)	65286	
Solo	65564	
Sorrell (Milan)	63556	
Souder (Wasola)	65773	
South County	63129	
(Saint Louis)		
South Fork	65776	
South Gifford (La Plata)	63549	
South Greenfield	65752	
South River (Palmyra)	63461	
South Shore	63301	
(Saint Charles)		
South Van Buren	63965	
(Van Buren)		
South West City	64863	
Spalding (Hannibal)	63401	
Spanish Lake	63138	
(Saint Louis)		
Sparta	65753	
Speed (Boonville)	65233	
Sperry (Kirksville)	63501	
Spickard	64679	
Spokane	65754	
Spring Bluff (Sullivan)	63080	
Spring Garden (Eugene)	65032	
Spring Lake (Kirksville)	63501	
Springfield	65800-810	
	65890, 65898-899	
Springfork (Sedalia)	65301	
Springtown	63660	
(Mineral Point)		
Squires	65755	
Stahl (Novinger)	63559	
Stanberry	64489	
Stanton	63079	
Stark City	64866	
Starkenburg (Rhineland)	65069	
Steedman	65077	
Steele	63877	
Steelville	65565-566	
Berryman	65565	
Courtois	65565	
Steffenville	63470	
Stella	64867	
Stephens (Columbia)	65202	
Stet64680		
Stewartsville	64490	
Stockton	65785	
Stones Corner (Joplin)	64801	
Stoney Point	63660	
(Mineral Point)		
Stony Hill (New Haven)	63068	
Stotesbury (Hume)	64752	
Stotts City	65756	
Stoutland	65567	
Stoutsville	65283	
Stover	65078	
Strafford	65757	
Strain (Sullivan)	63080	
Strasburg	64090	
Stringtown	64834	
(Carl Junction)		
Strother (Paris)	65275	
Sturdivant	63782	
Sturgeon	65284	
Sublette (Greentop)	63546	
Success	65570	
Sugar Creek	64054	
(Independence)		

Sullivan 63080
Sulphur Springs 63083
Summerfield (Belle) 65013
Summersville 65571
Summit (Mineral Point) 63660
Sumner 64681
Sunrise Beach 65079
Sunset Hills 63127
  (Saint Louis)
Sutherland (Windsor) 65360
Swedeborg 65572
Sweet Springs 65351
Swiss (Hermann) 65041
Syracuse 65354
Taberville (Rockville) 64780
Tallapoosa 63878
Taneyville 65759
Taos (Faucett) 64448, 65101
Tarkio 64491
Tarrants (Bowling Green) .. 63334
Taylor 63471
Tebbetts 65080
Tecumseh 65760
Tenmile (Macon) 63552
Teresita 65573
Thayer 65791
Theodosia 65761
Thomas Hill 65244
  (Clifton Hill)
Thomasville (Birch Tree) .. 65438
Thompson 65285
Thornfield 65762
Tiff 63674
Tiff City 64868
Tightwad (Clinton) 64735
Timber (Salem) 65560
Times Beach (Eureka) 63025
Tina 64682
Tipton 65081
Tolona (Lewistown) 63452
Town And Country 63011
  .... 63017, 63131
  (Ballwin)
Tracy (Platte City) 64079
Treloar 63378
Trenton 64683
Trimble 64492
Triplett 65286
Troy 63379
Truesdail (Warrenton) 63383
Truesdale (Warrenton) 63383
Truxton 63381
Tunas 65764
Turners 65765
Turney 64493
Tuscumbia 65082
Twin Oaks 63021, 63088
  (Ballwin)
Tyrone 65464, 65483
  (Elk Creek)
Udall 65766
Ulman 65083
Union 63084
Union City (Billings) 65610
Union Star 64494
Uniontown 63783
Unionville 63565
Unity Village 64063-064
  (Lees Summit)

University City 63124, 63130
  (Saint Louis)
Urbana 65767
Urbandale (Moberly) 65270
Urich 64788
Utica 64686
Valles Mines 63020, 63087
  (De Soto)
Valley City (Knob Noster) .. 65336
Valley Park 63088
Van Buren 63965
Vancleve (Meta) 65058
Vandalia 63382
Vandiver Village (Mexico) .. 65265
Vanduser 63784
Vanzant 65768
Velda Village 63121
  (Saint Louis)
Vera (Bowling Green) 63334
Verona 65769
Versailles 65084
Viburnum 65566
Vichy 65580
Vienna 65582
Vigus (Hazelwood) 63042
Villa Ridge 63089
Vineyard (Stotts City) 65756
Vinita Park (Saint Louis) 63114
Viola (Shell Knob) 65747
Vista 64789
Vulcan 63675
Waco 64869
Wainwright (Holts Summit) .. 65043
Wakenda 64687
Waldron 64092
Walker 64790
Walnut Grove 65770
Walnut Shade 65771
Wappapello 63966
Wardell 63879
Wardsville 65101
  (Jefferson City)
Warren (Monroe City) 63456
Warrensburg 64093
Warrenton 63383
Warsaw 65355
Warson Woods 63122
  (Saint Louis)
Washburn 65772
Washington 63090
Wasola 65773
Watson 64496
Waverly 64096
Wayland 63472
Waynesville 65583
Weatherby 64497
Weatherby Lake 64152
  (Kansas City)
Weaubleau 65774
Webb City 64870
Webster Groves 63119
  (Saint Louis)
Wein (New Cambria) 63558
Weingarten 63670
  (Sainte Genevieve)
Weldon Spring 63304
  (Saint Charles)
Wellington 64097
Wellston (Saint Louis) 63112

  63133
Wellsville 63384
Wentworth 64873
Wentzville 63385
Wesco 65586
West Alton 63386
West County (Saint Louis) .. 63146
West Ely (Hannibal) 63401
West Eminence 65466
  (Eminence)
West Plains 65775-776
  Lanton 65775
  Siloam Springs 65775
West Quincy (Taylor) 63471
Westboro 64498
Weston 64098
Westphalia 65085
Wheatland 65779
Wheaton 64874
Wheeling 64688
Whitakerville (Warsaw) 65355
Whiteoak 63880
Whiteside 63387
Whitewater 63785
Willard 65781
Williamsburg 63388
Williamstown 63473
Williamsville 63967
Willmathsville (Greentop) .. 63546
Willow Springs 65793
Wilton (Hartsburg) 65039
Winchester 63011, 63021
  (Ballwin)
Windsor 65360
Windyville 65783
Winfield 63389
Winigan 63566
Winona 65588
Winston 64689
Wisdom (Warsaw) 65355
Withers Mill 63401, 63461
  (Hannibal)
Wittenberg 63786
Wolf Island 63881
Womack (Fredericktown) .. 63645
Woodland (Palmyra) 63461
Woodlandville 65256
  (Harrisburg)
Woodlawn (Madison) 65263
Woodlinville (Rocheport) .. 65279
Woods Heights 64024
  (Excelsior Springs)
Woodson Terrace 63134
  (Saint Louis)
Woodville (Excello) 65247
Wooldridge 65287
Worth 64499
Worthington 63567
Wright City 63390
Wyaconda 63474
Wyatt 63882
Yarrow (Kirksville) 63501
Yates (Higbee) 65257
Youngstown (Novinger) 63559
Yount (Perryville) 63775
Yukon 65589
Zalma (Arab) 63733, 63787
Zanoni 65784
Zell (Sainte Genevieve) 63670

BELLE CENTER

BUILDINGS

Northpark Mall
101 N RANGE LINE RD ... 64801

BLACK JACK

APARTMENTS

Desmet Apt
1425 N NEW FLORISSANT RD
63033

Wellington Arms
11333 SUGAR PINE DR ... 63033

BLACK WALNUT

GOVERNMENT

St Charles City Center
200 N 2ND ST 63301

St Charles County Admin
118 N 2ND ST 63301

BRAZITO

APARTMENTS

Deville Southwest Apt
821 SOUTHWEST BLVD .. 65109

Jefferson Hts Apt
1600 Jefferson Heights Dr 65109

Jefferson West Apt
810 WILDWOOD DR 65109

BROWNS
STATION

APARTMENTS

Candlelight Ter Apt
1408 Business Loop 70 W 65202

Woodlake Village
2607 EASTWOOD DR 65202

Wynwood Townhouses
4901 AZTEC BLVD 65202

CHESTERFIELD

BUILDINGS

The Atrium At Chesterfiel
16305 Swingley Ridge Rd   63017

CLAYTON

BUILDINGS

Carondelet East
7710 CARONDELET AVE . 63105

Carondelet West
7730 CARONDELET AVE . 63105

Chromalloy Plaza
120 S CENTRAL AVE 63105

Pierre Laclede Center
7701 FORSYTH BLVD 63105

GOVERNMENT

St Louis County Govt Ctr
41 S CENTRAL AVE 63105

COLUMBIA

APARTMENTS

Ashwood Apt
1021 ASHLAND RD 65201

Broadmoor Apt
2012 W ASH ST 65203

Broadway Apt
2309 W BROADWAY 65203

Chateau Fontainebleau Apt
2806 W ROLLINS RD 65203

College Park Apt
301 CAMPUSVIEW DR 65201

Columbia Square Apt
1801 W WORLEY ST 65203

Forest Village Apt
3001 S PROVIDENCE RD 65203

Gatehouse Apt
2401 W BROADWAY 65203

Hawthorne Apt
510 HIGH ST 65201

Holiday House Apt
109 N STADIUM BLVD 65203

Keeneland Downs
8 KEENE ST 65201

Manor House Apt
306 HITT ST 65201

Montmartre Apt
104 CLINKSCALES RD 65203

Oak Towers
700 N GARTH AVE 65203

Off Broadway Apt
2801 W BROADWAY 65203

Paquin Towers
1201 PAQUIN ST 65201

Parkway Apt
217 W BROADWAY 65203

Stadium Apt
1301 OLD 63 S 65201

Tara Apt
1133 ASHLAND RD 65201

Tiger Vlg Apt
301 TIGER LN 65203

University Place
1205 UNIVERSITY AVE 65201

BUILDINGS

Biscayne Mall
301 N STADIUM BLVD 65203

Columbia Mall
2300 BERNADETTE DR ... 65203

Executive Building
601 E BROADWAY 65201

Guitar Building
28 N 8TH ST 65201

Parkade Plaza
601 Business Loop 70 W .. 65203

GOVERNMENT

Boone County City Building
701 E BROADWAY 65201

Boone County Court House
705 E WALNUT ST 65201

Federal Building
608 CHERRY ST 65201

Municipal Building
600 E BROADWAY 65201

CREVE COEUR

BUILDINGS

1 Cityplace Building
1 CITYPLACE DR 63141

Mercy Doctors Building
621 S NEW BALLAS RD .. 63141

HONEY CREEK

APARTMENTS

Broadmoor Apt
505 ELLIS BLVD 65101

BUILDINGS

Broadway Building
221 W HIGH ST 65101

Dawson Building
308 E HIGH ST 65101

Gordon Building
600 MONROE ST 65101

GOVERNMENT

Federal Building
101 W HIGH ST 65101

State Capitol
201 W CAPITOL AVE 65101

Supreme Court Building
207 W HIGH ST 65101

Truman Building
301 W HIGH ST 65101

INDEPENDENCE

BUILDINGS

Independence Center
18813 E 39TH ST S 64057

JOPLIN

BUILDINGS

Blvd Professional Park
2700 Mc Clelland Blvd 64804

KANSAS CITY

BUILDINGS

2 Pershing Square
2300 MAIN ST 64108

At & T Town Pavilion
1111 MAIN ST 64105

Bannister Mall
5600 E 95TH ST 64137

Blue Ridge Mall
4200 BLUE RIDGE BLVD . 64133

Board of Trade Building
127 10th STREET 64105

Board Of Trade Building
4800 MAIN ST 64112

Commerce Tower Building
911 MAIN ST 64105

Harry Truman Sports Compl
8500 STADIUM DR 64129

Municipal Auditorium
211 W 13TH ST 64105

One Kc Place
1200 MAIN ST 64105

One Pershing Square
2301 MAIN ST 64108

GOVERNMENT

Federal Building
601 E 12TH ST 64106

Jackson County Courthouse
415 E 12TH ST 64106

Kansas City City Hall
414 E 12TH ST 64106

Old Federal Building
911 WALNUT ST 64106

State Office Building
615 E 13TH ST 64106

United States Courthouse
811 GRAND BLVD 64106

HOTELS

KC Marriott Downtown
200 W 12TH ST 64105

RICHMOND HEIGHTS

BUILDINGS

Bellevue Medical Ctr East
1035 BELLEVUE AVE 63117

Bellevue Medical Ctr West
1031 BELLEVUE AVE 63117

SAINT JOSEPH

GOVERNMENT

Buchanan County Ct House
411 JULES ST 64501

SAINT LOUIS

APARTMENTS

Frontenac Apt
40 N Kingshighway Blvd ... 63108

Gentrys Landing
400 N 4TH ST 63102

Grand Towers Apt
3520 LACLEDE AVE 63103

Jefferson Arms Apt
415 N TUCKER BLVD 63101

Lennox Apt
827 WASHINGTON AVE ... 63101

Mansion House
300 Mansion House Ctr 63102

Plaza Sq Apt
20 PLAZA SQ 63103

BUILDINGS

500 Broadway Building
500 N BROADWAY 63102

Arcade Building
812 OLIVE ST 63101

Boatmens Plaza
1 BOATMENS PLZ 63101

Boatmens Tower
100 N BROADWAY 63102

Centerpointe Building
11885 LACKLAND RD 63146

Chemical Building
721 OLIVE ST 63101

Equitable Building
10 S BROADWAY 63102

Executive Office Building
515 OLIVE ST 63101

Frisco Building
906 OLIVE ST 63101

Kiel Auditorium
1416 MARKET ST 63103

Laclede Gas Building
720 OLIVE ST 63101

Marquette Building
314 N BROADWAY 63102

Mercantile Towers
1 MERCANTILE CTR 63101

Metropolitan Square
1 METROPOLITAN ST. 63102

Paul Brown Building
818 OLIVE ST 63101

Railway Exchange Building
611 OLIVE ST 63101

Saint Louis Centre
515 N 6TH ST 63101

South Side Natl Bank Building
3606 GRAVOIS AVE 63116

St Anthonys Medical Building
10004 KENNERLY RD 63128

GOVERNMENT

City Hall
1200 MARKET ST 63103

Civil Courts Building
10 N TUCKER BLVD 63101

Federal Building
1520 MARKET ST 63103

Municipal Courts
1320 MARKET ST 63103

Old Post Office
815 OLIVE ST 63101

Robert A Young Building
1222 SPRUCE ST 63103

US Court & Custom House
1114 MARKET ST 63101

HOSPITALS

Queeny Tower
4989 Barnes Hospital Plz ... 63110

HOTELS

Embassy Suites Hotel
901 N 1ST ST 63102

Residence Inn By Marriott
1881 CRAIGSHIRE RD .. 63146

Windsor Hotel
4209 LINDELL BLVD 63108

SPRINGFIELD

BUILDINGS

Battlefield Mall
2825 S GLENSTONE AVE 65804

Commerce Terrace Building
2200 E SUNSHINE ST 65804

Corporate Centre
1949 E SUNSHINE ST 65804

Hammons Tower
901 E SAINT LOUIS ST 65806

Holland Building
205 PARK CENTRAL E ... 65806

John Q Hammons Building
300 S JOHN Q HAMMONS
PKY 65806

Mc Daniel Building
318 PARK CENTRAL E ... 65806

Medical Towers
1443 N ROBBERSON AVE 65802

National Ave Medical Building
1900 S NATIONAL AVE 65804

North Town Mall
1923 E KEARNEY ST 65803

Plaza Towers
1736 E SUNSHINE ST 65804

South Oaks Centre
3303 S CAMPBELL AVE ... 65807

Woodruff Building
333 PARK CENTRAL E ... 65806

GOVERNMENT

Federal Building
222 N JOHN Q HAMMONS PKY
.... 65806

Springfield State Office Compl
149 PARK CENTRAL SQ .. 65806

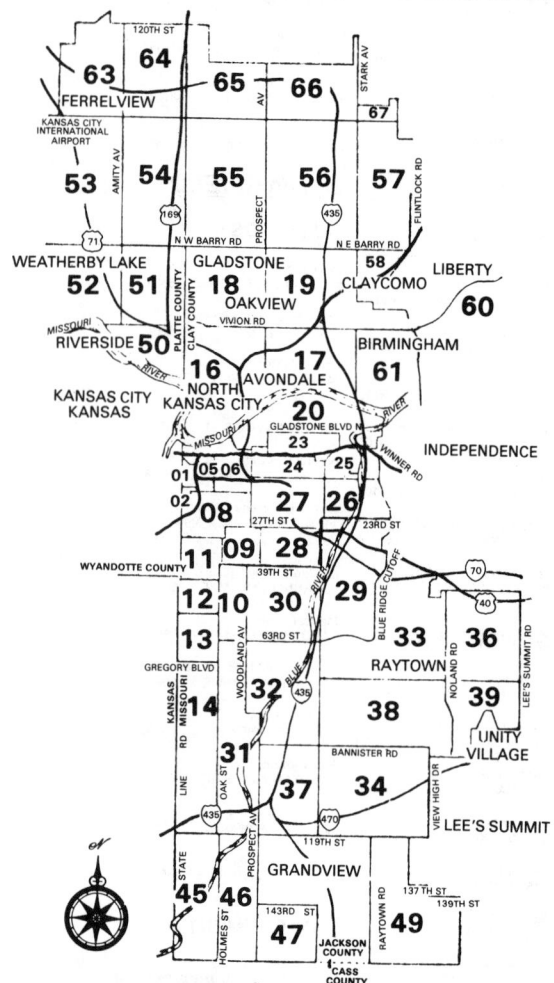

ZIP CODES
KANSAS CITY, MO
641 + TWO DIGITS SHOWN = ZIP CODE

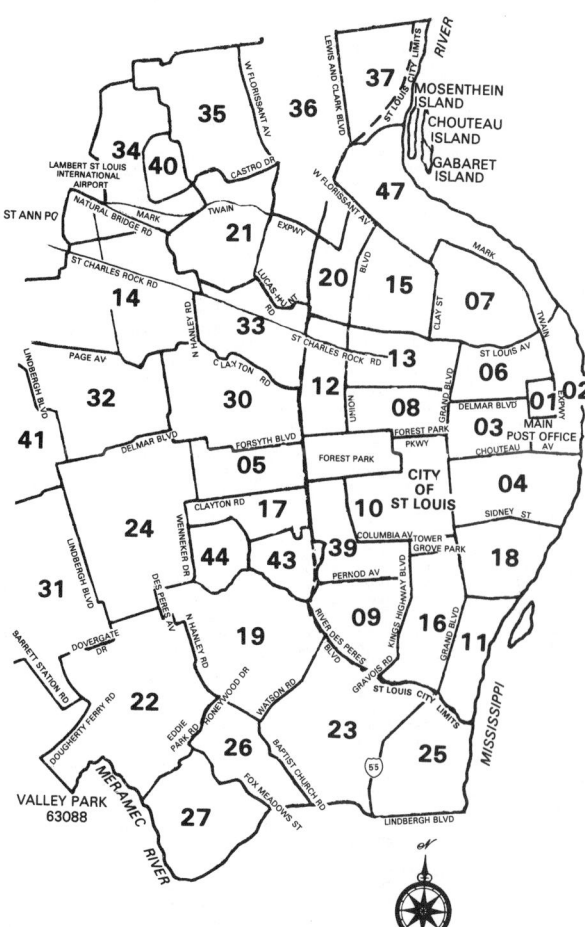

ZIP CODES

ST LOUIS, MO

631 + TWO DIGITS SHOWN = ZIP CODE

Inverness	59530	
Ismay	59336	
Jackson	59736	
Jardine (Gardiner)	59030	
Jefferson City	59638	
Joliet	59041	
Joplin	59531	
Jordan	59337	
Judith Gap	59453	
Kalispell	59901-904	
Creston	59902	
Evergreen	59901	
Kevin	59454	
Kila	59920	
Kinsey	59338	
Kirby (Busby)	59016	
Klein (Roundup)	59072	
Kremlin	59532	
Lake Mc Donald	59921	
Lakeside	59922	
Lambert	59243	
Lame Deer	59043	
Larslan	59244	
Laurel	59044	
Lavina	59046	
Ledger	59456	
Lennep (Martinsdale)	59053	
Lewistown	59457	
Libby	59923	
Lima	59739	
Lincoln	59639	
Lindsay	59339	
Livingston	59047	
Lloyd	59535	
Lockwood (Billings)	59101	
Lodge Grass	59050	
Lolo	59847	
Loma	59460	
Lonepine	59848	
Loring	59537	
Lothair	59461	
Lustre (Frazer)	59225	
Luther	59051	
Malta	59538	
Manhattan	59741	
Marion	59925	
Martin City	59926	
Martinsdale	59053	
Marysville	59640	
Mc Allister	59740	
Mc Cabe	59245	
Mc Leod	59052	
Medicine Lake	59247	
Medicine Springs (Conner)	59827	
Melrose	59743	
Melstone	59054	
Melville	59055	
Mildred	59341	
Miles City	59301	
Mill Iron	59342	
Milltown	59851	
Miner (Emigrant)	59027	
Missoula	59801-803	
	59806-808, 59812	
East Missoula	59801	
Evaro	59801	
Southgate	59801	
Moccasin	59462	
Moiese (Charlo)	59824	
Molt	59057	
Monarch	59463	

Montana City (Clancy)	59634	
Moore	59464	
Mosby	59058	
Musselshell	59059	
Myers (Hysham)	59038	
Nashua	59248	
Neihart	59465	
Niarada	59852	
Norris	59745	
Noxon	59853	
Nye	59061	
Oilmont	59466	
Olive	59343	
Olney	59927	
Opheim	59250	
Opportunity (Anaconda)	59711	
Otter	59062	
Outlook	59252	
Ovando	59854	
Pablo	59855	
Paradise	59856	
Park City	59063	
Peerless	59253	
Pendroy	59467	
Philipsburg	59858	
Pinesdale	59841	
Plains	59859	
Plentywood	59254	
Plevna	59344	
Polaris	59746	
Polebridge	59928	
Polson	59860	
Pompeys Pillar	59064	
Pony	59747	
Poplar	59255	
Potomac (Bonner)	59823	
Powderville	59345	
Power	59468	
Pray	59065	
Proctor	59929	
Pryor	59066	
Radersburg	59641	
Ramsay	59748	
Rapelje	59067	
Ravalli	59863	
Raymond	59256	
Raynesford	59469	
Red Lodge	59068	
Redstone	59257	
Reedpoint	59069	
Reserve	59258	
Rexford	59930	
Richey	59259	
Richland	59260	
Ringling	59642	
Rising Sun	59434	
(East Glacier Park)		
Roberts	59070	
Rocker (Butte)	59701	
Rocky Boy (Box Elder)	59521	
Rollins	59931	
Ronan	59864	
Roscoe	59071	
Rosebud	59347	
Roundup	59072-073	
Delphia	59073	
Klein	59072	
Roy	59471	
Rudyard	59540	
Ryegate	59074	
Saco	59261	

Saint Ignatius	59865	
Saint Marie	59231	
Saint Mary (Browning)	59417	
Saint Regis	59866	
Saint Xavier	59075	
Saltese	59867	
Sand Coulee	59472	
Sand Springs	59077	
Sanders	59076	
Santa Rita	59473	
Savage	59262	
Scobey	59263	
Seeley Lake	59868	
Shawmut	59078	
Shelby	59474	
Shepherd	59079	
Sheridan	59749	
Shonkin (Highwood)	59450	
Sidney	59270	
Silesia (Joliet)	59041	
Silver Gate	59081	
Silver Star	59751	
Silverbow (Butte)	59750	
Simms	59477	
Somers	59932	
Sonnette	59348	
Southgate (Missoula)	59801	
Springdale	59082	
Stanford	59479	
Stevensville	59870	
Stockett	59480	
Straw (Buffalo)	59418	
Stryker	59933	
Sula	59871	
Sumatra	59083	
Summit	59434	
(East Glacier Park)		
Sun River	59483	
Sunburst	59482	
Superior	59872	
Swan Lake (Bigfork)	59911	
Sweetgrass	59484	
Tampico (Glasgow)	59230	
Teigen	59084	
Terry	59349	
Thompson Falls	59873	
Three Forks	59752	
Toston	59643	
Townsend	59644	
Trego	59934	
Trident (Three Forks)	59752	
Trout Creek	59874	
Troy	59935	
Turah (Clinton)	59825	
Turner	59542	
Twin Bridges	59754	
Twodot	59085	
Ulm	59485	
Utica (Hobson)	59452	
Valier	59486	
Vandalia	59273	
Vaughn	59487	
Victor	59875	
Vida	59274	
Virginia City	59755	
Volborg	59351	
Walkerville (Butte)	59701	
Warmsprings	59756	
Warren (Bridger)	59014	
Washoe (Bearcreek)	59007	
Wayne (Belt)	59412	

West Glacier 59936	Wibaux 59353	Wise River 59762
West Yellowstone 59758	Willard 59354	Wolf Creek 59648
Westby 59275	Willow Creek 59760	Wolf Point 59201
White Sulphur Springs 59645	Wilsall 59086	Worden 59088
Whitefish 59937	Windham (Stanford) 59479	Wyola 59089
Whitehall 59759	Winifred 59489	Yaak (Troy) 59935
Whitetail 59276	Winnett 59087	Yellowtail 59035
Whitewater 59544	Winston 59647	Zortman 59546
Whitlash 59545	Wisdom 59761	Zurich 59547

IMPORTANT BUILDINGS

BILLINGS

GOVERNMENT

Billings City Hall
220 N 27TH ST 59101

Federal Building
316 N 26TH ST 59101

Yellowstone Courthouse
215 N 27TH ST 59101

BOZEMAN

BUILDINGS

Bozeman Hotel
321 E MAIN ST 59715

Farm Bureau
502 S 19TH AVE 59715

Federal
10 E BABCOCK ST 59715

Law & Justice Center
615 S 16TH AVE 59715

Main Mall
2825 W MAIN ST 59715

Martel Plaza
220 W LAMME ST 59715

Medial Arts Center
300 N WILLSON AVE 59715

University Square
200 S 23RD AVE 59715

GOVERNMENT

County Court House
301 W MAIN ST 59715

DEER LODGE

GOVERNMENT

Powell County Court House
409 MISSOURI AVE 59722

EAST MISSOULA

APARTMENTS

Missoula Manor Homes
909 W CENTRAL AVE 59801

Union Square
2400 Fort Missoula Rd 59801

HAMILTON

GOVERNMENT

County Courthouse
205 BEDFORD ST 59840

HELENA

GOVERNMENT

Accounting Div Admin
200102 PO BOX 59620

Adjutant General
202101 PO BOX 59620

Appellate Defenders
200145 PO BOX 59620

Architecture & Engineerin
200103 PO BOX 59620

Attorney General
201401 PO BOX 59620

Audit & Compliance
202942 PO BOX 59620

Board Of Investments
200126 PO BOX 59620

Board Of Public Education
200601 PO BOX 59620

Budget & Program Planning
200802 PO BOX 59620

Building Codes Bureau
200517 PO BOX 59620

Building Standards Sect
200517 PO BOX 59620

Capitol Employees Cred Un
200401 PO BOX 59620

Capitol Post Office
200144 PO BOX 59620

Central Payroll Division
200305 PO BOX 59620

Central Sevices Div
201404 PO BOX 59620

Child Support
202943 PO BOX 59620

Citizens Advocate Office
200803 PO BOX 59620

Coal Board
200523 PO BOX 59620

Comm Of Labor & Industry
201501 PO BOX 59620

Commissioner Of Higher Ed
203101 PO BOX 59620

Community Development Bur
200523 PO BOX 59620

Consumer Council
201703 PO BOX 59620

Coord Of Indian Affairs
200503 PO BOX 59620

Council On Vocational Edu
203201 PO BOX 59620

Court Administration
203002 PO BOX 59620

Crime Control Division
201408 PO BOX 59620

Criminal Justice Info Net
201406 PO BOX 59620

Data Processing Div
201405 PO BOX 59620

Department Of Health
200901 PO BOX 59620

Department Of Livestock
202001 PO BOX 59620

Department Of Revenue
202701 PO BOX 59620

Dept Fish Wildlife Parks
200701 PO BOX 59620

Dept Of Aeronautics
201031 PO BOX 59620

Dept Of Natural Resources
202301 PO BOX 59620

Dept Of State Lands
201601 PO BOX 59620

Dept Of Transportation
201001 PO BOX 59620

Developmental Disability
202923 PO BOX 59620

Director Dept Institution
201301 PO BOX 59620

Director Office S R S
202901 PO BOX 59620

Directors Office Admin
200101 PO BOX 59620

Directors Office Agri
200201 PO BOX 59620

Directors Office Commerce
200501 PO BOX 59620

Disability Determination
202931 PO BOX 59620

Economic Develment Board
200505 PO BOX 59620

Electrical Safety Sect
200517 PO BOX 59620

Environmental Quality Cou
201704 PO BOX 59620

Executive Office
200801 PO BOX 59620

Family Services
204001 PO BOX 59620

Financial Div Commerce
200512 PO BOX 59620

Fire Marshall Bureau
201417 PO BOX 59620

Gambling Control
201424 PO BOX 59620

General Services Division
200110 PO BOX 59620

Hail Insurance Unit
200202 PO BOX 59620

Hard Rock Mining Impact B
200523 PO BOX 59620

Health Facilities Authori
200506 PO BOX 59620

Highway Patrol Division
201419 PO BOX 59620

Highway Traffic Safety
201423 PO BOX 59620

Historic Preservation
201202 PO BOX 59620

Horseracing Board Of
200512 PO BOX 59620

House Of Representatives
201701 PO BOX 59620

Information Services Div
200113 PO BOX 59620

Investment Division
200125 PO BOX 59620

Job Service Office
201505 PO BOX 59620

Legislative Auditor
201705 PO BOX 59620

Legislative Council
201706 PO BOX 59620

Legislative Fiscal Analys
201711 PO BOX 59620

Legislative House & Senat
200400 PO BOX 59620

Lewis & Clark Human Serv
202936 PO BOX 59620

Lt Governors Office
201901 PO BOX 59620

Mail & Distribution Sect
200112 PO BOX 59620

Management Support
200107 PO BOX 59620

Mechanical Safety Sect
200517 PO BOX 59620

Mental Disabilities Board
200804 PO BOX 59620

Milk Control Board
200512 PO BOX 59620

Mont Historical Society
201201 PO BOX 59620

Montana Arts Council
202201 PO BOX 59620

Montana Benefits, Incorp
200126 PO BOX 59620

Montana Board Of Housing
200528 PO BOX 59620

Montana Lottery
200544 PO BOX 59620

Montana Promotion Divisio
200533 PO BOX 59620

Montana State Library
201800 PO BOX 59620

Off Of Public Instruction
202501 PO BOX 59620

Pac Nw Elect Power Cons B
200805 PO BOX 59620

Petro Tank Release Comp
200902 PO BOX 59620

Political Practices Comm
202401 PO BOX 59620

Probation And Parole
201313 PO BOX 59620

Profess Occupa Licensing
200513 PO BOX 59620

Property & Supply Bureau
200137 PO BOX 59620

Public Employees Retire
200131 PO BOX 59620

Public Safety Division
200517 PO BOX 59620

Public Service Regulation
202601 PO BOX 59620

Publications & Graphics
200132 PO BOX 59620

Purchasing Bureau
200135 PO BOX 59620

Records Management
202805 PO BOX 59620

Risk Mngt & Tort Defence
200124 PO BOX 59620

Science & Tech Alliance
200504 PO BOX 59620

Search
202937 PO BOX 59620

Secretary Of State
202801 PO BOX 59620

Section 8 Housing
200545 PO BOX 59620

Senate
201702 PO BOX 59620

State Auditors Office
200301 PO BOX 59620

State Law Library
203004 PO BOX 59620

State Personnel Division
200127 PO BOX 59620

Supreme Court Clerk
203003 PO BOX 59620

Supreme Court Judges
203001 PO BOX 59620

T R I C
202922 PO BOX 59620

Tax Appeal Board State
200138 PO BOX 59620

Teachers Retirement
200139 PO BOX 59620

Teams
202938 PO BOX 59620

Treasurers Office
200140 PO BOX 59620

Weights & Measures Bureau
200512 PO BOX 59620

MISSOULA

APARTMENTS

Clark Fork Manor
301 W FRONT ST 59802

GOVERNMENT

City Hall
435 RYMAN ST 59802

County Courthouse
200 W BROADWAY ST 59802

NEBRASKA
Abbreviation NE

Abbott (Grand Island)	68803
Abie	68001
Adams	68301
Agnew (Raymond)	68428
Ainsworth	69210
Air Park (Lincoln)	68524
Albany (Oxford)	68967
Albion	68620
Alda	68810
Alexandria	68303
Algernon (Mason City)	68855
Allen	68710
Alliance	69301
Alma	68920
Almeria (Taylor)	68879
Alvo	68304
Amelia	68711
Ames	68621
Amherst	68812
Anderson (Funk)	68940
Angora	69331
Anselmo	68813
Ansley	68814, 68819
Myrtle	68814
Antelope (Oneill)	68763
	68969, 68981
Antioch (Ellsworth)	69340
Arapahoe	68922
Arcadia	68815
Archer	68816
Arlington	68002
Armada (Miller)	68858
Arnold	69120
Arthur	69121
Ash Grove (Franklin)	68939
Ashby	69333
Ashland	68003
Ashton	68817
Assumption (Juniata)	68955
Atkinson	68713
Atlanta	68923
Auburn	68305
Aurora	68818
Avoca	68307
Axtell	68924
Ayr	68925
Bancroft	68004
Barada (Falls City)	68355
Barneston	68420
Bartlett	68622
Bartley	69020
Bassett	68714
Battle Creek	68715
Bayard	69334
Beatrice	68310, 68458
Ellis	68310
Glenover	68310
Hoag	68310
Riverside	68310
Rockford	68310
Beaver City	68926, 68946
Beaver Crossing	68313
Bee	68314
Beemer	68716
Belden	68717
Belgrade	68623
Belle Prairie (Strang)	68444

Bellevue	68005, 68123
	68147, 68157
Bellwood	68624
Belmont (Lincoln)	68521, 69339
Belvidere	68315
Benedict	68316
Benkelman	69021
Bennet	68317
Bennington	68007
Benson (Omaha)	68104
Berea (Alliance)	69301
Bertrand	68927
Berwyn	68819
Bethany (Lincoln)	68505
Beverly (Culbertson)	69024
Big Springs	69122
Bignell (Maxwell)	69151
Bingham	69335
Bixby (Sutton)	68979
Bladen	68928
Blaine (Hastings)	68901, 68924
Blair	68008-009
Bloomfield	68718
Bloomington	68929
Blue Hill	68930
Blue River Lodge (Crete)	68333
Blue Springs	68318
Boelus	68820
Bostwick (Superior)	68978
Boys Town	68010
Bradshaw	68319
Brady	69123
Brainard	68626
Brandon (Grant)	69140
Brayton (Wolbach)	68882
Brewster	68821
Bridgeport	69336
Bristol (Rockville)	68871
Bristow	68719
Broadwater	69125
Brock	68320
Broken Bow	68822
Brownlee (Thedford)	69166
Brownson (Sidney)	69162
Brownville	68321
Brule	69127
Bruning	68322
Bruno (Abie)	68001, 68014
Brunswick	68720
Bucktail (Paxton)	69155
Buffalo (Campbell)	68932
Burchard	68323
Burkett (Grand Island)	68803
Burr	68324
Burress (Fairmont)	68354
Burwell	68823, 68837
Bushnell	69128
Butte	68722
Byron	68325
Cadams (Superior)	68978
Cairo	68824
Callaway	68825
Cambridge	69022
Cameron (Wood River)	68883
Campbell	68932
Capehart (Omaha)	68123
Carleton	68326
Carroll	68723
Cedar (Pleasanton)	68866
Cedar Bluffs	68015
Cedar Creek	68016

Cedar Rapids	68627
Center	68724, 68949
Spade	68724
Centerville (Martell)	68404
Central City	68826
Ceresco	68017
Chadron	69337
Chambers	68725
Champion	69023
Chapman	68827
Chappell	69129
Cheney (Lincoln)	68526
Cherry Creek (Ravenna)	68869
Chester	68327
Clarks	68628
Clarkson	68629
Clatonia	68328
Clay (Litchfield)	68852
Clay Center	68933
Clearwater	68726
Cliff (Arnold)	69120
Clinton (Gordon)	69343
Cody	69211
Coleridge	68727
Colon	68018
Colton (Sidney)	69162
Columbus	68601-602
Richland	68601
Comstock	68828
Concord	68728
Cook	68329
Cordova	68330
Corner (Sargent)	68874
Cornlea	68630
Cortland	68331
Cosmo (Minden)	68959
Cotesfield	68829
Cottonwood	68949-950
(Holdrege)	
Cowles (Blue Hill)	68930
Crab Orchard	68332
Craig	68019
Crawford	69339
Creighton	68729
Creighton Univ (Omaha)	68131
Creston	68631
Crete	68333
Crofton	68730
Crookston	69212
Culbertson	69024
Curtis	69025
Cushing (Saint Paul)	68873
Custer (Callaway)	68825
Dakota City	68731
Dalton	69131
Danbury	69026
Dannebrog	68831
Dannevirke (Elba)	68835
Darr (Cozad)	69130
Davenport	68335
Davey	68336
David City	68632
Davis Creek (Arcadia)	68815
Dawson	68337
Daykin	68338
De Witt	68341
Decatur	68020
Delight (Callaway)	68825
Denman (Kenesaw)	68956
Denton	68339
Denver (Holstein)	68950

Deshler	68340
Deweese	68934
Dickens	69132
Diller	68342
Divide (Riverdale) .. 68870, 68940	
Dix	69133
Dixon	68732
Doane (Benkelman)	69021
Dodge	68633
Doniphan	68832
Dorchester	68343
Douglas	68344
Douglas Grove (Comstock)	68828
Du Bois	68345
Dubois (Du Bois)	68345
Dunbar	68346
Duncan	68634
Dunlap (Hemingford)	69348
Dunning	68833
Dwight	68635
Eagle	68347
East Custer (Oconto)	68860
Eaton (Heartwell)	68945
Eddyville	68834
Edgar	68935
Edison	68936
Elba	68835
Eldorado (Alma) 68920, 68944	
Elgin	68636
Eli (Valentine)	69201
Elim (Callaway)	68825
Elk Creek 68348, 68855	
Elkhorn	68022
Ellis (Beatrice)	68310
Ellsworth	69340
Elm (Litchfield)	68852
Elm Creek	68836
Elmwood	68349
Elsie	69134
Elsmere	69135
Elwood 68937, 68976	
Johnson Lake	68937
Elyria	68837
Emerald (Lincoln)	68528
Emerson 68733, 68967	
Emmet	68734
Enders	69027
Endicott	68350
Enterprise (North Loup)	68859
Ericson	68637
Eureka (North Loup)	68859
Eustis	69028
Ewing	68735
Exeter	68351
Fairbury	68352
Fairfield 68938, 68977	
Fairmont	68354
Falls City	68355
Farmers (Bloomington)	68929
Farnam	69029
Farwell	68838
Filley	68357
Firth	68358
Flats (Sutherland)	69165
Florence (Omaha) .. 68112, 68152	
Fordyce	68736
Fort Calhoun	68023
Fort Robinson (Crawford) .	69339
Foster	68737
Franklin	68939
Fremont	68025

Friend	68359
Fullerton	68638
Funk	68940
Gandy (Stapleton)	69163
Gardner (Riverdale)	68870
Garfield (Broken Bow)	68822
.... 68869, 68927	
Garland	68360
Garrison (David City)	68632
Geneva	68361
Genoa	68640
Geranium (Comstock)	68828
Gering	69341
Gibbon	68840
Gilead	68362
Giltner	68841
Gladstone (Fairbury)	68352
Glen (Crawford)	69339
Glenover (Beatrice)	68310
Glenrock (Auburn)	68305
Glenvil	68941
Goehner	68364
Gordon	69343
Gothenburg	69138
Graf (Tecumseh)	68450
Grafton	68365
Grainton (Wallace)	69169
Grand Island 68801-803	
Abbott	68803
Burkett	68803
Kuesters Lake	68801
Parkview	68801
Prairie Creek	68801
Washington	68801
Grant (Amherst) 68812, 68825	
.... 68963, 68972, 69140	
Brandon	69140
Grattan (Oneill)	68763
Greeley	68842
Greenwood	68366
Gresham	68367
Gretna	68028
Grover (Milford)	68405
Guide Rock	68942
Gurley	69141
Hadar	68738
Haig (Mitchell)	69357
Haigler	69030
Hallam	68368
Halsey	69142
Hamilton (Strang)	68444
Hamlet	69031
Hampton	68843
Hanover (Glenvil)	68941
Hansen (Hastings)	68901
Harbine (Jansen)	68377
Hardy	68943
Harrisburg	69345
Harrison (Litchfield)	68852
.... 68858, 68883, 69346	
Hartington	68739
Harvard 68944, 68954	
Eldorado	68944
Hastings 68901-902	
Blaine	68901
Hansen	68901
Ingleside	68901
Spencer Park	68901
West Blue	68901
Havelock (Lincoln)	68529
Hay Springs	69347

Hayes (Anselmo) ... 68813, 68959	
Hayes Center	69032
Hayland (Juniata)	68955
Hazard	68844
Heartwell	68945
Hebron (Gilead) 68362, 68370	
Hemingford 69348, 69354	
Dunlap	69348
Henderson	68371
Hendley	68946
Henry (Lyman)	69349
Herman	68029
Hershey	69143
Hickman	68372
Highland (Cortland)	68331
....	68950
Hildreth	68947
Hoag (Beatrice)	68310
Holbrook	68948
Holdrege 68949, 68969	
Center	68949
Cottonwood	68949
Holdridge	68949
Prairie	68949
Sheridan	68949
Holdridge (Holdrege)	68949
Holland (Hickman)	68372
Hollinger (Oxford)	68967
Holmesville	68374
Holstein	68950
Homer	68030
Hooper	68031
Horace (Scotia)	68875
Hordville	68846
Hoskins	68740
Howe (Auburn)	68305
Howells	68641
Hubbard	68741
Hubbell	68375
Humboldt	68376
Humphrey	68642
Huntley	68951
Hyannis	69350
Imperial	69033
Inavale	68952
Independent (North Loup) .	68859
Indianola	69034
Industry (Atlanta)	68923
Ingleside (Hastings)	68901
Inglewood (Fremont)	68025
Inland	68954
Inman	68742
Ithaca	68033
Jacinto (Dix)	69133
Jackson 68743, 68883	
Jansen	68377
Johnson	68378
Johnson Lake (Elwood)	68937
Johnstown	69214
Julian	68379
Juniata	68955
Kearney 68847-849	
Keene (Axtell)	68924
Kenesaw	68956
Kennard	68034
Keystone	69144
Kilfoil (Merna)	68856
Kilgore	69216
Kimball	69145
Kowanda (Oshkosh)	69154
Kramer (Crete)	68333

Kronborg (Marquette) 68854	
Kuesters Lake 68801	
(Grand Island)	
La Platte (Omaha) 68123	
La Vista (Omaha) 68128	
Laird (Loomis) 68958	
Lake (Wilcox) 68982	
Lakeside 69351	
Lamar 69035	
Lanham (Odell) 68415	
Laurel 68745	
Lavista (Omaha) 68128	
Lawrence 68957	
Lebanon 69036	
Leicester (Trumbull) 68980	
Leigh 68643	
Lemoyne 69146	
Leshara 68035	
Lewellen 69147	
Lewis (Saronville) 68975	
Lewiston 68380	
Lexington 68850	
Liberty 68381	
.... 68815, 68945	
Lincoln 68500-512, 68514	
.... 68516-517, 68520-524	
.... 68526-529, 68531-532	
.... 68542, 68544, 68572	
68583, 68588, 68947, 68959	
Air Park 68524	
Bar Code 68572	
Belmont 68521	
Bethany 68505	
Cheney 68526	
Emerald 68528	
Havelock 68529	
Prairie Home 68527	
Rokeby 68523	
State House 68509	
Lindsay 68644	
Linwood 68036	
Lisco 69148	
Litchfield 68852	
Little Blue (Glenvil) 68941	
Lodgepole 69149	
Logan (Amherst) 68812, 68853	
.... 68950, 68959, 68981	
Lone Tree 68826, 68933	
(Central City)	
Long Pine 69217	
Loomis 68958	
Lorenzo (Sidney) 69162	
Lorton 68382	
Louisville 68037	
Loup (Oconto) 68860	
.... 68864, 68866	
Loup City 68853	
Lowell (Gibbon) 68840	
Lushton (Henderson) 68371	
Lyman 69352	
Henry 69349	
Lynch 68746	
Lynn (Clay Center) 68933	
Lyons 68038	
Macon (Franklin) 68939	
Macy 68039	
Madison 68748	
Madrid 69150	
Magnet 68749	
Malcolm 68402	
Malmo 68040	

Manley 68403	
Marion (Franklin) 68939, 69026	
Marquette 68854	
Marshall (Clay Center) 68933	
Marsland 69354	
Martell 68404	
Martin (Wood River) 68883	
Mascot (Oxford) 68967	
Maskell 68751	
Mason City 68855	
Max 69037	
Maxwell 69151	
May (Norman) 68963	
Mayfield (Cairo) 68824	
Maywood 69038	
Mc Clean (Mclean) 68747	
Mc Cook 69001	
Mc Grew (Mcgrew) 69353	
Mead 68041	
Meadow Grove 68752	
Melbeta 69355	
Memphis 68042	
Merna 68856	
Merriman 69218	
Michigan (Ord) 68862	
Midland (Archer) 68816	
Milburn (Anselmo) 68813	
Milford 68405	
Millard (Omaha) 68137, 68144	
Miller 68858	
Milligan 68406	
Mills 68753	
Milton (Miller) 68858	
Minatare 69356	
Minden 68959, 68963	
Cosmo 68959	
Hayes 68959	
Lincoln 68959	
Logan 68959	
South Minden 68959	
Mirage (Axtell) 68924	
Mitchell 69357	
Monroe 68647	
Moorefield 69039	
Morrill 69358	
Morse Bluff 68648	
Mount Clare (Lawrence) ... 68957	
Mullally 68971	
(Republican City)	
Mullen 69152	
Murdock 68407	
Murphy (Phillips) 68865	
Murray 68409	
Myrtle (Ansley) 68814	
Naper 68755	
Naponee 68960	
Nebraska City 68410	
Nehawka 68413	
Neligh 68756	
Nelson 68961	
Nemaha (Cortland) 68331	
.... 68414	
Nenzel 69219	
New Helena (Anselmo) 68813	
Newark (Gibbon) 68840	
Newcastle 68757	
Newman Grove 68758	
Newport 68759	
Nickerson 68044	
Niobrara 68760	
Noble (Ord) 68862	

Nora (Nelson) 68961	
Norfolk 68701-702	
Norman 68963	
North Auburn (Auburn) 68305	
North Bend 68621, 68649	
(Ames)	
North Franklin (Campbell) . 68932	
North Loup 68859	
North Platte 69101	
.... 69103, 69132	
Northport (Bridgeport) 69336	
Nysted (Dannebrog) 68831	
O' Neill (Oneill) 68763	
Oak 68964	
Oak Creek (Loup City) 68853	
Oak Grove (Bloomington) . 68929	
Oakdale 68761	
Oakland 68045	
Obert 68762	
Oconto 68860	
Octavia 68650	
Odell 68415	
Odessa 68861	
Ogallala 69153	
Ohiowa 68416	
Omaha 68100-114, 68116-120	
.... 68122-124, 68127-128	
..... 68130-138, 68142, 68144	
.... 68147, 68152, 68154-155	
.... 68157, 68164, 68172	
.... 68175-82, 68198	
Bellevue 68123	
Bellevue 68147	
Bellevue 68157	
Benson 68104	
Capehart 68123	
Creighton Univ 68178	
Florence 68112	
Florence 68152	
La Platte 68123	
La Vista 68128	
Lavista 68128	
Millard 68137	
Millard 68144	
Papillion 68128	
Papillion 68133	
Papillion 68138	
Papillion 68157	
Ralston 68127	
Oneida (Wilcox) 68982	
Oneill 68763	
Ong 68452	
Orchard 68764	
Ord 68862	
Orleans 68966	
Osceola 68651	
Oshkosh 69154	
Osmond 68765	
Otoe 68417	
Overton 68863	
Oxford 68967	
Page 68766	
Palisade 69040	
Palmer 68864	
Palmyra 68418	
Panama 68419	
Papillion 68046, 68128	
.... 68133, 68138, 68157	
Parks 69041	
Parkview (Grand Island) ... 68801	
Paul (Nebraska City) 68410	

Washington 68068, 68801	Westmark (Bertrand) 68927	Wood Lake 69221
.... 68853, 68951, 68972	Weston 68070	Wood River (Oconto) 68860
Waterbury 68785	Westside (Bertrand) 68927	 68883
Waterloo 68069	Whiteclay 69365	Cameron 68883
Wauneta 69045	Whitman 69366	Harrison 68883
Wausa 68786	Whitney 69367	Jackson 68883
Waverly 68462	Wilber 68465	Martin 68883
Wayne 68787, 68860	Wilcox 68982	Worms (Saint Libory) 68872
Wayside (Chadron) 69337	Williamsburg (Bertrand) 68927	Wymore 68466
Webster (Loup City) 68853	Willow Island 69171	Wynot 68792
Weeping Water 68463	Willowdale (Oneill) 68763	Wyoming (Nebraska City) . 68410
Weissert 68880	Wilsonville 69046	Yale (Arcadia) 68815
Wellfleet 69170	Winnebago 68071	York 68467
West Blue (Hastings) 68901	Winnetoon 68789	Yutan 68073
West Point 68788	Winside 68790	Zero (Ayr) 68925
West Union (Sargent) 68874	Winslow 68072	
Western 68464	Wisner 68791	
Westerville 68881	Wolbach 68882	

ABBOTT

APARTMENTS

Centennial Towers
910 N BOGGS AVE 68803

Chalet Apt
3033 W CAPITAL AVE 68803

Continental Apt
3111 COLLEGE ST 68803

Crysallis Lutheran Home
2807 W FAIDLEY AVE 68803

Golden Towers
804 N BOGGS AVE 68803

Grandview Apt
3423 KELLY ST 68803

Hall County Housing
915 BAUMANN DR 68803

Windsor Sq
3027 W CAPITAL AVE 68803

BUILDINGS

Conestoga Mall
3404 W 13TH ST 68803

Grand Island Mall
2250 N WEBB RD 68803

Mall
2808 OLD FAIR RD 68803

Webb Plaza
2418 N WEBB RD 68803

BELLEVUE

APARTMENTS

Chandler Acres Apt
3416-518 GERTRUDE ST. 68147

Tantara Apt
3708-715 EMILINE ST 68147

Westridge Apts
3610-612 GAYLE AVE 68123

Westridge Apts
3702-706 GAYLE AVE 68123

BELMONT

APARTMENTS

Tomasek Apartments
2900 N 1ST ST 68521

Tomasek Apartments
201-31 ADAMS ST 68521

HOTELS

Dillon Inn
1301 W BOND CIR 68521

BENSON

APARTMENTS

Churchill Apt
2003-011 N 45TH ST 68104

Colonial Square Apt
4102-110 N 52ND ST 68104

Colony Apt
6303-313 TAYLOR ST 68104

Cottonwood Manor
4731-741 N 62ND ST 68104

Country Club Apt
5314-322 CORBY ST 68104

Freyer Apt
4313-318 N 65TH ST 68104

Highway House Apt
4701-705 BURDETTE ST . 68104

Holiday Apt
4502-506 N 49TH ST 68104

Lake View Manor Apt
4114-122 N 48TH ST 68104

Lakeshore Apt
4813-823 BOYD ST 68104

Maplewood Court Apt
4512-524 BEDFORD AVE . 68104

Mauldin Manor
4810 BOYD ST 68104

Mc Intire Apt
6207 MAPLE ST 68104

Northampton Arms Apt
6122 N 56TH ST 68104

Northampton Arms Apt
5705-825 Henninger Dr 68104

Northampton Arms Apt
5605 Northhampton Blvd .. 68104

Northampton Arms Apt
5635 Northhampton Blvd .. 68104

Park Lane Apt
5204 N 60TH ST 68104

Park Lane Apt
6006 PARK LANE DR 68104

Park Manor Apt
6636-640 MILITARY AVE .. 68104

Park Terrace Apt
6646-654 MILITARY AVE .. 68104

Parklane Apt
5205 N 60TH AVE 68104

Patan Apt
4602-618 REDMAN AVE .. 68104

Pickrel Apt
6012 BIRCH ST 68104

Pine Park Apt
5120-128 MILITARY AVE .. 68104

Pine Park Apt
5120-128 NW Radial Hwy. 68104

Regan Place Apt
4402 N 60TH AVE 68104

Rose Hill Apt
5504-516 CORBY ST 68104

Sahler Apt
4822-826 SAHLER ST 68104

Shalimar Apt
4525-535 N 66TH ST 68104

Shalimar Apt
4701-719 N 66TH ST 68104

Shalimar Apt
4807-825 N 66TH ST 68104

Shalimar Apt
6501-531 GRAND AVE 68104

Shirley-ann Apt
5820 ERSKINE ST 68104

Taylor Apt
4844-854 TAYLOR ST 68104

Tiffany Apt
4620-622 REDMAN AVE .. 68104

Vieue Carre Apt
1503 N 48TH ST 68104

Vieux Carre Apt
1501-513 N 48TH ST 68104

BETHANY

APARTMENTS

Chateau La Fleur
6100 VINE ST 68505

BLAIR

APARTMENTS

Parkview Manor
758 S 16TH ST 68008

COLUMBUS

APARTMENTS

Briarwood Apts
2722-806 25TH ST 68601

Camelot Apt
770 30TH AVE 68601

Carriage House Estates
2500 4TH AVE 68601

Colonial Courts Apt
2723 14TH ST 68601

Columbian Village
3717 27TH ST 68601

Columbus Place Apts
1305 8TH ST 68601

Cottonwood
1607 23RD ST 68601

Edgetown
2265 8TH AVE 68601

Johansen Apt
1158 39TH AVE 68601

Lakeview Apts
201-303 E 22ND ST 68601

Olivette Apts
2910 14TH ST 68601

Parkview Trlr Ct
858 33RD AVE 68601

Prairie View Building
3805 27TH ST 68601

Randall Apt
1555 26TH AVE 68601

Real Life
3600 30TH ST 68601

Sayers Apt
2021 14TH ST 68601

Schmid Apts
2809 14TH ST 68601

Village Apt
2481 E 6TH AVE 68601

Westport Apts
3914 25TH ST 68601

BUILDINGS

City Hall
2424 14TH ST 68601

Doctors Building
3005 19TH ST 68601

U S 30 Center Building
3100 23RD ST 68601

HOTELS

Downtowner Hotel
1354 27TH AVE 68601

FLORENCE

APARTMENTS

Country Pk Manor Apt
3110-112 WILLIT ST 68112

Florence Home
7915 N 30TH ST 68112

GRAND ISLAND

APARTMENTS

Bellwood Square Apt
2222 BELLWOOD DR 68801

Coventry Apt
1524 COVENTRY LN 68801

Francis Villa
1405 W KOENIG ST 68801

Holiday Garden
2004 N WHEELER AVE 68801

The Yancey
123 N LOCUST ST 68801

BUILDINGS

Court House
121 S PINE ST 68801

HOTELS

Kingswood Estates
2323 BELLWOOD DR 68801

HAVELOCK

GOVERNMENT

Havelock Station Usps
9998 PO BOX 68529

LA VISTA

APARTMENTS

Alpine Village
7001-005 S 86TH ST 68128

Alpine Village
8550-554 PLAZA BLVD 68128

Hi Pointe Apts
1501-529 Grandview Ave .. 68128

Huntington Park
621 FENWICK DR 68128

Huntington Park Apts
1502-510 Grandview Ave .. 68128

Huntington Park Apts
1506 GRANDVIEW PLZ ... 68128

Park Crest Apt
8501-519 BIRCH DR 68128

Park Crest Apt
8603-615 BIRCH DR 68128

Ridge Park Apt
8504 GRANVILLE PKY 68128

Tara Hills
201-209 Shillealagh Blvd. . 68128

The Pointe
8202 S 90TH PLZ 68128

The Pointe
8202-206 ELM DR 68128

Willowbrook
8722 Willowbrook Plz 68128

LINCOLN

APARTMENTS

Ambassador Apt
1330 LINCOLN MALL 68508

Capitol City Villa
2501 N ST 68510

Centerstore
100 N 12TH ST 68508

Country Club Village
2800 WOODS BLVD 68502

Gateway Manor
225 N 56TH ST 68504

Lake Park Apt
4000 S 56TH ST 68506

Lincoln Manor Apt
2626 N 49TH ST 68504

Mahoney Manor
4241 N 61ST ST 68507

Palisade Apt
1035 S 17TH ST 68508

President Apt
1340 LINCOLN MALL 68508

Rudge Memorial Home Apt
1810 E ST 68508

Tabitha
841 S 47TH ST 68510

University Towers
128 N 13TH ST 68508

Willow Wood Apt
1215 ARAPAHOE ST 68502

BUILDINGS

Abel Hall North
880 N 17TH ST 68508

Abel Hall South
860 N 17TH ST 68508

American Charter Center
206 S 13TH ST 68508

Atrium Building
1200 N ST 68508

Cather Hall
609 N 17TH ST 68508

Centrum Mall
1111 O ST 68508

Color Court Building
825 M ST 68508

Cornhusker Plz
301 S 13TH ST 68508

Ctu Building
1221 N ST 68508

Firstier Bank Building
233 S 13TH ST 68508

Golds Galleria
1033 O ST 68508

Harper Hall
1150 N 14TH ST 68508

Lincoln Benefit Life Building
134 S 13TH ST 68508

Lincoln Building
1001 O ST 68508

Lincoln Center Building
215 Centennial Mall S 68508

Lincoln Square Building
121 S 13TH ST 68508

NBC Center
1248 O ST 68508

Old Federal Building
129 N 10TH ST 68508

Pound Hall
513 N 17TH ST 68508

Sandoz Hall
820 N 17TH ST 68508

Schramm Hall
1130 N 14TH ST 68508

Selleck Quadrangle
600 N 15TH ST 68508

Smith Hall
1120 N 14TH ST 68508

Terminal Building
941 O ST 68508

Vistar Bank Building
6940 O ST 68510

GOVERNMENT

City-county Building
555 S 10TH ST 68508

New Federal Building
100 CENTENNIAL MALL N 68508

HOTELS

Lincoln Hilton Hotel
141 N 9TH ST 68508

MILLARD

APARTMENTS

Applecreek Apt
2212 S 139TH CT 68144

Applecreek Apt
2207-229 S 141ST CT 68144

Applecreek Apt
2212-234 S 141ST PLZ 68144

Deauville Apt
12728 DEAUVILLE DR 68137

Deauville Apt
12734 DEAUVILLE DR 68137

Deauville Apt
12760-88 DEAUVILLE DR 68137

Deauville Apt
12836 DEAUVILLE DR 68137

Deauville Apt
12720-794 GAIL PLZ 68137

Deauville Apt
12723-793 Woodcrest Plz . 68137

Georgetown Apt
2205-214 S 142ND CT 68144

Georgetown Apt
2312-327 S 142ND CT 68144

Georgetown Apt
2204-226 S 142ND PLZ 68144

Georgetown Apt
2307-315 S 143RD CT 68144

Georgetown Apt
2210-315 S 143RD PLZ 68144

Georgetown Apt
14162-314 Castelar Plz 68144

Heritage Hgts
11706-812 ARBOR ST 68144

Kingswood Manor
2721 S 134TH AVE 68144

Kingswood Manor
13302-322 Kingswood Dr. . 68144

Montclair
13407-427 Montclair Dr 68144

Royal Terrace Apt
2917-937 S 134TH AVE 68144

Terrace Park Apt
2502-526 S 114TH ST 68144

Terrace Park Apt
11417-515 ARBOR ST 68144

Village Ct Apt
2306-328 VILLAGE CT 68144

Walnut Hill Apt
4813-819 S 131ST ST 68137

Westbrook Manor Apt
14735 W PLZ 68137

Whispering Isle Apt
12130-240 ANNE ST 68137

Woodridge Apt
14115 BERRY PLZ 68137

Woodridge Apt
14112 V PLZ 68137

BUILDINGS

11111 M Building
11111 M ST 68137

Arbor Plaza I
11823 ARBOR ST 68144

Arbor Plaza II
11725 ARBOR ST 68144

Arbor Plaza III Office Building
11711 ARBOR ST 68144

Empire Prof Ofc Building
11329 P ST 68137

Execu-west Building
4780 S 131ST ST 68137

Executive Center
13426 A ST 68144

Metro Buss Cen Ofc Building
11128 JOHN GALT BLVD .. 68137

Oak Ridge Ofc Park Building
5010 S 118TH ST 68137

One Landmark Centre
14748 W CENTER RD 68144

P O Credit Union Building
4848 S 120TH ST 68137

Renaissance Building
13304 W CENTER RD 68144

Westwood Plaza
12165 W CENTER RD 68144

HOTELS

Comfort Inn
10919 J ST 68137

Hotel Carlisle
10909 M ST 68137

Residence Inn
11025 M ST 68137

Sheraton Inn Southwest
4888 S 118TH ST 68137

Super 8 Motel
10829 M ST 68137

Town House Inn
13929 GOLD CIR 68144

NORFOLK

APARTMENTS

Blaine Apt
607 BLAINE ST 68701

Catalina Apt
600 PARK AVE 68701

Cedardale
607 MICHIGAN AVE 68701

Chateau Apt
607 CEDAR AVE 68701

Cimmaron Apt
922 SYRACUSE AVE 68701

Cottonwood Apt
413 N 6TH ST 68701

Cottonwood Apt
603 VERGES AVE 68701

Country Club Apt
1402 COUNTRY CLUB RD 68701

Evergreen Apt
111 S PINE ST 68701

Glen Park Terrace
1300-317 IMPALA DR 68701

Glenmore Apt
1503-507 GLENMORE DR 68701

Green Gable Apt
812 S 8TH ST 68701

Greenland Village
901-907 SYRACUSE AVE   68701

Hespe Apt
1000-1300 HESPE DR 68701

Ioof Apt
1204 NORFOLK AVE 68701

Isabelle
1205-206 ISABELLE CIR .. 68701

Lakewood Apts
1400-406 Riverside Blvd ... 68701

Little Caesar Apt
103-113 Little Caesar Ave . 68701

Norfolk Apt
510 1ST STREET 68701

Normandy Apt
1001-007 N 6TH ST 68701

Northwestern Apt
1414 S 3RD ST 68701

Park Ave Apt
402 PARK AVE 68701

Queen City Apt
600 QUEEN CITY BLVD ... 68701

Rca Apt
1101 NORFOLK AVE 68701

Rebecca Lodge Apt
1700 PASEWALK AVE 68701

St. Joseph Res Care Fac
210 HARRIS DR 68701

Sunrise Apt
118 E PHILLIP AVE 68701

Sunset Square Apt
1314 PASEWALK AVE 68701

The Chateau
1824 VICKI LN 68701

The Meadows Apt
500 S 18TH ST 68701

Toby Apt
1100-106 S 9TH ST 68701

Valley View Apt
2801 PROSPECT AVE 68701

Verges Apt
1220-222 VERGES AVE ... 68701

Village Green Apts
1001 Village Green Dr 68701

Western Terrace Apt
311-313 N 12TH ST 68701

Westside Plaza Apt
2600 Westside Plaza Dr ... 68701

Woodwind Apt
115-125 N 25TH ST 68701

BUILDINGS

Centrum Building
123 N 4TH ST 68701

Holiday Plaza
1105 S 13TH ST 68701

Mcm Iii Building
125 S 4TH ST 68701

Norfolk Professional Building
101 N 4TH ST 68701

OMAHA

APARTMENTS

Appletree Apt
6205-215 S 97TH CT 68127

Appletree Apt
6425 S 98TH PLZ 68127

Appletree Apt
9865 MONROE PLZ 68127

Applewood Pointe
9509-516 S PLZ 68127

Applewood Pointe Apt
9566 PARK DR 68127

Ardmore Apt
4902 CALIFORNIA ST 68132

Belgrade Apt
1302-310 N 49TH ST 68132

Bentley Plaza Apts Building 4
835 N 95TH PLZ 68114

Briarwood Apt
5816 S 94TH PLZ 68127

California Hills Apt
612-640 N 46TH ST 68132

California Hills Apt
802 N 46TH ST 68132

Cambridge Apt
4912-924 S 96TH ST 68127

Cambridge Apt
4912-5148 S 97TH PLZ 68127

Cambridge Apt
9615-739 Mockingbird Dr .. 68127

Cambridge Apt
9606-739 OHERN PLZ 68127

Camelot Village
2020-417 N 92ND AVE 68134

Camelot Village
2416-526 N 93RD CT 68134

Camelot Village
2405-515 N 94TH PLZ 68134

Camelot Village
9251-415 CADY AVE 68134

Candlewick Apt
812-834 N 124TH CT 68154

Candlewick Apt
824 N 124TH PLZ 68154

Canterberry Sq
720 PARK AVE 68105

Canterbury Square
2934 LEAVENWORTH ST 68105

Canterbury Square Apt
719 S 30TH ST 68105

Carlanna Apt
906-908 S 27TH ST 68105

Caroline Apt
1616-618 MILITARY AVE ... 68111

Carthage Apt
1314 N 49TH AVE 68132

Carthage Apt
814 N 50TH AVE 68132

Carthage Apt
4919 HAMILTON ST 68132

Casa Linda Townhomes
108 S 49TH AVE 68132

Cass Street Apt
7511 CASS ST 68114

Castle Apt
1040-044 S 29TH ST 68105

Cedar Heights
3317-329 S 56TH ST 68106

Cedar Heights Apt
3316-328 S 54TH ST 68106

Cedar Heights Apt
5406-530 GROVER ST 68106

Cedar Heights Apt
5405-531 HASCALL ST 68106

Centaur Apt
1053-59 PARK AVE 68105

Center Apt
1902-938 S 38TH AVE 68105

Center Apt
1901-937 S 39TH ST 68105

Center Apt
3857 CENTER ST 68105

Center Apt
3856-62 FRANCES ST 68105

Century 21 Apt
5311-521 S 101ST PLZ 68127

Century 21 Apt
10005-49 R ST 68127

Century 21 Apt
10034-45 S PLZ 68127

Century 21 Apt
10004-49 T PLZ 68127

Century 21 Apts
5511 S 101ST PLZ 68127

Century Apt
909-915 N 48TH AVE 68132

Charter Oak Apt
8919 BURT ST 68114

Cherry Garden Ct Condo
814-25 S 37TH AVE 68105

Cherry Garden Ct Condo
813-17 S 38TH ST 68105

Cherry Hills
1014 N 48TH AVE 68127

Chula Vista
2968 POPPLETON AVE ... 68105

Citadel
5051-57 S 84TH CT 68127

Citadel
4963-76 S 86TH PKY 68127

Citadel
5028-66 S 86TH PKY 68127

Citadel
8405-515 OHERN ST 68127

Clar O Apt
568 S 33RD ST 68105

Clar O Apt
3304 JACKSON ST 68105

Coat Of Arms Apt
256-286 N 116TH CT 68154

Coat Of Arms Apt
11550-80 BURKE ST 68154

Coat Of Arms Apt
11552-608 Davenport Plz . 68154

Coat Of Arms Apt
11557-587 WAKELEY Plz . 68154

Colonial Hotel
3804 FARNAM ST 68131

Continental Apt
4310-334 S 25TH ST 68107

Cornish Apt
1404 S 10TH ST 68108

Cornish Apt
1009 WILLIAM ST 68108

Cornish Hts Apt
1320-360 S 75TH ST 68124

Cornish Hts Apt
1345-365 S 76TH ST 68124

Cornish Hts Apt
7610-634 BRIGGS ST 68124

Cottonwood Apt
1120-130 N 47TH AVE 68132

Cottonwood Apt
1115-121 N 48TH ST 68132

Cottonwood Apt
4750 LAFAYETTE AVE 68132

Cottonwood Apt
4752-58 NICHOLAS ST 68132

Country Club Village
9903-45 Q PLZ 68127

Country Club Village
9942 S PLZ 68127

Country Club Village
9929-46 T PLZ 68127

Country Club Village
9912-24 U ST 68127

Country Court Apt
5708-710 S 14TH ST 68107

Country House Apt
1325 S 30TH AVE 68105

Creighton Palms
320 N 20TH ST 68102

Dakota Apt
2709 DEWEY AVE 68105

Danforth Apt
3725 JACKSON ST 68105

De Freese Manor
2669 DODGE ST 68131

De Vaney Apt
1333-35 S 33RD ST 68105

De Vaney Apt
3221 WOOLWORTH AVE . 68105

Deerpark Apt
3223 S 24TH ST 68108

Dewey Apt
2612-18 DEWEY AVE 68105

Doretta Apt
1112 PARK AVE 68105

Driftwood Manor Apt
1130 S 29TH ST 68105

Dundee Apt
4544 NICHOLAS ST 68132

Dundee Apt
5019 UNDERWOOD AVE . 68132

Dundee Apt
4702 WAKELEY ST 68132

Dundee Arms Apt
4955-57 CUMING ST 68132

Dundee Court
4628-55 CAPITOL AVE 68132

Dundee Court
4602-04 CASS ST 68132

Dundee Court
4728-32 CHICAGO ST 68132

Dundee Court
4621-23 WAKELEY ST 68132

Dundee Park
4816-24 CASS ST 68132

Dundee Park Apt
417 N 49TH ST 68132

Dundee Park Apt
4904 DAVENPORT ST 68132

Dundee Place Apt
801 N 48TH ST 68132

Dundee Terrace Apt
4644-716 CUMING ST 68132

Dunsany Apt
1113-17 S 10TH ST 68108

Echo Manor Apt
4817-841 HOLMES ST 68117

Ed Low Terrace Apt
806 N 46TH ST 68132

Eden West Apt
1155-75 N 94TH PLZ 68114

Eden West Apt
902-945 N 95TH PLZ 68114

Eden West Apt
9404-416 CUMING PLZ 68114

Eden West Apt
9505-546 WESTERN CIR .. 68114

Eden West Apt
9402-475 WESTERN PLZ . 68114

Eight Hundred Ten Apt
810 N 46TH ST 68132

El Dorado Apt
605-607 S 36TH ST 68105

Elizabeth Apt
3701-05 JONES ST 68105

Ember Manor
5800-02 S 14TH ST 68107

Eton Apt
524-26 S 36TH ST 68105

Evans Tower
3600 N 24TH ST 68110

Fernshire Apt
725 S 37TH ST 68105

Field Club Apt
1015 S 38TH AVE 68105

Fiesta Apt
802-10 N 107TH AVE 68114

Fleetwood Apt
3417 JONES ST 68105

Florence Towers
5100 FLORENCE BLVD 68110

Florentine Apt
2105-319 BensonGdn.Blvd 68134

Florentine Condo
601 S 32ND AVE 68105

Four Pine Apt
2017 Benson Garden Blvd 68134

Four Seasons Apt
5052 GROVER ST 68106

Four Seasons Apt
5114 GROVER ST 68106

Fox Run Apt
3576-586 S 69TH CT 68106

Fox Run Apt
3506-656 S 69TH PLZ 68106

Fox Run Apt
3521-537 S 70TH ST 68106

Fox Run Apt
6925-945 GROVER ST 68106

Fox Run Apt
6954-974 HANSEN PLZ ... 68106

Frances Apt
1908-938 S 39TH ST 68105

Frances Apt
1907-937 S 40TH ST 68105

Frances Apt
3907-921 CENTER ST 68105

Frances Apt
3906-912 FRANCES ST ... 68105

Franklin Heights Apt
4455-457 FRANKLIN ST ... 68111

Garden Valley Courts
5530 N 16TH ST 68110

Garden Valley Courts
5702 N 16TH ST 68110

Genoa Apt
3828 CASS ST 68131

Glendale Apt
406 N 49TH ST 68132

Gordon Apts
622 N 50TH ST 68132

Grover Square Apt
3606 S 67TH CT 68106

Grover Square Apt
3605-717 S 68TH CT 68106

Grover Square Apt
3706-718 S 68TH PLZ 68106

Grover Square Apt
6755-811 A PLZ 68106

Grover Square Apt
6805-819 B PLZ 68106

Hacienda Apt
3106-136 N 111TH PLZ 68164

Hacienda Apt
3105 N 112TH PLZ 68164

Hacienda Apt
11102-143 Cottonwood Plz 68164

Hanscom Apt
1738 S 29TH ST 68105

Harken House Apt
816-28 N 46TH ST 68132

Harrisburg Sq Apt
4851-865 S 95TH PLZ 68127

Harrisburg Square
4712-864 S 94TH PLZ 68127

Harrisburg Square
4706-716 S 95TH PLZ 68127

Harrisburg Square
9411-525 HOLMES PLZ ... 68127

Harrisburg Square
9406-524 N AVENUE PLZ 68127

Heritage Apt
4903-921 CHICAGO ST ... 68132

Hillcrest Apt
7600 MAIN ST 68127

Hillside Apt
304-316 N 31ST ST 68131

Hilltop Apt
1019-121 N 48TH AVE 68132

Horizon Apt
1306-314 N 48TH AVE 68132

Horizon Apt
1305-313 N 49TH ST 68132

Howard Park Apt
3306-520 HOWARD ST 68105

Indian Hills Apt
8515-519 Indian Hills Dr 68114

J K Apt
817-821 N 47TH ST 68132

J M W Apt
2323 M ST 68107

Jackson Place
514 S 13TH ST 68102

Jackson Place
3007-09 JACKSON ST 68105

James Court
3058-62 Poppleton Ave 68105

Johnette Apt
524 PARK AVE 68105

Kent Apt
907-11 S 25TH ST 68105

Keystone Terrace Apt
2916-28 N 83RD ST 68134

Kingston Court Apt
1704-712 N 73RD ST 68114

Kirshenbaum Apt
5013-15 CALIFORNIA ST . 68132

Knickerbocker Apt
702 S 38TH ST 68105

Knickerbocker Apt
3801 JONES ST 68105

Kristine Apt
622 S 36TH ST 68105

Kutlers Manor
3515 LEAVENWORTH ST 68105

L And K Apt
5826-830 S 14TH ST 68107

La Gratta
2116 N 16TH ST 68110

Lafayette Hills
4509-34 LAFAYETTE AVE 68132

Lake Candlewood Apt
1306-544 N 120TH PLZ 68154

Lake Candlewood Apt
1311-541 N 122ND PLZ 68154

Lake Candlewood Apt
12206-16 CHARLES PLZ . 68154

Lake Forest Apt
3626-636 N 112TH AVE 68164

Lake Forest Apt
3516-526 N 112TH PLZ 68164

Lake Forest Apt
3605-615 N 113TH CT 68164

Lake Forest Apt
3505-516 N 113TH PLZ 68164

Lake Forest Apt
11306-316 BIRCH PLZ 68164

Lake Forest Apt
11255-393 EVANS ST 68164

Lake Forest Apt
3605-16 Lake Forest Dr 68164

Lake Forest Apt
11305-315 PRATT ST 68164

Lakeview Apt
5003-13 Country Club Cir . 68127

Lamp Street Apt
11004-108 LAMP ST 68154

Lamplighter Apt
2665-75 N 93RD ST 68134

Lancaster Apt
820 S 25TH AVE 68105

Lancaster Apt
2552-564 MARCY ST 68105

Lantern Tree Apt
7505-517 PIERCE PLZ 68124

Lantern Tree Apt
7506-717 Poppleton Plz 68124

Lar-gro Apt
817-915 N 48TH ST 68132

Latvian Village East
2901-959 PADDOCK PLZ . 68124

Laurelwood Apt
5816-926 N 99TH PLZ 68134

Laurelwood Apt
6006-016 N 99TH PLZ 68134

Laurelwood Apt
5316-925 N 100TH PLZ 68134

Laurelwood Apt
6005-105 N 100TH PLZ 68134

Laurelwood Apt
10011-31 ARCADIA PLZ ... 68134

Laurelwood Apt
10005-26 Crown Point Plz 68134

Laurelwood Apt
10008-28 HIMEBAUGH Plz 68134

Laurelwood Apt
9905-10025 KANSAS PLZ 68134

Laurelwood Apt
10015-26 OGDEN PLZ 68134

Leetom Apt
4804-808 DODGE ST 68132

Linden Manor Apt
1127 S 31ST ST 68105

Lions Head Apts Building 10
10910-14 PAUL PLZ 68154

Lions Head Apts Building 11
10922-934 PAUL PLZ 68154

Lions Head Apts Building 14
1324 N 110TH PLZ 68154

Lions Head Apts Building 17
11022-26 LAFAYETTE Plz. 68154

Lions Head Apts Building 18
1205-307 N 111TH PLZ 68154

Lions Head Apts Building 2
1423-431 N 109TH PLZ 68154

Lionshead Apts Building 24
1304-08 N 112TH PLZ 68154

Lionshead Apts Building 25
1318 N 112TH PLZ 68154

Lionshead Apts Building 26
1328 N 112TH PLZ 68154

Lionshead Apts Building 28
1420 N 112TH PLZ 68154

Livingston Plz
303 S 132ND ST 68154

Lyle Manor
817 PARK AVE 68105

Lynch Apts
1052 S 20TH ST 68108

Maple Manor
3028-044 N 97TH ST 68134

Maple Manor
2901-917 Maplewood Blvd. 68134

Maple Manor
3001-023 Maplewood Blvd. 68134

Maple Manor Apt
3002-026 N 97TH ST 68134

Marbee Apt
714 S 36TH ST 68105

Marianna Apt
424 S 35TH ST 68131

Mark Manor Apt
2423 S 18TH ST 68108

Martinique Apt
802-34 N 93RD ST 68114

Martinique Apt
802-38 N 94TH PLZ 68114

Martinique Apt
9302-325 BEMIS PLZ 68114

Martinique Apt
9314-334 BURT ST 68114

Mary Ann Apt
1021 PARK AVE 68105

Maryland Apt
1136 PARK AVE 68105

Mason Apt
1005 S 31ST ST 68105

Mason Apt
3070-075 MASON ST 68105

Mayfair Apts
2222 HOWARD ST 68102

Maywood 12 Apt
5402 S 77TH ST 68127

Mc Clusky Apt
616 S 37TH ST 68105

Melody Ann Apt
1034 PARK AVE 68105

Michael Apt
3307-309 HOWARD ST 68105

Middletown Apt
508 S 35TH AVE 68105

Middletown Apt
3550 HOWARD ST 68105

Miracle Hills Condos
11945 Miracle Hills Dr 68154

Miracle Hills Condos
11937 Miracle Hills Dr 68154

Mobob Apt
3518 CALIFORNIA ST 68131

Mockingbird
8562-64 ORCHARD AVE .. 68127

Mockingbird Manor
8610-616 LAKEVIEW DR . 68127

Mt Vernon Garden
5725 S 14TH ST 68107

Mt Vernon Gardens Apt
5702 S 13TH ST 68107

Mt Vernon Gardens Apt
5703 S 14TH ST 68107

Mt Vernon Manor North
5726 S 14TH ST 68107

Mt Vernon Manor South
5818 S 14TH ST 68107

Mt Vernon Place Apt
5718-720 S 14TH ST 68107

New Cassel
900 N 90TH ST 68114

Newtowne Apt
3316-516 N 102ND PLZ ... 68134

Newtowne Apt
3305-515 N 103RD PLZ ... 68134

Normandie Apt
2955 PACIFIC ST 68105

Normandie Apt
1102 PARK AVE 68105

North Place Apts
2114 S 45TH ST 68106

Norwick Apt
5312-420 N 117TH CT 68164

Norwick Apt
11706-24 NORWICK PLZ . 68164

Norwick Apt
11716-22 OGDEN PLZ 68164

Nottingham Apt
3302-306 BURT ST 68131

Novak Apt
4609 CALIFORNIA ST 68132

Odinas Apt
571 S 28TH ST 68105

Old Mill Apt
1156 N 108TH PLZ 68154

Old Mill Apt
1155-56 N 109TH PLZ 68154

Old Mill Apt
10817 N MILL CT 68154

Old Mill Apt
10917 WESTERN PLZ 68154

Omaha Regency Trlr Ct
17400 W DODGE RD 68118

Orac Apt
911 FOREST AVE 68108

Orleans Square
4740-752 S 83RD ST 68127

Pacific Gardens Apt
7701-713 PIERCE ST 68124

Park East Apt
1901 PARK AVE 68105

Park Plaza West
105 N 31ST AVE 68131

Park Tower North
1501 PARK AVE 68105

Park Tower South
1601 PARK AVE 68105

Park West Apt
514 PARK AVE 68105

Parkvale Apt
2964-72 Woolworth Ave 68105

Pattrick Apt
1405 S 10TH ST 68108

Peachtree Apt
8320-30 CALIFORNIA ST .. 68114

Peoria Hotel Apt
1109 S 10TH ST 68108

Peterson Apt
5306 S 32ND ST 68107

Phillips Apt
3325 CALIFORNIA ST 68131

Pittman Manor Apt
2901 PARKER ST 68111

Plaza Court Apt
518-24 S 35TH ST 68105

Ponderosa Point
6320 S 72ND ST 68127

Ponderosa Point
6410 S 72ND ST 68127

R A Manor
1015 TURNER BLVD 68105

Ramanda Manor
151 N 41ST ST 68131

Ramona Court Apt
3307 DEWEY AVE 68105

Red Apple Apt
540 S 30TH ST 68105

Redman View Apt
5712 N 42ND ST 68111

Regency Apt
919-1039 S 106TH PLZ 68114

Regency Apt
10304-351 Broadmoor Ct .. 68114

Regency Apt
10315-353 Fieldcrest Ct 68114

Regency Apt
10322-530 PACIFIC ST 68114

Regency Apt
712-1010 REGENCY PKY . 68114

Remington Hts Rtmt Ctr
12606 W DODGE RD 68154

Rene Apt
1015 PARK AVE 68105

Richland Park Apt
605-735 N 116TH ST 68154

Richland Park Apt
11502-672 BURT ST 68154

Richland Park West Building W
11710-14 BURT ST 68154

Richland Park West Building X
11724 BURT ST 68154

Richland Park West Building Y
11730-34 BURT ST 68154

Riviera
4601-620 CHICAGO ST ... 68132

Riviera Apt
4723-727 CASS ST 68132

Roni Lee Apt
4420-422 S 25TH ST 68107

Roosevelt Apt
420-635 N 48TH ST 68132

Roosevelt Apt
4724 DAVENPORT ST 68132

Rorick Apt
604 S 22ND ST 68102

Rose Apt
4605-729 CALIFORNIA ST 68132

Rose Apt
4609 CASS ST 68132

Roycroft Apt
5017 UNDERWOOD AVE . 68132

Saint Frances Apt
8929-933 CUMING ST 68114

Saint Regis Apt
619-21 S 37TH ST 68105

Satellite Apt
1138 S 29TH ST 68105

Selma Terrace
630-36 PARK AVE 68105

Sequoia Park Apt
7306-316 MAPLE ST 68134

Seventeen Apt
1017 S 31ST ST 68105

Seymour Apt
608-610 S 32ND AVE 68105

Sherman Apt
2501-503 N 16TH ST 68110

Sherri Park
10715-735 O ST 68127

Shirbley Apt
3320-328 CALIFORNIA ST 68131

Shirley Villa Apt
603 S 35TH AVE 68105

Siders Apt
1025 S 30TH AVE 68105

Sinos Apt
1122-124 PARK AVE 68105

Sky Haven
4805 S 90TH ST 68127

Sky Haven
8866 HOLMES ST 68127

Sky Haven
8828-842 M ST 68127

Sonland Apt
1130 S 31ST ST 68105

South Park Terrace Apt
5027-33 S 20TH ST 68107

Southpark Apt
3602-610 S 50TH ST 68106

Southpark Apt
5001-033 A ST 68106

Spring Manor
3101-123 S 69TH AVE 68106

Stephen Apt
3506-508 JACKSON ST ... 68105

Story Book Apt
1008-010 S 29TH ST 68105

Stratford
543 PARK AVE 68105

Stratford Terrace
2922 JACKSON ST 68105

Strohl Apt
5005 CALIFORNIA ST 68132

Studio 96 Apt
5632-636 S 96TH ST 68127

Sun Valley Apt
4460-468 REDMAN AVE ... 68111

Sunset Valley Condo
9101-107 ARBOR ST 68124

Sylvapt Apt
4915 DAVENPORT ST 68132

Telestar
1133 PARK AVE 68105

Telstar Apt
1135 PARK AVE 68105

Ten Twenty One Apt
1021 S 31ST ST 68105

Terene Apt
115 N 50TH ST 68132

The Prague
1402 S 13TH ST 68108

Thomasville Apt
5735 S 99TH CT 68127

Thomasville Apt
5920-6036 S 100TH PLZ .. 68127

Thomasville Apt
9916-926 BERRY PLZ 68127

Thomasville Apt
9905-925 SUFFOLK PLZ .. 68127

Thompsen Apt
1016-330 S 30TH AVE 68105

Thompsen Apt
3112 WOOLWORTH AVE .. 68105

Thompsen Apt
1332 S 30TH AVE 68105

Thousand And One Apt
1001-035 N 90TH ST 68114

Tier Nam Apt
4728-732 CASS ST 68132

Tiffany Apt
4816-824 CHICAGO ST ... 68132

Tiffany Manor Townhouses
4484-492 REDMAN AVE ... 68111

Tobin Ct Apt
4702-710 CASS ST 68132

Turner Garden Apt
1019-035 TURNER BLVD . 68105

Underwood Manor
706 N 50TH ST 68132

Underwood Manor
4919-931 WEBSTER ST .. 68132

Underwood Towers
4850 UNDERWOOD AVE . 68132

Underwood Towers
4903 UNDERWOOD AVE . 68132

Valencia Apt
551 S 35TH ST 68105

Valencia Apt
3419 HOWARD ST 68105

Valley Town Homes
3067 S 41ST ST 68105

Valley Town Homes
3069 S 41ST ST 68105

Valley Town Homes
3071 S 41ST ST 68105

Valley Town Homes
3073 S 41ST ST 68105

Valley Town Homes
3075 S 41ST ST 68105

Valley Town Homes
3089 S 41ST ST 68105

Valley Town Homes
3091 S 41ST ST 68105

Valley Town Homes
3093 S 41ST ST 68105

Vanderbilt Apts
11102 DECATUR PLZ 68154

Vanderbilt Apts
11105 FRANKLIN PLZ 68154

Vanderbilt Apts
11107 SEWARD PLZ 68154

Vel Ben Apt
613 S 19TH ST 68102

Victoria Apt
2642 HARNEY ST 68131

Villa D Amore
3102 S 69TH AVE 68106

Village Apt
2808 S 93RD PLZ 68124

Village Central Apt
3401 CALIFORNIA ST 68131

Ville Rouge Apt
4903-905 CALIFORNIA ST 68132

Virginia Apt
1148 PARK AVE 68105

Vista Apt
6310-346 S 96TH ST 68127

Wakeley Apt
4620-717 WAKELEY ST ... 68132

Warren House Apt
9755 MOCKINGBIRD DR . 68127

Washington Heights Apt
355-425 N 117TH CT 68154

Washington Heights Apt
414-425 N 118TH PLZ 68154

Washington Heights Apt
366-396 N 119TH PLZ 68154

Washington Heights Apt
11825-935 CASS PLZ 68154

Washington Heights Apt
11765-834 CHICAGO PLZ 68154

Washington Heights Apt
11705-936 WAKELEY PLZ 68154

Wentworth
5306-445 S 86TH CT 68127

Wentworth
5316-326 S 86TH PLZ 68127

Wentworth
8612-642 R PLZ 68127

Wentworth
8636-668 S PLZ 68127

Wentworth Apt
5406-530 S 86TH PLZ 68127

Wentworth Apt
8611-621 T PLZ 68127

Westbrook Garden Apt
1857-921 Robertson Dr 68114

Westbrook Gardens Apt
1854-920 N 81ST ST 68114

Wildwood
6710 S 83RD AVE 68127

Willow Creek Apt
7007-251 S 145TH ST 68138

Willow Park
5612-616 S 95TH TER 68127

Willow Park Apt
9609-733 PARK DR 68127

Wilshire Townhouses
4470-478 REDMAN AVE ... 68111

Woodland Apt
506 S 31ST ST 68105

Wycliffe West Office
15202 WYCLIFFE DR 68154

Yale Apt
814 S 38TH ST 68105

Zodiac Two Apt
1126-36 S 29TH ST 68105

BUILDINGS

1065 Building
1065 N 115TH ST 68154

1200 Landmark Center
1299 FARNAM ST 68102

7000 Building
7000 W CENTER RD 68106

7301 Building
7301 PACIFIC ST 68114

74 Dodge Plaza
7415 DODGE ST 68114

7400 Court
808 S 74TH PLZ 68114

8610 Building
8610 CASS ST 68114

8701 Dodge Building
8701 W DODGE RD 68114

94 Dodge Place
9394 W DODGE RD 68114

Aaa Auto Ass'n Building
910 N 96TH ST 68114

American Charter Building
8630 CASS ST 68114

American Nat Bank Building
8990 W DODGE RD 68114

Arbor Plaza Ofc Building
9015 ARBOR ST 68124

Bank Building
11207 W DODGE RD 68154

Barker Building
306 S 15TH ST 68102

Bergan Mercy Medical Cent
7710 MERCY RD 68124

Beta West Building
1201 FARNAM ST 68102

Blackstone Centre
302 S 36TH ST 68131

Bonanza Plaza Office Building
212 S 74TH ST 68114

Bozell & Jacobs Ofc Building
10250 REGENCY CIR 68114

Brandeis Braiker Building
210 S 16TH ST 68102

Brook Park Shop Ctr
3015 N 90TH ST 68134

Bryant Resource Center
2423 GRANT ST 68111

Capital Court Building
7070 CAPITOL CT 68132

Capitol Plaza Building
1815 CAPITOL AVE 68102

Center Pointe
9239 W CENTER RD 68124

Central Park Plaza
222 S 15TH ST 68102

Church Building
124 S 24TH ST 68102

Commercial Federal Tower
2120 S 72ND ST 68124

Continental Building
209 S 19TH ST 68102

Continental General Building
8901 INDIAN HILLS DR 68114

Corporate Plaza
11212 DAVENPORT ST 68154

Corporate Plaza
11222 DAVENPORT ST 68154

Dial Building
8801 W CENTER RD 68124

Doctors Building
4239 FARNAM ST 68131

Dodge Center Building
5002 DODGE ST 68132

Dodge Professional Center
8601 W DODGE RD 68114

Douglas County Society
5730 N 30TH ST 68111

Durham Plaza
8401 W DODGE RD 68114

Electric Building
409 S 17TH ST 68102

Embassy Plaza
9110 W DODGE RD 68114

Embassy Plaza West
9140 W DODGE RD 68114

Embassy Square
9202 W DODGE RD 68114

Embassy Tower
9300 UNDERWOOD AVE .. 68114

Empire State Building
300 S 19TH ST 68102

Essex Building
400 ESSEX CT 68114

Essex Building
10400 ESSEX CT 68114

Executive Building
1624 DOUGLAS ST 68102

Executive Plaza Building
6818 GROVER ST 68106

Farmers National Building
11516 NICHOLAS ST 68154

Farnam Building
1613 FARNAM ST 68102

Federal Building
215 N 17TH ST 68102

First National Center Bld
1620 DODGE ST 68102

First Natl Bank Building
11404 W DODGE RD 68154

First Westside Bank Building
222 S 72ND ST 68114

Firstier Bank Na Omaha
1620 FARNAM ST 68102

Firstier Place
8712 W DODGE RD 68114

Flatiron Building
1722 SAINT MARYS AVE . 68124

Ford Building
8031 W CENTER RD 68124

Fort Crest Ofc Building
5601 N 103RD ST 68134

Grain Exchange Building
1905 HARNEY ST 68102

Guarantee Center Two Building
8805 INDIAN HILLS DR 68114

Harney West V
10802 FARNAM DR 68154

Hickory Villa
510 1ST STREET 68124

Hillcrest Landing
7500 MAIN ST 68127

Hillside Elem Parrish
1312 ROBERTSON DR 68114

Historic Burlington Place
1004 FARNAM ST 68102

Historic Burlington Place
1004 Farnam On The Mall 68102

Historic Library Plz
1823 HARNEY ST 68102

IBM Building
450 REGENCY PKY 68114

Immanuel Professional Plz
6801 N 72ND ST 68122

Immanuel Reg Med Plz Building
210 REGENCY PKY 68114

Indian Hills Plaza
8901 W DODGE RD 68114

Indian Hills Prof Building
220 N 89TH ST 68114

Insurance Building
7101 MERCY RD 68106

Investors Office Center
11301 DAVENPORT ST 68154

John D Wear Building
7602 PACIFIC ST 68114

Keeline Building
319 S 17TH ST 68102

Law Building
500 S 18TH ST 68102

Le Dioyt Landmark Building
1001 FARNAM ST 68102

Le Dioyt Landmark Building
1001 Farnam On The Mall 68102

Mark 70 Building
6969 GROVER ST 68106

Maryland Plz Building
1325 S 72ND ST 68124

Medical Building
720 N 87TH ST 68114

Medical Court Building
410 S SADDLE CREEK RD 68131

Methodist College
8501 W DODGE RD 68114

Metro Technical College
5730 N 30TH ST 68111

Midwest Minor Medical
8552 CASS ST 68114

Miracle Hills Exec Ctr
11422 Miracle Hills Dr 68154

Morgan Place
8420 W DODGE RD 68114

Ne Credit Union League
4315 FRANCES ST 68105

Ninety-o-one Building
9001 ARBOR ST 68124

North Tower
4242 FARNAM ST 68131

Northwest Dental Building
5200 N 91ST AVE 68134

Northwest Sta, Usps
6012 N 102ND ST 68134

Norwest Bank Building
10010 REGENCY CIR 68114

Norwest Building
1919 DOUGLAS ST 68102

Oak Park Office Building
7363 PACIFIC ST 68114

Oak Park Office Building
7377 PACIFIC ST 68114

Oak Park Office Building
7389 PACIFIC ST 68114

Old Federal Building
106 S 15TH ST 68102

Old Mill Ofce Pk
10832 OLD MILL RD 68154

Old Mill Gateway Building
10843 OLD MILL RD 68154

Old Mill Ofce Park
10828-846 OLD MILL RD . 68154

Omaha Building
1650 FARNAM ST 68102

One Old Mill Building
101 S 108TH AVE 68154

One Prof Sq Building
10822 OLD MILL RD 68154

One Professional Sq
10826 OLD MILL RD 68154

One Two Zero Building
120 N 69TH ST 68132

Ops School
5730 N 30TH ST 68111

Pacific Hills Ofce Building C
12020 SHAMROCK PLZ ... 68154

Pacific Hills Ofce Building D
12120 SHAMROCK PLZ ... 68154

Pacific Hills Ofce Building E
1010 S 120TH ST 68154

Park East Medical Center
2566 SAINT MARYS AVE . 68105

Park Place Office Building
1044 N 115TH ST 68154

Parkview Prof Ctr
1055 N 115TH ST 68154

Philadelphia Place
256 N 115TH ST 68154

Philadelphia Place
268 N 115TH ST 68154

Physicians Building
10060 REGENCY CIR 68114

Presto X Building
4521 LEAVENWORTH ST 68106

Professional Building
3510 DODGE ST 68131

Regency Clubhouse
10506 PACIFIC ST 68114

Regency Fashion Ct
120 REGENCY PKY 68114

Regency Four Office Building
10040 REGENCY CIR 68114

Regency One Office Building
10050 REGENCY CIR 68114

Service Life Building
1904 FARNAM ST 68102

Seville Sq Ofce Building
14707 CALIFORNIA ST 68154

St Cecelia Convent
3843 WEBSTER ST 68131

State Office Building
1313 Farnam On The Mall 68102

Stonebrook Office Park
210-230 S 108TH AVE 68154

Sunset Valley Ofc Building
2580 S 90TH ST 68124

Terrace View Exec Ctr
1045 N 115TH ST 68154

The Center
1941 S 42ND ST 68105

The Century Building
11213 DAVENPORT ST 68154

The Mark
9290 W DODGE RD 68114

The Scoular Building
2027 DODGE ST 68102

Timber Ridge
11110 FORT ST 68164

Two Old Mill Building
10855 W DODGE RD 68154

Union Hall Building
1821 CALIFORNIA ST 68102

US Army
5730 N 30TH ST 68111

Veterans Adm Med Ctr
4101 WOOLWORTH AVE . 68105

West Dodge Medical Building
8300 DODGE ST 68114

West Maple Medical Center
2808 N 75TH ST 68134

Westmark Building
10707 PACIFIC ST 68114

Westport Professional Ctr
909 N 96TH ST 68114

Westroads Shopping Center
10000 CALIFORNIA ST 68114

Woodmen Tower
1700 FARNAM ST 68102

World Insurance Co
11808 GRANT ST 68164

Xerox Building
7171 MERCY RD 68106

HOSPITALS

Childrens Memorial Hosp
8301 DODGE ST 68114

Methodist Hospital
8303 DODGE ST 68114

HOTELS

Best Western Hotel
3650 S 72ND ST 68124

Club House
11515 MIRACLE HILLS DR 68154

Days Inn Hotel
3001 CHICAGO ST 68131

Embassy Suites Hotel
7270 CEDAR ST 68124

Hampton Inn
3301 S 72ND ST 68124

Hampton Inn
10728 L ST 68127

Holiday Inn
3321 S 72ND ST 68124

Holiday Inn
655 N 108TH AVE 68154

Homewood Suites
7010 HASCALL ST 68106

La Quinta Motor Inn
3330 N 104TH AVE 68134

Motel 6
10708 M ST 68127

New Tower Inn
7764 DODGE ST 68114

Radisson Redick Tower Htl
1504 HARNEY ST 68102

Ramada Inn
7007 GROVER ST 68106

Red Lion Inn
1616 DODGE ST 68102

Rodeway Inn
7101 GROVER ST 68106

Savannah Suites
4809 S 107TH AVE 68127

Super 8 Motel
7111 SPRING ST 68106

PAPILLION

BUILDINGS

Sarpy County Courthouse
1210 GOLDEN GATE DR . 68046

NEVADA
Abbreviation NV

Alamo 89001
Amargosa Valley 89020
Anderson Acres (Reno) 89506
Apache (Imlay) 89418
Arden (Las Vegas) 89118
Arthur (Wells) 89835
Ash Springs (Hiko) 89017
Aurora (Wellington) 89444
Austin 89310
Babbitt (Hawthorne) 89415
Baker 89311
Baker And Taylor (Reno) ... 89564
Battle Mountain 89820
Beatty 89003
Beowawe 89821
Black Springs (Reno) 89506
Blue Diamond 89004
Bonanza (Las Vegas) 89106
Bordertown (Reno) 89506
Bottle Creek (Winnemucca) 89445
Boulder City 89005-006
   Lakeshore 89005
   Willow Beach 89005
Bunkerville 89007
Cactus Springs 89124
   (Las Vegas)
Cal Nev Ari 89039
Calico Basin (Las Vegas) .. 89124
Calico Ridge (Henderson) .. 89015
Caliente 89008
Callville Bay (Las Vegas) .. 89124
Carlin 89822
Carp (Caliente) 89008
Carroll Station (Fallon) 89406
Carson City 89701-706
   .... 89710-714, 89721
   Clear Creek 89701
   Jacks Valley 89701
   Lakeview 89701
   Moundhouse 89701
   Moundhouse 89706
   New Empire 89701
   New Washoe City 89701
   Stewart 89701
   Washoe 89701
Carvers (Round Mountain) 89045
Caselton (Pioche) 89043
Cave Rock 89413, 89448
   (Glenbrook)
Centerville 89410
   (Gardnerville)
Central Valley (Smith) 89430
Charleston (Elko) 89801
Cherry Creek (Ely) 89301
Citibank (Las Vegas) .. 88901-905
Citibank Nevada 89163-164
   (Las Vegas)
Clear Creek (Carson City) . 89701
Coaldale (Tonopah) 89049
Cobre (Wells) 89835
Cold Spring (Fallon) 89406
Cold Springs (Reno) 89506
College Park 89030
   (North Las Vegas)
Contact (Jackpot) 89825
Cordero (Mc Dermitt) 89421
Cosgrave (Winnemucca) .. 89445
Cottonwood Cove 89046

   (Searchlight)
Cottonwood Creek (Reno) 89510
Cover City (Wells) 89835
Crescent Valley 89821
   (Beowawe)
Crystal (Pahrump) 89041
Crystal Bay 89402, 89450-451
Crystal Springs (Hiko) 89017
Currie (Ely) 89301
Dayton 89403
Deeth 89823
Denio 89404
Dike (Denio) 89404
Dixie Valley (Fallon) 89406
Dresslerville 89410
   (Gardnerville)
Dry Lake (Las Vegas) 89124
Dry Valley (Pioche) 89043
Duck Valley (Owyhee) 89832
Duckwater 89314
Dunphy (Beowawe) 89821
Dyer 89010
Eagle Valley (Pioche) 89043
East Ely (Ely) 89301, 89315
East Las Vegas 89121-122
   (Las Vegas)
Echo Bay (Overton) 89040
Elburz (Halleck) 89824
Elgin (Caliente) 89008
Elk Point (Zephyr Cove) 89448
Elko 89801-803
   Charleston 89801
   Jiggs 89801
   Lee 89801
   North Fork 89801
Elks Point (Zephyr Cove) .. 89448
Ely 89301
Empire 89405
Eureka 89316
Fallon 89406-407, 89496
   Carroll Station 89406
   Cold Spring 89406
   Dixie Valley 89406
   Frenchman 89406
   Middlegate 89406
   Peterson 89406
   Ragtown 89406
   Salt Wells 89406
   Stillwater 89406
Federal (Las Vegas) 89101
Fernley 89408
Fish Lake Valley 89049
   (Tonopah)
Frenchman (Fallon) 89406
Gabbs 89409
Galena (Reno) 89511
Gardnerville 89410
Garside (Las Vegas) 89102
   89107
Genoa 89411
Gerlach 89412
Glenbrook 89413
Golconda 89414
Gold Hill (Virginia City) 89440
Gold Point (Goldfield) 89013
Golden Valley (Reno) 89506
Goldfield 89013
Goodsprings (Jean) 89019
Grass Valley 89445
   (Winnemucca)
Green Valley (Henderson) . 89014

Greenbrae (Sparks) 89431
Halleck 89824
Happy Valley (Sparks) 89431
Hawthorne 89415-416
   Babbitt 89415
   Thorne 89415
   Whiskey Flats 89415
Hazen (Fernley) 89408
Henderson 89009
   .... 89011-012, 89014-016
   Calico Ridge 89015
   Green Valley 89014
Hidden Valley (Reno) 89502
Highway 40 (Denio) 89404
Hiko 89017
Huffaker (Reno) 89511
Humboldt (Imlay) 89418
Huntridge (Las Vegas) 89104
   89110
Imlay 89418
Incline Village 89450-452
   Crystal Bay 89450-451
Indian Springs 89018, 89070
Ione (Austin) 89310
Jackass Flats (Mercury) ... 89023
Jackpot 89825
Jacks Valley 89701
   (Carson City)
Jackson Mountain (Denio) 89404
Jarbidge 89826
Jean 89019, 89026
Jiggs (Elko) 89801
Johnnie (Pahrump) 89041
Jungo (Winnemucca) 89445
Kelmont East 89448
   (Zephyr Cove)
King River (Orovada) 89425
Kingsbury (Zephyr Cove) .. 89448
Kingston (Austin) 89310
Lake Village 89448
   (Zephyr Cove)
Lakeridge (Stateline) 89449
Lakeshore (Boulder City) .. 89005
Lakeview (Carson City) 89701
Lamoille 89828
Lane (Ely) 89301
Las Vegas 89101-134
   ... 89137, 89139, 89150-155
   .... 89158-160, 89163-164
   89170, 89177, 89180, 89185
   89191, 89193, 89195, 89199
   Arden 89118
   Bonanza 89106
   Cactus Springs 89124
   Calico Basin 89124
   Callville Bay 89124
   Citibank 88901-905
   Citibank Nv 89163-164
   Dry Lake 89124
   East Las Vegas
   89121-122
   Federal 89101
   Garside 89102
   Garside 89107
   Huntridge 89104
   Huntridge 89110
   Paradise 89109
   Red Rock 89107
   Red Rock Vista 89108
   Red Rock Vista
   89128-131

Tuscarora 89834	Weed Heights (Yerington) . 89447	Sulphur 89445
Unionville (Imlay) 89418	Weeks (Yerington) 89447	Weso 89445
University (Reno) 89507	Wellington 89444	Wittell (Zephyr Cove) 89448
Upper Valley (Lovelock) 89419	Wells 89835	Yerington 89447
Ursine (Pioche) 89043	Wendover 89883	Zephyr Cove 89448-449
Valley Of Fire (Overton) 89040	Weso (Winnemucca) 89445	Cave Rock 89448
Valmy 89438	Whiskey Flats (Hawthorne) 89415	Elk Point 89448
Verdi 89439	Wilkins (Wells) 89835	Elks Point 89448
Virginia City 89440	Willow Beach 89005	Kelmont East 89448
Virginia Foothills (Reno) 89511	(Boulder City)	Kingsbury 89448
Vista (Sparks) 89431	Winchester (Las Vegas) 89109	Lake Village 89448
Wabuska (Yerington) 89447	Winnemucca 89445-446	Marla Bay 89448
Wadsworth 89442	Bottle Creek 89445	Pinewild 89448
Warm Springs (Tonopah) .. 89049	Cosgrave 89445	Round Hill 89448
Washington (Reno) 89503	Grass Valley 89445	Skyland 89448
.... 89513, 89523	Jungo 89445	Stateline 89448
Washoe (Carson City) 89701	Paradise Hill 89445	Wittell 89448

CALICO RIDGE

GOVERNMENT

City Of Henderson
240 S WATER ST 89015

FEDERAL

BUILDINGS

Foley Federal Building
300 LAS VEGAS BLVD S . 89101

RENO

APARTMENTS

Park Towers
280 ISLAND AVE 89501

BUILDINGS

Arlington Towers
100 N ARLINGTON AVE ... 89501

First Inter Bank Building
1 E 1ST ST 89501

Valley Bank Plaza
50 W LIBERTY ST 89501

GOVERNMENT

Courthouse
75 COURT ST 89501

Federal Building
300 BOOTH ST 89509

NEW HAMPSHIRE
Abbreviation NH

Acworth	03601
Allenstown (Suncook)	03275
Alstead	03602
Alton	03809
Alton Bay	03810
Amherst	03031
Andover	03216, 03265
Potter Place	03265
Antrim	03440
Ashland	03217
Ashuelot	03441
Atkinson	03811
Auburn	03032
Barnstead	03218
Barrington	03825
Bartlett	03812
Bath	03740
Bedford	03110
Beebe River (Campton)	03223
Belmont	03220
Bennington	03442
Berlin	03570
Bethlehem	03574
Boscawen (Concord)	03303
Bow	03304
Bradford	03221
Brentwood (Exeter)	03833
Bretton Woods	03575
Bristol	03222
Brookline	03033
Campton	03223, 03285
Beebe River	03223
Canaan	03741
Candia	03034
Canterbury	03224
Center Barnstead	03225
Center Conway	03813
Center Harbor	03226
Center Ossipee	03814
Center Sandwich	03227
Center Strafford	03815
Center Tuftonboro	03816
Charlestown	03603
Chester	03036
Chesterfield	03443
Chocorua	03817
Claremont	03743
Colebrook	03576
Columbia (Colebrook)	03576
Concord	03300-303, 03305-306
Boscawen	03303
Penacook	03303
Contoocook	03229
Conway	03818
Cornish	03745
Cornish Flat	03746
Danbury	03230
Danville	03819
Deerfield	03037
Derry	03038
Dover	03820-822
Drewsville	03604
Dublin	03444
Dunbarton (Goffstown)	03045
Durham	03824
East Andover	03231
East Candia	03040
East Derry	03041

East Hampstead	03826
East Hebron	03232
East Kingston	03827
East Lempster	03605
East Rochester	03868
East Sullivan	03445
East Swanzey	03446
East Wakefield	03830
Eaton Center	03832
Elkins	03233
Enfield	03748
Enfield Center	03749
Epping	03042
Epsom	03234
Errol	03579
Etna	03750
Exeter	03833
Farmington	03835
Fitzwilliam	03447
Francestown	03043
Franconia	03580
Franklin	03235
Freedom	03836
Fremont	03044
Georges Mills	03751
Gilford (Laconia)	03246-247
Gilmanton	03237
Gilsum	03448
Glen	03838
Glencliff	03238
Goffstown	03045
Gonic	03839
Gorham	03581
Goshen	03752
Grafton	03240
Grantham	03753
Greenfield	03047
Greenland	03840
Greenville	03048
Groveton	03582
Guild	03754
Hampstead	03841
Hampton	03842-843
Hampton Falls	03844
Hancock	03449
Hanover	03755
Harrisville	03450
Haverhill	03765
Hebron	03241
Henniker	03242
Hill	03243
Hillsboro	03244
Hinsdale	03451
Holderness	03245
Hollis	03049
Hooksett	03106
Hopkinton (Contoocook)	03229
Hudson	03051
Intervale	03845
Jackson	03846
Jaffrey	03452
Jefferson	03583
Kearsarge	03847
Keene	03431-435
Kingston	03848
Laconia	03246-247
Gilford	03246-247
Lancaster	03584
Lebanon	03756, 03766
Lee (Durham)	03824
Lempster	03606

Lincoln	03251
Lisbon	03585
Littleton	03561
Lochmere	03252
Londonderry	03053
Lyme	03768
Lyme Center	03769
Lyndeborough	03082
Madbury (Dover)	03820
Madison	03849
Manchester	03100-109, 03111
Marlborough	03455
Marlow	03456
Meadows	03587
Melvin Village	03850
Meredith	03253
Meriden	03770
Merrimack	03054
Milan	03588
Milford	03055
Milton	03851
Milton Mills	03852
Mirror Lake	03853
Monroe	03771
Mont Vernon	03057
Moultonboro	03254
Mount Sunapee	03772
Mount Washington	03589
Munsonville	03457
Nashua	03060-063
New Boston	03070
New Castle	03854
New Durham	03855
New Hampton	03256
New Ipswich	03071
New London	03257
Newbury	03255
Newfields	03856
Newington (Portsmouth)	03801
Newmarket	03857
Newport	03773
Newton	03858
Newton Junction	03859
North Conway	03860
North Hampton	03862
North Haverhill	03774
North Salem	03073
North Sandwich	03259
North Stratford	03590
North Sutton	03260
North Walpole	03609
North Woodstock	03262
Northwood	03261
Nottingham	03290
Orford	03777
Ossipee	03864
Pelham	03076
Pembroke (Suncook)	03275
Penacook (Concord)	03303
Peterborough	03458, 03460
Piermont	03779
Pike	03780
Pittsburg	03592
Pittsfield	03263
Plainfield	03781
Plaistow	03865
Plymouth	03264
Portsmouth	03801-802, 03804
Newington	03801
Potter Place (Andover)	03265
Raymond	03077

333

Richmond (Winchester) 03470	South Tamworth 03883	Wentworth 03282
Rindge 03461	Spofford 03462	West Chesterfield 03466
Rochester 03866, 03867	Stinson Lake 03274	West Franklin 03235
Rollinsford 03805, 03869	Stoddard 03464	West Lebanon 03784
Rumney 03266	Strafford 03884	West Nottingham 03291
Rye03870	Stratham 03885	West Ossipee 03890
Rye Beach 03871	Sunapee 03782	West Peterborough 03468
Salem 03079	Suncook 03275	West Springfield 03284
Salisbury 03216, 03235,03268	Surry (Keene) 03431	West Stewartstown 03597
.... 03303	Tamworth 03886	West Swanzey 03469
Sanbornton 03269	Temple 03084	Westmoreland 03467
Sanbornville 03872	Tilton 03276	Whitefield 03598
Sandown 03873	Troy 03465	Wilmot Flat 03287
Seabrook 03874	Twin Mountain 03595	Wilton 03086
Silver Lake 03875	Union 03887	Winchester 03470
Somersworth 03878	Wakefield (Union) 03887	Windham 03087
South Acworth 03607	Walpole 03608	Winnisquam 03289
South Effingham 03882	Warner 03278	Wolfeboro 03894
South Hampton 03827	Warren 03279	Wolfeboro Falls 03896
(East Kingston)	Washington 03280	Wonalancet 03897
South Newbury 03272	Waterville Valley 03215	Woodstock 03293
South Sutton 03273	Weare 03281	Woodsville 03785

IMPORTANT BUILDINGS   NEW HAMPSHIRE

CONCORD

GOVERNMENT

Capitol Building
107 N MAIN ST 03301

City Hall
41 GREEN ST 03301

Federal Building
55 PLEASANT ST 03301

Merrimack County Court Hs
163 N MAIN ST 03301

State House Annex
25 CAPITOL ST 03301

MANCHESTER

GOVERNMENT

City Hall
908 ELM ST 03101

Federal Building
275 CHESTNUT ST 03101

Hillsborough Cnty Ct Hse
300 CHESTNUT ST 03101

NASHUA

GOVERNMENT

Hillsborough County Building
19 TEMPLE ST 03060

HOSPITALS

Memorial Hospital
2014 PO BOX 03061

Saint Joseph Hospital
2013 PO BOX 03061

PORTSMOUTH

MILITARY

Portsmouth Naval Shipyard
2001 PO BOX 03804

NEW JERSEY
Abbreviation NJ

Aberdeen (Matawan)	07747
Absecon	08201
Academy (Newark)	07102
Adelphia	07710
Albion (Berlin)	08009
Allamuchy	07820
Allendale	07401
Allenhurst 07709, 07711	
Allentown	08501
Allenwood	08720
Alloway	08001
Allwood (Clifton)	07012
Almonesson (Woodbury) ..	08096
Alpha (Phillipsburg)	08865
Alpine	07620
Ampere (East Orange)	07017
Ancora (Hammonton)	08037
Andover	07821
Anglesea (Wildwood)	08260
Annandale	08801
Arlington (Kearny)	07032
Asbury	08802
Asbury Gardens (Neptune)	07753
Asbury Park	07712
Ashland	08043
(Kirkwood Voorhees)	
Atco	08004
Atlantic City 08400-406, 08411	
Auburn (Swedesboro)	08085
Audubon	08106
Augusta	07822
Aura (Glassboro)	08028
Avalon	08202
Avenel 07001, 07098	
Avon (Avon By The Sea) ...	07717
Awosting (Hewitt)	07421
Baptistown	08803
Barnegat	08005
Barnegat Light	08006
Barnsboro (Sewell)	08080
Barrington	08007
Barry Lakes	07422
(Highland Lakes)	
Basking Ridge 07920, 07939	
Batsto (Hammonton)	08037
Bay Head	08742
(Point Pleasant Beach)	
Bayonne	07002
Bayville	08721
Bayway (Elizabeth)	07202
Beach Haven	08008
Beach Haven West	08050
(Manahawkin)	
Beachwood	08722
Beaver Lake (Franklin)	07416
Bedminster	07921
Beemerville (Sussex)	07461
Beesleys Point (Marmora)	08223
Belford	07718
Belle Mead	08502
Belleplain (Woodbine)	08270
Belleville	07109
Bellmawr 08031, 08099	
Bellmead (Belle Mead)	08502
Belmar	07719
Belvidere	07823
Bergen (Jersey City)	07304
Bergen Point (Bayonne)	07002

Bergenfield	07621
Bergenline (Union City)	07087
Berkeley (Bayville) . 08721, 08757	
Berkeley Heights	07922
Berlin	08009
Bernardsville	07924
Betsytown (Elizabeth)	07201
Beverly	08010
Billingsport (Paulsboro) ...	08066
Birmingham	08011
Bivalve (Port Norris)	08349
Blackwood	08012
Blackwood Ter	08096
(Woodbury)	
Blairstown	07825
Blawenburg	08504
Blenheim (Blackwood)	08012
Bloomfield	07003
Bloomingdale	07403
Bloomsbury	08804
Bogota	07603
Boonton	07005
Bordentown	08505
Bound Brook	08805
Bradevelt (Marlboro)	07746
Bradley Beach	07720
Bradley Park (Neptune)	07753
Branchburg (Somerville) ...	08876
Branchville 07826-827, 07890	
Brant Beach	08008
(Beach Haven)	
Brick 08723-724	
Osbornsville	08723
Brick Church	07018
(East Orange)	
Bridgeboro (Riverside)	08075
Bridgeport	08014
Bridgeton	08302
Bridgewater	08807
Brielle	08730
Brigantine	08203
Brighton Beach	08008
(Beach Haven)	
Broadway	08808
Brookdale (Bloomfield)	07003
Brooklawn	08030
(Gloucester City)	
Brookside	07926
Brotmanville (Bridgeton) ..	08302
Browns Mills	08015
Budd Lake	07828
Buena	08310
Bunker Hill (Sewell)	08080
Burleigh	08210
(Cape May Court House)	
Burlington	08016
Butler	07405
Buttzville	07829
Caldwell 07006-007	
North Caldwell	07006
West Caldwell ... 07006-007	
Califon	07830
Camden 08100-110	
East Camden	08105
Fairview	08104
Pennsauken	08105
South Camden	08104
Campbells Junction	07718
(Belford)	
Cape May	08204
Cape May Point	08212

Cardiff (Pleasantville)	08232
Carlstadt	07072
Carmel (Millville)	08332
Carneys Point	08069
(Penns Grove)	
Carteret	07008
Cassville (Jackson)	08527
Castle Point (Hoboken)	07030
Cecil (Williamstown)	08094
Cedar Beach	07758
(Port Monmouth)	
Cedar Bonnet Island	08050
(Manahawkin)	
Cedar Brook	08018
Cedar Grove	07009
Cedar Knolls	07927
Cedar Run (West Creek) ...	08092
Cedarville	08311
Centerton (Elmer)	08318
Central (East Orange)	07018
Chambersburg (Trenton) ...	08611
Changewater	07831
Chapel Heights (Sewell) ...	08080
Chatham	07928
Chatsworth	08019
Cherry Hill 08002-003, 08034	
....	08358
Ellisburg	08002
Erlton	08002
Woodcrest	08003
Chesilhurst	08089
(Waterford Works)	
Chester	07930
Chesterfield (Bordentown)	08505
Chestnut (Union)	07083
Cinnaminson (Riverton)	08077
Clark	07066
Clarksboro	08020
Clarksburg	08510
Clayton	08312
Clementon	08021
Clermont	08210
(Cape May Court House)	
Cliffside Park	07010
Cliffwood	07721
Cliffwood Beach (Keyport)	07735
Cliffwood Lake	07460
(Stockholm)	
Clifton 07011-015	
Allwood	07012
Delawanna	07014
Main Avenue	07011
Clinton	08809
Clinton Hill (Newark)	07108
Closter	07624
Cold Indian Springs	07712
(Asbury Park)	
Cold Spring (Cape May) ...	08204
Colesville (Sussex)	07461
Collings Lakes	08094
(Williamstown)	
Collingswood	08108
Cologne	08213
Colonia	07067
Colonial Terrace	07712
(Asbury Park)	
Colts Neck	07722
Columbia	07832
Columbus	08022
Convent Station	07961
(Morristown)	

Paterson 07508, 07538	Jericho (Woodbury) 08096	Liberty Corner 07938
Prospect Park .. 07508, 07538	Jersey City 07097, 07300	Lincoln Park 07035
Hamburg 07419	.... 07302-311, 07399	Lincroft 07738
Hamilton (Trenton) 08609-611	Bergen Station 07304	Linden 07036
.... 08619-620	Five Corners 07308	Lindenwold (Clementon) ... 08021
.... 08629, 08690-691	General Lafayette 07309	Lindy Lake (Butler) 07405
Hamilton Township 08330	Greenville 07305	Linwood 08221-222, 08227
(Mays Landing)	Hudson City 07307	Prudential Ins ..08222, 08227
Hammonton 08037	Journal Square 07306	Steelmanville 08221
Hampton 08827	Pershing 07399	Lionshead Lake (Wayne) .. 07470
Hancocks Bridge 08038	Jerseyville (Freehold) 07728	Little Falls 07424
Harrington Park 07640	Jobstown 08041	Little Ferry 07643
Harrison 07029	Johnsonburg 07846	Little Silver 07739
Harrisonville 08039	Journal Square 07306	Little York 08834
Harvey Cedars 08008	(Jersey City)	Livingston 07039
(Beach Haven)	Juliustown 08042	Loch Arbour (Allenhurst) 07711
Hasbrouck Heights 07604	Keansburg 07734	Locust (Rumson) 07760
Haskell 07420	Kearny (Harrison) 07029	Lodi 07644
Haven Beach (Bch Haven) 08008	.... 07032, 07099	Long Beach 08008
Haworth 07641	Arlington 07032	(Beach Haven) ....
Hawthorne 07506-507	South Kearny 07032	Long Branch 07740
Paterson 07506-507	West Arlington 07032	Long Valley 07853
Hazlet 07730	Keasbey 08832	Longport 08403
Heislerville 08324	Kendall Park 08824	Loveladies (Beach Haven) 08008
Helmetta 08828	Kenilworth 07033	Lower Montville 07045
Hewitt 07421	Kenvil 07847	(Montville)
Hi Nella (Somerdale) 08083	Keyport 07735	Lumberton 08048
Hibernia 07842	Kingston 08528	Lyndhurst 07071
High Bridge 08829	Kinnelon (Butler) 07405	Lyons 07939
High Crest (Butler) 07405	Kirkwood 08040, 08043	Lyonsville (Boonton) 07005
High Point (Sussex) 07461	(Kirkwood Voorhees)	Madison 07940
Highland Lakes 07422	Kresson (Marlton) 08053	Magnolia 08049
Highland Park 08904	Lacey (Forked River) 08731	Mahwah 07430, 07495, 07498
Highlands 07732	Lacey Township 08734	Main Avenue (Clifton) 07011
Hightstown 08520	(Lanoka Harbor)	Malaga 08328
Hillcrest (Paterson) 07502	Lafayette 07848	Manahawkin 08050
Hillsborough (Somerville) .. 08876	Lake Como (Spring Lake) . 07762	Manalapan (Englishtown) . 07726
Hillsdale 07642	Lake Hiawatha 07034	Manasquan 08736
Hillside 07205	Lake Hopatcong 07849	Manchester (Lakehurst) 08733
Hilltop (Blackwood) 08012	Lake Intervale (Boonton) .. 07005	.... 08757, 08759
Ho Ho Kus 07423	Lake Pine (Marlton) 08053	Mantoloking 08738
Hoboken 07030	Lake Stockholm 07460	Mantua 08051
Holgate (Beach Haven) 08008	(Stockholm)	Mantua Heights (Mantua) . 08051
Holmdel 07733, 07777	Lake Swannanoa 07438	Manville 08835
Hopatcong 07843	(Oak Ridge)	Maple Shade 08052
Hope 07844	Lake Tamarack 07460	Maplecrest (Maplewood) ... 07040
Hopewell 08525	(Stockholm)	Maplewood 07040
Howell 07731	Lakehurst 08733, 08759	Margate City 08402
Hudson City (Jersey City) . 07307	Manchester 08733	Marlboro 07746
Hudson Heights 07047	Lakeland (Blackwood) 08012	Marlton 08053
(North Bergen)	Lakewood 08701	Marlton Lakes (Atco) 08004
Hurffville (Sewell) 08080	Lambertville 08530	Marmora 08223
Ideal Beach (Keansburg) .. 07734	Landing 07850	Martinsville 08836
Imlaystown 08526	Landisville 08326	Masonville (Mount Laurel) . 08054
Ind Hillside (Hillside) 07205	Lanoka Harbor 08734	Matawan 07747
Indian Mills (Vincentown) .. 08088	Laurel Lake (Millville) 08332	Mauricetown 08329
Industrial Hillside 07205	Laurel Springs 08021	Mayetta (West Creek) 08092
(Hillside)	(Clementon)	Mays Landing 08330
Interlaken (Asbury Park) ... 07712	Laurence Harbor 08879	Mayville 08210
Ironbound (Newark) 07105	(South Amboy)	(Cape May Court House)
Ironia 07845	Lavallette 08735	Maywood 07607
Irvington 07111	Lawnside 08045	Mc Afee 07428
Iselin 08830	Lawrenceville (Trenton) 08648	Mckee City 08232
Island Heights 08732	Layton 07851	(Pleasantville)
Jackson (Jersey City) 07305	Lebanon 08833	Meadows (Secaucus) 07096
.... 08527	Ledgewood 07852	Medford 08055
Cassville 08527	Leeds Point 08220	Mendham 07945
Jacobstown (Wrightstown) 08562	Leesburg 08327	Menlo Park (Edison) 08837
Jamesburg 08831	Lenola (Moorestown) 08057	Mercerville (Trenton) 08619
Jefferson Township 07438	Leonardo 07737	Merchantville 08109
(Oak Ridge)	Leonia 07605	Meriden (Boonton) 07005

Merrill Lynch 08988-989
  (New Brunswick)
Metropark South 08878
  (South Amboy)
Metuchen 08840
Miami Beach (Villas) 08251
Mickleton 08056
Middlebush (Somerset) 08873
Middlesex 08846
Middletown 07748
Middleville 07855
Midland Park 07432
Midvale (Wanaque) 07465
Milford 08848
Millburn 07041
Millhurst (Freehold) 07728
Millington 07946
Millstone (Clarksburg) 08510
  08876
Milltown 08850
Millville 08332
Milmay 08340
Milton (Oak Ridge) 07438
Mine Hill (Dover) 07801
Minotola 08341
Mizpah 08342
Monitor (West New York) .. 07093
Monmouth (Eatontown) 07724
Monmouth Beach 07750
Monmouth Hills 07732
  (Highlands)
Monmouth Junction 08852
Monmouth Park 07757
  (Oceanport)
Monroe (Cranbury) 08512
Monroeville 08343
Montague 07827
Montclair 07042-043
  Upper Montclair 07043
Montgomery (Skillman) 08558
Montvale 07645
Montville 07045
Moonachie 07074
Moorestown 08057
Morgan (South Amboy) 08879
Morganville 07751
Morris Plains 07950
Morristown 07960-963
  Convent Station 07961
Morsemere (Ridgefield) 07657
Mount Arlington 07856
Mount Ephraim 08059
Mount Freedom 07970
Mount Holly 08060
Mount Laurel 08054
Mount Royal 08061
Mount Tabor 07878
Mountain Lakes 07046
Mountain View (Wayne) 07470
Mountainside 07092
Muhlenberg (Plainfield) 07060
Mullica Hill 08062
Murray Hill 07974
  (New Providence)
Musical Heritage 07713
  (Asbury Park)
Mystic Island (Tuckerton) .. 08087
National Park 08063
Navesink 07752
Neptune 07753-754

Asbury Gardens 07753
Bradley Park 07753
Shark River Hills 07753
Whitesville 07753
Neshanic Station 08853
Netcong 07857
Netherwood (Plainfield) 07062
New Brunswick 08901-906
  ...... 08922, 08933, 08988-989
  Merrill Lynch 08988-08989
New Egypt 08533
New Gretna 08224
New Hanover (Cookstown) . 08511
New Lisbon 08064
New Milford 07646
New Monmouth 07748
  (Middletown)
New Providence 07974
New Vernon 07976
Newark 07100-108, 07112
  .... 07114, 07175, 07184
  .... 07188-189, 07191-195
  07197-199
  Academy 07102
  Clinton Hill 07108
  Ironbound 07105
  Midtown 07102
  North 07104
  Roseville 07107
  South 07112, 07114
  Vailsburg 07106
  Washington Park 07102
  Weequahic 07112
  West 07103
Newfield 08344
Newfoundland 07435
Newport 08345
Newton 07860
Newtonville 08346
Norma 08347
Normandy Beach 08739
North (Newark) 07104
North Arlington 07031
North Beach 08008
  (Beach Haven)
North Bergen 07047
North Branch (Somerville) . 08876
North Brunswick 08902
North Caldwell (Caldwell) .. 07006
North Cape May 08204
  (Cape May)
North Center (Bloomfield) . 07003
North Dennis 08214
  (Dennisville)
North Elizabeth 07208
  (Elizabeth)
North Haledon 07508, 07538
  (Haledon)
North Hanover 08562
  (Wrightstown)
North Long Branch 07740
  (Long Branch)
North Middletown 07734
  (Keansburg)
North Plainfield (Plainfield) 07060
  07062-063
North Wildwood 08260
  (Wildwood)
Northfield 08225
Northvale 07647
Norwood 07648

Nutley 07110
Oak Ridge 07438
Oak Valley (Wenonah) 08090
Oakhurst 07755
Oakland 07436
Oaklyn 08107
Ocean (Asbury Park) 07712
  .... 07755, 08758
Ocean Beach (Lavallette) . 08735
Ocean City 08226
Ocean Gate 08740
Ocean Grove 07756
Ocean Mall (Asbury Park) . 07712
Ocean Township 08758
  (Waretown)
Ocean View 08230
Oceanport 07757
Oceanville 08231
Ogdensburg 07439
Old Bridge 08857
Old Tappan (Westwood) 07675
Oldbridge (Old Bridge) 08857
Oldwick 08858
Oradell 07649
Orange 07050-051
Ortley Beach 08751
  (Seaside Heights)
Osbornsville (Brick) 08723
Osgli (Newark) 07187
Outwater (Garfield) 07026
Overbrook (Cedar Grove) . 07009
Oxford 07863
Packanack Lake (Wayne) . 07470
Palermo (Marmora) 08223
Palisade (Fort Lee) 07024
Palisades Park 07650
Palmer Square 08540, 08542
  (Princeton)
Palmyra 08065
Pamrapo (Bayonne) 07002
Paradise Lakes (Alloway) . 08001
Paramus 07652-653
Park Avenue (Union City) .. 07087
Park Ridge 07656
Parkandbush (Elizabeth) ... 07202
Parkertown (Tuckerton) 08087
Parlin 08859
Parsippany 07054
Passaic 07055
Paterson 07501-514, 07522
  07524, 07530, 07533, 07538
  07543-544
  Hillcrest 07502
  Haband Co 07530
  Hillcrest 07502
  Peoples Park ... 07513, 07543
  South Paterson 07503, 07533
Pattenburg (Asbury) 08802
Paulsboro 08066
Peahala Park 08008
  (Beach Haven)
Peapack 07977
Pedricktown 08067
Pemberton 08068
Pennington 08534
Penns Grove 08069
Pennsauken 08105, 08109-110
  (Camden)
  Camden 08110
  Delair 08110
Pennsville 08070

Peoples Park (Paterson) ...	07513
....	07543
Pequannock	07440
Perrineville	08535
Pershing (Jersey City)	07399
Perth Amboy	08861-863
Petersburg (Woodbine) ...	08270
Peterstown (Elizabeth)	07201
Phalanx (Colts Neck)	07722
Phillipsburg	08865
Pine Beach	08741
Pine Brook	07058
Pine Cliff Lake	07480
(West Milford)	
Pine Grove (Marlton)	08053
Pine Hill (Clementon)	08021
Pine Valley (Clementon) ...	08021
Pinehurst (Absecon)	08201
Pines Lake (Wayne)	07470
Piscataway	08854-855
Pitman	08071
Pittsgrove (Elmer)	08318
Pittstown	08867
Plainfield	07060-063
Muhlenberg	07060
Netherwood	07062
North Plainfield	07060
North Plainfield ...	07062-063
Scotch Plains	07060
Watchung	07060
Plainsboro	08536
Plaza (Secaucus)	07096
Pleasantville	08232-233
Pluckemin	07978
Plumsted (New Egypt)	08533
Point Pleasant	08742
(Point Pleasant Beach)	
Pomona	08240
Pompton Falls	07442
(Pompton Lakes)	
Pompton Junction	07457
(Riverdale)	
Pompton Plains	07444
Porchtown (Newfield)	08344
Port Elizabeth	08348
Port Monmouth	07758
Port Murray	07865
Port Norris	08349
Port Reading	07064
Port Republic	08241
Port-au-peck (Oceanport) ..	07757
Pottersville	07979
Powerville (Boonton)	07005
Preakness (Wayne)	07470
Princeton	08540-544
Palmer Square	08540, 08542
West Windsor	08540
Princeton Junction	08550
Prospect Park	07508, 07538
(Haledon)	
Quakertown	08868
Quinton	08072
Radburn (Fair Lawn)	07410
Rahway	07065
Ramsey	07446
Rancocas	08073
Rancocas Woods	08054
(Mount Laurel)	
Randolph	07869
Raritan	08869
Readington	08870

Red Bank	07701-704, 07799
Fair Haven	07701
Fairview	07701
Shrewsbury	07701
Suburban	07701
Westboro	07701
Richland	08350
Richwood	08074
Ridgefield	07657
Ridgefield Park	07660
Ridgewood	07450-452
Glen Rock	07450
Ringoes	08551
Ringwood	07456
Rio Grande	08242
Ritz (Garfield)	07026
River Edge	07661
River Vale (Westwood)	07675
Riverdale	07457
Riverside	08370, 08075
Riverton	08076, 08077
Rivervale (Westwood)	07675
Robbinsville (Trenton)	08691
Rochelle Park	07662
Rockaway	07866
Rockaway Valley	07005
(Boonton)	
Rockleigh (Northvale)	07647
Rocky Hill	08553
Roebling	08554
Roosevelt	08555
Roseland	07068
Roselle	07203
Roselle Park	07204
Rosemont	08556
Rosenhayn	08352
Roseville (Newark)	07107
Rumson	07760
Runnemede	08078
Rutherford	07070
Saddle Brook	07662
(Rochelle Park)	
Saddle River	07458
Salem	08079
Sands Point (Oceanport) ..	07757
Sayreville	08871-872
Schooleys Mountain	07870
Scobeyville (Eatontown) ...	07724
Scotch Plains (Plainfield) ..	07060
....	07076, 07090
Scullville (Mays Landing) ..	08330
Sea Bright (Rumson)	07760
Sea Girt	08750
Sea Isle City	08243
Seabrook (Bridgeton)	08302
Seaside Heights	08751
Seaside Park	08752
Seaville (Ocean View)	08230
Secaucus	07094, 07096
Meadows	07096
Plaza	07096
Sergeantsville	08557
Sewaren	07077
Sewell	08080
Shady Lake	07405, 07480
(Butler)	
Shamong (Vincentown)	08088
Shark River Hills	07753
(Neptune)	
Shark River Manor	07719
(Belmar)	

Sharptown (Woodstown) ...	08098
Shaw Crest (Wildwood) ...	08260
Shiloh	08353
Ship Bottom (Bch Haven) .	08008
Short Hills	07078
Shrewsbury	07701-702
Shrewsbury Township	07724
(Eatontown)	
Sicklerville	08081
Silver Lake (Stockholm) ...	07460
Silverton (Toms River)	08753
Singac (Little Falls)	07424
Skillman	08558
Skyline Lakes (Ringwood)	07456
Smithville (Absecon)	08201
Somerdale	08083
Somers Point	08244
Somerset	08873
....	08875, 08890
East Millstone	08873
East Millstone	08875
Franklin	08873
Middlebush	08873
Zarepath	08873
Somerville	08807, 08876-877
(Bridgewater)	
Branchburg	08876
Finderne	08876
Hillsborough	08876
Millstone	08876
North Branch	08876
South Branch	08876
South (Newark)	07112, 07114
South Amboy	08878-879
South Belmar (Belmar)	07719
South Bound Brook	08880
South Branch (Somerville)	08876
South Brunswick	08512
(Cranbury)	
South Camden (Camden) .	08104
South Dennis	08245
South Egg Harbor	08215
(Egg Harbor City)	
South Hackensack	07606
South Kearny (Kearny)	07032
South Orange	07079
South Paterson ...	07503, 07533
(Paterson)	
South Plainfield	07080
South River	08882
South Seaside Park	08752
(Seaside Park)	
South Seaville	08246
South Toms River ...	08753, 08757
(Toms River)	
South Vineland (Vineland)	08360
Southampton (Vincentown)	08088
Sparta	07871
Spotswood	08884
Spray Beach (Bch Haven)	08008
Spring Lake	07762
Springfield	07081
Staffordville	08092
(West Creek)	
Stanhope	07874
Stanton	08885
Steelmantown (Woodbine)	08270
Steelmanville (Linwood)	08221
Stewartsville	08886
Stillwater	07875
Stirling	07980

IMPORTANT BUILDINGS NEW JERSEY

ACADEMY

GOVERNMENT

Federal Building
970 BROAD ST 07102

M L King Jr Federal Building
50 WALNUT ST 07102

New Jersey State
1100 RAYMOND BLVD 07102

Us Courthouse
2 FEDERAL SQ 07102

AUDUBON

APARTMENTS

Audubon Towers
600 W NICHOLSON RD ... 08106

BAYWAY

APARTMENTS

Chilton Towers
220 W JERSEY ST 07202

BETSYTOWN

BUILDINGS

Hersh Towers
125 BROAD ST 07201

Martin Building
1139 E JERSEY ST 07201

GOVERNMENT

Union County Courthouse
2 BROAD ST 07201

CAMDEN

APARTMENTS

Cooper River Plaza
5105 N PARK DR 08109

Ferry Station
2011 FERRY AVE 08104

Haddonview South
1 MACARTHUR BLVD 08108

John F Kennedy Towers
2021 WATSON ST 08105

Myrtle Place
4001 MYRTLE AVE 08105

Northgate I
433 N 7TH ST 08102

Northgate II
500 N 7TH ST 08102

Pennsauken Towers
8001 MAPLE AVE 08109

Riverview Towers
130 MICKLE BLVD 08103

BUILDINGS

Camden Co Admin Building
539 MARKET ST 08102

Cooper Pky East
6981 N PARK DR 08109

Cooper Pky West
6981 N PARK DR 08109

Ferry Office Building
2101 FERRY AVE 08104

Ferry Plaza
1800 E DAVIS ST 08104

Hall Of Justice
101 S 5TH ST 08103

Mickle Towers
200 MICKLE BLVD 08103

Parkade Building
519 FEDERAL ST 08103

CHAMBERSBURG

APARTMENTS

Kingsbury Square
2 KINGSBURY SQ 08611

South Village 1
312 LALOR ST 08611

South Village 2 Office
28 STOKELY AVE 08611

CHERRY HILL

APARTMENTS

Cadbury Retirement Home
2150 ROUTE 38 08002

Cherry Hill Apts East
2151 ROUTE 38 08002

Cherry Hill Apts West
2141 ROUTE 38 08002

Colonial
836 Cooper Landing Rd 08002

Habitat
966 PARK BLVD 08002

Hampshire House
606 Cooper Landing Rd 08002

Kyoto
2995 CHAPEL AVE W 08002

Provincial Apts West
106 CHESTNUT ST 08002

Somerset
801 Cooper Landing Rd 08002

Toledo
3005 CHAPEL AVE W 08002

BUILDINGS

Ave Of Commerce
2428 ROUTE 38 08002

Barclay House
1200 MARLTON PIKE E ... 08034

Cherry Hill Plaza
1415 MARLTON PIKE E ... 08034

Chestnut Place Condos
111 CHESTNUT ST 08002

Commerce Center Building A
1800 CHAPEL AVE W 08002

Commerce Center Building B
1810 CHAPEL AVE W 08002

Commerce Center Building C
1820 CHAPEL AVE W 08002

Executive Campus
12 EXECUTIVE CAMPUS 08002

Executive Mews
1930 MARLTON PIKE E ... 08003

One Cherry Hill
1 MALL DR 08002

Provincial Executive Building
2201 ROUTE 38 08002

South Jersey Med Ctr
1401 MARLTON PIKE E ... 08034

Sussex House
1001 KINGS HWY N 08034

DOVER

APARTMENTS

Jamestown Vlg Apts
0 JAMES ST 08753

EDISON

APARTMENTS

Senior Citizens Apts
1061 INMAN AVE 08820

GOVERNMENT

Municipal Building
100 MUNICIPAL BLVD 08817

HOTELS

Clarion Hotel
2055 LINCOLN STREET .. 08817

Ramada Inn
3050 WOODBRIDGE AVE 08837

ELIZABETH

APARTMENTS

Tudor Court
800 N BROAD ST 07208

EWING

APARTMENTS

Beechwood Gardens
225 BEECHWOOD AVE ... 08618

Bellevue Plaza Apts
447 BELLEVUE AVE 08618

Carteret Arms
333 W STATE ST 08618

Claridge House
1130 STUYVESANT AVE .. 08618

East Gate Apts
1501 PARKSIDE AVE 08638

Glen Cairn Arms Apts Frt
301 W STATE ST 08618

Glen Cairn Arms Apts Rear
301 W STATE ST 08618

Highgate Apts
1 HIGHGATE DR 08618

J Conner French Tower
630 W STATE ST 08618

James Abbott Apts
490 HOFFMAN AVE 08618

Josepheson Apts
237 OAKLAND ST 08618

Lafayette House
777 W STATE ST 08618

Luther Towers
489 W STATE ST 08618

Office Condominium
1450 PARKSIDE AVE 08638

Park Place Apts
1460 PARKSIDE AVE 08638

Parkside Manor Apts
1441 PARKSIDE AVE 08638

Parkwood Apts
1100 EDGEWOOD AVE 08618

Regency House
1315 W STATE ST 08618

River Bank Apts
2030 RIVERSIDE DR 08618

Rowan Towers
620 W STATE ST 08618

Scudders Falls East
325 W Upper Ferry Rd 08628

Versailles Apts
220 SULLIVAN WAY 08628

BUILDINGS

Ewing Twp Municipal
1872 PENNINGTON RD ... 08618

GLEN ROCK

BUILDINGS

Amica
66 GLEN AVE 07452

C F Post
20 WILSEY SQ 07450

Lincoln Building
45 N BROAD ST 07450

Medical Arts
385 S MAPLE AVE 07452

Medical Arts Building
127 UNION ST 07450

Zecher
1250 E Ridgewood Ave 07450

HOSPITALS

Valley Hospital
223 N VAN DIEN AVE 07450

GROVEVILLE

APARTMENTS

Dover Manor Apts
4134 S BROAD ST 08620

Hillcrest Garden Apts
617 HILLTOP DR 08620

Sunnybrae Gardens
4134 S BROAD ST 08620

HAMILTON

APARTMENTS

Hamilton Gardens
2300 S BROAD ST 08610

Miller Homes
125 LINCOLN AVE 08609

Trenton Center East
511 GREENWOOD AVE ... 08609

Trenton Center West
465 GREENWOOD AVE ... 08609

Winding Brook Apts
1 BRADFORD AVE 08610

HIGHLAND PARK

GOVERNMENT

Highland Park Boro Hall
221 S 5TH AVE 08904

JERSEY CITY

BUILDINGS

Jersey Journal Building
30 JOURNAL SQ 07306

Trust Company
921 BERGEN AVE 07306

LAWRENCEVILLE

APARTMENTS

Westgate Apts
550 LAWRENCEVILLE RD 08648

MAHWAH

BUILDINGS

International Crossroads
1 INTERNATIONAL BLVD 07495

MONTCLAIR

COLLEGES

Montclair State College
1 NORMAL AVE 07043

NEW BRUNSWICK

APARTMENTS

Jack Pincus Building
550 REMSEN AVE 08902

Senior Citizens Building
75 NEILSON ST 08901

Uaw Sr Citizens Building
90 NEILSON ST 08901

GOVERNMENT

County Admin Building
1 JOHN F KENNEDY SQ . 08901

NB Government Comm Comple
710 HERMANN RD 08902

New Brunswick City Hall
76 BAYARD ST 08901

PALMER SQUARE

APARTMENTS

Holly House Apts
0 BUNN DR 08540

Lawrence Ct Apts
0 WEST DR 08540

Meadowlane Apts
465 MEADOW RD 08540

Millstone River
0 LAKEVIEW TER 08540

PATERSON

APARTMENTS

Alexander Hamilton Proj
202 ALABAMA AVE 07513

Christopher Columbus Proj
7 MATLOCK ST 07522

Colt Arms
52 GODWIN ST 07501

Dean Mcnulty
196 GRAND ST 07501

Dr Andrew Mcbride Apt
22 ELLISON ST 07501

Dr Norman Cotton
163 GRAHAM AVE 07501

Federation Apts
510 E 27TH ST 07514

Gordon Canfield Apts
160 WARD ST 07505

Gov Towers East
225 20TH AVE 07501

Gov Towers North
211 20TH AVE 07501

Gov Towers West
195 20TH AVE 07501

Kent Village
779 11TH AVE 07514

Kent Village
45 E 40TH ST 07514

Martin De Porres Village
1 GREEN ST 07501

Masiello Apts
255 ATLANTIC ST 07503

Park East Terrace
807 11TH AVE 07514

Redwood Village
311 REDWOOD AVE 07522

Rev William Griffin
199 CARROLL ST 07501

Riverview Towers
145 PRESIDENTIAL BLVD 07522

Triangle Village
85 PATERSON ST 07501

BUILDINGS

Hudson United Bank
100 HAMILTON PLZ 07505

County Administration Bld
317 PENNSYLVANIA AVE 07503

Court House
77 HAMILTON ST 07505

Romaine
136 WASHINGTON ST 07505

GOVERNMENT

City Hall
155 MARKET ST 07505

County Administration Bui
317 PENNSYLVANIA AVE 07503

Federal Plz
200 FEDERAL PLZ 07505

Passaic County Court Hous
77 HAMILTON ST 07505

HOSPITALS

Mount Carmel Guild
396 STRAIGHT ST 07501

Preakness
0 PO BOX 07509

COLLEGES

Passaic County Comm Coll
1 COLLEGE BLVD 07505

TOMS RIVER

COLLEGES

Ocean County College
2001 PO BOX 08754

TRENTON

BUILDINGS

Broad St Bank Building
143 E STATE ST 08608

Federal Building
402 E STATE ST 08608

Trenton Trust Building
28 W STATE ST 08608

COLLEGES

Trenton State College
550 PO BOX 08625

Trenton State College
4700 PO BOX 08650

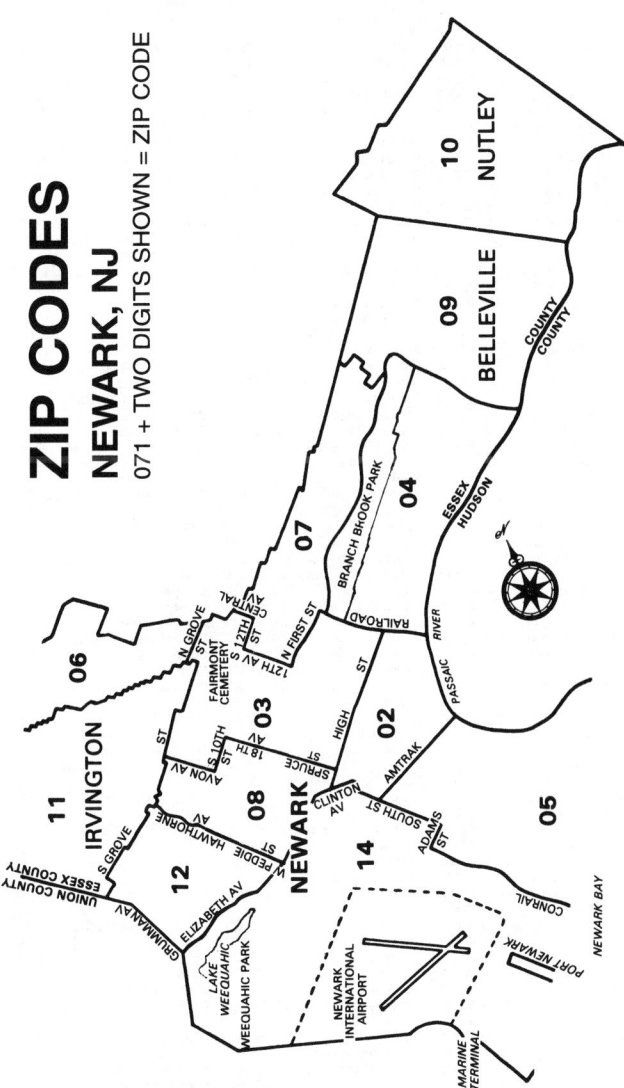

ZIP CODES
NEWARK, NJ
071 + TWO DIGITS SHOWN = ZIP CODE

Lower Ranchito	87581	Ojo Caliente (Zuni) . 87327, 87549		Qway (Quay)	88433
(Vallecitos)		Ojo Feliz	87735	Radium Springs	88054
Lucy (Willard)	87063	Ojo Sarco	87550	Rainsville	87736
Luis Lopez (Socorro)	87801	Old Albuquerque	87104	Ramah	87321, 87357
Lumberton	87547	(Albuquerque)		Tinaja	87321
Luna	87824	Old Picacho (Fairacres)	88033	Ramon (Yeso)	88136
Lyden (Velarde)	87582	Omega (Quemado)	87829	Ranches De Taos	87557
Madrid (Cerrillos)	87010	Organ	88052	(Ranchos De Taos)	
Magdalena	87825	Orogrande	88342	Ranchito (Taos)	87571
Malaga	88263	Paguate	87040	Ranchitos (Bernalillo)	87004
Maljamar	88264	Pajarito	87105, 87532	Rancho West	87124
Mangas Springs	88061	(Albuquerque)		(Rio Rancho)	
(Silver City)		Panorama Heights	87124	Raton	87740
Manzano (Mountainair)	87036	(Rio Rancho)		Red Hill (Quemado)	87829
Manzano Base	87115	Paradise Hills	87114	Red River	87558
(Albuquerque)		(Albuquerque)		Redrock	88055
Maxwell	87728	Paraje (Casa Blanca)	87007	Regina	87046
Mayhill	88339	Pastura (Santa Rosa)	88435	Rehoboth	87322
Mc Alister	88427	Pecos	87552	Rencona (Rowe)	87562
Mc Donald	88262	Pena Blanca	87041	Reserve	87830
Mc Intosh	87032	Penablanca (Pena Blanca)	87041	Ribera	87560
Mccartys (San Fidel)	87049	Penasco	87553	Rincon	87940
Mcgaffey (Fort Wingate)	87316	Pendaries (Rociada)	87742	Rinconado (Embudo)	87531
Medanales	87548	Pep	88126	Rio Chiquito (Chimayo)	87522
Melrose	88124	Peralta	87042, 87068	Rio Lucio (Penasco)	87553
Mentmore	87319	Perea (Fort Wingate)	87316	Rio Rancho	87124
Mesa Poleo (Coyote)	87012	Pescado (Zuni)	87327	Rito De Las Sillas	87064
Mescalero	88340	Petaca	87554	(Youngsville)	
Mesilla	88046	Philadelphia (Cubero)	87014	Riverside (Espanola)	87532
Mesilla Park	88047	Philmont (Cimarron)	87714		88201, 88210
Mesita (Laguna)	87026	Picacho	88343	Road Forks (Lordsburg)	88045
Mesquite	88048	Picuris (Penasco)	87553	Rociada	87742
Mexican Springs	87320	Pie Town	87827	Rock Canyon	87935
Miami	87729	Pilar (Taos)	87571	(Elephant Butte)	
Midway (Roswell)	88201	Pine (Pecos)	87552	Rodarte	87561
Milagro (Encino)	88321	Pine View (Vadito)	87579	Rodeo	88056
Milan	87021	Pinedale (Gallup)	87301	Rodey (Hatch)	87937
Mills	87730	Pinehill	87357	Rogers	88132
Milnesand	88125	Pinon	88344	Romeroville (Las Vegas)	87701
Mimbres	88049	Pinos Altos	88053	Rosebud (Amistad)	88410
Mogollon (Glenwood)	88039	Pinoswells (Cedarvale)	87009	Roswell	88201-202
Monero (Lumberton)	87547	Pintada (Santa Rosa)	88435	Elkins	88201
Montezuma	87731	Placita (Vadito)	87579, 87939	Midway	88201
Monticello	87939	Placitas	87043, 87515	Riverside	88201
Monument	88265	Playas	88009	Rowe	87562
Mora	87732	Plaza Blanca (Rutheron)	87563	Roy	87743
Moriarty	87035	Pleasant Hill (Texico)	88135	Ruidoso	88345
Moses (Seneca)	88437	Pleasanton (Glenwood)	88039	Ruidoso Downs	88346
Mosquero	87733	Pojoaque Valley	87501	Rutheron	87563
Mount Dora	88429	(Santa Fe)		Sabinal (Bosque)	87006
Mountain Park	88325	Polvadera	87828	Sacramento	88347
Mountainair	87036	Ponderosa	87044	Saint Vrain	88133
Mule Creek	88051	Ponderosa Pines (Tijeras)	87059	Salem	87941
Nageezi	87037	Portales (Lingo)	88123, 88130	San Acacia	87831
Nambe (Santa Fe)	87501	Arch	88130	San Antonio	87008, 87832
Nara Visa	88430	University	88130	(Cedar Crest)	
Naschitti (Tohatchi)	87325	Pot Creek (Taos)	87571	San Cristobal	87564
Navajo	87328	Prewitt	87045	San Felipe Pueblo	87001
Navajo Dam	87419	Progresso (Willard)	87063	(Algodones)	
New Laguna	87038	Pueblito	87566	San Fidel	87049
New York (Cubero)	87014	(San Juan Pueblo)		San Francisco (Bosque)	87006
Newcomb	87325, 87455	Pueblitos (Belen)	87002	San Francisco Plaza	87830
(Tohatchi)		Pueblo Pintado (Cuba)	87013	(Reserve)	
Newkirk	88431	Puerto De Luna	88432	San Ildefonso Pueblo	87501
Nogal	88341	Punta De Agua	87036	(Santa Fe)	
North Carmen (Mora)	87732	(Mountainair)		San Jon (Bard)	88411, 88434
North Hurley (Hurley)	88043	Quarteles (Espanola)	87532	San Jose	87537, 87565
North San Ysidro (Ilfeld)	87538	Quay	88433	(Hernandez)	
Nutrias (Tierra Amarilla)	87575	Quemado	87829	San Juan	87565
Ocate	87734	Querinda Park (Red River)	87558	Soham	87565
Ojito (Lindrith)	87029, 87521	Questa	87556	South San Ysidro	87565

San Juan (San Jose)	87565	Sheep Springs	87325, 87364
San Juan Pueblo	87566	(Tohatchi)	
San Lorenzo (Hanover)	88041	Sherman (Hanover)	88041
San Mateo	87050	Shiprock	87420
San Miguel	87560, 88058	Sierra Blanca (Ruidoso)	88345
(Ribera)		Sierra Vista (Alto)	88312
San Patricio	88348	Sierra Vista Estates	88312
San Pedro (Espanola)	87532	(Cedar Crest)	
San Rafael	87051	Sile (Pena Blanca)	87041
San Ysidro	87053	Silver City (Arenas Valley)	
Sanctuario (Chimayo)	87522		88022, 88036, 88053
Sandia Base	87115-116		88061-062
(Albuquerque)		Gila Hot Springs	88061
Sandia Knoll	87047	Little Walnut Village	88061
(Sandia Park)		Mangas Springs	88061
Sandia Park	87047	Smith Lake	87365
Sandia Pueblo	87004, 87047	Socorro	87801
(Bernalillo)		Sofia (Grenville)	88424
Sanostee	87420, 87461	Soham (San Jose)	87565
(Shiprock)		Solano	87746
Santa Ana Pueblo	87004	Sombrillo (Espanola)	87532
(Bernalillo)		South Carmen (Ledoux)	87725
Santa Clara Pueblo	87532	South San Ysidro	87565
(Espanola)		(San Jose)	
Santa Cruz	87567	Springer (Miami)	87729, 87747
Santa Fe	87500-506	Abbott	87747
Agua Fria	87501	Springstead	87311
Canada De Los Alamos		(Church Rock)	
	87501	Standing Rock	87313
Canoncito	87501	(Crownpoint)	
Chupadero	87501	Stanley	87056
Cuyamungue	87501	Star Lake (Cuba)	87013
Jacona	87501	Stead	88438
La Cienega	87501	Sunland Park	88063
Nambe	87501	Sunshine (Deming)	88030
Pojoaque Valley	87501	Sunspot	88349
San Ildefonso Pueblo	87501	Taiban	88134
Seton Village	87501	Tajique	87057
Tesuque Pueblo	87501	Talpa (Ranchos De Taos)	87557
Santa Rosa	88432, 88435	Taos	87571
(Puerto De Luna)		Taos Ski Valley	87525
Pastura	88435	Tatum	88213, 88267
Pintada	88435	Tererro	87573
Santa Teresa	88008	Tesuque	87574
Santo Domingo Pueblo	87052	Tesuque Pueblo	87501
Santo Nino (Santa Cruz)	87567	(Santa Fe)	
Santo Tomas (La Mesa)	88044	Texico	88135
Sapello	87745	Thomas (Clayton)	88415
Seama (Cubero)	87014	Thoreau	87323
Seboyeta	87055	Three Rivers (Tularosa)	88352
Seboyetita (Seboyeta)	87055	Tierra Amarilla	87575
Sedan	88436	Tijeras	87059
Sena	87568	Timberon	88350
Senator Clarke Field	87301	Tinaja (Ramah)	87321
(Gallup)		Tinnie	88351
Seneca	88437	Tocito (Shiprock)	87420
Separ (Lordsburg)	88045	Tohatchi	87325
Serafina	87569	Tohlakai (Gallup)	87301
Servilleta Plaza	87539	Tolar (Taiban)	88134
(La Madera)		Tome	87060
Seton Village (Santa Fe)	87501	Torreon (Cuba)	87013, 87061
Seven Rivers (Lakewood)	88254	Tortugas (Mesilla Park)	88047
Seven Springs	87025	Trampas	87576
(Jemez Springs)		Trechado (Fence Lake)	87315
		Trementina	88439
		Tres Piedras	87577
		Tres Ritos (Vadito)	87579
		Truchas	87578
		Truth Consequences	87901
		Tucumcari	88401, 88416, 88441
		Tularosa	88352
		Turley (Blanco)	87412
		Twin Lakes (Gallup)	87301
		Two Gray Hills (Tohatchi)	87325
		Tyrone	88065
		University	87106, 88130
		(Albuquerque)	
		University Park	88003
		(Las Cruces)	
		Upper Anton Chico	87711
		(Anton Chico)	
		Upper Pueblo (Sena)	87568
		Ute Park	87749
		Vadito	87579
		Vado	88072
		Valdez	87580
		Valle Escondido (Taos)	87571
		Vallecitos	87581
		Vallecitos De Los Indios	87025
		(Jemez Springs)	
		Valmora	87750
		Vanadium (Bayard)	88023
		Vanderwagen	87326
		Vaughn	88353
		Veguita	87062
		Velarde	87582
		Ventero (Amalia)	87512
		Villanueva	87583
		Volcano Cliffs	87120
		(Albuquerque)	
		Wagon Mound	87735, 87752
		(Ojo Feliz)	
		Levy	87752
		Waterflow	87421
		Watrous	87750, 87753
		(Valmora)	
		Weed	88354
		West Las Vegas	87701
		(Las Vegas)	
		White Horse (Cuba)	87013
		White Lakes (Stanley)	87056
		White Rock	87313, 87544
		(Crownpoint)	
		Whites City	88268
		Whitewater (Hurley)	88043
		Willard	87063
		Williams Acres (Gallup)	87301
		Williamsburg	87942
		Winston	87943
		Yatahey (Gallup)	87301, 87375
		Gallup	87375
		Yeso	88136
		Youngsville	87064
		Zamora (Tijeras)	87059
		Zia Pueblo (San Ysidro)	87053
		Zuni	87327
		Zuni Pueblo (Zuni)	87327

AGUA FRIA

HOSPITALS

Saint Vincent Hosp
455 SAINT MICHAELS DR 87501

COLLEGES

College Of Santa Fe
1600 Saint Michaels Dr 87501

ALBUQUERQUE

HOSPITALS

Carrie Tingley Hospital
1127 University Blvd NE ... 87102

Lovelace Clinic
5200 GIBSON BLVD SE ... 87108

Lovelace Medical Center
5400 GIBSON BLVD SE ... 87108

Memorial Hospital
806 CENTRAL AVE SE 87102

Presbyterian Hospital
1100 CENTRAL AVE SE ... 87106

St Joseph NE Heights Hosp
4701 Montgomery Blvd NE 87109

St Josephs Hospital
601 GRAND AVE NE 87102

University Of NM Hospital
2211 LOMAS BLVD NE 87106

Veterans
2100 Ridgecrest Dr SE 87108

ARCH

HOSPITALS

Plains Regional Med Ctr
60 PO BOX 88130

CLOVE

GOVERNMENT

Curry County Courthouse
700 N MAIN ST 88101

CLOVIS

HOSPITALS

Clovis High Plains Hosp
1688 PO BOX 88102

GILA HOT SPRINGS

GOVERNMENT

Federal Building
2610 N SILVER ST 88061

LAS CRUCES

GOVERNMENT

County Courthouse
251 W AMADOR AVE 88005

Federal Building
200 E GRIGGS AVE 88001

COLLEGES

New Mexico State Univer
30001 PO BOX 88003

LAS VEGAS

BUILDINGS

New Mex Highlands Univ
901 UNIVERSITY AVE 87701

HOSPITALS

NM State Hospital
1388 PO BOX 87701

SILVER CITY

BUILDINGS

Grant County Courthouse
898 PO BOX 88062

COLLEGES

Western NM University
680 PO BOX 88062

TUCUMCARI

HOSPITALS

Dan C Trigg Mem Hospital
608 PO BOX 88401

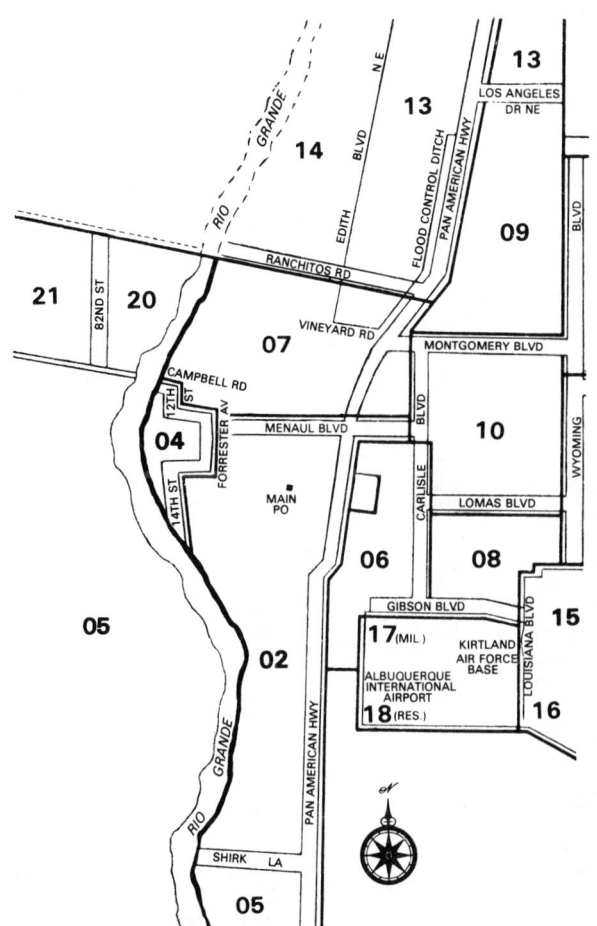

ZIP CODES
ALBUQUERQUE, NM
871 + TWO DIGITS SHOWN = ZIP CODE

West Gilgo Beach 11702
Bache Halsey Stuart Shields
  (New York) 10292
Bacon Hill 12871
  (Schuylerville)
Bagatelle (Wyandanch) 11798
Bainbridge 13733
Baiting Hollow 11933
  (Calverton)
Bakers Mills 12811
Bald Mountain (Greenwich) 12834
Baldwin Harbor (Baldwin) .. 11510
Baldwin Place 10505
Baldwinsville 13027
Ballston Lake 12019
Ballston Spa 12020
Balmat 13609
Balmville (Newburgh) 12550
Bangall 12506
Bangor (North Bangor) 12966
Banksville (Bedford) 10506
Bar Harbor 11762
  (Massapequa Park)
Barbourville (Deposit) 13754
Bardonia (Nanuet) 10954
Barker 13746, 14012
  (Chenango Forks)
Barkersville 12850
  (Middle Grove)
Barnerville (Howes Cave) . 12092
Barnes Corners (Rodman) .. 13610
Barnes Hole (Amagansett) . 11930
Barneveld 13304
Barnum Island 11558
  (Island Park)
Barrytown 12507
Barryville 12719
Bartlett (Rome) 13440
Bartlett Hollow 13775
  (Franklin)
Barton 13734
Basom 14013
Batavia 14020-021
  Bushville 14020
Batchellerville 12134
  (Northville)
Bates (Preston Hollow) 12469
Bath 14810
Bathgate (Bronx) 10457
Battenville (Greenwich) 12834
Battery Park City North 10282
  (New York)
Battery Park City South 10280
  (New York)
Baxter Estates 11050
  (Port Washington)
Bay Haven (Island Park) 11558
Bay Hills (Huntington) 11743
Bay Park (East Rockaway) . 11518
Bay Point (Sag Harbor) 11963
Bay Shore 11706
Bay Terrace (Flushing) 11360
Bayberry (Liverpool) 13088-090
Bayberry Point (Islip) 11751
Baychester (Bronx) 10469
Baycrest (Huntington) 11743
Bayport 11705
Bayshore (Bay Shore) 11706
Bayside (Flushing) 11360-361
Bayview (Southold) 11971
Bayville 11709

Beach Hampton 11930
  (Amagansett)
Beacon 12508
Bear Mountain 10911
Bearsville 12409
Beaver Dams 14812
Beaver Falls 13305
Beaver Meadow (Plymouth) 13832
Beaver River (Lowville) 13367
Beckers Corners (Selkirk) . 12158
Bedell (Fleischmanns) 12430
Bedford 10506
Bedford Hills 10507
Beechurst (Flushing) 11357
Beekmantown 12901
  (Plattsburgh)
Beixeden (Southold) 11971
Belcher (Salem) 12865
Belden (Harpursville) 13787
Belfast 14711
Belfort (Croghan) 13327
Belgium (Baldwinsville) 13027
Bella Vista (Centerport) 11721
Belle Crest 11731
  (East Northport)
Belle Isle (Warners) 13164
Belle Terre 11777
  (Port Jefferson)
Bellerose (Jamaica) 11426
Belleville 13611
Bellevue (Schenectady) ... 12306
Bellmore 11710
Bellona 14415
Bellport 11713
Bellvale 10912
Belmont 14813
Bemis Heights 12170
  (Stillwater)
Bemus Point 14712
Bennettsville 13733
  (Bainbridge)
Benson (Northville) 12134
Benson Mines (Star Lake) . 13690
Bergen 14416
Bergen Park 11746
  (Huntington Station)
Berkshire 13736
Berlin 12022
Berne 12023
Bernhards Bay 13028
Berwyn (La Fayette) 13084
Bethel 12720
Bethlehem (Delmar) 12054
Bethlehem Center 12077
  (Glenmont)
Bethpage 11714
Big Brook (Westernville) ... 13486
Big Flats 14814
Big Indian 12410
Big Island (Goshen) 10924
Big Moose (Eagle Bay) 13331
Billings 12510
Biltmore Shores 11758
  (Massapequa)
Bing (Binghamton) 13900
Binghamton 13900-905
  Bing 13900
  Broadacres 13905
  Choconut Center 13905
  Conklin Forks 13903
  Dickinson 13905

East Side 13904
East Vestal 13903
Glen Castle 13901
Hawleyton 13903
Hillcrest 13901
Hinmans Corners 13905
Hospital 13904
Kattelville 13901
Nimmonsburg 13901
Park Terrace 13903
Port Dickinson 13901
Southview 13903
West Chenango 13905
West Colesville 13904
Westview 13905
Black Creek 14714
Black River 13612
Blasdell 14219
Blauvelt 10913
Bleecker (Gloversville) 12078
Blenheim (North Blenheim) 12131
Bliss 14024
Blodgett Mills 13738
Bloomfield (Holcomb) 14469
Blooming Grove 10914
Bloomingburg 12721
Bloomingdale 12913
Bloomington 12411
Bloomville 13739
Blossvale 13308, 13401
Blue Mountain Lake 12812
Blue Point 11715
Blue Ridge (Schroon Lake) 12870
Blue Stores (Germantown) 12526
Bluff Point (Keuka Park) ... 14478
Boght Corners (Cohoes) ... 12047
Bohemia 11716
Boiceville 12412
Bolivar 14715
Bolton Landing 12814
Bombay 12914
Bonney (Smyrna) 13464
Boonville 13309
Borough Hall (Jamaica) 11424
Boston 14025
Botanical (Bronx) 10458
Bouckville 13310
Boulevard (Bronx) .. 10459, 10474
Boultons Beach 13685
  (Sackets Harbor)
Bouquet (Essex) 12936, 12994
Bovina (Bovina Center) 13740
Bovina Center 13740
Bowens Corners (Fulton) . 13069
Bowling Green (New York) 10004
Bowling Green Brm 10275
  (New York)
Bownansville 14026
Box Hill (Saint James) 11780
Boylston (Lacona) 13083
Boyntonville 12090
  (Hoosick Falls)
Bradford 14815
Bradley (Liberty) 12754
Brainard 12024
Brainardsville 12915
Braman Corners 12053
  (Delanson)
Bramanville (Howes Cave) 12092
Branchport 14418
Brandreth (Long Lake) 12847

Brandywine (Schenectady)	12304
Brant	14027
Brant Lake	12815
Brantingham	13312
Brasher Falls	13613
Brasie Corners	13642
(Gouverneur)	
Brawer Hill (Coram)	11727
Breakabeen (Middleburgh)	12122
Breesport	14816
Breezy Point	11697
(Far Rockaway)	
Brentwood	11717
Brewerton	13029
Brewster	10509
Briar Park (Wantagh)	11793
Briarcliff Manor	10510
Bridgehampton	11932
Bridgeport	13030
Bridgewater	13313
Brier Hill	13614
Brighton	13439, 14610
(Richfield Springs)	
Brightside	13436
(Raquette Lake)	
Brightwaters	11718
Brisben (Oxford)	13830
Bristol (Amityville)	11701
Broad Channel	11693
(Far Rockaway)	
Broadacres (Binghamton)	13905
Broadalbin	12025
Broadlawn Manor	11701
(Amityville)	
Brockport	14420
Brocton	14716
Bronx	10400, 10451-475
Allerton	10467
Bathgate	10457
Baychester	10469
Botanical	10458
Boulevard	10459
Boulevard	10474
Castle Hill	10462
City Island	10464
Claremont Park	10457
Clason Point	10473
Cornell	10473
Cranford	10470
Crotona Park	10460
Dreiser Loop	10475
Einstein	10475
Esplanade	10469
Fieldston	10463
Fordham	10458
Highbridge	10452
Hillside	10469
Hub	10455
Jerome Avenue	10468
Kingsbridge	10463
Longwood	10459
Melcourt	10451
Morris Heights	10453
Morris Park	10461
Morrisania	10456
Mosholu	10467
Mott Haven	10454
Mount Carmel	10458
Oak Point	10455
Parkchester	10462
Parkway	10462

Pilgrim	10461
Riverdale	10471
Soundview	10472
Spuyten Duyvil	10463
Stadium	10452
Throggs Neck	10465
Tremont	10457
University Heights	10452
Van Cott	10467
Van Nest	10462
Wakefield	10466
West Farms	10460
Westchester	10461
Williamsbridge	10467
Woodlawn	10470
Bronxville	10708
Brookdale (Norfolk)	13667-668
Brookfield	12994, 13314
(Whallonsburg)	
Brookhaven	11719
Brooklyn ..	11200-26,11228-11249
	11251-252, 11254-256
Brooksburg (Windham)	12496
Brooktondale	14817
Brookview	12026
Brookville	11545, 11548
(Glen Head)	
Browns Hollow	13317
(Canajoharie)	
Brownville	13615
Bruceville (High Falls)	12440
Brunswick (Troy)	12180
Brushton	12916
Brutus (Weedsport)	13166
Bryant (New York)	10036
Buchanan	10511
Buckram (Locust Valley)	11560
Bucks Bridge (Canton)	13617
Buel (Canajoharie)	13317
Buffalo	14200-228, 14231, 14233
	14240-241, 14260-261
	14263-267, 14269-273
	14276, 14280
Amherst	14221, 14228,14231
Blasdell	14219
Cheektowaga ..	14206, 14215
	14225, 14227
Eggertsville	14226
Hamburg	14219
Jingo	14233
Kenmore	14217, 14223
Lackawanna	14218
Scoreball	14276
Sloan	14212
Snyder	14226
South Cheektowaga ...	14227
Tonawanda	
	14207, 14217, 14223
West Amherst	14228
West Seneca	
	14210, 14218, 14220, 14224
Williamsville ..	14221, 14231
Bulls Head (Rochester)	14611
Bullville	10915
Bundyville (Oswego)	13126
Burden Lake	12018
(Averill Park)	
Burdett	14818
Burke	12917
Burlingham	12722
Burlington Flats	13315

Burnt Hills	12019, 12027
(Ballston Lake)	
Burnwood (East Branch)	13756
Burt	14028
Burtonsville (Esperance)	12066
Bushville (Batavia)	14020
Buskirk	12028
Butternuts	13776
(Gilbertsville)	
Bville (Baldwinsville)	13027
Byron	14422
Cabinhill (De Lancey)	13752
Cadosia (Hancock)	13783
Cadyville	12918
Cairo	12413
Calcium	13616
Caledonia	14423
Callicoon	12723
Callicoon Center	12724
Calverton	11933
Cambria Heights (Jamaica)	11411
Cambridge	12816
Camden	13316
Cameron	14819
Cameron Mills	14820
Camillus	13031
Campbell	14821
Campbell Hall	10916
Campville (Endicott)	13760
Camroden (Rome)	13440
Canaan	12029
Canaan Lake (Patchogue) .	11772
Canada Lake	12032
(Caroga Lake)	
Canajoharie	13317
Canal Street (New York)	10013
Canandaigua	14424-425
Farmington	14425
Canaseraga	14822
Canastota	13032
Candor	13743
Caneadea	14717
Canisteo	14823
Canoe Place	11946
(Hampton Bays)	
Canoga (Seneca Falls)	13148
Canton	13617
Cape Vincent	13618
Captree Island (Babylon)	11702
Cardiff (La Fayette)	13084
Carle Place	11514
Carlisle	12031
Carmel	10512
Carmen (Schenectady)	12303
Caroga Lake	12032
Carousel Center	13290
(Syracuse)	
Carthage	13619, 13631
Champion	13619
Denmark	13619
Herrings	13619
West Carthage	13619
Wilna	13619
Carver Park (Yaphank)	11980
Cassadaga	14718
Cassville	13318
Castile	14427
Castle Creek	13744
Castle Hill (Bronx)	10462
Castle Point	12511
Castleton On Hudson	12033

Castorland	13620
Catatonk (Owego)	13827
Cathedral (New York)	10025
Cato	13033
Catskill	12414
Cattaraugus	14719
Cattown (Fly Creek)	13337
Caughdenoy	13036
(Central Square)	
Cayuga	13034
Cayuta	14824
Cazenovia	13035
Cedarcroft (Greenlawn)	11740
Cedarhurst	11516
Cedarvale (Syracuse)	13215
Cedarville (Ilion)	13357
Celoron	14720
Cementon	12415
Center Berlin (Berlin)	12022
Center Brunswick (Troy)	12180
Center Cambridge	12816
(Cambridge)	
Center Moriches	11934
Centereach	11720
Centerlisle (Lisle)	13797
Centerport	11721
Centerville	13756, 14029
(East Branch)	
Central (Jamaica)	11435
Central Bridge	12035
Central Islip	11722
Central Nyack (Nyack)	10960
Central Park (Bethpage)	11714
Central Square	13036
Central Valley	10917
Centre Village	13787
(Harpursville)	
Centuck (Yonkers)	10710
Ceres	14721
Chadwicks	13319
Chaffee	14030
Champion (Carthage)	13619
Champlain	12919
Chappaqua	10514
Charleston Four Corners	12166
(Sprakers)	
Charlotteville	12036
Charlton (Ballston Lake)	12019
Chase Lake (Glenfield)	13343
Chase Lincoln (Rochester)	14643
Chase Mills	13621
Chaseville (Maryland)	12116
Chasm Falls	12953, 12995
(Malone)	
Chateaugay	12920
Chatham	12037
Chatham Center (Valatie)	12184
Chaumont	13622
Chauncey (Ardsley)	10502
Chautauqua	14722
Chazy	12921
Cheektowaga	14206, 14212
	14215, 14225, 14227
Buffalo	14225
Buffalo	14227
South Cheektowaga	14227
Cheeselovers (Westbury)	11595
Chelsea	12512
Chemung	14825
Chenango Bridge	13745
Chenango Forks	13746

Chenango Lake (Norwich)	13815
Cherokee (New York)	10028
Cherry Creek	14723
Cherry Grove (Sayville)	11782
Cherry Plain	12040
Cherry Valley	13320
Cherrytown (Kerhonkson)	12446
Chester	10918
Chestertown	12817
Chestnut Ridge	10977
(Spring Valley)	
Cheviot (Germantown)	12526
Chichester	12416
Childwold	12922
Chilson (Ticonderoga)	12883
China (Deposit)	13754
Chinatown (New York)	10013
Chippewa Bay	13623
Chitt (Chittenango)	13037
Chittenango	13037
Choconut Center	13905
(Binghamton)	
Church Street (New York)	10007
Churchville	13478, 14428
(Verona)	
Clifton	14428
Churubusco	12923
Cicero	13039
Cincinnatus	13040
Circleville	10919
City Island (Bronx)	10464
Clare (Russell)	13684
Claremont Park (Bronx)	10457
Clarence	14031
Clarence Center	14032
Clarendon	14429
Clark Mills	13321
Clarks Mills (Greenwich)	12834
Clarkson	14430
Clarkstown (New City)	10956
Clarksville	12041
Claryville	12725
Clason Point (Bronx)	10473
Claverack	12513
Clay	13039, 13041
Clayton	13624
Clayville	13322
Clearview Landing	11791
(Syosset)	
Cleaver (Walton)	13856
Clemons	12819
Clermont (Germantown)	12526
Cleveland	13042
Cleverdale	12820
Clifton (Churchville)	14428
Clifton Park	12065
Clifton Springs	14432
Climax	12042
Clinton	13323
Clinton Corners	12514
Clintondale	12515
Clintonville (Keeseville)	12924
Clockville	13043
Clough Corners	13862
(Whitney Point)	
Clyde	14433
Clymer	14724
Cobb (Water Mill)	11976
Cobleskill	12043
Cochecton	12726
Cochecton Center	12727

Coeymans	12045
Coeymans Hollow	12046
Cohocton	14826
Cohoes	12047
Coila (Cambridge)	12816
Colchester	13755, 13856
(Downsville)	
Cold Brook	13324
Cold Spg Harbor	11724
(Cold Spring Harbor)	
Cold Spring	10516
Cold Spring Harbor	11724
Cold Spring Hills	11743
(Huntington)	
Cold Springs	11798, 13027
(Wyandanch)	
Colden	14033
Colesville (Harpursville)	13787
Colgate (Hamilton)	13346
College (New York)	10030
College Point (Flushing)	11356
Colliersville	13747
Collins	14034
Collins Center	14035
Collins Landing	13607
(Alexandria Bay)	
Collinsville	13433
(Port Leyden)	
Colonial Park (New York)	10039
Colonial Springs	11798
(Wyandanch)	
Colonie (Albany)	12205, 12212
Colosse (Parish)	13131
Colton	13625
Columbia (Ilion)	13357
Columbia University	10025
(New York)	
Columbiaville	12050
Columbus (New Berlin)	13411
Columbus Circle	10023
(New York)	
Colvin (Syracuse)	13205
Colvin Elmwood (Syracuse)	13207
Commack	11725
Comstock	12821
Concord Village (Babylon)	11702
Conesus	14435
Conewango Valley	14726
Conger Corners	13480
(Waterville)	
Congers	10920
Conifer (Tupper Lake)	12986
Conklin	13748
Conklin Forks	13903
(Binghamton)	
Conklingville (Hadley)	12835
Conlei Park (East Islip)	11730
Connelly	12417
Connetquot (East Islip)	11730
Connoquot (Bohemia)	11716
Conquest (Port Byron)	13140
Constable	12926
Constableville	13325
Constantia	13044
Continental Village	10566
(Peekskill)	
Cook Falls (Roscoe)	12776
Cooks Corners (Brushton)	12916
Cooksburg	12469
(Preston Hollow)	
Coonrod (Rome)	13440

(Dickinson Center)
East Durham 12423
East Elmhurst (Flushing) 11369
East Fishkill 12533
(Hopewell Junction)

East Floyd 13354
(Holland Patent)
East Freetown 13055
East Genoa (Locke) 13092
East Glenville 12302
(Schenectady)
East Half Hollow Hills 11746
(Huntington Station)
East Hebron (Salem) 12865
East Herkimer (Herkimer) .. 13350
East Homer 13056
East Huntington 11743
(Huntington)
East Irvington 10533
(Irvington)
East Jefferson 12093
(Jefferson)
East Jewett 12424
East Kingston (Kingston) .. 12401
East Lake Ronkonkoma 11779
(Ronkonkoma)
East Line (Ballston Spa) ... 12020
East Maine (Johnson City) . 13790
East Masonville 13839
(Sidney Center)
East Mcdonough (Oxford) . 13830
East Meadow 11554
East Meredith 13757
East Nassau 12062
East Nichols (Nichols) 13812
East Oakfield (Oakfield) 14125
East Otto 14729
East Palermo 13036
(Central Square)
East Palmyra 14444
East Park (Hyde Park) 12538
East Pitcairn 13648
(Harrisville)
East Poestenkill 12018
(Averill Park)
East Randolph 14730
East Ridge (Hankins) 12741
East Rodman (Rodman) 13682
East Schodack 12063
East Side (Binghamton) 13904
East Sidney (Franklin) 13775
East Stone Arabia 13428
(Palatine Bridge)
East Syracuse 13057
East Vestal (Binghamton) . 13903
East View (Valhalla) 10595
East Walden (Walden) 12586
East Wawarsing 12489
(Wawarsing)
East White Plains 10604
(White Plains)
East Windham 12439
(Hensonville)
East Windsor (Windsor) 13865
East Winfield 13491
(West Winfield)
Eastchester 10709
Easton (Greenwich) 12834
Eastport 11941
Eastside (East Hampton) .. 11937

Eastwood (Syracuse) 13206
Eaton 13334
Eatons Neck (Northport) 11768
Eben (Potsdam) 13676
Echo 11776
(Port Jefferson Station)
Eddy (Canton) 13617
Eddyville (Kingston) 12401
Eden 14057
Edenville (Warwick) 10990
Edgemere (Far Rockaway) 11690
Edgemont (Scarsdale) 10583
Edgewood (Brentwood) 11717
Edgewood Park 13607
(Alexandria Bay)
Edinburg (Northville) 12134
.... 12835
Edmeston 13335
Edson (Windsor) 13865
Edwards 13635
Edwardsville (Hammond) .. 13646
Eggertsville (Amherst) 14226
Einstein (Bronx) 10475
Elba 14058
Elbridge 13060
Eldred 12732
Elizabethtown 12932
Elizaville 12523
Elk Creek (Schenevus) 12155
Elka Park 12427
Ellenburg 12933
Ellenburg Center 12934
Ellenburg Depot 12935
Ellenville 12428
Ellicottville 14731
Ellington 14732
Ellisburg 13636
Elm Grove (Morris) 13808
Elma 14059
Elmdale (Gouverneur) 13642
Elmhurst (Flushing) 11373
Elmhurst-a (Flushing) 11380
Elmira . 14900-905, 14925, 14975
Elmont (Floral Park) 11003
Elmsford 10523
Elmwood (Syracuse) 13207
Elnora (Clifton Park) 12065
Elsmere (Delmar) 12054
Elwood (East Northport) 11731
Emerson (Port Byron) 13140
Emeryville (Gouverneur) ... 13642
Emmons (Oneonta) 13820
Empeyville (Camden) 13316
Empire State (New York) ... 10001
Empire State Building 10118
(New York)
Empire State Plaza 12223
(Albany)
Endicott 13760-761, 13763
Campville 13760
Crestview Heights 13760
Endwell 13760
Union 13760
West Corners 13760
West Endicott 13760
Endwell (Endicott) .. 13760, 13762
Ephratah (Fort Plain) 13339
Erieville 13061
Erin 14838
Esopus 12429
Esperance 12066

Esplanade (Bronx) 10469
Essex 12936
Etna 13062
Evans Mills 13637
Exeter (Burlington Flats) ... 13315
Fabius 13063
Factoryville 12928
(Crown Point)
Fair Harbor (Bay Shore) 11706
Fair Haven 13064, 13156
North Fair Haven 13064
Fairdale (Hannibal) 13074
Fairfield 13336
Fairmount (Syracuse) 13219
Fairport 14450
Falconer 14733
Fallsburg 12733
Fancher 14452
Far Rockaway . 11600, 11690-697
Arverne 11692
Breezy Point 11697
Broad Channel 11693
Edgemere 11690
Fort Tilden 11695
Inwood 11696
Neponsit 11694
Rockaway Beach 11693
Rockaway Park 11694
Rockaway Point 11697
Roxbury 11690
Wave Crest 11690
Fara Park (Lindenhurst) 11757
Farleys Point 13160
(Union Springs)
Farmers Mills (Carmel) 10512
Farmersville 14060
(Farmersville Station)
Farmersville Station 14060
Farmingdale ... 11735-737, 11774
East Farmingdale 11735
South Farmingdale 11735
Farmington (Canandaigua) 14425
Farmingville 11738, 11749
Farnham 14061
Fayette 13065
Fayetteville 13066
Felts Mills 13638
Fenner (Cazenovia) 13035
Fenton (Port Crane) 13833
Fergusonville (Schenevus) 12155
Ferndale 12734
Fernwood (Pulaski) 13142
Feura Bush 12067
Fieldston (Bronx) 10463
Filer Corners (Morris) 13808
Fillmore 14735
Findley Lake 14736
Fine 13639
Fineview 13640
Fire Island (Bay Shore) 11706
Fire Place (East Hampton) . 11937
Fire Place Neck 11719
(Brookhaven)
Fish Creek 13325
(Constableville)
Fish House (Broadalbin) ... 12025
Fishers 14453
Fishers Landing 13641
Fishkill 12524
Fishkill Plains 12590
(Wappingers Falls)

Glass Lake (Averill Park) ...	12018	
Glen Aubrey	13777	
Glen Castle (Binghamton) .	13901	
Glen Cove	11542	
Glen Head	11545	
Glen Oaks (Floral Park)	11004	
Glen Park (Watertown)	13601	
Glen Spey	12737	
Glen Wild	12738	
Glenburnie	12861	
(Putnam Station)		
Glendale (Flushing)	11385	
....	13343	
Glenfield	13343	
Glenford	12433	
Glenham	12527	
Glenmont	12077	
Glens Falls 12801, 12803-804		
Queensbury	12801	
West Glens Falls	12801	
Glenville (Schenectady) ...	12302	
....	12325	
Schenectady	12325	
Glenwood	14069	
Glenwood Landing	11547	
Gloversville	12078	
Godeffroy	12739	
Gold Grounds	11968	
(Southampton)		
Goldens Bridge	10526	
Goodyears Corners	13081	
(King Ferry)		
Gordon Heights (Medford) .	11763	
Gorham	14461	
Goshen	10924	
Goulds Mill (Lyons Falls) ..	13368	
Gouverneur	13642	
Governors Island	10004	
(New York)		
Gowanda	14070	
Gracie (New York)	10028	
Gracie Area 2 (New York) ..	10128	
Grafton	12082	
Grahamsville 12740, 12782		
Granby Center (Fulton)	13069	
Grand Central Brm	10164	
(New York)		
Grand Gorge	12434	
Grand Island	14072	
Grandview (Nyack)	10960	
Grangerville	12871	
(Schuylerville)		
Granite (Kerhonkson)	12446	
Granite Springs	10527	
Grant (Cold Brook)	13324	
Grant Park (Hewlett)	11557	
Grantville (Norfolk)	13667	
Granville	12832	
Graphite (Hague)	12836	
Grassy Point	10980	
(Stony Point)		
Gravesville (Poland)	13431	
Gray (Cold Brook)	13324	
Great Bend	13643	
Great Hog Neck (Peconic) .	11958	
Great Neck 11020-025, 11027		
Allenwood	11021	
Great Neck	11020	
Harbor Hills	11023	
Kenilworth	11024	
Kensington	11021	

Kings Point	11024	
Lake Gardens	11022	
Old Village 11023-024		
Russell Gardens	11021	
Saddle Rock	11023	
Saddle Rock Estates ..	11021	
Thomaston	11021	
Great River	11739	
Great South Bay (Babylon)	11702	
Great South Beach	11782	
(Sayville)		
Great Valley	14741	
Greece 14616, 14626		
(Rochester)		
Greeley Square	10001	
(New York)		
Green Acres	11581	
(Valley Stream)		
Green Island (Troy)	12183	
Green Pastures (Jericho) ...	11753	
Greenburgh (White Plains)	10607	
Greene	13778	
Greenfield	12833	
(Greenfield Center)		
Greenfield Center	12833	
Greenfield Park	12435	
Greenfld Park	12435	
(Greenfield Park)		
Greenhurst	14742	
Greenlawn	11740	
Greenport	11944	
Greenvale	11548	
Greenville	12083	
Greenway (Rome)	13440	
Greenwich	12834	
Greenwood	14839	
Greenwood Lake	10925	
Greenwood Village	11702	
(Babylon)		
Gregorytown (Downsville) .	13755	
Greig	13345	
Grenell (Clayton)	13624	
Gridleyville	13864	
(Willseyville)		
Grindstone (Clayton)	13624	
Grossinger (Ferndale)	12734	
Groton	13073	
Groveland 14462, 14545		
Grover Hills (Mineville)	12956	
Guffin Bay (Dexter)	13634	
Guilderland	12084	
Guilderland Center	12085	
Guilford	13780	
Gulf Summit (Windsor)	13865	
Gurn Spring (Gansevoort) .	12831	
Hadley	12835	
Hagaman	12086	
Hagedorns Mills (Galway) .	12074	
Hagerman (Bellport)	11713	
....	11772	
Hague	12836	
Hailesboro	13645	
Haines Falls	12436	
Halcott Center	12430	
(Fleischmanns)		
Halcottsville	12438	
Hales Eddy (Hancock)	13783	
Halesite (Huntington)	11743	
Half Hollow (Deer Park)	11729	
Half Hollow Hills	11746	
(Huntington Station)		

Halfmoon (Clifton Park)	12065	
....	12188	
Hall	14463	
Hallock Acres (Smithtown) .	11787	
Hallsville (Fort Plain)	13339	
Hambletville (Deposit)	13754	
Hamburg 14075, 14219		
Hamden	13782	
Hamilton	13346	
Hamilton Grange	10031	
(New York)		
Hamlin	14464	
Hammond	13646	
Hammondsport	14840	
Hampton	12837	
Hampton Bays	11946	
Hampton Park	11968	
(Southampton)		
Hancock	13783	
Hankins	12741	
Hannacroix	12087	
Hannawa Falls	13647	
Hannibal	13074	
Harbor Acres	11050	
(Port Washington)		
Harbor Green	11758	
(Massapequa)		
Harbor Heights	11743	
(Huntington)		
Harbor Hills (Great Neck) ...	11023	
....	11777	
Harbor Island	11558	
(Island Park)		
Harbor Isle (Island Park)	11558	
Harbor View (Lawrence)	11559	
Harbor Village	11743	
(Huntington)		
Harborfields (Greenlawn) ..	11740	
Hardscrapple	11937	
(East Hampton)		
Harford	13784	
Harkness (Peru)	12972	
Harmony Corners	12020	
(Ballston Spa)		
Harpersfield	13786	
Harpursville 13787, 13826		
Belden	13787	
Centre Village	13787	
Colesville	13787	
South Nineveh	13787	
Harrietstown	12983	
(Saranac Lake)		
Harriman	10926	
Harris	12742	
Harrisburg (Lowville)	13367	
Harrison	10528	
Harrisville	13648	
Hart Lot (Elbridge)	13060	
Hartford	12838	
Hartsdale	10530	
Hartwick	13348	
Harvard (East Branch)	13756	
Hastings	13076	
Hastings On Hudson	10706	
Hatchs Corner (Russell) ...	13684	
Hauppauge 11760, 11788		
Islandia	11788	
Smithtown	11788	
Haven (Wurtsboro)	12790	
Haverstraw	10927	
Hawkeye (Au Sable Forks)	12912	

359

Richmond Hill 11418	
Rochdale Village 11434	
Rosedale 11422	
Saint Albans 11412	
South Richmond Hill 11419	
Woodhaven 11421	
James Hill (Centerport) ... 11721	
Jamesport 11947	
Jamestown 14701-704	
Jamesville 13078	
Janesville (Cobleskill) 12043	
Jasper 14855	
Java Center 14082	
Java Village 14083	
Jay 12941	
Jefferson 12093, 12414	
East Jefferson 12093	
North Harpersfield 12093	
Jefferson Park 13698	
(Woodville)	
Jefferson Valley 10535	
Jeffersonville 12748	
Jenksville (Berkshire) 13736	
Jericho 11753, 11853, 12910	
Green Pastures 11753	
Muttontown 11753	
Jerome Avenue (Bronx) ... 10468	
Jersey Colony (Southold) ... 11971	
Jerusalem (Bethpage) 11714	
Jewell Manor (Liverpool) ... 13088	
Jewett 12444	
Jewett Center (Hunter) 12442	
Jingo (Buffalo) 14233	
Johnsburg 12843	
Johnson 10933	
Johnson City 13790	
Johnsonville 12094	
Johnstown 12095	
Johnsville 13452	
(Saint Johnsville)	
Jones Beach (Wantagh) 11793	
Jonesville (Clifton Park) ... 12065	
Jordan 13080	
Jordanville 13361	
Junction Boulevard 11372	
(Flushing)	
Junius (Waterloo) 13165	
Kanona 14856	
Kasoag (Altmar) 13302	
Katonah 10536	
Kattelville (Binghamton) 13901	
Kattskill Bay 12844	
Kauneonga Lake 12749	
Kayuta Lake (Forestport) .. 13338	
Keene 12942	
Keene Valley 12943	
Keeseville 12911	
.... 12924, 12944	
Au Sable Chasm 12911	
Clintonville 12924	
Kelly Corners 12455	
(Margaretville)	
Kelsey (Hancock) 13783	
Kendall 14476	
Kenilworth (Great Neck) 11024	
Kenmore 14217, 14223	
Buffalo 14217	
Hiler 14217	
Tonawanda 14217	
Kennedy 14747	
Kenoza Lake 12750	
Kensington (Great Neck) ... 11021	
Kent (Carmel) 10512, 14477	
Kenwood (Oneida) 13421	
Kerhonkson 12446	
Ketchumville (Berkshire) ... 13736	
Keuka Park 14478	
Kew Gardens (Jamaica) ... 11415	
Kiamesha Lake 12751	
Kill Buck 14748	
Killawog 13794	
Kinderhook 12106	
King Ferry 13081	
Kings Park 11754	
Kings Point (Great Neck) ... 11024	
Kings Settlement 13815	
(Norwich)	
Kings Station 12831	
(Gansevoort)	
Kingsbridge (Bronx) 10463	
Kingsbury (Hudson Falls) .. 12839	
Kingston 12401	
Kirk (South Plymouth) ... 13844	
Kirkland (Clinton) 13323	
Kirkville 13082	
Kirkwood 13795	
Kirschnerville (Croghan) ... 13327	
Kiskatom (Catskill) 12414	
Kismet (Bay Shore) 11706	
Kitchawan (Ossining) 10562	
Knapp Creek 14749	
Knapps Station (Norwood) ... 13668	
Knickerbocker (New York) . 10002	
Knollwood Beach 11743	
(Huntington)	
Knowlesville 14479	
Knowsville (Watertown) 13601	
Knox 12107	
Knoxboro 13362	
Kodak Park (Rochester) ... 14652	
Kortright (Bloomville) 13739	
Kringsbush 13452	
(Saint Johnsville)	
Kripplebush (Accord) 12404	
.... 12484	
Krumville (Olivebridge) 12461	
La Fargeville 13656	
La Fayette 13084	
La Grange (Lagrangeville) ... 12540	
La Salle (Niagara Falls) ... 14304	
Lackawanna 14218	
Lacona 13083	
Ladentown (Pomona) 10970	
Lafargeville 13656	
(La Fargeville)	
Lafayette (La Fayette) 13084	
Lagrangeville 12540	
Lairdsville (Clinton) 13323	
Lake Bonaparte 13648	
(Harrisville)	
Lake Carmel (Carmel) 10512	
Lake Clear 12945	
Lake Colby (Saranac Lake) ... 12983	
Lake Delaware (Delhi) 13753	
Lake Delta (Rome) 13440	
Lake Desolation 12850	
(Middle Grove)	
Lake Devenoge 12743	
(Highland Lake)	
Lake Gardens 11022	
(Great Neck)	
Lake George 12845	
Lake Grove 11755	
Lake Hill 12448	
Lake Hills (Ronkonkoma) ... 11779	
Lake Huntington 12752	
Lake Katonah (Katonah) ... 10536	
Lake Katrine 12449	
Lake Kitchawan 10590	
(South Salem)	
Lake Luzerne 12846	
Lake Mahopac (Mahopac) ... 10541	
Lake Minnewaska 12561	
(New Paltz)	
Lake Mohegan 10547	
(Mohegan Lake)	
Lake Panamoka (Ridge) 11961	
Lake Peekskill 10537	
Lake Placid 12946	
Lake Pleasant 12108	
Lake Ronkonkoma 11779	
(Ronkonkoma)	
Lake Secor (Mahopac) 10541	
Lake View 14085	
Lakeland 11779, 13209	
(Ronkonkoma)	
Lakemont 14857	
Lakeport (Chittenango) 13037	
Lakeview 11552, 11570, 14085	
(West Hempstead)	
Lakeville 11040, 14480	
(New Hyde Park)	
Lakewood 14750	
Lancaster 14086	
Landia (Syosset) 11791	
Lanesville 12450	
Langdon (Kirkwood) 13795	
Langdon Corners (Canton) ... 13617	
Lansing 14882	
Lansingburg (Troy) 12182	
Lapeer (Marathon) 13803	
Larchmont 10538	
Lassellsville 13452	
(Saint Johnsville)	
Latham 12110-111, 12128	
Verdoy 12110	
West Latham 12110	
Lathams Corners 13843	
(South New Berlin)	
Lattingtown 11560	
(Locust Valley)	
Lattintown (Marlboro) 12542	
Laughing Waters 11971	
(Southold)	
Laurel 11948	
Laurel Hollow 11724, 11791	
(Cold Spring Harbor)	
Laurel Hollow Park 11780	
(Saint James)	
Laurens 13796	
Lawrence 11559	
Lawrenceville 12472, 12949	
(Rosendale)	
Lawtons 14091	
Lawyersville 12113	
Lazy Point (Amagansett) ... 11930	
Le Ray (Evans Mills) 13637	
Le Roy 14482	
Lebanon 13085	
Lebanon Center 13332	
(Earlville)	
Lebanon Springs 12114	
Ledyard (Aurora) ... 13026, 13081	

Lee (Rome) 13440
Lee Center 13363
Leeds 12451
Leibhardt (Accord) 12404
Leicester 14481
Lenox (Canastota) 13032
Lenox Hill (New York) 10021
Leon 14751
Leonardsville 13364
Leonta (Franklin) 13775
Leroy (Le Roy) 14482
Levittown 11756
Lew Beach 12753
Lewis 12950, 13489
Lewisboro (South Salem) .. 10590
Lewiston 14092
Lexington 12452
Leyden (Port Leyden) 13433
Liberty 12754
Lido Beach (Long Beach) .. 11561
Lily Dale 14752
Lima 14485
Limerick 13657
Limestone 14753
Lincklaen (De Ruyter) 13052
Lincoln (Clockville) 13043
Lincolndale 10540
Lincolnton (New York) 10037
Linden Hill (Flushing) 11354
Lindenhurst 11757
Lindley 14858
Linlithgo (Germantown) 12526
Linwood (Pavilion) 14525
Lisbon 13658
Lisle 13797
Little Bow (Gouverneur) 13642
Little Falls 13365
Little Genesee 14754
Little Hog Neck (Peconic) .. 11958
Little Ipswich (Sosset) 11791
Little Neck (Flushing) 11362
Little Plains 11731
(East Northport)
Little Valley 14755
Little York 13087, 13642
Liverpool 13088-090
Bayberry 13088-090
Dominion Park 13090
Galeville 13088
Jewell Manor 13088
Salina 13088
Livingston 12541
Livingston Manor 12758
Livingstonville 12122
(Middleburgh)
Livonia 14487
Livonia Center 14488
Lloyd (Highland) 12528
Lloyd Harbor (Huntington) .. 11743
Lloyds Neck (Huntington) .. 11743
Loch Sheldrake 12759
Locke 13092
Lockport 14094-095
Pendleton 14094
Lockwood 14859
Locust Grove 11791, 13309
(Syosset)
Locust Valley 11560
Locustwood (Floral Park) ... 11003
Lodi 14860
London Terrace (New York) 10011

Lonelyville (Bay Shore) 11706
Long Beach 11561
Long Eddy 12760
Long Island City . 11100-06, 11120
Astoria 11101-106
Sunnyside 11104
Long Lake 12847
Longwood (Bronx) 10459
Loon Lake (Onchiota) 12968
Lordville (Hancock) 13783
Lorraine 13659
Loudonville (Albany) 12211
Lounsberry (Nichols) 13812
Low Hampton (Whitehall) .. 12887
Lower Genegantslet Corner
(Greene) 13778
Lower Oswegatchie 13670
(Oswegatchie)
Lower Rotterdam 12306
(Schenectady)
Lowman 14861
Lowville 13367
Lutheranville 12064
(East Worcester)
Luzerne (Lake Luzerne) 12846
Lycoming 13093
Lykers (Sprakers) 12166
Lynbrook 11563-564
Lyncourt (Syracuse) 13208
Lyndonville 14098
Lyon Mountain 12952, 12955
Merrill 12955
Standish 12952
Lyons 14489
Lyons Falls 13368
Lyonsdale (Lyons Falls) 13368
Lyonsville (Accord) 12404
(Baldwinsville)
Lysander 13027, 13094
Mabbettsville (Millbrook) ... 12545
Mac Dougall (Romulus) 14541
Macedon 14502
Machias 14101
Macomb (Gouverneur) 13642
Madison 13402
Madison Park 11731
(East Northport)
Madison Square 10010
(New York)
Madison Square Brm 10160
(New York)
Madrid 13660
Madrid Springs (Madrid) ... 13660
Mahopac 10541
Mahopac Falls 10542
Maidstone Park 11937
(East Hampton)
Maine 13802
Malden Bridge 12115
Malden On Hudson 12453
Mallory 13103
Malone 12953
Maltaville (Ballston Spa) ... 12020
Malverne 11565
Mamaroneck 10543
Manchester 14504
Mandana (Skaneateles) ... 13152
Manhasset 11030
Manhasset Hills 11040
(New Hyde Park)
Manhattan (See New York City)

Manhattanville (New York) 10027
Manheim (Dolgeville) 13329
Manitou (Garrison) 10524
Manlius 13104
Mannetto Hills (Syosset) 11791
Mannsville 13661
Mannville (Watervliet) 12189
Manorhaven 11050
(Port Washington)
Manorville 11949
Maple Grove (Morris) 13808
Maple Springs 14756
Maple Valley (Westford) 13488
Maple View 13107
Maplecrest 12454
Mapletown (Canajoharie) .. 13317
Maplewood (Watervliet) 12189
Marathon 13803
Marcellus 13108
Marcellus Falls 13108
(Marcellus)
Marconiville (Copiague) 11726
Marcy 13403
Margaretville 12455
Mariaville 12137
(Pattersonville)
Marietta 13110
Marilla 14102
Marine Midland 10259, 14639
(New York)
Marion 14505
Marlborough (Marlboro) 12542
Marshville (Canajoharie) ... 13317
Martinsburg 13404
Martisco (Marcellus) 13108
Martville 13111
Maryhill (Mount Sinai) 11766
Maryknoll 10545
Maryland 12116
Masonville 13804
Maspeth (Flushing) 11378
Mass Park 11762
(Massapequa Park)
Massapequa 11758
Massapequa Park 11762
Massawepie 12986
(Tupper Lake)
Massena 13662
Massena Ctr (Massena) 13662
Massena Sprgs (Massena) .. 13662
Masten Lake (Wurtsboro) .. 12790
Mastic 11950
Mastic Beach 11951
Matinecock 11560
(Locust Valley)
Mattituck 11952
Mattydale (Syracuse) 13211
Maybrook 12543
Mayfair (Schenectady) 12302
Mayfair Park (Seaford) 11783
Mayfield 12117
Mayville 14757
Maywood 11701, 12205
(Amityville)
Mcclure (Deposit) 13754
Mcconnellsville 13401
(Mc Connellsville)
Mccurdy's (Rochester) 14645
Mcdonough (Mc Donough) .. 13801
Mcgraw (Mc Graw) 13101
Mckeever (Forestport) 13338

(Wappingers Falls)
New Hampton 10958
New Hartford 13413
New Haven 13121
New Hempstead 10977
(Spring Valley)
New Hope (Moravia) 13118
New Hyde Park . 11040-44, 11099
Garden City Park 11040
Herricks 11040
Lakeville Estates 11040
Manhasset Hills 11040
North H P 11040
Visa 11041
New Kingston 12459
New Lebanon 12125
New Lisbon 13415
New Milford 10959
New Paltz 12561
New Rochelle 10800-805
Rochelle 10800
Wykagyl 10804
New Russia 12964
New Square 10977
(Spring Valley)
New Suffolk 11956
New Windsor 12553
New Woodstock 13122
New York
For individual street listings
see page 373
.... 10000-041, 10043-048
.... 10055, 10060, 10079-081
.... 10087, 10090, 10094-096
10098-26, 10128-133, 10138
10149-8, 10184-5, 10196-197
10199-200, 10203, 10211-13
.... 10242, 10249, 10256-261
.... 10265,10268-282
.... 10285-286, 10292
Audubon 10032
Bankers Trust 10256
Bar Code Church Street
.... 10242
Barclay Bank 10265
Bowling Green 10004
Bowling Green Brm 10275
Canal Street 10013, 10213
Chinatown 10013
Church Street
.... 10007, 10249, 10277
College 10030
Colonial Park 10039
Cooper 10003, 10211
Empire State 10001
Federal Reserve 10045
Fort George 10040
Fort Washington 10032
Franklin D Roosevelt
.... 10022, 10126
G P O 10001
G P O Official Mail 10199
Gracie 10130
Grand Central .. 10017, 10164
Greeley Square 10001
Hamilton Grange 10031
Hell Gate 10029
Irving Trust 10257
Island 10044
Knickerbocker 10002
Lenox Hill 10131

Lincolnton 10037
Madison Square Brm .. 10160
Manhattanville 10027
Marden Kane Inc 10094
Marine Midland 10259
Merrill Lynch 10080
Midtown 10018, 10138
Morgan Guaranty 10260
Morningside 10026
Murray Hill Brm 10157
Muscular Dystrophy 10149
Old Clelsea Brm 10114
Peck Slip 10038
Peck Slip Brm 10273
Postal Data Center 10099
Prince 10012
Radio City Brm 10102
Rockefeller Center Brm 10124
South Pole 10090
Times Square Brm 10109
Triborough 10035
Trinity 10006, 10212
Village 10014
Wall Street 10005
Wall Street Brm 10269
Washington Bridge 10033
New York Mills 13417
Newark 14513
Newark Valley 13811
Newburgh 12550-553
Balmville 12550
Middle Hope 12550
Roseton 12550
Town 12550
West Newburgh 12550
Newcomb 12852, 12879
Tahawus 12879
Newfane 14108
Newfield 14867
Newport 13416
Newstead (Akron) 14001
Newton Falls 13666
Newton Hook (Stuyvesant) 12173
Newtonville 12128
Newtown (Hampton Bays) . 11946
Niagara (Niagara Falls) 14300
Niagara Falls 14300-305
La Salle 14304
Niagara 14300
North Falls 14300
Wheatfield 14304
Nichols 13812
Nicholville 12938
.... 12965
Fort Jackson 12938
Hopkinton 12940
North Lawrence 12938
North Lawrence 12940
Niles (Skaneateles) 13152
Nimmonsburg (Binghamton)13901
Nineveh 13813
Nineveh Junction (Afton) .. 13730
Niobe 14758
Niskayuna 12309
Nissequogue (Saint James) 11780
Niverville 12130
Noblesboro (Cold Brook) .. 13324
Norfolk 13667
North (Yonkers) 10703
North Afton (Afton) 13730
North Amityville 11701

(Amityville)
North Argyle (Argyle) 12809
North Babylon 11703
North Baldwin (Baldwin) 11510
North Bangor 12966, 12991
Bangor 12966
West Bangor 12991
North Bay 13123
North Bayshore 11706
(Bay Shore)
North Bellmore (Bellmore) . 11710
North Bellport (Bellport) 11713
North Blenheim 12131
North Boston 14110
North Branch 12766
North Bridgewater 13318
(Cassville)
North Broadalbin 12025
(Broadalbin)
North Brookfield 13418
North Castle (Armonk) 10504
North Chatham 12132
North Chili 14514
North Chittenango 13037
(Chittenango)
North Clymer 14759
North Cohocton 14868
North Collins 14111
North Columbia (Ilion) 13357
North Creek 12853
North East (Millerton) 12546
North Evans 14112
North Fair Haven 13064
(Fair Haven)
North Falls 14300
(Niagara Falls)
North Fenton 13746
(Chenango Forks)
North Franklin (Oneonta) .. 13820
North Gage (Utica) 13502
North Granville 12854
North Great River 11722
(Central Islip)
North Greece 14515
North Greenbush 12198
(Wynantskill)
North Hampton 11946
(Hampton Bays)
North Hannibal (Oswego) .. 13126
North Harpersfield 12093
(Jefferson)
North Haven (Sag Harbor) . 11963
North Hebron (Granville) ... 12832
North Highland 10516
(Cold Spring)
North Hills 11040, 11576
(New Hyde Park)
North Hillsdale 12529
(Hillsdale)
North Hoosick 12133
North Hudson 12855
North Ilion (Frankfort) 13340
North Java 14013, 14113
(Basom)
North Kortright 13750
(Davenport)
North Lawrence 11559
.... 12938, 12967
(Lawrence)
North Lindenhurst 11757
(Lindenhurst)

North Long Beach 11558
  (Island Park)
North Massapequa 11758
  (Massapequa)
North Merrick (Merrick) 11566
North New Hyde Park 11040
  (New Hyde Park)
North Norwich 13814
North Patchogue 11772
  (Patchogue)
North Petersburg 12138
  (Petersburg)
North Pharsalia 13844
  (South Plymouth)
North Pitcher 13124
North Pole (Lake Placid) ... 12946
North River 12856
North Rose 14516
North Russell (Canton) 13617
North Salem 10560
North Sanford (Deposit) 13754
North Sea 11963, 11968
  (Sag Harbor)
North Seaford (Seaford) 11783
North Shore Beach 11778
  (Rocky Point)
North Smithtown 11787
  (Smithtown)
North Stockholm 13668
  (Norwood)
North Syracuse 13212
  (Syracuse)
North Tarrytown 10591
  (Tarrytown)
North Tonawanda 14120
North Valley Stream 11580
  (Valley Stream)
North Victory (Martville) 13111
North Wantagh (Wantagh) . 11793
North Western 13419
North White Plains 10603
  (White Plains)
North Wilmurt (Remsen) ... 13438
North Winfield 13491
  (West Winfield)
North Woodmere 11581
  (Valley Stream)
Northampton 11901, 12134
  (Riverhead)
Northbush (Johnstown) 12095
Northfield (Walton) 13856
Northhill (Roslyn) 11576
Northport 11768
Northville 11901, 12134
  (Riverhead)
  Batchellerville 12134
  Benson 12134
  Edinburg 12134
  Hope 12134
  Northampton 12134
  Sacandaga 12134
Norton Hill 12135
Norwich 13815
Norwood 13668
Novac (Sag Harbor) 11963
Nunda 14517
Nyack 10960
Oak Beach (Babylon) 11702
Oak Hill 12460
Oak Hills (Calverton) 11933
Oak Island (Babylon) 11702

Oak Island Beach 11702
  (Babylon)
Oak Point (Bronx) .. 10455, 13646
Oakdale 11769, 13790
  Idle Hour 11769
Oakfield 14125
Oakfield Village 11793
  (Wantagh)
Oakhaven (East Islip) 11730
Oakland Gardens 11364
  (Flushing)
Oaks Corners 14518
Oaksville (Fly Creek) 13337
Obernburg 12767
Occanum (Windsor) 13865
Ocean Bay Park 11706
  (Bay Shore)
Ocean Beach 11770
Oceanside 11572
Oconee (Bay Shore) 11706
Odessa 14869
Ogdensburg 13669
Ohio (Cold Brook) 13324
Olcott 14126
Old Bethpage 11804
Old Brookville 11545, 11548
  (Glen Head)
Old Chatham 12136
Old Chelsea (New York) 10011
Old Clelsea Brm 10114
  (New York)
Old Field 11733, 11790
  (East Setauket)
Old Field Point 11733
  (East Setauket)
Old Field South 11790
  (Stony Brook)
Old Fields 11932
  (Bridgehampton)
Old Forge 13420
Old Village 11023-024
  (Great Neck)
Old Westbury 11568
Olean 14760
Olive (Olivebridge) 12461
Olivebridge 12461
Oliverea (Big Indian) 12410
Olmstedville 12857
Omar (La Fargeville) 13656
Onchiota 12968
Oneida 13421
Oneida County Airport 13424
  (Oriskany)
Oneonta 13820, 13861
  Emmons 13820
  Milford Center 13820
  North Franklin 13820
  West End 13820
Onondaga Hill (Syracuse) . 13215
Onondaga Nation (Nedrow) 13120
Ontario 14519
Ontario Center 14520
Oppenheim (Dolgeville) 13329
Oquaga Lake (Deposit) 13754
Oran 13125
Orangeburg 10962
Orangetown (Nyack) 10960
Orchard Park 14127
Oregon (Mattituck) 11952
Orient 11957
Orient Point (Orient) 11957

Oriskany 13424
Oriskany Falls 13425
Orwell 13426
Oscawana Lake 10579
  (Putnam Valley)
Osceola (Camden) 13316
Ossining 10562
Oswegatchie 13654, 13670
  (Heuvelton)
  Lower Oswegatchie 13670
Oswego 13126
Oswego Center (Oswego) 13126
Otego 13825
Otisco (Tully) 13159
Otisco Valley (Marietta) 13110
Otisville 10963, 12970
Otsdawa (Otego) 13825
Otsego (Fly Creek) 13337
Otselic (Georgetown)
  .... 13072, 13129
Otter Creek (Glenfield) 13343
Otter Lake (Forestport) 13338
Otto 14766
Ouaquaga 13826
Ovid 14521
Owasco 13130
Owego 13827
Owls Head 12969
Oxbow (Antwerp) ... 13608, 13671
Oxford 13830
Oyster Bay 11771
Oyster Bay Cove 11791
  (Syosset)
Ozone Park (Jamaica) 11416-417
Paddy Hill (Brownville) 13615
Paines Hollow (Mohawk) .. 13407
Painted Post 14870
Palatine Bridge 13428
Palenville 12463
Palermo (Fulton) 13069
Palisades 10964
Palmer (Corinth) 12822
Palmyra 14522
Pamelia (Evans Mills) 13637
Panama 14767
Panorama (Rochester) 14625
Pantigo (East Hampton) 11937
Paradox (Ticonderoga) 12858
Paris 13429
Paris Station (Sauquoit) 13456
Parish 13131
Parishville 13672
Parishville Center 13676
  (Potsdam)
Park Terrace (Binghamton) 13903
Parkchester (Bronx) 10462
Parkside (Flushing) 11375
Parksville 12768
Parkway (Bronx) 10462
Patchin (New York) 10011
Patchogue 11772
Patent (Hartwick) 13348
Patria (Warnerville) 12187
Patterson 12563
Pattersonville 12137
Paul Smiths 12970
Pavilion 14525
Pawling 12564
Peakville (East Branch) 13756
Pearl River 10965

Peasleeville 12985
  (Schuyler Falls)
Peck Slip (New York) 10038
Peck Slip Brm (New York) . 10273
Peconic 11958
Peekskill 10566
Pelham 10803
Pembroke (Corfu) 14436
Penataquit (Bay Shore) 11706
Pendleton (Lockport) 14094
Penfield 14526
Penn Yan 14527
Pennellville 13132
Perch River (Dexter) 13634
Perkinsville 14529
Perry 14530
Perrys Mills (Champlain) ... 12919
Perrysburg 14129
Perryville 13133
Perth (Amsterdam) 12010
Peru 12972
Peruville (Groton) 13073
Peter Stuyvesant 10009
  (New York)
Peterboro 13134
Petersburg 12138
Pharsalia 13758
  (East Pharsalia)
Phelps 14532
Phila (Philadelphia) 13673
Philadelphia 13673
Philipse Manor 10591
  (Tarrytown)
Philipstown (Cold Spring) . 10516
Phillipsport 12769
Philmont 12565
Phoenicia 12464
Phoenix 13135
Piercefield 12973
Pierces Corner 13642
  (Gouverneur)
Pierceville (Eaton) 13334
Piermont 10968
Pierrepont (Canton) 13617
Pierrepont Manor 13674
Piffard 14533
Pike 14130
Pilgrim (Bronx) 10461
Pillar Point (Dexter) 13634
Pilot Knob 12844
  (Kattskill Bay)
Pine (Albany) 12203
Pine Aire (Brentwood) 11717
Pine Bush 12566
Pine City 14871
Pine Crest Dunes 11958
  (Peconic)
Pine Grove (Glenfield) 13343
Pine Hill 12465, 13471
Pine Island 10969
Pine Lake (Caroga Lake) . 12032
Pine Meadows (Altmar) 13302
Pine Neck (Sag Harbor) ... 11963
Pine Plains 12567
Pine Valley 14872
Pine Woods (Bouckville) ... 13310
Pinelawn (Huntington) 11743
Pineville (Altmar) 13302, 13856
Pioneer (Ballston Spa) 12020
Pipe Stave Hollow 11766
  (Mount Sinai)

Piseco 12139
Pitcairn (Harrisville) 13648
Pitcher 13136
Pitcher Hill (Syracuse) 13212
Pitt (New York) 10002
Pittsfield (New Berlin) 13411
Pittsford 14534
Plainedge (Levittown) 11756
Plainfield 13491
  (West Winfield)
Plainview 11803
Plainville 13137
Plandome (Manhasset) 11030
Planetarium (New York) 10024
Platt Cove (Elka Park) 12427
Plattekill 12568
Plattsburgh 12901, 12903
    Beekmantown 12901
    South Plattsburgh 12901
Pleasant Valley 12569
Pleasantdale (Troy) 12182
Pleasantville ... 00401, 10570-572
    Readers Digest 00401
Pleasantville 10570
Plessis 13675
Plum Island (Greenport) ... 11944
Plumbrook (Norfolk) 13667
Plymouth 13832
Pocantico Hills 10591
  (Tarrytown)
Poestenkill 12140
Point Lookout 11569
Point O Woods 11706
  (Bay Shore)
Point Rock (Taberg) 13471
Point Vivian 13607
  (Alexandria Bay)
Pok (Poughkeepsie) 12600
Poland 13431
Polkville (Cortland .13045, 13101
Pomona 10970
Pomonok (Flushing) 11365
Pompey 13138
Pond Eddy 12770
Ponquogue 11946
  (Hampton Bays)
Poolville 13432
Pope Mills (Heuvelton) 13654
Poplar Ridge 13139
Poquott (East Setauket) ... 11733
Port Authority (New York) .. 10011
Port Byron 13140
Port Chester 10573
Port Crane 13833
Port Dickinson 13901
  (Binghamton)
Port Ewen 12466
Port Gibson 14537
Port Henry 12974
Port Jefferson 11777
Port Jefferson Station 11776
Port Jervis 12771, 12785
Port Kent 12975
Port Leyden 13433
Port Lookout 11569
  (Point Lookout)
Port Of Egypt (Southold) ... 11971
Port Of Missing Men 11968
  (Southampton)
Port Ontario (Pulaski) 13142
Port Washington 11050-055

Baxter Estates 11050
Flower Hill 11050
Harbor Acres 11050
Manorhaven 11050
Sands Point 11050
The Terrace 11050
Portageville 14536
Portchester 10573
  (Port Chester)
Porter Corners 12859
Portland 14769
Portlandville 13834
Portville 14770
Postmaster (Flushing) 11351
Potsdam 13676, 13669
Potter Hollow 12469
  (Preston Hollow)
Pottersville 12860
Poughkeepsie 12600-603
    Arlington 12603
    Pok 12600
    Red Oaks Mill 12603
    South Road 12601
Poughquag 12570
Pound Ridge 10576
Pratts Hollow 13434
Prattsburg 14873
Prattsville 12468
Preble 13141
Prendergast Point 14757
  (Mayville)
Preston (Oxford) 13830
Preston Hollow 12469
Prince (New York) 10012
Princetown (Duanesburg) . 12056
Promised Land 11930
  (Amagansett)
Prospect 13435
Providence (Middle Grove) 12850
Pulaski 13142
Pulteney 14874
Pultneyville 14538
Pulvers Corners 12567
  (Pine Plains)
Punxheld (Manorville) 11949
Purchase 10577
Purdys 10578
Purdys Mills (Altona) 12910
Purling 12470
Putnam Lake 10509, 12563
  (Brewster)
Putnam Station 12861
Putnam Valley 10579
Pyrites 13677
Quaker Hill (Pawling) 12564
Quaker Springs 12871
  (Schuylerville)
Quaker Street 12141
Queensbury 12801, 12804
  (Glens Falls)
    Glens Falls 12804
Quinneville 13746
  (Chenango Forks)
Quioque 11978
  (Westhampton Beach)
Quogue 11959
Radio City (New York) 10019
Radison (Baldwinsville) 13027
Rainbow Beach 11953
  (Middle Island)
Rainbow Lake 12976

Rampasture(Hampton Bay) 11946
Rams Island 11964
  (Shelter Island)
Randallsville (Hamilton) ... 13346
Randolph 14772
Ransomville 14131
Rapollo Park (Smithtown) .. 11787
Raquette Lake 13436
Ravena 12143
Ray Brook 12977
Raymertown (Troy) 12180
Raymondville 13678
Readburn (Walton) 13856
Reber (Willsboro) 12996
Red Creek 13143
Red Falls (Prattsville) 12468
Red Hook .. 12504, 12507, 12571
  (Annandale On Hudson)
  Milan 12571
  Upper Red Hook 12571
Red Mills (Ogdensburg) ... 13669
Red Oaks Mill 12603
  (Poughkeepsie)
Red Rock (East Chatham) 12060
Redfield 13437
Redford 12978
Redwood 11963, 13679
  (Sag Harbor)
Reeves Park (Riverhead) ... 11901
Rego Park (Flushing) 11374
Reidsville 12186
  (Voorheesville)
Remsen 13438
Remsenburg 11960
Rensselaer 12144
Rensselaer Falls 13680
Rensselaerville 12147
Retsof 14539
Rexford (Alplaus) ... 12008, 12148
  Vischer Ferry 12148
Rexville 14877
Reydon Shores (Southold) .. 11971
Rhinebeck 12572
Rhinecliff 12574
Ricard (Altmar) 13302
Riceville (Gloversville) 12078
Richburg 14774
Richfield 13439
  (Richfield Springs)
Richford 13835
Richland 13144
Richmond Hill (Jamaica) ... 11418
Richmondville 12149
Richville 13681
Ridge 11961
Ridge Mills (Rome) 13440
Ridgefields Highlands 11743
  (Huntington)
Ridgewood (Flushing) 11385
Rifton 12471
Riley Cove (Ballston Spa) .. 12020
Riparius 12862
Ripley 14775
Riverbank (Warrensburg) .. 12885
Riverdale (Bronx) ... 10471, 13440
  .... 12862, 13795, 13838
Riverhead 11901
Riverside (Riverhead) 11901
Riverside Park (Kingston) .. 12401
Road Behind The Lot 11937
  (East Hampton)

Roanoke (Riverhead) 11901
Robbins Island 11956
  (New Suffolk)
Robbins Rest 11770
  (Ocean Beach)
Roch (Rochester) 14600
Rochdale Village 11434
  (Jamaica)
Rochelle (New Rochelle) .. 10800
Rochester . 14600-27, 14638-639
  14642-47, 14649-653, 14660
  14664, 14673, . 14683, 14694
  14694
  Brighton 14610
  Bulls Head 14611
  Chase Lincoln 14643
  Eastman Kodak 14651
  Greece 14616, 14626
  Irondequoit 14617
  Marine Midland 14639
  Mccurdy's 14645
  Panorama 14625
  Ridgemont 14626
  Security Norstar 14638
  Strong Memorial Hos .. 14642
  Twelve Corners 14618
  Westgate 14624
  Xerox 14644
  Xerox Corp 14664
Rock City Falls 12863
Rock Cut (Jamesville) 13078
Rock Glen 14550
  (Silver Springs)
Rock Hill 12775
Rock Stream 14878
Rock Tavern 12575
Rockaway Beach 11693
  (Far Rockaway)
Rockaway Park 11694
  (Far Rockaway)
Rockaway Point 11697
  (Far Rockaway)
Rockdale (Mount Upton) ... 13809
Rockefeller Center 10020
  (New York)
Rockefeller Center Brm 10124
  (New York)
Rockhurst (Cleverdale) 12820
Rockland M P C 10951
Rockville Center ....
  .... 11570-572, 11592
Rockwell Springs (Nedrow) 13120
Rockwells Mills 13843
  (South New Berlin)
Rockwood (Johnstown) 12095
Rocky Point 11778
Rodman 13610, 13682
  Barnes Corners 13610
  East Rodman 13682
Roessleville (Albany) 12205
Rolling Meadows 12401
  (Kingston)
Rome 13440-442, 13449
  Bartlett 13440
  Camroden 13440
  Coonrod 13440
  Floyd 13440
  Greenway 13440
  Lake Delta 13440
  Lee 13440
  Ridge Mills 13440

Riverdale 13440
  Seifert Corners 13440
  Spencer Settlement 13440
  Stanwix 13440
Romulus 14541
Roneck Park (Amityville) 11701
Ronkonkoma 11779
Roosevelt 11575
Roosevelt Field 11530
  (Garden City)
Roosevelt Island 10044
  (New York)
Rooseveltown 13683
Root (Sprakers) 12166
Roscoe 12776
Rose 14542
Rose Grove (Southampton) 11968
Roseboom 13450
Rosedale (Jamaica) 11422
Rosendale 12472
Roseton (Newburgh) 12550
Roslyn 11576
Roslyn Harbor 11545, 11548
  (Glen Head)
Roslyn Heights 11577
Ross Corners (Vestal) 13850
Rossburg 14776
Rossie (Hammond) 13646
Rotterdam (Schenectady) . 12303
Rotterdam Junction 12150
Round Lake 12151
Round Top 12473
Rouses Point 12979
Roxbury 11690, 12474
  (Far Rockaway)
  Hubbell Corners 12474
Ruby 12475
Ruby Corner (Hammond) .. 13646
Rural Grove (Sprakers) 12166
Rural Hill (Woodville) 13698
Rush 14543
Rushford 14777
Rushville 14544
Russell 13684
Russell Gardens 11021
  (Great Neck)
Russia (Poland) 13431
Rutland (Felts Mills) 13638
Rye 10580
Rye Brook (Port Chester) .. 10573
Sabael 12864
Sabattis (Long Lake) 12847
Sabbath Day Point 12874
  (Silver Bay)
Sacandaga (Northville) 12134
Sachem (Holbrook) 11741, 11779
Sackets Harbor 13685
Sacketts Lake 12701
  (Monticello)
Saddle Rock (Great Neck) . 11023
Saddle Rock Estates 11021
  (Great Neck)
Sag Harbor 11963
Sagaponack 11962
Sagtikos Manor 11706
  (Bay Shore)
Saint Albans (Jamaica) 11412
Saint Bonaventure 14778
Saint Huberts 12943
  (Keene Valley)
Saint James 11780

South Bay (Canastota) 13032	South Road 12601	Stanley 14561
South Bay Village 12827	(Poughkeepsie)	Stanwix (Rome) 13440
(Fort Ann)	South Russell (Russell) 13684	Star Island (Montauk) 11954
South Berne (Berne) 12023	South Rutland 13688	Star Lake 13690
South Bethlehem 12161	South Salem 10590	Starkville (Fort Plain) 13339
South Bolivar (Bolivar) 14715	South Schodack 12162	Staten Island 10300-314
South Bombay (Moira) 12957	South Setauket 11720	Steamburg 14783
South Brookfield 13485	(Centereach)	Stella Niagara 14144
(West Edmeston)	South Stony Brook 11790	Stephentown 12168-169
South Butler 13154	(Stony Brook)	Sterling 13156
South Byron 14557	South Trenton (Barneveld) . 13304	Sterling Forest 10979
South Cairo 12482	South Vestal (Vestal) 13850	Sterlington (Sloatsburg) ... 10974
South Cheektowaga 14227	South Wales 14139	Stetsonville (New Lisbon) . 13415
(Cheektowaga)	South Westerlo 12163	Steuben (Holland Patent) .. 13354
South Colton 13687	South Worcester 12197	Stevers Mills 12025
South Columbia 13439	(Worcester)	(Broadalbin)
(Richfield Springs)	Southampton 11968-969	Stewart Manor 11530
South Danby 13864	Four Acres 11968	(Garden City)
(Willseyville)	Gold Grounds 11968	Stilesville (Deposit) 13754
South Dayton 14138	Hampton Park 11968	Stillwater 12170
South Durham (Acra) 12405	North Sea 11968	Stirling (Greenport) 11944
South Edmeston 13466	Port Of Missing Men ... 11968	Stittville 13469
South Edwards (Edwards) . 13635	Rose Grove 11968	Stockbridge (Munnsville) .. 13409
South Fallsburg 12779	Sebanoc 11968	Stockport 12050, 13783
South Farmingdale 11735	Towd 11968	(Columbiaville)
(Farmingdale)	Tuckahoe 11968	Stockton 14784
South Floral Park 11003	Wickapogue 11968	Stockwell (Waterville) 13480
(Floral Park)	Southeast (Brewster) 10509	Stokes (Lee Center) 13363
South Glens Falls 12803	Southfields 10975	Stone Arabia (Fort Plain) .. 13339
South Granville 12832	Southold 11971	Stone Mills 13656
(Granville)	Southview (Binghamton) ... 13903	(La Fargeville)
South Hamilton 13332	Southwest Oswego 13126	Stone Ridge 12484
(Earlville)	Southwood (Jamesville) 13078	Stony Brook 11790
South Hannibal (Hannibal) . 13074	Sparkill 10976	Stony Creek 12878
South Hartford 12838, 13810	Speculator 12164	Stony Point 10980
(Hartford)	Speedsville (Berkshire) 13736	Stoodley Corners 12302
South Hauppauge 11722	Speigletown (Troy) 12182	(Schenectady)
(Central Islip)	Spencer 14883	Stormville 12582
South Haven (Brookhaven) . 11719	Spencer Settlement (Rome) . 13440	Stottville 12172
South Hempstead 11550	Spencerport 14559	Stow 14785
(Hempstead)	Spencertown 12165	Straits Corners (Owego) ... 13827
South Holbrook (Holbrook) . 11741	Speonk 11972	Stratford 13470
South Huntington 11746	Spinnerville (Ilion) 13357	Strathmore (Manhasset) 11030
(Huntington Station)	Split Rock (Camillus) 13031	Streetroad (Ticonderoga) .. 12883
South Ilion (Ilion) 13357	Sprakers 12166	Strongs Neck 11733
South Jamesport 11970	Spring Brook 14140	(East Setauket)
South Jewett (Hunter) 12442	Spring Glen 12483	Strykersville 14145
South Kortright 13842	Spring Lake (Port Byron) .. 13140	Sturges Corner 13750
South Lebanon (Earlville) .. 13332	Spring Valley 10977	(Davenport)
South Lima 14558	Springfield Center 13468	Stuyvesant 12173
South Millbrook 12545	Springfield Gardens 11413	Stuyvesant Falls 12174
(Millbrook)	(Jamaica)	Suassa Park 11777
South New Berlin 13843	Springport 13160	(Port Jefferson)
South Nineveh 13787	(Union Springs)	Suffern 10901
(Harpursville)	Springs (East Hampton) ... 11937	Sugar Loaf 10981
South Nyack (Nyack) 10960	Springvale (Norwich) 13815	Sugarbush (Onchiota) 12968
South Onon (Nedrow) 13120	Springville 14141	Sullivan (Chittenango) 13037
South Onondaga (Nedrow) . 13120	Springwater 14560	Summerhill (Locke) 13092
South Otselic 13155	Sprout Brook 13317	Summit 12175
South Owego (Owego) 13827	(Canajoharie)	Summitville 12781
South Oxford (Oxford) 13830	Spruceton (West Kill) 12492	Sundown 12782
South Ozone Park .. 11420, 11436	Spuyten Duyvil (Bronx) 10463	Sunken Meadow 11768
(Jamaica)	Squiretown 11946	(Northport)
South Plainedge 11758	(Hampton Bays)	Sunmount (Tupper Lake) .. 12986
(Massapequa)	Stacysburg 12580	Sunnyside 11104
South Plattsburgh 12901	Stacy Basin (Durhamville) . 13054	(Long Island City)
(Plattsburgh)	Stadium (Bronx) 10452	Sunside (Cairo) 12413
South Plymouth 13844	Stafford 14143	Suny At Buffalo 14260-261
South Pole (New York) 10090	Stamford 12167	(Buffalo)
South Richmond Hill 11419	Standish (Lyon Mountain) . 12952	Suny Stony Brook 11794
(Jamaica)	Stanfordville 12581	(Stony Brook)

Van Buren Point	14166
Van Cott (Bronx)	10467
Van Deusenville	13317
(Canajoharie)	
Van Etten	14889
Van Hornesville	13475
Van Nest (Bronx)	10462
Varysburg	14167
Venetian Shores	11757
(Lindenhurst)	
Venice Center	13147
(Scipio Center)	
Verbank	12585
Verdoy (Latham)	12110
Vermillion (Mexico)	13114
Vermontville	12989
Vernon	13476
Vernon Center	13477
Vernon Valley	11731
(East Northport)	
Verona	13478
Verona Beach	13162
Verplanck	10596
Versailles	14168
Vesper (Tully)	13159
Vestal	13850-851
Ross Corners	13850
South Vestal	13850
Tracy Creek	13850
Twin Orchards	13850
Willow Point	13850
Victor	14564
Victory Mills	12884
Vienna (Blossvale)	13308
Village (New York)	10014
Village Of The Branch	11787
(Smithtown)	
Virgil (Cortland)	13045
Vischer Ferry (Rexford)	12148
Volney (Fulton)	13069
Voorheesville	12186
Waccabuc	10597
Waddington	13694
Wadhams	12990
Wading River	11792
Wadsworth (Piffard)	14533
Wainscott	11975
Waits (Owego)	13827
Wakefield (Bronx)	10466
Walden	12586
Wales Center	14169
Walesville (Whitesboro)	13492
Walker Valley	12588
Wall Street (New York)	10005
Wall Street Brm	10269
(New York)	
Wallace (Avoca)	14809
Wallkill	12589
Walloomsac	12090
(Hoosick Falls)	
Walton	13856
Walworth	14568
Wampsville	13163
Wanakena	13695
Wantagh	11793
Wappingers Falls	12590
Warners	13164
Warnerville	12187
Warren	13439
(Richfield Springs)	
Warrensburg	12885

Warsaw	14569
Warwick	10990
Washington Bridge	10033
(New York)	
Washington Mills	13479
Washingtonville	10992
Wassaic	12592
Water Island (Patchogue)	11772
Water Mill	11976
Waterford	12188
Waterloo	13165
Waterport	14571
Waterside Park	11768
(Northport)	
Watertown	13601-603
Fort Drum	13602-13603
Glen Park	13601
Knowsville	13601
Waterville	13480
Watervliet	12189
Watkins Glen	14891
Watson (Lowville)	13367
Wave Crest	11690
Waverly	14892
Wawarsing	12489
Wayland	14572
Wayne	14893
Webster	14580
Webster Crossing	14584
Weedsport	13166
Wegatchie (Antwerp)	13608
Welcome (Mount Vision)	13810
Wellesley Island	13640
(Fineview)	
Wells	12190
Wells Bridge	13859
Wells Park (Islip)	11751
Wellsburg	14894
Wellsville	14895
Weltonville	13811
(Newark Valley)	
Wesley Chapel (Suffern)	10901
West Amboy (W. Monroe)	13167
West Amherst (Amherst)	14228
West Amityville	11758
(Massapequa)	
West Babylon	11704, 11707
Babylon	11704
Babylon	11707
Santapogue	11704
Santapogue	11707
West Bainbridge	13733
(Bainbridge)	
West Bangor	12991, 13602
(North Bangor)	
West Bay Shore	11706
(Bay Shore)	
West Berne (Berne)	12023
West Bloomfield	14585
West Branch (Ava)	13303
West Brentwood	11717
(Brentwood)	
West Burlington	13482
West Bush (Gloversville)	12078
West Camp	12490
West Candor (Candor)	13743
West Carthage	13619
(Carthage)	
West Charlton	12010
(Amsterdam)	
West Chazy	12992

West Chenango	13905
(Binghamton)	
West Clarksville	14786
West Colesville	13904
(Binghamton)	
West Copake	12593
West Corners (Endicott)	13760
West Coxsackie	12192
(Coxsackie)	
West Danby	14883, 14896
West Davenport	13860
West Deer Park	11798
(Wyandanch)	
West Delhi (Delhi)	13753
West Durham (Durham)	12422
West Eaton	13484
West Edmeston	13485
West End (Oneonta)	13820
West Endicott (Endicott)	13760
West Exeter	13487
West Falls	14170
West Farms (Bronx)	10460
West Fort Ann (Fort Ann)	12827
West Fulton	12194
West Gilgo Beach	11702
(Babylon)	
West Glens Falls	12801
(Glens Falls)	
West Glenville	12010
(Amsterdam)	
West Groton (Groton)	13073
West Hampton Beach	11978
(Westhampton Beach)	
West Harpersfield	13786
(Harpersfield)	
West Harrison	10604
(White Plains)	
West Haverstraw	10993
West Hebron (Salem)	12865
West Hempstead	11552
West Henrietta	14586
West Hills (Huntington)	11743
West Huntington	11743
(Huntington)	
West Hurley	12491
West Islip	11795
West Kill	12492
West Latham (Latham)	12110
West Laurens (Laurens)	13796
West Lebanon	12195
West Lee (Lee Center)	13363
West Leyden	13489
West Lowville (Lowville)	13367
West Mecox (Water Mill)	11976
West Meredith	13757
(East Meredith)	
West Milton	12020
(Ballston Spa)	
West Monroe	13167
West Neck (Huntington)	11743
West Newark	13811
(Newark Valley)	
West Newburgh (Newburgh)	12550
West Nyack	10994-995
West Oneonta	13861
West Parishville	13676
(Potsdam)	
West Park	12493
West Pierrepont (Canton)	13617
West Plattsburgh	12962
(Morrisonville)	

West Point 10996-997
West Potsdam (Potsdam) . 13676
West Richmondville 12149
  (Richmondville)
West Ronkonkoma 11779
  (Ronkonkoma)
West Rush (Rush) 14543
West Saint James 11787
  (Smithtown)
West Sand Lake 12196
West Saugerties 12477
  (Saugerties)
West Sayville 11796
West Schuyler (Utica) 13502
West Seneca (Buffalo) 14210
  .... 14218, 14220, 14224
  Buffalo 14224
West Shokan 12494
West Smithtown 11787
  (Smithtown)
West Stockholm 13696
West Taghkanic (Ancram) . 12502
West Tiana 11946
  (Hampton Bays)
West Turin 13325
  (Constableville)
West Valley 14171
West Valley Falls 12185
  (Valley Falls)
West Village (New York) 10014
West Windsor (Windsor) ... 13865
West Winfield 13491
West Yaphank (Medford) 11763
Westbrookville 12785
Westbury (Old Westbury) ... 11568
  11590, 11593-595, 11597
  Cheeselovers 11595
  Dept Of Motor Vehicles 11593
  New Cassel 11590
Westchester (Bronx) 10461
Westchester Cnty Airport .. 10604
Westdale 13483
Westerlo 12055, 12193
  (Dormansville)
Western (North Western) .. 13419
Western Nassau 11599
  (Garden City)
Westernville 13486
Westfield 14787
Westford 13488
Westgate (Rochester) 14624
Westhampton 11977
Westmere (Albany) 12203
Westminster Park 13607
  (Alexandria Bay)
Westmoreland 13490
Westons Mills 14788
Westover (Johnson City) .. 13790
Westport 12993
Westtown 10998

Westvale (Syracuse) 13219
Westview (Binghamton) 13905
Westville (Schenevus) 12155
Westville Center 12926
  (Constable)
Wevertown 12886
Whaley Lake (Holmes) 12531
Whallons Bay (Essex) 12936
Whallonsburg 12994
Wheatfield 14120, 14304
  (North Tonawanda)
Wheatley (Old Westbury) ... 11568
Wheatley Heights 11798
  (Wyandanch)
Wheelerville 12032
  (Caroga Lake)
Whippleville 12995
White Creek 12057
  (Eagle Bridge)
White Lake 12786, 13494
White Plains ... 10600-607, 10625
  .... 10629, 10633, 10650
  East White Plains 10604
  Gedney 10605
  Greenburgh 10607
  North White Plains 10603
  West Harrison 10604
  Westchester County Airport ..
  10604
White Sulphur Springs 12787
Whitehall 12887
Whitelaw (Canastota) 13032
Whites Store 13843
  (South New Berlin)
Whitestone (Flushing) 11357
Whitestown (Whitesboro) .. 13492
Whitesville 14897
Whitfield (Accord) 12404
Whitman (Masonville) 13804
Whitney Point 13862
Whittier (Kingston) 12401
Wiccopee 12533
  (Hopewell Junction)
Wickapogue 11968
  (Southampton)
Wickman Park (Greenport) 11944
Wildwood (Wading River) .. 11792
Willard 14588
Willet 13863
Williams Lake (Rosendale) 12472
Williamsbridge (Bronx) 10467
Williamson 14589
Williamstown 13493
Williamsville 14221
  .... 14228, 14231
  Amherst 14221
  Amherst 14231
  Buffalo 14221
  Buffalo 14231
Williston Park 11596

Willow 12495
Willow Point (Vestal) 13850
Willowvale (Chadwicks) 13319
Willsboro 12996
Willseyville 13864
Wilmington 12997
Wilna (Carthage) 13619
Wilson 14172
Wilton 12866
Wincoma (Huntington) 11743
Windham 12496
Windmill Farms (Armonk) . 10504
Windsor 13865
Winfield (West Winfield) ... 13491
Wingdale 12594
Winston Park 11746
  (Huntington Station)
Winthrop 13697
Witherbee 12998
Wolcott 14590
Wolf Lake (Wurtsboro) 12790
Woodbourne 12788
Woodbury 11797
Woodbury Falls 10930
  (Highland Mills)
Woodcliff Park 11933
  (Calverton)
Woodgate 13494
Woodhull 14898
Woodlawn (Bronx) 10470
Woodmere 11598
Woodridge 12789
Woods Corners (Norwich) . 13815
Woodsburgh (Woodmere) .. 11598
Woodside (Flushing) 11377
Woodstock 12498
Woodville 13698
Worcester 12197
Worth (Lorraine) 13659
Wreck Lead (Island Park) ... 11558
Wurtsboro 12790
Wyandanch 11798
Wykagyl (New Rochelle) ... 10804
Wynantskill 12198
Wyoming 14591
Xerox (Rochester) 14644
Yaleville (Norwood) 13668
Yankee Lake (Wurtsboro) .. 12790
Yaphank 11980
Yonkers 10700-710
  Centuck 10710
  East 10704
  North 10703
  South 10705
York 14592
Yorkshire 14173
Yorktown Heights 10598
Yorkville 10128, 13495
  (New York)
Youngs (Unadilla) 13849
Youngstown 14174
Youngsville 12791
Yulan 12792
Zacks Inlet (Seaford) 11783

Example:

Park Pl	 07	All houses have the zipcode 10007
Park Row	1 - 43 38	All houses numbered 1-43 have the zipcode 10038
	44 - 166 .... E 07	All even numbered houses 44-166 have the zipcode 10007
	45 - 165 ...... O 38	All odd numbered houses 44-165 have the zipcode 10038
Pleasant Ave		
	1 - 299 29	All houses numberd 1-299 have the zipcode 10029
	300 - OUT 35	All houses numbered 300 or greater have the zipcode 10035

1st Ave
1 - 346	E 09
1 - 343	O 03
345	10
347 - 444	10
445 - 699	16
700 - 876	17
877 - 1096	22
1097 - 1099	O 21
1098 - 1100	E 22
1101 - 1532	21
1533 - 1537	O 28
1534 - 1538	E 21
1539 - 1667	28
1668 - 1678	E 28
1669 - 1679	O 28
1680 - 1855	28
1856 - 2255	29
2256	35
2257	29
2258 - 2449	35
2451 - 2499	O 35

2nd Ave
1 - 343	03
344 - 459	10
460 - 746	16
747 - 922	17
923 - 1139	22
1140	21
1141	22
1142 - 1537	21
1538 - 1540	E 28
1539 - 1541	O 21
1542 - 1680	28
1681 - 1855	28
1856 - 1862	E 29
1857 - 1863	O 28
1864 - 2259	29
2260 - 2499	35

3rd Ave
1 - 243	03
244 - 356	10
357 - 604	16
605	58
606 - 618	16
619 - 796	17
797 - 963	22
964	55
965 - 1009	22
1010 - 1409	21
1410 - 1549	28
1550 - 1709	28
1710 - 2121	29
2122	35
2123	29
2124 - 2399	35

4th Ave
	03

5th Ave
1 - 34	11
1 - 133	O 03

36 - 38	11
40 - 152	E 11
135 - 151	O 10
153 - 217	10
218 - 348	E 01
219 - 231	O 10
233 - 459	O 16
350	18
352 - 370	E 01
372 - 498	E 18
461 - 519	O 17
500	10
502 - 594	E 36
521	75
523 - 549	O 17
551	76
553 - 609	O 17
596 - 628	E 20
611 - 743	O 22
630	11
632 - 638	E 20
640 - 664	E 19
666	03
668 - 770	E 19
745	51
747 - 765	O 22
767	53
769	22
771 - 787	22
788 - 990	21
991 - 1059	28
1060 - 1150	28
1151 - 1313	29
1314 - 1416	E 26
1315 - 1415	O 29
1417 - 2117	35
2118	37
2119	35
2120 - 2399	37
800A - 800B	21

6th Ave
1 - 204	13
205 - 335	14
336 - 414	E 11
337 - 415	O 14
416 - 650	11
651 - 773	10
774 - 960	01
961 - 1080	18
1081 - 1219	36
1220 - 1241	20
1242 - 1254	E 12
1243 - 1253	O 20
1255 - 1279	20
1280 - 1289	19
1290	04
1291 - 1344	19
1345	05
1346 - 1499	19

7th Ave
1 - 241	11
242	01
243	11
244 - 379	01
380 - 418	E 21
381 - 439	O 01
420 - 440	E 19
441 - 449	01
450	23
451 - 461	01
462 - 576	18
577 - 720	36
721 - 887	19
889 - 941	19
1800 - 2000	26
2001 - 2259	27
2260 - 2499	30
2500 - 2699	39

7th S Ave
	14

8th Ave
1 - 67	14
68 - 78	E 11
69 - 79	O 14
80 - 278	11
279 - 420	01
421	99
422 - 499	01
500 - 637	18
638 - 789	36
790 - 996	19
2031 - 2037	O 26
2039 - 2224	26
2225	27
2226	26
2227 - 2482	27
2483 - 2487	O 30
2484 - 2488	E 27
2489 - 2728	30
2729 - 2999	39

9th Ave
1 - 43	14
44 - 227	11
228 - 340	01
341	99
342 - 449	01
450 - 559	18
560 - 700	36
701 - 925	19
3700 - 4199	34

10th Ave
1 - 59	14
60 - 236	11
237 - 239	O 01
238 - 240	E 11
241 - 449	01
450 - 555	18
556 - 685	36
686 - 702	E 19
687 - 703	O 36
704 - 1000	19
3700 - 4099	34

ALBANY

APARTMENTS

Bnai Brith Apts
400 HUDSON AVE 12203

Central Towers
400 CENTRAL AVE 12206

Dewitt Clinton Apts
142 STATE ST 12207

Eloise Apts
11 S LAKE AVE 12203

Executive House Apts
175 S SWAN ST 12210

Nelson House
5 SAMARITAN RD 12208

Ohav Sholom
115 KRUMKILL RD 12208

River Hill Apts
2 Van Rensselaer Blvd 12204

Sophia Apts
426 WHITEHALL RD 12208

Towne Towers Apartments
12 CALIFORNIA AVE 12205

Townsend Apts
45 CENTRAL AVE 12206

Twrs Colonie Douglas Hse
424 SAND CREEK RD 12205

Twrs Colonie Hanover Hse
420 SAND CREEK RD 12205

Twrs Colonie Lyman Hse
422 SAND CREEK RD 12205

Village One
587 BROADWAY 12204

Westview Homes
680 CENTRAL AVE 12206

BUILDINGS

Colonie Center
1425 CENTRAL AVE 12205

Crossgates Mall
120 Washington Ave. Ext .. 12203

Labor Temple
890 3RD ST 12206

Shop & Save Plaza
900 CENTRAL AVE 12206

Stuyvesant Plaza
1475 WESTERN AVE 12203

GOVERNMENT

City Hall
24 EAGLE ST 12207

County Court House
16 EAGLE ST 12207

Federal Building
445 BROADWAY 12207

Leo Obrien Building
0 LEO OBRIEN BLDG 12207

MILITARY

Armed Forces Reserve Ctr
780 WASHINGTON AVE ... 12203

ALBIA

APARTMENTS

Adam Court Apts
101 Industrial Park Rd 12180

Burns Apts
720 FEDERAL ST 12180

Caldwell Apts
17 STATE ST 12180

Kennedy Towers
2100 6TH AVE 12180

Oneil Apts
2121 6TH AVE 12180

St Marys Woodland Vlg
2902 TIBBITS AVE 12180

Troy Towers Apts
2000 6TH AVE 12180

BUILDINGS

Hendrick Hudson
200 BROADWAY 12180

AMHERST

APARTMENTS

Boulevard Towers Apts
120 MEYER RD 14226

Drexel Hill Apts
205 EVANS ST 14221

Georgetown Apts
321 EVANS ST 14221

Pomeroy Apartments
3901 MAIN ST 14226

BUILDINGS

Clarence Mall
4401 TRANSIT RD 14221

Eastern Hills Mall
4545 TRANSIT RD 14221

AQUEDUCT

APARTMENTS

Hillcrest Vlg E
1503 HILLSIDE AVE 12309

Niskayuna Garden Apts
1197 HILLSIDE AVE 12309

Tall Oaks Apt
2475 BROOKSHIRE DR ... 12309

Van Antwerp Vill
1365 VAN ANTWERP RD . 12309

BAYBERRY

HOSPITALS

North Medical Center
5100 W TAFT RD 13088

BELLEVUE

APARTMENTS

Mohawk Manor
473 DUANESBURG RD ... 12306

BINGHAMTON

APARTMENTS

5 Riverside Towers
5 RIVERSIDE DR 13905

Carlisle Apts
150 MOELLER ST 13904

Chenango Place
110 CHENANGO ST 13901

Country Towne Apts
100 ROBERTS ST 13901

Ely Park Apts
1 ELY PARK BLVD 13905

North Shore Towers Building 1
45 EXCHANGE ST 13901

North Shore Towers Building 2
24 ISBELL ST 13901

North Shore Village
14 ISBELL ST 13901

River House
38 FRONT ST 13905

The Windermere
260 WASHINGTON ST 13901

Woodburn Court I
21 EXCHANGE ST 13901

Woodburn Court Ii
100 SUSQUEHANNA ST .. 13901

BUILDINGS

Bache Building
71 STATE ST 13901

Binghamton Plz
33 W STATE ST 13901

Chase Lincoln 1st Building
2 COURT ST 13901

Chenango Plaza
1318 FRONT ST 13901

Colonial Plz
349 CHENANGO ST 13901

Colonial Plz
32 W STATE ST 13901

Foundry Plaza
10 GLENWOOD AVE 13905

Giant Plaza
1290 FRONT ST 13901

Good Shephard Home
80 FAIRVIEW AVE 13904

Key Bank Building
59 COURT ST 13901

Marine Midland Plz
1 MARINE MIDLAND PLZ   13901

Metrocenter
49 COURT ST 13901

Midtown Mall
15 CHENANGO ST 13901

Northgate Plaza
1250 FRONT ST 13901

Oneil Building
102 STATE ST 13901

Press Building
19 CHENANGO ST 13901

Professional Building
117 HAWLEY ST 13901

Security Mutual Building
80 EXCHANGE ST 13901

Station Square
45 LEWIS ST 13901

Stephens Sq
81 STATE ST 13901

GOVERNMENT

Binghamton City Off Building
38 HAWLEY ST 13901

Binghamton County Veterans Arena
1146 PO BOX 13902

Broome County
1766 PO BOX 13902

Federal Building
15 HENRY ST 13901

State Office Building Annex
164 HAWLEY ST 13901

HOTELS

Del Motel
124 PO BOX 13904

Econo Lodge
196 PO BOX 13904

COLLEGES

Broome Community College
1017 PO BOX 13902

College In The Woods
6006 PO BOX 13902

Dickinson Community
6007 PO BOX 13902

Glenn Bartle Library
6012 PO BOX 13902

Graduate Community
6010 PO BOX 13902

Hillside Community
6014 PO BOX 13902

Hinman College
6009 PO BOX 13902

Newing College
6008 PO BOX 13902

Suny Admissions
6001 PO BOX 13902

Suny Alumni
6004 PO BOX 13902

Suny Career Development
6013 PO BOX 13902

Suny Financial Aid
6011 PO BOX 13902

Suny Foundation
6005 PO BOX 13902

Suny General Business
6000 PO BOX 13902

Suny Registrar
6002 PO BOX 13902

Suny Student Accounts
6003 PO BOX 13902

BLASDELL

APARTMENTS

Coach Lite Village Apts
3300 MCKINLEY PKY 14219

BRANDYWINE

BUILDINGS

Mohawk Mall
400 BALLTOWN RD 12304

BRIGHTON

APARTMENTS

1600 East Ave Apts
1600 EAST AVE 14610

Carlton Apts
1211 PARK AVE 14610

Cobbs Hill Village
645 NORRIS DR 14610

Colby Apts
1225 PARK AVE 14610

Coolidge Apts
1650 EAST AVE 14610

East Ave Towers Apts
2505 EAST AVE 14610

East Blvd Manor Apts
76 EAST BLVD 14610

Linden Ave Apts
81 LINDEN AVE 14610

Oak Hill Ter Apts
2470 EAST AVE 14610

Parkwin Apts
1190 PARK AVE 14610

Renaissance Apts
2500 EAST AVE 14610

Royal Manor Apts
75 EAST BLVD 14610

Valley Manor Apts
1570 EAST AVE 14610

BROOKLYN

GOVERNMENT

Federal Court
225 CADMAN PLZ E 11201

NY State Supreme Court
360 ADAMS ST 11201

BUFFALO

APARTMENTS

1290 Delaware Apts
1290 DELAWARE AVE 14209

800 W Ferry Apts
800 W FERRY ST 14222

Ambassador Apts
175 NORTH ST 14201

Brent Manor Apts
366 ELMWOOD AVE 14222

Campanile Apts
925 DELAWARE AVE 14209

Canterbury Courts Apts
2 LEXINGTON AVE 14222

Commodore Apts
1240 DELAWARE AVE 14209

Delaware Court Apts
1022 DELAWARE AVE 14209

Delaware Towers
1088 DELAWARE AVE 14209

Edgebrook Estates
65 EDGEBROOK EST 14227

Elliott Apts
175 LINWOOD AVE 14209

Elm-nor Apts
209 ELMWOOD AVE 14222

Executive Towers Apts
849 DELAWARE AVE 14209

Fairfax House
715 DELAWARE AVE 14209

Gates Circle Apts
1306 DELAWARE AVE 14209

Hyde Park Apts
196 NORTH ST 14201

Kenmore Towers
3015 DELAWARE AVE 14217

Kenmore Village Apts
657 COLVIN AVE 14217

Kenton Presbyterian Vlg
3735 DELAWARE AVE 14217

Linwood Elderly Housing
333 LINWOOD AVE 14209

Mayflower Apts
66 SUMMER ST 14209

North Court Apts
197 NORTH ST 14201

Park Lane Apt
33 GATES CIR 14209

Sherwood Apts
140 LINWOOD AVE 14209

St Johns Tower
865 MICHIGAN AVE 14203

Stuyvesant Apts
245 ELMWOOD AVE 14222

Touraine Apts
274 DELAWARE AVE 14202

Westbrook Apts
675 DELAWARE AVE 14209

Westbury Apts
210 DELAWARE AVE 14202

Windsor Apts
703 W FERRY ST 14222

BUILDINGS

Brisbane Building
403 MAIN ST 14203

Buffalo Convention Center
1 Convention Center Plz ... 14202

Buffalo Memorial Aud
140 MAIN ST 14202

Cathedral Park Tower
37 FRANKLIN ST 14202

Chemical Bank Building
69 DELAWARE AVE 14202

Convention Center Tower
43 COURT ST 14202

Crosby Building
170 FRANKLIN ST 14202

Ellicott Sq Building
295 MAIN ST 14203

Fleet Bank Building
12 FOUNTAIN PLZ 14202

Guaranty Building
30 CHURCH ST 14202

Hubbard Building
47 W HURON ST 14202

Liberty Building
424 MAIN ST 14202

M & T Building
1 M AND T PLZ 14203

M & T Center
3 FOUNTAIN PLZ 14203

Main Seneca Building
237 MAIN ST 14203

Marine Midland Ctr
1 MARINE MIDLAND CTR 14203

Niagara Frontier Building
290 MAIN ST 14202

Olympic Towers
300 PEARL ST 14202

Rand Building
14 LAFAYETTE SQ 14203

Root Building
86 W CHIPPEWA ST 14202

Statler Towers
107 DELAWARE AVE 14202

Tishman Building
10 LAFAYETTE SQ 14203

Waterfront Village Center
60 LAKEFRONT BLVD 14202

Waterfront Village Center
40 LA RIVIERE DR 14202

GOVERNMENT

Buffalo City Court Building
50 DELAWARE AVE 14202

Buffalo City Hall
65 NIAGARA SQ 14202

Edward E Rath Building
95 FRANKLIN ST 14202

Erie County Building
25 DELAWARE AVE 14202

Erie County Courthouse
92 FRANKLIN ST 14202

Federal Building
111 W HURON ST 14202

General Donavan Building
125 MAIN ST 14203

MJ Dillon Fed Court Building
68 COURT ST 14202

TJ Dulski Fed Office Building
111 W HURON ST 14202

US Courthouse
68 COURT ST 14202

WJ Mahoney St Office Building
65 COURT ST 14202

HOSPITALS

Buffalo General Hospital
100 HIGH ST 14203

Sheehan Memorial Hospital
425 MICHIGAN AVE 14203

HOTELS

Buffalo Hilton Hotel
120 CHURCH ST 14202

BULLS HEAD

APARTMENTS

Danforth Towers
160 WEST AVE 14611

Glide Court Apts
133 GLIDE ST 14611

Plymouth Gardens
1400 PLYMOUTH AVE S ... 14611

The Westmore Apts
327 WEST AVE 14611

Valley Ct Apts
1170 GENESEE ST 14611

Winslow Apts
565 CHILI AVE 14611

CANANDAIGUA

APARTMENTS

Finger Lakes Manor
190 PARRISH ST 14424

Lakeside Village Apts
275 JEFFERSON AVE 14424

GOVERNMENT

Canandaigua Court House
27 MAIN ST 14424

COLVIN

APARTMENTS

Bernardine Apt
417 CHURCHILL AVE 13205

Greenwich Manor Apt
681 E SENECA TPKE 13205

Loretto Adult Home
710 E BRIGHTON AVE 13205

Valley Vista
122 W SENECA TPKE 13205

COLVIN ELMWOOD

APARTMENTS

Shady Willow Estates
139 FORD AVE 13207

Valley Court
300 MAINS AVE 13207

DEERFIELD

APARTMENTS

Algonquinn Apts
1434 GENESEE ST 13502

Amalott Apts Front
1416 GENESEE ST 13502

Candlewyck Ln Apts
2 CANDLEWYCK LN 13502

Genesee Towers
110 GENESEE ST 13502

Goldbas Apartments
440 WHITESBORO ST 13502

Highland Courts Apts
1506 WHITESBORO ST ... 13502

Humphrey Gardens
221 HERKIMER RD 13502

Kanatena Apts
1504 GENESEE ST 13502

Kennedy Plaza Apts
2 KENNEDY PLZ 13502

Lilley Cooper Memorial Ap
276 GENESEE ST 13502

Manor Apts
1400 GENESEE ST 13502

Michael Walsh Apts
1216 GRAY AVE 13502

Oneida Mobile Ct
865 STATE ROUTE 5 13502

Roosevelt Apts
1514 GENESEE ST 13502

Skyline Mobile Ct
786 STATE ROUTE 5 13502

Strawberry Hills Trl Pk
831 STATE ROUTE 5 13502

Victoria Apts
1420 GENESEE ST 13502

Washington Courts
440 WHITESBORO ST 13502

BUILDINGS

258 Building
258 GENESEE ST 13502

Kempf Building
250 GENESEE ST 13502

Winston Building
230 GENESEE ST 13502

GOVERNMENT

City Hall
1 KENNEDY PLZ 13502

EAST

APARTMENTS

Pkway House
61 BRONX RIVER RD 10704

Secor Terrace
1122 YONKERS AVE 10704

The Parkway Terrace
43 BRONX RIVER RD 10704

The Westview
11 BRONX RIVER RD 10704

Wakefield Towers
85 BRONX RIVER RD 10704

EAST GLENVILLE

GOVERNMENT

Glenville Town Hall
18 GLENRIDGE RD 12302

Navy Depot
0 NAVY DEPOT 12302

EASTWOOD

APARTMENTS

Grant Village
100 VILLAGE DR 13206

Grant Village
100 EDTIM RD 13206

ELMIRA

BUILDINGS

Mark Twain Building
147 W GRAY ST 14901

GOVERNMENT

Chem Co Govt Building
228 LAKE ST 14901

Chemung Cty Justice Building
203 WILLIAM ST 14901

City Hall
317 E CHURCH ST 14901

FLEETWOOD

APARTMENTS

Birchview
40 E BIRCH ST 10552

Cadillac
50 FLEETWOOD AVE 10552

Cadillac Apts
40 FLEETWOOD AVE 10552

Cedarcrest Apts
472 GRAMATAN AVE 10552

Esplanade Gardens
531 E LINCOLN AVE 10552

Fleetridge
642 LOCUST ST 10552

Fleetridge East
636 N TERRACE AVE 10552

Fleetridge South
600 LOCUST ST 10552

Fleetwood View
60 BROAD ST W 10552

Plymouth House
625 GRAMATAN AVE 10552

Terrace Arms
651 N TERRACE AVE 10552

Vernon Manor
465 E LINCOLN AVE 10552

BUILDINGS

The Pennwood
101 ELLWOOD AVE 10552

FLUSHING

BUILDINGS

Bulova Corporate Center
7520 ASTORIA BLVD 11370

GEDNEY

APARTMENTS

Bristol House Coops
10 NOSBAND AVE 10605

Bryant Gardens
1 BRYANT CRES 10605

Claridge
101 Old Mamaroneck Rd .. 10605

Gaylord
2 OVERLOOK RD 10605

Gedney House
59 Old Mamaroneck Rd 10605

Surrey Strathmore Apts
90 BRYANT AVE 10605

GREECE

APARTMENTS

English Village
1100 ENGLISH RD 14616

GREENBURGH

APARTMENTS

Fulton Pk
25 COUNTY CENTER RD 10607

HINSDALE

APARTMENTS

Orchard Estates Apt
101 ROXBORO CIR 13211

BUILDINGS

Pickard Building
5858 E MOLLOY RD 13211

IRONDEQUOIT

APARTMENTS

Park Titus Apts
455 TITUS AVE 14617

LYNCOURT

APARTMENTS

Butternut Arms Apt
1312 BUTTERNUT ST 13208

Court Street Arms
304 COURT ST 13208

North Court Apt
1106 1ST NORTH ST 13208

Vinette Towers Apt
947 POND ST 13208

MOUNT VERNON

APARTMENTS

August P Petrillo
110 N 3RD AVE 10550

Caledonia Court
5 S 16TH AVE 10550

Carriage House
131 E PROSPECT AVE 10550

Chester Courts
101 ELM AVE 10550

Cortlandt Arms
269 W 1ST ST 10550

Levister Towers
230 S 7TH AVE 10550

Macedonia Towers
150 S 5TH AVE 10550

Monticello
30 PARK AVE 10550

The Belle Fontaine
64 ELM AVE 10550

The Lenox
111 N 3RD AVE 10550

The Quincy
11 PARK AVE 10550

The Williamsburg
33 N 3RD AVE 10550

NEW ROCHELLE

APARTMENTS

Calton Court
43 CALTON RD 10804

Faymore Gardens
140 PELHAM RD 10805

Glen Island Manor
600 PELHAM RD 10805

Huguenot Towers
50 GUION PL 10801

Huguenot Towers North
80 GUION PL 10801

Kensington
35 CLINTON PL 10801

Larochelle Manor
111 LOCKWOOD AVE 10801

Peldale Apts
838 PELHAMDALE AVE ... 10801

Pelham Hall
300 PELHAM RD 10805

Pelmar Apts
666 PELHAM RD 10805

The Kenmore
266 PELHAM RD 10805

Trinity Coop Apts
164 CHURCH ST 10805

Wykagyl Garden
1273 NORTH AVE 10804

BUILDINGS

Kaufman Building
271 NORTH AVE 10801

HOSPITALS

New Rochelle Hospital
16 GUION PL 10801

COLLEGES

College Of New Rochelle
29 CASTLE PL 10805

NEW WINDSOR

APARTMENTS

Continental Manor
186 TEMPLE HILL RD 12553

Kingswood Gardens Apts
810 BLOOMING GROVE TPKE ..
.... 12553

Knox Village Apts
835 Blooming Grove Tpke 12553

Oakwood Terrace Apts
320 Blooming Grove Tpke 12553

Sycamore Gardens Apts
431 Blooming Grove Tpke 12553

NIAGARA FALLS

BUILDINGS

Hooker Chemical Building
360 RAINBOW BLVD S 14303

NORTH

APARTMENTS

Father Finian Twrs
1 FR Finian Sullivan Dr 10703

Grey Oaks
495 ODELL AVE 10703

Highview Twrs
87 HIGH ST 10703

NORTH WHITE PLAINS

APARTMENTS

Biltmore Tower
30 LAKE ST 10603

Chatham
44 N BROADWAY 10603

Dorchester
50 N BROADWAY 10603

Edgebrook
1 LAWRENCE DR 10603

Fairview
100 MANHATTAN AVE 10603

Fairview
33 OAK ST 10603

Half Moon
11 LAKE ST 10603

Heritage Tower
15 STEWART PL 10603

Madison House
70 FERRIS AVE 10603

River Pk
70 VIRGINIA RD N 10603

Summit House
155 FERRIS AVE 10603

Tanglewood Apts
260 CHURCH ST 10603

POUGHKEEPSIE

GOVERNMENT

County Court House
10 MARKET ST 12601

Dutchess Cty Office Building
22 MARKET ST 12601

ROCHESTER

APARTMENTS

Alexandrian Apts
300 ALEXANDER ST 14607

Algonquin Apts
34 GOODMAN ST S 14607

Apollo Apts
81 THURSTON RD 14619

Ardsley Apts
699 MAIN ST E 14605

Avondale Apts
370 MEIGS ST 14607

Barrington Apts
152 BARRINGTON ST 14607

Biltmore Apts
357 ALEXANDER ST 14607

Borinquen Apartments
100 BORINQUEN PLZ 14605

Bretton Hall Apts
325 ALEXANDER ST 14607

Brookview Apts
504 BROOKS AVE 14619

Brownstone Apts
241 ALEXANDER ST 14607

Buckingham Apts
713 PARK AVE 14607

Campus Apts
1126 DEWEY AVE 14613

Cedarwood Towers
2052 MAIN ST E 14609

Colonial Apts
28 PARK AVE 14607

Colony Apts
1361 LAKE AVE 14613

Delmar Apts
962 MONROE AVE 14620

Dunn Towers Apts
200 DUNN TOWER DR 14606

Ellis East Apts
747 EAST AVE 14607

Genesee Gateway Apts
185 MOUNT HOPE AVE ... 14620

Goler House Apts
60 CRITTENDEN BLVD 14620

Haddon Hall
505 UNIVERSITY AVE 14607

Keeler Manor Apts
1624 CLINTON AVE N 14621

Keeler Park Apts
601 SENECA MANOR DR 14621

Lake Tower Apts
321 LAKE AVE 14608

Lake View Towers
4575 LAKE AVE 14612

Manhattan Sq Apts
10 Manhattan Square Dr ... 14607

Midtown Manor
475 BROAD ST E 14607

Normandy Apts
253 ALEXANDER ST 14607

Palisades Apts
345 ALEXANDER ST 14607

Plaza Apts
35 CHESTNUT ST 14604

Poplar Way Apts
1011 UNIVERSITY AVE 14607

Ridge Hudson Tower
401 SENECA MANOR DR 14621

River View Towers
60 RIVER ST 14612

Roosevelt Apts
267 OXFORD ST 14607

Royal Apts
80 THURSTON RD 14619

Saint Paul Court Apts
1564 SAINT PAUL ST 14621

Saint Simmons Ter
360 SAINT PAUL ST 14605

Seneca Towers
200 SETH GREEN DR 14621

Shelbourne Apts
517 UNIVERSITY AVE 14607

Shire At Culverton
2515 CULVER RD 14609

Southview Towers
500 SOUTH AVE 14620

Strathmore Apts
970 MONROE AVE 14620

The Berkeley Apts
214 BERKELEY ST 14607

The Flanders
440 THURSTON RD 14619

The Harvard Apts
85 MEIGS ST 14607

The Milburn Apts
189 MILBURN ST 14607

The Plaza Apts
125 SAINT PAUL ST 14604

The Savannah
15 SAVANNAH ST 14607

The Seville Apts
445 POST AVE 14619

Vassar Apts
593 PARK AVE 14607

Whittier Apts
270 GOODMAN ST S 14607

Woodview Apts
1835 SAINT PAUL ST 14621

BUILDINGS

Academy Building
13 FITZHUGH ST S 14614

Alliance Building
183 MAIN ST E 14604

Case Building
82 SAINT PAUL ST 14604

Chestnut Plaza
50 CHESTNUT ST 14604

Columbia Building
31 MAIN ST E 14614

Corporate Place
255 EAST AVE 14604

Cox Building
36 SAINT PAUL ST 14604

Cutler Building
42 EAST AVE 14604

East Ave Commons
111 EAST AVE 14604

Ebenezer Watts Building
47 FITZHUGH ST S 14614

Ellwanger And Barry Building
39 STATE ST 14614

Executive Office Building
36 MAIN ST W 14614

First Federal Building
328 MAIN ST E 14604

First Federal Plz
28 MAIN ST E 14614

Four Corners Building
1 MAIN ST W 14614

Hiram Sibley Building
311 ALEXANDER ST 14604

Medical Arts Building
277 ALEXANDER ST 14607

Norstar Tower
1 EAST AVE 14604

Powers Building
16 MAIN ST W 14614

Reynolds Arcade Building
16 MAIN ST E 14614

Riverside Convention Ctr
123 MAIN ST E 14604

Seneca Building
20 CLINTON AVE S 14604

Tallman Building
25 MAIN ST E 14614

Temple Building
14 FRANKLIN ST 14604

Terminal Building
65 W BROAD ST 14614

The Loft
180 SAINT PAUL ST 14604

Time Square Building
45 EXCHANGE BLVD 14614

Triangle Building
335 MAIN ST E 14604

Union Trust Building
19 MAIN ST W 14614

War Memorial
100 EXCHANGE BLVD 14614

Washington Building
155 MAIN ST W 14614

Wilder Building
8 EXCHANGE BLVD 14614

GOVERNMENT

City Hall
30 CHURCH ST 14614

County Office Building
39 MAIN ST W 14614

Federal Building
100 STATE ST 14614

Public Safety Building
150 PLYMOUTH AVE S 14614

HOTELS

Cadillac Hotel
45 CHESTNUT ST 14604

East Avenue Inn
384 EAST AVE 14607

Radisson Hotel
70 STATE ST 14614

COLLEGES

RBI
1850 RIDGE RD E 14622

Rochester Business Inst
1850 RIDGE RD E 14622

SCHENECTADY

APARTMENTS

Netherland Village
1455 DORWALDT BLVD ... 12308

Sheridan Vill
1301 GERLING ST 12308

Ten Eyck Apts
375 BROADWAY 12305

Wade Lupe Apts
15 LAFAYETTE ST 12305

GOVERNMENT

City Hall
105 JAY ST 12305

County Court House
620 STATE ST 12305

SOUTH

APARTMENTS

Sunnyside Manor
2 SUNNYSIDE DR 10705

The Edendale
123 VALENTINE LN 10705

The Wencrest
25 SUNNYSIDE DR 10705

Valdale
200 VALENTINE LN 10705

SYRACUSE

APARTMENTS

Almus Oliver Apt
300 BURT ST 13202

Cedar Ridge Apt
201 SEELEY RD 13224

Clinton Plz
550 S CLINTON ST 13202

Dewitt Heights
401 SMITH ST 13224

Executive Quarters
1060 E GENESEE ST 13210

Harrison House
80 PRESIDENTIAL PLZ ... 13202

Imperial Gardens Apt
989 JAMES ST 13203

Ivy Ridge Apt
100 IVY RIDGE RD 13210

James Apt
600 JAMES ST 13203

Jefferson Towers
50 PRESIDENTIAL PLZ ... 13202

Kennedy Square Apt
893 E FAYETTE ST 13210

Madison Tower
60 PRESIDENTIAL PLZ ... 13202

Mount St James
338 JAMESVILLE AVE 13210

Plaza Apt
1108 E GENESEE ST 13210

Regency Towers Apt
770 JAMES ST 13203

Remington House
103 REMINGTON AVE 13210

Ross Towers Apt
710 LODI ST 13203

Rugby Arms Apt
204 DORCHESTER AVE .. 13203

Skyline Building
753 JAMES ST 13203

Toomey Abbott
1207 ALMOND ST 13210

Townsend Towers
500 HARRISON ST 13202

BUILDINGS

1 Lincoln Center
108 W FAYETTE ST 13202

499 Building
499 S WARREN ST 13202

500 Building
500 S SALINA ST 13202

Atrium Building
2 CLINTON SQ 13202

Corporate Center Building
90 PRESIDENTIAL PLZ ... 13202

Empire Building
472 S SALINA ST 13202

Gridley Building
103 E WATER ST 13202

Hills Building
217 MONTGOMERY ST ... 13202

Jefferson Building
204 E JEFFERSON ST 13202

Kemper Building
224 HARRISON ST 13202

Lafayette Building
210 E FAYETTE ST 13202

Loew Building
108 W JEFFERSON ST 13202

Medical Plaza
407 UNIVERSITY AVE 13210

Monroe Building
333 E ONONDAGA ST 13202

Mony II
120 MADISON ST 13202

Mony Plaza
100 MADISON ST 13202

Onondaga Plaza
217 S SALINA ST 13202

Powelson Building
400 MONTGOMERY ST ... 13202

Presidential Plz Med Building
600 E GENESEE ST 13202

Romax Building
731 JAMES ST 13203

State Tower Building
109 S WARREN ST 13202

Syracuse Building
224 HARRISON ST 13202

University Building
120 E WASHINGTON ST .. 13202

White Memorial Building
100 E WASHINGTON ST .. 13202

Wilson Building
306 S SALINA ST 13202

GOVERNMENT

City Hall
233 E WASHINGTON ST .. 13202

Civic Center
421 MONTGOMERY ST ... 13202

County Court House
401 MONTGOMERY ST ... 13202

Onondaga County Office Bl
600 S STATE ST 13202

Public Safety Building
511 S STATE ST 13202

State Office Building
333 E WASHINGTON ST .. 13202

UTICA

APARTMENTS

Academy At Southgate
10 FOERY DR 13501

Brandegee Garden Apts
827 JAY ST 13501

Chancellor Apts
417 BLEECKER ST 13501

Georgian Ct Apts
2410 ONEIDA ST 13501

Historical Pk Apts
100 RUTGER ST 13501

Holland House Apts
1629 GENESEE ST 13501

Knamm Apts
33 SCOTT ST 13501

Macratovin Apts
7 DEVEREUX ST 13501

Marino Ruggiero Apts
415 BLEECKER ST 13501

Matt Apart
1790 ARMORY DR 13501

N D Peters Manor
1600 ARMORY DR 13501

Obilston Apts
1431 GENESEE ST 13501

Ropewalk Apts
1427 ONEIDA ST 13501

Six Nations Apts
601 JAY ST 13501

Steinhorst Sq Apts
612 SOUTH ST 13501

Twin Towers
509 2ND ST 13501

Woodside Apts
2400 ONEIDA ST 13501

BUILDINGS

Alexander Pirnie Fed Building
10 BROAD ST 13501

Bankers Trust Building
185 GENESEE ST 13501

Mayro Building
239 GENESEE ST 13501

Paul Building
209 ELIZABETH ST 13501

Security Building
124 BLEECKER ST 13501

Union Station Building
321 MAIN ST 13501

GOVERNMENT

County Office Building
800 PARK AVE 13501

NYS Parkway Armory
1700 PARKWAY E 13501

Oneida County Court House
200 ELIZABETH ST 13501

State Office Building
207 GENESEE ST 13501

COLLEGES

Suny College
3050 PO BOX 13504

WHITE PLAINS

APARTMENTS

Alex Hamilton
5 FRANKLIN AVE 10601

Benjamin Franklin
1 BROAD PKY 10601

Broad Park Lodge
292 MAIN ST 10601

Grant House
235 S LEXINGTON AVE ... 10606

Harding Terrace
98 HARDING AVE 10606

Prospect Terrace
14 SOUNDVIEW AVE 10606

The Brentwood
300 MAIN ST 10601

The Winton
210 MARTINE AVE 10601

Tompkins Manor
505 CENTRAL PARK AVE 10606

Tower Club
76 S LEXINGTON AVE 10606

Westbrook
10 FRANKLIN AVE 10601

White Swan
1 S BROADWAY 10601

BUILDINGS

County Center
198 CENTRAL PARK AVE 10606

Galleria Mall
100 MAIN ST 10601

Northcourt
175 MAIN ST 10601

White Plains Plaza
1 N BROADWAY 10601

GOVERNMENT

County Courthouse
111 GROVE ST 10601

Michalean Office Building
148 MARTINE AVE 10601

YONKERS

APARTMENTS

Arden House
300 N BROADWAY 10701

Crest Manor
377 N BROADWAY 10701

Greystone
1100 WARBURTON AVE .. 10701

Hudson House
632 WARBURTON AVE 10701

Jefferson Terrace
108 JEFFERSON ST 10701

Phillips Towers
100 RIVERDALE AVE 10701

Phillipse Towers
80 RIVERDALE AVE 10701

River Towers II
615 WARBURTON AVE 10701

Rye Towers
270 N BROADWAY 10701

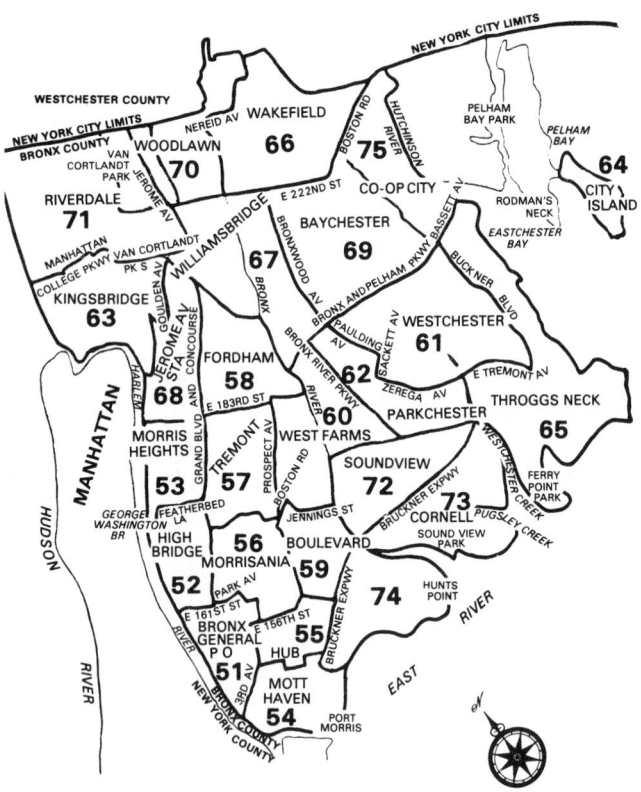

ZIP CODES

BRONX, NY

104 + TWO DIGITS SHOWN = ZIP CODE

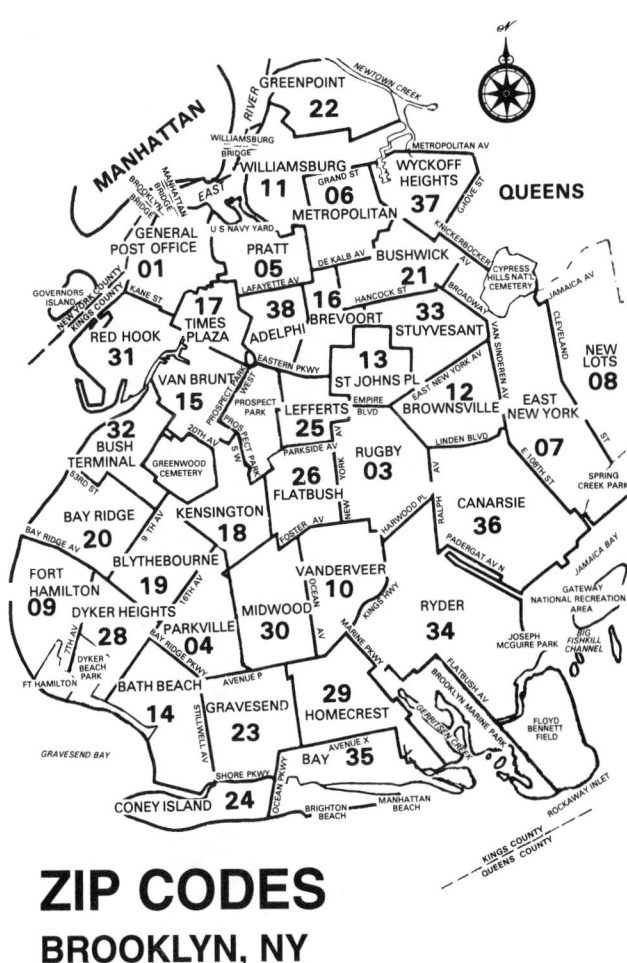

ZIP CODES

BROOKLYN, NY

112 + TWO DIGITS SHOWN = ZIP CODE

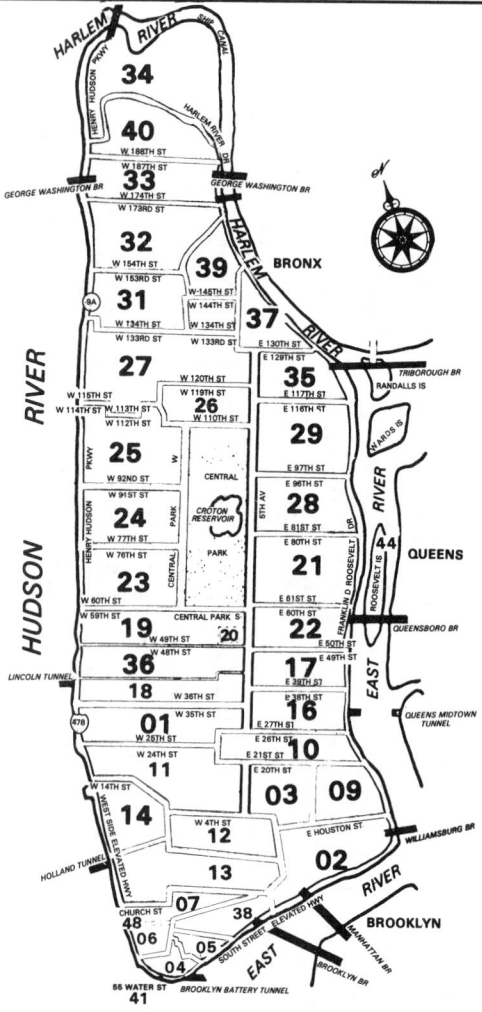

ZIP CODES

MANHATTAN, NY
100 + TWO DIGITS SHOWN = ZIP CODE

NORTH CAROLINA
Abbreviation NC

Aberdeen 28315
Abshers (Traphill) 28685
Acme (Riegelwood) 28456
Adams (Boone) 28607
Advance 27006
Aho (Blowing Rock) 28605
Ahoskie 27910
Alamance 27201
Alarka (Bryson City) 28713
Albemarle 28001-002
   Millingport 28001
   North Albemarle 28001
   Palestine 28001
   Plyler 28001
   River Haven 28001
   South Albemarle 28001
Albertson 28508
Alexander 28701
Alexander Mills 28043
   (Forest City)
Alexis 28006
All Healing Springs 28681
   (Taylorsville)
Allen Jay (High Point) 27263
Alliance 28509
Allison (Ruffin) 27326
Almond 28702
Altamahaw 27202
Altamont (Newland) 28657
Amantha (Sugar Grove) 28679
Amity (Cleveland) 27013
Anderson (Kitty Hawk) 27949
Andrews 28901
Angier 27501
Ansonville 28007
Apex 27502
Apple Grove (Lansing) 28643
Aquadale (Norwood) 28128
Aquone 28703
Arapahoe 28510
Ararat 27007
Arcadia (Lexington) 27292
Archdale (High Point) 27263
Archers Lodge (Clayton) ... 27520
Arden 28704
Ardmore (Winston Salem) . 27103
Arlington (Jonesville) 28642
Arnold (Lexington) 27292
Ash 28420
Ash Hill (Ararat) 27007
Asheboro 27203-204
   Farmer 27203
Asheville 28800-806
   .... 28810, 28813-816
   Biltmore 28813
   Downtown 28802
   Grace 28814
   Oteen 28815
   West Asheville . 28806, 28816
Ashford (Marion) 28752
Ashland (Creston) 28615
Assembly (Lake Junaluska) 28745
Atkinson 28421
Atlantic 28511
Atlantic Beach 28512
Aulander 27805
Aurora 27806
Austin (Elkin) 28621

Autryville 28318
Avent Ferry (Raleigh) 27606
Avon 27915
Ayden 28513
Aydlett 27916
Ayersville (Mayodan) 27027
Badin 28009
Bagley (Kenly) 27542
Bahama 27503
Bailey 27807
Bakersville 28705
Baldwin (West Jefferson) .. 28694
Ball (Lansing) 28643
Balm (Banner Elk) 28604
Balsam 28707
Balsam Grove 28708
Bamboo (Blowing Rock) ... 28605
Banner Elk 28604, 28691
   Balm 28604
   Beech Mountain 28604
   Elk Valley 28604
   Foscoe 28604
   Grandfather 28604
   Kellersville 28604
   Matney 28604
   Norwood Hollow 28604
   Rominger 28604
   White Rock 28604
Barber 27008
Barco 27917
Barium Springs 28010
Barnardsville 28709
Barnesville 28319
Barrett (Ennice) 28623
Barriers Mill 28124
   (Mount Pleasant)
Bat Cave 28710
Bath 27808
Baton (Granite Falls) 28630
Battleboro 27809
Bayboro 28515
Bear Creek 27207
Bear Poplar (Mount Ulla) .. 28125
Beaufort 28516
Beaver Creek 28694
   (West Jefferson)
Bee Log (Burnsville) 28714
Beech Bottom (Newland) .. 28657
Beech Creek 28679
   (Sugar Grove)
Beech Mountain 28604
   (Banner Elk)
Belew Creek 27009
   (Belews Creek)
Belews Creek 27009
Belhaven 27810
Bellarthur 27811
Bells Cross Roads 28166
   (Troutman)
Belmont 28012
Belvidere 27919
Belwood (Lawndale) 28090
Benham (Elkin) 28621
Bennett 27208
Benson 27504
Bermuda Run (Advance) .. 27006
Bessemer City 28016
Bethabara (Winston Salem) 27106
Bethania 27010
Bethel 27812, 28692
Bethlehem (Hickory) 28601

Beulaville 28518
Biggs Park (Lumberton) 28358
Biltmore (Asheville) 28813
Biscoe 27209
Bixby (Advance) 27006
Black Creek 27813
Black Mountain 28711
Blackburn (Newton) 28658
Bladenboro 28320
Blanch 27212
Blounts Creek 27814
Blowing Rock 28605
Bluff (Hot Springs) 28743
Bly (Lansing) 28643
Boger City (Lincolnton) 28092
Boiling Springs 28017, 28461
Bolivia 28422
Bolton 28423
Bonlee 27213
Bonnie Doone 28303
   (Fayetteville)
Boogertown (Gastonia) 28052
Boomer 28606
Boone 28607-608
Boonville 27011
Bostic 28018
Boulevard (Eden) 27288
Bowdens (Warsaw) 28398
Bradfords Cross Roads 28677
   (Statesville)
Brandon (Lansing) 28643
Branon (Yadkinville) 27055
Brasstown 28902
Brevard 28712
Bridgeton 28519
Bridgewater (Morganton) .. 28655
Brightwood 27214
   (Browns Summit)
Brindle Town (Morganton) . 28655
Broadway 27505
Brook Cove (Walnut Cove) 27052
Brooks Cross Roads 27020
   (Hamptonville)
Brown Mountain Beach 28645
   (Lenoir)
Browns Summit 27214
Brownwood (Todd) 28684
Broyhill Furniture 28633
   (Lenoir)
Brumnage Creek 28740
   (Greenmountain)
Brunswick 28424
Bryson City 28713
Buck Shoals 27020
   (Hamptonville)
Buckhorn (Efland) 27243
Buffalo Cove (Lenoir) 28645
Buies Creek 27506
Bullock 27507
Bunn 27508
Bunnlevel 28323
Burch (Elkin) 28621
Burgaw 28425
Burkemont (Morganton) 28655
Burlington 27215-217
   Glen Raven 27215
   Kayser Roth 27220
Burningtown (Franklin) 28734
Burnsville 28135, 28714
   (Polkton)
   Bee Log 28714

Busick (Browns Summit) ... 27214
Butner 27509
Butters 28324
Buxton 27920
Bynum 27228
Calabash 28459, 28467
(Shallotte)
Caldwell (Huntersville) 28078
Call (North Wilkesboro) 28659
Calvin (Morganton) 28655
Calypso 28325
Camden 27921
Cameron 28326
Cameron Village (Raleigh) .. 27605
Camp Lejeune 28542, 28547
Jacksonville 28542
Lejeune 28542
Camp Springs (Reidsville) .. 27320
Canden (Candor) 27229
Candler 28715
Candor 27229
Canton 28716
Cape Carteret 28584
(Swansboro)
Cape Fear (Wilmington) 28401
Carbonton (Sanford) 27330
Caroleen 28019
Carolina Beach 28428
Carolina Hills (Fletcher) 28732
Carpenter Bottom 28652
(Minneapolis)
Carrboro 27510
Carthage 28327
Cartoogechaye (Franklin) . 28734
Cary 27511-513, 27518-519
Casar 28020
Cashiers 28717
Castalia 27816
Castle Hayne 28429
Casville (Ruffin) 27326
Caswell Beach 28465
(Oak Island)
Catawba 28609
Catawba Heights (Belmont) 28012
Cedar Falls 27230
Cedar Grove 27231
Cedar Island 28520
Cedar Mountain 28718
Cedar Valley (Lenoir) 28645
Celeste Hinkle 28677
(Statesville)
Center (Yadkinville) 27055
Centerview (Kannapolis) ... 28081
Cerro Gordo 28430
Chadbourn 28431
Champion (Ferguson) 28624
Chapel Hill ... 27514-516, 27599
Charles (Statesville) 28677
Charlotte . 28200-237, 28241-247
.... 28250, 28253-256, 28258
.... 28260-262, 28265-266
.... 28269-270, 28272-275
.... 28277-78, 28280-290
.... 28294, 28296-297, 28299
Cameron Brown 28296
Mint Hill 28227
Cherokee 28719
Cherry Lane 28627
(Glade Valley)
Cherry Point 28533
Cherrygrove (Reidsville) ... 27320

Cherryville 28021
Chesterfield (Morganton) .. 28655
Chestnut Dale (Newland) .. 28657
Chestnut Hill (Crumpler) ... 28617
Chimney Rock 28720
China Grove 28023
Chinquapin 28521
Chocowinity 27817
Churchland (Lexington) 27292
Claremont 28610
Clarendon 28432
Clarkton 28433
Clayton 27520
Clemmons 27012
Cleveland 27013
Cleveland Springs 28150
(Shelby)
Cliffdale (Bostic) 28018
Cliffside 28024
Clifton (Warrensville) 28693
Climax 27233
Clinchcross (Marion) 28752
Clingman (Ronda) 28670
Clinton 28328
Clyde 28721
Coats 27521
Cofield 27922
Coinjock 27923
Colerain 27924
Coleridge (Ramseur) 27316
Colfax 27235
College (Durham) 27708
Collettsville 28611
Collington (Kitty Hawk) 27949
Colon (Sanford) 27330
Columbia 27925
Columbus 28722
Comet (Lansing) 28643
Comfort 28522
Como 27818
Concord 28025-027
Flowes Store 28025
North Concord 28025
Sidestown 28025
Conetoe 27819
Connellys Springs 28612
Conover 28613
Conway 27820
Cool Spring (Cleveland) 27013
Cooleemee 27014
Copeland (Dobson) 27017
Corapeake 27926
Cordova 28330
Corinth (Bostic) 28018
Cornelius 28031,28036, 28078
Smithville 28031
Corolla 27927
Correll Park (Salisbury) 28144
Cotton Grove (Lexington) .. 27292
Cottonville (Norwood) 28128
Council 28434
Country Park Acres 27408
(Greensboro)
Countyline (Harmony) 28634
Courtney (Yadkinville) 27055
Cove City 28523
Cowee (Franklin) 28734
Crabtree Valley (Raleigh) .. 27612
Cramerton 28032
Cranberry 28614
Cranberry Gap (Newland) . 28657

Creedmoor 27522, 27564
Northside 27522, 27564
Creston 28615
Creswell 27928
Cricket 28659
(North Wilkesboro)
Crisp (Macclesfield) 27852
Cross Mill (Marion) 28752
Crossnore 28616
Crouse 28033
Crowders (Gastonia) 28052
Crumpler 28617
Culberson 28903
Cullasaja (Franklin) 28734
Cullowhee 28723
Cumberland 28331
Cumnock 27237
Currie 28435
Currituck 27929
Cycle (Hamptonville) 27020
Dallas 28034
Dalton (Pinnacle) 27043
Dana 28724
Danbury 27016
Daniels-rhyne 28092
(Lincolnton)
Darby (Ferguson) 28624
Darkridge (Elk Park) 28622
Davidson 28036
Davis 28524
Deep Gap 28618
Deep River (High Point) 27260
Deep Run 28525
Deerfield (Boone) 28607
Dehart (Hays) 28635
Delco 28436
Delight (Lawndale) 28090
Denny (Ferguson) 28624
Denton 27239
Denver 28037
Devotion (Dobson) 27017
Dillsboro 28725
Dimmette (Ronda) 28670
Dobbinsville (Ellenboro) ... 28040
Dobson 27017
Dockery (Traphill) 28685
Dolinger (Lansing) 28643
Doolie (Mooresville) 28115
Doran (Shelby) 28150
Dortches (Rocky Mount) ... 27801
Dosier (Pfafftown) 27040
Double Island 28740
(Greenmountain)
Double Shoals (Lawndale) . 28090
Doughton (Thurmond) 28683
Dover 28526
Downtown (Asheville) 28802
Draco (Lenoir) 28645
Drake (Battleboro) 27809
Draper (Eden) 27288
Drexel 28619
Duan (Newton) 28658
Dublin 28332
Dudley 28333
Dudley Shoals 28630
(Granite Falls)
Duke (Durham) 27706, 27708
Duncan (Fuquay Varina) ... 27526
Dunn 28334-335
Duraleigh (Raleigh) 27612
Durants Neck 27930, 27944

Hertford	27930	
Durham	27700-713, 27715	
	27717,27722	
Duke University		
	27706, 27708, 27710	
East P A	27711	
Eno Valley	27712	
North Durham	27712	
Research Triangle Park	27709	
Shannon Plaza	27707, 27713	
Eagle (Hamptonville)	27020	
Eagle Rock	27523	
Eagle Springs	27242	
Earl	28038	
East Bend	27018	
East Fayetteville	28301	
(Fayetteville)		
East Flat Rock	28726	
East Franklin (Franklin)	28734	
East Lake (Manns Harbor)	27953	
East Laport (Cullowhee)	28723	
East Laurinburg	28352	
(Laurinburg)		
East Marion (Marion)	28752	
East Monbo (Statesville)	28677	
East Spencer	28039	
Eastover (Fayetteville)	28301	
Eden	27288-289	
Boulevard	27288	
Draper	27288	
Leaksville	27288	
Meadow Summit	27288	
New Leaksville	27288	
Spray	27288	
Edenton	27932	
Edgemont (Lenoir)	28645	
Edneyville	28727	
Edward	27821	
Edwards Crossroads	28675	
(Sparta)		
Efland	27243	
Ela (Bryson City)	28713	
Elizabeth City	27906-907, 27909	
Elizabethtown	28337	
Elk Park	28622	
Elk Valley (Banner Elk)	28604	
Elkin	28621	
Ellenboro	28040	
Ellendale (Taylorsville)	28681	
Eller (Winston Salem)	27107	
Ellerbe	28338	
Ellijay (Franklin)	28734	
Ellisboro (Madison)	27025	
Elm City	27822	
Elmwood (Statesville)	28677	
Elon College	27244	
Emerald Isle	28594	
Emerson (Clarkton)	28433	
Emerywood (High Point)	27262	
Emit (Middlesex)	27557	
Enfield	27823	
Engelhard	27824	
Enka	28728	
Ennice	28623	
Enola (Morganton)	28655	
Eno Valley	27712	
Enterprise (Lexington)	27292	
Erastus (Cullowhee)	28723	
Ernul	28527	
Erwin	28339	
Erwin Heights	27360	

Essex (Hollister)	27844	
Estelle (Milton)	27305	
Ether	27247	
Etowah	28729	
Eufola (Statesville)	28677	
Eure	27935	
Eureka (Fremont)	27830	
Eutaw (Fayetteville)	28303	
Everetts	27825	
Evergreen	28438	
Fair Bluff	28439	
Fairfield	27826	
Fairmont	28340	
Fairplains	28659	
(North Wilkesboro)		
Fairview	28730	
Fairview Cross Roads	27017	
(Dobson)		
Faison	28341	
Faith	28041	
Falcon	28342	
Falkland	27827	
Fallston	28042	
Farmer (Asheboro)	27203	
Farmers Store (Lansing)	28643	
Farmington (Mocksville)	27028	
Farmville	27828	
Fayetteville	28301-309	
	28311, 28314	
Bonnie Doone	28303	
East Fayetteville	28301	
Eastover	28301	
Eutaw	28303	
Haymount	28305	
Lafayette	28304	
Lakedale	28306	
Ponderosa	28303	
Vander	28301	
Fearrington Village	27312	
(Pittsboro)		
Feezor (Lexington)	27292	
Ferguson	28624	
Fig (Creston)	28615	
Finger (Mount Pleasant)	28124	
Finley (Lenoir)	28645	
Fisher Town (Kannapolis)	28081	
Five Points (Raleigh)	27608	
Flat Rock	27043, 28731	
(Pinnacle)		
Flat Springs (Elk Park)	28622	
Flay (Cherryville)	28021	
Fleetwood	28626	
Fletcher	28732	
Flint Hill (Troy)	27371	
Flowes Store (Concord)	28025	
Fontana Dam	28733	
Footsville (Yadkinville)	27055	
Forest City	28043	
Forest Oaks (Greensboro)	27406	
Fork (Advance)	27006	
Fort Barnwell (Dover)	28526	
Fort Bragg	28307	
Fort Caswell (Oak Island)	28465	
Fort Raleigh City	27954	
(Manteo)		
Foscoe (Banner Elk)	28604	
Fountain	27829	
Fountain Hill (Peachland)	28133	
Four Oaks	27524	
Foxfire (Jackson Springs)	27281	
Frank (Newland)	28657	

Franklin	28734	
Franklinton	27525	
Franklinville	27248	
Freemans Mills	27260	
(High Point)		
Fremont	27830	
Friendship (Greensboro)	27410	
Frisco	27936	
Frog Level (Forest City)	28043	
Frog Pond (Oakboro)	28129	
Frogsboro (Leasburg)	27291	
Fulp (Walnut Cove)	27052	
Fuquay Varina	27526	
Gamewell (Lenoir)	28645	
Garland	28441	
Garner	27529	
Garysburg	27831	
Gaston	27832	
Gastonia	28051-056	
Boogertown	28052	
Crowders	28052	
Groves	28052	
Pinkney	28052	
Ragan Village	28054	
Ranlo	28054	
Rex	28052	
Ridge	28052	
Smyre	28052	
South Gastonia	28052	
Spencer Mountain	28054	
Victory	28052	
West Gastonia	28052	
Gates	27937	
Gatesville	27938	
George (Woodland)	27897	
Germanton	27019	
Gerton	28735	
Gibson	28343	
Gibsonville	27249	
Gilkey (Rutherfordton)	28139	
Glade Valley	28627	
Glass (Kannapolis)	28081	
Glen Alpine	28628	
Glen Raven (Burlington)	27215	
Glendale Springs	28629	
Glendon	27251	
Glenola (High Point)	27260	
Glenville	28736	
Glenwood	28737	
Globe (Lenoir)	28645	
Gloucester	28528	
Godwin	28344	
Gold Hill	28071	
Golden (Bostic)	28018	
Golden Gate (Greensboro)	27405	
Goldsboro	27530-534	
Grantham	27530	
Patetown	27530	
Walnut Creek	27530	
Webtown	27530	
Goldston	27252	
Gordontown (Lexington)	27292	
Goshen (Wilkesboro)	28697	
Grace (Asheville)	28814	
Gragg (Lenoir)	28645	
Graham	27253	
Grandfather (Banner Elk)	28604	
Grandview Heights	28607	
(Boone)		
Grandy	27939	
Granite Falls	28630	

Mooresville 28115
Moratock (Troy) 27371
Moravian Falls 28654
Mordecai (Raleigh) 27604
Morehead City 28557
Morganton 28655, 28680
  Bridgewater 28655
  Brindle Town 28655
  Burkemont 28655
  Calvin 28655
  Chesterfield 28655
  Enola 28655
  Joy 28655
  Magnolia 28655
  Oak Hill 28655
  Petersburg 28655
  Pleasant Grove 28655
  Pumpkin Center 28655
  Salem 28655
  Sunnyside 28655
Morlan Park (Salisbury) 28144
Morrisville 27560
Mortimer (Lenoir) 28645
Morven 28119
Mount Airy 27030-031
  Round Peak 27030
  White Sulphur Springs 27030
Mount Gilead 27306
Mount Herman (Lenoir) ... 28645
Mount Holly 28120
Mount Mourne 28123
Mount Olive 28365
Mount Pleasant 27011, 27807
  (Boonville) 28124, 28657
  Barriers Mill 28124
  Finger 28124
Mount Tabor 27106
  (Winston Salem)
Mount Ulla 28125
Mount Vernon (Cleveland) 27013
Mount Zion (Greensboro) .. 27405
Mountain Home 28758
Mountain Park 28676
  (State Road)
Mountain View (Hickory) ... 28602
Moxley (Traphill) 28685
Moyock 27958
Muddy Creek 27103
  (Winston Salem)
Mulberry 28659
  (North Wilkesboro)
Murfreesboro 27855
Murphy 28906
Myers (Hays) 28635
Nags Head 27959
Nakina 28455
Naples 28760
Nashville 27856
Nathans Creek (Crumpler) 28617
Navassa (Wilmington) 28404
Nebo (Boonville) 27011, 28761
Needmore (Bryson City) ... 28713
Neuse (Raleigh) 27661
New Bern 28560-564
New Hill 27562
New House (Shelby) 28150
New Leaksville (Eden) 27288
New London 28127
New Salem (Randleman) .. 27317
Newell 28126
Newland 28657

Newlife (Hays) 28635
Newport 28570
Newsom (Denton) 27239
Newton 28658
Newton Grove 28366
Norlina 27563
Norman 28367
North (Winston Salem) 27105
North Albemarle 28001
  (Albemarle)
North Concord (Concord) .. 28025
North Cove (Marion) 28752
North Durham (Durham) ... 27712
North Elkin (Elkin) 28621
North Hills 27609, 27614
  (Raleigh)
North Wilkesboro ... 28656, 28659
  28674
  Call 28659
  Cricket 28659
  Fairplains 28659
  Hunting Creek 28659
  Lowes Co Inc 28656
  Mulberry 28659
  Quarry 28659
  Spurgeon 28659
  Windy Gap 28659
Northside 27522, 27564
  (Creedmoor)
Norton (Cullowhee) 28723
Norwood 28128
Norwood Hollow 28604
  (Banner Elk)
Oak City 27857
Oak Grove 28086
  (Kings Mountain)
Oak Hill (Lenoir) ... 28645, 28655
Oak Island 28461, 28465
  (Southport)
  Caswell Beach 28465
  Fort Caswell 28465
  Long Beach 28465
  Yaupon Beach 28465
Oak Park (Arden) 28704
Oak Ridge 27310
Oakboro 28129
Oakdale 27282, 28677
  (Jamestown)
Ocean Isle Beach ... 28459, 28469
  (Shallotte)
Ocono Lufty (Cherokee) 28719
Ocracoke 27960
Ogden (Wilmington) 28405
Okeewemee (Troy) 27371
Old Fort 28762
Old Sparta (Macclesfield) .. 27852
Olde Farm (Spring Lake) .. 28390
Oldtown (Winston Salem) . 27106
Olin 28660
Olive Branch (Marshville) .. 28103
Olivers Crossroads 28658
  (Newton)
Olivette (Lenoir) 28645
Olivia 28368
Ophir (Troy) 27711
Oregon Hill (Ruffin) 27326
Oriental 28571
Orion (Jefferson) 28640
Orrum 28369
Osbornville (Union Grove) 28689
Osceola (Browns Summit) 27214

Osgood (Sanford) 27330
Osmond (Leasburg) 27291
Ossipee (Elon College) 27244
Oteen (Asheville) 28815
Otto 28763
Overhills (Cameron) 28326
Oxford 27565
Pactolus (Greenville) 27834
Paint Rock (Hot Springs) .. 28743
Palestine (Albemarle) 28001
Palmyra 27859
Pantego 27860
Parker (Creston) 28615
Parks Crossroads 27316
  (Ramseur)
Parkton 28371
Parkview (Kinston) 28503
Parmele 27861
Parsonville (Purlear) 28665
Patetown (Goldsboro) 27530
Patterson 28661
Patterson Springs 28150
  (Shelby)
Paw Creek 28130
Paynes Store 28681
  (Taylorsville)
Peace Haven Estates 27104
  (Winston Salem)
Peachland 28133
Peden (Scottville) 28672
Pelham 27311
Pembroke 28372
Pendleton 27862
Penland 28765
Penrose 28766
Peoria (Sugar Grove) 28679
Perch (Pinnacle) 27043
Perkinsville (Boone) 28607
Petersburg (Morganton) ... 28655
Petersville (Lexington) 27292
Pfafftown 27040
Pikeville 27863
Pilot Mountain 27041
Pine Hall 27042
Pine Knoll (Hope Mills) 28348
Pine Knoll Shores 28512
  (Atlantic Beach)
Pine Level 27568
Pine View (Sanford) 27330
Pinebluff 28373
Pinehurst 28374
Pineola 28662
Pinetops 27864
Pinetown 27865
Pineville 28134
Piney Creek 28663
Pink Hill 28572
Pinkney (Gastonia) 28052
Pinnacle 27043
Pisgah Forest 28768
Pittsboro (Bynum) .. 27228, 27312
  Fearrington Village 27312
Plaza (Greensboro) 27408
Pleasant Gap 28740
  (Greenmountain)
Pleasant Garden 27313
Pleasant Gardens (Marion) 28752
Pleasant Grove 28655
  (Morganton)
Pleasant Hill 27866, 28621
Plumtree 28664

Plyler (Albemarle) 28001
Plymouth 27962
Point Harbor 27964
Polkton 28135
Polkville 28136
Pollocksville 28573
Ponderosa (Fayetteville) ... 28303
Pooletown (Richfield) 28137
Porter (Norwood) 28128
Portsmouth (Ocracoke) ... 27960
Potecasi 27867
Powells Point 27966
Powells Store (Ruffin) 27326
Powellsville 27967
Prentiss (Franklin) 28734
Price (Stoneville) 27048
Princeton 27569
Proctorville 28375
Propst Crossroads 28658
    (Newton)
Prospect Hill 27314
Providence 27315, 28752
Pumpkin Center 28092, 28655
    (Lincolnton)
Purlear 28665
Pyatte (Newland) 28657
Quarry (North Wilkesboro) 28659
Queen (Troy) 27371
Quick (Ruffin) 27326
Radical (Mc Grady) 28643
Raeford (Mccain) ... 28361, 28376
Ragan Village (Gastonia) .. 28054
Raleigh 27600-615, 27619-629
    .... 27634-636, 27640, 27650
    27656, 27658, 27661, 27668
    .... 27675-676, 27690, 27695
    27697-699
    Avent Ferry 27606
    Avent Ferry Rd 27606
    Brentwood 27604
    Cameron Village 27605
    Crabtree Valley 27612
    Duraleigh 27612
    Highwoods 27625
    Mccullers 27603
    Mordecai 27604
    Neuse 27661
    North Hills ... 27609, 27614
    South Hills 27606
    State University 27607
    Tower 27610
    Wake Crossroads 27604
    Westgate 27676
    Wilders Grove 27604
Ramseur 27316
Randleman 27317
Rankin (Greensboro) 27405
Ranlo (Gastonia) 28054
Red Cross (Climax)27233, 28129
Red Oak 27868
Red Springs 28377
Reddies River (Wilbar) 28696
Redland (Advance) 27006
Reedy Creek (Lexington) .. 27292
Reese (Vilas) 28692
Reidsville 27320-323
    Burlington House 27321
    Camp Springs 27320
    Chase Packaging Inc .. 27322
    Cherrygrove 27320
    Harrison Cross Roads 27320

Midway 27320
Monroeton 27320
Relief (Greenmountain) 28740
Rex (Gastonia) 28052, 28378
Rhine (Jefferson) 28640
Rhodhiss 28667
Rhodhizz (Rhodhiss) 28667
Rich Square 27869
Richfield 28137
Richlands 28574
Richmond Hill (Boonville) .. 27011
Ridge (Gastonia) 28052
Ridgecrest 28770
Ridgefield (Greensboro) ... 27410
Ridgeway 27570
Riegelwood 28456
River Haven (Albemarle) ... 28001
Riverside (Franklin) 28734
Roanoke Rapids 27870
Roaring Creek (Newland) . 28657
Roaring Gap 28668
Roaring River 28669
Robbins 27325
Robbinsville 28771
Robersonville 27871
Rock Creek (Snow Camp) 27349
Rockford (Dobson) 27017
Rockingham 28379
Rockwell 28138
Rocky Mount 27801-804
    Dortches 27801
Rocky Point 28457
Rodanthe 27968
Roduco 27969
Rolesville 27571
Rominger (Banner Elk) 28604
Ronda 28670
Roper 27970
Rose Hill 28458
Roseboro 28382
Rosman 28772
Rougemont 27572
Round Peak (Mount Airy) .. 27030
Rowland 28383
Roxboro 27573
Roxobel 27872
Royal Oaks (Kannapolis) .. 28081
Royal Pines (Arden) 28704
Rudd (Browns Summit) 27214
Ruffin 27326
Rural Hall 27045, 27094, 27098-9
    Stanleyville 27045
Rusk (Elkin) 28621
Rutherfordton 28139
Rutherwood (Boone) 28607
Saddle (Ennice) 28623
Saint Pauls 28384
Salem (Morganton) 28655
Salemburg 28385
Salisbury 28144-147
    Correll Park 28144
    Morlan Park 28144
Salter Path 28575
Saluda 28773
Salvo 27972
Sands (Boone) 28607
Sandy Mush (Forest City) . 28043
Sandy Ridge 27046, 27235
Sanford 27237, 27330-331
    (Cumnock)
    Carbonton 27330

Colon 27330
Haw Branch 27330
Jonesboro Heights ... 27330
Osgood 27330
Pine View 27330
Shallowell 27330
Swan Station 27330
Tramway 27330
White Hill 27330
Sapphire 28774
Saratoga 27873
Saw Mills (Granite Falls) .. 28630
Saxapahaw 27340
Scaly Mountain 28775
Scotland Neck 27874
Scotts 28699
Scottville 28672
Scranton 27875
Seaboard 27876
Seagrove 27341
Sealevel 28577, 28581
Sedalia 27342
Sedgefield (Greensboro) ... 27407
Sedges Garden 27105
    (Winston Salem)
Selma 27576
Semora 27343
Senia (Newland) 28657
Setzer Gap (Lenoir) 28645
Seven Lakes (West End) .. 27376
Seven Springs 28578
Severn 27877
Sevier (Marion) 28752
Seward (Pfafftown) 27040
Shacktown (Yadkinville) ... 27055
Shady Brook (Kannapolis) 28081
Shallotte 28459, 28467-470
    Calabash 28459
    Ocean Isle Beach 28459
    South Brunswick 28459
    South Brunswick 28470
    Sunset Beach 28459
Shallowell (Sanford) 27330
Shannon 28386
Shannon Plaza 27707, 27713
Sharon (Statesville) 28677
Sharpsburg 27878
Shatley Springs 28617
    (Crumpler)
Shawboro 27973
Shelby 28150-152
    Cleveland Springs 28150
    Doran 28150
    Kingstown 28150
    New House 28150
    Patterson Springs 28150
    Swainsville 28150
Sherrills Ford 28673
Sherwood (Vilas) 28692
Shiloh 27974
Shingle Hollow 28139
    (Rutherfordton)
Shoal (Pinnacle) 27043
Shoe (Wilbar) 28696
Shulls Mills (Boone) 28607
Sidestown (Concord) 28025
Siler City 27344
Silk Hope (Siler City) 27344
Siloam 27047
Silver Valley (Lexington) .. 27292
Silverstone (Zionville) 28698

Simpson 27879
Sims 27880
Skyland 28776
Smethport 28694
(West Jefferson)
Smithfield 27577
Smithville (Cornelius) 28031
Smyre (Gastonia) 28052
Smyrna 28579
Sneads Ferry 28460
Snow Camp 27349
Snow Hill 28580
Soapstone Mountain 27355
(Staley)
Sophia 27350
Soul City (Manson) 27553
South Albemarle 28001
(Albemarle)
South Brunswick 28459, 28470
(Shallotte)
South Gastonia (Gastonia) 28052
South Greensboro 27406
(Greensboro)
South Hills (Raleigh) 27606
South Lexington 27292
(Lexington)
South Mills 27976
South Newton (Newton) 28868
Southern Pines 28387-388
Southern Shores 27949
(Kitty Hawk)
Southmont 27351
Southport 28461, 28465
Boiling Springs 28461
Oak Island 28461
Sparta 28675
Spear (Newland) 28657
Speed 27881
Speedwell (Cullowhee) 28723
Spencer 28159
Spencer Mountain 28054
(Gastonia)
Spindale 28160
Spray (Eden) 27288
Spring Creek 28743
(Hot Springs)
Spring Hope 27882
Spring Lake 28390
Spring Valley 27406
(Greensboro)
Springfield (Hays) 28635
Spruce Pine 28777
Spurgeon 28659
(North Wilkesboro)
Stacy 28581
Staley 27355
Stallings (Matthews) 28105
Stamey Branch (Newland) 28657
Stanfield 28163
Stanley 28164
Stanleyville (Rural Hall) 27045
Stantonsburg 27883
Star 27356
Startown (Newton) 28658
State Road 28676
Statesville 28677, 28687
Bradfords Cross Roads 28677
Celeste Hinkle 28677
Charles 28677
East Monbo 28677
Elmwood 28677

Eufola 28677
Loray 28677
Love Valley 28677
Oakdale 28677
Sharon 28677
West Statesville 28677
Stedman 28391
Stella 28582
Stem 27581
Stokes 27884
Stokesdale 27357
Stoneville 27048
Stonewall 28583
Stoney Creek (Whitsett) 27377
Stony Fork (Deep Gap) 28618
Stony Knoll (Dobson) 27017
Stony Point 28678
Stonycreek (Elon College) 27244
Stovall 27582
Stratford (Sparta) 28675
Stumpy Point 27978
Sturgills (Lansing) 28643
Sugar Grove 28679
Sugar Hill (Marion) 28752
Summerfield 27358
Summit 27405, 28665
(Greensboro)
Sunbury 27979
Sunnyside (Morganton) 28655
Sunset Beach 28459, 28468
(Shallotte)
Shallotte 28468
Sunset Harbor (Bolivia) 28422
Sunshine (Bostic) 28018
Supply 28462
Surf City (Holly Ridge) 28445
Sussex (Grassy Creek) 28631
Swainsville (Shelby) 28150
Swan Station (Sanford) 27330
Swancreek (Jonesville) 28642
Swannanoa 28778
Swanquarter 27885
Swansboro 28584, 28594
Cape Carteret 28584
Sweetwater (Sugar Grove) 28679
Swepsonville 27359
Sylva 28779
Tabor City 28463
Talleys Crossing 27284
(Kernersville)
Tamarack (Todd) 28684
Tapoco 28780
Tar Heel 28392
Tarawa Terrace 28543
Tarboro 27886
Tate Street (Greensboro) .. 27403
Taylorsville 28681
Teachey 28464
Tennessee Acres 27405
(Greensboro)
Terrell 28682
Theta (Jefferson) 28640
Thomasville 27360-361
Erwin Heights 27360
Three Mile (Newland) 28657
Thurmond 28683
Tillery 27887
Timberlake 27583
Toast 27049
Tobaccoville 27050
Todd 28684

Toliver (Todd) 28684
Toluca (Lawndale) 28090
Tom Creek (Marion) 28752
Topia (Scottville) 28672
Topsail Beach 28445
(Holly Ridge)
Topton 28781
Tower (Raleigh) 27610
Townsville 27584
Tramway (Sanford) 27330
Transport Clearings 28276
(Charlotte)
Traphill 28685
Treetop (West Jefferson) .. 28694
Trenton 28585
Trinity 27370
Triplett 28686
Troutman 28166
Troy 27371
Trust (Hot Springs) 28743
Tryon 28782
Tuckasegee 28783
Tuckerdale (Lansing) 28643
Turkey 28393
Turnersburg 28688
Tuxedo 28784
Twin Oaks (Sparta) 28675
Tyner 27980
Tyro (Lexington) 27292
Unaka (Murphy) 28906
UNC-Greensboro 27413
Union (Franklin) 28734
Union Cross 27284
(Kernersville)
Union Grove 28669
Union Mills 28167
Upper Pig Pen 28740
(Greenmountain)
Upton (Lenoir) 28645
Uwharie (Troy) 27371
Valdese 28690
Vale 28168
Valle Crucis 28691
Valley (Newland) 28657
Valmead (Lenoir) 28645
Vanceboro 28586
Vandalia (Greensboro) 27406
Vandemere 28587
Vander (Fayetteville) 28301
Vannoy (Wilbar) 28696
Vashti (Hiddenite) 28636
Vass 28394
Vaughan 27586
Vein Mountain (Marion) 28752
Victory (Gastonia) 28052
Vienna (Pfafftown) 27040
Viewmont (Hickory) 28601
Vilas 28692
Waco 28169
Wade 28395
Wadesboro 28170
Wadeville (Mount Gilead) .. 27306
Wagoner (Jefferson) 28640
Wagram 28396
Wake Crossroads 27604
Wake Forest 27587-588
Wakulla 28397
Walkertown 27051
Wallace 28466
Wallburg 27373
Walnut (Marshall) 28753

NORTH CAROLINA

ASHEVILLE

GOVERNMENT

Biltmore Finance Station
28813 PO BOX 28813

Grace Station
28804 PO BOX 28804

Oteen Finance Station
28815 PO BOX 28815

Pak N Post #1
4001 PO BOX 28805

Pak-n-post #2
10001 PO BOX 28806

West Asheville Station
28806 PO BOX 28806

BETHLEHEM

GOVERNMENT

City Hall
76 N CENTER ST 28601

BONNIE DOONE

APARTMENTS

Carriage Hills
2109 ELVIRA ST 28303

Georgetown Apts
3211 TALLYWOOD DR 28303

Ponderosa Apts
5501 YADKIN RD 28303

IMPORTANT BUILDINGS

The Family Lodge
243 N REILLY RD 28303

Williamsburg Apts
6465 YADKIN RD 28303

BOOGERTOWN

GOVERNMENT

Gaston Cty Admin
212 W MAIN AVE 28052

Gastonia City Hall
177 S SOUTH ST 28052

GOVERNMENT

Gaston Cty Court House
151 S SOUTH ST 28052

CAPE FEAR

APARTMENTS

Canterbury Woods
1401 CAMERON CT 28401

Cypress Grove
2 CYPRESS GROVE DR .. 28401

Summer Hill
2019 FALL DR 28401

BUILDINGS

First Union Bank Building
201 N FRONT ST 28401

Wachovia Bank Building
101 N FRONT ST 28401

Wallace Building
244 PRINCESS ST 28401

GOVERNMENT

Federal Building
2 PRINCESS ST 28401

N H Cty Adm Building
320 CHESTNUT ST 28401

GOVERNMENT

Federal Building
152 N FRONT ST 28401

CHAPEL HILL

BUILDINGS

University Mall
201 S ESTES DR 27514

CHARLOTTE

BUILDINGS

77 Executive Pk
500 ARCHDALE DR 28217

Arboretum Contract
21001 PO BOX 28277

BB&T Center
200 S TRYON ST 28202

Cameron Brown Building
301 S MCDOWELL ST 28204

Charlotte Apparel Mart
200 N COLLEGE ST 28202

Charlotte Merchandise Mar
2500 E Independence Blvd 28205

City Fair
211 N COLLEGE ST 28202

Colwick Towers
4401 COLWICK RD 28211

Commerce Ctr
129 W TRADE ST 28202

Convention Center
101 S COLLEGE ST 28202

Court Arcade
725 E TRADE ST 28202

E Independence Plaza Building
700 E STONEWALL ST 28202

Eastland Mall Office
5471 CENTRAL AVE 28212

Executive Building
623 E TRADE ST 28202

Executive Plaza
501 ARCHDALE DR 28217

First Citizens Bank Plaza
128 S TRYON ST 28202

Freedom Village Shp Ctr
2947 FREEDOM DR 28208

Gateway Center
901 W TRADE ST 28202

Home Fed Building
139 S TRYON ST 28202

Law Building
730 E TRADE ST 28202

Metroview Building
1900 RANDOLPH RD 28207

Midtown Square Mall
401 S Independence Blvd . 28204

NC Federal Center
230 S TRYON ST 28202

Park Rd Shopping Center
4201 PARK RD 28209

Park Seneca Building
1515 MOCKINGBIRD LN .. 28209

Randolph Medical Center
1928 RANDOLPH RD 28207

Southern Nat Center
200 S COLLEGE ST 28202

Southpark Mall
4400 SHARON RD 28211

Tryon Mall
4500 N TRYON ST 28213

UCB Building
212 S TRYON ST 28281

Woodlawn Green Office Pk
204 E WOODLAWN RD ... 28217

GOVERNMENT

Charlotte Meck Govt Ctr
600 E 4TH ST 28202

City Hall
600 E TRADE ST 28202

County Office Building
720 E 4TH ST 28202

Courthouse Annex
700 E TRADE ST 28202

Meck County Court House
800 E 4TH ST 28202

Meck County Office Building
700 N TRYON ST 28202

Nc State Office Building
500 W TRADE ST 28202

GOVERNMENT

Airport Station
4800 EXPRESS DR 28219

Foxcroft East Contract
4001 PO BOX 28226

One First Union Center
301 S COLLEGE ST 28202

Us Courthouse Building
401 W TRADE ST 28202

CLEVELAND SPRINGS

GOVERNMENT

Law Enforcement Ctr
100 JUSTICE PL 28150

CORRELL PARK

GOVERNMENT

Rowan County Building
402 N MAIN ST 28144

Rowan County Courthouse
210 N MAIN ST 28144

DEEP RIVER

BUILDINGS

First Factors
101 S MAIN ST 27260

International Home Furnis
210 E COMMERCE AVE ... 27260

Radio Building
164 S MAIN ST 27260

GOVERNMENT

City Municipal Building
211 S HAMILTON ST 27260

DURHAM

BUILDINGS

West Port Ctr
1725 Carpenter Fletcher ... 27713

EAST FAYETTEVILLE

BUILDINGS

Federal Building
301 GREEN ST 28301

First Citizens Bank Building
109 GREEN ST 28301

Wachovia Building
225 GREEN ST 28301

GOVERNMENT

Court House
117 DICK ST 28301

FAYETTEVILLE

APARTMENTS

Briarwood Arms
1 BRIAR CIR 28306

Colony Place
1 EMERSON CT 28306

Glendale
1100 Marlborough Rd 28304

Queen Anne
412 OAKRIDGE AVE 28305

Southwood
6541 RAEFORD RD 28304

Towers West
810 EXECUTIVE PL 28305

Treetop
910 GREENLEAF DR 28314

GREENSBORO

BUILDINGS

Federal Building
324 W MARKET ST 27401

First Union Bank
300 N GREENE ST 27401

Jefferson Standard Building
101 N ELM ST 27401

North Carolina Trust Ctr
301 N ELM ST 27401

Renaissance Plaza
230 N ELM ST 27401

Southeastern Building
102 N ELM ST 27401

Wachovia Building
201 N ELM ST 27401

HOSPITALS

Charter Hills Hosp
700 WALTER REED DR ... 27403

GREENVILLE

BUILDINGS

Hendrix Building
321 S EVANS ST 27858

Minges Building
301 S EVANS ST 27858

Pitt County Courthouse
100 W 3RD ST 27858

Wilcar Building
223 W 10TH ST 27834

GOVERNMENT

Federal Building
215 S EVANS ST 27858

JACKSONVILLE

APARTMENTS

Azalea Garden
904 GUM BRANCH RD 28540

Brynn Marr Village
300 VILLAGE DR 28546

Hinson Arms Apts
1230 RICHLANDS HWY ... 28540

MCCULLERS

BUILDINGS

Albemarle Building
325 N SALISBURY ST 27603

Caswell Building
200 W JONES ST 27603

Cooper Building
225 N MCDOWELL ST 27603

Cotton Building
222 N DAWSON ST 27603

Dobbs Building
430 N SALISBURY ST 27603

Elks Building
121 W JONES ST 27603

Legislative Office Building
300 N SALISBURY ST 27603

Old Education Building
116 W EDENTON ST 27603

Randall Building
831 W MORGAN ST 27603

Shore Memorial Building
214 W JONES ST 27603

HOSPITALS

Dorothea Dix Hospital
820 S BOYLAN AVE 27603

MONROE

GOVERNMENT

Court House
500 N MAIN ST 28112

MORDECAI

BUILDINGS

Archdale Building
512 N SALISBURY ST 27604

NEW BERN

APARTMENTS

Colony Village
3000 BRUNSWICK AVE ... 28562

Fox Chase Village
2821 NEUSE BLVD 28562

Robins Nest Apts
1425 RED ROBIN LN 28562

GOVERNMENT

Federal Building
415 MIDDLE ST 28560

PEACE HAVEN ESTATES

BUILDINGS

One Piedmont Plaza
1920 W 1ST ST 27104

Two Piedmont Plaza
2000 W 1ST ST 27104

RALEIGH

BUILDINGS

Archives-library
109 E JONES ST 27601

Bath Building
306 N WILMINGTON ST ... 27601

Highway Building
1 S WILMINGTON ST 27601

Justice Building
2 E MORGAN ST 27601

Revenue Building
2 S SALISBURY ST 27601

Ruffin Building
1 W MORGAN ST 27601

GOVERNMENT

Agriculture Building
2 W EDENTON ST 27601

Labor Building
4 W EDENTON ST 27601

Nc Legislature
16 W JONES ST 27601

WILMINGTON

APARTMENTS

Campus Edge
450 RACINE DR 28403

Chateau Terrace
1201 COLUMBUS CIR 28403

Clear Run
5362 NEW CENTRE DR ... 28403

College Acres
4863 College Acres Dr 28403

College Green
820 N MACMILLAN AVE ... 28403

College Manor
4601 FILLMORE DR 28403

Colonial Parke
5034 HUNT CLUB RD 28403

Fountain Head
601 PLUM NEARLY LN 28403

Governours Square
3330 S COLLEGE RD 28412

Mill Creek
401 MILL CREEK CT 28403

University Arms
4901 PEPYS LN 28403

University Place
902 N MACMILLAN AVE ... 28403

WINSTON SALEM

BUILDINGS

First Union Bank
310 W 4TH ST 27101

Ncnb Building
102 W 3RD ST 27101

One Triad Park
200 W 2ND ST 27101

Reynolds
401 N MAIN ST 27101

Wachovia Building
301 N MAIN ST 27101

GOVERNMENT

Courthouse
1 W 3RD ST 27101

Federal Building
251 N MAIN ST 27101

Hall Of Justice
200 N MAIN ST 27101

NORTH DAKOTA
Abbreviation ND

Abercrombie 58001
Absaraka 58002
Adams 58210
Adrian (Montpelier) 58472
Agate 58310
Alamo 58830
Alexander 58831
Alfred 58411
Alice 58003
Alkabo (Grenora) 58845
Almont 58520
Alsen 58311
Ambrose 58833
Amenia 58004
Amidon 58620
Anamoose 58710
Aneta 58212
Antler 58711
Appam (Alamo) 58830
Apple Valley (Menoken) 58558
Ardoch 58213
Arena 58412
Argusville 58005
Armourdale (Rocklake) 58365
Arnegard 58835
Arthur 58006
Arvilla 58214
Ashley 58413
Aurelia (Donnybrook) 58734
Aylmer (Anamoose) 58710
Ayr 58007
Backoo (Walhalla) 58282
Baker (York) 58386
Baldwin 58521
Balfour 58712
Balta 58313
Bantry 58713
Barlow (Carrington) 58421
Barney 58008
Bartlett (Lakota) 58344
Barton 58315
Bathgate 58216
Battleview (Powers Lake) . 58773
Beach 58621
Belcourt 58316
Belden (Stanley) 58784
Belfield 58622
Benedict 58716
Bentley (New Leipzig) 58562
Bergen (Voltaire) 58792
Berlin 58415
Berthold 58718
Berwick (Towner) 58788
Beulah 58523
Binford 58416
Bisbee 58317
Bismarck 58501-502
.... 58504-507
     Lincoln 58504
     Livona 58504
Blaisdell (Berthold) 58718
Blanchard 58009
Bloom (Jamestown) 58401
Blue Grass (New Salem) .. 58563
Bonetraill (Williston) 58801
Bordulac (Carrington) 58421
Bottineau 58318
Bowbells 58721

Coteau 58721
Bowdon 58418
Bowesmont (Drayton) 58225
Bowman 58623
Braddock 58524
Brampton (Cogswell) 58017
Brantford (New Rockford) . 58356
Breien (Solen) 58570
Bremen 58319
Briarwood (Fargo) 58104
Brinsmade 58320
Brisbane (Carson) 58529
Brocket 58321
Buchanan 58420
Bucyrus (Hettinger) 58639
Buffalo 58011
Buffalo Springs (Bowman) 58623
Buford (Williston) 58801
Burlington 58722
Burnstad (Wishek) 58495
Burt (Mott) 58646
Butte 58723
Buxton 58218
Caledonia 58219
Calio (Munich) 58352
Calvin 58323
Cando 58324
Cannon Ball 58528
Carbury (Souris) 58783
Carpio 58725
Carrington 58421
Carson 58529
Cartwright 58838
Casselton 58012
Cathay 58422
Cavalier 58220
Cayuga 58013
Center 58530
Chaffee 58014
Charbonneau (Alexander) . 58831
Charlson (New Town) 58763
Chaseley 58423
Christine 58015
Churchs Ferry 58325
Clementsville (Wimbledon) 58492
Cleveland 58424
Clifford 58016
Clifton (Martin) 58758
Clyde (Munich) 58352
Cogswell 58017
Coleharbor 58531
Colfax 58018
Colgan (Fortuna) 58844
Colgate (Hope) 58046
Columbus 58727
Concrete (Cavalier) 58220
Conway (Forest River) 58233
Cooperstown 58425
Corinth (Alamo) 58830
Coteau (Bowbells) 58721
Coulee (Kenmare) 58746
Courtenay 58426
Crary 58327
Crete (Gwinner) 58040
Crocus (Rocklake) 58365
Crosby 58730
Crystal 58222
Cummings 58223
Dahlen 58224
Danzig (Ashley) 58413
Davenport 58021

Dawson 58428
Dazey 58429
Deering 58731
Delamere (Milnor) 58060
Denbigh (Towner) 58788
Denhoff 58430
Des Lacs 58733
Devils Lake 58301
Dickey 58431
Dickinson 58601-602
     Lehigh 58601
     New Hradec 58601
Dodge 58625
Donnybrook 58734
Douglas 58735
Dover (Carrington) 58421
Doyon 58328
Drake 58736
Drayton 58225
Driscoll 58532
Dunn Center 58626
Dunning (Maxbass) 58760
Dunseith 58329
Durbin (Mapleton) 58059
Dwight (Wahpeton) 58075
Eagles Nest (Glen Ullin) ... 58631
Eckelson 58432
Eckman (Maxbass) 58760
Edgeley 58433
Edinburg 58227
Edmore 58330
Edmunds (Pingree) 58476
Egeland 58331
Eldridge (Jamestown) 58401
Elgin 58533
Ellendale 58436
Elliott (Lisbon) 58054
Embden (Wheatland) 58079
Emerado 58228
Emmet (Garrison) 58540
Emrick (Cathay) 58422
Enderlin 58027
Englevale (Fort Ransom) .. 58033
Epping 58843
Erie58029
Esmond 58332
Fairdale 58229
Fairfield 58627
Fairmount 58030
Falkirk (Washburn) 58577
Fallon (Flasher) 58535
Fargo 58102-109
.... 58121-24, 58126
     Briarwood 58104
     Frontier 58104
     North River 58102
     Prairie Rose 58104
     Reilies Acres 58102
Fessenden 58438
Fillmore (Esmond) 58332
Fingal 58031
Finley 58230
Flasher 58535
Flaxton 58737
Flora (Maddock) 58348
Fonda (Rolette) 58366
Forbes 58439
Fordville 58231
Forest River 58233
Forman 58032
Fort Clark (Center) 58530

Moffit 58560	Raleigh 58564	Stirum 58069
Mohall 58761	Raub (Ryder) 58779	Strasburg 58573
Monango 58471	Rawson (Alexander) 58831	Straubville (Cogswell) 58017
Montpelier 58472	Ray58849	Streeter 58483
Mooreton 58061	Reeder 58649	Surrey 58785
Moscow (Alsen) 58311	Regan 58477	Sutton 58484
Mott 58646	Regent 58650	Sydney (Jamestown) 58401
Mountain 58262	Reiles Acres (Fargo) 58102	Sykeston 58486
Munich 58352	Revere (Hannaford) 58448	Tagus (Berthold) 58718
Munster (New Rockford) ... 58356	Reynolds 58275	Tappen 58487
Mylo 58353	Rhame 58651	Taylor 58656
Nanson (Rolette) 58366	Rhoades (Grassy Butte) 58634	Temple (Tioga) 58852
Napoleon 58561	Richardton 58652	Temvik (Linton) 58552
Nash (Grafton) 58237	Riverdale 58565	Thompson 58278
Neche 58265	Riverside (West Fargo) 58078	Thorne (Rolette) 58366
Nekoma 58355	Robinson 58478	Timmer (Solen) 58570
Nelvik (Ashley) 58413	Rocklake 58365	Tioga 58852
New England 58647	Rogers 58479	Tokio 58379
New Hradec (Dickinson) ... 58601	Rolette 58366	Tolley 58787
New Leipzig 58562	Rolla 58367	Tolna 58380
New Rockford 58356	Rose Hill (Carrington) 58421	Tower City 58071
New Salem 58563	Roseglen 58775	Towner 58788
New Town 58763	Ross 58776	Trenton 58853
Newburg 58762	Roth (Souris) 58783	Trotters 58657
Newtown (New Town) 58763	Round Prairie (Williston) ... 58801	Turtle Lake 58575
Niagara 58266	Rugby 58368	Tuttle 58488
Niobe (Kenmare) 58746	Ruso 58778	Twin Buttes (Halliday) 58636
Nome 58062	Russell (Newburg) 58762	Underwood 58576
Noonan 58765	Ruthville (Minot) 58701	Upham 58789
Norma (Kenmare) 58746	Rutland 58067	Urbana (Spiritwood) 58481
North River (Fargo) 58102	Ryder 58779	Valley City 58072
Northgate (Flaxton) 58737	Saint Anthony 58566	Velva 58790
Northwood 58267	Saint Gertrude (Raleigh) ... 58564	Venturia 58489
Nortonville (Jud) 58454	Saint John 58369	Verona 58490
Norwich 58768	Saint Michael 58370	Voltaire 58792
Oakes 58474	Saint Thomas 58276	Voss (Minto) 58261
Oberon 58357	San Haven (Dunseith) 58329	Wabek (Plaza) 58771
Omemee (Willow City) 58384	Sanborn 58480	Wahpeton 58074-076
Ops (Forest River) 58233	Sanger (Center) 58530	Dwight 58075
Oriska 58063	Sanish (New Town) 58763	Galchutt 58075
Orr (Inkster) 58244	Sarles 58372	Walcott 58077
Orrin 58359	Saundersville (Harvey) 58341	Wales 58281
Osnabrock 58269	Sawyer 58781	Walhalla 58282
Ostby (Willow City) 58384	Schefield (New England) .. 58647	Walum (Hannaford) 58448
Overly 58360	Scranton 58653	Wano (Edgeley) 58433
Oxbow (Horace) 58047	Selfridge 58568	Warren (Davenport) 58021
Page 58064	Selz (Harvey) 58341	Warsaw (Minto) 58261
Palermo 58769	Sentinel (Sentinel Butte) ... 58654	Warwick 58381
Park River 58270	Sentinel Butte 58654	Washburn 58577
Parshall 58770	Sharon 58277	Watford City 58854
Pekin 58361	Sheldon 58068	Webster 58382
Pembina 58271	Shepard (Cooperstown) 58425	Wellsburg (Harvey) 58341
Penn 58362	Sherwood 58782	Werner (Halliday) 58636
Perth 58363	Sheyenne 58374	West Fargo 58078
Petersburg 58272	Shields 58569	Westby (Grenora) 58845
Pettibone 58475	Sibley (Dazey) 58429	Westfield (Hague) 58542
Pick City (Hazen) 58545	Silva (Rugby) 58368	Westhope 58793
Pickardville (Mc Clusky) ... 58463	Simcoe (Granville) 58741	Wheatland 58079
Pillsbury 58065	Solen 58570	Wheelock (Ray) 58849
Pingree 58476	Souris 58783	White Earth 58794
Pisek 58273	South Heart 58655	White Shield (Garrison) 58540
Plaza 58771	South Prairie (Minot) 58701	Whitman (Michigan) 58259
Pleasant Lake (Rugby) 58368	Southam (Crary) 58327	Wild Rice (Horace) 58047
Porcupine (Shields) 58569	Spencer (Kenmare) 58746	Wildrose 58795
Portal 58772	Spiritwood 58481	Williston 58801-802
Portland 58274	Springbrook (Epping) 58843	Bonetraill 58801
Powers Lake 58773	Stanley 58784	Buford 58801
Prairie Rose (Fargo) 58104	Stanton 58571	Round Prairie 58801
Prairieview (Max) 58759	Starkweather 58377	Willow City 58384
Price (Center) 58530	Steele 58482	Wilton 58579
Prosper (Harwood) 58042	Sterling 58572	Wimbledon 58492

Windsor (Cleveland)	58424	Woodbury (Jamestown)	58401	Zap	58580
Wing	58494	Woodworth	58496	Zeeland	58581
Wishek	58495	Wyndmere	58081		
Wolford	58385	York	58386		
Wolseth (Glenburn)	58740	Ypsilanti	58497		
Wood Lake (Tokio)	58379	Zahl	58856		

BISMARCK

APARTMENTS

Crescent Manor
107 E BOWEN AVE 58504

Kensington
114 N 3RD ST 58501

Patterson Place
420 E MAIN AVE 58501

Plaza Tower
1111 N 1ST ST 58501

BUILDINGS

Broadway Business Center
2900 E BROADWAY AVE . 58501

Dakota Norwest Building
400 E BROADWAY AVE ... 58501

Gateway Mall
2700 STATE ST 58501

Gold Seal Plaza
918 E DIVIDE AVE 58501

Kirkwood Office Tower
919 S 7TH ST 58504

Logans On Third
120 N 3RD ST 58501

Medical Arts Building
810 E ROSSER AVE 58501

Northbrook Mall
1929 N WASHINGTON ST 58501

Parkade Building
515 E BROADWAY AVE ... 58501

Provident Life Building
316 N 5TH ST 58501

Randall Building
4023 STATE ST 58501

Regency Business Center
3333 E BROADWAY AVE . 58501

Russell Building
4007 STATE ST 58501

GOVERNMENT

Burleigh County
5518 PO BOX 58502

City Of Bismarck
5503 PO BOX 58502

Federal Building
220 E ROSSER AVE 58501

Heritage Center
612 E BOULEVARD AVE .. 58505

Highway Building
608 E BOULEVARD AVE .. 58505

Liberty Memorial Building
604 E BOULEVARD AVE .. 58505

Municipal Airport
2301 UNIVERSITY DR 58504

North Dakota State Office Building
900 E BOULEVARD AVE .. 58505

North Dakota Captiol Building
600 E BOULEVARD AVE .. 58505

The Dacotah Foundation
600 S 2ND ST 58504

HOSPITALS

Medcenter One
5525 PO BOX 58502

St Alexius Medical Center
5510 PO BOX 58502

HOTELS

Holiday Inn
1015 PO BOX 58502

FARGO

APARTMENTS

Fargo High Rise
101 2ND ST S 58103

New Horizon Manor
2525 BROADWAY 58102

Pioneer Manor
201 11TH ST N 58102

Twin Towers
1110 3RD AVE N 58102

University Manor
1201 2ND AVE N 58102

BUILDINGS

Black Building
118 BROADWAY 58102

City Hall
200 3RD ST N 58102

Court House
211 9TH ST S 58103

Gate City Building
500 2ND AVE N 58102

Pioneer Building
203 10TH ST N 58102

Professional Building
100 4TH ST S 58103

GOVERNMENT

New Federal Building
657 2ND AVE N 58102

OHIO
Abbreviation OH

Aberdeen 45101
Academia (Mount Vernon) 43050
Ada 45810
Adairo (Shiloh) 44878
Adams (Cambridge) 43725
.... 43821, 43832
Adamsville 43802
Addison (Gallipolis) 45631
Addyston 45001
Adelphi 43101
Adena 43901
Adrian 44801
Akron 44300-317, 44319-322
.... 44325-326, 44328-329
.... 44331, 44333-334, 44372
.... 44393, 44396-399
   Copley 44321
   East Akron 44305
   Ellet 44312
   Fairlawn 44333
   General Tire 44329
   Goodyear Tire 44316
   Kenmore 44314
   Loral Systems 44315
   Maple Valley 44320
   North Hill 44310
   Portage Lakes 44319
   South Arlington 44306
   Uniroyal Goodrich 44397
   West Akron 44307
Albany 45710
Albion (West Salem) 44287
Alexander (Athens) 45701
Alexandria 43001
Alfred (Coolville) 45723
Alger 45812
Alledonia 43902
Allensburg (Hillsboro) 45133
Allensville (Mc Arthur) 45651
Allentown (Wheelersburg) . 45694
Alliance 44601
Alltel (Hudson) 44238
Alma (Waverly) 45690
Alpha 45301
Alton (Galloway) 43119
Altoona (Wellston) 45692
Alvada 44802
Alvordton 43501
Amanda 43102
Amboy (Conneaut) 44030
Amelia 45102
Amesville 45711, 45777
   Sharpsburg 45777
Amherst 44001
Amity 43050, 43064
   (Mount Vernon)
Amlin 43002
Amsden 44803
Amsterdam 43903
Anderson (Cincinnati) 45230
.... 45244-245, 45254-255
Andover 44003
Ankenytown 43019
   (Fredericktown)
Anna 45302
Ansonia 45303
Antioch 43143, 43793
   (Mount Sterling)

Antiquity (Racine) 45771
Antrim (Harpster) 43323
Antwerp 45813
Apple Creek 44606
Apple Grove (Racine) 45771
Apple Valley (Howard) 43028
Appleton (Johnstown) 43031
Arabia (Pedro) 45659
Arbolia (Richwood) 43344
Arcadia 44804
Arcanum 45304
Archbold 43502
Archers Fork 45767
   (New Matamoras)
Arion (Mc Dermott) 45652
Arlington 45814
Arlington Heights 45215
   (Cincinnati)
Armstrong Mills 43933
   (Jacobsburg)
Arnold (Plain City) 43064
Ash Ridge (Georgetown) .. 45121
Ashland 44805
Ashley 43003
Ashley Corner 45694
   (Wheelersburg)
Ashtabula 44004-005
Ashville 43103
Athalia (Proctorville) 45669
Athens 45701
Atlanta (New Holland) 43145
Atlas (Barnesville) 43713
Attica 44807
Atwater 44201
Auburn 44022, 44681
   (Chagrin Falls)
Auburn Corners (Mantua) . 44255
Augusta 44607
Aurora 44202
Austin (Frankfort) 45628
Austinburg 44010
Austintown (Youngstown) .. 44515
Ava 43711
Avlon (Bremen) 43107
Avon 44011
Avon Lake 44012
Avondale (Lakeview) 43331
.... 44708, 45229
Axtel (Vermilion) 44089
Bailey Lakes (Ashland) 44805
Baileys Mills 43713
   (Barnesville)
Bainbridge 44022, 45612
   (Chagrin Falls)
   Barretts Mills 45612
   Fruitdale 45612
   Humboldt 45612
   Morgantown 45612
   Nipgen 45612
   Paint 45612
   Paxton 45612
   Spargursville 45612
Bakersville 43803
Baltic 43804
Baltimore 43105
Bangs (Mount Vernon) 43050
Bannock 43972
Barberton 44203
Bardwell (Mount Orab) 45154
Barlow 45712
Barnesville 43713

Barretts Mills 45612
   (Bainbridge)
Bartlett 45713
Barton 43905
Bascom 44809
Bashan (Long Bottom) 45743
Basil (Baltimore) 43105
Batavia 45103
Batesville 43713, 43773
   (Barnesville)
Bath 44210
Bay View (Sandusky) 44870
Bay Village 44140
Bayard (Minerva) 44657
Bazetta (Cortland) 44410
Beach City 44608
Beachwood (Cleveland) 44122
Bealsville 43716
Beaumont (Athens) 45701
Beavan (Newport) 45768
Beaver 43773, 45613
   (Quaker City)
Beaver Creek 45430-432
.... 45434, 45440
   (Dayton)
Beaver Park (Lorain) 44053
Beaverdam 45808
Beavertown 45767
   (New Matamoras)
Becks Mills (Millersburg) ... 44654
Bedford 44146
Bedford Heights 44128, 44146
   (Cleveland)
Beechwold (Columbus) 43214
Belden (Grafton) 44044
Belfast (Hillsboro) 45133
Bellaire 43906
Bellaire Gardens (Marion) . 43302
Bellbrook 45305
Belle Addition 43324
   (Huntsville)
Belle Point (Ostrander) 43061
Belle Valley 43717
Belle Vernon (Sycamore) .. 44882
Bellefontaine 43311
Bellepoint (Delaware) 43015
Bellevue 44811
Bellview Heights 43906
   (Bellaire)
Bellville 44813
Belmont 43718
Belmore 45815
Beloit 44609
Belpre 45714
Bentleyville 44022, 44139
   (Chagrin Falls)
Benton 44654, 44882
   (Millersburg)
Benton Ridge 45816
Bentonville 45105
Berea 44017
Bergholz 43908
Berkey 43504
Berkshire (Sunbury) 43074
Berlin 44610
Berlin Center 44401
Berlin Heights 44814
Berne 43155, 43724
   (Sugar Grove)
Bernice (Newcomerstown) 43832
Berwick (New Riegel) 44853

Bessemer (Nelsonville) 45764
Bethany (Middletown) 45042
Bethel (Mount Sterling) 43143
.... 45106, 45745
   Mount Olive 45106
Bethesda 43719
Bethlehem 44662, 44875
   (Navarre)
Bettsville 44815
Beulah Beach (Vermilion) .. 44089
Beverly 45715
Bevis (Cincinnati) 45247
Bexley (Columbus) 43209
Bidwell 45614
Big Plain (London) 43140
Big Prairie 44611
Big Run (Cutler) 45724
Big Springs 43347
   (Rushsylvania)
Birmingham 43749, 44816
   (Kimbolton)
Bishopville (Glouster) 45732
Black Horse (Ravenna) 44266
Blackfork (Oak Hill) 45656
Blackhawk (Lakeview) 44331
Blacklick 43004, 43099
Blacktop (Lore City) 43755
Bladen (Crown City) 45623
Bladensburg 43005
Blaine 43909
Blainesville (Maynard) 43937
Blake (Seville) 44273
Blakeslee 43505
Blanchester 45107
Blissfield 43805
Bloom (Lithopolis) 43136
Bloom Center (Lewistown) .. 43333
Bloomdale 44817
Bloomfield 43011, 43762
   (Centerburg)
Blooming Grove (Galion) ... 44833
Bloomingburg 43106
Bloomingdale 43910
Bloomingville (Sandusky) .. 44870
Bloomville 44818
Blue Ash (Cincinnati) 45242
Blue Ball (Franklin) 45005
Blue Creek 45616
Blue Rock 43720
Bluffton 45817
Boardman 44512-513
   (Youngstown)
Bokes Creek 43358
   (West Mansfield)
Bolivar 44612
Bond Hill (Cincinnati) 45237
Bonn (Whipple) 45788
Bono (Martin) 43445
Bookwalter 43128
   (Jeffersonville)
Booth (Newcomerstown) 43832
Boston (Barnesville) 43713
.... 44264, 45133
Boston Heights (Hudson) .. 44236
Botkins 45306
Boughtonville (Willard) 44890
Bourneville 45617
Bowerston 44695
Bowersville 45307
Bowling Green 43332, 43402-403

(La Rue)
Braceville (Newton Falls) .. 44444
Bradford 45308
Bradner 43406
Bradrick (Chesapeake) 45619
Brady Lake 44211
Bradyville (Manchester) 45144
Branch Hill (Loveland) 45140
Brandon (Mount Vernon) ... 43050
Bratenahl (Cleveland) 44108
Brecksville 44141
Bremen 43107
Brewster 44613
Briarwood Beach 44215
   (Chippewa Lake)
Brice 43109
Bridgeport 43912
Bridgetown (Cincinnati) 45211
Briggs (Cleveland) 44134
Briggsdale (Columbus) 43223
Brilliant 43913
Brinkhaven 43006
Bristol (New Lexington) 43764
Bristolville 44402
Broadview Heights 44147
Broadway 43007
Broadwell (Stewart) 45778
Brokaw (Stockport) 43787
Bronson (Norwalk) 44857
Brook Park (Cleveland) 44142
Brookfield 43732, 44403
   (Cumberland)
   Yankee Lake 44403
Brooklyn (Cleveland) 44144
Brooklyn Heights 44131
   (Cleveland)
Brookpark (Cleveland) 44142
Brookville 45309
Brookwood (Cincinnati) 45239
Brown (New Plymouth) 45654
Brown Heights (Cambridge) 43725
Brownhelm (Amherst) 44001
Brownstown 43351
   (Upper Sandusky)
Brownsville 43721
.... 45601, 45767
   Zanesville 43721
Browntown (Georgetown) .. 45121
Brunswick 44212
Brush Creek (Otway) 45657
Brush Ridge (Marion) 43302
Bryan 43506
Buchtel 45716
Buck (Kenton) 43326
Buck Run (Rockbridge) 43149
Buckeye (Zanesville) 43701
Buckeye Lake 43008
Buckeye Village (Attica) 44807
Buckeyeville (Cambridge) .. 43725
Buckingham (Corning) 43730
Buckland 45819
Bucks (Baltic) 43804
Bucyrus 44820
Buena Vista 43149, 45684
   (Rockbridge)
Buffalo 43722, 43772
Buford 45110
Bulkhead (Lewistown) 43333
Bunker Hill (Millersburg) ... 44654
Burbank 44214
Burghill 44404

Burgoon 43407
Burkettsville 45310
Burkhart (Lewisville) 43754
Burlingham (Shade) 45776
Burlington (South Point) 45680
Burnet Woods (Cincinnati) . 45220
Burr Oak (Glouster) 45732
Burr Oaks 43143
   (Mount Sterling)
Burton 44021
Burton City (Orrville) 44667
Burton Lake (Burton) 44021
Bushnell (Conneaut) 44030
Butler 43843, 44822
   (Walhonding)
   North Liberty 44822
Butlerville 45162
   (Pleasant Plain)
Byer (Wellston) 45692
Byesville 43723
Byhalia (Richwood) 43344
Byhaliw (West Mansfield) .. 43358
Byington (Latham) 45646
Byrd (Decatur) 45115
Cadiz 43907
Cadmus (Patriot) 45658
Cairo 45820
Calais 43773, 43788
   (Quaker City)
Calcutta (East Liverpool) ... 43920
Caldwell 43724
Caledonia 43314
California (Cincinnati) 45228
Cambridge 43725, 43750
   Adams 43725
   Brown Heights 43725
   Buckeyeville 43725
   Cassell 43725
   Center 43725
   Claysville 43725
   College Hill 43725
   Fairdale 43725
   Harriett 43725
   Indian Camp 43725
   Knox 43725
   Liberty 43725
   Sunny Meade 43725
   Westland 43725
Camden 45311
Cameron 43914
Camp Creek (Rarden) 45671
Camp Dennison 45111
Camp Falling Rock 43055
   (Newark)
Camp Washington 45225
   (Cincinnati)
Campbell 44405
Campbellsport (Ravenna) . 44266
Canaan 43064, 44217
   (Plain City)
Canaanville (Athens) 45701
Canal Fulton 44614
Canal Lewisville 43812
   (Coshocton)
Canal Winchester 43110
Candleville (Mt. Gilead) 43338
Candy Town (Nelsonville) . 45764
Canfield 44406
Cannelville (Roseville) 43777
Canton . 44700-12, 44714, 44718
..... 44720-721, 44730, 44735

.... 44750, 44760, 44767	
.... 44798-799	
County Fair	44708
Dueber	44706
East Canton	44730
Hills And Dales	44708
Jackson Belden	44718
Lake Cable	44730
Lake Slagle	44720
Mapleton	44730
Mcdonaldsville	44720
Mckinley	44704
North Canton ... 44709, 44720	
North Industry	44707
Osnaburg	44730
Reedurban	44710
Richville	44706
Waco	44707
Carbon Hill	43111
Carbondale	45717
Cardington	43315
Carey	43316
Carlisle (Franklin)	45005
Carmel (Hillsboro)	45133
Caroline (Attica)	44807
Carpenter (Albany)	45710
Carroll	43112
Carrollton	44615
Carrothers (Attica)	44807
Carthage 45216, 45735	
(Cincinnati)	
Carthagena (Celina)	45822
Cass (Dresden)	43821
Cassel (Cambridge)	43725
Casstown	45312
Castalia	44824
Castine (Arcanum)	45304
Catawba	43010
Catawba Island	43452
(Port Clinton)	
Cavallo (Walhonding)	43843
Cecil	45821
Cedarville	45314
Celeryville (Willard)	44890
Celina 45822, 45826	
Carthagena	45822
Center (Cambridge)	43725
.... 43793, 45715	
Centerburg	43011
Centerpoint (Oak Hill)	45656
Centerton (Willard)	44890
Centerville (Prospect)	43342
.... 43718, 45429, 45440	
.... 45458-459, 45475, 45685	
Central City (Newark)	43055
Central Point (Columbus) ..	43223
Cessna (Kenton)	43326
Ceylon (Huron)	44839
Chagrin Falls 44022-023	
Auburn	44022
Bainbridge	44022
Bentleyville	44022
Hunting Valley	44022
Moreland Hills	44022
Orange	44022
Russell Township	44022
South Russell	44022
Chalfants (Glenford)	43739
Chambersburg (Minerva) ..	44657
Champion (Warren)	44483
Chandlersville	43727

Chapel Hill (Corning)	43730
Chardon	44024
Charlestown (Ravenna)	44266
Charm	44617
Chasetown (Fayetteville) ...	45118
Chaseville	43772
(Pleasant City)	
Chatfield	44825
Chatham (Newark)	43055
.... 44256, 44275	
Chauncey	45719
Chautauqua (Miamisburg)	45342
Chenoweth	43143
(Mount Sterling)	
Cherokee Heights	43324
(Huntsville)	
Cherokee Landing	43331
(Lakeview)	
Cherry Fork	45618
Cherry Grove (Cincinnati) .	45245
Cherry Valley (Andover)	44003
Chesapeake	45619
Cheshire	45620
Chester 44026, 45720	
Chesterhill	43728
Chesterland	44026
Chesterville	43317
Cheviot (Cincinnati)	45211
Chickasaw	45826
Chillicothe	45601
Chilo	45112
Chippewa 43331, 44230	
(Lakeview)	
Chippewa Lake	44215
Christiansburg	45389
Christopher Columbus	43215
(Columbus)	
Cincinnati 45200-255, 45258	
.... 45262-264, 45267-271	
.... 45273-275, 45277, 45296	
.... 45298-299, 45944, 45999	
Airport	45275
Ameritrust	45271
Amf	45275
Anderson . 45230, 45254-255	
Arlington Heights	45215
Avondale	45229
Bevis	45247
Blue Ash	45242
Bond Hill	45237
Bridgetown	45211
Brookwood	45239
Bulk Mail Center	45235
Burnet Woods	45220
Business Reply	45273
California	45228
Camp Washington	45225
Carthage	45216
Cherry Grove	45245
Cheviot	45211
Clifton 45219-45220	
Colerain 45251-45252	
College Hill	45224
Commercial Accounts .	45274
Commercial Accts	45274
Corryville	45219
Covedale	45238
Cumminsville	45223
Deer Park	45236
Del Fair	45238
Delhi	45238

Dent 45247-45248	
Dillonvale	45236
Dunlap	45247
East End	45226
Elmwood Place	45216
Envir Pro Agency	45268
Evanston	45207
Evendale 45215, 45241	
Fairfax	45227
Fairmont	45211
Fairmount	45214
Fidelity Investments	45277
Fifth Third Bank	45263
Finneytown	45224
Forest Park	45240
Glen Este	45245
Glendale	45246
Golf Manor	45237
Green Township 45247-45248	
Greenhills	45218
Groesbeck	
45239, 45247, 45251, 45253	
Hazelwood	45242
Huntington Nat'l Bank .	45270
Hyde Park	45208
Indian Hill	45243
IRS 45298, 45944, 45999	
Ivorydale	45217
Kennedy Heights	45213
Kenwood	45236
Lincoln Heights	45215
Lockland	45215
Losantiville	45237
Mack 45211, 45248	
Madeira	45243
Madison Place	45227
Madisonville	45227
Mariemont	45227
Montgomery	45242
Mount Carmel	45244
Mount Washington	45230
Mt Auburn	45219
Mt Lookout	45208
Newtown 45244-45245	
North College Hill	
.... 45224, 45231, 45239	
Northside	45223
Norwood	45212
O'bryonville	45208
Oakley	45209
Parkdale	
.... 45218, 45240, 45246	
Pleasant Ridge	45213
Pleasant Run Farms ...	45240
Price Hill	45205
Provident Bank	45269
Queen City	45210
Queen City	45214
Reading	45215
Riverside	45204
Roselawn 45222, 45237	
Rossmoyne	45236
Saint Bernard	45232
Saylor Park	45233
Shademore	45244
Sharonville	45241
Silverton	45236
Springdale	45246
Star Bank	45264
Stock Yards	45225
Sycamore	45242

Ellisonville (Ironton) 45638
Elliston (Graytown) 43432
Ellsberry (Aberdeen) 45101
Ellsworth 44416
Elm Grove (Piketon) 45661
Elmore 43416
Elmville (Hillsboro) . 45133, 45660
Elmwood Place 45216
(Cincinnati)
Elyria 44035-036, 44039
North Ridgeville 44035
Ridgeville 44035
Empire 43926
Englewood 45315, 45322
(Clayton)
Union 45322
Enon 45323
Enterprise (Logan) 43138
Epworth Heights 45140
(Loveland)
Era (Mount Sterling) 43143
Eris (Urbana) 43078
Essex (Richwood) 43344
Etna 43018
Euclid (Cleveland) 44117
44119, 44123, 44132, 44143
Evansport 43519
Evanston (Cincinnati) 45207
Evendale 45215, 45241
(Cincinnati)
Everett (Peninsula) 44264
Ewing (Logan) 43138
Ewington (Vinton) 45686
Excello (Middletown) 45044
Fairborn 45324
Fairdale (Cambridge) 43725
Fairfax 45133, 45227
(Hillsboro)
Fairfield (Somerdale) 44678
.... 45014, 45724
Hamilton 45014
Fairhope (Louisville) 44641
Fairlawn (Akron) 44333
Fairmont (Cincinnati) 45211
Fairmount (Cincinnati) 45214
Fairpoint 43927
Fairport Harbor 44077
(Painesville)
Fairview 43736, 43772, 45133
Quaker City 43736
Fairview Park (Cleveland) . 44126
Falls (Logan) 43138
Fallsburg (Newark) . 43055, 43822
Fargo (Sunbury) 43074, 43334
Farmdale 44417
Farmer 43520
Farmerstown (Baltic) 43804
Farmersville 45325
Farnham (Conneaut) 44030
Fawcett (Peebles) 45660
Fayette 43521, 45680
Fayetteville 45118
Federal (Glouster) 45732
Feed Springs 44683
(Uhrichsville)
Feesburg 45119
Felicity 45120
Findlay 45839-840
Finneytown (Cincinnati) 45224
Fire Brick (Oak Hill) 45656
Firestone Park (Akron) 44301

Fitchville (New London) 44851
Five Mile (Mount Orab) 45154
Five Points 43143
(Mount Sterling)
Flat Rock 44828
Flatiron (Crooksville) 43731
Fleatown (Newark) 43055
Fleming 45729
Fletcher 43772, 45326
(Pleasant City)
Flintridge (Newark) 43055
Floodwood (Nelsonville) ... 45764
Florence (London) .. 43140, 43724
Flushing 43977
Fly 45730
Forest 45843
Forest Park (Cincinnati) 45240
Forestdale (Ironton) 45638
Fort Jennings 45844
Fort Loramie 45845
Fort Recovery 45846
Fort Scott Camps 45030
(Harrison)
Fort Seneca 44829
Foster (Maineville) 45039
Fostoria 44830
Fountain Park (Woodstock) 43084
Fountain Square 45202
(Cincinnati)
Fowler 44418
Fowlers Mill (Chardon) 44024
Fox (Circleville) 43113
Frampton (Newark) 43055
Frankfort 45628
Franklin (Newark) .. 43055, 44216
.... 44680, 44699, 45005
Blue Ball 45005
Carlisle 45005
Franklinton (Columbus) 43222
Frazeysburg 43822
Frederick (Wheelersburg) . 45694
Fredericksburg 44627
Fredericksdale 43779
(Sarahsville)
Fredericktown 43019
Fredonia 43023, 43055
(Granville)
Freedom (Windham) 44288
Freeport 43973
Fremont 43420
Fresno 43824
Friendship 45630
Frost (Coolville) 45723
Fruitdale (Bainbridge) 45612
Fulda (Caldwell) 43724
Fulton 43321
Fultonham 43735, 43738
(East Fultonham)
Gage (Patriot) 45658
Gahanna (Columbus) 43230
Galena 43021
Galion 44833
Gallia (Patriot) 45658
Gallipolis 45631
Galloway 43119
Gambier 43022
Ganges (Shelby) 44875
Gann (Brinkhaven) 43006
Garden (Guysville) 45735
Garden City 45694
(Wheelersburg)

Garden Isle (Lodi) 44254
Garfield Heights 44105
.... 44125, 44128
(Cleveland)
Garrettsville 44231
Gates Mills 44040
Gateway (Westerville) 43081
Gaysport (Blue Rock) 43720
Geneva (Bremen) .. 43107, 44041
Cork 44041
Harpersfield 44041
Saybrook 44041
Trumbull 44041
Genoa 43430
Georges Run 43938
(Mingo Junction)
Georgesville (Grove City) .. 43123
Georgetown 45121
Germantown (Farmersville) 45325
.... 45327, 45745
Getaway (Chesapeake) 45619
Gettysburg 45328
Gibisonville (Rockbridge) .. 43149
Gibson (Salesville) 43778
Gibsonburg 43431
Gilboa (Ottawa) 45875
Gilmore (Port Washington) 43837
Girard 44420
Glandorf 45848
Glasgow 43837
(Port Washington)
Glass Rock (Glenford) 43739
Glen Este (Cincinnati) 45245
Glen Robbins (Rayland) 43943
Glen Roy (Wellston) 45692
Glencoe 43928
Glendale (Cincinnati) 45246
Glenford 43739
Glenmont 44628
Glenwillow (Solon) 44139
Gloria Glens 44215
(Chippewa Lake)
Glouster 45732
Gnadenhutten 44629
Gomer 45809
Good Hope 43149, 43160
(Rockbridge)
Goose Run (Glouster) 45732
Gordon 45304, 45329
(Arcanum)
Gore (Logan) 43138
Goshen (Mechanicsburg) .. 43044
.... 43326, 44460, 45122
Cozaddale 45122
Edenton 45122
Grafton 44044
Grand Prairie (Marion) 44302
Grand Rapids 43522
Grand River 44045
Grandview 45767
(New Matamoras)
Grandview Heights 43212
(Columbus)
Grange Hall 43143
(Mount Sterling)
Granger (Medina) 44256
Granville 43023
Gratiot 43740
Gratis 45330
Graysville 45734, 45789
Greenbrier 45734

Harmon Ridge 45734	Hanging Rock (Ironton) 45638	Highland 45132
Hartshorn 45734	Hannibal 43931	Highland Heights 44143
Long Run 45734	Hanover (Newark) 43055	(Cleveland)
Pleasant Ridge 45734	Hanoverton 44423	Highland Hills 44122, 44128
Rinard Mills 45734	Happy Hollow 45764	(Cleveland)
Sprague 45734	(Nelsonville)	Highland Park 45629
Straight Fork 45734	Harbor (Ashtabula) 44004	(Franklin Furnace)
Washington 45734	Harbor Hills (Hebron) 43025	Highlandtown (Salesville) . 43778
Way Ridge 45734	Harbor View 43434	Highwater (Newark) 43055
Wayne 45734	Harlem Springs 44631	Hilliard 43026
Graytown 43432	Harmon (Navarre) 44662	Hillman (Georgetown) 45121
Greasy Ridge (Scottown) .. 45678	Harmon Ridge (Graysville) 45734	Hillsboro 45133
Great Bend (Portland) 45770	Harper (Bellefontaine) 43311	Hilltop (Columbus) 43204
Green (Woodsfield) 43793	Harpersfield (Geneva) 44041	Hinckley 44233
44720, 44232, 45658, 45684	Harpster 43323	Hiram 44234
Green Camp 43322	Harriett 43725, 45133	Hiramsburg (Cumberland) . 43732
Green Springs 44836	(Cambridge)	Hitchcock (Oak Hill) 45656
Green Township 45247-248	Harriettsville 45745	Hobson (Middleport) 45760
(Cincinnati)	(Lower Salem)	Hockingport 45739
Greenbrier (Graysville) 45734	Harrington (Warsaw) 43844	Holgate 43527
Greencastle (Carroll) 43112	Harrisburg 43126, 44641	Holland 43528
Greendale (Logan) 43138	Harrison (Ashville) 43103	Hollansburg 45332
Greene (North Bloomfield) .. 44450	.... 43311, 43771, 45030	Hollister (Glouster) 45732
Greenfield .. 45123, 45165, 45658	Crosby 45030	Holloway 43985
Rainsboro 45123	Fort Scott Camps 45030	Holmesville 44633
Greenford 44422	New Baltimore 45030	Homer 44235, 43027
Greenhills (Cincinnati) 45218	New Haven 45030	Homerville 44235
Greens Run (Glouster) 45732	Harrison Adams 43070	Homeworth 44634
Greensburg 44232	(Rosewood)	Hooksburg (Stockport) 43787
Greentown 44630	Harrisonville (Pomeroy) 45769	Hooven 45033
Greenville 45331	Harrisville 43974	Hopedale 43976
Greenwich 44837	Harrod 45850	Hopetown (Chillicothe) 45601
Greenwood (Senecaville) .. 43780	Harshasville (Peebles) 45660	Hopewell 43746
Greer (Glenmont) 44628	Hartford 44424	Horton (West Mansfield) ... 43358
Grelton 43523	Hartland (Norwalk) 44857	Houston 45333
Griffith (Woodsfield) 43793	Hartleyville (Glouster) 45732	Howard 43028
Groesbeck (Cincinnati) 45239	Hartsgrove (Rome) 44085	Howenstein (East Sparta) . 44626
.... 45247, 45251	Hartshorn (Graysville) 45734	Howland (Warren) 44484
Grove City 43123	Hartville 44632	Hoytville 43529
Groveport 43125	Harveysburg 45032	Hubbard 44425
Grover Hill 45849	Haskins 43525	Huber Heights (Dayton) 45424
Guernsey (Kimbolton) 43749	Havana (Willard) 44890	Hudson 44236-238
Guilford (Seville) 44273	Havensport (Carroll) 43112	Hue (New Plymouth) 45654
Guilford Lake 44423, 44432	Haverhill 45636	Humboldt (Bainbridge) 45612
(Hanoverton)	Haviland 45851	Hunter (Bethesda) 43719
Gustavus 44417, 44428	Haydenville 43127	Hunterdon (Glouster) 45732
(Farmdale)	Hayesville 44838	Hunting Valley 44022
Guyan (Crown City) 45623	Haynes 43135, 43152	(Chagrin Falls)
Guysville 45735	(Laurelville)	Huntsburg 44046
Gypsum 43433	Hazelwood (Cincinnati) 45242	Huntsville 43324
Hackney (Beverly) 45715	Heath (Newark) 43055-056	Huron 44839
Hallsville 45633	Hebardsville (Athens) 45701	Hyde Park (Cincinnati) 45208
Hamburg (Lancaster) 43130	Hebbardsville (Albany) 45710	Hyland Park 45629
Hamden 45634	Hebron 43025	(Franklin Furnace)
Hamersville 45130	Hecla (Ironton) 45638	Iberia 43325
Hamilton 45011-015, 45018	Hedges (Huntsville) 43324	Idaho (Piketon) 45661
.... 45020	Helena 43435	Ilesboro (Logan) 43138
Champion Intrntl 45020	Helmick (Warsaw) 43844	Independence (Cleveland) . 44131
Liberty Township 45011	Hemlock (Corning) 43730	Indian Camp (Cambridge) . 43725
Lindenwald 45015	Hemlock Grove (Pomeroy) 45769	Indian Hill (Cincinnati) 45243
Millville 45013	Hendrysburg (Barnesville) 43713	Indian Lake (Huntsville) 43324
New Miami 45011	Henley 45652, 45657	.... 43331, 43348
Pease Co 45023	(Mc Dermott)	Ink (Tiffin) 44883
Princeton 45015	Henrietta (Amherst) 44001	Iron City (Bellefontaine) ... 43311
Rossville 45013	Hepburn (Kenton) 43326	Iron Point (Shawnee) 43782
Saint Clair 45011	Hickman (Newark) 43055	Irondale (Dresden) . 43821, 43932
West American Ins 45026	Hicksville 43526	Cream City 43932
Hamler 43524	Hide Away Hills (Bremen) . 43107	Ironspot (Roseville) 43777
Hamlet (Amelia) 45102	Higginsport 45131	Ironton 45638
Hammondsville 43930	High Hill 43727	Irwin 43029
Hanersville (Gallipolis) 45631	(Chandlersville)	Island View (Lakeview) 43331

Isle Saint George 43436
Isleta (West Lafayette) 43845
Isleta Corners 43832
   (Newcomerstown)
Ithaca (Arcanum) 45304
Ivorydale (Cincinnati) 45217
Jackson (Circleville) 43113
.... 43748, 44217, 44287
.... 44875, 45640, 45730
  Cove 45640
  Limerick 45640
  Pattonville 45640
  Petrea 45640
  Ridgeland 45640
  Rockyhill 45640
  Walnut Hills 45640
Jackson Belden (Canton) .. 44718
Jackson Center 45334
Jackson Lake (Oak Hill) 45656
Jackson Ridge 43793
  (Woodsfield)
Jacksontown 43030
Jacksonville 45660, 45740
  (Peebles)
Jacobsburg 43933
Jaite (Brecksville) 44141
Jamestown 45335
Jasper 45642
Jasper Mills 43160
  (Washington Court House)
Jefferson (Carroll) 43112
.... 43128, 43162
.... 43311, 43821, 43840
.... 44047, 45656, 45684
  Denmark 44047
  Lenox 44047
  New Lyme 44047
  Rays Corners 44047
  Sheffield Township 44047
Jeffersonville 43128
Jelloway (Danville) 43014
Jenera 45841
Jerome (Dublin) 43017, 43064
Jeromesville 44840
Jerry City 43437
Jersey (Pataskala) 43062
Jerusalem 43747
Jewell 43530
Jewett 43986
Jobs (Shawnee) 43782, 45732
Johnstown 43031
Johnsville (Shauck) 43349
Jonesboro 43160
  (Washington Court House)
Jump (Kenton) 43326
Junction City 43748
Justus (Navarre) 44662
Kalida 45853
Kanauga (Gallipolis) 45631
Kansas 44841
Keene 43828
Kelleys Island 43438
Kelloggsville (Conneaut) ... 44030
Kenmore (Akron) 44314
Kennard (Cable) 43009
Kennedy Heights 45213
  (Cincinnati)
Kennonsburg (Quaker City) 43773
Keno (Long Bottom) 45743
Kensington 44427
Kent 44240, 44242-243

Kenton 43326
Kenwood (Cincinnati) 45236
Kerr (Woodsfield) ... 43793, 45643
Kettering (Dayton) 45409
.... 45419-420, 45429-430
..... 45432, 45439-440, 45459
Kettlersville 45336
Kidron 44636
Kilbourne 43032
Kile (Plain City) 43064
Kilgore (Carrollton) 44615
Killbuck 44637
Kilvert (Stewart) 45778
Kimball (Monroeville) 44847
Kimberly (Nelsonville) 45764
Kimbolton 43749
King Mines (Lore City) 43755
Kings Creek (Urbana) 43078
Kings Island 45034
  (Kings Mills)
Kings Landing (Lakeview) . 43331
Kings Mills 45034
Kingston 45644
Kingsville 44048, 44068
Kinnickinnick 45601
  (Chillicothe)
Kinsman 44428
Kiousville 43143
  (Mount Sterling)
Kipling 43750
Kipton 44049
Kirby 43330
Kirkersville 43033
Kirtland 44026, 44094
  (Chesterland)
Kitchen (Oak Hill) 45656
Kitts Hill 45645
Knollwood Village 43113
  (Circleville)
Knox (Cambridge) .. 43725, 44638
Kunkle 43531
Kyger (Cheshire) 45620
L Hocking 45742
  (Little Hocking)
La Rue 43332
Lacarne 43439
Lafayette (London) 43140
.... 44256, 45854
Lima 45854
Lafferty 43951
Lagrange 44050
Laings 43752
Lake (Bellefontaine) 43311
Lake Aquilla (Chardon) 44024
Lake Cable (Canton) 44730
Lake Fork (Jeromesville) ... 44840
Lake Milton 44429
Lake Slagle (Canton) 44720
Lake White (Waverly) 45690
Lakeline (Willoughby) 44095
Lakemore 44250
Lakeridge (Huntsville) 43324
Lakeside (Lakeview) 43331
Lakeside Marblehead 43440
Lakeview 43331
Lakeville 44638
Lakewood 44107
Lamira (Belmont) 43718
Lancaster 43130, 43132
Landon (Maineville) 45039
Langsville 45741

Lansing 43934
Latham 45646
Lattasburg (West Salem) ... 44287
Lattasville (Frankfort) 45628
Latty 45855
Laura 45337
Laurel 43149, 45157
  (Rockbridge)
Laurelville 43135
.... 43152, 43156
  Haynes 43135
  South Perry 43135
Lawrence (Canal Fulton) ... 44614
Lawshe (Peebles) .. 45660, 45679
Layland (Killbuck) 44637
Layman (Cutler) 45724
Leavittsburg 44430
Lebanon 45036
.... 45745, 45770
  Otterbien Home 45036
Lecta (Scottown) 45678
Lee (Cleveland) 44120
Lees Creek 45138
Leesburg 45135
Leesville 44639
Leetonia 44431
Leipsic (Belmore) ... 45815, 45856
  West Leipsic 45856
Leistville (Circleville) 43113
Lemert (Sycamore) 44882
Lemoyne 43441
Lena (Conover) 45317
Lenox (Jefferson) 44047
Leonardsburg (Delaware) . 43015
Lerado (Williamsburg) 45176
Leroy (Painesville) 44077
Letart (Racine) 45771
Levanna (Ripley) 45167
Lewis Center 43035
Lewisburg 45338
Lewistown 43333
Lewisville 43754
Lexington (Mansfield) 44904
Liberty (Cambridge) 43725
.... 45693, 45745
Licking (Nashport) 43830
Licking View (Zanesville) .. 43701
Lilly Chapel 43162
  (West Jefferson)
Lima 45801-802
..... 45804-809, 45819, 45854
  Cridersville 45806
  Elida 45807
Limaville 44640
Limerick (Jackson) 45640
Lincoln (Fulton) 43338
.... 44905, 45658
Lincoln Heights 44903, 45215
  (Mansfield)
Lincoln Village 43228
  (Columbus)
Lindale (Amelia) 45102
Lindentree (Mineral City) ... 44656
Lindenwald (Hamilton) 45015
Lindsey 43442
Linndale (Cleveland) 44135
Linton (Plainfield) 43836
Linwood Park (Vermilion) .. 44089
Linworth (Columbus) 43085
Lippincott (Urbana) 43078
Lisbon 44432

Litchfield	44253
Lithopolis	43136
Little Bullskin (Patriot)	45658
Little Hocking	45742
Little London (Shelby)	44875
Little Sandusky 43323, 43351
(Harpster)
Little Texas (Newark)	43055
Little Washington	44903
(Mansfield)
Little York (Nevada)	44849
Liverpool (Valley City)	44280
Lock (Centerburg)	43011
Lockbourne	43137
Lockland (Cincinnati)	45215
Lockville (Carroll)	43112
Lockwood	44450
(North Bloomfield)
Locust Grove (Peebles)	45660
Lodi	44254
Logan	43138
Logan Elm Village	43113
(Circleville)
Logansville (De Graff)	43318
Lombardsville	45652
(Mc Dermott)
London	43140
Londonderry	45647
Long Bottom	45743
Long Run (Graysville)	45734
Longstreth (Nelsonville)	45764
Loomis (Belmont)	43718
Lorain	44052-055
Beaver Park	44053
Sheffield	44055
South Lorain	44055
Loral Systems (Akron)	44315
Lordstown (Warren)	44481
Lore City	43755
Losantiville (Cincinnati)	45237
Lottridge (Coolville)	45723
Louden (Peebles)	45660
Loudonville	44842
Louisville	44641
Loveland 45111, 45140
(Camp Dennison)
Branch Hill	45140
Epworth Heights	45140
Murdock	45140
Seilcrest Acres	45140
Springvale	45140
Steelville	45140
Symmes Township	45140
Twenty Mile Stand	45140
Twightwee	45140
Lovell (Upper Sandusky)	43351
Lowell (Tiffin) 44883, 45744
Lowellville	44436
Lower Newport (Newport)	45768
Lower Salem	45745
Lucas	44843
Lucasville 45648, 45699
Luckey	43443
Ludington (Corning)	43730
Ludlow Falls	45339
Luray (Hebron)	43025
Lykens (Bloomville)	44818
Lyn May (Cleveland)	44124
Lynchburg	45142
Lyndhurst (Cleveland)	44124
Lyndon (South Salem)	45681

Lynn (Kenton)	43326
Lynx	45650
Lyons	43533
Lyra (Wheelersburg)	45694
Lytle (Waynesville)	45068
Macedonia	44056
Mack (Cincinnati) ... 45211, 45248
Macksburg	45746
Madeira (Cincinnati)	45243
Madison 43160, 43760
.... 43773, 43821
.... 44057, 44903, 45656
(Washington Court House)
North Madison	44057
South Madison	44057
Madison Lake (London)	43140
Madison Mills	43143
(Mount Sterling)
Madison Place	45227
(Cincinnati)
Madisonville (Cincinnati)	45227
Magnetic Springs	43036
Magnolia	44643
Maineville	45039
Mainsville	43764
(New Lexington)
Malaga	43757
Malinta	43535
Mallet Creek (Medina)	44256
Malta	43758
Malvern	44644
Manchester	45144
Manley Hill (Shawnee)	43782
Mansfield 44900-907, 44999
Cool Ridge Heights	44905
East Mansfield	44905
Lexington	44904
Lincoln	44905
Lincoln Heights	44903
Little Washington	44903
Madison	44903
Pavonia	44903
Steam Corners	44904
Windsor	44903
Mantua	44255
Maple Grove 44883, 45601
(Tiffin)
Maple Heights 43724, 44137
(Caldwell)
Cleveland	44137
Maple Valley (Akron)	44320
Mapleshade (Gallipolis)	45631
Mapleton (Canton)	44730
Maplewood	45340
Marathon	45145
Marble Cliff (Columbus)	43212
Marblehead	43440
(Lakeside Marblehead)
Marcy (Canal Winchester)	43110
Marengo	43334
Maria Stein	45860
Mariemont (Cincinnati)	45227
Marietta	45750
Marion 43301-302, 43305-307
Bellaire Gardens	43302
Brush Ridge	43302
Grand Prairie	43302
Readers Digest	43307
Vernon Heights	43302
West Town	43302
Mark Center	43536

Marne (Newark)	43055
Marr (Sycamore Valley)	43789
Marseilles	43351
(Upper Sandusky)
Marshall (Hillsboro)	45133
Marshallville	44645
Martel	43335
Martin	43445
Martins Ferry	43935
Martinsburg	43037
Martinsville	45146
Mary Ann (Newark)	43055
Marysville	43040-041
Mason	45040
Massie (Harveysburg)	45032
Massieville (Chillicothe)	45601
Massillon	44646-648
Masury	44438
Materials Park (Novelty)	44073
Maumee	43537
Maximo	44650
Maxville (Logan)	43138
May Hill (Seaman)	45679
Mayfield Heights	44124
(Cleveland)
Maynard	43937
Maysville (Logan) ... 43138, 44606
Mc Arthur	45651
Mc Claimsville	43143
(Mount Sterling)
Mc Clintocksburg	44444
(Newton Falls)
Mc Clure ... 43041, 43534, 43041
Mc Comb	45858
Mc Connelsville	43756
Mc Cuneville (Shawnee)	43782
Mc Cutchenville	44884
Mc Dermott	45652
Mc Donald	44437
Mc Donald (Kenton)	43326
Mc Donaldsville (Canton)	44720
Mc Guffey	45859
Mc Kean (Newark)	43055
Mc Kinley (Canton)	44704
Mc Kinley Heights (Niles)	44446
Mc Leish (Glouster)	45732
Mc Luney (Crooksville)	43731
Mc Morran (Bellefontaine)	43311
Mc Zena (Lakeville)	44638
Meade (Kingston)	45644
Meadowbrook (Zanesville)	43701
Meadowbrook Lake	44224
(Cuyahoga Falls)
Mecca (Cortland)	44410
Mechanic (Baltic)	43804
Mechanicsburg	43044
Mechanicstown	44651
Medina 44256, 44258, 44259
Chatham	44256
Granger	44256
Lafayette	44256
Mallet Creek	44256
Montville	44256
River Styx	44256
Weymouth	44256
Medway	45341
Meeksville (Mc Arthur)	45651
Melmore	44845
Melody Lake (Zanesville)	43701
Melrose	45861
Mendon	45862

Mentor 44060-061
   Concord 44060
   Kirtland Hills 44060
Mercerville (Crown City) 45623
Mesopotamia 44439
Metamora 43540
Metzger (Chillicothe) 45601
Mexico (Sycamore) 44882
Miami (Miamitown) . 45041, 45056
Miami Island (Huntsville) ... 43324
Miami University (Oxford) .. 45056
Miamisburg 45342-343
   Chautauqua 45342
Miamitown 45041
Miamiville 45147
Middle Bass 43446
Middle Point 45863
Middlebourne 43773
   (Quaker City)
Middlebranch 44652
Middleburg 43336, 43724
Middleburg Heights 44130
   (Cleveland)
Middlefield 44062
Middleport 45760
Middletown (Cable) 43009
   45042-044
   Bethany 45042
   Excello 45044
   Warren County 45044
   West Middletown 45042
Midford Heights 43331
   (Lakeview)
Midland 45148
Midland City 45629
   (Franklin Furnace)
Midpark (Cleveland) 44130
Midtown (Zanesville) 43701
Midvale 44653
Midway (Lakeview) 43331
Mifflin (Ashland) ... 44805, 45646
Milan 44846
Milford 45150
Milford Center 43045
Millbury 43447
Milledgeville 43142
Miller (Crown City) 45623
Miller City 45864
Millersburg 44654
Millersport 43046
Millerstown (Saint Paris) ... 43072
Millersville (Helena) 43435
Millertown (Corning) 43730
Millfield 45761
Millport (Ashville) ... 43103, 44427
Millville (Hamilton) 45013
Millwood (Danville) 43014
   .... 43028, 43773
Milton Center 43541
Miltonsburg (Woodsfield) .. 43793
Mineral (New Marshfield) .. 45766
Mineral City 44656
Mineral Ridge 44440
Mineral Springs (Peebles) . 45660
Minersville (Pomeroy) 45769
Minerva 44657
Minerva Park (Columbus) . 43229
Minford 45653
Mingo 43047
Mingo Junction 43938
Minnewauken Island 43324

(Huntsville)
Minster 45865
Mishler (Mogadore) 44260
Mitiwanga (Huron) 44839
Modoc (Glouster) 45732
Mogadore 44260
Mohawk (Warsaw) 43844
Mohicanville 44840
   (Jeromesville)
Moline (Walbridge) 43465
Monclova 43542
Monday (Nelsonville) 45764
Monday Creek (Logan) 43138
Mononcue 43351
   (Upper Sandusky)
Monroe (London) ... 43140, 43143
   43749, 45073, 45099, 44695
   45050
Monroe Center (Conneaut) 44030
Monroe Mills (Howard) 43028
Monroeville 44847
Montezuma 45866
Montgomery 43332, 45242
   (La Rue)
Montpelier 43543
Montville 44064, 44256
Moons 43160
   (Washington Court House)
Moorefield (Cadiz) 43907
Moores Junction 43731
   (Crooksville)
Mooresville (Chillicothe) 45601
Moraine (Dayton) 45439
Moreland Hills 44022
   (Chagrin Falls)
Morgansville (Malta) 43758
Morgantown (Bainbridge) .. 45612
Morges (Magnolia) 44643
Morning Sun (Camden) 45311
Morral 43337
Morrisons (Zanesville) 43701
Morristown 43759
Morrow 45152
Moscow 45153
Moultrie (Minerva) 44657
Moundbuilders (Newark) ... 43055
Moundsville (Caldwell) 43724
Moundville 43019
   (Fredericktown)
Moundwood (Huntsville) ... 43324
Mount Air (Columbus) 43085
Mount Blanchard 45867
Mount Carmel (Cincinnati) 45244
Mount Cory 45868
Mount Eaton 44659
Mount Ephraim 43779
   (Sarahsville)
Mount Gilead 43338
Mount Holly (Waynesville) . 45068
Mount Hope 44660
Mount Joy (Otway) 45657
Mount Liberty 43048
Mount Olive (Bethel) 45106
Mount Olivett 43713
   (Barnesville)
Mount Orab 45154
Mount Perry 43760
Mount Pisgah 45157
   (New Richmond)
Mount Pleasant (Logan) ... 43138
   .... 43939, 44720

Mount Repose (Milford) 45150
Mount Saint Joseph 45051
Mount Sterling 43143
Mount Union (Alliance) 44601
Mount Vernon 43050, 43203
   Academia 43050
   Amity 43050
   Bangs 43050
   Brandon 43050
Mount Victory 43340
Mount Washington 45230
   (Cincinnati)
Mountville (Glouster) 45732
Mowrystown 45155
Moxahala 43761
Moxahala Park 43701
   (Zanesville)
Mt Auburn (Cincinnati) 45219
Mt Lookout (Cincinnati) 45208
Mudsock 43358, 45658
   (West Mansfield)
Muirfield (Dublin) 43017
Mule Town (Minford) 45653
Munks Corners (Columbus) 43227
Munroe Falls 44262
Murdock (Loveland) 45140
Murray City 43144
Museville (Blue Rock) 43720
Mutual 43044, 43078
   (Mechanicsburg)
Nankin 44848
Napoleon 43545
Nashport 43830
Nashville 44661
Navarre 44662
Neapolis 43547
Neelysville 43756
   (Mc Connelsville)
Neffs 43940
Negley 44441
Nelley Island 43324
   (Huntsville)
Nellie (Warsaw) 43844
Nelson (Garrettsville) 44231
Nelsonville 45764
Nevada 44849
Neville 45156
New Albany 43054, 44460
New Alexander 44625
   (East Rochester)
New Alexandria 43938
   (Mingo Junction)
New Athens 43981
New Baltimore (Harrison) .. 45030
New Bavaria 43548
New Bedford 43804, 43824
   (Baltic)
New Bloomington 43341
New Boston (Portsmouth) . 45662
New Bremen 45869
New California 43064
   (Plain City)
New Carlisle 45344
New Castle 43716, 45638
   (Beallsville)
New Concord 43762
New Cumberland 44656
   (Mineral City)
New Dover (Marysville) 43040
New England (Stewart) 45778
New England Hill 43782

(Shawnee)	
New Floodwood	45764
(Nelsonville)	
New Franklin (Minerva)	44657
New Garden (Hanoverton)	44423
New Guilford (Walhonding)	43843
New Hagerstown	44695
(Bowerston)	
New Hampshire	45870
New Harmony	45176
(Williamsburg)	
New Harrisburg	44615
(Carrollton)	
New Haven	44850, 45030
New Holland	43145
New Knoxville	45871
New Lebanon	45345
New Lexington	43764
New London	44851
New Lyme	44047, 44085
(Jefferson)	
New Madison	45346
New Market	44701, 45133
(Canton)	
New Marshfield	45766
New Marshfld	45766
(New Marshfield)	
New Martinsburg	43160
(Washington Court House)	
New Matamoras	45767
New Miami (Hamilton)	45011
New Middletown	44442
New Paris	45347
New Philadelphia	44663
New Pittsburg (Plymouth)	44865
New Plymouth	45654
New Plymouth Heights	45629
(Franklin Furnace)	
New Princeton (Warsaw)	43844
New Richmond	45157
New Riegel	44853
New Rome (Columbus)	43228
New Rumley	43984
New Salem (Pleasantville)	43148
New Springfield	44443
New Straitsville	43766
New Vienna	45159
New Washington	44854
New Waterford	44445
New Weston	45348
New Winchester (Bucyrus)	44820
Newark	43055-058, 43093
Camp Falling Rock	43055
Central City	43055
Clay Lick	43055
Fleatown	43055
Flintridge	43055
Frampton	43055
Hanover	43055
Heath	43056
Hickman	43055
Highwater	43055
Little Texas	43055
Marne	43055
Mary Ann	43055
Mckean	43055
Moundbuilders	43055
Newton	43055
Reform	43055
Rockey Fork	43055
State Farm Insurance	43093

Toboso	43055
Vanatta	43055
Vanburen	43055
Wilkins Corners	43055
Newburg Heights	44127
(Cleveland)	
Newburgh Heights	44105
(Cleveland)	
Newbury	44065
Newcastle (Walhonding)	43843
Newcomerstown	43832
Newell Run (Newport)	45768
Newman (Prospect)	43342
Newport (London)	43140
	44683, 45768, 45845
Beavan	45768
Lower Newport	45768
Newell Run	45768
Schley	45768
Yankeeburg	45768
Newton (Newark)	43055
Newton Falls	44444
Newtonsville	45158
Newtown	43917, 45244-245
(Dillonvale)	
Ney	43549
Niles	44446
Nimisila (Clinton)	44216
Nipgen (Bainbridge)	45612
Noble (Cleveland)	44132
North Baltimore	45872
North Bend	45052
North Benton	44449
North Bloomfield	44450
North Canton	44709, 44720-721
(Canton)	
North College Hill	45224
	45231, 45239
(Cincinnati)	
North Condit (Sunbury)	43074
North E Waterworks	44705
(Canton)	
North Eaton	44028, 44044
(Columbia Station)	
North Fairfield	44855
North Georgetown	44665
North Greenfield	43358
(West Mansfield)	
North Hampton	45349
North Hill (Akron)	44310
North Hills (Logan)	43138
North Industry (Canton)	44707
North Jackson	44451
North Kenova	45680
(South Point)	
North Kingsville	44068
North Lawrence	44666
North Lewisburg	43060
North Liberty (Butler)	44822
North Lirna	44452
North Madison (Madison)	44057
North Monroeville	44847
(Monroeville)	
North Olmsted	44070
North Perry (Perry)	44081
North Randall (Cleveland)	44128
North Ridgeville	44035, 44039
(Elyria)	
Elyria	44039
North Robinson	44856
North Royalton	44133

North Salem (Kimbolton)	43749
North Star	45350
North Uniontown	45133
(Hillsboro)	
North Westerville	43081
(Westerville)	
North Woodbury	44813
(Bellville)	
North Zanesville	43701
(Zanesville)	
Northampton	44221
(Cuyahoga Falls)	
Northfield	44056, 44067
(Macedonia)	
Sagamore Hills	44067
Northridge (Dayton)	45413-414
Northside (Cincinnati)	45223
Northup (Patriot)	45658
Northville (Urbana)	43078
Northwest (Columbus)	43220
Northwood	43605, 43619
(Toledo)	
Norton (Waldo)	43356, 44203
Norwalk	44857
Norwich	43767
Norwood (Cincinnati)	45212
Nova	44859
Novelty	44072-073
O'bryonville (Cincinnati)	45208
Oak Grove (Nelsonville)	45764
Oak Harbor	43449
Oak Hill	45656
Oak Run (Mount Sterling)	43143
Oakdale (Glouster)	45732
Oakfield	43731, 44450
(Crooksville)	
Oakland (Amanda)	43102
Oakland Park (Columbus)	43224
Oakley (Cincinnati)	45209
Oakwood (Dayton)	45409
	45419, 45873
Oakwood Village (Bedford)	44146
Oberlin	44074
Obetz (Columbus)	43207
Oceola	44860
Oconnor Landing	43310
(Belle Center)	
Octa	43160
(Washington Court House)	
Ohio City	45874
Okeana	45053
Okolona	43550
Olbers (Glouster)	45732
Old Fort	44861
Old Plymouth Heights	45629
(Franklin Furnace)	
Old Sawmill (Dublin)	43017
Old Straitsville	43766
(New Straitsville)	
Old Town (Portland)	45770
Old Washington	43768
Olena (Norwalk)	44857
Olive (Long Bottom)	45743
Olive Green (Sunbury)	43074
Olivesburg (Ashland)	44805
Olmsted Falls	44138
Omega (Waverly)	45690
Oneida (Malvern)	44644
Ontario	44862
Opperman (Cumberland)	43732
Orange (Newcomerstown)	43832

Rappsburg (Scottown) 45678	
Rarden 45671	
Ratcliffburg 45647	
(Londonderry)	
Rathbone (Delaware) 43015	
Ravenna 44266	
Rawson (Jenera) 45841, 45881	
Ray45672	
Rayland 43943	
Raymond 43067	
Rays Corners (Jefferson) .. 44047	
Readers Digest (Marion) .. 43307	
Reading (Somerset) 43783	
.... 44665, 45215	
Red Diamond (Mc Arthur) . 45651	
Redfield (New Lexington) .. 43764	
Redhaw (Polk) 44866	
Redoak (Ripley) 45167	
Redtown (Glouster) 45732	
Reed (Attica) 44807	
Reedsville 45772	
Reedtown (Attica) 44807	
Reedurban (Canton) 44710	
Reese (Columbus) 43207	
Reesville 45166	
Reform (Newark) 43055	
Rehoboth (New Lexington) 43764	
Reily (Oxford) 45056	
Reinersville 43756	
(Mc Connelsville)	
Reminderville (Aurora) 44202	
Rendville (Corning) 43730	
Reno 45773	
Renrock (Cumberland) 43732	
Republic 44867	
Resaca (Plain City) 43064	
Reynoldsburg 43068	
Riceland (Orrville) 44667	
Rich Hill (Centerburg) 43011	
Richfield 44286	
Richland (Marion) .. 43302, 43310	
.... 43359, 43780, 44628	
Richmond 43944, 44890	
Richmond Dale 45673	
Richmond Heights 44143	
(Cleveland)	
Richmondale 45673	
(Richmond Dale)	
Richville (Canton) 44706	
Richwood 43344	
Ridge (Carey) 43316	
Ridgefield (Monroeville) 44847	
Ridgeland (Jackson) 45640	
Ridgeville (Elyria) 44035	
Ridgeville Corners 43555	
Ridgeway 43345	
Ridgewood (Zanesville) 43701	
Rinard Mills (Graysville) ... 45734	
Ringgold (Malta) 43758	
Ringo (Marengo) 43334	
Ringold (Circleville) 43113	
Rio Grande 45674	
Ripley (Shreve) 44676, 45167	
Levanna 45167	
Redoak 45167	
Stringtown 45167	
Risingsun 43457	
Rittman 44270	
River Bend (Columbus) 43223	
River Corners (Spencer) ... 44275	
River Styx (Medina) 44256	

Riveredge (Cleveland) 44135	
Riverlea (Columbus) 43085	
Riverside 45204, 45431	
(Cincinnati)	
Riverside Park 44683	
(Uhrichsville)	
Rix Mills (New Concord) ... 43762	
Roadway Express (Akron) 44393	
Roaming Shores 44084-085	
(Rock Creek)	
Roanoke (Uhrichsville) 44683	
Roberts (Roseville) 43777	
Robertsville 44670	
Robins (Byesville) 43723	
Rochester (Wellington) 44090	
Rock Camp 45675	
Rock Creek 44084	
Rock Mills 43160	
(Washington Court House)	
Rockbridge 43149	
Rockey Fork (Newark) 43055	
Rockford 45882	
Rockland (Belpre) 45714	
Rockville (Stout) 45684	
Rocky Ridge 43458	
Rocky River 44116	
Rockyhill (Jackson) 45640	
Rodney (Gallipolis) 45631	
Rogers 44455	
Rolandus (Racine) 45771	
Rome 44085, 44878	
.... 45669, 45684	
Hartsgrove 44085	
New Lyme 44085	
Roaming Shores 44085	
Rootstown 44272	
Roscoe (Coshocton) 43812	
Rose Farm (Crooksville) ... 43731	
Rosedale (Irwin) 43029	
Roselawn 45222, 45237	
(Cincinnati)	
Roseville 43777	
Rosewood 43070	
Ross 45061	
Rossburg 45348, 45362	
(New Weston)	
Rossford 43460	
Rossmoyne (Cincinnati) 45236	
Rossville (Hamilton) 45013	
Roundhead 43346	
Rowsburg (Polk) 44866	
Roxabell (Frankfort) 45628	
Roxbury (Stockport) 43787	
Royalton (Lancaster) 43130	
Royersville (Ironton) 45638	
Rubyville (Lucasville) 45648	
Rudolph 43462	
Ruggles (New London) 44851	
Ruggles Beach (Huron) 44839	
Ruraldale (Blue Rock) 43720	
Rush (Uhrichsville) 44683	
Rushcreek (Bremen) 43107	
Rushsylvania 43347	
Rushtown (Mc Dermott) 45652	
Rushville 43150	
Russell (Novelty) 44072	
Russell Township 44022	
(Chagrin Falls)	
Russells Point 43348	
Russellville 45168	
Russia 45363	

Rutland 45775	
Sabina 45169	
Sagamore Hills 44067	
(Northfield)	
Saint Bernard 45216-217	
.... 45232	
(Cincinnati)	
Saint Clair (Hamilton) 45011	
Saint Clairsville 43950	
Saint Henry 45883	
Saint Johns 45884	
Saint Joseph (Mogadore) .. 44260	
Saint Louisville 43071	
Saint Martin 45118	
(Fayetteville)	
Saint Marys 45885	
Saint Paris 43072	
Salem (Newcomerstown) .. 43832	
.... 44460, 45745	
Goshen 44460	
New Albany 44460	
Patmos 44460	
Salem Center (Langsville) . 45741	
Salesville 43778	
Salineville 43945	
Salt Creek (Mount Hope) .. 44660	
Salt Rack (Morral) 43337	
Saltillo (New Lexington) 43764	
Samantha (Leesburg) 45135	
San Margherita (Columbus) 43204	
Sand Hill (Reno) 45773	
Sand Ridge (Millfield) 45761	
Sandrun (Nelsonville) 45764	
Sandusky 44870-871	
Bay View 44870	
Bloomingville 44870	
Sandy Spring (Stout) 45684	
Sandyville 44671	
Santoy (Corning) 43730	
Sarahsville 43779	
Sardinia 45171	
Sardis 43946	
Sassafrass Point 43331	
(Lakeview)	
Savannah 44874	
Saybrook 44004, 44041	
(Ashtabula)	
Saylor Park (Cincinnati) 45233	
Sayre (Crooksville) 43731	
Schley (Newport) 45768	
Scio 43988	
Scioto Furnace 45677	
Scioto Village (Delaware) .. 43015	
Sciotoville (Portsmouth) ... 45662	
Scott 45886	
Scottown 45678	
Scroggsfield (Carrollton) .. 44615	
Seaman 45679	
Sears Roebuck (Toledo) ... 43655	
Sebring 44672	
Sedalia 43151	
Seilcrest Acres 45140	
(Loveland)	
Selma (South Charleston) . 45368	
Seminole Island 43324	
(Huntsville)	
Senecaville 43780	
Seven Hills (Cleveland) 44131	
Seven Mile 45062	
Seville 44273	
Sewellsville 43713	

(Barnesville)
Shade 45776
Shademore (Cincinnati) 45244
Shadeville (Lockbourne) ... 43137
Shadyside 43947
Shaker Heights 44118
.... 44120, 44122
(Cleveland)
Shalersville (Mantua) 44255
Shandon 45063
Shanesville (Sugarcreek) .. 44681
Shannon (Dresden) 43821
Sharon (Caldwell) 43724
Sharon Center 44274
Sharon Township (Shelby) 44875
Sharonville (Cincinnati) 45241
Sharpsburg (Amesville) 45777
Shauck 43349
Shawnee 43782
Shawnee Hills (Powell) 43065
Shawnee Island 43324
(Huntsville)
Sheffield (Lorain) 44055
Sheffield Lake 44054
Sheffield Township 44047
(Jefferson)
Shelby 44875
Shenadoah (Shiloh) 44878
Shenandoah (Greenwich) .. 44837
Shephard (Columbus) 43219
Sheridan (South Point) 45680
Sherrodsville 44675
Sherwood 43556
Shiloh 44878
Shincrock (Huron) 44839
Shore (Cleveland) 44123
Short Creek 43989
Shreve 44676
Siam (Attica) 44807
Sidney 45365, 46367
Silver Lake 44224
(Cuyahoga Falls)
Silverton (Cincinnati) 45236
Sims Station 43338
(Mount Gilead)
Sinking Spring 45172
Smithfield 43948
Smithville 43351, 44677
(Upper Sandusky)
Solon 44139
Somerdale 44678
Somerset 43783
Somerton (Barnesville) 43713
Somerville 45064
Sonora (Zanesville) 43701
South Amherst (Amherst) .. 44001
South Arlington (Akron) 44306
South Bloomfield 43103
(Ashville)
South Bloomingville 43152
South Charleston 45368
South Condit (Sunbury) 43074
South Euclid 44118, 44121
(Cleveland)
South Lebanon 45065
South Logan (Logan) 43138
South Lorain (Lorain) 44055
South Madison (Madison) . 44057
South Newbury (Newbury) 44065
South Olive (Caldwell) 43724
South Perry (Laurelville) ... 43135

South Plymouth 43160
(Washington Court House)
South Point 45680
South Russell 44022
(Chagrin Falls)
South Salem 45681
South Solon 43153
South Vienna 45369
South Webster 45682
South Zanesville 43701
(Zanesville)
Southington 44470
Spargursville 45612
(Bainbridge)
Sparta 43350
Speidel (Bethesda) 43719
Spencer 44275
Spencerville 45887
Spg Valley 45370
(Spring Valley)
Spiller (Portland) 45770
Sprague (Graysville) 45734
Spring Hills 43357
(West Liberty)
Spring Mountain (Warsaw) 43844
Spring Valley 45370
Springboro 45066
Springdale (Cincinnati) 45246
Springfield 45501-506
Springhills (De Graff) 43318
Springvale (Loveland) 45140
Springville (Carey) . 43316, 44676
Stafford 43786
Stanleyville (Whipple) 45788
Starr (New Plymouth) 45654
State Road 44223
(Cuyahoga Falls)
Staunton 43160
(Washington Court House)
Steam Corners (Mansfield) 44904
Steelville (Loveland) 45140
Sterling 44276
Steuben (Monroeville) 44847
Steubenville 43952
Stewart 45778
Stewartsville 43960
Stillwater 44679
Stillwell (Killbuck) 44637
Stiversville (Portland) 45770
Stock Yards (Cincinnati) ... 45225
Stockdale 45683
Stockport 43770, 43787
(Pennsville)
Brokaw 43787
Dale 43787
Hooksburg 43787
Palmer 43787
Pennsville 43787
Roxbury 43787
Todds 43787
Windsor 43787
Stone Creek 43840
Stonelick (Batavia) 45103
Stony Ridge 43463
Stout 45684
Stoutsville 43154
Stovertown (Zanesville) 43701
Stow (Cuyahoga Falls) 44224
Straight Fork 45734
(Graysville)
Strasburg 44680

Stratford (Delaware) 43015
Stratton 43961
Stream Side 45629
(Franklin Furnace)
Streetsboro 44241
Stringtown (Felicity) 45120
.... 45167, 45701
Strongsville 44136
Struthers 44471
Stryker 43557
Suffield (Mogadore) 44260
Sugar Grove 43155
Sugar Grove Lake (Galion) 44833
Sugar Tree Ridge 45133
(Hillsboro)
Sugarcreek 44681
Sullivan 44880
Sulphur Springs 44881
Summerfield 43788
Summerford (London) 43140
Summersville (Richwood) . 43344
Summit Station 43073
Summitville 43962
Sunbury 43074
Sundale (Norwich) 43767
Sunny Meade (Cambridge) 43725
Sunset Isle (Huntsville) 43324
Sunshine (Stout) 45684
Swanton 43558
Sybene (South Point) 45680
Sycamore 44882
.... 45242, 45249
Belle Vernon 44882
Benton 44882
Deunquat 44882
Lemert 44882
Mexico 44882
Plankton 44882
Sycamore Township 45236
.... 45242, 45249
(Cincinnati)
Sycamore Valley 43789
Sylvania 43560
Symmes Township 45140
.... 45242, 45249
(Loveland)
Syracuse 45779
Tacoma (Barnesville) 43713
Taft (Cincinnati) 45213, 45236
Tallmadge 44278
Tarlton 43156
Taylortown (Shelby) 44875
Tecumseh Island 43324
(Huntsville)
Temperanceville 43713
(Barnesville)
Terrace Park 45174
Terre Haute (Urbana) 43078
Thackery (Urbana) 43078
Thatcher (Circleville) 43113
The Plains 45780
Thivener (Gallipolis) 45631
Thompson 44086
Thornville 43076
Thurman 45685
Thurston 43157
Tick Ridge 43143
(Mount Sterling)
Tidd Dale (Brilliant) 43913
Tidewater (Edison) 43320
Tiffin 44883

Tiltonsville 43963
Timberlake (Willoughby) ... 44095
Tipp City 45371
Tippecanoe 44699
Tiro 44887
Toboso (Newark) 43055
Todds (Stockport) 43787
Toledo 43600-615, 43617, 43620
. 43623-24, 43635, 43652-57
.... 43659-661, 43666-667
.... 43681-682, 43697, 43699
    Northwood 43605
    Oregon 43605
    Owens Corning 43659
    Owens Illinois 43666
    Sears Roebuck 43655
Tontogany 43565
Torch 45781
Toronto 43964
Tradersville (London) 43140
Trail (Dundee) 44624
Trail Run (New Matamoras) 45767
Tranquility (Seaman) 45679
Tremont City 45372
Trenton 45067
Tri Village (Columbus) 43212
Triadelphia (Malta) 43758
Trimble 45782
Trinway 43842
Trotwood (Dayton) . 45416, 45426
Troy (Burton)
.... 44021, 45373, 45374
Truetown (Millfield) 45761
Trumbull (Geneva) 44041
Truro (Reynoldsburg) 43068
Tucson (Chillicothe) 45601
Tunnel Hill (Warsaw) 43844
Tuppers Plains 45783
Turkey Foot (Lakeview) 44331
Tuscarawas 44682
Twenty Mile Stand 45140
    (Loveland)
Twightwee (Loveland) 45140
Twin (Bourneville) 45617
Twinsburg 44087
Tyndall (Coshocton) 43812
Uhrichsville 44683
Union 43160, 43311
.... 43759, 45322
    (Washington Court House)
Union City 45390
Union Furnace 43158
Union Station (Granville) ... 43023
Unionport 43966
Uniontown 44685
Unionville 44088
Unionville Center 43077
Uniopolis 45888
Unity 44413, 45693
    (East Palestine)
University (Columbus) 43210
University Heights 44118
    (Cleveland)
Upper Arlington (Columbus) 43212
.... 43220-221
Upper Sandusky 43351
Urbana 43078
Urbancrest (Grove City) 43123
Utica 43080
Utopia (Georgetown) 45121
Valley (Pleasant City) 43772

Valley City 44280
Valley View 44125, 44131
    (Cleveland)
Valleydale (Cincinnati) 45216
Valleyview (Columbus) 43204
Van Buren 45389
Van Wert 45891
Vanatta (Newark) 43055
Vanburen (Newark) 43055
Vandalia 45377
Vanlue 45890
Vaughnsville 45893
Venedocia 45894
Vera Cruz (Fayetteville) 45118
Vermilion 44089
Vernon (Kinsman) .. 44428, 44875
Vernon Heights (Marion) ... 43302
Verona 45378
Versailles 45380
Vesuvius (Pedro) 45659
Veto (Belpre) 45714
Vickery 43464
Vicksville (Glouster) 45732
Vienna 44473
Vigo (Chillicothe) 45601
Vincent 45784
Vinton 45686
Waco (Canton) 44707
Wade (New Matamoras) 45767
Wadsworth 44281
Wagon Wheel 43143
    (Mount Sterling)
Wagram (Pataskala) 43062
Waite Hill (Willoughby) 44094
Wakatomika (Dresden) 43821
Wakefield 45687
Wakeman 44889
Walbridge 43465
Waldo 43356
Walhonding 43772, 43843
    (Pleasant City)
    Butler 43843
    Cavallo 43843
    New Guilford 43843
    Newcastle 43843
    Perry 43843
Walnut (Patriot) 45658
Walnut Creek 44687
Walnut Grove 43311
    (Bellefontaine)
Walnut Hills 45206, 45640
    (Cincinnati)
Walnutrun (London) 43140
Walton Hills (Bedford) 44146
Wamsley (Otway) 45657
Wapak (Wapakoneta) 45895
Wapakoneta 45895
Warner (Lower Salem) 45745
Warnock 43967
Warren 44481-488
    Business Reply 44488
    Champion 44483
    Courtesy Reply 44487
    Howland 44484
    Lordstown 44481
Warren County 45044
    (Middletown)
Warrensburg 43015, 43061
    (Delaware)
Warrensville Heights 44122
.... 44128

    (Cleveland)
Warsaw 43844
Washington (Circleville) 43113
.... 43138, 43160, 43716
.... 43749, 43832, 43842
44638, 44699, 45656, 45734
Washingtonville 44490
Waterbury 43348
    (Russells Point)
Waterford 43019, 45786
    (Fredericktown)
Waterloo 43110, 45688
    (Canal Winchester)
Watertown 45787
Waterville 43566
Watkins (Marysville) 43040
Wauseon 43567
Waverly 45690
Way Ridge (Graysville) 45734
Wayland 44285
Wayne (Circleville) 43113
.... 43466, 43773
.... 44093, 44624, 45734
Waynesburg 44688
Waynesfield 45896
Waynesville 45068
Webb Summit (Logan) 43138
Wellington 44090
Wellston 45692
Wellsville 43968
Welshfield (Burton) 44021
Wesley (Bartlett) 45713
West Akron (Akron) 44307
West Alex 45381
    (West Alexandria)
West Alexandria 45381
West Andover (Andover) ... 44003
West Bedford (Warsaw) 43844
West Belpre (Belpre) 45714
West Carrollton 44615
.... 45439, 45449
    (Carrollton)
West Chester 44699
.... 45069, 45071
    (Tippecanoe)
    Pisgah 45069
West Clarksfield 44889
    (Wakeman)
West Elkton 45070
West End (Ashtabula) 44004
West Fairport 44045
    (Grand River)
West Farmington 44491
West Jackson (Richwood) . 43344
West Jefferson 43162
West Lafayette 43845
West Lancaster 43128
    (Jeffersonville)
West Lebanon (Dalton) 44618
West Leipsic (Leipsic) 45856
West Liberty 43357
West Logan (Logan) 43138
West London (London) 43140
West Manchester 45382
West Mansfield 43358
West Marietta (Marietta) ... 45750
West Mecca (Cortland) 44410
West Middletown 45042
    (Middletown)
West Millgrove 43467
West Milton 45383

West Point 44492, 44833
West Portsmouth 45662
(Portsmouth)
West Richfield 44286
(Richfield)
West Rushville 43163
West Salem 44287
West Town (Marion) 43302
West Union 45693
West Unity 43570
West Williamsfield 44093
(Williamsfield)
West Worthington 43234-235
(Columbus)
Westboro (Midland) 45148
Western Hills 45233, 45238
(Cincinnati)
Westerville 43081-082, 43086
Gateway 43081
North Westerville 43081
Westfield (Ashley) 43003
Westfield Center 44251
Westlake 44145
Westland 43228, 43725
(Columbus)
Weston 43569
Westville 43083, 44609
Westwood (Cincinnati) 45248
Weymouth (Medina) 44256
Wharton 43359
Wheelersburg 45694
Whigville (Summerfield) ... 43788
Whipple 45788
Whispering Valley 43333
(Lewistown)
Whistler (Kingston) 45644
White Cottage 43791
White Oak 45239, 45247
(Cincinnati)
White Sulphur (Ostrander) 43061
Whitehall (Columbus) 43213
Whitehouse 43571
Whiteoak (Mount Sterling) 43143
Wickliffe 44092
Widowville (Ashland) 44805
Wilberforce 45384
Wilbren (New Lexington) ... 43764
Wilkesville 45695
Wilkins Corners (Newark) . 43055
Will O Bee (Willoughby) 44094
Willard 44888, 44890
Willetsville (Hillsboro) 45133
Williamsburg 45176
Williamsfield 44093
Williamsport 43164, 43338
Williamstown 45897

Williston 43468
Willoughby 44094-095
Eastlake 44095
Kirtland 44094
Lakeline 44095
Timberlake 44094
Waite Hill 44094
Will O Bee 44094
Willowick 44094-44095
Willoughby Hills 44092
(Wickliffe)
Willow Lakes (Zanesville) . 43701
Willow Wood 45696
Willowick 44092, 44094-095
(Wickliffe)
Wills Creek (Conesville) 43811
Willshire 45898
Wilmington 45177
Wilmot 44689
Wilson (Beallsville) 43716
Winchester 45697
Windham 44288
Windsor (Stockport) 43787
.... 44099, 44903
Winesburg 44690
Winfield (Dover) 44622
Wingett Run 45789
Winona 44493
Winterset (Lore City) 43755
Wintersville 43952
(Steubenville)
Winton Place 45216, 45232
(Cincinnati)
Withamsville (Cincinnati) .. 45245
Wolf (Newcomerstown) 43832
Wolf Run 43970
Woodlawn (Cincinnati) 45215
Woodmere (Cleveland) 44122
Woodsfield 43793
Woodstock 43084
Woodville 43469
Wooster 44691
Worthington (Columbus) ... 43085
Wren 45899
Wright Patterson 45431, 45433
(Dayton)
Wrightstown (Glouster) 45732
Wrightsville (Manchester) .. 45144
Wyandot (Nevada) 44849
Wyoming (Cincinnati) 45215
Xenia 45385
Xerox (Columbus) 43267
Yale (Deerfield) 44411
Yankee Lake (Brookfield) .. 44403
Yankeeburg (Newport) 45768
Yankeetown (Hamersville) . 45130

Yatesville (Bloomingburg) . 43106
Yellow Bud (Chillicothe) 45601
Yellow Springs 45387
York (Crooksville) ... 43731, 45764
York Center (Raymond) 43067
Yorkshire 45388
Yorkville 43971
Yost (Glenford) 43739
Young Hickory 43732
(Cumberland)
Youngstown 44500-507
.... 44509-515, 44555
.... 44598-599
Austintown 44515
Boardman 44512-44513
Business Reply 44598
Cornersburg 44511
Courtesy Reply 44599
Poland 44514
Youngsville (Seaman) 45679
Zaleski 45698
Zanesfield 43360
Zanesville 43701-702, 43721
Buckeye 43701
Darlington 43701
Dillon Falls 43701
Licking View 43701
Meadowbrook 43701
Melody Lake 43701
Midtown 43701
Morrisons 43701
Moxahala Park 43701
North Zanesville 43701
Owens Hill 43701
Pleasant Grove 43701
Ridgewood 43701
Sonora 43701
South Zanesville 43701
Stovertown 43701
Willow Lakes 43701
Zanns Corners (Waverly) .. 45690
Zeno (Cumberland) 43732
Zoar 44697
Zoarville (Mineral City) 44656

AKRON

APARTMENTS

Alcazar
627 W MARKET ST 44303

Avalon
214 N PORTAGE PATH 44303

Blair House
255 N PORTAGE PATH 44303

Buchtel House
770 E BUCHTEL AVE 44305

Carlton House
275 N PORTAGE PATH 44303

Cotter House
50 COTTER AVE 44305

Diplomat Apts
1350 N HOWARD ST 44310

Fir Hill Towers
77 FIR HL 44304

Highland Square Apts
733 W MARKET ST 44303

Highland Towers
900 W MARKET ST 44313

Hill Chateau
26 E TALLMADGE AVE 44310

Ontario Apts
264 W MARKET ST 44303

Saferstein Towers #1
525 DIAGONAL RD 44320

Saferstein Towers #2
585 DIAGONAL RD 44320

BUILDINGS

1st Federal Building
326 S MAIN ST 44308

1st National Tower Building
106 S MAIN ST 44308

Akron Centre
50 S MAIN ST 44308

Chapel Hill Mall
2000 BRITTAIN RD 44310

Citi Center
146 S HIGH ST 44308

Edison Building
76 S MAIN ST 44308

Huntington Building
137 S MAIN ST 44308

Peoples Federal Building
39 E MARKET ST 44308

Society Building
159 S MAIN ST 44308

Summit Mall
3265 W MARKET ST 44333

GOVERNMENT

City Cty Safety Building
217 S HIGH ST 44308

Courthouse
209 S HIGH ST 44308

Federal Building
2 S MAIN ST 44308

Municipal Building
166 S HIGH ST 44308

State Office Building
161 S HIGH ST 44308

AUBURN

BUILDINGS

Stepnorth I
100 N MAIN ST 44022

BEAVER PARK

APARTMENTS

Executive Apts
5537 BEAVERCREST DR   44053

BUILDINGS

Professional Building
3600 KOLBE RD 44053

BEECHWOLD

APARTMENTS

Worthington Terrace Apt
60 Broadmeadows Blvd 43214

BEXLEY

APARTMENTS

Bexley Towers
2877 E BROAD ST 43209

Heritage Tower
1145 COLLEGE AVE 43209

Heritage Tower
1145 COLUMBUS LANCASTER
RD 43209

BRATENAHL

APARTMENTS

Bratenahl Place
1 BRATENAHL PL 44108

CANTON

APARTMENTS

Downtowner Motor Inn
621 MARKET AVE N 44702

BUILDINGS

Amer Trust Bank Building
116 CLEVELAND AVE NW 44702

Bank One Towers
101 CENTRAL PLZ S 44702

Belden Village Tower
4450 Belden Village St NW 44718

Bliss Towers
217 2ND ST NW 44702

Carnegie Building
236 3RD ST SW 44702

Commercial Building
205 MARKET AVE S 44702

Harter Bank Building
126 2ND ST NE 44702

Mellett Building
115 DEWALT AVE NW 44702

Natl City Bank Building
315 TUSCARAWAS ST W 44702

Renkert Building
306 MARKET AVE N 44702

William R Day Building
121 CLEVELAND AVE SW 44702

GOVERNMENT

City Hall Building
218 CLEVELAND AVE SW 44702

CENTERVILLE

BUILDINGS

Dayton Mall
2700 STATE ROUTE 725 . 45459

Dayton Mall
2700 MIAMISBURG
CENTERVILLE RD 45459

CHAMPION

GOVERNMENT

Municipal Building
141 SOUTH ST SE 44483

Warren City Hall
391 MAHONING AVE NW . 44483

CHRISTOPHER COLUMBUS

APARTMENTS

Americana
370 S 5TH ST 43215

Bolinger Tower
750 N HIGH ST 43215

Greystone Court Apt
815 N HIGH ST 43215

Jaycee Arms
266 E MAIN ST 43215

Mcdowell Center
241 MCDOWELL ST 43215

Nazareth Tower
300 E RICH ST 43215

One Americana
380 S 5TH ST 43215

Sunshine Terrace
272 S GIFT ST 43215

The Waterford Tower
155 W MAIN ST 43215

Thurber Tower
645 NEIL AVE 43215

Townley Court
580 E TOWN ST 43215

BUILDINGS

Aep Building
1 RIVERSIDE PLZ 43215

Atlas Building
8 E LONG ST 43215

Bank Building
17 S HIGH ST 43215

Bryden Building
700 BRYDEN RD 43215

Buckeye Federal
42 E GAY ST 43215

Columbus Center
100 E BROAD ST 43215

Connor Building
233 S HIGH ST 43215

Court House Annex
410 S HIGH ST 43215

Gay High Building
51 N HIGH ST 43215

High Long
5 E LONG ST 43215

Huntington Bank Building
41 S HIGH ST 43215

Huntington Trust
37 W BROAD ST 43215

IBM
140 E TOWN ST 43215

Lincoln Leveque
50 W BROAD ST 43215

Midland Building
250 E BROAD ST 43215

Motorist Building
471 E BROAD ST 43215

National City Bank
155 E BROAD ST 43215

Ohio Center
400 N HIGH ST 43215

One Capital South
175 S 3RD ST 43215

One Columbus
10 W BROAD ST 43215

One Marconi
274 MARCONI BLVD 43215

One Nationwide Plaza
1 W NATIONWIDE BLVD .. 43215

One Nationwide Plaza
1 NATIONWIDE PLZ 43215

One Nationwide Plaza
1 W NATIONWIDE PLZ 43215

Scoa Building
33 N HIGH ST 43215

Society Bank Building
88 BROAD ST. 43215

State Office Building
65 S FRONT ST 43215

Three Nationwide Plaza
3 NATIONWIDE PLZ 43215

Three Nationwide Plaza
245 N HIGH ST 43215

Trautman Building
209 S HIGH ST 43215

Two Nationwide Plaza
2 E NATIONWIDE BLVD ... 43215

Two Nationwide Plaza
2 NATIONWIDE PLZ 43215

Workmans Compensation Bld
30 W SPRING ST 43215

GOVERNMENT

Beacon Building
50 W GAY ST 43215

City Of Columbus
99 N FRONT ST 43215

City Of Columbus
90 W BROAD ST 43215

Front Street Building
109 N FRONT ST 43215

New Federal Building
200 N HIGH ST 43215

State House Capital
60 STATE HOUSE 43215

State Office Tower
30 E BROAD ST 43215

State Office Tower
77 S HIGH ST 43215

Us Government
85 MARCONI BLVD 43215

CINCINNATI

APARTMENTS

Adams Landing
900 ADAMS XING 45202

Blue Fountain Apt
1673 CEDAR AVE 45224

East Oak Manor Apt
310 OAK ST 45219

Edgecliff Apt
2210 VICTORY PKY 45206

Garfield Tower
111 GARFIELD PL 45202

Hammond North Apt
5300 HAMILTON AVE 45224

Queens Tower Apt
810 MATSON PL 45204

Regency Apt
2444 MADISON RD 45208

Riverview Terrace
2401 INGLESIDE AVE 45206

Summit View Apt
2660 LEHMAN RD 45204

The Gramercy
135 GARFIELD PL 45202

BUILDINGS

1st Nat Bank Building
105 E 4TH ST 45202

1st Nat Bank Ctr
425 WALNUT ST 45202

4th National Bank Building
18 E 4TH ST 45202

580 Building
580 WALNUT ST 45202

5th & Race Tower
120 W 5TH ST 45202

Alms & Doepke Building
222 E CENTRAL PKY 45202

American Building
30 E CENTRAL PKY 45202

Atlas Bank Building
524 WALNUT ST 45202

Atrium I
201 E 4TH ST 45202

Atrium II
221 E 4TH ST 45202

Bartlett Building
36 E 4TH ST 45202

Carew Tower
441 VINE ST 45202

Central Trust Center
201 E 5TH ST 45202

Central Trust Tower
5 W 4TH ST 45202

Cincinnati Commerce Cente
600 VINE ST 45202

Commerce Building
100 E 8TH ST 45202

Daylight Building
659 VAN METER ST 45202

Dixie Terminal Building
49 E 4TH ST 45202

Doctors Building
19 GARFIELD PL 45202

Enquirer Building
617 VINE ST 45202

Executive Building
35 E 7TH ST 45202

Federal Reserve Bank
150 E 4TH ST 45202

Federated Building
7 W 7TH ST 45202

Fifth Third Center
511 WALNUT ST 45202

Formica Building
120 E 4TH ST 45202

Gwynne Building
602 MAIN ST 45202

Hunter Saving Loan Building
14 E 4TH ST 45202

Jewelers Exchange Building
37 W 7TH ST 45202

Kroger Building
1014 VINE ST 45202

Lytle Tower Apt
405 BROADWAY ST 45202

Mercantile Library Building
414 WALNUT ST 45202

Merchants Building
34 W 6TH ST 45202

Provident Bank Building
630 VINE ST 45202

Provident Tower
1 E 4TH ST 45202

Sami Burke Building
800 BROADWAY ST 45202

Terrace Hilton Building
15 W 6TH ST 45202

Tri State Building
432 WALNUT ST 45202

Walnut Towers
898 WALNUT ST 45202

GOVERNMENT

City Hall
801 PLUM ST 45202

Federal/John Peck Building
550 MAIN ST 45202

Ham County Courthouse
1000 MAIN ST 45202

US Post Office & Ct House
100 E 5TH ST 45202

HOSPITALS

Garfield House Hotel
2 GARFIELD PL 45202

HOTELS

Cincinnatian Hotel
601 VINE ST 45202

Vernon Manor Hotel
400 OAK ST 45219

CLEVELAND

APARTMENTS

Berkshire Cleveland
11820 EDGEWATER DR .. 44107

Bohn Towers
1300 SUPERIOR AVE E 44114

Carlyle
12900 LAKE AVE 44107

Carter Manor
1012 PROSPECT AVE E ... 44115

Chesterfield Apts
1120 CHESTER AVE 44114

Commodore Apts
1990 FORD DR 44106

Edgewater Towers
11720 EDGEWATER DR .. 44107

Fenway Manor
1986 E 107TH ST 44106

Imperial House
11900 EDGEWATER DR .. 44107

Lakeshore Towers
12506 EDGEWATER DR .. 44107

Marine Towers East
12520 EDGEWATER DR .. 44107

Marine Towers West
12540 EDGEWATER DR .. 44107

Reserve Square
1700 E 13TH ST 44114

Three Village Condos
5200 THREE VILLAGE DR 44124

University Towers
1575 EAST BLVD 44106

Waterford
12500 EDGEWATER DR .. 44107

Winton Place
12700 LAKE AVE 44107

BUILDINGS

1001 Building
1001 EUCLID AVE 44115

1010 Euclid Building
1010 EUCLID AVE 44115

666 Euclid Building
668 EUCLID AVE 44114

B P America Building
200 PUBLIC SQ 44114

Bank One Building
1255 EUCLID AVE 44115

Bank One Center
600 SUPERIOR AVE E 44114

Blue Cross Blue Shield
2060 E 9TH ST 44115

Bond Court Building
1300 E 9TH ST 44114

Bulkley Building
1501 EUCLID AVE 44115

Burke Lakefront Airport
1501 N MARGINAL DR 44114

Caxton Building
812 HURON RD E 44115

Center West Building
20950 Center Ridge Rd 44116

Centerline Building I
19201 VILLAVIEW RD 44119

Citizens Building
850 EUCLID AVE 44114

Cleve Hopkins Intl Arpt
5300 RIVERSIDE DR 44135

Cleveland Stadium
1085 W 3RD ST 44114

Colonial Arcade
530 EUCLID AVE 44115

County Administration Bld
1219 ONTARIO ST 44113

Courthouse Sq Development
310 W LAKESIDE AVE 44113

Diamond Building
1100 SUPERIOR AVE E 44114

Dodge Building
1901 E 13TH ST 44114

East Ohio Gas Building
1717 E 9TH ST 44114

Eaton Center
1111 SUPERIOR AVE E 44114

Euclid Arcade
510 EUCLID AVE 44115

Fidelity Building
1940 E 6TH ST 44114

Film Exchange Building
2108 PAYNE AVE 44114

Finance Building
750 PROSPECT AVE E 44115

Galleria/tower At Erievw
1301 E 9TH ST 44114

Guildhall Building
45 PROSPECT AVE NW 44115

Hanna Building
1422 EUCLID AVE 44115

Huntington Building
925 EUCLID AVE 44115

I N A Building
14701 DETROIT AVE 44107

Illuminating Building
55 PUBLIC SQ 44113

Investment Plaza
1801 E 9TH ST 44114

Justice Center
1200 ONTARIO ST 44113

Kaiser Medical Building
50 SEVERANCE CIR 44118

Keith Building
1621 EUCLID AVE 44115

L T V Steel Building
25 PROSPECT AVE NW 44115

Lakewood Center West
14650 DETROIT AVE 44107

Lakewood Ctr North
14600 DETROIT AVE 44107

Landmark Office Towers
101 PROSPECT AVE NW .. 44115

Lincoln Building
1367 E 6TH ST 44114

M K Ferguson Building
1500 W 3RD ST 44113

Marion Building
1276 W 3RD ST 44113

Midland Building
101 PROSPECT AVE NW .. 44115

National City Bank Building
629 EUCLID AVE 44114

National City E 6th Building
1965 E 6TH ST 44114

Natl City Center
1900 E 9TH ST 44114

Nineteen Hundred Euclid
1900 EUCLID AVE 44115

Northern Ohio Bank Building
1370 ONTARIO ST 44113

Ohio Savings Plaza
1801 E 9TH ST 44114

One Cleveland Center
1375 E 9TH ST 44114

One Erieview Plaza
1 ERIEVIEW PLZ 44114

One Playhouse Sq Building
1375 EUCLID AVE 44115

Osborn Med Building
1020 HURON RD E 44115

Park Building
140 PUBLIC SQ 44114

Park Chester Building
10605 CHESTER AVE 44106

Penton Plaza
1111 CHESTER AVE 44114

Perry Payne Building
740 W SUPERIOR AVE 44113

Playhouse Sq Plaza
1220 HURON RD E 44115

Plaza Nine Building
55 ERIEVIEW PLZ 44114

Prospect 4th Building
2077 E 4TH ST 44115

Renaissance Office Twr
1350 EUCLID AVE 44115

Reserve Square
1250 SUPERIOR AVE E 44114

Ritz Carlton Office Building
250 W HURON RD 44113

Rockefeller Building
614 W SUPERIOR AVE 44113

Rockwell Building
601 ROCKWELL AVE 44114

Skylight Office Tower
1660 W 2ND ST 44113

Society Bank Building
800 SUPERIOR AVE E 44114

Society National Bk Building
127 PUBLIC SQ 44114

Standard Building
1370 ONTARIO ST 44113

Statler Office Tower
1127 EUCLID AVE 44115

Suburban West Building
20800 Center Ridge Rd 44116

Terminal Tower
50 PUBLIC SQ 44113

The Arcade
401 EUCLID AVE 44114

The Avenue
230 W HURON RD 44113

Transohio Tower
2000 E 9TH ST 44115

Union Building
1836 EUCLID AVE 44115

United Office Building
2012 W 25TH ST 44113

Western Reserve Building
1468 W 9TH ST 44113

Westgate Towers
20525 Center Ridge Rd 44116

Westview Towers
21010 Center Ridge Rd 44116

GOVERNMENT

A J Celebreeze Fed Building
1240 E 9TH ST 44199

City Hall
601 LAKESIDE AVE E 44114

County Courthouse
1 W LAKESIDE AVE 44113

Frank J Lausche Building
615 W SUPERIOR AVE 44113

State Office Building
615 W SUPERIOR AVE 44113

HOTELS

Alcazar Hotel
2450 DERBYSHIRE RD ... 44106

Ritz Carlton Hotel
1515 W 3RD ST 44113

CLINTONVILLE

APARTMENTS

Canterbury Apts
3440 RIVER RD 43202

BUILDINGS

Canterbury Apts
3440 Olentangy River Rd .. 43202

COLUMBUS

APARTMENTS

Broadway Terrace
1100 E BROAD ST 43205

Cambridge Arms
926 E BROAD ST 43205

Eastland Manor
4225 MACSWAY AVE 43232

Lutheran Senior City
935 N CASSADY AVE 43219

Mt Vernon Plaza Hi Rise
1035 ATCHESON ST 43203

Park Towers
1620 E BROAD ST 43203

Poindexter Building
1253 Mount Vernon Ave 43203

Royal York Apts
1445 E BROAD ST 43205

Sawyer Towers
529 SAWYER BLVD 43203

Summit Chase
1000 URLIN AVE 43212

Taylor Terrace
88 E 1ST AVE 43201

BUILDINGS

Canyon Medical
5969 E BROAD ST 43213

Lincoln Tower
1800 CANNON DR 43210

Port Columbus Intl Airpo
4600 E 17TH AVE 43219

Port Columbus Intl Airpo
4600 International Gtwy 43219

CUYAHOGA FALLS

APARTMENTS

Sutliff Apartment 1
1850 2ND ST 44221

DAYTON

APARTMENTS

10 Wilmington Place
10 WILMINGTON AVE 45420

Biltmore
210 N MAIN ST 45402

Carillon House
2230 S PATTERSON BLVD 45409

Commodore Apt
522 W GRAND AVE 45405

Dayton Towers
425 Dayton Towers Dr 45410

Rockwood Apt
515 W GRAND AVE 45405

The Lakewoods
980 WILMINGTON AVE 45420

BUILDINGS

111 W First St Building
111 W 1ST ST 45402

American Building
4 S MAIN ST 45402

Barclay Building
137 N MAIN ST 45402

Centre City Building
40 S MAIN ST 45402

Citizens Federal Centre
1 Citizens Federal Ctr 45402

Citizens Federal Centre
112 N MAIN ST 45402

Dayton Convention Center
22 DAVE HALL PLZ 45402

Dayton Convention Center
22 E 5TH ST 45402

Fidelity Building
211 S MAIN ST 45402

First National Building
1 FIRST NATIONAL PLZ .. 45402

Hulman Building
120 W 2ND ST 45402

IBM Building
33 W 1ST ST 45402

Kettering Tower
40 N MAIN ST 45423

Knott Building
40 S MAIN ST 45402

Miami Valley Tower
40 W 4TH ST 45402

Reibold Building
117 S MAIN ST 45402

Safety Building
335 W 3RD ST 45402

Salem Mall
5200 SALEM AVE 45426

Society Bank Building
32 N MAIN ST 45402

West 1st Plaza
333 W 1ST ST 45402

GOVERNMENT

Federal Building
200 W 2ND ST 45402

Municipal Building
101 W 3RD ST 45402

HOSPITALS

Stillwater Hospital
8100 N MAIN ST 45415

ELIDA

APARTMENTS

Gatehouse Square Apts
2275 N CABLE RD 45807

ELYRIA

APARTMENTS

Elyria Retirement Comm
145 ACADEMY CT 44035

HOWLAND

APARTMENTS

Arbor Manor Apt
1380 ARBOR AVE SE 44484

BUILDINGS

Market Place
5000 E MARKET ST 44484

LEXINGTON

APARTMENTS

Lakewood Apts
1 LAKEWOOD DR 44904

Village Green Apt
201 W MAIN ST 44904

LIMA

APARTMENTS

Andover Apts
1050 MACKENZIE DR 45805

Birches
725 S CABLE RD 45805

C And J Apts
2350 N COLE ST 45801

Dominion Building Apt
108 E HIGH ST 45801

Furl Williams Apt
936 W ROBB AVE 45801

Hampton Green Apts
400 S MUMAUGH RD 45804

Lima Estates
510 E NORTH ST 45801

Lima Towers
790 S MAIN ST 45804

Lima West Apts
1855 N COLE ST 45801

Pilgrim Place
449 S MAIN ST 45804

Richlieu Apt
1475 EDGEWOOD DR 45805

Town Square Apts
72 TOWN SQ 45801

Wilshire Apt
1500 DEERFIELD DR 45805

BUILDINGS

311 Building
311 E MARKET ST 45801

Bank One Tower
121 W HIGH ST 45801

Colonial Building
212 N ELIZABETH ST 45801

Martin Building
658 W MARKET ST 45801

Metropolitan Bank Building
127 N ELIZABETH ST 45801

National Bank Building
43 TOWN SQ 45801

St Ritas Medical Building
718 W MARKET ST 45801

GOVERNMENT

Allen County Court House
301 N MAIN ST 45801

Lima Municipal Building
50 TOWN SQ 45801

LINCOLN HEIGHTS

APARTMENTS

Manor Apts
210 OHIO ST 44903

Woodcliff Apts
300 WOOD ST 44903

LORAIN

BUILDINGS

Lorain City Hall
200 W ERIE AVE 44052

LORDSTOWN

APARTMENTS

Apple Gate Apt
1150 SALT SPRINGS RD . 44481

Reeves Apt
295 W MARKET ST 44481

Warner House
182 HIGH ST NE 44481

BUILDINGS

Bank One Building
106 E MARKET ST 44481

Second National Tower
108 MAIN AVE SW 44481

The First Place
159 E MARKET ST 44481

GOVERNMENT

Cnty Administration Building
160 HIGH ST NW 44481

Trumbull Cnty Court Hse
161 HIGH ST NW 44481

MANSFIELD

APARTMENTS

Apostolic Christian Apt
455 LOGAN RD 44907

Brittany Pk Apts
616 CLINE AVE 44907

Zeidiker
160 W 2ND ST 44902

BUILDINGS

Barrington One
13 PARK AVE W 44902

City
30 N DIAMOND ST 44902

Courthouse
50 PARK AVE E 44902

Jackson Betts Fed Building
180 N DIAMOND ST 44902

Richland Trust Bld
3 N MAIN ST 44902

MASSILLON

BUILDINGS

Administrative Offices
1 JAMES DUNCAN PLZ ... 44646

Law And Safety Building
2 JAMES DUNCAN PLZ ... 44646

NORTHWOOD

APARTMENTS

Ravine Park Village
2300 SEAMAN ST 43605

BUILDINGS

Woodville Mall
3725 WILLISTON RD 43619

SPRINGFIELD

APARTMENTS

Cardinal Village Apt
2981 VESTER AVE 45503

Cole Manor
315 S BURNETT RD 45505

Colonial Arms
1576 E HIGH ST 45505

Governors Manor
2100 E HIGH ST 45505

Grayhill Homes Apt
220 MONTGOMERY AVE . 45506

High Royal
1592 E HIGH ST 45505

Royal York Apts
1910 E HIGH ST 45505

Southern Apts
501 S LIMESTONE ST 45505

Springfield Towers
363 E HIGH ST 45505

Tubman Towers
17 W JOHNSON ST 45506

Westwind
2107 TROY RD 45504

BUILDINGS

Banc Ohio Building
4 W MAIN ST 45502

Columbia Gas Building
101 W HIGH ST 45502

Credit Life Building
1 S LIMESTONE ST 45502

Mc Adams Building
31 E HIGH ST 45502

Riverbend Building
333 N LIMESTONE ST 45503

The Arcue Building
6 W HIGH ST 45502

The Tecumseh Building
34 W HIGH ST 45502

GOVERNMENT

City Building
76 E HIGH ST 45502

Clark County Court House
101 N LIMESTONE ST 45502

TOLEDO

APARTMENTS

Brand Whitlock Homes
392 NEBRASKA AVE 43602

West Park Place Apt
3501 EXECUTIVE PKY 43606

BUILDINGS

Bell Building
709 MADISON AVE 43624

Community Services
1 STRANAHAN SQ 43604

Control Data Bus Tech Ctr
1946 N 13TH ST 43624

Edison Plaza
300 MADISON AVE 43604

Fiberglas Tower
1 LEVIS SQ 43604

Fifth Third Center
608 MADISON AVE 43604

Franklin Park Mall
5001 MONROE ST 43623

Gardner Building
500 MADISON AVE 43604

Huntington Bank Building
515 MADISON AVE 43604

Libbey Owens Ford Building
811 MADISON AVE 43624

Lucas County Ct House
700 ADAMS ST 43624

Michael V Disalle
1 GOVERNMENT CTR 43604

Miracle Mile Shopping Ctr
4925 JACKMAN RD 43613

National City Bank Building
405 MADISON AVE 43604

North Towne Mall
343 New Towne Square Dr 43612

Ohio Building
420 MADISON AVE 43604

Southwyck Mall
2040 S REYNOLDS RD 43614

Spitzer Building
520 MADISON AVE 43604

Summit Center
333 N SUMMIT ST 43604

Toledo Trust Building
245 N SUMMIT ST 43604

United Savings Building
240 N HURON ST 43604

Webstrand
4 SEAGATE 43604

Westgate Shopping Center
3301 W CENTRAL AVE 43606

GOVERNMENT

Federal Offices Building
234 N SUMMIT ST 43604

Municipal Court Building
555 N ERIE ST 43624

Safety Building
525 N ERIE ST 43624

U S Court House
1716 SPIELBUSCH AVE .. 43624

COLLEGES

Medical College Of Ohio
10008 PO BOX 43699

Owens Technical College
10000 PO BOX 43699

WARREN

APARTMENTS

Riverview Apt
250 TOD AVE NW 44485

Riverview Apt
700 BUCKEYE ST NW 44485

YOUNGSTOWN

APARTMENTS

Amedia Plaza Apartments
131 BOARDMAN ST 44503

Edgewood Apartments
55 DEWEY ST. 44507

Gutnecht Towers
110 WOOD ST. 44503

Gypsy Ln Manor
465 GYPSY LN 44504

International Tower
25 MARKET ST. 44503

Norton Manor
1400 SPRINGDALE ST. 44505

Parkway Towers
291 PARK ST. 44504

Pelton Apartments
224 WOOD ST. 44502

Phoenix House
850 MERIDIAN ST. 44509

BUILDINGS

City Centre One
100 FEDERAL ST. 44503

Dollar Bank Building
16 WICK ST. 44503

Federal Building
18 N PHELPS ST 44503

Home Saving and Loan Bldg
275 FEDERAL ST. 44503

Legal Arts Centre
101 MARKET ST. 44503

Mahoning Bank Bldg
26 MARKET ST. 44503

Metropolitan Tower
1 Federal Plaza Central 44503

Ohio One Building
25 BOARDMAN ST. 44503

Phar Mor Center
20 FEDERAL ST. 44503

Realty Building
47 Federal Plaza Central .. 44503

Stambaugh Building
44 Federal Plaza Central .. 44503

Wick Building
34 FEDERAL ST. 44503

GOVERNMENT

City Hall
26 S PHELPS ST 44503

Mahoning Cnty Court House
120 MARKET ST 44503

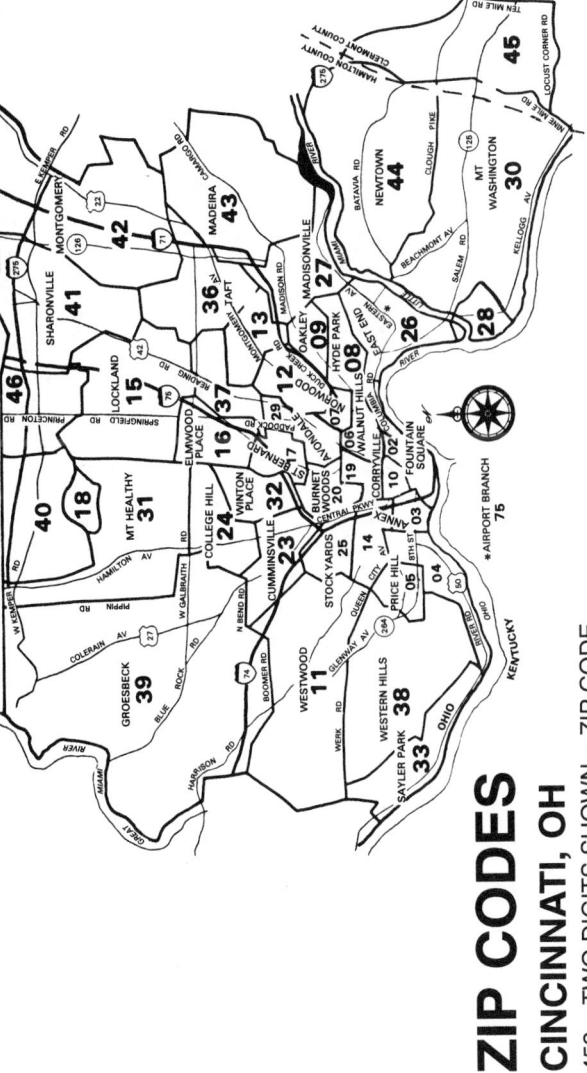

ZIP CODES
CINCINNATI, OH
452 + TWO DIGITS SHOWN = ZIP CODE

.... 73034, 73083	
Edna (Bristow) 74010	
El Reno 73036	
Eldorado 73537	
Elgin 73538	
Elk City 73644, 73648	
Elmer 73539	
Elmore City 73035	
Elmwood (Beaver) 73932	
Enid 73701-703, 73705-706	
Enterprise (Stigler) 74462	
Erick 73645, 73656	
Eucha 74342	
Eufaula 74432	
Fairfax 74637	
Fairland 74343	
Fairmont 73736	
Fairview 73737	
Fanshawe 74935	
Fargo 73840	
Farris (Atoka) 74542	
Faxon 73540	
Fay 73646	
Felt 73937	
Finley 74543	
Fittstown 74842	
Fitzhugh 74843	
Fletcher 73541	
Foraker (Shidler) 74652	
Forgan 73938	
Fort Cobb 73038	
Fort Gibson 74434	
Fort Sill 73503	
Fort Supply 73841	
Foss 73647	
Foster 73039	
Fox 73435	
Foyil 74031	
Francis 74844	
Frederick 73542	
Freedom 73842	
Gage 73843	
Gans 74936	
Garber 73738	
Garvin 74736	
Gate 73844	
Gay (Hugo) 74743	
Geary 73040	
Gene Autry 73436	
Geronimo 73543	
Glencoe 74032	
Glenoak (Bartlesville) 74003	
Glenpool 74033	
Golden 74737	
Goltry 73739	
Goodwell 73939	
Gore 74435	
Gotebo 73041	
Gould 73544	
Gowen 74545	
Gracemont 73042	
Grady (Terral) 73569	
Graham 73437	
Grandfield 73546	
Granite 73547	
Grant 74738	
Grayson (Henryetta) 74437	
Greenfield 73043	
Grove 74344	
Guthrie 73044	
Guymon 73942	

Hailey (Hallett) 74034	
Haileyville 74546	
Hallett 74034	
Halliburton (Duncan) 73536	
Hallis (Hallett) 74034	
Hammon 73650	
Hanna 74845	
Harden City (Stonewall) ... 74871	
Hardesty 73944	
Harmon (Arnett) 73832	
Harrah 73045	
Hartshorne 74547	
Haskell 74436	
Hastings 73548	
Haworth 74740	
Haywood 74501, 74548	
(Mcalester)	
Headrick 73549	
Healdton 73438	
Heavener 74937	
Helena 73741	
Hendrix 74741	
Hennepin 73046	
Hennessey 73742	
Henryetta 74437	
Herd (Pawhuska) 74056	
Higgins (Wilburton) 74578	
Hillsdale 73743	
Hinton 73047	
Hitchcock 73744	
Hitchita 74438	
Hobart 73651	
Hockerville (Quapaw) 74363	
Hodgen 74939	
Hoffman (Henryetta) 74437	
Hog Shooter 74003	
(Bartlesville)	
Holdenville 74848	
Hollis 73550	
Hollister 73551	
Hominy 74035	
Honobia 74549	
Hooker 73945	
Hopeton 73746	
Howe 74940	
Hoyt 74440	
Hugo 74743	
Hulbert 74441	
Hunter 74640	
Hydro 73048	
Idabel 74745	
Indiahoma 73552	
Indianola 74442	
Inola 74036	
Isabella 73747	
Jay 74346	
Jenks 74037	
Jennings 74038	
Jet 73749	
Jones 73049	
Kansas 74347	
Kaw (Kaw City) 74641	
Kaw City 74641	
Keefeton (Muskogee) 74401	
Kellyville 74039	
Kemp 74747	
Kendrick (Stroud) 74079	
Kenefic 74748	
Kenton 73946	
Keota 74941	
Ketchum 74349	

Keyes 73947	
Kiefer 74041	
Kingfisher 73750	
Kingston 73439	
Kinta 74552	
Kiowa 74553	
Knowles 73847	
Konawa 74849	
Krebs 74554	
Kremlin 73753	
Kulli (Idabel) 74745	
Lahoma 73754	
Lamar 74850	
Lamont 74643	
Lane 74555	
Langley 74350	
Langston 73050	
Laverne 73848	
Lawton 73501-503	
.... 73505-507, 73558	
Leach (Rose) 74364	
Lebanon 73440	
Leedey 73654	
Leflore 74942	
Lehigh 74556	
Lenapah 74042	
Leon 73441	
Leonard 74043	
Lequire 74943	
Lexington 73051	
Lincolnville (Quapaw) 74363	
Lindsay 73052	
Loco 73442	
Locust Grove 74352	
Logan 73849	
Lone Grove 73443	
Lone Wolf 73655	
Longdale 73755	
Lookeba 73053	
Lotsee (Sand Springs) 74063	
Loveland 73553	
Loyal 73756	
Lucien 73757	
Luther 73054	
Macomb 74852	
Madill 73446	
Manchester 73758	
Mangum 73554	
Manitou 73555	
Mannford 74044	
Mannsville 73447	
Maramec 74045	
Marble City 74945	
Marietta 73448	
Marland 74644	
Marlow (Bray) 73012, 73055	
Marshall 73056	
Martha 73556	
Martin (Muskogee) 74401	
Mason (Okemah) 74859	
Maud 74854	
May 73851	
Mayfield 73656	
Maysville 73057	
Mazie 74353	
Mc Loud 74851	
Mc Millan (Madill) 73446	
Mcalester 74501-502	
Haywood 74501	
Richville 74501	
Scipio 74501	

Mccurtain 74944
Mclain (Muskogee) 74401
Mead 73449
Medford 73759
Medicine Park 73557
Meeker 74855
Meers 73558
Meno 73760
Meridian 73058
Messer (Hugo) 74743
Miami 74354-355
Midwest City 73110, 73130
      (Oklahoma City)
Milburn 73450
Milfay 74046
Mill Creek 74856
Millerton 74750
Milo (Ardmore) 73401
Minco 73059
Moffett 74946
Monroe 74947
Moodys 74444
Moore 73160, 73165, 73170
      Oklahoma City 73160
      Warr Acres 73160
Mooreland 73852
Morris 74445
Morrison 73061
Mounds 74047
Mountain Park 73559
Mountain View 73062
Moyers 74557
Muldrow 74948
Mulhall 73063
Muse 74949
Muskogee 74401-403
      Bacone 74401
      Beland 74401
      Keefeton 74401
      Martin 74401
      Mclain 74401
      Summitt 74401
      Wybark 74401
Mustang 73064
Mutual 73853
Nardin 74646
Nash 73761
Nashoba 74558
Nelagony (Pawhuska) 74056
New Lima (Wewoka) 74884
New Tulsa (Coweta) 74429
Newalla 74857
Newby (Bristow) 74010
Newcastle 73065
Newkirk 74647
Nichols Hills 73116, 73120
      (Oklahoma City)
Nicoma Park 73066
Ninnekah 73067
Noble 73068
Norfolk (Cushing) 74023
Norman 73019, 73026, 73037
      73069-072
North Miami 74358
Nowata 74048
Noxie (Wann) 74083
Nuyaka (Okmulgee) 74447
Oakhurst 74050
Oakland (Madill) 73446
Oaks 74359
Oakwood 73658

Ochelata 74051
Octavia (Smithville) 74957
Oilton 74052
Okarche 73762
Okay 74446
Okeene 73763
Okemah 74859
Okesa (Bartlesville) 74003
Oklahoma City 73100-132
      73134-137
      .... 73139-157, 73159-160
      .... 73162-165, 73167
      .... 73169-170, 73172-173
      .... 73177-180, 73184-185
      .... 73189-190, 73193-199
      Del City 73115
      Midwest City 73110
      Midwest City 73130
      Moore 73165
      Moore 73170
      Nichols Hills 73116
      Nichols Hills 73120
      The Village 73120
      Village 73114
      Warr Acres 73122
      Warr Acres 73132
Okmulgee 74447
Oktaha 74450
Olney (Coalgate) 74538
Olustee 73560
Omega 73764
Oologah 74053
Optima (Hooker) 73945
Orienta (Fairview) 73737
Orlando 73073
Osage 74054
Oscar 73561
Overbrook 73453
Owasso 74055
Paden 74860
Page (Hodgen) 74939
Panama 74951
Panola 74559
Paoli 73074
Park Hill 74451
Pauls Valley 73075
Pawhuska 74009, 74056
      (Bowring)
      Herd 74056
      Nelagony 74056
      Pearsonia 74056
Pawnee 74058
Pearsonia (Pawhuska) 74056
Peckham (Newkirk) 74647
Peggs 74452
Pensacola (Vinita) 74301
Peoria (Quapaw) 74363
Perkins 74059
Pernell 73076
Perry 73077
Pershing (Barnsdall) 74002
Pettit (Park Hill) 74451
Pharoah 74862
Phillips (Coalgate) 74538
Phillips Petroleum 74004
      (Bartlesville)
Picher 74360
Pickens 74752
Piedmont 73078
Pierce (Checotah) 74426
Pink (Tecumseh) 74873

Pittsburg 74560
Platter 74753
Pocasset 73079
Pocola 74902
Ponca City 74601-604
Pond Creek 73766
Pooleville (Ardmore) 73401
Porter 74454
Porum 74455
Poteau 74953
Prague 74864
Preston 74456
Proctor 74457
Prue 74060
Pryor 74361-362
Purcell 73080
Putnam 73659
Qualls (Park Hill) 74451
Quapaw 74363
Quinton 74561
Ralston 74650
Ramona 74061
Randlett 73562
Ratliff City 73081
Rattan 74562
Ravia 73455
Red Oak 74563
Red Rock 74651
Redbird 74458
Reed (Mangum) 73554
Rentiesville 74459
Reydon 73660
Richville (Mcalester) 74501
Ringling 73456
Ringold 74754
Ringwood 73768
Ripley 74062
Rocky 73661
Roff 74865
Roland 74954
Roosevelt 73564
Rose 74364
Rosston 73855
Rubottom (Wilson) 73463
Rufe 74755
Rush Springs 73082
Ryan 73565
Saint Louis 74866
Salem (Henryetta) 74437
Salina 74365
Sallisaw 74955
Sand Springs 74063
Sapulpa 74066-067
Sasakwa 74867
Savanna 74565
Sawyer 74756
Sayre 73662
Schlegal (Cushing) 74023
Schulter 74460
Scipio (Mcalester) 74501
Seiling 73663
Selman (Buffalo) 73834
Seminole 74818, 74868
Sentinel 73664
Shady Point 74956
Shamrock 74068
Sharon 73857
Shattuck 73864
Shawnee 74801-802, 74838
      Bethel Acres 74801
      Dale 74801

Shidler	74652	Texhoma	73949	Wanette	74878
Shults (Idabel)	74745	Texola	73668	Wann	74083
Silver City (Jennings)	74038	Thackerville	73459	Wapanucka	73461
Skiatook	74070	The Village	73120	Wardville	74576
Slick	74071	(Oklahoma City)		Warner	74469
Smithville	74957	Thomas	73669	Warr Acres	73122
Snow	74567	Tiawah (Claremore)	74017		73132, 73160
Snyder	73566	Tipton	73570	(Oklahoma City)	
Soper	74759	Tishomingo	73460	Washington	73093
South Coffeyville	74072	Tom (Haworth)	74740	Washita	73094
(S Coffeyville)		Tonkawa	74653	Watonga	73772
Southard	73770	Topsy (Spavinaw)	74366	Watova (Nowata)	74048
Sparks	74869	Tryon	74875	Watson	74963
Spavinaw	74366	Tullahassee	74466	Watts	74964
Spelter City (Henryetta)	74437	Tulsa	74100-108	Waukomis	73773
Spencer	73084		74110, 74112, 74114-117	Waurika	73573
Spencerville	74760		74119-121, 74126-137	Wayne	73095
Sperry	74073		74141, 74145-150	Waynoka	73860
Spiro	74959		74152-153, 74155-159	Weatherford	73096
Springer	73458		74169-172, 74182-187	Webbers Falls	74470
Sterling	73567		74189, 74192-194	Welch	74369
Stidham	74461	Abumps	74189	Weleetka	74880
Stigler	74462	Turley	74126	Welling	74471
Stillwater	74074-078	West Tulsa	74107	Wellston	74881
College	74074	Williams Center	74172	Welty	74882
Stilwell	74960	Tupelo	74572	West Tulsa (Tulsa)	74107
Stonewall	74871	Turley (Tulsa)	74126	Westport (Cleveland)	74020
Strang	74367	Turpin	73950	Westville	74965
Stratford	74872	Tuskahoma	74574	Wetumka	74883
Stringtown	74569	Tuskegee (Bristow)	74010	Wewoka	74884
Strong City (Cheyenne)	73628	Tussy	73088	Wheatland	73097
Stroud	74079	Tuttle	73089	White Oak (Vinita)	74301
Stuart	74570	Twin Hills (Okmulgee)	74447	Whitefield	74472
Sulphur	73086	Twin Oaks	74368	Whitesboro	74577
Summerfield	74966	Tyrone	73951	Wilburton	74578
Summit (Muskogee)	74401	Union City	73090	Williams Center (Tulsa)	74172
Sweetwater	73666	Valliant	74764	Willow	73673
Swink	74761	Velma	73091	Wilson	73463
Taft	74463	Vera	74082	Winganon (Chelsea)	74016
Tahlequah	74464-465	Verden	73092	Wister	74966
Talala	74080	Verdigris (Claremore)	74017	Wolco (Barnsdall)	74002
Talihina	74571	Vernon (Hanna)	74845	Woodville (Kingston)	73439
Tallant (Barnsdall)	74002	Vian	74962	Woodward	73801-802
Taloga	73667	Vici	73859	Wright City	74766
Tamaha (Stigler)	74462	Village (Oklahoma City)	73114	Wyandotte	74370
Tatums	73087	Vinita	74301	Wybark (Muskogee)	74401
Tecumseh	74873	Vinson	73571	Wynnewood	73098
Temple	73568	Wade (Bennington)	74723	Wynona	74084
Terlton	74081	Wagoner	74467, 74477	Yale	74085
Terral (Oscar)	73561, 73569	Wainwright	74468	Yarnaby (Hendrix)	74741
Grady	73569	Wakita	73771	Yukon	73085, 73099
Texanna (Checotah)	74426	Walters	73572	Zena (Jay)	74346

BACONE

GOVERNMENT

County Court House
412 COURT ST 74401

Municipal Building
112 S 3RD ST 74401

BARTLESVILLE

BUILDINGS

Aurora Building
415 S DEWEY AVE 74003

First Court Place
501 SE Frank Phillips Blvd 74003

Price Tower Annex
500 S DEWEY AVE 74003

Washington Park Mall
2350 SE Washington Blvd 74006

GOVERNMENT

City Administration
600 S DEWEY AVE 74003

Washington County Cd
420 S JOHNSTONE AVE .. 74003

HOSPITALS

Jane Phillips Hospital
3500 E Frank Phillips Blvd 74006

COLLEGE

GOVERNMENT

City Of Stillwater
723 S LEWIS ST 74074

Payne County Courthouse
606 S HUSBAND ST 74074

EDMOND

HOSPITALS

Edmond Memorial Hospital
1 S BRYANT AVE 73034

MOORE

HOSPITALS

Moore Community Hosp
1500 SE 4TH ST 73160

NICHOLS HILLS

HOSPITALS

Mercy Health Center
4300 W MEMORIAL RD ... 73120

Mercy Hospital
4300 W MEMORIAL RD ... 73120

NORMAN

GOVERNMENT

Cleveland Co Courthouse
200 S PETERS AVE 73069

OKLAHOMA CITY

BUILDINGS

100 Park Avenue Building
100 PARK AVE 73102

101 Park Avenue Building
101 PARK AVE 73102

1st National Center
120 N ROBINSON AVE 73102

50 Penn Place
50 PENN PL 73118

American 1st Tower
101 N ROBINSON AVE 73102

Bancfirst
101 N BROADWAY AVE ... 73102

Capitol Investors
217 N HARVEY AVE 73102

City Hall
200 N WALKER AVE 73102

Colcord
15 N ROBINSON AVE 73102

Conners
2501 LINCOLN ST. 73105

Court Plaza
228 ROBERT S KERR AVE 73102

Fidelity Plaza
201 ROBERT S KERR AVE 73102

First City Place
204 N ROBINSON AVE 73102

First Oklahoma Tower
210 PARK AVE 73102

Hightower
105 N HUDSON AVE 73102

Jim Thorpe
2101 LINCOLN ST. 73105

Leadership Square
211 N ROBINSON AVE 73102

Liberty Tower
100 N BROADWAY AVE ... 73102

Mid America
20 N BROADWAY AVE 73102

Midland Ctr
134 ROBERT S KERR AVE 73102

Oliver Hodge
2500 LINCOLN ST. 73105

Park Harvey Center
200 N HARVEY AVE 73102

Robinson Renaissance
119 N ROBINSON AVE 73102

Sequoyah
2400 LINCOLN ST. 73105

State Capitol
2300 N LINCOLN BLVD 73105

Wiley Post Historical
2100 LINCOLN ST. 73105

GOVERNMENT

Ok County Office
320 Robert S Kerr Ave 73102

HOSPITALS

Baptist Hospital
3300 NW Expressway St ... 73112

Childrens Hospital
940 NE 13TH ST 73104

Deaconess Hospital
5501 N PORTLAND AVE ... 73112

Oklahoma allergy Clinic
750 13TH ST. 73104

Oklahoma Memorial Hosp
800 NE 13TH ST 73104

Ou Health Science Center
1100 N LINDSAY AVE 73104

Presbyterian Hospital
700 NE 13TH ST 73104

Southwest Medical Center
1001 44TH ST. 73109

St Anthony Hospital
1000 N LEE AVE 73102

VA Hospital
921 13TH ST. 73104

Will Rogers Memorial Hospital
2401 LINCOLN ST. 73105

TULSA

BUILDINGS

Beacon Building
406 S BOULDER AVE 74103

Center Office Building
707 S HOUSTON AVE 74127

Denver Building
624 S DENVER AVE 74119

Eastland Mall
14002 E 21ST ST 74134

Hillcrest Physicians
1145 S UTICA AVE 74104

GOVERNMENT

Page Belcher Federal Building
333 W 4TH ST 74103

US Courthouse
333 W 4TH ST 74103

Delake (Lincoln City)	97367
Dellwood (Coos Bay)	97420
Denmark (Langlois)	97450
Depoe Bay	97341
Detroit	97342
Dever Conner (Albany)	97321
Dew Valley (Bandon)	97411
Dexter	97431
Diamond	97722
Diamond Lake (Chemult)	97731
Dillard	97432
Disston (Culp Creek)	97427
Dixonville (Roseburg)	97470
Dodson (Cascade Locks)	97014
Donald	97020
Dora (Myrtle Point)	97458
Dorena	97434
Douglas Gardens	97477
(Springfield)	
Dover (Eagle Creek)	97022
Drain	97435
Drew (Tiller)	97484
Drewsey	97904
Dufur	97021
Dundee	97115
Dunes City (Florence)	97439
Durham (Portland)	97224
Durkee	97905
Eagle Creek	97022
Eagle Crest (Redmond)	97756
Eagle Crest Corners	97304
(Salem)	
Eagle Point	97524
East Gardiner (Reedsport)	97467
East Lake (La Pine)	97739
Eastside (Coos Bay)	97420
Eastwood (Roseburg)	97470
Echo	97826
Eddyville	97343
Edenbower (Roseburg)	97470
Elgarose (Roseburg)	97470
Elgin	97827
Elk City (Toledo)	97391
Elkton	97436
Ellendale (Dallas)	97338
Elmira	97437
Elsie (Seaside)	97138
Empire (Coos Bay)	97420
Englewood (Coos Bay)	97420
Enterprise	97828
Eola (Salem)	97304
Estacada	97023
Eugene	97401-405, 97408
	97412, 97440, 97455
Acorn Park	97402
Coburg	97401, 97408
College Crest	97401
Crow	97401
Fir Grove	97401
Four Corners	97402
Goshen	97405
Irving	97401
River Road	97404
Santa Clara	97404
South Side	97405
University	97401
University	97403
West Side	97402
Fairoaks (Sutherlin)	97479
Fairview	97024, 97423
Fall Creek	97438

Falls City	97344
Farmington Mall	97007
(Beaverton)	
Fayetteville (Shedd)	97377
Fern Corner (Dallas)	97338
Fields	97710
Finn Rock (Vida)	97488
Fir Grove (Eugene)	97401
Fir Villa (Dallas)	97338
Fish Lake Resort	97524
(Eagle Point)	
Five Corners (Lakeview)	97630
Florence	97439
Forest Grove	97116
Fort Klamath	97626
Fort Rock	97735
Fort Stevens (Hammond)	97121
Fortune Branch (Glendale)	97442
Fossil	97830
Foster	97345
Four Corners	97301, 97402
(Salem)	
Fox	97831
Franklin (Junction City)	97448
Frenchglen	97736
Friend (Dufur)	97021
Fruitdale (Grants Pass)	97526
Fruitland (Salem)	97301
Gales Creek	97117
Galice (Merlin)	97532
Garden Home (Portland)	97223
Gardiner	97441
Garibaldi	97118
Gaston	97119
Gates	97346
Gateway (Madras)	97741
Gaylord (Myrtle Point)	97458
Gazley (Myrtle Creek)	97457
Gearhart (Seaside)	97138
Gervais	97026
Gilchrist	97737
Gilliams (Dallas)	97338
Gladstone	97027
Glasgow (North Bend)	97459
Glenada (Florence)	97439
Glenbrook (Monroe)	97456
Glendale	97442
Gleneden Beach	97388
Glengary (Roseburg)	97470
Glenwood (Forest Grove)	97116
Glide	97443
Globe (Walton)	97490
Gold Beach	97444
Gold Hill	97525
Goshen (Eugene)	97405
Grand Island (Dayton)	97114
Grand Ronde	97347
Granite (Sumpter)	97877
Grants Pass ... 97526-527, 97543	
Fruitdale	97526
Hugo	97526
South Grants Pass	97526
Three Pines	97526
Grass Valley	97029
Gravelford (Myrtle Point)	97458
Green (Roseburg)	97470
Green Acres (Coos Bay)	97420
Greenacres (Scottsburg)	97473
Greenberry (Corvallis)	97330
Greenleaf	97430, 97445
(Deadwood)	

Greenway (Portland)	97223
Gresham	97030, 97080
	97230, 97233, 97236
Hager (Klamath Falls)	97601
Haines	97833
Halfway	97834
Halls Ferry (Salem)	97302
Halsey	97348
Hammond	97121
Happy Valley	97236, 97266
(Portland)	
Harbor (Brookings)	97415
Harlan (Eddyville)	97343
Harper	97906
Harriman (Klamath Falls)	97601
Harrisburg	97446
Hauser (North Bend)	97459
Hayesville (Salem)	97305
Hazel Green (Salem)	97305
Hebo	97122
Heceta Beach (Florence)	97439
Helix	97835
Helvetia (Hillsboro)	97123-124
Hemlock (Westfir)	97492
Henley (Klamath Falls)	97601
Heppner	97836
Hereford	97837
Hermiston	97838
Hildebrand (Bonanza)	97623
Hillsboro	97123-124
Helvetia	97123-124
Orenco	97123-124
Scholls	97123
West Union	97123-124
Hines	97738
Hollywood (Salem)	97303
Hood River	97031
Hopewell (Salem)	97304
Horton (Blachly)	97412, 97448
Hoskins (Philomath)	97370
Hubbard	97032
Hugo (Grants Pass)	97526
Hunter Creek (Gold Beach)	97444
Huntington	97907
Idanha	97350
Idleyld Park	97447
Illahe (Agness)	97406
Illinois Valley	97523
(Cave Junction)	
Imbler	97841
Imnaha	97842
Independence	97351
Indian Ford (Sisters)	97759
Ione	97843
Ironside	97908
Irrigon	97844
Irving (Eugene)	97401
Island City (La Grande)	97850
Jacksonville	97530
Jamieson	97909
Jasper (Fall Creek)	97438
Jefferson	97352
Jennings Lodge (Portland)	97267
Jewell (Seaside)	97138
John Day	97845
Johnson City (Portland)	97267
Jonesboro (Juntura)	97911
Jordan (Scio)	97374
Jordan Valley	97910
Joseph	97846
Junction City	97448

Juntura	97911
Kahneeta (Warm Springs)	97761
Keating (Baker City)	97814
Keizer (Salem)	97303, 97307
Salem	97307
Kellogg (Oakland)	97462
Keno	97627
Kent	97033
Kerby	97531
Kernville (Lincoln City)	97367
Kimberly	97848
King City (Portland)	97224
Kings Valley (Monmouth)	97361
Kingsley Field	97601
(Klamath Falls)	
Kinzua (Fossil)	97830
Kirk (Chiloquin)	97624
Klamath Falls	97601-603
	97625
Altamont	97601
Chelsea	97601
Hager	97601
Harriman	97601
Henley	97601
Kingsley Field	97601
Lake Of The Woods	97601
Oit	97603
Oretech	97601
Pelican City	97601
Rocky Point	97601
Shady Pine	97601
Weyerhaeuser Townsite	
	97601
Wocus	97601
Worden	97601
La Grande	97850
La Pine	97739
Labish Village (Salem)	97305
Lacomb (Lebanon)	97355
Lafayette	97127
Lake Grove	97034-035
(Lake Oswego)	
Lake Of The Woods	97603
(Klamath Falls)	
Lake Oswego	97034-035
Lake Grove	97034-035
Mountain Park	97034-035
Oswego	97034
Lakecreek (Eagle Point)	97524
Lakeside	97449
Lakeview	97630
Lancaster (Junction City)	97448
Langlois	97450
Latham (Cottage Grove)	97424
Laurel Grove (Bandon)	97411
Lawen	97740
Leaburg (Walterville)	97489
Lebanon	97355
Lee (Coquille)	97423
Lees Camp (Tillamook)	97141
Leland (Springfield)	97478
Lewisburg (Corvallis)	97330
Lewisville (Monmouth)	97361
Lexington	97839
Libby (Coos Bay)	97420
Liberal (Molalla)	97038
Lime (Huntington)	97907
Lincoln (Ashland)	97520
Lincoln Beach	97341
(Depoe Bay)	
Lincoln City	97367

Linnton (Portland)	97231
Little Albany (Tidewater)	97390
Logsden	97357
London (Cottage Grove)	97424
Long Creek	97856
Long Mountain	97524
(Eagle Point)	
Lookingglass (Roseburg)	97470
Lorane	97451
Lorella (Bonanza)	97623
Lostine	97857
Lowell	97452
Lyons	97358
Macleay (Salem)	97301
Madras	97741
Malin	97632
Manhattan Beach	97136
(Rockaway)	
Manning	97125
Manzanita	97130
Mapleton	97453
Marcola	97454
Marion	97359
Marion Forks (Idanha)	97350
Market (Coos Bay)	97420
Marquam (Molalla)	97038
Marylhurst	97036
Maupin	97037
Mayville (Fossil)	97830
Maywood Park (Portland)	97220
Mc Kenzie Bridge	97413
(Blue River)	
Mc Minnville	97128
(Mcminnville)	
Mc Nary (Umatilla)	97882
Mccoy (Rickreall)	97371
Mccredie Springs	97463
(Oakridge)	
Mckee Bridge	97530
(Jacksonville)	
Mckinley (Myrtle Point)	97458
Meacham	97859
Meadow View	97448
(Junction City)	
Medford	97501-504
Central Point West	97501
South Medford	97501
Table Rock	97501
West Main	97501
Mehama	97384
Melrose (Roseburg)	97470
Merlin	97532
Merrill	97633
Metolius (Madras)	97741
Midland	97634
Mikkalo	97861
Mill City	97360
Millersburg (Albany)	97321
Millington (Coos Bay)	97420
Millwood (Umpqua)	97486
Milo (Pleasant Hill)	97455
Milton Freewater	97862
Milwaukie (Portland)	97222
	97267, 97269
Minerva (Florence)	97439
Minnow (Dexter)	97431
Mist (Clatskanie)	97016
Mitchell	97750
Modoc Point (Chiloquin)	97624
Mohawk (Springfield)	97477
Mohler (Nehalem)	97131

Molalla	97038
Monitor (Woodburn)	97071
Monmouth	97361
Monroe	97456
Monument	97864
Moro	97039
Mosier	97040
Mount Angel	97362
Mount Hood	97041
(Mount Hood Parkdale)	
Mount Vernon	97865
Mount View (Ashland)	97520
Mountain Park	97034-035
(Lake Oswego)	
Mulino	97042
Multnomah (Portland)	97219
Murphy	97533
Murphys Camp	97473
(Scottsburg)	
Myrtle Creek	97457
Myrtle Point	97458
Nashville (Philomath)	97370
Neahkahnie (Nehalem)	97131
Nehalem	97131
Nelscott (Lincoln City)	97367
Neotsu	97364
Nesika Beach	97444
(Gold Beach)	
Neskowin	97149
Netarts	97143
New Idaho (Lakeview)	97630
New Idanha (Idanha)	97350
New Pine Creek	97635
Newberg	97132
Newport	97365-366
Agate Beach	97365
Otter Crest	97365
Newton Creek (Roseburg)	97470
Nonpareil (Sutherlin)	97479
North Albany (Albany)	97321
North Beach (Florence)	97439
North Bend	97459
North Howell (Silverton)	97381
North Plains	97133
North Powder	97867
North Rosebg (Roseburg)	97470
North Santiam (Aumsville)	97325
Norway	97458, 97460
(Myrtle Point)	
Noti	97461
Nyssa	97913
O' Brien (O Brien)	97534
Oak Grove	97222, 97267-268
(Portland)	
Oak Lodge (Portland)	97267
Oak Park (Salem)	97305
Oakdale (Dallas)	97338
Oakland	97462
Oakridge	97463
Oakville (Shedd)	97377
Ocean City (Lincoln City)	97367
Oceanside	97134
Odell	97044
Oit (Klamath Falls)	97601
Old Town (Oakland)	97462
Ontario	97914
Ophir	97464
Oregon City	97045
Orenco (Hillsboro)	97123-124
Oretech (Klamath Falls)	97601
Oswego (Lake Oswego)	97034

Summit (Philomath) 97370	Two Mile (Bandon) 97411
Sumner (Coos Bay) 97420	Tyee (Umpqua) 97486
Sumpter 97877	Tygh Valley 97063
Sunny Valley (Wolf Creek) 97497	Ukiah 97880
Sunriver (Bend) 97707	Umatilla 97882
Surf Pines (Warrenton) 97146	Umpqua 97486
Surprise Valley 97457	Union 97883
(Myrtle Creek)	Union Creek (Prospect) 97536
Sutherlin 97479	Union Gap (Oakland) 97462
Suver (Independence) 97351	Unity 97884
Suver Junction (Monmouth) 97361	Unity Bridge (Fall Creek) ... 97438
Sweet Home 97386	University 97401, 97403
Swisshome 97480	(Eugene)
Table Rock (Medford) 97501	Upper Soda (Cascadia) 97329
Taft (Lincoln City) 97367	Vale 97918
Takilma (Cave Junction) 97523	Valley Falls (Lakeview) 97630
Talbot (Jefferson) 97352	Valley Junction 97396
Talent 97540	(Willamina)
Tangent 97389	Vaughn (Veneta) 97487
Tektronix (Beaverton) 97077	Veneta 97487
Tenmile 97481	Verboort (Forest Grove) 97116
Terrebonne 97760	Vernonia 97064
The Dalles 97058	Vida 97488
Three Pines (Grants Pass) 97526	Vista (Salem) 97302
Thurston 97482	Walden (Cottage Grove) 97424
Tide (Swisshome) 97480	Waldport 97394
Tidewater 97390	Walker (Creswell) 97426
Tigard 97223-224, 97281	Wallowa 97885
(Portland)	Walterville 97489
Tillamook 97141	Walton 97490
Tiller 97484	Wamic (Tygh Valley) 97063
Timber 97144	Wankers Corners 97068
Timberline Lodge 97028	(West Linn)
(Government Camp)	Warm Springs 97761
Toketee Falls 97447	Warner Valley (Adel) 97620
(Idleyld Park)	Warren 97053
Toledo 97391	Warrenton 97121, 97146
Tollgate (Sisters) 97759	(Hammond)
Tolovana Park 97145	Camp Rilea 97146
Tongue Point (Astoria) 97103	Surf Pines 97146
Trail 97541	Wasco 97065
Trent (Dexter) 97431	Waterloo (Lebanon) 97355
Tri-city (Myrtle Creek) 97457	Weatherby (Durkee) 97905
Triangle Lake (Blachly) 97412	Wecoma Beach 97367
Troutdale 97060	(Lincoln City)
Tualatin 97062	Wedderburn 97491
Tumalo (Bend) 97701	Welches 97067
Turner (Marion) 97359, 97392	Wemme (Welches) 97067
Twin Rocks (Rockaway) 97136	West Linn 97068

West Main (Medford) 97501	
West Oak (Oakridge) 97463	
West Salem (Salem) 97304	
West Scio (Scio) 97374	
West Side 97402, 97630	
(Eugene)	
West Slope (Portland) 97225	
West Stayton (Aumsville) .. 97325	
West Union 97123-124	
(Hillsboro)	
Westfall 97920	
Westfir 97492	
Westlake 97493	
Weston 97886	
Westport (Clatskanie) 97016	
Weyerhaeuser Townsite ... 97601	
(Klamath Falls)	
Wheatland (Salem) 97303	
Wheeler 97147	
White City 97503	
Wilbur 97494	
Wilderville 97543	
Willamette (West Linn) 97068	
Willamette City 97463	
(Oakridge)	
Willamina 97396	
Williams 97544	
Willowcreek (Vale) 97918	
Wilsonville 97070	
Wimer (Rogue River) 97537	
Winberry (Fall Creek) 97438	
Winchester 97495	
Winchester Bay 97467	
(Reedsport)	
Winston 97496	
Winterville (Bandon) 97411	
Wocus (Klamath Falls) 97601	
Wolf Creek 97497	
Wonder (Wilderville) 97543	
Wood Village (Troutdale) ... 97060	
Woodburn 97071	
Worden (Klamath Falls) 97601	
Wren (Philomath) 97370	
Wyeth (Cascade Locks) 97014	
Yachats 97498	
Yamhill 97148	
Yoncalla 97499	
Yonna (Bonanza) 97623	
Zigzag (Rhododendron) 97049	

OREGON   IMPORTANT BUILDINGS

ALFALFA

BUILDINGS

Bend City Hall
720 NW WALL ST 97701

ALOHA

APARTMENTS

Al-len
6200 SW HALL BLVD 97005

Allentowne Village
14100 SW ALLEN BLVD ... 97005

Aloha Park
875 SW 185TH AVE 97006

Amber Lantern
18140 SW SHAW ST 97007

Antoinette Plaza
11985 SW CENTER ST 97005

Audubon Square
7580 SW Scholls Ferry Rd 97005

Bayridge
17500 NW CORNELL RD . 97006

Beaver Creek
12270 SW CENTER ST 97005

Beaverton Garden Court
4105 SW HOCKEN AVE ... 97005

Beaverton Mobilodge
14385 SW JENKINS RD ... 97005

Birnam West
13225 SW ALLEN BLVD ... 97005

Brookside Estates
6750 SW Scholls Ferry Rd 97005

Canyon Plaza
3750 SW 108TH AVE 97005

Casa Royale
6320 SW LOMBARD AVE . 97005

Castlewood Arms
13555 SW JENKINS RD ... 97005

Cedars West
12625 SW COLONY LN ... 97005

Chateau Ecole
2435 SW ECOLE AVE 97005

Conestoga Park
9900 SW Conestoga Dr 97005

Country Oaks
13795 SW ELECTRIC ST . 97005

Crescent Ridge
7860 SW HALL BLVD 97005

Crown West
11655 SW ALLEN BLVD ... 97005

Dayle Ann
5840 SW ERICKSON AVE 97005

Devonshire Manor
18150 SW ROSA RD 97007

Downing Hills
9385 SW DOWNING DR .. 97005

Drum Castle
4085 SW 160TH AVE 97007

Edgewood Downs
7799 SW Scholls Ferry Rd 97005

Endicott Woods
9450 SW 146TH TER 97007

Fairway Downs
8600 SW Scholls Ferry Rd 97005

Farmington
13787 SW Farmington Rd 97005

Farmington Oaks
18850 SW Farmington Rd 97007

Garden Brook Terrace
3950 SW 102ND AVE 97005

Gem Lane Village
12520 SW GEM LN 97005

Greenway Square
9495 SW DOWNING DR .. 97005

Greenway Terrace
9595 SW PRAIRIE TER 97005

Greystone Square
13590 SW ELECTRIC ST . 97005

Heather Court
18745 SW Farmington Rd 97007

Heather Place
4905 SW SPENCER AVE . 97005

Hollytree
5335 SW MURRAY BLVD . 97005

Iron Horse Lane
11850 SW Iron Horse Ln ... 97005

Kalevala Village
5500 SW 180TH AVE 97007

Kimberly West
7851 SW HALL BLVD 97005

Kings Court
16300 SW ESTUARY DR . 97006

Kristin
11875 SW 7TH ST 97005

Lone Pine
2800 SW 185TH AVE 97006

Marcia Lee
14245 SW WALKER RD ... 97006

Meadowbrook Vlg
6970 SW KING BLVD 97005

Menlo Manor
13720 SW 6TH ST 97005

Nut Tree Mobile Estates
14205 SW JENKINS RD ... 97005

Oak View Village
2335 SW BRIGGS RD 97005

Overlook At Murrayhill
14505 SW OSPREY DR ... 97007

Parkland Aloha
5400 SW 180TH AVE 97007

Patrician
18000 SW SHAW ST 97007

Pine Grove
5160 SW 180TH AVE 97007

Pine Rdg Park
6900 SW 195TH AVE 97007

Ranken Square
4200 SW 107TH AVE 97005

Reef
5200 SW 141ST AVE 97005

Richland Terrace
15195 SW WALKER RD ... 97006

Ridgeview
7850 SW HALL BLVD 97005

Rochelle
17350 SW SHAW ST 97007

Royal Crest
11700 SW ALLEN BLVD ... 97005

Royal Pines
9555 SW ALLEN BLVD 97005

Sandwood Townhouses
6155 SW KING BLVD 97005

Scholls Bridge
6745 SW Scholls Ferry Rd 97005

Scottsdale Park
13995 SW BUTNER RD ... 97006

Seminole Mobile Estates
100 SW 195TH AVE 97006

Shannon Oaks
8350 SW Greenway Blvd .. 97005

Sorrento View
12365 SW Conestoga Dr .. 97005

Spencer House
13665 SW LARCH PL 97005

Springbrook
6300 SW 188TH CT 97007

Springbrook
10080 SW 5TH ST 97005

Stephanie Terrace
15000 SW Farmington Rd 97007

Sterling Pointe
14300 SW TEAL BLVD 97005

Stone Creek
5005 SW MURRAY BLVD . 97005

Sussex Village
6800 SW HALL BLVD 97005

The Firs
12995 SW ALLEN BLVD ... 97005

The Fountains
4550 SW MURRAY BLVD . 97005

The Lakes
18370 NW CORNELL RD . 97006

Tiffany Terrace
3825 SW 178TH AVE 97007

Townhouse
13520 SW ELECTRIC ST . 97005

Valley Park
4925 SW JAMIESON RD .. 97005

Villa La Pine
14630 SW Farmington Rd 97007

Village At Forest Glen
13775 SW Old Scholls Ferry
Rd 97005

Village Victorian
16290 SW SHAW ST 97007

West Royal
6170 SW LOMBARD AVE . 97005

Westpark
17700 SW SHAW ST 97007

Willow Brook
14095 SW WALKER RD ... 97005

Wood Creek
3280 SW 170TH AVE 97006

Woodland Vlg
4420 SW 99TH AVE 97005

BUILDINGS

Blanton Plaza
3835 SW 185TH AVE 97007

Cascade Plaza
8775 SW CASCADE AVE . 97005

Cascade Square
8625 SW CASCADE AVE . 97005

Center Plaza West
12655 SW CENTER ST 97005

Commercial Plaza
4800 SW GRIFFITH DR 97005

Farmington Mall
17455 SW Farmington Rd   97007

Greentree West
10950 SW 5TH ST 97005

Park Plaza West
10700 SW BEAVERTON
HILLSDALE HWY 97005

Quadrant Business Campus
1865 NW 169TH PL 97006

Summercrest Plaza
16300 SW HART RD 97007

Valley Plaza
9400 SW BEAVERTON HILLSDALE
HWY 97005

Westgate Square
3800 SW Cedar Hills Blvd . 97005

GOVERNMENT

Post Office
4550 SW BETTS AVE 97005

Post Office
3800 SW 185TH AVE 97007

FOUR CORNERS

COLLEGES

Willamette University
900 STATE ST SE 97301

GRESHAM

APARTMENTS

Aldercrest
21900 SE ALDER DR 97030

Ash Mountain
2950 NE 23RD ST 97030

Bellacres Mobile Estate
2980 NE DIVISION ST 97030

Camlu
1350 W POWELL BLVD 97030

Colonial Heights
890 NW DIVISION ST 97030

East Park
140 SW EASTMAN PKY ... 97080

Florence Terrace
159 SW FLORENCE AVE . 97080

Golfside
1999 NE DIVISION ST 97030

Green Tee Estates
900 NE FRANCIS AVE 97030

Greenbrook
200 SW FLORENCE AVE . 97080

Gresham Garden Court
815 SE 223RD AVE 97030

Hollyridge
2700 W POWELL BLVD 97030

Kelly Creek
2775 NE DIVISION ST 97030

Meyers Square
2800 SE 1ST ST 97080

Stevens Trailer Park
1445 NW VICTORIA AVE .. 97030

Suburban Mobile Estates
21016 SE STARK ST 97030

The Turn At Gresham
24050 SE STARK ST 97030

Town Fair Terrace
1167 NW WALLULA AVE .. 97030

Village Retirement Ctr
4501 W POWELL BLVD 97030

Vista Villa
250 SE VISTA AVE 97080

Wilmar East
1071 SE KANE RD 97080

Yorktown Gardens
340 NE CLEVELAND AVE   97030

BUILDINGS

Mountain Vw Prof Plz
25500 SE STARK ST 97030

Mt Hood Medical Building
24900 SE STARK ST 97030

Mt Hood Professional Ctr
22400 SE STARK ST 97030

GOVERNMENT

City Hall
1333 NW EASTMAN PKY   97030

Post Office
103 W POWELL BLVD 97030

Usps Midway Station
840 SE 122ND AVE 97233

HOTELS

Golden Knight
750 E POWELL BLVD 97030

HALLS FERRY

GOVERNMENT

Vista Station
3300 PO BOX 97302

HAPPY VALLEY

APARTMENTS

Monterey Terrace Condos
8717 SE MONTEREY AVE 97266

GOVERNMENT

Usps Lents Station
8225 SE INSLEY ST 97266

HELVETIA

GOVERNMENT

Washington Co Courthouse
155 N 1ST AVE 97124

JENNINGS LODGE

GOVERNMENT

USPS Oak Grove Branch
3860 SE NAEF RD 97267

LAKE GROVE

APARTMENTS

Alderwood
50 KERR PKY 97035

Bay Roc
668 MCVEY AVE 97034

Bay Vista
295 3RD ST 97034

Botticelli Villas
3800 BOTTICELLI ST 97035

Burnham
200 BURNHAM RD 97034

Carman Oaks
3800 CARMAN DR 97035

Eagle Crest
45 EAGLE CREST DR 97035

Edgewater
195 2ND ST 97034

Hunt Club
6142 BONITA RD 97035

Ivy Club
215 GREENRIDGE DR 97035

Lake Grove
3930 LAKE GROVE AVE .. 97035

Lake Oswego
258 EVERGREEN ST 97034

Lakeview
300 1ST ST 97034

Mcnary Highlands
3433 MCNARY PKY 97035

Mountain Lake Terrace
86 KINGSGATE RD 97035

Mountain Park Town Center
1 JEFFERSON PKY 97035

Oswegan
199 E AVE 97034

Oswego Lake Shore
540 S STATE ST 97034

Oswego Terrace
16250 PACIFIC HWY 97034

Park Place
48 EAGLE CREST DR 97035

Parkridge
200 GREENRIDGE DR 97035

Quailhill
12375 Mount Jefferson Ter 97035

Ridgecrest
47 EAGLE CREST DR 97035

Ridgeview
44 EAGLE CREST DR 97035

Talisman
750 1ST ST 97034

Tamerlane
685 1ST ST 97034

Tanglewood II
4 TOUCHSTONE 97035

Tanglewood II
100 KERR PKY 97035

Westlake Meadows
5300 PARKVIEW DR 97035

BUILDINGS

Five Centerpointe
5 CENTERPOINTE DR 97035

Four Centerpointe
4 CENTERPOINTE DR 97035

Frazier
543 3RD ST 97034

Kruse Way Plaza
4500 KRUSE WAY 97035

Kruse Way Plaza Ii
4550 KRUSE WAY 97035

Kruse Way Suites
4000 KRUSE WAY PL 97035

Kruse Woods I
5285 MEADOWS RD 97035

Lake Place Ctr
363 S STATE ST 97034

Lakeside Plaza
8 N STATE ST 97034

Mercantile Village
4015 MERCANTILE DR 97035

One Centerpointe
1 CENTERPOINTE DR 97035

Oregon State Bar Center
5200 MEADOWS RD 97035

Six Centerpointe
6 CENTERPOINTE DR 97035

Three Centerpointe
3 CENTERPOINTE DR 97035

Two Centerpointe
2 CENTERPOINTE DR 97035

GOVERNMENT

City Hall
380 A AVE 97034

MILITARY

National Guard Armory
1915 S SHORE BLVD 97034

GOVERNMENT

Lake Grove Station
15875 Boones Ferry Rd 97035

Main Post Office
501 4TH ST 97034

MILWAUKIE

APARTMENTS

Crystal Lake
10500 SE 26TH AVE 97222

The Bluffs
12601 SE RIVER RD 97222

The Crossing
12200 SE McLoughlin Blvd 97222

GOVERNMENT

USPS Milwaukie Finance St
11222 SE MAIN ST 97222

PORTLAND

APARTMENTS

King Tower
901 SW KING AVE 97205

Panorama
735 SW SAINT CLAIR AVE 97205

Park Vista
2323 SW PARK PL 97205

Portland Towers
950 SW 21ST AVE 97205

Vista Saint Clair
1000 SW VISTA AVE 97205

Westmoreland Union Manor
6404 SE 23RD AVE 97202

Wimbledon Square
2831 SE COLT DR 97202

BUILDINGS

American Bank
621 SW MORRISON ST ... 97205

Bank Of America Financial
121 SW MORRISON ST ... 97204

Bank Of California Tower
707 SW Washington St 97205

Benjamin Franklin Plaza
1 SW COLUMBIA ST 97258

Cascade
520 SW 6TH AVE 97204

Columbia Square
111 SW COLUMBIA ST 97201

Commonwealth
421 SW 6TH AVE 97204

Crown Plaza
1500 SW 1ST AVE 97201

First Interstate Tower
1300 SW 5TH AVE 97201

Harrison Square
1800 SW 1ST AVE 97201

Koin Center
222 SW COLUMBIA ST 97201

Lloyd
700 NE MULTNOMAH ST . 97232

Lloyd Center Tower
825 NE MULTNOMAH ST . 97232

Lloyd Five Hundred
500 NE MULTNOMAH ST . 97232

Mayer
1130 SW MORRISON ST . 97205

Morgan
720 SW Washington St 97205

One Main Place
101 SW MAIN ST 97204

Pacwest Center
1211 SW 5TH AVE 97204

Pittock Block
921 SW Washington St 97205

Security Pacific Plaza
1001 SW 5TH AVE 97204

Standard Insurance Ctr
900 SW 5TH AVE 97204

Standard Plaza
1100 SW 6TH AVE 97204

Terminal Sales
1220 SW MORRISON ST . 97205

Two Hundred Market
200 SW MARKET ST 97201

US Bancorp Tower
111 SW 5TH AVE 97204

GOVERNMENT

City Hall
1220 SW 5TH AVE 97204

Federal
511 NW BROADWAY 97209

Green Wyatt Federal
1220 SW 3RD AVE 97204

Justice Center
1120 SW 3RD AVE 97204

Multnomah Co Courthouse
1021 SW 4TH AVE 97204

Pioneer Courthouse
555 SW YAMHILL ST 97204

Portland
1120 SW 5TH AVE 97204

US Courthouse
620 SW MAIN ST 97205

GOVERNMENT

USPS Creston Station
5010 SE FOSTER RD 97206

USPS East Portland Statio
1020 SE 7TH AVE 97214

USPS Rose City Park Stati
2425 NE 50TH AVE 97213

USPS Sellwood Station
6723 SE 16TH AVE 97202

HOTELS

Heathman
1009 SW BROADWAY 97205

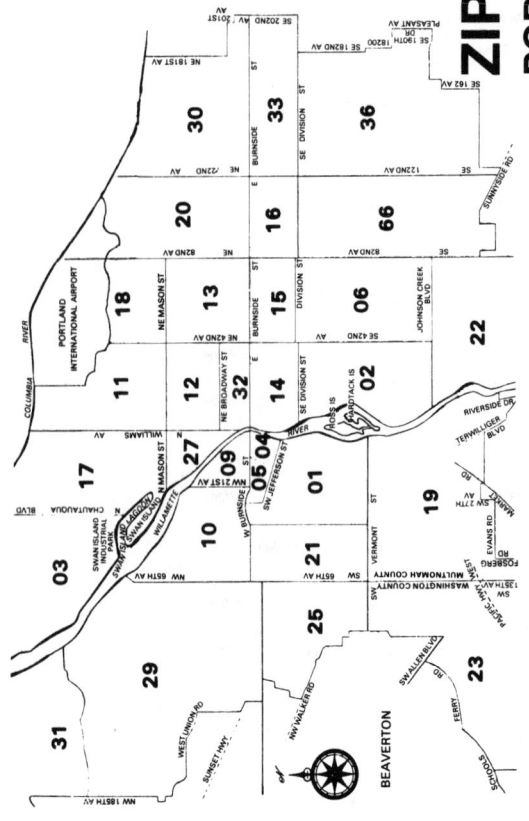

ZIP CODES
PORTLAND, OR
972 + TWO DIGITS
SHOWN = ZIP CODE

PENNSYLVANIA
Abbreviation PA

Aaronsburg 16820
Abbott (Galeton) 16922
Abbottstown 17301
Aberdeen (Elizabethtown) . 17022
Abington 19001, 19111
    Ogontz Campus 19001
    Roslyn 19001
Academia (Port Royal) 17082
Academy Corners 16928
    (Knoxville)
Accomac (York) 17406
Ackermanville 18010
Acme 15610
Acosta 15520
Adah 15410
Adamsburg 15611
Adamsdale 17972
    (Schuylkill Haven)
Adamstown 19501
Adamsville 16110
Addison 15411
Adrian 16210
Africa (Mercersburg) 17236
Airville 17302
Akron 17501
Aladdin (Schenley) 15682
Alba 16910
Albany (Kempton) 19529
Albion 16401, 16475
Albrightsville 18210
Alburtis 18011
Alcoa Center 15069
    (New Kensington)
Aldan (Clifton Heights) 19018
Aldenville 18401
Aleppo 15310
Alexander Springs 17004
    (Belleville)
Alexandria 16611
Alfarata (Mc Clure) 17841
Alinda (Landisburg) 17040
Aline 17853
    (Mount Pleasant Mills)
Aliquippa 15001
Allegheny (Pittsburgh) 15212
Alleghenyville (Mohnton) .. 19540
Allendale (Camp Hill) 17011
Allenport 15412, 17066
Allensville 17002
Allentown 18100-106, 18175
    18195
    Wescosville 18106
Allenwood 17810
Allison 15413, 17751
Allison Park 15101
Allport 16821
Alltel (Kittanning) 16215
Almedia (Bloomsburg) 17815
Alpine (Lewisberry) 17339
Alsace Manor (Temple) 19560
Altamont (Frackville) 17931
Altenwald (Waynesboro) ... 17268
Altoona 16601-603
    Greenwood 16601
    Juniata 16601
    Lakemont 16602
Alum Bank 15521
Alverda 15710

Alverton 15612
Amaranth (Warfordsburg) . 17267
Amberson 17210
Ambler 19002
Ambridge 15003
Amity 15311, 19518
Analomink 18320
Andalusia (Bensalem) 19020
Anderson (Granville) 17029
Andersonburg (Loysville) .. 17047
Andersontown 17055
    (Mechanicsburg)
Andover (Mc Connellsburg) 17233
Andreas 18211
Andrews Bridge 17509
    (Christiana)
Andrews Settlement 16923
    (Genesee)
Angelica (Mohnton) 19540
Anita 15711
Annville 17003
Ansonia (Wellsboro) 16901
Antes Fort 17720
Anthony (Turbotville) 17772
Antis (Bellwood) 16617
Antrim 16901, 17225
    (Wellsboro)
Apollo 15613
Aqua (Chambersburg) 17201
Aquashicola 18012
Arcadia 15712, 17563
Arch Rock (Mifflintown) ... 17059
Archbald 18403
Arcola 19420
Ardara 15615
Ardmore 19003
Ardsley (Glenside) 19038
Arendtsville 17303
Aristes 17920
Armagh 15920, 17063
Armbrust 15616
Armstrong (Williamsport) .. 17701
Arnold (New Kensington) .. 15068
Arnot 16911
Arnots Addition 17970
    (Saint Clair)
Arona 15617
Arsenal (Pittsburgh) 15201
Artemas 17211
Asaph (Wellsboro) 16901
Ashbury (Orangeville) 17859
Ashfield 18212
Ashland 17921
Ashley (Wilkes Barre) 18706
Ashville 16613, 16629
Aspers 17304
Aspinwall (Pittsburgh) 15215
Aston 19014
Atglen 19310
Athens 18810
Athol (Earlville) 19519
Atkinsons Mills 17051
    (Mc Veytown)
Atlantic 16111
Atlas (Mount Carmel) 17851
Atlasburg 15004
Auburn 17922
Audubon 19403, 19407
    (Norristown)
    Norristown 19407
Aughwick (Mount Union) ... 17066

Augustaville (Sunbury) 17801
Aultman 15713
Austin 16720
Austinburg (Knoxville) 16928
Austinville 16914
    (Columbia Cross Roads)
Avalon (Pittsburgh) 15202
Avella 15312
Avis 17721
Avoca (Pittston) 18641
Avon (Lebanon) 17042
Avondale 19311
Avonmore 15618
Ayr 17212, 17233
    (Big Cove Tannery)
Bachmanville (Hershey) 17033
Baden 15005
Baederwood (Jenkintown) . 19046
Bailey (Newport) 17074
Baileys Corner 16926
    (Granville Summit)
Bainbridge 17502
Bairdford 15006
Bakers Summit 16614
Bakerstown 15007
Bala Cynwyd 19004
Bald Eagle (Mill Hall) 17751
Baldwin (Pittsburgh) 15234
Balls Mills 17728
    (Cogan Station)
Bally 19503
Bamford (Landisville) 17538
Bangor (Ackermanville) 18010
    .... 18013, 18050
    East Bangor 18013
    Roseto 18013
Bankstown 17052
    (Mapleton Depot)
Bannerville (Mc Clure) 17841
Barbours (Williamsport) 17701
Baresville (Hanover) 17331
Bareville (Leola) 17540
Barkeyville (Harrisville) 16038
Barking (New Kensington) . 15068
Barnesboro 15714
Barnesville 18214
Barneytown 17052
    (Mapleton Depot)
Barnitz (Carlisle) 17013
Barree (Alexandria) 16611
Barrville (Reedsville) 17084
Barry (Hegins) 17938
Bart 17503
Barto 19504
Bartonsville 18321
Bartville (Christiana) 17509
Basket (Oley) 19547
Bastress (Williamsport) 17701
Bath 18014
Baumgardner 17584
    (Willow Street)
Baumstown (Birdsboro) 19508
Bausman 17504
Beach Haven 18601
Beach Lake 18405
Beale (Port Royal) 17082
Beallsville 15313
Bear Creek 18602
Bear Gap (Elysburg) 17824
Bear Lake 16402
Bear Valley (Shamokin) ... 17872

Brier Hill 15415
Brisbin 16620
Bristol 19007
Bro Dart (Williamsport) 17705
Broad Axe (Ambler) 19002
Broad Top 16621
Brockport 15823
Brockton 17925
Brockway 15824
Brodbecks (Glenville) 17329
Brodheadsville 18322
Brogue 17309
Brogueville (Felton) 17322
Brommerstown (Auburn) 17922
Brook Park (Lewisburg) 17837
Brookfield (Westfield) 16950
Brookhaven 19015
Brookland (Ulysses) 16948
Brookline 15226, 19083
   (Pittsburgh)
Brooklyn 18813
Brookside (Shippensburg) ... 17257
.... 17771, 17963
Brookville 15825
Broomall 19008
Broughton (Pittsburgh) 15236
Brown 17084, 17727
   (Reedsville)
Browndale (Forest City) 18421
Brownfield 15416
Brownstone 17036
   (Hummelstown)
Brownstown 15906, 17508
   (Johnstown)
Brownsville 15417
.... 17976, 19565
   West Brownsville 15417
Bruin 16022
Brunnerville (Lititz) 17543
Brush Valley 15720
Brushtown 17241, 17731
   (Newville)
Bryan Mills (Hughesville) .. 17737
Bryansville (Delta) 17314
Bryn Athyn 19009
Bryn Mawr 19010
Brysonia (Biglerville) 17307
Buck (Quarryville) 17566
Buck Hill Falls 18323
Buck Run (Pottsville) 17901
Buck Valley 17267
   (Warfordsburg)
Buckhorn (Bloomsburg) 17815
Buckingham 18912
Buena Vista 15018
.... 17268, 17527
Buffalo (Liverpool) .. 17045, 17837
Buffalo Mills 15534
Buffalo Springs (Lebanon) .. 17042
Bulger 15019
Bungy (Mansfield) 16933
Bunker Hill 17042, 17901
   (Lebanon)
Bunkertown 17049
   (Mc Alisterville)
Bunola 15020
Burgettstown 15021
Burlington 18814
Burnham 17009
Burnside 15721, 17872
Burnt Cabins 17215

Bushkill 18324, 18371, 18373
Bustleton 19115, 19152
   (Philadelphia)
Butler 16001, 16003
   Bon Aire 16001
   Meridian 16001
   Nixon 16001
   Plaza 16001
   Point 16001
Buttonwood (Trout Run) 17771
Butztown (Bethlehem) 18017
Buyerstown (Kinzers) 17535
Byrnedale 15827
Byrnesville (Centralia) 17927
Bywood (Upper Darby) 19082
Cabot (Marwood) 16023
Cadogan 16212
Cains (Gap) 17527
Cairnbrook 15924
Caldwell (Lock Haven) 17745
California 15419, 17777
Callensburg 16213
Callery 16024
Calumet 15621
Calvert (Trout Run) 17771
Calvin 16622
Camargo (Quarryville) 17566
Camb Springs 16403
   (Cambridge Springs)
Cambra 18611
Cambridge Springs 16403
Cammal (Jersey Shore) 17723
Camp Curtin (Harrisburg) ... 17110
Camp Grove (Herndon) 17830
Camp Hill
   ..... 17001, 17011-012, 17089
   Allendale 17011
   Cumberland Park 17011
   Eberleys Mill 17011
   Hill 17011
   Lower Allen 17011
   Ranavilla 17011
   Rossmoyne 17011
   Shiremanstown 17011
   White Hill 17011
Campbelltown 17010
Camptown 18815
Canadensis 18325
Canadohta Lake 16438
   (Union City)
Canoe Camp (Mansfield) .. 16933
Canonsburg 15317
Canton 17724, 17743
   Beech Flats 17724
   Cedar Ledge 17724
   East Canton 17724
   Ellenton 17724
   Gleason 17724
   Union 17724
   Ward 17724
   West Leroy 17724
Caprivi (Carlisle) 17013
Carbondale 18407
Cardale 15420
Carlisle 17013
Carlisle Springs 17013
   (Carlisle)
Carlton 16311
Carmichaels 15320
Carnegie 15106
Carroll 17090, 17747

   (Shermans Dale)
Carroll Park (Wynnewood) . 19096
Carroll Valley 17320
   (Fairfield)
Carrolltown 15722
Carson (Pittsburgh) 15203
Carsontown (Waterville) ... 17776
Carsonville (Halifax) 17032
Carter Camp (Galeton) 16922
Carversville 18913
Cascade (Trout Run) 17771
Cashtown 17201, 17310
   (Chambersburg)
Cassandra 15925
Cassville 16623
Castanea 17726, 17745
Caste Village 15236
   (Pittsburgh)
Castle 16101-102, 16105
   (New Castle)
Castle Shannon 15234
   (Pittsburgh)
Castor (Philadelphia) 19149
Catasauqua 18032
Catawissa 17820
Cathead (Sabinsville) 16943
Cecil 15321
Cedar Lane (East Earl) 17519
Cedar Ledge (Canton) 17724
Cedar Run 17727
Cedar Springs (Mill Hall) ... 17751
Cedarbrook (Wyncote) 19095
Cedarhurst (Pittsburgh) 15243
Cedars 19423
Center 17047, 17059
   (Loysville)
Center City 17701
   (Williamsport)
Center Mills (Aspers) 17304
Center Moreland 18657
   (Tunkhannock)
Center Square (Blue Bell) .. 19422
Center Valley 18034
Centerport 19516
Centerville 16404
.... 16925, 17062, 17601
Central (Benton) 17814
Central City 15926
Central Manor 17582
   (Washington Boro)
Centralia 17927
Centre (New Bloomfield) ... 17068
.... 17842, 19541
Centre Hall 16828
Chadds Ford 19317
Chain (New Ringgold) 17960
Chalfont 18914
Chalkhill 15421
Chambers Hill 17111
   (Harrisburg)
Chambersburg 17201
Chambersville 15723
Champion 15622
Chandlers Valley 16312
Chapman 17760, 17864
   (North Bend)
Charleroi 15022
Charleston (Wellsboro) 16901
Charlestown (Mercersburg) . 17236
Charlton 17112, 17745
   (Harrisburg)

Charmian 17214
   (Blue Ridge Summit)
Charnita (Fairfield) 17320
Chatham 16935, 19318
   (Middlebury Center)
Cheesetown 17201
   (Chambersburg) ....
Cheltenham 19012
Cherokee Ranch (Temple) 19560
Cherry Flats (Mansfield) 16933
Cherry Grove 17264
   (Three Springs)
Cherry Hill (Albion) 16401
Cherry Run (Weikert) 17885
Cherry Tree 15724
Cherryville 17966, 18035
   (Ravine) ....
Chest Springs 16624
Chester 19013-016, 19022
   Eddystone 19013
   Feltonville 19013
   Parkside 19013
   Village Green 19013
Chester Heights 19017
Chester Springs 19425
Chester Township 19013
   (Chester)
Chestnut Hill 19118
   (Philadelphia)
Chestnut Level 17566
   (Quarryville)
Chestnut Ridge 15422
Cheswick 15024
Cheyney 19319
Chichester (Aston) 19014
Chicora 16025
Childs (Carbondale) 18407
Chillisquaque (Montandon) 17850
Chinchilla 18410
Christiana 17509
Church Hill (Mercersburg) . 17236
Church Hill Manor 17084
   (Reedsville)
Churchill (Pittsburgh) 15221
Churchtown (Narvon) 17555
Churchville (Southampton) 18966
Cisna Run (Loysville) 17047
Cito (Mc Connellsburg) 17233
Clairton 15025
Clarence 16829
Clarendon 16313
Claridge 15623
Clarington 15828
Clarion 16214
Clark 16113
Clarks Mills 16114
Clarks Summit 18411
Clarksburg 15725
Clarkstown (Muncy) 17756
Clarksville 15322
Clay (Ephrata) 17522
Clay Hill (Chambersburg) .. 17201
Claylick (Mercersburg) 17236
Claysburg 16625
Claysville 15323
Clayton (Bally) 19503
Clear Spring (Dillsburg) 17019
Clearfield 16830
Clearville 15535
Cleona (Lebanon) 17042
Clermont (Harrisburg) 17112

Cleveland (Catawissa) 17820
Cleversburg 17257
   (Shippensburg)
Clifford 18413
Clifton Heights 19018
Climax 16216
Clinton 15026, 17752
Clintondale (Mill Hall) 17751
Clintonville 16372
Clune 15727
Cly (York Haven) 17370
Clymer 15728, 16943
Cmphill (Camp Hill) 17011
Coal (Shamokin) 17872
Coal Cabin Beach (Delta) . 17314
Coal Center 15423
Coal Run (Coal Township) . 17866
Coal Township 17866
Coaldale (Lykens) .. 17048, 18218
Coalport 16627
Coatesville 19320
Cobblerville (Newville) 17241
Coburn 16832
Cochranton 16314
Cochranville 19330
Cocolamus 17014
Codorus 17311
Coffeetown (Palmyra) 17078
Cogan House (Trout Run) . 17771
Cogan Station 17728
Cokeburg 15324
Colebrook 17015, 17734
Colebrookdale (Boyertown) 19512
Colemanville (Pequea) 17565
Colerain (Kirkwood) 17536
Coles (Mahanoy City) 17948
Coles Creek (Benton) 17814
Colesburg (Coudersport) .. 16915
College Misericordia 18612
   (Dallas)
College Park (Lewisburg) .. 17837
Collegeville 19426, 19473
   Graterford 19426
   Rahns 19426
   Trappe 19426
Collingdale (Darby) 19023
Collins (Quarryville) 17566
Collinsville (Airville) 17302
Collomsville 17701
   (Williamsport)
Colmar 18915
Colonial Crest 17112
   (Harrisburg)
Colonial Hills 17044
   (Lewistown)
Colonial Park 17109
   (Harrisburg)
Columbia 17512
Columbia Cross Roads 16914
Columbus 16405
Colver 15927
Colwyn (Darby) 19023
Comly (Turbotville) 17772
Commerce (Philadelphia) .. 19108
Commodore 15729
Compass (Gap) 17527
Concord 17217
Concordville ... 19331, 18939-340
Conestoga 17516
Conewago 17022, 17331
   (Elizabethtown)

Confluence 15424
Congo (Barto) 19504
Conneaut Lake 16316
Conneautville 16406
Connellsville 15425
Connersville 17851
   (Mount Carmel)
Connerton (Girardville) 17935
Connoquenessing 16027
Conoy (Bainbridge) 17502
Conshohocken 19428
Conway 15027
Conyngham 17927, 18219
   (Centralia)
Cooke (Carlisle) 17013
Cooks Run (Westport) 17778
Cooksburg 16217
Coolspring 15730
Coon Hunter (Middleburg) . 17842
Coopersburg 18036
Cooperstown 16317
Cooperville (Christiana) 17509
Coplay 18037
Coral 15731
Coraopolis 15108
Corliss (Pittsburgh) 15204
Cornwall 17016, 17083
Cornwall Center 17016
   (Cornwall)
Cornwells Heights 19020
   (Bensalem)
Corry 16407
Corsica 15829
Cosytown (Greencastle) 17225
Couchtown (Loysville) 17047
Coudersport 16915
Coulters 15028
Country Manor 17112
   (Harrisburg)
Coupon 16629
Courtdale (Wilkes Barre) ... 18704
Courtney 15029
Cove (Duncannon) 17020
Cove Gap (Mercersburg) .. 17236
Covington 16917
Cowan (Mifflinburg) 17844
Cowanesque 16918
Cowans Village 17224
   (Fort Loudon)
Cowansville 16218
Cowley (Granville Summit) 16926
Crabtree 15624
Crafton 15205, 15275-276
   (Pittsburgh)
Craigheads (Carlisle) 17013
Craigs (Mahanoy City) 17948
Craigsville (Worthington) .. 16262
Craley 17312
Cramer (Seward) 15954
Cranberry 16319
Cranberry Township 16033
   (Evans City)
Cranesville 16410
Crawford (Jersey Shore) ... 17740
Creamery 19430
Creekside 15732, 15739
Creighton 15030
Cresco 18326
Cresmont (Frackville) 17931
Cress (Waynesboro) 17268
Cresson 16630, 16699

Cressona 17929
Crestmont (Lock Haven) 17745
Creswell (Conestoga) 17516
Crooked Creek 16935
   (Middlebury Center)
Crosby 16724
Cross Fork 17729
Cross Keys 17021, 17350
   (East Waterford)
Cross Roads (Felton) 17322
Crossgrove (Mc Clure) 17841
Crossingville (Edinboro) 16412
Crown 16220
Croydon 19021
Crucible 15325
Crum Lynne 19022
Crystal Spring 15536
Cuba Mills (Mifflintown) 17059
Cuddy 15031
Cumberland Park 17011
   (Camp Hill)
Cumbola 17930
Cummings (Waterville) 17776
Cummingstown (Carlisle) .. 17013
Curllsville 16221
Curryville 16631
Curtisville 15032
Curwensville 16833
Custer City 16725
Cyclone 16726
Cynwyd (Bala Cynwyd) 19004
Daggett (Millerton) 16936
Dagus Mines 15831
Daisytown 15427, 15902
Dale (Johnstown) ... 15902, 19504
Dallas 18612, 18690
Dallastown 17313
Dalmatia 17017
Dalton 18414
Damascus 18415
Danboro 18916
Danielsville 18038
Danville 17821-822
Darby 19023
Darby Township 19036
   (Glenolden)
Dark Water (Saint Clair) 17970
Darlington 16115, 19063
Darragh 15625
Dauberville 19517
Dauphin 17018
Davidsburg (Dover) 17315
Davidson (Muncy Valley) .. 17758
Davidsville 15928
Davistown (Mount Morris) .. 15349
Dawson 15428
Dayton 16222, 17098
De Lancey 15733
De Turksville 17963
   (Pine Grove)
De Young 16728
Decatur (Mc Clure) 17841
Deer Lake (Orwigsburg) 17961
Deerfield (Knoxville) 16928
Defense Depot 17055
   (Mechanicsburg)
Defiance 16633
Deiblers (Danville) 17821
Delano 18220
Delaware 17059, 17777
   (Mifflintown)

Dellville (Duncannon) 17020
Delmar (Wellsboro) 16901
Delmont 15626
Delta 17314
Denbo 15429
Denholm (Mifflintown) 17059
Denver 17517
Deodate (Elizabethtown) ... 17022
Derrick City 16727
Derrs (Benton) 17814
Derry
   15627, 17033, 17099, 17821
Devault 19432
Devon 19333
Devonshire Heights 17112
   (Harrisburg)
Dewart 17730
Diamondtown 17851
Dianaville 17331
Dice (Mifflinburg) 17844
Dickerson Run 15430
Dickey (Mercersburg) 17236
Dickinson 17218, 17324
Dickson City 18519
Dieners Hill (Pottsville) 17901
Dilliner 15327
Dillsburg 17019
Dilltown 15929
Dimock 18816
Dingmans Ferry 18328
Distant 16223
District (Boyertown) 19512
Dixonville 15734
Dogtown 16923, 17870
   (Genesee)
Donaldson (Tremont) 17981
Donegal 15628, 15646
Donegal Heights 17552
   (Mount Joy)
Donnally Mills 17062
   (Millerstown)
Donnellytown (Carlisle) 17013
Donora 15033
Dooleyville 17851
   (Mount Carmel)
Dormont (Pittsburgh) 15216
Dornsife 17823
Dorset (New Ringgold) 17960
Dott (Warfordsburg) 17267
Doubling Gap (Newville) 17241
Douglass (Gilbertsville) 19525
Douglassville 19518
Doutyville (Shamokin) 17872
Dover 17315
Downingtown 19335, 19372
Downtown (Pittsburgh) 15222
Doyles Mills (Mifflin) 17058
Doylesburg 17219
Doylestown 18901, 18933
   New Britain 18901
Draper (Wellsboro) 16901
Dravosburg 15034
Drehersville (Orwigsburg) . 17961
Dresher 19025
Drexel Hill 19026
Drexel Hills 17070
   (New Cumberland)
Drexelbrook (Drexel Hill) .. 19026
Drifting 16834
Drifton 18221
Driftwood 15832

Drocton (Renovo) 17764
Drumore 17518
Drums 18222
Drury Run (Renovo) 17764
Dry Run 17219-220
   (Doylesburg)
Dry Valley Crossroads 17889
   (Winfield)
Dryville (Mertztown) 19539
Du Bois 15801
Dublin (Fort Littleton) 17223
   .... 17239, 18917
Duboistown (Williamsport) .. 17701
Dudley 16634
Duffield (Chambersburg) ... 17201
Duke Center 16729
Dunbar 15431
Duncan (Wellsboro) 16901
Duncannon 17020
Duncansville 16635
Duncott (Pottsville) 17901
Dundore (Port Trevorton) .. 17864
Dunkelbergers (Shamokin) 17872
Dunlevy 15432
Dunlo 15930
Dunmore (Scranton) 18512
Dunnstown (Lock Haven) .. 17745
Dupont (Pittston) 18641
Duquesne 15110
Durham 18039
Durlach (Ephrata) 17522
Duryea (Pittston) 18642
Dushore 18614
Dysart 16636
Eagles Mere 17731
Eagleville 19403, 19408
   (Norristown)
   Norristown 19408
Earl 17557, 19512
   (New Holland)
Earlington 18918
Earlville 19519
East Bangor (Bangor) 18013
East Berlin 17316
East Brady 16028
East Brunswick 17960
   (New Ringgold)
East Buffalo (Lewisburg) ... 17837
East Butler 16029
East Cameron 17828
   (Gowen City)
East Canton (Canton) 17724
East Charleston 16933
   (Mansfield)
East Chillisquaque 17847
   (Milton)
East Earl 17519
East Falls (Philadelphia) ... 19129
East Freedom 16637
East Germantown 19138
   (Philadelphia)
East Greenville 18041
East Hanover (Annville) 17003
East Hickory 16321
East Kane (Kane) 16735
East Keating (Westport) 17778
East Lancaster 17605
   (Lancaster)
East Lansdowne 19050
   (Lansdowne)
East Lawrenceville 16929

(Lawrenceville)
East Lewisburg (Milton) 17847
East Liberty (Pittsburgh) 15206
East Mc Keesport 15035
East Millsboro 15433
East Mines (Saint Clair) 17970
East Muncy (Muncy) 17756
East Newport (Newport) 17074
East Pennsboro (Enola) 17025
East Petersburg 17520
East Pittsburgh 15112
East Prospect 17317
East Renovo (Renovo) 17764
East Salem (Mifflintown) ... 17059
East Smethport 16730
East Smithfield 18817
East Springfield 16411
East Stroudsburg 18301
East Texas 18046
East Vandergrift 15629
East Waterford 17021
East York (York) 17402
Eastland Hills 17268
(Waynesboro)
Easton 18040, 18042-045
   Forks Township 18040
   Palmer 18043, 18045
   Palmer Township 18045
   West Easton 18042
   Williams Township 18042
Eastpoint 17765
(Roaring Branch)
Eastville (Loganton) 17747
Eastwick (Philadelphia) 19153
Eau Claire 16030
Ebenezer (Lebanon) 17042
Ebensburg 15931
Eberleys Mill (Camp Hill) .. 17011
Ebervale 18223
Echo Valley (Tremont) 17981
Eckville (Kempton) 19529
Eddington (Bensalem) 19020
Eddystone 19013, 19022
(Chester)
Eden 17566, 17601
(Quarryville)
Edenburg (Hamburg) 19526
Edenville 17201, 17252
(Chambersburg)
Edgegrove (Hanover) 17331
Edgely (Bristol) 19007
Edgemont 17109, 19028
(Harrisburg)
Edgewater Park 19067
(Morrisville)
Edgewood 15218, 17872
(Pittsburgh)
Edinboro 16412, 16444
Edinburg 16116
Edisonville (Strasburg) 17579
Edmon 15630
Edwardsville 18704
(Wilkes Barre)
Effort 18330
Ehrenfeld (South Fork) 15956
Eighty Four 15330
Elco 15434
Eldersville 15036
Elderton 15736
Eldora (Peach Bottom) 17563
Eldred 16731, 17754, 17964

Eleven Mile (Genesee) 16923
Elgin 16413
Elimsport (Allenwood) 17810
Elizabeth 15037, 17543
Elizabethtown 17022
Elizabethville 17023
Elk (Gaines) 16921
Elk Grove (Benton) 17814
Elkins Park 19012, 19117
(Cheltenham)
Elkland 16920
Ellen Gowan (Shenandoah) 17976
Ellendale (Dauphin) 17018
Ellenton (Canton) ... 17724, 17768
Elliottsburg 17024
Elliottson (Carlisle) 17013
Ellisburg (Genesee) 16923
Ellport (Ellwood City) 16117
Ellsworth 15331
Ellwood City 16117
Elm 17521
Elmer (Westfield) 16950
Elmhurst 18416
Elmora 15737
Elrama 15038
Elstonville (Manheim) 17545
Elton 15934
Elverson 19520
Elwyn (Media) 19063
Elwyn Terrace (Manheim) . 17545
Elysburg 17824
Emeigh 15738
Emerald (Slatington) 18080
Emigsville 17318
Emlenton 16373
Emmaus 18049
Emmaus 18049, 18098-099
Emporium 15834
Emsworth (Pittsburgh) 15202
Endeavor 16321-322
(East Hickory)
Enders (Halifax) 17032
Englesville (Boyertown) 19512
Englewood (Frackville) 17931
English Center 17776
(Waterville)
Enhaut (Harrisburg) 17113
Enola 17025
Enon Valley 16120
Enterline (Halifax) 17032
Entlerville (Newville) 17241
Entriken 16638
Ephrata 17522, 17549
   Clay 17522
   Durlach 17522
   Farmersville 17522
   Hahnstown 17522
   Hinkletown 17522
   Lincoln 17522
   Murrell 17522
   Napierville 17522
   Voganville 17522
   Weidmanville 17522
Equinunk 18417
Erdenheim (Philadelphia) .. 19118
Erdman (Lykens) 17048
Erie16500-512, 16514-515
   .... 16522, 16530-534, 16538
   16541, 16544, 16546, 16550
   .... 16553-554, 16558, 16563
   16565

Belle Valley 16509
   Perry Square 16507
   Presque Isle 16505
   South Erie 16508
   Wesleyville 16510
Erly (Elliottsburg) 17024
Ernest 15739
Erwinna 18920
Eshbach (Bechtelsville) 19505
Eshcol (Millerstown) 17062
Espy (Bloomsburg) 17815
Espyville (Linesville) 16424
Essington 19029
Estherton (Harrisburg) 17110
Etna (Pittsburgh) 15223
Etown (Elizabethtown) 17022
Etters 17319
Eulalia (Coudersport) 16915
Evans City 16033
Evansville (Fleetwood) 19522
Evendale (Richfield) 17086
Everett 15537
Everhartville (Newport) 17074
Everson 15631
Eville (Elizabethville) 17023
Excelsior 17825, 17872
Exchange (Danville) 17821
Exeter (Pittston) 18643
Export 15632
Exton 19341, 19353
Eyers Grove (Millville) 17846
Eynon (Archbald) 18403
Factoryville 18419
Fagleysville 19525
(Gilbertsville)
Fair Acres 17070
(New Cumberland)
Fairbank 15435
Fairchance 15436
Fairdale (Carmichaels) 15320
Fairfield 17320, 17754
   Carroll Valley 17320
   Charnita 17320
   Greenstone 17320
Fairhill (Philadelphia) 19133
Fairhope 15012, 15538
(Belle Vernon)
   Glencoe 15538
Fairland (Lititz) 17543
Fairlawn (Cogan Station) .. 17728
Fairless Hills 19030
Fairmount (Quarryville) 17566
Fairmount City 16224
Fairmount Springs 17814
(Benton)
Fairoaks (Ambridge) 15003
Fairplay (Gettysburg) 17325
Fairview 16415, 17025
   17044, 17070, 17268, 17872
Fairview Drive (Hanover) .. 17331
Fairview Heights 19533
(Leesport)
Fairview Village 19409
Fairville (Lewisburg) 17837
Fallentimber 16639
Falling Spring 17040, 17201
(Landisburg)
Falls 18615, 19054
Falls Creek 15840
Fallsington (Levittown) 19054
Falmouth (Bainbridge) 17502

Fannett (Doylesburg) 17219	Foresthill (Mifflinburg) 17844	Ganister (Williamsburg) 16693
Fannettsburg 17221	Forestville 16035, 17901	Gans 15439
Farmdale (Mount Joy) 17552	Forks (Orangeville) 17859	Gap 17527
Farmersville (Ephrata) 17522	Forks Township (Easton) ... 18042	Garards Fort 15334
Farmington 15437	Forksville 18616	Garden City (Media) 19063
Farragut (Montoursville) 17754	Fort Hill 15540	Gardenview (Reedsville) ... 17084
Farrandsville 17734	Fort Hunter (Harrisburg) 17110	Gardenville 18926
Farrell 16121	Fort Littleton 17223	Gardners 17324
Farwell (Renovo) 17764	Fort Loudon 17224	Garfield (Bernville) 19506
Fassett (Gillett) 16925	Fort Robinson (Loysville) .. 17047	Garland 16416
Fawn Grove 17321	Fort Washington ... 19025, 19034	Garrett 15542
Faxon (Williamsport) 17701	(Dresher)	Gastonville 15336
Fayette (Mc Alisterville) ... 17049	Upper Dublin 19034	Gatchellville (New Park) 17352
Fayette City 15438	Fortney (Lewisberry) 17339	Gay Street (West Chester) 19381
Fayetteville 17222	Forty Fort (Wilkes Barre) .. 18704	Geigertown 19523
Fayfield (York) 17402	Fountain (Hegins) 17938	Genesee 16923, 16941
Fearnot (Sacramento) 17968	Fountain Hill (Bethlehem) . 18015	Andrews Settlement ... 16923
Feasterville Trevose 19053	Fountain Springs 17921	Dogtown 16923
Felton 17322	(Ashland)	Eleven Mile 16923
Feltonville (Chester) 19013	Fountainville 18923	Ellisburg 16923
Fenelton 16034	Fox (Shunk) 17768	Gold 16923
Fermanagh (Mifflintown) ... 17059	Fox Chapel (Pittsburgh) 15238	Hickox 16923
Fern Glen (Nuremberg) 18241	Fox Chase (Philadelphia) .. 19111	Keech 16923
Ferndale (Johnstown) 15905	Fox Hill (Waynesboro) 17268	Kinney 16923
.... 17872, 17985, 18921	Foxburg 16036	North Bingham 16923
Fernville (Bloomsburg) 17815	Foxcroft (Jenkintown) 19046	North Bingham 16941
Fernwood (Lansdowne) 19050	Frackville 17931, 17932	Raymond 16923
Fertility (Lancaster) 17602	Frailey (Tremont) 17981	West Bingham 16923
Fetterville (Narvon) 17555	Franconia 18924	Geneva (Conneaut Lake) .. 16316
Fidelity (Philadelphia) 19109	Frankford (Philadelphia) 19124	Georgetown 15043, 17340
Fields Station 17771	Franklin 16323	Germansville 18053
(Trout Run)	.... 17820, 17846, 17861	Germantown (Lykens) 17048
Finleyville 15332	Rocky Grove 16323	.... 17340, 19144
Fisher 16225	Franklin Center (Media)	Gettysburg 17325-326
Fisherdale (Elysburg) 17824	.... 19063, 19091	Gettysburg Junction 17013
Fishers Ferry (Sunbury) 17801	Franklin Mint (Media) 19091	(Carlisle)
Fishertown 15539	Franklintown 17323	Gibbon Glade 15440
Fisherville (Halifax) 17032	Frazer (Malvern) 19355	Gibraltar (Birdsboro) 19508
Fishing Creek 17859	Frederick 19435	Gibson 18820
(Orangeville)	Fredericksburg 17026	Gibsonia 15044
Fishing Creek Valley 17112	Fredericksville 19539	Gifford 16732
(Harrisburg)	(Mertztown)	Gilbert 18331
Five Points 17772, 19606	Fredericktown 15333	Gilberton 17934
(Turbotville)	Fredonia 16124	Gilbertsville 19525
Fiveforks (Waynesboro) 17268	Freeburg 17827	Gillett 16925
Fivepointville (Denver) 17517	Freedom 15042	Gipsy 15741
Fleetville 18420	Freeland 18224	Girard 16417
Fleetwood 19522	Freemansburg (Bethlehem) 18017	Girardville 17935
Fleming 16835	Freeport 16229	Gitts Run (Hanover) 17331
Flemington (Lock Haven) .. 17745	Frenchville 16836, 16850	Glades (York) 17402
Flicksville 18050	Freysville (Red Lion) 17356	Gladwyne 19035
Flinton 16640	Friedens 15541	Glasgow 16644
Flintville (Lebanon) 17042	Friedensburg 17933	Glassport 15045
Floradale (Biglerville) 17307	Friedsville 18818	Gleason (Canton) 17724
Floreffe (Clairton) 15025	Frisbie (Orwigsburg) 17961	Gleasonton (North Bend) .. 17760
Florin (Mount Joy) 17552	Fritztown (Reading) 19608	Glen Campbell 15742
Flourtown 19031	Frogtown 17070	Glen Carbon (Pottsville) 17901
Fogelsville 18051	(New Cumberland)	Glen Dower (Pottsville) 17901
Folcroft 19032	Frostburg 15740	Glen Forney (Waynesboro) 17268
Folsom 19033	Fruitville (Lancaster) 17601	Glen Hope 16645
Fombell 16123	Fryburg 16326	Glen Lyon 18617
Fontana (Lebanon) 17042	Frystown (Myerstown) 17067	Glen Mawr (Hughesville) ... 17737
Forbes Road 15633	Fulton (Peach Bottom) 17563	Glen Mills 19342
Force 15841	Furlong 18925	Glen Richey 16837
Ford City 16226	Furniss (Peach Bottom) 17563	Glen Riddle Lima ... 19037, 19063
Ford Cliff 16228	Gabelsville (Boyertown) 19512	Media 19037
Forest City 18421	Gaines 16921	Glen Rock 17327
Forest Grove 18922	Galeton 16922	Glencoe (Fairhope) 15538
Forest Hills (Pittsburgh) 15221	Galilee (Damascus) 18415	Glendon (Mahanoy City) ... 17948
Forest Knolls 17575	Gallitzin 16641	Glenhope (Glen Hope) 16645
(Silver Spring)	Gamble (Trout Run) 17771	Gleniron (Millmont) 17845

Glenmoore 19343
Glenolden 19036
Glenshaw 15116
Glenside 19038
Glenville 17329
Glenwillard 15046
Glenwood (Harrisburg) 17109
Glenworth (Pottsville) 17901
Gnatstown (Hanover) 17331
Gold (Genesee) 16923
Goldsboro (Etters) 17319
Good (Waynesboro) 17268
Good Spring (Tremont) 17981
Goodhope 17055
   (Mechanicsburg)
Goodville 17094, 17528
   (Thompsontown)
Goodyear (Gardners) 17324
Goosetown (Watsontown) . 17777
Gordon 17936
Gordonville 17529
Gouglersville (Reading) 19608
Gouldsboro 18424
Gowen City 17828
Graceton (Homer City) 15748
Gracey (Harrisonville) 17228
Gradyville 19039
Grampian 16838
Grampian Hills 17701
   (Williamsport)
Grand Valley 16420
Grangeville (Hanover) 17331
Grantham 17027
Grantville 17028
Granville 17029
Granville Summit 16926
Grapeville 15634
Grassflat 16839
Graterford (Collegeville) ... 19426
Gratz 17030
Gray 15544
Grays Landing 15461
   (Masontown)
Graysville 15337
Greason (Carlisle) 17013
Great Bend 18821
Greble (Myerstown) 17067
Greeley 18425
Green Fields 17098
   (Williamstown)
Green Lane 18054
Green Park 17031
Green Point (Jonestown) .. 17038
Green Ridge (Aston) 19014
Green Springs (Hanover) .. 17331
Green Tree (Pittsburgh) 15220
Greenbank (New Holland) . 17557
Greenbrier (Rebuck) 17867
Greenburr (Loganton) 17747
Greenbury (Pottsville) 17901
Greencastle 17225
Greene 17201, 17747
   (Chambersburg)
Greene Junction 15425
   (Connellsville)
Greenfield Manor 19601
   (Reading)
Greenock 15047
Greensboro 15338
Greensburg 15601, 15605-606
Greenspring (Newville) 17241

Greenstone (Fairfield) 17320
Greentown 18426
Greentree 15220, 15242
   (Pittsburgh)
Greenvillage 17201
   (Chambersburg)
Greenville 16125
Greenwich (Kutztown) 19530
Greenwood (Altoona) 16601
   .... 17094, 17846
Greenwood Hills 17109
   (Harrisburg)
Gregg (Allenwood) 17810
Greshville (Boyertown) 19512
Griesemersville 19512
   (Boyertown)
Grimesville 17701
   (Williamsport)
Grimville (Kutztown) 19530
Grindstone 15442
Groffdale (New Holland) ... 17557
Grovania (Danville) 17821
Grove City 16127
Grover 17735
Guernsey (Biglerville) 17307
Guilford (Chambersburg) .. 17201
Guys Mills 16327
Gwynedd 19436
Gwynedd Valley 19437
Hadley 16130
Hahnstown (Ephrata) 17522
Haleeka (Cogan Station) .. 17728
Halfville (Lititz) 17543
Halifax 17032
Halls (Muncy) 17756
Hallstead 18822
Hamburg 19526
Hametown (Glen Rock) 17327
Hamilton 15744, 16939, 17201
   17801
Hamlin 18427
Hammersley Fork (Renovo) 17764
Hampden 17055, 19604
   (Mechanicsburg)
Hampton (New Oxford) 17350
Hancock (Mertztown) 19539
Haneyville (Lock Haven) ... 17745
Hannastown 15635
Hanover 17331-333
Happy Valley (Elysburg) ... 17824
Harborcreek 16421
Harford 18823
Harleigh 18225
Harlem (Barto) 19504
Harleysville 19438, 19441
Harmonsburg 16422
Harmony 16037
Harrisburg 17100-113
   .... 17120-130, 17140, 17177
   .... 17120-130, 17140, 17177
   Beaufort Farm 17110
   Blue Cross 17177
   Blue Ridge 17112
   Blue Shield 17140
   Bressler 17113
   Camp Curtin 17110
   Capitol Blue Cross 17177
   Chambers Hill 17111
   Clermont 17112
   Colonial Cres 17112
   Colonial Park 17109
   Country Manor 17112

   Devonshire Heights 17112
   Enhaut 17113
   Estherton 17110
   Fort Hunter 17110
   Glenwood 17109
   Greenwood Hill 17109
   Heckton 17110
   Kline Village 17104
   Lawnford Acre 17111
   Lawnton 17111
   Lenker Manor 17111
   Linglestown 17112
   Lower Paxton 17109
   Lucknow 17110
   Manada Gap 17112
   Oakleigh 17111
   Oberlin 17113
   Oberlin Gardens 17113
   Paxtang 17111
   Paxtang Manor 17111
   Paxtonia 17112
   Penbrook 17103, 17109
   Piketown 17112
   Progress 17109
   Ridgeview 17112
   Ritzie Vlg 17112
   Rutherford 17111
   Skyline View 17112
   Steelton 17113
   Swatara 17111
   West End 17102
   West Hanover 17112
   Wilhelm 17111
   Windsor Farms 17110
Harrison City 15636
Harrison Valley 16927
Harrisonville 17228
Harristown (Paradise) 17562
Harrisville 16038
Hartleton 17829
Hartsfield (Liberty) 16930
Hartstown 16131
Harveys Lake 18618
Harwick 15049
Hastings 16646, 16675
Hatboro 19040
Hatfield 19440
Haverford 19041
Havertown 19083
Hawk Run 16840
Hawksville (Quarryville) 17566
Hawley 18428, 18438
   Lords Valley 18428
Hawstone (Lewistown) 17044
Hawthorn 16230
Hays Grove (Newville) 17241
Hazel Hurst 16733
Hazelwood (Pittsburgh) 15207
Hazen (Brookville) 15825
Hazleton 18201
Hebe (Herndon) 17830
Heberlig (Newville) 17241
Hebron 16915, 17042
   (Coudersport)
Heckschersville 17901
   (Pottsville)
Heckton (Harrisburg) 17110
Hecla (New Ringgold) 17960
Hector 16943, 16948
   (Sabinsville)
Hegins 17938

Heidelburg (Carnegie) 15106	
Heidlersburg (Gettysburg) .. 17325	
Heilmandale (Lebanon) 17042	
Heilwood 15745	
Helfenstein 17939	
Hellam (York) 17406	
Hellen Mills (Brockton) 17925	
Hellertown 18055	
Hemlock Grove 17758	
(Muncy Valley)	
Hendersonville 15339	
Henryville 18332	
Hensel (Quarryville) 17566	
Hepburn (Cogan Station) .. 17728	
Hepburnville 17728	
(Cogan Station)	
Hepler (Klingerstown) 17941	
Hereford 18056	
Herman 16039	
Herminie 15637	
Hermitage 16148	
Herndon 17830	
Herrick Center 18430	
Herrville (Willow Street) 17584	
Hershey 17033	
Hershey Heights (Hanover) 17331	
Heshbon Park 17701	
(Williamsport)	
Hessdale (Strasburg) 17579	
Hesston 16647	
Hibbs 15443	
Hickory 15340	
Hickorytown (Carlisle) 17013	
Hickox (Genesee) 16923	
Hidden Valley 15502	
High Spire (Highspire) 17034	
Highland Park (Camp Hill) . 17011	
.... 17044, 19082	
Highmount (York) 17406	
Highspire 17034	
Highville (Conestoga) 17516	
Hill (Camp Hill) 17011	
Hill Church (Boyertown) 19512	
Hiller 15444	
Hilliards 16040	
Hills Terrace 17948	
(Mahanoy City)	
Hillsdale 15746	
Hillsgrove 18619	
Hillside (Pottsville) 17901	
Hillsville 16132	
Hilltown 18927	
Hinkletown (Ephrata) 17522	
Hobart (Hanover) 17331	
Hockersville 17033, 17241	
(Hershey)	
Hoernerstown 17036	
(Hummelstown)	
Hoffer (Port Trevorton) 17864	
Hogestown 17055	
(Mechanicsburg)	
Hokendauqua (Whitehall) . 18052	
Holbrook 15341	
Holicong 18928	
Holland (Southampton) 18966	
Hollidaysburg 16648	
Hollsopple 15935, 15953	
Seanor 15935	
Hollywood (Jenkintown) 19046	
Holmes 19043, 19098	
Holmesburg (Philadelphia) 19136	

Holtwood 17532	
Home 15747	
Homer (Coudersport) 16915	
Homer City 15748	
Homestead 15120	
Homesville (Ashland) 17921	
Homewood 15208, 17019	
(Pittsburgh)	
Honesdale 18431	
Honey Brook 19344	
Honey Grove 17035	
Hookstown 15050	
Hooversville 15936	
Hop Bottom 18824	
Hopeland 17533	
Hopewell 16650, 17240	
Hopwood 15445	
Horningford (Lewistown) ... 17044	
Horsham 19044	
Host (Womelsdorf) 19567	
Hostetter 15638	
Houston 15342	
Housum (Chambersburg) . 17201	
Houtzdale 16651	
Howard 16841	
Howe (Newport) 17074	
Hoytville (Morris) 16938	
Hublersburg (Bellefonte) .. 16823	
Hubley (Valley View) 17983	
Huey (Rimersburg) 16248	
Hughesville 17737	
Hulmeville (Langhorne) 19047	
Hummels Store (Mohnton) 19540	
Hummels Wharf 17831	
Hummelstown 17036	
Hunker 15639	
Hunlock Creek 18621	
Hunter (Shamokin) 17872	
Hunters Run (Gardners) ... 17324	
Hunterstown (Gettysburg) . 17325	
Huntersville (Muncy) 17756	
Hunting Park 19140	
(Philadelphia)	
Huntingdon 16652, 16654	
Huntingdon Valley 19006	
Huntington Mills 18622	
Huntsdale (Carlisle) 17013	
Hustontown 17228-229	
(Harrisonville)	
Hutchinson 15640	
Hyde 16843	
Hyde Park 15641	
Hydetown 16328	
Hyndman 15545, 15564	
Hyner 17738	
Ickesburg 17037	
Idaville 17337	
Imler 16655	
Immaculata 19345	
Imperial 15126	
Independence 17864	
(Port Trevorton)	
Indian Head 15446	
Indian Lake 15926	
(Central City)	
Indiana 15701, 15705	
Indianola 15051	
Industry 15052	
Inez (Coudersport) 16915	
Inglenook (Halifax) 17032	
Inglesmith (Artemas) 17211	

Ingomar 15127	
Ingram (Pittsburgh) 15205	
Intercourse 17534	
Iola (Millville) 17846	
Iona (Lebanon) 17042	
Irishtown (New Oxford) 17350	
Ironton (Coplay) 18037	
Ironville (Columbia) 17512	
Irvine 16329, 16368-369	
Irving (Pine Grove) 17963	
Irvona 16645, 16656	
(Glen Hope)	
Irwin 15642	
Isabella 15447	
Island Park (Sunbury) 17801	
Ithan (Villanova) 19085	
Iva (Paradise) 17562	
Ivyland (Warminster) 18974	
Jackson (Lawrenceville) 16929	
.... 17006, 17032, 17765	
17814, 17830, 17870, 18825	
Jackson Center 16133	
Jackson Hall 17201	
(Chambersburg)	
Jackson Summit 16936	
(Millerton)	
Jacksonville (Kempton) 19529	
Jacksonwald (Reading) 19606	
Jacobs Creek 15448	
Jacobs Mills (Hanover) 17331	
Jacobus (York) 17407	
Jalappa (Hamburg) 19526	
James City 16734	
James Creek 16657	
Jamestown 16134	
Jamison 18929	
Jamison City (Benton) 17814	
Jarrettown (Dresher) 19025	
Jeannette 15644	
Jefferson 15344	
.... 17032, 17922, 19506	
Jeffersonville 19401, 19403	
(Norristown)	
Jenkintown 19046	
Jenners 15546	
Jennerstown 15547	
Jericho Mills 17059	
(Mifflintown)	
Jermyn 18433	
Jerome 15937	
Jersey Mills 17739	
Jersey Shore 17723	
.... 17727, 17740	
Cammal 17723	
Crawford 17740	
Larrys Creek 17740	
Larryville 17740	
Limestone 17740	
Mchenry 17723	
Mifflin 17740	
Oriole 17740	
Piatt 17740	
Porter 17740	
Ramsey 17740	
Rauchtown 17740	
Ross Siding 17723	
Salladasburg 17740	
Tomb 17740	
Watson 17740	
Jerseytown (Bloomsburg) . 17815	
Jessup 18434	

Rose Valley 19063
Upper Providence 19063
Wallingford 19063
Wawa 19063
Mehoopany 18629
Meiser (Middleburg) 17842
Meiserville 17853
(Mount Pleasant Mills)
Melcroft 15462
Melrose Park (Cheltenham) 19012
.... 19117, 19126
Mendenhall 19357
Menges Mills 17346
Menno (Belleville) 17004
Mentcle 15761
Mercer 16137
Mercersburg 17236
Meridian (Butler) 16001
Merion Station 19066
Merrian (Mount Carmel) 17851
Merrittstown 15463
Mertztown 19539
Meshoppen 18630
Metal (Fort Loudon) 17224
Mexico 17056
Meyersdale 15552
Middle City East 19102
(Philadelphia)
Middle City West 19103
(Philadelphia)
Middle Creek 17843
(Beaver Springs)
Middle Paxton (Dauphin) .. 17018
Middle Spring 17257
(Shippensburg)
Middleburg 17842
Middlebury Center 16935
Middleport 17953
Middlesex (Carlisle) 17013
Middleswarth (Middleburg) 17842
Middletown 17057, 19056
Londonderry 17057
Lower Swatara 17057
Royalton 17057
Shope Gardens 17057
Midland 15059
Midvalley (Wilburton) 17888
Midway 15060
Mifflin 17058, 17061, 17740
Doyles Mills 17058
Mccoysville 17058
Nook 17058
Walnut 17058
Mifflinburg 17844
Mifflintown 17059
Mifflinville 18631
Milan 18831
Milanville 18443
Mildred 18632
Mile Hill (Sunbury) 17801
Mile Run (Sunbury) 17801
Milesburg 16853
Milford (Mifflintown) 17059, 18337
Milford Square 18935
Mill Creek ... 17060, 17756, 17901
Mill Grove (Catawissa) 17820
Mill Hall 17751, 17767
Allison 17751
Bald Eagle 17751
Cedar Springs 17751
Clintondale 17751

Parvin 17751
Porter 17751
Rote 17751
Mill Run 15464
Mill Village 16427
Millardsville (Myerstown) .. 17067
Millcreek (Newmanstown) . 17073
Millersburg 17061
Millerstown 17062
Millersville 17551
Millerton 16936
Millheim 16854
Millmont 17845
Millport 16748, 17540
(Shinglehouse)
Millrift 18340
Mills 16937
Millsboro 15348
Millvale (Pittsburgh) 15209
Millville 17846
Millway (Lititz) 17543
Milmont Park (Folsom) 19033
Milnesville 18239
Milnor (Greencastle) 17225
Milroy 17063
Milton 17847
Milton Grove (Mount Joy) .. 17552
Mina (Coudersport) 16915
Mineral Point 15942
Mineral Springs 16855
Minersville 17954
Mingoville 16856
Minisink Hills 18341
Miquon 19452
Mocanaqua (Shickshinny) . 18655
Modena 19358
Mohns Hill (Reading) 19608
Mohnton 19540
Mohrsville 19541
Molino (Orwigsburg) 17961
Molltown (Fleetwood) 19522
Monaca 15061
Monessen 15062
Mongul (Shippensburg) 17257
Monongahela 15063
Monroe (Cocolamus) 17014
Monroeton 18832
Monroeville 15140, 15146
(Pitcairn)
Mont Alto 17237
Mont Clare 19453
Montandon 17850
Monterey 17214, 17540, 19530
(Blue Ridge Summit)
Montgomery 17236, 17752
(Mercersburg)
Brady 17752
Clinton 17752
Maple Hill 17752
Montgomeryville 18936
Montour (Pittsburgh) 15244
Montoursville 17754
Montrose 18801
Montsera (Carlisle) 17013
Mooredale (Carlisle) 17013
Mooresburg (Danville) 17821
Moosic 18507
Morann 16663
Mordansville (Bloomsburg) 17815
Morea Colliery 17948
(Mahanoy City)

Moreland (Muncy) 17756
Morgan 15064
Morgantown 19543
Morris 16938
Morris Run 16939
Morrisdale 16858
Morrisville 19067
Morton 19070
Morysville (Boyertown) 19512
Moscow 18444
Moselem (Hamburg) 19526
Moselem Springs 19522
(Fleetwood)
Moshannon 16859
Mosherville (Gillett) 16925
Moulstown (Hanover) 17331
Mount Aetna 19544
Mount Airy .. 17557, 17578, 19119
(New Holland)
Mount Allen 17055
(Mechanicsburg)
Mount Bethel 18343
Mount Braddock 15465
Mount Carbon (Pottsville) . 17901
Mount Hope (Manheim) 17545
Mount Jewett 16740, 16751
Mount Joy 17022, 17552
(Elizabethtown)
Donegal Heights 17552
Farmdale 17552
Florin 17552
Milton Grove 17552
Mount Laffee (Pottsville) .. 17901
Mount Lebanon 15228
(Pittsburgh)
Mount Morris 15349
Mount Nebo (Pequea) 17565
Mount Oliver (Pittsburgh) .. 15210
Mount Patrick (Liverpool) .. 17045
Mount Penn (Reading) 19606
Mount Pleasant 15666
.... 16938, 17006, 17019
.... 17042, 17059, 17063
.... 17331, 17901, 19506
Mount Pocono 18344
Mount Rock 17044, 17257
(Lewistown)
Mount Royal (Dover) 17315
Mount Tabor (Gardners) ... 17324
Mount Vernon (Gap) 17527
Mount Washington 15211
(Pittsburgh)
Mount Wilson (Lebanon) ... 17042
Mount Wolf 17347
Mount Zion (Carlisle) 17013
.... 17042, 17402
Mountain Top 18707
Mountainhome 18342
Mountrock (Carlisle) 17013
Mountville 17554
Mowersville 17257
(Shippensburg)
Mowry (Ashland) 17921
Moylan (Media) 19065
Muddy Creek Forks 17302
(Airville)
Muhlenberg Park (Reading) 19605
Muir 17957
Muncy 17756
Muncy Valley 17758, 17770
Beaver Lake 17758

463

Beech Glen	17758
Davidson	17758
Hemlock Grove	17758
Laporte	17758
Nordmont	17758
North Mountain	17758
Shrewsbury	17758
Strawbridge	17758
Munderf (Brookville)	15825
Munhall (Homestead)	15120
Munson	16860
Murrell (Ephrata)	17522
Murrysville	15668
Muse	15350
Myerstown	17067, 17324
Frystown	17067
Greble	17067
Kutztown	17067
Millardsville	17067
Reistville	17067
Naginey (Milroy)	17063
Nanticoke	18634
Napierville (Ephrata)	17522
Narberth	19072
Narvon	17555
Nashville (Spring Grove)	17362
Natalie (Mount Carmel)	17851
Natrona Heights	15065
Nauvoo (Morris)	16938
Nazareth	18064
Needmore	17212, 17238
(Big Cove Tannery)	
Belfast	17238
Sipes Mill	17238
Neelyton	17239
Neffs	18065
Neffsville (Lancaster)	17601
Nelson	16940
Nemacolin	15351
Nescopeck	18635
Neshannock (New Castle)	16105
Nesquehoning	18240
Nether Providence	19086
(Wallingford)	
Neville Island	15225
(Pittsburgh)	
New Albany	18833
New Alexandria	15670
New Baltimore	15553
New Bedford	16140
New Berlin	17855
New Berlins	19545
(New Berlinville)	
New Berlinville	19545
New Bethlehem	16242
New Bloomfield	17068
New Bridgeville	17356
(Red Lion)	
New Brighton	15066
New Britain (Doylestown)	18901
New Buffalo	17069
New Castle	16101-103
	16105, 16107-108, 17970
Castle	16105
Mahoningtown	16102
Neshannock	16105
New Chester (New Oxford)	17350
New Columbia	17856
New Cumberland	17070
New Danville (Lancaster)	17603
New Derry	15671

New Eagle	15067
New Enterprise	16664
New Florence	15944
New Franklin	17201
(Chambersburg)	
New Freedom	17349
New Freeport	15352
New Galilee	16141
New Geneva	15467
New Germantown	17071
New Hanover	19525
(Gilbertsville)	
New Holland	17557
New Hope	18938
New Jerusalem	19522
(Fleetwood)	
New Kensington	15068-069
New Kingstown	17072
New London	19360
New Market	17070
(New Cumberland)	
New Milford	18834
New Millport	16861
New Milltown (Kinzers)	17535
New Mines (Branchdale)	17923
New Oxford	17350
New Paris	15554
New Park	17352
New Philadelphia	17959
New Process (Warren)	16366
New Providence	17560
New Ringgold	17960
New Salem	15468
New Schaefferstown	19506
(Bernville)	
New Smithville (Kutztown)	19530
New Stanton	15672
New Street (Pottsville)	17901
New Texas (Peach Bottom)	17563
New Tripoli	18066
New Wilmington	16142, 16172
Newberry (Williamsport)	17701
Newberrytown (Etters)	17319
Newburg	17240
Newell	15466
Newfield (Ulysses)	16948
Newfoundland	18445
Newlin (Catawissa)	17820
Newmanstown	17073
Newport	17074
Newportville (Levittown)	19056
Newprt (Newport)	17074
Newry	16665
Newton Hamilton	17075
Newtown	17512, 18940
(Columbia)	
Wrightstown	18940
Newtown Square	19073
Newville	17241
Niantic (Barto)	19504
Nicetown (Philadelphia)	19140
Nicholson	18441, 18446
(Lenoxville)	
Nickel Mines (Paradise)	17562
Nicktown	15762
Niles Valley	16935
(Middlebury Center)	
Ninepoints (Christiana)	17509
Nineveh	15353, 17921
Nisbet	17759
Nixon (Butler)	16001

Nobend (Hyner)	17738
Noblestown (Oakdale)	15071
Nook (Mifflin)	17058
Nordmont (Muncy Valley)	17758
Normalville	15469
Norristown	19401, 19403-409
	19487-489
Audubon	19403
Eagleville	19403
Jeffersonville	19401, 19403
North Apollo	15673
North Bend (Hyner)	17738, 17760
Chapman	17760
Gleasonton	17760
North Bingham	16923, 16941
(Genesee)	
North Charleroi	15022
(Charleroi)	
North Cornwall (Lebanon)	17042
North Cumberld	17070
(New Cumberland)	
North East	16428
North Fork (Westfield)	16950
North Heidelberg	19506
(Bernville)	
North Hills (Glenside)	19038
North Huntingdon (Irwin)	15642
North Lebanon (Lebanon)	17042
North Londonderry	17078
(Palmyra)	
North Manheim	17901
(Pottsville)	
North Middleton	17013
(Carlisle)	
North Mountain	17758
(Muncy Valley)	
North Newton (Newville)	17241
North Philadelphia	19132
(Philadelphia)	
North Springfield	16430
North Union (Zion Grove)	17985
North Versailles	15137
North Wales (Gwynedd)	19436
	19454-455, 19477
North Warren (Warren)	16365
North Washington	16048
Northampton	18067
Northeast Madison	17047
(Loysville)	
Northpoint	15763
Northumberland	17857
Norvelt	15674
Norwood	19074
Nossville (Blairs Mills)	17213
Nottingham	19362
Noxen	18636
Noyes (Renovo)	17764
Nu Mine	16244
Nuangola	18637
Numidia	17858
Nuremberg	18241
Nyesville (Chambersburg)	17201
Oak Grove (Pine Grove)	17963
Oak Lane	19012, 19126
(Cheltenham)	
Oak Park (Northumberland)	17857
Oak Ridge	16245
Oak Shade (Quarryville)	17566
Oakbottom (Quarryville)	17566
Oakdale	15071
Oakford	19053

(Feasterville Trevose)	
Oakland (Pittsburgh)	15213
Oakland Mills	17076
Oakleigh (Harrisburg)	17111
Oaklyn (Sunbury)	17801
Oakmont	15139
Oakryn (Peach Bottom)	17563
Oaks	19456
Oakview (Drexel Hill)	19026
Oakville	17257, 17527
(Shippensburg)	
Observatory (Pittsburgh)	15214
Odin (Coudersport)	16915
Ogden (Marcus Hook)	19061
Ogdensburg	17765
(Roaring Branch)	
Ogletown (Windber)	15963
Ogontz (Philadelphia)	19117
Ogontz Campus (Abington)	19001
Ohiopyle	15470
Oil City	16301
Oil Creek (Oil City)	16301
Okome (Jersey Mills)	17739
Olanta	16837, 16863
(Glen Richey)	
Old Forge	18518
Old Line (Manheim)	17545
Old Lycoming	17701
(Williamsport)	
Old Port (Port Royal)	17082
Old Zionsville	18068
Oley	19547
Oley Furnace	19547
Oliveburg	15764
Oliver	15472, 17044, 17073
Olney (Philadelphia)	19120
Olyphant	18447
Oneida	18242
Ono	17077
Ontelaunee (Reading)	19605
Opp (Muncy)	17756
Orangeville	17859
Orbisonia	17243
Ore Valley (York)	17403
Orefield	18069
Oregon (Leola)	17540
Oregon Hill (Morris)	16938
Oreland	19075
Oreville (Mertztown)	19539
Oriental (Liverpool)	17045
Oriole (Jersey Shore)	17740
Ormsby (Cyclone)	16726
Orrstown	17244
Orrtanna	17353
Orson	18449
Orviston	16864
Orwigsburg	17961
Orwin (Tower City)	17980
Osceola	16942
Osceola Mills	16666, 16670
Osterburg	16667
Oswayo (Coudersport)	16915
Ottawa (Danville)	17821
Ottsville	18942
Outwood (Pine Grove)	17963
Oval (Nisbet)	17759
Overbrook	19096, 19151
(Wynnewood)	
Oxford	19363
Oyster Point (Lancaster)	17601
Pageville (Albion)	16401

Paint (Windber)	15963
Paintersville (Lewistown)	17044
Palm	18070
Palmdale (Hershey)	17033
Palmer (Easton)	18043
Palmer Township (Easton)	18042
Palmerton	18071
Palmyra	17078
Palo Alto (Pottsville)	17901
Paoli	19301
Paradise	17562, 17963
Bellemont	17562
Harristown	17562
Iva	17562
Lapark	17562
Leaman Place	17562
Nickel Mines	17562
Vintage	17562
Paradise Park	17068
(New Bloomfield)	
Pardeesville	18243
Paris (Burgettstown)	15021
Park (Vandergrift)	15690
Park Heights (Hanover)	17331
Park Place (Mahanoy City)	17948
Parker	16049
Parker Ford	19457
Parkesburg	19365
Parkhill	15945
Parkland (Langhorne)	19047
Parkside (Chester)	19013
Parkside Manor	19015
(Brookhaven)	
Parkville (Hanover)	17331
Parkway Center	15220
(Pittsburgh)	
Parnassus	15068
(New Kensington)	
Parrs Mill (Catawissa)	17820
Parryville	18244
Parvin (Mill Hall)	17751
Paschall (Philadelphia)	19142
Passmore (Bechtelsville)	19505
Passyunk (Philadelphia)	19148
Pattersonville (Ringtown)	17967
Patton	16668
Paupack	18451
Paxinos	17860
Paxtang (Harrisburg)	17111
Paxtonia (Harrisburg)	17112
Paxtonville	17861
Peach Bottom	17314, 17563
(Delta)	
Arcadia	17563
Eldora	17563
Fulton	17563
Furniss	17563
Mcsparren	17563
New Texas	17563
Oakryn	17563
Penn Hill	17563
Pleasant Grove	17563
Wrightsdale	17563
Peach Glen	17375
Pealertown (Orangeville)	17859
Peckville	18452
Pen Argyl	18072
Pen Mar (Waynesboro)	17268
Penbrook	17103, 17109
(Harrisburg)	
Penfield	15849

Penllyn (Blue Bell)	19422
Pennsylvania	15675, 17013
	17020, 17331, 17737, 19506
Pennsylvania Avon	17870
(Selinsgrove)	
Pennsylvania Center	19102
(Philadelphia)	
Pennsylvania Hill	17563
(Peach Bottom)	
Pennsylvania Hills	15235
(Pittsburgh)	
Pennsylvania Junction	19102
(Philadelphia)	
Pennsylvania Run	15765
Pennsylvania Valley	19072
(Narberth)	
Pennsylvania Wynne	19096
(Wynnewood)	
Penndel (Langhorne)	19047
Pennersville (Waynesboro)	17268
Penns Creek	17862
Penns Park	18943
Pennsburg	18073
Pennside (Reading)	19606
Pennville (Hanover)	17331
Penryn	17564
Pequea	17565
Perdix (Duncannon)	17020
Perkasie	18944
Perkiomenville	18074
Perry (Hamburg)	19526
Perry Square (Erie)	16507
Perry Village	17068
(New Bloomfield)	
Perryopolis	15473
Perryville	17728
(Cogan Station)	
Perulack (East Waterford)	17021
Peters (Mercersburg)	17236
Petersburg	16669
Petrolia	16050
Philadelphia	19092-093
	19099-155, 19160-162
	19170-173, 19175
	19177-179, 19181-185
	19187-188, 19191-193
	19196-197, 19244, 19255
A A R P Ins	19187
Abington	19111
Boulevard	19149
Bridesburg	19137
Bustleton	19115, 19152
Castor	19149
Chestnut Hill	19118
Commerce	19108
East Falls	19129
East Germantown	19138
Eastwick	19153
Fairhill	19133
Frankford	19124
Germantown	19144
Holmesburg	19136
Hunting Park	19140
I R S	19244, 19255
Kensington	19125
Kingsessing	19143
Lamott	19126
Lawncrest	19111
Lawndale	19111
Lester	19113
Logan	19141

465

Poplar Grove (Lititz) 17543	Puritan (Portage) 15946	Red Cross (Dornsife) 17823
Port Allegany 16743	Quakake 18245	Red Hill 18073, 18076
Port Carbon 17965	Quakertown 18951	(Pennsburg)
Port Clinton 19549	Quarryville 17566	Red Lion 17356
Port Matilda 16870	Quecreek 15555	Red Rock (Benton) 17814
Port Royal 17082	Queen 16670	Redrun (Stevens) 17578
Port Trevorton 17864	Queen City (Catawissa) 17820	Reed (Halifax) 17032
Port Vue (Mc Keesport) 15133	Quentin 17083	Reed Station (Paxinos) 17860
Portage 15946	Quigglevilla 17728	Reeders 18352
Porter (Jersey Shore) 17740	(Cogan Station)	Reeders Grove (Elysburg) 17824
.... 17751, 17980	Quincy 17247	Reeds Gap (Honey Grove) 17035
Porters Sideling 17354	Racine (Beaver Falls) 15010	Reedsville 17084
Portersville 16051	Radnor (Wayne) 19087	Refton 17568
Portland 18351	Rahns (Collegeville) 19426	Rehrersburg 19550
Portland Mills (Ridgway) ... 15853	Railroad 17355	Reiffton (Reading) 19606
Potter Brook (Westfield) 16950	Ralpho (Shamokin) 17872	Reilly (Branchdale) 17923
Pottersdale 16871	Ralston 17763	Reinerton (Tower City) 17980
Potts Grove 17865	Ramey 16671	Reinholds 17569
Pottstown 19464-465	Ramsey (Jersey Shore) 17740	Reistville (Myerstown) 17067
Sanatoga 19464	Ranavilla (Camp Hill) 17011	Renfrew 16053
Stowe 19464	Rankin (Braddock) 15104	Reno 16343
Pottsville 17901, 17974	Ranshaw (Coal Township) .. 17866	Renovo 17764
Becks 17901	Ransom 18653	Republic 15475
Buck Run 17901	Rauchtown (Jersey Shore) .. 17740	Revere 18953
Bunker Hill 17901	Rauschs (New Ringgold) .. 17960	Revloc 15948
Dieners Hill 17901	Raven Creek (Benton) 17814	Rew 16744
Duncott 17901	Raven Run (Lost Creek) 17946	Reward (Millerstown) 17062
Forestville 17901	Ravine 17966	Rexford (Gaines) 16921
Glen Carbon 17901	Rawlinsville (Holtwood) 17532	Rexmont 17085
Glen Dower 17901	Raymond (Genesee) 16923	Reynoldsville 15851
Glenworth 17901	Rea 15356	Rhawnhurst (Philadelphia) . 19111
Greenbury 17901	Reading 19600-612, 19640	Rheems 17570
Heckschersville 17901	Berkley 19605	Rices Landing 15357
Hillside 17901	Berkshire Heights 19610	Riceville 16432
Jonestown 17901	Bernharts 19605	Richboro 18954
Mechanicsville 17901	Five Points 19606	Richeyville 15358
Mill Creek 17901	Fritztown 19608	Richfield 17086
Mount Carbon 17901	Gouglersville 19608	Richland 15904, 17087
Mount Laffee 17901	Greenfield Manor 19601	(Johnstown)
Mount Pleasant 17901	Hampden 19604	Richlandtown 18955
New Street 17901	Jacksonwald 19606	Richmond (Mansfield) 16933
North Manheim 17901	Kenhorst 19607	.... 19134, 19530
Palo Alto 17901	Laureldale 19605	Richmondale (Forest City) 18421
Phoenix Park 17901	Lincoln Park 19609	Richvale (Blairs Mills) 17213
Pine Hill 17901	Lorane 19606	Riddlesburg 16672
Primrose 17901	Mohns Hill 19608	Ridgeview (Harrisburg) 17112
Wadesville 17901	Mount Penn 19606	Ridgeville (Danville) 17821
Powys (Cogan Station) 17728	Muhlenberg Park 19605	Ridgewood (Birdsboro) 19508
Poyntelle 18454	Ontelaunee 19605	Ridgway 15853
Presque Isle (Erie) 16505	Pennside 19606	Ridley Park 19078
Presto 15142	Reiffton 19606	Riegelsville 18077
Preston Hill 17935	River View Park 19605	Rife (Millersburg) 17061
(Girardville)	Saint Lawrence 19606	Rillton 15678
Preston Park 18455	Shillington 19607	Rimersburg 16248
Pricedale 15072	Sinking Spring 19608	Rinely (Stewartstown) 17363
Pricetown (Fleetwood) 19522	Springmont 19609	Ringgold 15770
Primos (Clifton Heights) 19018	State Hill 19608	Ringtown 17967, 19539
Primrose (Pottsville) 17901	Stony Creek Mills 19606	Brandonville 17967
Pringle (Wilkes Barre) 18704	Tuckerton 19605	Pattersonville 17967
Proctor (Williamsport) 17701	West Lawn 19609	Union 17967
Progress (Harrisburg) 17109	West Reading 19602	River View Park (Reading) 19605
Prompton 18456	West Reading 19611	Riverside 17868
Prospect 16052	West Wyomissing 19609	Rixford 16745
Prospect Park 19076	Wyomissing 19610	Roadside (Waynesboro) 17268
Prospectville (Ambler) 19002	Wyomissing Hills 19609	Roaring Branch 17765
Prosperity 15329	Reamstown 17567	Roaring Creek (Catawissa) 17820
Providence 17560	Rebersburg 16872	Roaring Spring 16673
(New Providence)	Rebuck 17867	Robertsdale 16674
Pulaski 16143	Rector 15677	Robeson (Birdsboro) 19508
Punxsutawney 15730, 15767	Red Bank (Mifflinburg) 17844	Robesonia 19551
(Coolspring)	Red Bridge (Chambersburg)17201	Robinson 15949

Shirley (Mount Union)	17066
Shirleysburg	17260
Shocks Mills (Marietta)	17547
Shoemakers	17948
(Mahanoy City)	
Shoemakersville	19555
Shohola	18458
Shope Gardens	17057
(Middletown)	
Shorbes Hill (Hanover)	17331
Shortsville	16935
(Middleburg Center)	
Shraders (Reedsville)	17084
Shrewsbury	17361
.... 17737, 17758	
Shumans (Bloomsburg)	17815
Shunk	17768
Siddonsburg (Dillsburg)	17019
Sidman	15955
Sigel	15860
Siglerville (Milroy)	17063
Silver Creek	17959
(New Philadelphia)	
Silver Lake (Lewisberry) ...	17339
Silver Spring 17055, 17575	
(Mechanicsburg)	
Forest Knolls	17575
Silverdale	18962
Simmonstown (Gap)	17527
Simpson (Carbondale)	18407
Singersville (Dauphin)	17018
Sinking Spring (Reading) ..	19608
Sinnamahoning	15861
Sinsheim (Spring Grove) ...	17362
Sipes Mill (Needmore)	17238
Sipesville	15561
Six Mile Run	16679
Skippack	19474
Skyline View (Harrisburg) ..	17112
Skytop	18357
Slackwater (Millersville)	17551
Slate Hill (Delta)	17314
Slate Run	17769
Slatedale	18079
Slateville (Kempton)	19529
Slatington	18080
Slickville	15684
Sligo	16255
Slippery Rock	16057
Slovan	15078
Smethport	16749
Smicksburg	16256
Smithfield	15478
Smithmill	16680
Smithton	15479
Smithville	17560
(New Providence)	
Smock	15480
Smokerun	16681
Smoketown 17201, 17576	
(Chambersburg)	
Smyrna (Christiana)	17509
Snedekerville	16914
(Columbia Cross Roads)	
Snow Shoe	16874
Snyder Corner (Red Lion) .	17356
Snyders (New Ringgold) ...	17960
Snydersburg	16257
Snydertown	17877
Solebury	18963
Somers Lane	16929

(Lawrenceville)	
Somerset 15501-502, 15510	
Somerton (Philadelphia) ...	19116
Sonestown	17770
Soradoville (Mc Clure)	17841
Soudersburg	17577
Souderton 18924, 18964	
(Franconia)	
Bethton	18964
South Canaan	18459
South Connellsville	15425
(Connellsville)	
South Creek (Gillett)	16925
South Enola (Enola)	17025
South Erie (Erie)	16508
South Fork	15956
South Gibson	18842
South Hanover	17036
(Hummelstown)	
South Heights	15081
South Hermitage (Narvon)	17555
South Hills (Pittsburgh)	15216
South Hills Village	15241
(Pittsburgh)	
South Londonderry	17033
(Hershey)	
South Manheim (Auburn) ..	17922
South Middleton	17007
(Boiling Springs)	
South Montrose	18843
South Mountain	17261
South Newton	17266
(Walnut Bottom)	
South Renovo (Renovo)	17764
South Sterling	18460
South Williamsport	17701
(Williamsport)	
Southampton (Orrstown) ...	17244
.... 18954, 18966	
Churchville	18966
Holland	18966
Southeastern 19397-399	
Southmont (Johnstown)	15905
Southview	15361
Southwark (Philadelphia) ..	19147
Southwest	15685
Southwest Madison	17047
(Loysville)	
Spangler	15775
Spangsville (Boyertown) ...	19512
Spartansburg	16434
Spears Grove	17021
(East Waterford)	
Specktown (Lykens)	17048
Speedwell (Lititz)	17543
Spinnerstown	18968
Sporting Hill 17055, 17545	
(Mechanicsburg)	
Spraggs	15362
Sprankle Mills	15776
Spring (Landisburg) 17040, 17812	
Spring Church	15686
Spring City	19475
Spring Creek	16436
Spring Garden (Kinzers) ...	17535
.... 17810, 17972, 19122-123	
Spring Glen	17978
Spring Grove	17346
.... 17354, 17362	
(Menges Mills)	
Nashville	17362

Sinsheim	17362
Stoverstown	17362
Spring House	19477
Spring Mills	16875
Spring Mount	19478
Spring Run	17262
Spring Valley (Temple)	19560
Springboro	16435
Springdale	15144
Springfield 16914, 17241	
.... 19064, 19118	
(Columbia Cross Roads)	
Media	19064
Springmont (Reading)	19609
Springs	15562
Springtown (Fannettsburg)	17221
.... 17777, 18081	
Springvale (Red Lion)	17356
Springville 17535, 18844	
(Kinzers)	
Sproul	16682
Spruce Creek	16683
Spruce Hill (Port Royal) ...	17082
Spry (York)	17402
Squirrel Hill	15217
(Pittsburgh)	
Stack Town (Bainbridge) ...	17502
Stahlstown	15687
Standard Brands	18762
(Wilkes Barre)	
Stanhope (Pine Grove)	17963
Star Junction	15482
Starford	15777
Starlight	18461
Starr (Tionesta)	16353
Starrucca	18462
Starview (Mount Wolf)	17347
State Hill (Gap) 17527, 19608	
State Line	17263
Steelstown (Annville)	17003
Steelton (Harrisburg)	17113
Steelville	19370
Steinsville (Kempton)	19529
Sterling	18463
Stevens	17578
Stevensville	18845
Stewartstown	17363
Sticks (Glenville)	17329
Stillwater	17878
Stockdale	15483
Stockertown	18083
Stokesdale (Wellsboro)	16901
Stoneboro	16153
Stonersville (Birdsboro)	19508
Stonetown (Birdsboro)	19508
Stoneybreak	17267
(Warfordsburg)	
Stonington (Sunbury)	17801
Stony Creek Mills	19606
(Reading)	
Stony Point 17047, 17262	
(Loysville)	
Stony Run	19557
Stonybrook (York)	17402
Stonycreek (Johnstown) ...	15906
Stonyfork (Wellsboro)	16901
Stouchsburg (Womelsdorf)	19567
Stoufferstown	17201
(Chambersburg)	
Stoughstown	17257
(Shippensburg)	

ABINGTON

APARTMENTS

Rhawn Terrace Apts
1811 RHAWN ST 19111

Wexford House Apts
8030 RYERS AVE 19111

ALLEGHENY

APARTMENTS

Allegheny Center
10 ALLEGHENY CTR 15212

BUILDINGS

Allegheny Center
4 ALLEGHENY CTR 15212

Martin Building
119 FEDERAL ST 15212

HOSPITALS

Allegheny General Hosp
320 E NORTH AVE 15212

Mercy providence Hospital
1004 ARCH ST 15212

ALLENTOWN

GOVERNMENT

Federal Building
442 W HAMILTON ST 18101

Lehigh County Court House
455 W HAMILTON ST 18101

ALTOONA

APARTMENTS

11th St Towers
1100 11TH ST 16601

Blair Towers
1600 8TH AVE 16602

Green Ave Towers
911 GREEN AVE 16601

BUILDINGS

Black & Yon Building
1107 12TH ST 16601

Blair Medical Center
501 HOWARD AVE 16601

Exec House #1
615 HOWARD AVE 16601

Exec House #2
600 CHESTNUT AVE 16601

Gables Office Building
1331 12TH AVE 16601

Ida Towers
1010 12TH ST 16601

Penn Alto
1130 13TH ST 16601

GOVERNMENT

City Hall Building
1200 13TH AVE 16601

ANDALUSIA

APARTMENTS

Bensalem Commons Apts
944 STATION AVE 19020

Bensalem Woods Apts
2300 BYBERRY RD 19020

Berkeley Trace Apts
3806 BENSALEM BLVD ... 19020

Carriage Apts
2819 KATE ST. 19020

Cedar Park Apts
831 CEDAR AVE 19020

Center Point West Apts
2290 GALLOWAY RD 19020

Century Lane Apts
2835 CENTURY LN 19020

Colonial Park Apts
957 BRISTOL PIKE 19020

Cornwells Manor
850 STATION AVE 19020

Cornwells Station Apts
717 STATION AVE 19020

Country Commons Apts
3338 RICHLIEU RD 19020

Country Lights Mews
3300 NESHAMINY BLVD . 19020

Creek Side Apts
2500 KNIGHTS RD 19020

Crestwood Apts
3241 HULMEVILLE RD 19020

Elmwood Park Apts
3300 STREET RD 19020

Gate House Apts
138 STATE RD 19020

Hillbrook Place Apts
2517 DUNKSFERRY RD .. 19020

Karlin Woods Apts
1900 PARK AVE 19020

Kingswood Apts
3110 KNIGHTS RD 19020

Knights Crossing Apts
3404 KNIGHTS RD. 19020

Lafayette Gardens Apts
520 BRISTOL PIKE 19020

Longmeadow Apts
3060 BRISTOL RD 19020

Quaker Ridge Apts
3131 KNIGHTS RD 19020

Regency Apts
2049 BROWN AVE 19020

Salem Village Apts
3550 STREET RD 19020

Shaminy Brook Apts
2900 KNIGHTS RD 19020

Thunder Hollow Apts
3228 BRISTOL RD 19020

Wood River Village
3200 BENSALEM BLVD ... 19020

BUILDINGS

Atrium Office Building
2075 BYBERRY RD 19020

Bensalem Twp Admin Building
2400 BYBERRY RD 19020

Constitution Building
1950 STREET RD 19020

Four Greenwood Square
3325 STREET RD 19020

Glenview Corp Ctr
3340 TILLMAN DR 19020

Neshaminy Medical Ctr
4802 NESHAMINY BLVD . 19020

One Greenwood Square
3333 STREET RD 19020

One Woodhaven Mall
1336 BRISTOL PIKE 19020

Three Greenwood Square
3329 STREET RD 19020

Two Greenwood Square
3331 STREET RD 19020

ARSENAL

APARTMENTS

Saint Augustine Plaza
230 36TH ST 15201

ASTON

APARTMENTS

Aston Arms Condos
224 PENNELL RD 19014

Brandywine Manor Apts
785 CHERRY TREE RD ... 19014

Cherrytree Apts
700 CHERRY TREE RD ... 19014

Concord Court Apts
900 CONCORD RD 19014

Donna Joell Apts
149 BETHEL RD 19014

Hidden Valley Apts
777 CHERRY TREE RD ... 19014

Twin Oaks Condominium Ctr
4009 MARKET ST 19014

Valley Brook Apts
230 PENNELL RD 19014

BUILDINGS

Aston Shopping Ctr
255 CONCORD RD 19014

Faccolo Shopping Ctr
223 PENNELL RD 19014

Village Green Shop Ctr
239 CONCORD RD 19014

AVALON

APARTMENTS

Avalon Arms
841 CALIFORNIA AVE 15202

California
909 CALIFORNIA AVE 15202

Chaize Place
923 CALIFORNIA AVE 15202

Emsworth Manor Apts
8179 OHIO RIVER BLVD .. 15202

Kingston Apts
301 S HOME AVE 15202

Lincoln House
245 LINCOLN AVE 15202

Metowers
1001 NEW BRIGHTON RD 15202

Queensbury Apts
220 S HOME AVE 15202

The Summit
420 N CHESTNUT ST 15202

Tiffany
925 CALIFORNIA AVE 15202

BALDWIN

APARTMENTS

Chateaugay
500 HOODRIDGE DR 15234

BELLE VALLEY

APARTMENTS

Glenwood Towers
4601 Glenwood Park Ave . 16509

BENSALEM

APARTMENTS

Croydon Station Apts
909 BRISTOL PIKE 19021

Glen Hollow Apts
1100 NEWPORTVILLE RD 19021

Glenn Hollow Apts
1701 NEWPORT RD 19021

BETHLEHEM

GOVERNMENT

City Hall
10 E CHURCH ST 18018

BLOOMFIELD

APARTMENTS

Friendship Gardens
273 S WINEBIDDLE ST 15224

Garfield Hi-rise
5330 FERN ST 15224

BOSTON

APARTMENTS

Virginia Manor Apts
1300 VIRGINIA ST 15135

BOTTS

HOSPITALS

Memorial Hospital
325 S BELMONT ST 17403

BOULEVARD

APARTMENTS

Devereaux Ct Apts
2946 DEVEREAUX AVE ... 19149

BRENTWOOD

APARTMENTS

Brentmor
3840 BROWNSVILLE RD . 15227

Brittany
3500 BROWNSVILLE RD . 15227

London Hall
3100 BROWNSVILLE RD . 15227

BROOKHAVEN

APARTMENTS

Allcutt Apts
900 MAIN ST 19015

Bridgewater Apts
280 BRIDGEWATER RD .. 19015

Camelot Court Apts
532 W BROOKHAVEN RD 19015

Hilltop Condos
5200 HILLTOP DR 19015

Trimble Run Apts
280 BRIDGEWATER RD .. 19015

BUILDINGS

Municipal Building
4098 EDGMONT AVE 19015

Penway Industrial Park
601 UPLAND AVE 19015

BROOKLINE

APARTMENTS

Eagle Manor Apts
34 E EAGLE RD 19083

Eagle Towers Apts
2323 DARBY RD 19083

Haverford Arms Apts
66 S EAGLE RD 19083

Haverford Hills Condos
400 GLENDALE RD 19083

Hollow Run Apts
1901 W CHESTER PIKE .. 19083

Holly House Apts
48 W EAGLE RD 19083

Lawrence Hill Apts
1930 LAWRENCE RD 19083

Robindale Apts
1921 LAWRENCE RD 19083

Southmore Court Apts
2031 DARBY RD 19083

Wyndmoor Court Apts
117 S EAGLE RD 19083

BUILDINGS

Belfield Medical Building
1 N BELFIELD AVE 19083

Falcon Center
525 W CHESTER PIKE 19083

Haverford Twp Admin Building
2325 DARBY RD 19083

Havertown Medical Building
850 W CHESTER PIKE 19083

Llanerch Medical Center
510 DARBY RD 19083

BROUGHTON

APARTMENTS

Cloverleaf Towers
60 CLOVER DR 15236

Maidenbridge Apts
100 WHITE HAMPTON LN 15236

BUSTLETON

APARTMENTS

Arthurs Court Apts
8111 CASTOR AVE 19152

Benton Court Apts
1822 BENTON ST 19152

Benton Gardens
8739 FRONTENAC ST 19152

Borbeck Court
7801 BUSTLETON AVE 19152

Bradford Arms
2100 BENSON ST 19152

Bustleton Arms
7701 BUSTLETON AVE 19152

Chapelcroft Apt Associate
9629 BUSTLETON AVE 19115

Curtis Apts
1838 MOWER ST 19152

Elevator Apts
2901 WELSH RD 19152

Emerald Way
2201 STRAHLE ST 19152

Emerson
1821 EVARTS ST 19152

Emerson Apts
1841 EVARTS ST 19152

Emerson West
1801 EVARTS ST 19152

Evans Court
9530 EVANS ST 19115

Evans West Apts
9522 EVANS ST 19115

Fairfield Apts
7922 FAIRFIELD ST 19152

Fox Chase Road Apts
1801 FOX CHASE RD 19152

Glendale Arms
2121 GLENDALE AVE 19152

Glendale Court Apts
2101 GLENDALE AVE 19152

Glendale House
2100 GLENDALE AVE 19152

Grant Gardens Apts
2101 MICHENER ST 19115

Grenadier Apts
2701 WELSH RD 19152

Hartel Court Apts
2300 HARTEL AVE 19152

Hermitage Apts
8229 ROOSEVELT BLVD . 19152

Hillside Apts
1751 WELSH RD 19115

Holme Circle Apts
2800 AXE FACTORY RD .. 19152

Longwood Manor
2401 HOFFNAGLE ST 19152

Manchester Apts
2786 MANCHESTER AVE 19152

Manchester Apts
2800 WELSH RD 19152

Manchester Apts
2801 WALNUT HILL ST 19152

Manchester Walk Apts
2650 WELSH RD 19152

Mar-rose Manor
2121 RHAWN ST 19152

Marigold Apts
8130 BUSTLETON AVE 19152

Park Circle Apts
8223 ROOSEVELT BLVD . 19152

Pearle Gate Manor
1635 HOFFNAGLE ST 19152

Rhawnwood Apts
2727 RHAWN ST 19152

Rosemary Apts
9633 BUSTLETON AVE 19115

Ryan Manor
7750 ROOSEVELT BLVD . 19152

Saint Laurent Apts
1865 WELSH RD 19115

Samuel Tabas House
2101 STRAHLE ST 19152

Scotch Lane Apts
9200 BUSTLETON AVE 19115

Stanwood Court Apts
2715 STANWOOD ST 19152

The Concord
1725 HOFFNAGLE ST 19152

Tustin Court Apts
8410 BUSTLETON AVE 19152

Valmont Towers Apts
7600 ROOSEVELT BLVD . 19152

Welch Court Apts
2630 WELSH RD 19152

Winchester Walk Apts
7901 ROOSEVELT BLVD . 19152

BUILDINGS

8040 Building
8040 ROOSEVELT BLVD . 19152

8400 Building
8400 BUSTLETON AVE 19152

Boulevard Medical Center
8350 ROOSEVELT BLVD . 19152

Northeast Medical Building
7310 CASTOR AVE 19152

Path Building
8220 CASTOR AVE 19152

Smylie Times Building
8001 ROOSEVELT BLVD . 19152

Tulip Tree Office Park
250 GEIGER RD 19115

BYWOOD

APARTMENTS

7200 Merion Trace
7113 W CHESTER PIKE ... 19082

Ambassador Terrace
30 S STATE RD 19082

Ashby Apts
6820 LUDLOW ST 19082

Barclay Square Apts
1600 GARRETT RD 19082

Birchwood Apts East
8115 W CHESTER PIKE ... 19082

Birchwood Apts West
8125 W CHESTER PIKE .. 19082

Boulevard Apts
216 S CAROL BLVD 19082

Carole House Apts
8650 W CHESTER PIKE .. 19082

Diamond Apts
139 S STATE RD 19082

Elizabeth Manor
7100 W CHESTER PIKE .. 19082

Harrison Arms
385 HARRISON AVE 19082

Hazel Apts
7246 HAZEL AVE 19082

Highland Crossings Apts
201 HIGHLAND AVE 19082

Highland Hall
26 PARK AVE 19082

Jeannette Court Apts
130 LONG LN 19082

Joseph Court
160 LONG LN 19082

Kenneth House Apts
8433 W CHESTER PIKE .. 19082

Killegarry Apts
15 GARRETT RD 19082

Killegarry Apts
7022 TERMINAL SQ 19082

Long Lane Court Apts
146 LONG LN 19082

Marlyn Apts
1505 BYWOOD AVE 19082

Marshall Garden Apts
7131 MARSHALL RD 19082

Marshall Woods Apts
6500 MARSHALL RD 19082

Oakwood Apts
8723 W CHESTER PIKE .. 19082

Park Lane East Apts
250 BEVERLY BLVD 19082

Parkview Apts
44 VICTORY AVE 19082

Parkview Court
6700 MARSHALL RD 19082

Parkwood Manor Apts
87 S STATE RD 19082

Penzel Apts
0 S STATE RD 19082

Prescott House
6724 MARSHALL RD 19082

Sheldrake Apts
50 S STATE RD 19082

Shirley Court Apts
7201 BRADFORD RD 19082

Springton Manor
355 SPRINGTON RD 19082

Stonehurst Apts
2 COPLEY RD 19082

Stonehurst Court
7200 WALNUT ST 19082

BUILDINGS

69th Street Terminal Building
6901 MARKET ST 19082

Greater Del Vly Bank Building
201 S 69TH ST 19082

Mcclatchy Building
2 S 69TH ST 19082

Plaza West Office Building
8600 W CHESTER PIKE .. 19082

Upper Darby Township Building
100 GARRETT RD 19082

CARSON

APARTMENTS

Carson Towers
2117 E CARSON ST 15203

CASTLE

APARTMENTS

Lawrence Manor
211 W MOODY AVE 16101

Mcgrath Manor
814 W WASHINGTON ST . 16101

Neshannock Woods Apts
101 CAMBRIDGE ST 16105

Riverside Apts
125 W NORTH ST 16101

Skyview Towers
219 N BEAVER ST 16101

BUILDINGS

Centennial Building
7 S MILL ST 16101

Central Building
101 S MERCER ST 16101

First Federal Plaza
25 N MILL ST 16101

Frew Building
12 W WASHINGTON ST ... 16101

Temple Building
125 E NORTH ST 16101

HOTELS

Castle Arms Hotel
134 N MERCER ST 16101

CEDARHURST

APARTMENTS

General Neville Apts
1150 BOWER HILL RD 15243

CENTERVILLE

COLLEGES

Lancaster Bible College
901 EDEN RD 17601

CHESTER

APARTMENTS

Bannaker Plaza Apts
2101 W 7TH ST 19013

Chester Towers Apts
1101 Avenue Of The States 19013

Chestnut Park Apts
327 E 23RD ST 19013

Civic Apts
122 W 5TH ST 19013

Mill Race Apts
758 E 25TH ST 19013

Oak Grove Apts
500 E 24TH ST 19013

Palmer House Apts
1420 ESREY ST 19013

Park Howard Apts
18 W 22ND ST 19013

Renshaw Terrace Apts
1315 RENSHAW RD 19013

Saint James Pl Apts
314 E 24TH ST 19013

Ventura Apts
1000 MACDADE BLVD 19013

Wallingford View Apts
2701 CHESTNUT ST 19013

Walnut Park Apts
325 E 24TH ST 19013

GOVERNMENT

Federal Building
160 E 7TH ST 19013

CHESTNUT HILL

BUILDINGS

The Hill Building
717 BETHLEHEM PIKE 19118

CHURCHILL

APARTMENTS

Ambassador Apts
1601 PENN AVE 15221

Brinton Towers
3000 LOCUST ST 15221

Bryn Mawr Apts
100 BRYN MAWR CT W ... 15221

Carriage House
1515 PENN AVE 15221

Penn Lincoln Apt
789 PENN AVE 15221

HOSPITALS

Forbes Health System
225 PENN AVE 15221

COMMERCE

BUILDINGS

Commerce Building
401 N BROAD ST 19108

North American Building
401 N BROAD ST 19108

CORLISS

APARTMENTS

Rockledge Apts
3207 FARONIA ST 15204

CRAFTON

APARTMENTS

Brett Manor
1860 BRETT ST 15205

Crafton Towers
1215 FOSTER ST 15205

Noble Manor Towers
2440 BALDWICK RD 15205

HOTELS

Greentree Marriott Hotel
101 MARRIOTT DR 15205

DAISYTOWN

BUILDINGS

Garden Terrace Apts
730 BLOOM ST 15902

DARLINGTON

APARTMENTS

Baldwin Apts
3125 PENNELL RD 19063

Colonial Manor Apts
900 N JACKSON ST 19063

Colonial Ter Apts
440 S ORANGE ST 19063

County Court Apts
1 VETERANS SQ 19063

Gayley Park Apts
410 GAYLEY ST 19063

Gayley Park Apts
30 E JEFFERSON ST 19063

Glen Riddle Park Apts
1016 W BALTIMORE PIKE 19063

Glen Riddle Station Apts
275 GLEN RIDDLE RD 19063

Greenhurst Apts
38 W STATE ST 19063

Hickory Hill Apts
520 N LEMON ST 19063

Holly House Apts
501 N PROVIDENCE RD . 19063

Hunt Club Apts
119 STATE RD 19063

Jamestown Apts
499 W JEFFERSON ST 19063

Jeffersonian Apts
275 W JEFFERSON ST 19063

Lexington Apts
460 LINDEN LN 19063

Lima Estates
411 N MIDDLETOWN RD . 19063

Malvern Court Apts
21 W STATE ST 19063

Martins Run Ret Home
11 MARTINS RUN 19063

Media Station Apts
340 MEDIA STATION RD .. 19063

Media Towers Apts
295 E JEFFERSON ST 19063

Midtown Apts
27 E STATE ST 19063

Monticello Apts
400 S ORANGE ST 19063

Orange Hill Apts
501 N ORANGE ST 19063

Plymouth Hall Apts
20 VETERANS SQ 19063

Providence Court Apts
42 STATE RD 19063

Rose Tree Crossing Apts
1295 N PROVIDENCE RD 19063

Tunbridge Apts
274 GLEN RIDDLE RD 19063

West State Ct Apts
421 W STATE ST 19063

Williamsburg Apts
435 LINDEN LN 19063

Winchester Apts
313 E JEFFERSON ST 19063

Winter Apts
215 MANCHESTER AVE .. 19063

Woodlyn Apts
210 E JEFFERSON ST 19063

Woodview Apts
940 N PROVIDENCE RD . 19063

Yorktown Apts
475 LINDEN LN 19063

BUILDINGS

Bob West Building
42 E BALTIMORE AVE 19063

Childcare Service Building
311 W FRONT ST 19063

Georgetown Building
101 CHESLEY DR 19063

Granite Farm Estates
1343 W BALTIMORE PIKE 19063

Granite Run Mall
1067 W BALTIMORE PIKE 19063

Hampton Building
112 CHESLEY DR 19063

Independence Building
110 CHESLEY DR 19063

Jamestown Building
102 CHESLEY DR 19063

Jefferson Building
106 CHESLEY DR 19063

Lafayette Building
103 CHESLEY DR 19063

Legal Arts Building
344 W FRONT ST 19063

Madison Building
108 CHESLEY DR 19063

Main Line Federal Building
2 S ORANGE ST 19063

Media Medical Prof Building
280 N PROVIDENCE RD . 19063

Riddle Health Care Ctr
1078 W BALTIMORE PIKE 19063

Rose Tree Corporate Ctr
1400 N PROVIDENCE RD 19063

Rose Tree Office Complex
1223 N PROVIDENCE RD 19063

William Penn Building
109 CHESLEY DR 19063

Yorktown Building
105 CHESLEY DR 19063

GOVERNMENT

Delaware County Courthouse
201 WEST FRONT ST 19063

DORMONT

APARTMENTS

Embassy Apts
230 BEVERLY RD 15216

Lebanon Hall Apts
318 WASHINGTON RD 15216

DOWNTOWN

APARTMENTS

Gateway Towers
320 Fort Duquesne Blvd ... 15222

Midtown Towers
643 LIBERTY AVE 15222

Roosevelt Arms
609 PENN AVE 15222

BUILDINGS

1 Gateway Ctr
420 Fort Duquesne Blvd ... 15222

1 Oliver Plaza
210 6TH AVE 15222

1 Ppg Place
1 PPG PL 15222

100 5th Ave Building
100 5TH AVE 15222

2 Gateway Ctr
603 STANWIX ST 15222

2 Ppg Place
2 PPG PL 15222

2nd Federal Building
335 5TH AVE 15222

3 Gateway Ctr
401 LIBERTY AVE 15222

3 Ppg Place
3 PPG PL 15222

300 6th Ave Building
300 6TH AVE 15222

4 Gateway Ctr
444 LIBERTY AVE 15222

4 Ppg Place
4 PPG PL 15222

4 Smithfield Building
4 SMITHFIELD ST 15222

5 Gateway Ctr
60 BLVD OF THE ALLIES . 15222

5 Ppg Place
5 PPG PL 15222

5th Avenue Place
120 5TH AVE 15222

6 Ppg Place
6 PPG PL 15222

711 Building
711 PENN AVE 15222

Allegheny Towers
625 STANWIX ST 15222

Arrot Building
401 WOOD ST 15222

Bell Telephone
201 STANWIX ST 15222

Benedum Trees Building
223 4TH AVE 15222

Centre City Towers
650 SMITHFIELD ST 15222

Century Building
130 7TH ST 15222

Clark Building
717 LIBERTY AVE 15222

Cng Tower
625 LIBERTY AVE 15222

Commonwealth Building
316 4TH AVE 15222

Convention Tower
960 PENN AVE 15222

David Lawrence Convention
1001 PENN AVE 15222

Fulton Building
107 6TH ST 15222

Heinz Hall
600 PENN AVE 15222

Investment Building
239 4TH AVE 15222

Kossman Building
400 STANWIX ST 15222

Liberty Center
1001 LIBERTY AVE 15222

National Steel Ctr
20 STANWIX ST 15222

Oliver Building
535 SMITHFIELD ST 15222

One Pnc Plaza
249 5TH AVE 15222

Park Building
355 5TH AVE 15222

Smithfield Building
610 SMITHFIELD ST 15222

Smithfield Diamond Building
415 SMITHFIELD ST 15222

Standard Life Building
345 4TH AVE 15222

Times Building
336 4TH AVE 15222

Two Pnc Plaza
630 LIBERTY AVE 15222

Union Bank Building
306 4TH AVE 15222

United Steelworkers Building
60 BLVD OF THE ALLIES . 15222

Westinghouse Building
11 STANWIX ST 15222

GOVERNMENT

New Federal Building
1000 LIBERTY AVE 15222

PA State Office Building
300 LIBERTY AVE 15222

HOTELS

Vista International Hotel
1000 PENN AVE 15222

EAST GERMANTOWN

APARTMENTS

Awbury Manor
1262 E WASHINGTON LN 19138

Cope House Apts
6101 BOYER ST 19138

Franklin Park Garden
6300 CHEW AVE 19138

Gro Marr Apts
944 E JOHNSON ST 19138

Robert Court
7441 LIMEKILN PIKE 19138

Washington Lane Apts
6201 CRITTENDEN ST 19138

BUILDINGS

Mt Airy Medical Center
7353 LIMEKILN PIKE 19138

EAST LIBERTY

APARTMENTS

Alder Court
6112 ALDER CT 15206

Auburn Towers Apts
6290 AUBURN ST 15206

Essex House
5713 CENTRE AVE 15206

Frontanac
490 S HIGHLAND AVE 15206

Harriet Tubman Ctr
550 NEGLEY RUN BLVD . 15206

Highland Manor
341 S HIGHLAND AVE 15206

Highwood
372 S HIGHLAND AVE 15206

Kenmawr Apts
401 SHADY AVE 15206

Kennilworth Apts
5700 CENTRE AVE 15206

Liberty Park Apts
6209 BROAD ST 15206

Negley Gardens
400 N NEGLEY AVE 15206

Parklane Apts
5700 BUNKERHILL ST 15206

Penn Circle Towers
6231 PENN AVE 15206

Penn Plaza
5600 PENN AVE 15206

Penn Shady
226 SHADY AVE 15206

Pennley Park Apt
5601 PENN AVE 15206

BUILDINGS

Highland Building
121 S HIGHLAND MALL ... 15206

Liberty Building
6101 PENN MALL E 15206

Medical Ctr East
211 N WHITFIELD ST 15206

EASTWICK

BUILDINGS

Mercy Eastwick Arts Building
2801 ISLAND AVE 19153

EDGEWOOD

APARTMENTS

Garden Court Apts
2235 S BRADDOCK AVE .. 15218

ELKINS PARK

APARTMENTS

Briar House Apts
8302 OLD YORK RD 19117

Brookside Ter Apts
534 E CHURCH RD 19117

Chelbourne Plaza
46 TOWNSHIP LINE RD 19117

Colonial Apts
7900 HIGH SCHOOL RD ... 19117

Elkins Court Apts
700 ELKINS AVE 19117

Elkins Park Apts
415 E CHURCH RD 19117

Elkins Park Garden Apts
8000 HIGH SCHOOL RD ... 19117

Elkins Park House
7900 OLD YORK RD 19117

Laurwyck Manor
22 TOWNSHIP LINE RD 19117

Meeting House Court
681 MEETINGHOUSE RD . 19117

One Breyer Estates
100 BREYER DR 19117

Park Spring Manor Apts
7876 SPRING AVE 19117

Regina Rose Apts
515 STAHR RD 19117

Rolling Hill Apts
26 TOWNSHIP LINE RD 19117

Station Mews
7804 MONTGOMERY AVE 19117

BUILDINGS

309 Professional Ctr
309 TOWNSHIP LINE RD .. 19117

Courtyard Of Shops
8121 OLD YORK RD 19117

Elkins Park Square
8080 OLD YORK RD 19117

Executive Plaza
7848 OLD YORK RD 19117

Medical Arts Building
60 TOWNSHIP LINE RD 19117

One Breyer Office Park
8380 OLD YORK RD 19117

Two Breyer Office Park
8360 OLD YORK RD 19117

Yorktown Courtyard
8119 OLD YORK RD 19117

ERIE

APARTMENTS

Barnabas Ct
5416 E LAKE RD 16511

Center City
814 SASSAFRAS ST 16501

Conrad House
5436 E LAKE RD 16511

Friendship Arms
111 E 11TH ST 16501

Gerald S Salsbury Building
4004 PACIFIC AVE 16506

Grandview Manor
4210 DAVISON AVE 16504

Harborview House
210 W 6TH ST 16507

J Leonard Ostrow Apt
4220 DAVISON AVE 16504

Kenilworth Apts
353 W 6TH ST 16507

Mercy Terrace Apts
430 E GRANDVIEW BLVD 16504

Methodist Towers
160 W 8TH ST 16501

Mid City Towers
12 E 9TH ST 16501

Pittsburgh
2182 W 8TH ST 16505

Richford Arms
515 STATE ST 16501

Robison Apts
210 W 8TH ST 16501

Scalise Apts
516 E 6TH ST 16507

Schaaf
10 E 34TH ST 16504

Schaaf Apts
3309 STATE ST 16508

Schmidt Towers
153 6TH ST. 16501

Sharp Apts
727 FRENCH ST 16501

Thirty Five Thirty Five
3535 STATE ST 16508

Tullio Towers
21 W 9TH ST 16501

BUILDINGS

Baldwin Building
1001 STATE ST 16501

Erie Medical Arts Building
225 W 25TH ST 16502

First National Bank Building
717 STATE ST 16501

Highpoint Towers
2314 SASSAFRAS ST 16502

Law Building
925 FRENCH ST 16501

Marine Bank Building
901 STATE ST 16501

Masonic Building
32 W 8TH ST 16501

Professional Building
1611 PEACH ST 16501

Rothrock Building
121 W 10TH ST 16501

Sumner E Nichols Building
155 W 8TH ST 16501

GOVERNMENT

Erie City Hall
626 STATE ST 16501

Erie County Court House
140 W 6TH ST 16501

Federal Building
617 STATE ST 16501

US Court House
617 STATE ST 16501

FAIRHILL

APARTMENTS

Hancock Apts
174 W ALLEGHENY AVE .. 19133

FALLS

APARTMENTS

Creek Village Apts
130 TULLYTOWN RD 19054

Galilee Village
25 PENN VALLEY RD 19054

Pennsbury Woods
9101 NEW FALLS RD 19054

Village At Newport
8590 NEW FALLS RD 19054

Village Of Pennbrook
9071 MILL CREEK RD 19054

BUILDINGS

Fallsington Industrl Park
0 HEADLEY PL 19054

FEASTERVILLE TREVOSE

APARTMENTS

Arbor Lane Apts
600 OLD STREET RD 19053

Bridgetown Commons
1825 BRIDGETOWN PIKE 19053

Chalet Village Apts
95 HEIGHTS LN 19053

Colonial Point Apts
2555 OLD TREVOSE RD . 19053

Croftwood Apts
400 E STREET RD 19053

Hickory Hills Apts
315 STEELE RD 19053

Top Of The Hill Apts
301 HEIGHTS LN 19053

BUILDINGS

1 Neshaminy Interplex
1 INTERPLEX DR 19053

2 Neshaminy Interplex
2 INTERPLEX DR 19053

2500 Neshaminy Interplex
2500 INTERPLEX DR 19053

2607 Neshaminy Interplex
2607 INTERPLEX DR 19053

2655 Neshaminy Interplex
2655 INTERPLEX DR 19053

2700 Neshaminy Interplex
2700 INTERPLEX DR 19053

3 Neshaminy Interplex
3 INTERPLEX DR 19053

4 Neshaminy Interplex
4 INTERPLEX DR 19053

5 Neshaminy Interplex
5 INTERPLEX DR 19053

6 Neshaminy Interplex
6 INTERPLEX DR 19053

7 Neshaminy Interplex
7 INTERPLEX DR 19053

8 Neshaminy Interplex
8 INTERPLEX DR 19053

Buck Hotel Prof Center
1216 BUCK RD 19053

Bucks County Mall
105 E STREET RD 19053

Feasterville Shop Plaza
1045 BUSTLETON PIKE .. 19053

One Allied Drive
1 ALLIED DR 19053

GOVERNMENT

TWP Administration Building
1500 DESIRE AVE 19053

FERNDALE

APARTMENTS

Carriage Hills Apts
545 GOUCHER ST 15905

Edwards Hill Apts
1781 GOUCHER ST 15905

Loughner Plaza
51 AKERS ST 15905

Norwood Gardens Apts
1781 GOUCHER ST 15905

BUILDINGS

Valley Pike Manor
1029 FRANKLIN ST 15905

FERTILITY

GOVERNMENT

City Hall
120 N DUKE ST 17602

Courthouse
50 N DUKE ST 17602

FIDELITY

BUILDINGS

Fidelity Building
123 S BROAD ST 19109

FRANKFORD

APARTMENTS

Arrott Arms Apts
1336 ARROTT ST 19124

Boulevard Apts
4732 ROOSEVELT BLVD . 19124

Carver Hall
4840 OXFORD AVE 19124

Darrah Apts
1655 HARRISON ST 19124

Fillmore Terrace Apts
4860 FILLMORE TER 19124

Foulkrod Apts
1340 FOULKROD ST 19124

Greenwood Court Apts
1346 FOULKROD ST 19124

Harrison Apts
1661 HARRISON ST 19124

Jaclyn Apts
5243 COTTAGE ST 19124

Leiper Park Apts
4712 LEIPER ST 19124

Northwood Court Apts
5231 OXFORD AVE 19124

Northwood Manor Apts
.1320 FOULKROD ST 19124

Northwood Towers
5245 OXFORD AVE 19124

Parkview Apts
3901 ROOSEVELT BLVD . 19124

Penn Street Apts
5008 PENN ST 19124

Sanford Apts
5000 AKRON ST 19124

Sorensen Arms Apts
4616 LEIPER ST 19124

The Apartment Center
5051 OXFORD AVE 19124

The Apartment Center
4925 SAUL ST 19124

The Mackley Apts
1401 E BRISTOL ST 19124

Toland House
4601 LEIPER ST 19124

Wistar Park Apts
4924 SAUL ST 19124

GERMANTOWN

APARTMENTS

Alden Park Manor
5500 WISSAHICKON AVE 19144

Baynton Manor
5307 BAYNTON ST 19144

Bel-air Apts
427 W CHELTEN AVE 19144

Birchwood Hill Apts
5115 WISSAHICKON AVE 19144

Blythewood Estates Apts
2991 W School House Ln . 19144

Cambridge Apts
2967 W School House Ln . 19144

Chelten Arms
500 W CHELTEN AVE 19144

Chelten Place Apts
319 W CHELTEN AVE 19144

Chelten Place Apts
5709 MORRIS ST 19144

Cloverly Apts
437 W School House Ln ... 19144

Colonial Gardens
5427 WAYNE AVE 19144

Congress Hall Apts
447 W CLAPIER ST 19144

Copley Manor Apts
123 W TULPEHOCKEN ST 19144

Copper Beech Court
5400 WISSAHICKON AVE 19144

Duval Manor Apts
6350 GREENE ST 19144

English Manor Apts
243 W TULPEHOCKEN ST 19144

Enon Tolen Apts
245 W QUEEN LN 19144

Erringer Place
414 W MANHEIM ST 19144

Fairfax Apts
5501 WAYNE AVE 19144

Fairmount Apts
357 W JOHNSON ST 19144

Fernhill Apts
333 W Abbottsford Ave 19144

Fishers Crossing Apts
4901 STENTON AVE 19144

Four Freedoms House
6101 MORRIS ST 19144

Frebar Apts
5017 WISSAHICKON AVE 19144

Germantown House
5457 WAYNE AVE 19144

Greene Arms Apts
5925 GREENE ST 19144

Greene Manor Apts
259 W JOHNSON ST 19144

Gypsy Lane Apts
4000 GYPSY LN 19144

Hampshire House
5008 MCKEAN AVE 19144

Hampton Court Apts
139 W TULPEHOCKEN ST 19144

Harvey Court Apts
109 W HARVEY ST 19144

Hathaway House
515 W CHELTEN AVE 19144

Independence Plaza
3120 W School House Ln . 19144

Johnson Park Apts
330 W JOHNSON ST 19144

Karen Park Apts
601 W PARK LN 19144

Kenilworth Apts
2979 W School House Ln . 19144

Kings Manor Apts
519 W KING ST 19144

Lafayette Gardens Apts
709 E CHURCH LN 19144

Magnolia Homes
5919 MAGNOLIA ST 19144

Manheim Gardens
501 W MANHEIM ST 19144

Marchwood Apts
5515 WISSAHICKON AVE 19144

Mayfair House
401 W JOHNSON ST 19144

Morris Manor Apts
5721 MORRIS ST 19144

Oliver Hall Apts
6100 MCCALLUM ST 19144

Park Heights Apts
5555 WISSAHICKON AVE 19144

Park Plaza Apts
689 W WALNUT LN 19144

Penn Lee Court Apts
557 E CHURCH LN 19144

President Apts
425 W CHELTEN AVE 19144

Qu-wayne Apts
5224 WAYNE AVE 19144

Queen Lane Apts
301 W QUEEN LN 19144

School Lane House Apts
5450 WISSAHICKON AVE 19144

Stokes Rowe Apts
5600 GERMANTOWN AVE 19144

Tarleton House
607 E CHURCH LN 19144

Tulwane Apts
6214 WAYNE AVE 19144

Valley Green Apts
5720 WISSAHICKON AVE 19144

Wal Lane House
401 W WALNUT LN 19144

Wallingford Apts
215 W WALNUT LN 19144

Walnut Lane West Apts
700 W WALNUT LN 19144

Walnut Ln Apts
242 W WALNUT LN 19144

Wayne Court Apts
5409 WAYNE AVE 19144

Wayne Iris Apts
5321 WAYNE AVE 19144

Wayne Manor Apts
6200 WAYNE AVE 19144

Waynemore Apts
5203 WAYNE AVE 19144

Waynemore Apts
179 W HANSBERRY ST ... 19144

Wincrest Apts
250 E JOHNSON ST 19144

Wissahickon Building
5225 SCHUYLER ST 19144

Wissahickon Gardens
549 W MANHEIM ST 19144

GREEN TREE

APARTMENTS

Greentree Gardens
833 GREENTREE RD 15220

Va Mansions East
2120 GREENTREE RD 15220

Va Mansions West
2160 GREENTREE RD 15220

BUILDINGS

1 Parkway Center
875 GREENTREE RD 15220

10 Parkway Center
875 GREENTREE RD 15220

11 Parkway Center
875 GREENTREE RD 15220

2 Parkway Center
875 GREENTREE RD 15220

3 Parkway Center
875 GREENTREE RD 15220

5 Parkway Center
875 GREENTREE RD 15220

6 Parkway Center
875 GREENTREE RD 15220

Manor Oak Village
1910 COCHRAN RD 15220

GREENFIELD MANOR

GOVERNMENT

Court House
633 COURT ST 19601

Reading City Hall
815 WASHINGTON ST 19601

HOSPITALS

Community General
135 N 6TH ST 19601

HAMPDEN

COLLEGES

Albright College
1621 N 13TH ST 19604

HARRISBURG

GOVERNMENT

City Government Center
10 N 2ND ST 17101

Dauphin Co War Vets Building
112 MARKET ST 17101

Dauphin County Ct House
101 MARKET ST 17101

HOMEWOOD

APARTMENTS

Homewood House
7130 FRANKSTOWN AVE 15208

Kelly St Hi Rise
7030 KELLY ST 15208

HULMEVILLE

APARTMENTS

Attleboro Retirement Vlg
290 WINCHESTER AVE ... 19047

Bellevue Court Apts
401 BELLEVUE AVE 19047

Dorilyn Terrace Apts
190 Bristol Oxford Vly Rd .. 19047

Middletown Trace Apts
800 TRENTON RD 19047

Orchard Square Apts
1801 OLD LINCOLN HWY 19047

Oxford Grant Apts
255 E LINCOLN HWY 19047

BUILDINGS

Old Post Office Building
198 N PINE ST 19047

One Oxford Vly Ofc Building B
2300 E LINCOLN HWY 19047

Oxford Business Center
586 MIDDLETOWN BLVD 19047

Oxford Falls Plz Office Building
444 OXFORD VALLEY RD 19047

Saint Marys Hosp Med Building
1205 LANGHORNE NEWTOWN
RD 19047

Saint Marys Hospital Building
1201 LANGHORNE NEWTOWN
RD 19047

Summit Square Office Building
1717 LANGHORNE NEWTOWN
RD 19047

Victorian Commons
1709 LANGHORNE NEWTOWN
RD 19047

HUNTING PARK

APARTMENTS

Ambassador Apts
2101 W VENANGO ST 19140

Opportunity Towers
1727 W Hunting Park Ave . 19140

Plymouth Hall
2201 W VENANGO ST 19140

Tower Apts
2100 W TIOGA ST 19140

Venango House
2104 W VENANGO ST 19140

JEFFERSONVILLE

APARTMENTS

Timberlake Apts Building A
2801 STANBRIDGE ST 19401

Timberlake Apts Building B
2803 STANBRIDGE ST 19401

JOHNSTOWN

APARTMENTS

Bloomfield Apts
329 THEATRE DR 15904

Centre Towne Apts
399 WALNUT ST 15901

Connor Towers
527 VINE ST 15901

Joseph Johns Towers
350 MARKET ST 15901

Lincoln Lee Manor
231 WALNUT ST 15901

Richland Towers
343 THEATRE DR 15904

Town House Towers
420 VINE ST 15901

BUILDINGS

Bt Financial Pl
551 MAIN ST 15901

Carnegie Building
605 MAIN ST 15901

Central Park Commons Building
430 MAIN ST 15901

Central Park Plaza
132 PARK PL 15901

Fisher Building
607 MAIN ST 15901

Galleria
500 Industrial Park Rd 15904

Park Building
423 MAIN ST 15901

Pennsylvania Traffic Building
319 WASHINGTON ST 15901

PNC Bank
227 FRANKLIN ST 15901

R A Seifert Med Building
321 MAIN ST 15901

Richland Mall
3200 ELTON RD 15904

Swank Building
616 MAIN ST 15901

U S National Bank Building
216 FRANKLIN ST 15901

Vine St Towers
525 VINE ST 15901

Wallace Building
406 MAIN ST 15901

GOVERNMENT

City Hall Building
401 MAIN ST 15901

U S Post Office Building
111 FRANKLIN ST 15901

KENHORST

COLLEGES

Alvernia College
400 Saint Bernadine St 19607

KINGSESSING

APARTMENTS

Arvilla Apts
4537 OSAGE AVE 19143

Baltimore Court Apts
6000 BALTIMORE AVE 19143

Bronson House
816 S 47TH ST 19143

Brooklyn Arms Apts
6030 LARCHWOOD AVE .. 19143

Cedar Park Apts
4818 CHESTER AVE 19143

Chester Hall
4725 CHESTER AVE 19143

Chester Plaza
4605 CHESTER AVE 19143

Clark Park Apts
4520 SPRINGFIELD AVE . 19143

Elvista Apts
4534 OSAGE AVE 19143

Farragut Hall
4618 CHESTER AVE 19143

Florence Court
800 S 49TH ST 19143

Garden Court A Apts
349 S 47TH ST 19143

Garden Court Apts
4643 PINE ST 19143

Garden Court B Apts
351 S 47TH ST 19143

Garden Court Plaza
4701 PINE ST 19143

Garden Court South
4740 PINE ST 19143

King Gardens Apts
1123 S 47TH ST 19143

Larchwood Terrace Apts
500 S 47TH ST 19143

Osage Garden Apts
419 S 48TH ST 19143

Osage Manor Apts
4524 OSAGE AVE 19143

Pine Vista Apts
4800 PINE ST 19143

Plaza Apts
2061 S 58TH ST 19143

Presbyterian Home Apts
2000 S 58TH ST 19143

Royal Chester Court
4601 CHESTER AVE 19143

Sylvania Garden Apts
414 S 48TH ST 19143

Trinity Apts
1008 S 48TH ST 19143

University Apts
801 S 47TH ST 19143

Winchester Apts
4815 CHESTER AVE 19143

Winchester House Apts
4804 CHESTER AVE 19143

LANCASTER

BUILDINGS

Greist Building
8 N QUEEN ST 17603

HOSPITALS

Community Hospital
3002 PO BOX 17604

Lancaster General
3555 PO BOX 17604

Saint Joseph
3509 PO BOX 17604

COLLEGES

Franklin And Marshall
3003 PO BOX 17604

Lancaster Theological Seminary
555 W JAMES ST 17603

LESTER

BUILDINGS

One International Court
100 STEVENS DR 19113

Two International Court
200 STEVENS DR 19113

LEVITTOWN

APARTMENTS

Birchview Apts
7200 MARION AVE 19055

Blue Ridge Apts
3501 BRISTOL OXFORD
VALLEY RD 19057

Brittany Springs Apts
3401 BRISTOL OXFORD
VALLEY RD 19057

Chesterfield Apts
1338 NEW RODGERS RD 19056

Country Club Apts
1228 NEW RODGERS RD 19056

Country Manor Apts
2151 LINCOLN HWY 19056

Crestwood Condos
3101 BRISTOL OXFORD
VALLEY RD 19057

Foxwood Manor Apts
2180 NEW RODGERS RD 19056

Hamilton Park Apts
2130 NEW RODGERS RD 19056

Kenwood Court Apts
1522 HAINES RD 19055

Longview Apts
1501 WOODBOURNE RD 19057

Millcreek Gardens Apts
6750 MILL CREEK RD 19057

Racquet Club E Apts
1970 NEW RODGERS RD 19056

Roman Apts
7030 MILL CREEK RD 19057

Sherwood Gardens
2000 NEW RODGERS RD 19056

Twin Terrace Apts
201 WOODBOURNE RD .. 19056

Woodbourne Apts
1350 WOODBOURNE RD 19057

BUILDINGS

Middletown Prof Building
1400 NEW RODGERS RD 19056

LOGAN

BUILDINGS

Grange Building
5601 N BROAD ST 19141

Klein Professional Building
5401 OLD YORK RD 19141

MC KEESPORT

APARTMENTS

Baehr Apts
801 WALNUT ST 15132

Hi View Garden
520 COURSIN ST 15132

Midtown Plaza
516 SINCLAIR ST 15132

Richmark
2807 LINCOLN WAY 15131

Royal Oak Village
152 ROYAL OAK DR 15131

Sr Citizen Hi Rise Apts
601 6TH ST 15132

MC KNIGHT

COLLEGES

La Roche College
9000 BABCOCK BLVD 15237

MEDIA

APARTMENTS

Crum Creek Condos
700 AVONDALE RD 19086

Linda Court Apts
830 W SPRINGFIELD RD 19064

Philmar Court Apts
533 PHILMAR CT 19064

Rolling Green Apts
257 N STATE RD 19064

Shel Drake Apts
24 N STATE RD 19064

Springfield Place Apts
420 E WOODLAND AVE ... 19064

Springwood Garden Apts
610 E WOODLAND AVE ... 19064

Thomson Park Apts
512 STIDMAN DR 19064

Wallingford Arms
27 WALLINGFORD AVE ... 19086

BUILDINGS

Springfield Mall
1250 BALTIMORE PIKE ... 19064

Springfield Park Shop Ctr
910 E WOODLAND AVE ... 19064

Springhaven Square
891 BALTIMORE PIKE 19064

Victoria Mill Off Ctr
1489 BALTIMORE PIKE ... 19064

GOVERNMENT

Springfield Twp Building
50 POWELL RD 19064

MIDDLE CITY EAST

APARTMENTS

1500 Locust Building
1500 LOCUST ST 19102

Academy House
1420 LOCUST ST 19102

Delancey Court
317 S 15TH ST 19102

Newport Apts
1530 SPRUCE ST 19102

Pine Tree Apts
1500 PINE ST 19102

Sprucemont
257 S 16TH ST 19102

Stiles Alumni Hall
325 N 15TH ST 19102

The Bellrich
301 S 15TH ST 19102

The Drake
1512 SPRUCE ST 19102

The Metropolitan
117 N 15TH ST 19102

The Nash
1527 SPRUCE ST 19102

The Touraine
1520 SPRUCE ST 19102

Versailles Apts
1530 LOCUST ST 19102

Vida Apts
235 S 15TH ST 19102

Westbury Apts
271 S 15TH ST 19102

BUILDINGS

1401 Walnut Building
1401 WALNUT ST 19102

1420 Walnut Building
1420 WALNUT ST 19102

1425 Walnut Building
1425 WALNUT ST 19102

1429 Walnut Building
1429 WALNUT ST 19102

1500 Walnut Building
1500 WALNUT ST 19102

1510 Chestnut St Building
1510 CHESTNUT ST 19102

1515 Locust Building
1515 LOCUST ST 19102

1515 Market St Building
1515 MARKET ST 19102

1520 Locust Building
1520 LOCUST ST 19102

1530 Chestnut St Building
1530 CHESTNUT ST 19102

2 Penn Center
1500 John F Kennedy Blvd 19102

230 S Broad Street Building
230 S BROAD ST 19102

American Patriot Building
112 S 16TH ST 19102

Atlantic Building
260 S BROAD ST 19102

Bellet Building
1505 RACE ST 19102

Broad & Locust Building
230 S BROAD ST 19102

Centre Square East Building
1500 MARKET ST 19102

Centre Square West Building
1500 MARKET ST 19102

Crozier Building
1422 CHESTNUT ST 19102

Exchange Building
1411 WALNUT ST 19102

Federal Building
1421 CHERRY ST 19102

Four Mellon Bank Center
1421 CHESTNUT ST 19102

Franklin Office Center
1427 VINE ST 19102

Gibson Building
260 S 15TH ST 19102

Greenwood Building
1528 WALNUT ST 19102

Jewish Federation Building
226 S 16TH ST 19102

Lewis Tower Building
225 S 15TH ST 19102

Medical Arts Building
1601 WALNUT ST 19102

Morton Building
220 S 16TH ST 19102

One Benj Franklin Pky
1 Benjamin Franklin Pky ... 19102

One Franklin Plaza
200 N 16TH ST 19102

One Penn Square West
30 S 15TH ST 19102

Packard Building
111 S 15TH ST 19102

Pennsylvania Building
1500 CHESTNUT ST 19102

Pennwalt Building
3 Benjamin Franklin Pky ... 19102

Professional Building
1521 LOCUST ST 19102

Robinson Building
42 S 15TH ST 19102

Rothenberg Building
1518 WALNUT ST 19102

The Bellevue
1401 CHANCELLOR ST ... 19102

The Bellevue
200 S BROAD ST 19102

The Drexel Building
1435 WALNUT ST 19102

The Spectacor Building
230 S 15TH ST 19102

Two Mellon Bank Center
2 MELLON BANK CTR 19102

Ugi Building
1401 ARCH ST 19102

GOVERNMENT

Municipal Services Building
1401 John F Kennedy Blvd 19102

MIDDLE CITY WEST

APARTMENTS

1820 Rittenhouse Apts
1820 RITTENHOUSE SQ . 19103

2101 Walnut Co-op
2101 WALNUT ST 19103

2201 Condominium
2201 CHERRY ST 19103

2400 Chestnut St Apts
2400 CHESTNUT ST 19103

Ambassador Town House
2101 CHESTNUT ST 19103

Carlton House Apts
1801 John F Kennedy Blvd 19103

Lincoln Rittenhouse
222 W RITTENHOUSE SQ 19103

Locust Point Apts
2429 LOCUST ST 19103

Logan Square East
2 FRANKLIN TOWN BLVD 19103

One Franklin Town Blvd
1 FRANKLIN TOWN BLVD 19103

One Rittenhouse Square
135 S 18TH ST 19103

Penn Center House
1900 John F Kennedy Blvd 19103

Rittenhouse Claridge
201 S 18TH ST 19103

Rittenhouse Regency
225 S 18TH ST 19103

Rittenhouse Savoy
1810 RITTENHOUSE SQ . 19103

Riverloft Apts
2300 WALNUT ST 19103

Rivers Edge Apts
2301 CHERRY ST 19103

Riverside Presbytn Tower
158 N 23RD ST 19103

Roosevelt Hotel
2220 WALNUT ST 19103

Sidney Hillman Apts
22 S 22ND ST 19103

The Arches
100 N 22ND ST 19103

The Chatham
135 S 20TH ST 19103

The Dorchester
226 W RITTENHOUSE SQ 19103

The Wellington
135 S 19TH ST 19103

Towne House
301 S 19TH ST 19103

Walnut Plaza
2135 WALNUT ST 19103

Wanamaker House
2020 WALNUT ST 19103

Warwick Apts
1701 LOCUST ST 19103

Westminister Apts
2215 ARCH ST 19103

William Penn House Apts
1919 CHESTNUT ST 19103

Windsor Apts
1700 Benjamin Franklin Pky19103

BUILDINGS

1615 Walnut Building
1615 WALNUT ST 19103

1616 Walnut Building
1616 WALNUT ST 19103

1700 Market Building
1700 MARKET ST 19103

1700 Walnut Building
1700 WALNUT ST 19103

1737 Chestnut St Building
1737 CHESTNUT ST 19103

1800 Kennedy Building
1800 John F Kennedy Blvd 19103

1818 Market Building
1818 MARKET ST 19103

1831 Chestnut St Building
1831 CHESTNUT ST 19103

1880 Kennedy Building
1880 John F Kennedy Blvd 19103

1913 Walnut St Building
1913 WALNUT ST 19103

1920 Chestnut St Building
1920 CHESTNUT ST 19103

2000 Market Building
2000 MARKET ST 19103

2401 Walnut Building
2401 WALNUT ST 19103

3720 Associates Building
37 S 20TH ST 19103

Allman Building
1701 WALNUT ST 19103

Architects Building
117 S 17TH ST 19103

Belgravia
1811 CHESTNUT ST 19103

Blue Cross Building
1901 MARKET ST 19103

Carlton House
1819 John F Kennedy Blvd 19103

Eight Penn Center
1628 John F Kennedy Blvd 19103

Eleven Penn Center
1835 MARKET ST 19103

Five Penn Center
1601 MARKET ST 19103

Four Penn Center
1616 John F Kennedy Blvd 19103

Jackson Cross Building
100 N 20TH ST 19103

Keystone Building
2040 MARKET ST 19103

Medical Building
1736 PINE ST 19103

Medical Tower
255 S 17TH ST 19103

Mulberry Atrium
2133 ARCH ST 19103

Mutual Benefit Life Building
1845 WALNUT ST 19103

Nine Penn Center
1735 MARKET ST 19103

One Commerce Square
2005 MARKET ST 19103

One Liberty Place
1650 MARKET ST 19103

One Logan Square
1 LOGAN ST. 19103

One Penn Center
1617 John F Kennedy Blvd 19103

Provident Mutual Building
1600 MARKET ST 19103

Provident Natl Bank Building
120 S 17TH ST 19103

Ritt Sq Professional Building
275 S 19TH ST 19103

Robert Morris Building
100 N 17TH ST 19103

Seven Penn Center
1635 MARKET ST 19103

Six Penn Center
20 N 17TH ST 19103

Stock Exchange Building
1900 MARKET ST 19103

Sun Oil Co Building
1608 WALNUT ST 19103

Ten Penn Center
1801 MARKET ST 19103

The Atrium
1900 MARKET ST 19103

The Marketplace
2400 MARKET ST 19103

Two Commerce Square
2001 MARKET ST 19103

Umi Building
1760 MARKET ST 19103

United Engineers Building
30 S 17TH ST 19103

United Fund Building
7 Benjamin Franklin Pky ... 19103

GOVERNMENT

School District Adm Building
2120 WINTER ST 19103

MOUNT AIRY

APARTMENTS

Allen Lane Apts
7057 CRESHEIM RD 19119

Allens Court Apts
19 W ALLENS LN 19119

Ardleigh Gardens
615 E UPSAL ST 19119

Ardleigh Manor Apts
303 E Mount Pleasant Ave . 19119

Ardleigh Manor Apts
7125 SPRAGUE ST 19119

Ardleigh Manor Apts
322 E DURHAM ST 19119

Blakemore St Apts
6788 BLAKEMORE ST 19119

Boyer House Apts
7500 DEVON ST 19119

Canterbury Apts
33 E ROUMFORT RD 19119

Carriage House Apts
15 CARPENTER LN 19119

Cliveden Apts
49 E CLIVEDEN ST 19119

Cliveden Hall
601 W CLIVEDEN ST 19119

Cliveden Manor
1009 E CLIVEDEN ST 19119

Cliveden Street East Apts
262 E CLIVEDEN ST 19119

Cresheim Valley Apts
7200 CRESHEIM RD 19119

Cresheimbrook Condos
7300 CRESHEIM RD 19119

Crittenden Manor Building 1
6801 CRITTENDEN ST 19119

Crittenden Manor Building 2
6813 CRITTENDEN ST 19119

Donna Apts
406 W Mount Pleasant Ave 19119

Emlen Arms
6733 EMLEN ST 19119

Fisher Building
6928 GERMANTOWN AVE 19119

Fitzsimons Day Mem Building
6920 GERMANTOWN AVE 19119

Franklin Villa Apts
200 W SEDGWICK ST 19119

Germantown Manor Apts
412 W HORTTER ST 19119

Gorgas Court
107 E GORGAS LN 19119

Kentwell Hall
6640 SPRAGUE ST 19119

King Philip Apts
6439 GREENE ST 19119

Krapf Memorial Apts
6996 GERMANTOWN AVE 19119

Lincoln Terrace Apts
7000 LINCOLN DR 19119

Malvern Hall
6655 MCCALLUM ST 19119

Malvern Hall East Wing
6655 MCCALLUM ST 19119

Malvern Hall West Wing
6655 MCCALLUM ST 19119

Marita Apts
359 W MOUNT AIRY AVE .. 19119

Martoni Apts
31 W ALLENS LN 19119

Mount Pleasant Arms
265 W Mount Pleasant Ave 19119

Pastorius Court Apts
501 W HORTTER ST 19119

Pelham Apts
332 W HORTTER ST 19119

Pelham Court
6809 EMLEN ST 19119

Pelham Park Manor
229 W UPSAL ST 19119

Princeton Gardens
7326 GERMANTOWN AVE 19119

Rose Court Apts
144 W ALLENS LN 19119

Rosemary Gardens Apts
219 ROSEMARY LN 19119

Schiedt Building
6970 GERMANTOWN AVE 19119

Schmidt Memorial Cottage
6926 GERMANTOWN AVE 19119

Sedgwick Apts
630 W SEDGWICK ST 19119

Sedgwick Court Apts
625 E VERNON RD 19119

Sedgwick Gardens
440 W SEDGWICK ST 19119

Simon Gardens
6732 CHEW AVE 19119

Simon Gardens Apts
6731 MUSGRAVE ST 19119

Stenton Arms Apts
6533 BELFIELD AVE 19119

Stenton Arms Apts
6690 SPRAGUE ST 19119

Stenton Arms Apts
458 E SHARPNACK ST 19119

Stenton Hall
740 E VERNON RD 19119

The Mccallum
6635 MCCALLUM ST 19119

Twin Manor Apts
255 W HORTTER ST 19119

Upsal Apts
500 E UPSAL ST 19119

Upsal Gardens
246 W UPSAL ST 19119

Upsal Manor Apts
13 E UPSAL ST 19119

Upsal Park Apts
329 E UPSAL ST 19119

Vernon Hall
615 E VERNON RD 19119

Vernon House
6445 GREENE ST 19119

W Allen Lane Apts
136 W ALLENS LN 19119

Wiltshire Arms Apts
7206 CRITTENDEN ST 19119

MOUNT LEBANON

APARTMENTS

Abbeyville
135 ABBEYVILLE RD 15228

Avon Court
15 BOWER HILL RD 15228

Gay Lebanon
440 COCHRAN RD 15228

Lebanon Vue
400 COCHRAN RD 15228

Pendale
460 WASHINGTON RD 15228

Washingtonian
1680 WASHINGTON RD .. 15228

BUILDINGS

Stevenson Williams Building
666 WASHINGTON RD 15228

MOUNT OLIVER

APARTMENTS

Richard L Caliguiri Plaza
803 E WARRINGTON AVE 15210

MOUNT WASHINGTON

APARTMENTS

Lagrande Apts
1411 GRANDVIEW AVE 15211

Mountvue Apts
5 GRANDVIEW AVE 15211

NORTH PHILADELPHIA

APARTMENTS

Allegheny Arms
1510 W ALLEGHENY AVE 19132

OAKLAND

APARTMENTS

5th Neville Apts
4705 5TH AVE 15213

Ambassador
4733 CENTRE AVE 15213

Cathedral Mansions
4716 ELLSWORTH AVE ... 15213

Centre Ave
4750 CENTRE AVE 15213

Devon Towers
4920 CENTRE AVE 15213

Devonshire
4910 CENTRE AVE 15213

Devonshire Apts
331 DEVONSHIRE ST 15213

Dithridge Towers
144 N DITHRIDGE ST 15213

Fairfax
4614 5TH AVE 15213

Forbes Craig
4531 FORBES AVE 15213

Hampshire Hall
4730 CENTRE AVE 15213

Hampton Hall
166 N DITHRIDGE ST 15213

King Edward
4609 BAYARD ST 15213

Park Mansions
5023 FREW ST 15213

Park Plaza
128 N CRAIG ST 15213

Pennsylvania
300 N DITHRIDGE ST 15213

Royal Windsor
222 MELWOOD AVE 15213

Royal York
3955 BIGELOW BLVD 15213

Schenley Arms
4041 BIGELOW BLVD 15213

Schenley House
151 N CRAIG ST 15213

Shadyoak
601 CLYDE ST 15213

University Square #1
4625 5TH AVE 15213

University Square #2
4601 5TH AVE 15213

Webster Hall
101 N DITHRIDGE ST 15213

Webster Towers
240 MELWOOD AVE 15213

Wellington Apts
245 MELWOOD AVE 15213

Winchester Apts
540 N NEVILLE ST 15213

BUILDINGS

3500 Fifth Ave
3500 5TH AVE 15213

Physicians Building
121 UNIVERSITY PL 15213

OLNEY

APARTMENTS

Hillside Gardens
6060 Crescentville Rd 19120

OVERBROOK

APARTMENTS

Brockton Court
1315 N 75TH ST 19151

Crown Apts
7312 RUSKIN RD 19151

Drexel Arms Apts
6311 OVERBROOK AVE ... 19151

Farrington Apts
7700 BROCKTON RD 19151

Hastings Manor Apts
6312 SHERWOOD RD 19151

Iorio Apts
6526 W GIRARD AVE 19151

Lebanon Court Apts
1105 N 63RD ST 19151

Lotus Village East
1121 N 66TH ST 19151

Lotus Village West
1120 N 66TH ST 19151

Pennbrook Apts
2130 N 63RD ST 19151

Phillips Apts
7212 HAVERFORD AVE ... 19151

Weymouth Apts
6310 SHERWOOD RD 19151

Woodbine Court Apts
7400 HAVERFORD AVE ... 19151

Woodcrest Gdns
1411 N 76TH ST 19151

Wynnewood Hall Apts
6318 CITY AVE 19151

PASSYUNK

APARTMENTS

Loft Apts
2032 S JUNIPER ST 19148

Stella Maris Apts
730 STELLA MARIS ST 19148

BUILDINGS

Food Distribution Ctr
3301 S GALLOWAY ST 19148

PENN HILLS

APARTMENTS

Laurel Village Apts
700 PENN CENTER BLVD 15235

Penn Towers
1100 PENN Center Blvd ... 15235

Penn Towers Apts
11979 FRANKSTOWN RD 15235

Valmar Gardens
2750 ROBINSON BLVD 15235

PHILADELPHIA

APARTMENTS

4203 Apts
4203 CHESTER AVE 19104

4205 Apts
4205 CHESTER AVE 19104

4401 Apts
4401 SPRUCE ST 19104

4415 Apts
4415 SPRUCE ST 19104

4417 Apts
4417 SPRUCE ST 19104

Abbott Square
530 S 2ND ST 19147

Abby House Apts
450 DOMINO LN 19128

Adelphia House
1229 CHESTNUT ST 19107

Admiral Court Apts
247 S 48TH ST 19139

Almar Apts
5711 ERDRICK ST 19135

Andover Apts
1133 E MOUNT AIRY AVE 19150

Ashton Acres
9601 ASHTON RD 19114

Ashwood Apts
6050 OVERBROOK AVE .. 19131

Atrium Apts
2555 WELSH RD 19114

Bakers Bay
5100 CONVENT LN 19114

Bakers Bay
5000 N CONVENT LN 19114

Bala Apts
2499 N 50TH ST 19131

Bank Street Court Apts
24 S BANK ST 19106

Barb-bee Apts
5719 COTTAGE ST 19135

Beacon Hill Apts
1330 PINE ST 19107

Beekman Place
2746 BELMONT AVE 19131

Beekman Place
1720 LOMBARD ST 19146

Berkley Court
5040 CITY AVE 19131

Berkshire Apts
4103 SPRUCE ST 19104

Black Horse Alley Apts
12 S LETITIA ST 19106

Blair Meadows Townhouses
190 SHAWMONT AVE 19128

Blenheim Apts
4311 SPRUCE ST 19104

Blue Grass Estates
9243 BLUE GRASS RD 19114

Branden Apts
4035 CHESTNUT ST 19104

Bridge View Place
315 NEW ST 19106

Bridgeview Plaza
6320 KEYSTONE ST 19135

Brith Sholom House
3939 Conshohocken Ave .. 19131

Brynfield Apts
5050 WYNNEFIELD AVE .. 19131

Burlington House Apts
1321 SPRUCE ST 19107

Calvert Hall
4045 BALTIMORE AVE 19104

Cameron Apts
616 WALNUT LN 19128

Canterbury Court Apts
9951 ACADEMY RD 19114

Carlene Apts
2500 BELMONT AVE 19131

Carousel Apts
2465 N 50TH ST 19131

Carriage House Apts
1311 LOMBARD ST 19147

Castle Hill Apts
4301 SPRUCE ST 19104

Cathedral East
750 E CATHEDRAL RD 19128

Cathedral Village
600 E CATHEDRAL RD 19128

Center City One Apts
1326 SPRUCE ST 19107

Center Post Apts
55 N 40TH ST 19104

Chalfonte Condo
10115 VERREE RD 19116

Chancellor Apts
206 S 13TH ST 19107

Chancery Lane Apts
134 ARCH ST 19106

Chestnut Arms Apts
4039 CHESTNUT ST 19104

Chestnut House
122 CHESTNUT ST 19106

Chestnut Terrace
7412 STENTON AVE 19150

Cheswick Sq Apts
7949 RIDGE AVE 19128

Chocolate Works
231 N 3RD ST 19106

Church St Apts
222 CHURCH ST 19106

Church View Court Apts
11 N 2ND ST 19106

Churchview Common Apts
122 CHURCH ST 19106

Clarenden Court Apts
3750 CLARENDEN RD 19114

Comly Apts
4900 COMLY ST 19135

Comly Court Apts
5923 HEGERMAN ST 19135

Comly Crest Apts
4820 COMLY ST 19135

Commodore Apts
4207 CHESTER AVE 19104

Concord Hall Apts
4418 SPRUCE ST 19104

Cottage Apts
5728 COTTAGE ST 19135

Deauville Apts
6725 RIDGE AVE 19128

Dominola Apts
425 DOMINO LN 19128

Duffield House
3701 Conshohocken Ave .. 19131

Dupont Court
631 DUPONT ST 19128

Dupont Towers Apts
6100 HENRY AVE 19128

Elizabeth Court
4017 BALTIMORE AVE 19104

Elkin Court Apts
7531 THOURON AVE 19150

Emerson Hall Apts
4209 CHESTER AVE 19104

Esther Klein Apts
2610 BELMONT AVE 19131

Executive House
6100 CITY AVE 19131

Fairmount Terrace Apts
3601 Conshohocken Ave .. 19131

Fairview Arms Apts
5219 WYNNEFIELD AVE .. 19131

Fairway Plaza Apts
5000 WOODBINE AVE 19131

Florence Apts
6607 FRANKFORD AVE ... 19135

Florence Garden Apts
506 S 41ST ST 19104

Forrest Village Apts
8440 WILLIAMS AVE 19150

Franklin House
269 S 9TH ST 19107

Gainor Apts
2217 N 51ST ST 19131

Glademore Apts
126 S 49TH ST 19139

Green Country Court
7841 RIDGE AVE 19128

Greenbrier Apts
3901 Conshohocken Ave .. 19131

Greenshire Apts
2801 PENNSYLVANIA AVE 19130

Haddington Townhouses
519 N 54TH ST 19131

Hamilton Court Apts
3818 CHESTNUT ST 19104

Harbor View Towers
9503 STATE RD 19114

Hawthorne Apts
712 S 12TH ST 19147

Hegerman House
5817 HEGERMAN ST 19135

Hen Ridge Apts
215 ROCK ST 19128

Henridge Apts
218 E SALAIGNAC ST 19128

Hopkinson House
602 S WASHINGTON SQ . 19106

Imperial Apts
247 S JUNIPER ST 19107

Imperial Towers
3801 Conshohocken Ave .. 19131

Iroquois Apts
2805 N 47TH ST 19131

Jackson Court Apts
4433 PEARSON AVE 19114

Jackson Court Apts
5912 JACKSON ST 19135

Joshua House Apts
2607 WELSH RD 19114

Kearsley Apt
2100 N 49TH ST 19131

Keystone House
6424 KEYSTONE ST 19135

Kirkstone Apts
5724 KEYSTONE ST 19135

Laverock Apts
1000 IVY HILL RD 19150

Lebanon Arms
5100 LEBANON AVE 19131

Lennox Apts
250 S 13TH ST 19107

Letitia Court Apts
11 S LETITIA ST 19106

Leverington Court Apts
631 LEVERINGTON AVE .. 19128

Lincoln Green Apts
4000 Presidental Blvd 19131

Linden Court Apts
3701 LINDEN AVE 19114

Linden Court Apts
9181 ACADEMY RD 19114

Locust Apts
801 LOCUST ST 19107

Lombard Mews
812 LOMBARD ST 19147

Longshore Apts
4100 LONGSHORE AVE .. 19135

Manayunk Apts
3901 MANAYUNK AVE 19128

Mantua Hall Housing Proje
3500 FAIRMOUNT AVE 19104

Mariners Court
221 VINE ST 19106

Marliss Court Apts
1061 E MOUNT AIRY AVE 19150

Martin Luther King Apts
1311 FITZWATER ST 19147

Mayfair Court Apts
6100 FRANKFORD AVE ... 19135

Mayfair Gardens Apts
6637 CHARLES ST 19135

Mercy Douglas
4511 WALNUT ST 19139

Mid Town Apts
1218 WALNUT ST 19107

Mill Creek Apts
729 N 46TH ST 19139

Mill Creek Housing
4505 FAIRMOUNT AVE 19139

Mount Airy Arms
1651 E MOUNT AIRY AVE 19150

Mount Carmel Gardens Apts
5700 RACE ST 19139

Mulberry Court Apts
225 ARCH ST 19106

Mullberry Court Apts
4015 DEVEREAUX ST 19135

Museum Towers
1801 BUTTONWOOD ST . 19130

Netherlands Apts
4322 CHESTNUT ST 19104

Old Quaker Building
3514 LANCASTER AVE 19104

Old Swedes Court
1 CHRISTIAN ST 19147

Olde City Place Apts
209 N 4TH ST 19106

On Lok House
219 N 10TH ST 19107

One Independence Place
241 S 6TH ST 19106

Orlowitz Hall
1000 WALNUT ST 19107

Osage Manor Apts
4416 OSAGE AVE 19104

Osborne Apts
206 OSBORNE ST 19128

Overmont House
4001 MONUMENT RD 19131

Pa Col Podiatric Dorms
801 CHERRY ST 19107

Packard Motor Car Building
317 N BROAD ST 19107

Park Place Apts
5738 FRANKFORD AVE ... 19135

Park Plaza Condominiums
3900 FORD RD 19131

Park Tower Apts
4001 Conshohocken Ave .. 19131

Park Towers
3651 RED LION RD 19114

Parker Place
312 PARKER AVE 19128

Passyunk Apts
746 E PASSYUNK AVE 19147

Pavillion
3901 Conshohocken Ave .. 19131

Penn Hall Apts
4101 BALTIMORE AVE 19104

Penn Wynne House
2201 BRYN MAWR AVE ... 19131

Penns Landing Apts
130 SPRUCE ST 19106

Penns View Apts
303 VINE ST 19106

Pfeiffer House Apts
222 RACE ST 19106

Pinewood Court Apts
1026 PINE ST 19107

Presidential Apts Adams
3900 CITY AVE 19131

Presidential Apts Jeffrsn
3900 CITY AVE 19131

Presidential Apts Madison
3900 CITY AVE 19131

Presidential Apts Wshngtn
3900 CITY AVE 19131

Queen Apts
328 QUEEN ST 19147

Randall School Condos
915 BAINBRIDGE ST 19147

Ridge Carlton
7373 RIDGE AVE 19128

Rieder House
10102 JAMISON AVE 19116

Riverpark House
3600 Conshohocken Ave .. 19131

Rochelle Arms
320 ROCHELLE AVE 19128

Royal Palm Court Apts
315 S 45TH ST 19104

Sandlewood Apts
9309 ASHTON RD 19114

Sandra Court Apts
7000 RIDGE AVE 19128

Sanford Arms Apts
10150 BRIDLE RD 19116

Sanford Arms Apts
755 KENTWOOD ST 19116

Sherwood Court
4423 PINE ST 19104

Shurs Lane Apts
407 SHURS LN 19128

Simpson Fletcher House
5353 MASTER ST 19131

Smythe Stores
107 ARCH ST 19106

Society Hill Towers
220 LOCUST ST 19106

Somerset Villas Apts
200 E SOMERSET ST 19134

Southwark Plaza
401 WASHINGTON AVE ... 19147

Southwark Plaza Apts
1021 S 4TH ST 19147

Spruce Hall Apts
4141 SPRUCE ST 19104

Spruce Hill Apts
4317 SPRUCE ST 19104

Spruce Hill Court Apts
4400 SPRUCE ST 19104

Sprucewood Apts
4105 SPRUCE ST 19104

Steeplechase
3600 RED LION RD 19114

Steven Smith Towers
1030 BELMONT AVE 19104

Stony Wood Terrace Apts
2525 WELSH RD 19114

Strawberry Court Apts
15 S BANK ST 19106

Sugar Refinery Apts
225 CHURCH ST 19106

Summit Gardens
701 SUMMIT AVE 19128

Summit Park East
8201 HENRY AVE 19128

Surrey Hall
329 S 42ND ST 19104

Suzalee Apts
1238 N 54TH ST 19131

Sylvania House
1324 LOCUST ST 19107

The Castings Apts
136 N BREAD ST 19106

The Cosmopolitan
221 S 12TH ST 19107

The Courts At Powelton
3500 POWELTON AVE 19104

The Fairfax Apts
4247 LOCUST ST 19104

The Lexington
3601 POWELTON AVE 19104

The Malt House
136 N 2ND ST 19106

The Marine Club Apts
1100 S BROAD ST 19146

The Milestone Apts
1327 SPRUCE ST 19107

The Rosamond Apts
4107 CHESTER AVE 19104

The Waterfront Apts
33 S LETITIA ST 19106

The Wireworks Apts
301 RACE ST 19106

Thouron Apts
7535 THOURON AVE 19150

Two Independence Place
233 S 6TH ST 19106

University Square Apts
3901 MARKET ST 19104

Valley View
6901 VALLEY AVE 19128

Valley View Apts
7950 HENRY AVE 19128

Wadsworth Manor
1116 E MOUNT AIRY AVE 19150

Wadsworth Manor
1117 E SYDNEY ST 19150

Walker Court Apts
4214 LONGSHORE AVE .. 19135

Walnut Hill Apts
4111 WALNUT ST 19104

Walnut Park Plaza
6250 WALNUT ST 19139

Walnut Square Apts
201 S 13TH ST 19107

Washington Square West
220 S 11TH ST 19107

Waterfront Ii Apts
106 S FRONT ST 19106

Waters Edge Apts
9523 STATE RD 19114

Waverly Court Apts
1934 WAVERLY ST 19146

Webster Manor
4224 OSAGE AVE 19104

Wellington Spruce Apts
1228 SPRUCE ST 19107

Welshwood Apts
2661 WILLITS RD 19114

West Park Housing Project
4445 HOLDEN ST 19104

West Park Housing Project
400 N BUSTI ST 19104

Westfield Apts
2237 BRYN MAWR AVE ... 19131

Wistar Alley Apts
30 N 3RD ST 19106

Wm B Moore Manor
1999 RIDGE AVE 19121

Woodbridge Mews
9401 ASHTON RD 19114

Woodenbridge Run Apts
3100 GRANT AVE 19114

Woodmere Apts
8200 HENRY AVE 19128

BUILDINGS

1100 Vine Assocs Building
1100 VINE ST 19107

1200 Walnut St Building
1200 WALNUT ST 19107

320 Building
320 WALNUT ST 19106

Abbott Building
201 N BROAD ST 19107

Academy Plaza Medical Ctr
10101 ACADEMY RD 19114

Ara Services Building
1101 MARKET ST 19107

Auerbach Building
121 N BROAD ST 19107

Avenue Of The Arts Building
1346 CHESTNUT ST 19107

Bailey Building
1218 CHESTNUT ST 19107

Bankers Security Building
1315 WALNUT ST 19107

Becker Building
1211 CHESTNUT ST 19107

Biddle Building
1217 SANSOM ST 19107

Bourse Building
21 S 5TH ST 19106

Butcher & Singer Building
211 S BROAD ST 19107

Caterbury Plaza
10431 ACADEMY RD 19114

Cheltenham Square Mall
2385 W Cheltenham Ave .. 19150

Chestnut East Building
841 CHESTNUT ST 19107

Chestnut Offices
124 CHESTNUT ST 19106

Constitution Place
325 CHESTNUT ST 19106

Continental Bank Building
1201 CHESTNUT ST 19107

Continental Building
400 MARKET ST 19106

Control Data Bs & Tech Ct
5070 PARKSIDE AVE 19131

Corestates Plaza
401 MARKET ST 19106

Daniel Building
22 N 3RD ST 19106

Dewey Building
1 N 13TH ST 19107

Edison Building
130 N 9TH ST 19107

Eight O One Associates
801 ARCH ST 19107

Empire Building
145 S 13TH ST 19107

Federal Reserve Bank Building
100 N 6TH ST 19106

Fineman Building
1314 CHESTNUT ST 19107

Franklin Med Building
829 SPRUCE ST 19107

Gallery I
901 MARKET ST 19107

Gallery Ii
1001 MARKET ST 19107

Garfield G Duncan Building
700 SPRUCE ST 19106

Garfield G Duncan Building
301 S 8TH ST 19106

Gateway Building
3535 MARKET ST 19104

Gilbert Building
1315 CHERRY ST 19107

Girard Medical Building
133 S 36TH ST 19104

Goldtex Building
315 N 12TH ST 19107

Green Tree Building
414 WALNUT ST 19106

Human Design Systems Building
3440 MARKET ST 19104

John Wanamakers Building
100 PENN SQ E 19107

John Wanamakers Building
1300 MARKET ST 19107

Juniper Building
129 N 12TH ST 19107

Lafayette Building
437 CHESTNUT ST 19106

Land Title Building
100 S BROAD ST 19110

Market Street Building
1234 MARKET ST 19107

Medical Office Building
1100 WALNUT ST 19107

Mellon Independence Ctr
701 MARKET ST 19106

Memorial Medical Building
5735 RIDGE AVE 19128

Monell Chemical Senses
3500 MARKET ST 19104

Mutch Building
51 N 39TH ST 19104

Neff Building
740 SANSOM ST 19106

Northeast Medical Center
9150 MARSHALL ST 19114

Nw Ayers Building
210 W WASHINGTON SQ 19106

One East Penn Sq Building
11 N JUNIPER ST 19107

One East Penn Square
1 E PENN SQ 19107

One Independence Mall
615 CHESTNUT ST 19106

One University City Building
4025 CHESTNUT ST 19104

PA Manufacturers Building
925 CHESTNUT ST 19107

Pennsylvania Mutual Towers
510 WALNUT ST 19106

Philadelphia Life Building
615 CHESTNUT ST 19106

Philadelphia National Bank Building
1345 CHESTNUT ST 19107

Presidental Commons Building
3900 CITY AVE 19131

Psfs Building
12 S 12TH ST 19107

Public Ledger Building
620 CHESTNUT ST 19106

Robert Morris Building
919 WALNUT ST 19107

Rohm & Haas Building
28 S 6TH ST 19106

Royal Insurance Building
330 MARKET ST 19106

Science Center
3600 SCIENCE CTR 19104

Science Center
3550 MARKET ST 19104

Scott Administration Building
1020 WALNUT ST 19107

Sheridan Building
125 S 9TH ST 19107

Social Services Building
311 S JUNIPER ST 19107

Society Hill Building
116 S 7TH ST 19106

Sovereign Building
714 MARKET ST 19106

Stephen Girard Building
21 S 12TH ST 19107

Teamsters Building
127 N 4TH ST 19106

The Bank Building
421 CHESTNUT ST 19106

The Belmont Building
221 N 13TH ST 19107

The Cast Iron Building
718 ARCH ST 19106

The Curtis Center
625 WALNUT ST 19106

Thom Jefferson Main Building
132 S 10TH ST 19107

Thomas Jefferson Building
1015 CHESTNUT ST 19107

Thompson Building
1000 SANSOM ST 19107

Univ City Science Ctr
3624 MARKET ST 19104

Washington Square Building
106 S 7TH ST 19106

Water Dept Building
101 N BROAD ST 19107

White Building
105 S 12TH ST 19107

Widener Building
100 S PENN SQ 19107

Widener Building
1339 CHESTNUT ST 19107

GOVERNMENT

City Hall
0 CITY HALL 19107

Federal Building
600 ARCH ST 19106

Gsa Building
900 MARKET ST 19107

Police Administration
700 RACE ST 19106

Us Customs House
200 CHESTNUT ST 19106

Us Federal Court House
601 MARKET ST 19106

Wm J Green Building
600 ARCH ST 19106

HOSPITALS

Ambulatory Care Center
3998 RED LION RD 19114

Donner Building
3400 SPRUCE ST 19104

Dulles Agnew Building
3400 SPRUCE ST 19104

Gates Pavilion
3400 SPRUCE ST 19104

Gibson Building
3400 SPRUCE ST 19104

Maloney Building
3400 SPRUCE ST 19104

Piersol Center
3400 SPRUCE ST 19104

Ravdin Institute
3400 SPRUCE ST 19104

Silverstein Pavilion
3400 SPRUCE ST 19104

White Building
3400 SPRUCE ST 19104

COLLEGES

Annenberg Center
3680 WALNUT ST 19104

Annenberg School
3620 WALNUT ST 19104

Blockley Hall
418 SERVICE DR 19104

Colonial Penn Center
3641 LOCUST WALK 19104

David Rittenhouse Labs
209 S 33RD ST 19104

Dept Of Chemistry Building
3301 SPRUCE ST 19104

Eisenlohr Annex
3808 WALNUT ST 19104

Eisenlohr Hall
3812 WALNUT ST 19104

Evans Building
4001 SPRUCE ST 19104

Franklin Building
3451 WALNUT ST 19104

Franklin Field
235 S 33RD ST 19104

Furness Building
220 S 34TH ST 19104

Goddard Labs
0 37TH And Hamilton Walk 19104

Grad School Of Education
3700 WALNUT ST 19104

Grad School Of Fine Arts
210 S 34TH ST 19104

Graduate Tower A
3600 CHESTNUT ST 19104

Graduate Tower B
3650 CHESTNUT ST 19104

Harrison House
3901 SPRUCE ST 19104

Harrison Labs
3301 SPRUCE ST 19104

Harrison Labs
235 S 34TH ST 19104

Hayden Hall
240 S 33RD ST 19104

Hollenbach Center
3000 SOUTH ST 19104

Houston Hall
3417 SPRUCE ST 19104

Irvine Auditorium
3401 SPRUCE ST 19104

Johnson Pavillion
3600 HAMILTON WALK 19104

Leidy Labs
415 S UNIVERSITY AVE .. 19104

Lewis Hall
100 S 34TH ST 19104

Lippincott Library
3420 WALNUT ST 19104

Mayer Hall
3817 SPRUCE ST 19104

Medical Education Building
3600 HAMILTON WALK 19104

Meyerson Hall
210 S 34TH ST 19104

Moore School
200 S 33RD ST 19104

Morgan Building
205 S 34TH ST 19104

Music Building
201 S 34TH ST 19104

Nursing Education Building
420 SERVICE DR 19104

Psychology Annex
3720 WALNUT ST 19104

Richards Building
0 37TH And Hamilton Walk 19104

Rosenthal Building
3800 SPRUCE ST 19104

Skinner Hall
200 S 36TH ST 19104

Smith Hall
215 S 34TH ST 19104

Steinberg Dietrich Hall
3620 LOCUST WALK 19104

Stiteler Building
208 S 37TH ST 19104

Towne Building
220 S 33RD ST 19104

U Of P Dental School
4001 SPRUCE ST 19104

U Of P Fine Arts Library
220 S 34TH ST 19104

U Of P Law School
3400 CHESTNUT ST 19104

U Of P Wharton School
3620 LOCUST WALK 19104

Van Pelt Library
3420 WALNUT ST 19104

Vance Hall
3733 SPRUCE ST 19104

Wayne Hall
3905 SPRUCE ST 19104

Web Dubois House
3900 WALNUT ST 19104

Weightman Hall
235 S 33RD ST 19104

PITTSBURGH

APARTMENTS

5100 Apartments
5100 5TH AVE 15232

5th Aiken Apts
5405 5TH AVE 15232

5th Negley Apts
5700 5TH AVE 15232

Alder Village
5944 ALDER ST 15232

Arlington Apts
515 S AIKEN AVE 15232

Belcrest
811 S NEGLEY AVE 15232

Belvedere Apts
5523 ELLSWORTH AVE ... 15232

Bigelow Apts
700 BIGELOW SQ 15219

Castleton
5612 HEMPSTEAD RD 15217

Centre Negley
5551 CENTRE AVE 15232

Citiline Towers
700 FORBES AVE 15219

College Gardens
5840 ELWOOD ST 15232

Colonial Terrace
5440 5TH AVE 15232

Coronado Apts
5260 CENTRE AVE 15232

General Forbes
5636 FORBES AVE 15217

Georgian Apts
5437 ELLSWORTH AVE ... 15232

Hempstead
5620 HEMPSTEAD RD 15217

Laurel Ridge Apts
106 15TH ST 15229

Marlin Arms
5245 CENTRE AVE 15232

Maxon Towers
6315 FORBES AVE 15217

Morrowfield Apts
2715 MURRAY AVE 15217

Mt Royal Towers
7070 FORWARD AVE 15217

Murray Beacon
1914 MURRAY AVE 15217

Negley Ct
5628 5TH AVE 15232

Normandy Apts
5520 5TH AVE 15232

Royal Manor
767 COLLEGE AVE 15232

Royal Plaza Apts
5506 5TH AVE 15232

Shady Apts
2123 SHADY AVE 15217

South Aiken Apts
545 S AIKEN AVE 15232

Ten Negley Apts
5700 ELLSWORTH AVE ... 15232

Warwick Plz
5048 5TH AVE 15232

Washington Plaza
1420 CENTRE AVE 15219

Wendover Apts
5562 HOBART ST 15217

Wightman
2130 WIGHTMAN ST 15217

Woodland Apts
5836 5TH AVE 15232

Woodland Manor
5925 5TH AVE 15232

BUILDINGS

1 Mellon Bank Center
500 GRANT ST 15219

2 Mellon Bank Center
523 GRANT ST 15219

3 Mellon Bank Ctr
525 WILLIAM PENN PL 15219

Alcoa Building
425 6TH AVE 15219

Allegheny Building
429 FORBES AVE 15219

Chamber Of Commerce
411 7TH AVE 15219

Chatham Center
112 WASHINGTON PL 15219

Civic Arena
300 AUDITORIUM PL 15219

Civic Building
200 ROSS ST 15219

Commerce Court Building
4 STATION SQ 15219

Frick Building
437 GRANT ST 15219

Gateway View Plaza
1600 W CARSON ST 15219

Grant Building
310 GRANT ST 15219

Gulf Tower
439 7TH AVE 15219

H K Porter Building
601 GRANT ST 15219

John H Reed Building
435 6TH AVE 15219

Koppers Building
436 7TH AVE 15219

Landmark Building
1 STATION SQ 15219

Law & Finance Building
429 4TH AVE 15219

Lawyers Building
428 FORBES AVE 15219

Manor Building
564 FORBES AVE 15219

Mc Crady Nicklas Building
304 ROSS ST 15219

One Oxford Centre
301 GRANT ST 15219

St Clair Building
1725 WASHINGTON RD .. 15241

U S Steel Building
600 GRANT ST 15219

Union Trust Building
523 GRANT ST 15219

USX Tower
600 GRANT ST 15219

GOVERNMENT

City County Building
414 GRANT ST 15219

County Court House
436 GRANT ST 15219

County Office Building
542 FORBES AVE 15219

Uspo & Courts Building
700 GRANT ST 15219

HOSPITALS

Mercy Hospital
1400 LOCUST ST 15219

Veterans Hospital
0 UNIVERSITY DRIVE C .. 15240

HOTELS

Sheraton Hotel
7 STATION SQ 15219

PITTSTON

GOVERNMENT

City Hall
35 BROAD ST 18640

READING

HOSPITALS

Reading Hospital
300 S 6TH AVE 19611

Saint Joseph Hospital
316 PO BOX 19603

COLLEGES

Reading Area Community
10 S 2ND ST 19602

SCRANTON

GOVERNMENT

City Hall
340 N WASHINGTON AVE 18503

Court House Annex
200 ADAMS AVE 18503

Lacka Cty Court House
200 N WASHINGTON AVE   18503

UNIVERSITY PARK

APARTMENTS

Allen Park Apts
1013 S ALLEN ST 16801

Allen Way Apts
110 E FOSTER AVE 16801

Beaver Hill Apts
340 E BEAVER AVE 16801

Cedar Brook Apts
320 E BEAVER AVE 16801

Collegate Arms
218 S SPARKS ST 16801

Crestmont Apts
901 S ALLEN ST 16801

Dorchester Apts
600 W COLLEGE AVE 16801

Fairmount Hill Apts
215 W FAIRMOUNT AVE .. 16801

Foster Ave Apts
736 E FOSTER AVE 16801

Heritage Oaks Apts
10 VAIRO BLVD 16803

Hetzel Plaza
500 E COLLEGE AVE 16801

Imperial Towers
425 WAUPELANI DR 16801

Lenwood Apts
917 S ALLEN ST 16801

Lexington House Apt
518 UNIVERSITY DR 16801

Logan House
333 LOGAN AVE 16801

Mt Nittany Apts
1006 S PUGH ST 16801

Mt Nittany Residence
301 ROLLING RIDGE DR . 16801

Orlando Apts
221 S BARNARD ST 16801

Park Hill Apts
478 E BEAVER AVE 16801

The Lofts
728 BELLAIRE AVE 16801

Univ Ter Apts
925 BELLAIRE AVE 16801

University Gate Way Apts
616 E COLLEGE AVE 16801

University Towers Apts
458 E COLLEGE AVE 16801

BUILDINGS

Alexander Court
309 E BEAVER AVE 16801

Ambassador Apts
421 E BEAVER AVE 16801

Armenara Plaza
444 E COLLEGE AVE 16801

Barcroft Apts
522 E COLLEGE AVE 16801

Beaver Plaza
222 W BEAVER AVE 16801

Beaver Ter Apts
456 E BEAVER AVE 16801

Century Towers Apts
710 S ATHERTON ST 16801

Colony Apts
532 E COLLEGE AVE 16801

Executive House Apts
411 WAUPELANI DR 16801

Gardner Apts
472 E COLLEGE AVE 16801

Lions Gate Apts
424 WAUPELANI DR 16801

Nittany Garden Apts
445 WAUPELANI DR 16801

Nittany Mall Building
2901 E COLLEGE AVE 16801

Penn Towers Apts
255 E BEAVER AVE 16801

Regency Square
200 HIGHLAND AVE 16801

South Hills Office Building
1315 S ALLEN ST 16801

University Ter Apts
825 BELLAIRE AVE 16801

WEST CHESTER

BUILDINGS

Chester Cty Courthouse
2 N HIGH ST 19380

WILKES BARRE

GOVERNMENT

Federal Building
197 S MAIN ST 18701

Veterans Administration
19 N MAIN ST 18701

WILKINSBURG

HOSPITAL

Forbes Metropolitan Hospital
225 PENN ST. 15221

YORK

GOVERNMENT

City Hall
50 W KING ST 17401

State Building
130 N DUKE ST 17401

York County Court House
28 E MARKET ST 17401

HOSPITALS

Memorial Hospital
15118 PO BOX 17405

York Hospital
15198 PO BOX 17405

COLLEGES

York College Of PA
15199 PO BOX 17405

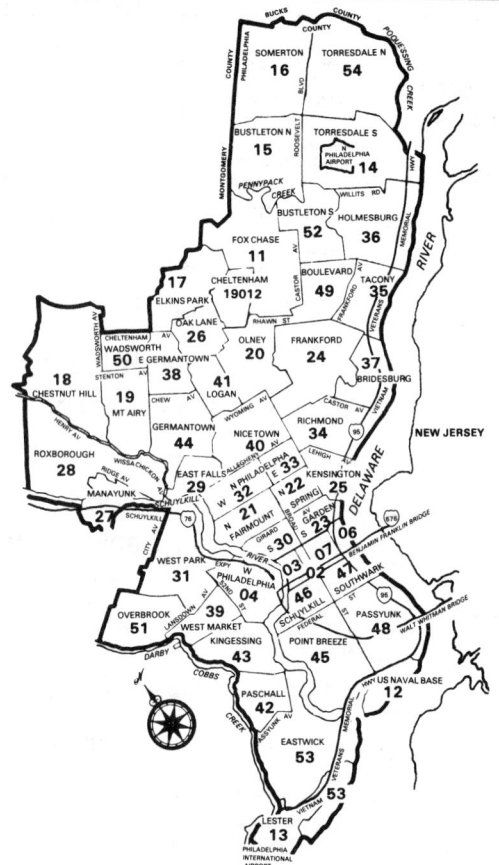

ZIP CODES
PHILADELPHIA, PA
191 + TWO DIGITS SHOWN = ZIP CODE

BAYAMON

APARTMENTS

Jard De Caparra
0 CALLE VIA PERIFERICA 00959

GUAYNABO

APARTMENTS

Ave Lopategui
0 URB Col De Parkville 00969

Cond Parkside
0 CALLE 6 PARKSIDE 00968

Parq Mediterraneo
0 CALLE CAPRI 00969

LEVITTOWN

APARTMENTS

Urb Valparaiso
0 CALLE 3 00949

Hoxsie	02889	West Barrington	02806	Westerly	02891
Lakewood	02888	(Barrington)		White Rock (Westerly)	02891
Natick	02886	West Glocester	02814	Wickford	02852
Norwood	02888	(Chepachet)		(North Kingstown)	
Oakland Beach	02886	West Greenville	02828	Wood River Junction	02894
Pawtuxet	02888	(Greenville)		Woodville (Hope Valley)	02832
Pilgrim	02888	West Greenwich	02817	Woonsocket	02895-896
Warwick Neck (Warwick)	02889	West Kingston	02892	North Smithfield	02895-896
Watch Hill (Westerly)	02891	West Warwick	02893	Wyoming	02898
Weekapaug (Westerly)	02891				

IMPORTANT BUILDINGS

APPONAUG

APARTMENTS

Brookside Village Building 1
3687 POST RD 02886

Brookside Village Building 2
3687 POST RD 02886

Brookside Village Building 3
3687 POST RD 02886

Brookside Village Building 4
3687 POST RD 02886

Cowesett Hills Apts
3595 POST RD 02886

Hardig Brook Vlg
331 CENTERVILLE RD 02886

Royal Crest Building 1
1 CEDAR POND DR 02886

Villa Del Rio Apt A
303 GREENWICH AVE 02886

Villa Del Rio Apt B
305 GREENWICH AVE 02886

Villa Del Rio Apt C
309 GREENWICH AVE 02886

Villa Del Rio Apt D
311 GREENWICH AVE 02886

Villa Del Rio Apt E
307 GREENWICH AVE 02886

BUILDINGS

Courthouse Building
222 QUAKER LN 02886

R I Mall
650 BALD HILL RD 02886

T F Green Airport
2000 POST RD 02886

Warwick Mall
400 BALD HILL RD 02886

CENTREDALE

APARTMENTS

Charles Place
460 CHARLES ST 02904

CONIMICUT

APARTMENTS

Bayside Country Club Apts
212 SANDY LN 02889

Meadowbrook Terrace Apts
2220 WARWICK AVE 02889

GASPEE POINT

APARTMENTS

Fairfax Village
900 POST RD 02888

Narr Village
400 NARRAGANSETT PKY 02888

BUILDINGS

Warwick Terrace Apts
2215 ELMWOOD AVE 02888

PAWTUCKET

BUILDINGS

Jfk Building
175 BROAD ST 02860

Mcdevitt Building
23 BROAD ST 02860

PROVIDENCE

APARTMENTS

Beneficent House
1 CHESTNUT ST 02903

Bradford House
100 ATWELLS AVE 02903

Corliss Landing
555 S MAIN ST 02903

Foxpoint Manor
575 WICKENDEN ST 02903

Regency
1 REGENCY PLZ 02903

Regency East
3 REGENCY PLZ 02903

Regency West
2 REGENCY PLZ 02903

Wayland Manor
500 ANGELL ST 02906

Westminster Place Apt
700 CAHIR ST 02903

BUILDINGS

Arcade Building
130 WESTMINSTER ST ... 02903

Fleet Center
50 KENNEDY PLZ 02903

Fleet Natl Bank Building
111 WESTMINSTER ST 02903

Hospital Trust Building
15 WESTMINSTER ST 02903

Hospital Trust Tower
1 HOSPITAL TRUST PLZ . 02903

Physicians Office Building
110 LOCKWOOD ST 02903

Turks Head Building
76 WESTMINSTER ST 02903

Union Trust Building
170 WESTMINSTER ST ... 02903

Veterans Memorial
83 PARK ST 02903

Westminster Building
180 WESTMINSTER ST ... 02903

Westminster Square
10 DORRANCE ST 02903

GOVERNMENT

Federal Building
1 EXCHANGE TER 02903

Federal Building
380 WESTMINSTER ST ... 02903

John O Pastore Fed Building
2 EXCHANGE TER 02903

Judicial Complex
1 DORRANCE PLZ 02903

Ri State House
82 SMITH ST 02903

Ri State Office Building
2 CAPITOL HL 02903

Ri State Office Building
101 SMITH ST 02903

State Court House
250 BENEFIT ST 02903

HOTELS

Omni Biltmore Plaza
11 DORRANCE ST 02903

SMITHFIELD

COLLEGE

Bryant College
1150 DOUGLAS ST. 02917

WARWICK

BUILDING

Brookside Village
1150 POST ROAD 02886

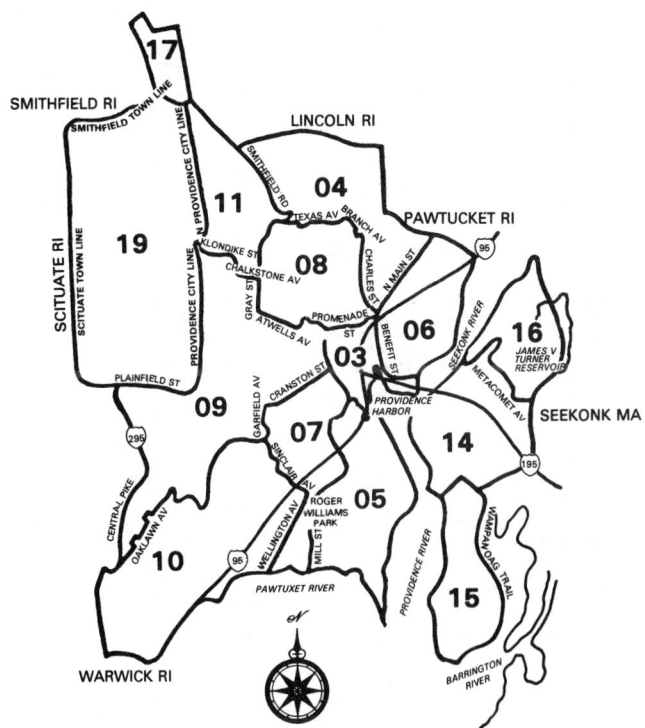

ZIP CODES
PROVIDENCE, RI
029 + TWO DIGITS SHOWN = ZIP CODE

SOUTH CAROLINA
Abbreviation SC

Abbeville 29620
Abney (Kershaw) 29067
Adams Run 29426
Aiken 29801-804, 29808
Airport (Greenville) 29612
Alcolu 29001
Alcot (Bishopville) 29010
Allendale 29810
Alvin (Saint Stephen) 29479
Anderson 29621-625
Andrews 29510
Antioch (Camden) 29020
Arcadia 29320
Arcadia Lakes (Columbia) . 29206
Ashland (Bishopville) 29010
Ashton (Islandton) 29929
Atkins (Lynchburg) 29080
Atlantic Beach 29582
       (North Myrtle Beach)
Awendaw 29429
Aynor 29511, 29544
Ballentine 29002
Bamberg 29003
Barkersville 29916
       (Early Branch)
Barnwell 29812-814
       Snelling 29812
Barr (Lexington) 29072
Barton (Fairfax) 29827
Batesburg 29006
Batesville (Greenville) 29607
Bath 29816
Bayview (Columbia) 29204
Beaufort 29901-905
       Burton 29902
       Laurel Bay 29902
       Parris Island 29902
       Parris Island 29905
Beckhamville 29055
       (Great Falls)
Beech Island 29841-842
       (North Augusta)
       North Augusta 29842
Bellinger (Hardeeville) 29927
Belton 29627
Belvedere (Columbia) 29204
       29841
Bendale (Columbia) 29203
Bennettsville 29512
Berlin (Salley) 29137
Bethcar (Wagener) 29164
Bethel (Clover) 29710
Bethera 29430
Bethune 29009
Bigcreek (Chappells) 29037
Bishopville 29010
Blacksburg 29702
Blackstock 29014
Blackville 29817
Blair 29015
Blake (Yemassee) 29945
Blenheim 29516
Bloomville (Manning) 29102
Bluff Estates (Columbia) . 29209
Bluffton 29910
Blythewood 29016
Bolen Town (Orangeburg) .. 29115
Bon Air (Sumter) 29150

Bonneau 29431
Bordeaux (Mc Cormick) ... 29835
Borden 29017
Bowling Green 29703
Bowman 29018
Bowyer (Holly Hill) 29059
Boykin (Rembert) 29128
Bradley 29819
Branchville 29432
Breeze Hill (Langley) 29834
Brighton (Garnett) 29922
Brighton Beach (Bluffton) .. 29910
Britts (Mc Cormick) 29835
Broad Street (Sumter) 29150
Brogdon (Sumter) 29150
Brunson 29911
Bucksport (Conway) 29527
Buffalo 29321
Burnettown (Warrenville) ... 29851
Burton (Beaufort) 29902
Cades 29518
Calhoun Falls 29628
Callison (Bradley) 29819
Camden 29020
Cameron 29030
Campobello 29322
Canadys 29433
Capitol (Columbia) 29211
Capitol View (Columbia) .. 29209
Carlisle 29031
Cartersville 29161
       (Timmonsville)
Cassatt 29032
Catawba 29704
Cateechee (Norris) 29667
Cayce 29033
Cedar Terrace (Columbia) . 29209
Centenary 29519
Central 29630
Chapin 29036
Chappells 29037
Charleston 29401-420
       29422-425
       Hanahan 29406
       Hanahan 29410
       James Island 29412
       North Charleston 29411
       North Charleston ......
       29418-420
       Pinehaven 29405
       Saint Andrews 29407
Cheraw 29520
Cherokee Falls 29702
       (Blacksburg)
Cherry Grove Beach 29582
       (North Myrtle Beach)
Chesnee 29323
Chester 29706
Chesterfield 29709
Claremont (Rembert) 29128
       29150
Clarks Hill 29821
Clearwater 29822
Clemson 29631-634
Cleora (Edgefield) 29824
Cleveland 29635
Clifton 29324
Clinton 29325
Clio 29525
Clover 29710
Clyde (Mc Bee) 29101

Cochrantown (Conway) ... 29526
Coiubia (Columbia) 29200
Cola (Columbia) 29200
College Park (Ladson) 29456
Colliers (Modoc) 29838
Columbia 29200-212
       .... 29214-228, 29230, 29240
       .... 29250, 29260, 29290
       29292
       Arcadia Lakes 29206
       Bayview 29204
       Belvedere 29204
       Bendale 29203
       Bluff Estates 29209
       Capitol 29211
       Capitol View 29209
       Cedar Terrace 29209
       Coiubia 29200
       Cola 29200
       Crafts Farrow 29203
       Crane Forest 29203
       Denny Terrace 29203
       Dutch Fork 29210
       Eastmont 29209
       Eau Claire 29203
       Edgewood 29204
       Fairfield Terrace 29203
       Farrow Terrace 29203
       Five Points 29205
       Forest Acres 29206
       Fort Jackson 29207
       Galaxy 29209
       Greenview 29203
       Harbison 29212
       Haskell Heights 29203
       Hazelwood Acres 29209
       Hollywood Hills 29203
       Killian 29203
       Leesburg 29209
       Lincolnshire 29203
       Market Center 29201
       Mountain Brook 29209
       North Pointe 29223
       Northeast 29223
       Olympia 29201
       Ravenwood 29206
       Ridgewood 29203
       Sandwood 29206
       Stark Terrace 29203
       Twin Lake Hill 29209
Conestee 29636
Congaree (Eastover) 29044
Converse 29329
Conway 29526-527
       Bucksport 29527
       Cochrantown 29526
Coosaw (Seabrook) 29940
Cope 29038
Cordesville 29434
Cordova 29039
Cornwell (Blackstock) 29014
Cottageville 29435
Coward 29530
Cowpens 29330
Crafts Farrow (Columbia) .. 29203
Crane Forest (Columbia) .. 29203
Crescent Beach 29582
       (North Myrtle Beach)
Creston (Cameron) 29030
Crocketville 29913
Cross 29436

Cross Anchor	29331
Cross Hill	29332
Cypress Crossroads	29069
(Lamar)	
Dale	29914
Dalzell	29040
Darlington	29532, 29540
Daufuskie Island	29915
Davis Crossroads	29148
(Summerton)	
Davis Station	29041
De Kalb (Westville)	29175
Delmar (Leesville)	29070
Delta (Whitmire)	29178
Denmark	29042
Denny Terrace (Columbia)	29203
Dillon	29536
Dixiana (West Columbia)	29169
Donalds	29638
Dorchester	29437
Douglass (Blackstock)	29014
Drayton	29333
Due West	29639
Dunbarton (Jackson)	29831
Duncan	29334, 29390-391
Dunkins Mill (Rembert)	29128
Dusty Bend (Camden)	29020
Dutch Fork (Columbia)	29210
Early Branch	29916
Easley	29640-642
Eastmont (Columbia)	29209
Eastover	29044
Eau Claire (Columbia)	29203
Edgefield	29824
Edgemoor	29712
Edgewood (Columbia)	29204
Edisto Island	29438
Edmund (Lexington)	29072
Effingham	29541
Ehrhardt	29081
Elgin	29045
Elko	29826
Elliott	29046
Elloree	29047
Emory (Saluda)	29138
Enoree	29335
Estill	29918, 29939
Nixville	29918
Eureka (Trenton)	29847
Eutaw Springs	29048
(Eutawville)	
Eutawville	29048
Fair Play	29643
Fairfax	29827
Fairfield	29928
(Hilton Head Island)	
Fairfield Terrace	29203
(Columbia)	
Fairforest	29336
Fairview Crossroads	29070
(Leesville)	
Farrow Terrace (Columbia)	29203
Fechtig (Early Branch)	29916
Felderville (Elloree)	29047
Fingerville	29338
Five Points (Columbia)	29205
Florence	29501-506
Quinby	29501
Quinby	29506
Floyd Dale	29542
Folly Beach	29439

Forest Acres (Columbia)	29206
Foreston (Manning)	29102
Fork	29543
Fort Jackson (Columbia)	29207
Fort Lawn	29714
Fort Mill	29715-716
Tega Cay	29715
Fort Motte	29135
(Saint Matthews)	
Fountain Inn	29644
Fripp Island	29920
(St Helena Island)	
Frogmore	29920
(St Helena Island)	
Fruit Hill (Saluda)	29138
Furman	29921
Gable	29051
Gadsden	29052
Gaffney	29340-342
Gaillard Crossroads	29040
(Dalzell)	
Galaxy (Columbia)	29209
Galivants Ferry	29544
Garden City	29576
(Murrells Inlet)	
Gardens Corner	29945
(Yemassee)	
Garnett	29922
Gaston	29053
Georgetown	29440, 29442
Maryville	29440
Gifford	29923
Gilbert	29054
Gillisonville (Ridgeland)	29936
Glendale	29346
Glenn Springs (Pauline)	29374
Gloverville	29828
Glympville (Pomaria)	29126
Goat Island Resort	29148
(Summerton)	
Goose Creek	29445
Grahamville (Ridgeland)	29936
Gramling	29348
Graniteville	29829
Gray Court	29645
Grays (Early Branch)	29916
Great Falls	29055
Greeleyville	29056
Green Pond	29446
Green Sea	29545
Greenbrier (Winnsboro)	29180
Greenview (Columbia)	29203
Greenville	29601-616, 29698
Airport	29612
Batesville	29607
Park Place	29608
Greenwood	29646-649
Greer	29650-652
Gresham	29546
Grover	29447
Hagood (Rembert)	29128
Hamer	29547
Hammond Crossroads	29135
(Saint Matthews)	
Hampton (Crocketville)	29913
	29924
Hanahan (Charleston)	29406
	29410
Harbison (Columbia)	29212
Harbour Town	29928
(Hilton Head Island)	

Hardeeville	29927
Harleyville	29448
Hartsville	29550-551
Haskell Heights	29203
(Columbia)	
Hazelwood Acres	29209
(Columbia)	
Heath Springs	29058
Hebron (Cades)	29518
Hemingway	29554
Hibernia (Monetta)	29105
Hickory Grove	29717
Highway Four Forty One	29150
(Sumter)	
Hilda	29813
Hilton Head Island	
(Daufuskie Island)	
	29915, 29925-926
	29928, 29938, 29948
Fairfield	29928
Harbour Town	29928
Hodges	29653, 29695
Holly Hill	29059
Hollywood (Saluda)	29138, 29449
Meggett	29449
Rantowels	29449
Yonges Island	29449
Hollywood Hills	29203
(Columbia)	
Holtson Crossroads	29006
(Batesburg)	
Honea Path	29654
Hopkins	29061
Horatio	29062
Horrel Hill (Hopkins)	29061
Hoyt Heights (Sumter)	29150
Huger	29450
Inman	29349
Irmo	29063
Islandton	29929
Isle Of Palms	29451
Iva	29655
Jackson	29831
Jacksonboro	29452
James Island (Charleston)	29412
Jamestown	29453
Jamison (Orangeburg)	29115
Jefferson	29718
Jenkinsville	29065, 29106
Jericho (Adams Run)	29426
Joanna	29351
Johns Island	29455, 29457
Johnsonville	29555
Johnston	29832
Johnstown (Bath)	29816
Jones Crossroads	29105
(Monetta)	
Jonesville	29353
Jordan (Manning)	29102
Kathwood	29169
(West Columbia)	
Kelton (Jonesville)	29353
Kershaw	29067
Killian (Columbia)	29203
Kinards	29355
Kings Creek	29719
Kingstree	29556
Kingville (Gadsden)	29052
Kirkland (Camden)	29020
Kirkwood (Camden)	29020
Kitchings Mill (Salley)	29137

Kline 29814
Kneece (Batesburg) 29006
La France 29656
Ladson 29456
Lake City 29560
Lake Murray (Chapin) 29036
Lake Murray Shores 29070
    (Leesville)
Lake View 29563
Lake Wylie (Clover) 29710
Lamar 29069
Lancaster 29720-721
Lando 29724
Landrum 29356
Lane 29564
Langley 29834
Latta 29565
Laurel Bay (Beaufort) 29902
Laurens 29360
Lebanon (Winnsboro) 29180
Leeds (Carlisle) 29031
Leesburg (Columbia) 29209
Leesville 29070
Lexington 29071-073
    Barr 29072
    Edmund 29072
    Macedon 29072
    Oak Grove 29072
    Red Bank 29072
Liberty 29657
Liberty Hill 29074, 29835
Limehouse (Hardeeville) ... 29927
Lincolnshire (Columbia) ... 29203
Little Mountain 29075
Little River 29566
Little Rock 29567
Livingston 29076
Lobeco 29931
Lockhart 29364
Lodge 29082
Lone Star 29077
Long Creek 29658
Longs 29568
Longtown (Ridgeway) 29130
Loris 29569
Lowndesville 29659
Lucknow (Bishopville) 29010
Lugoff 29078
Luray 29932
Lydia 29079
Lyman 29365
Lynchburg 29080
Macedon (Lexington) 29072
Madison (Westminster) 29693
Manning 29102
Manville (Bishopville) 29010
Marietta 29661
Marion 29571
Market Center (Columbia) . 29201
Martin 29836
Maryville (Georgetown) 29440
Mauldin 29662
Mayesville 29104
Mayo 29368
Mc Bee 29101
Mc Clellanville 29458
Mc Coll 29570
Mc Connells 29726
Mc Cormick 29835, 29899
Mckenzie Crossroads 29114
    (Olanta)

Mechanicsville 29010
    (Bishopville)
Meeting Street 29824
    (Edgefield)
Meggett (Hollywood) 29449
Midway (Bamberg) 29003
Miley 29933
Millford (Pinewood) 29125
Minturn 29573
Mitchellville (Ridgeland) ... 29936
Mitford (Blackstock) 29014
    29055
Mixville (Warrenville) 29851
Modoc 29838
Moncks Corner 29430, 29461
    (Bethera)
    Oakley 29461
Monetta 29105
Monticello 29106
Montmorenci 29839
Moore 29369
Moselle (Islandton) 29929
Moss (Edgefield) 29824
Motbridge (Lynchburg) 29080
Mount Carmel 29840
Mount Croghan 29727
Mount Holly 29445
    (Goose Creek)
Mount Pleasant 29464-465
Mountain Brook (Columbia) 29209
Mountain Rest 29664
Mountville 29370
Mullins 29574
Murrells Inlet 29576
Myrtle Beach 29572, 29575
    .... 29577-578, 29579, 29587
    North Gate 29577
    Socastee 29577
    Surfside Beach 29575
    Surfside Beach 29587
Neeses 29107
Nesmith 29580
Nevadun (Ridgeland) 29936
New Ellenton 29809
New Holland (Wagener) 29164
New Holland Crossroads .. 29006
    (Batesburg)
New Zion 29111
Newberry 29108
Newry 29665
Nichols 29581
Ninety Six 29666
Nixville (Estill) 29918
Norris 29667
North 29112
North Augusta 29841-842
    Beech Island 29841
    Belvedere 29841
North Charleston 29404-406
    .... 29411, 29418-420
    (Charleston)
North Gate (Myrtle Beach) 29577
North Myrtle Beach 29582
    29597-598
    Atlantic Beach 29582
    Cherry Grove Beach ... 29582
    Crescent Beach 29582
    Ocean Drive Beach 29582
    Windy Hill Beach 29582
North Pointe (Columbia) ... 29223
North Santee (Summerton) 29148

Northeast (Columbia) 29223
Norway 29113
Oak Dale (New Zion) 29111
Oak Grove (Lexington) 29072
Oakley (Moncks Corner) ... 29461
Oats (Lamar) 29069
Ocean Drive Beach 29582
    (North Myrtle Beach)
Olanta 29114
Olar 29843
Olympia (Columbia) 29201
Ora (Laurens) 29360, 29645
Orangeburg 29115-117
    Bolen Town 29115
    Jamison 29115
    Pecan Way Terrace 29115
Osborn (Adams Run) 29426
Oswego (Sumter) 29150
Pacolet 29372
Pacolet Mills 29373
Pageland 29728
Pamplico 29583
Panola (Pinewood) 29125
Park Place (Greenville) 29608
Parksville 29844
Parlers (Santee) 29142
Parris Island (Beaufort) 29902
    29905
Patrick 29584
Pauline 29374
Pawleys Island 29585
Paxville (Manning) 29102
Peak 29122
Pecan Way Terrace 29115
    (Orangeburg)
Pelion 29123
Pelzer 29669
Pendleton 29670
Peniel Crossroads 29161
    (Timmonsville)
Perry 29124
Pickens 29671
Piedmont 29673
Pinehaven (Charleston) 29405
Pineland 29934
Pineridge (Mc Bee) 29101
    29169
Pineville 29468
Pinewood 29125
Pinopolis 29469
Pisgah (Rembert) 29128
Pleasant Hill 29058
    (Heath Springs)
Pleasant Lane (Edgefield) . 29824
Plum Branch 29845
Pocataligo (Yemassee) 29945
Pomaria 29126
Pontiac (Elgin) 29045
Port Royal 29935
Poston 29588
Pritchardville (Bluffton) 29910
Promised Land (Bradley) .. 29819
Prosperity 29127
Purysburgh (Hardeeville) .. 29927
Quinby (Florence) .. 29501, 29506
Rains 29589
Rantowels (Hollywood) 29449
Ravenel 29470
Ravenwood (Columbia) 29206
Red Bank (Lexington) 29072
Red Hill (Camden) 29020

Reevesville 29471
Reidville 29375
Rembert 29128
Richburg 29729
Richland 29675
Richland Springs (Saluda) 29138
Ridge Spring 29129
Ridgeland 29912, 29936
    Coosawhatchie 29912
    Gillisonville 29936
    Grahamville 29936
    Mitchellville 29936
    Nevadun 29936
Ridgeville 29472
Ridgeway 29130
Ridgewood (Columbia) 29203
Rion 29132
Ritter (Walterboro) 29488
River Hills (Clover) 29710
Robertville (Garnett) 29922
Robinson (Mc Bee) 29101
Rock Hill 29730-734
Rockton (Winnsboro) 29180
Rocky Springs (Wagener) . 29164
Roebuck 29376
Rowesville 29133
Ruby 29741
Ruffin 29475
Russellville 29476
Saint Andrews 29407
    (Charleston)
Saint Charles 29104
    (Mayesville)
Saint George 29477
Saint Helena 29920
    (St Helena Island)
Saint Helena Island 29920
    (St Helena Island)
Saint Matthews 29135
Saint Paul (Summerton) 29148
Saint Stephen 29479
Salem 29676
Salkehatchie (Yemassee) . 29945
Salley 29137
Salters 29590
Saluda 29138
Saluda Gardens 29169
    (West Columbia)
Samaria (Batesburg) 29006
Sandwood (Columbia) 29206
Sandy Springs 29677
Santee 29142
Sardinia 29143
Sardis (Timmonsville) 29161
Savannah River Plant 29831
    (Jackson)
Scotia 29939
Scottsville (Mayesville) 29104
Scranton 29591
Seabrook (Dale) 29914, 29940
    Coosaw 29940
Seigling (Allendale) 29810
Seivern (Wagener) 29164
Sellers 29592
Seneca 29672, 29678-679
Shamokin (Camden) 29020
Sharon 29742
Sheldon 29941
Shiloh (Lynchburg) 29080
Shirley (Garnett) 29922
Shoals Junction (Donalds) 29638

Shulerville (Jamestown) 29453
Silver (Manning) 29102, 29125
Silverstreet 29145
Simpson (Ridgeway) 29130
Simpsonville 29680-681
Singleton 29135
    (Saint Matthews)
Six Mile 29682
Slater 29683
Slighs (Prosperity) 29127
Smallwood (Ridgeway) 29130
Smoaks 29481
Smyrna 29743
Snelling (Barnwell) 29812
Socastee (Myrtle Beach) ... 29577
Society Hill 29593
South Of The Border 29547
    (Hamer)
Spartanburg 29301-307
    .... 29316, 29318-319
    Valley Falls 29303
Spring Hill (Rembert) 29128
Spring Mills (Kershaw) 29067
Springdale 29169
    (West Columbia)
Springfield 29146
Stark Terrace (Columbia) .. 29203
Starr 29684
Startex 29377
State Park 29147
Stateburg (Sumter) 29150
Steedman (Leesville) 29070
Stiefeltown (Warrenville) ... 29851
Stockman (Prosperity) 29127
Stokes Bridge 29010
    (Bishopville)
Stoneboro (Heath Springs) 29058
Stoney Hill (Prosperity) 29127
Stover (Blackstock) 29014
Stuckey (Hemingway) 29554
Sullivans Island 29482
Summerland (Batesburg) .. 29006
Summerton 29148
Summerville 29483-485
Summit (Leesville) 29070
Sumter 29150-151, 29153-154
    Bon Air 29150
    Broad Street 29150
    Brogdon 29150
    Claremont 29150
    Highway Four Forty One
    29150
    Hoyt Heights 29150
    Oswego 29150
    Stateburg 29150
Sunset 29685
Surfside Beach 29575, 29587
    (Myrtle Beach)
Swansea 29160
Sycamore 29846
Tamassee 29686
Tarboro (Tillman) 29943
Tatum 29594
Taxahaw (Kershaw) 29067
Taylors 29687
Tega Cay (Fort Mill) 29715
Thor (Pelion) 29123
Tigerville 29688
Tillman 29943
Timmonsville 29161
Townville 29689

Travelers Rest 29690
Trenton 29847
Trio 29595
Troy 29848
Tuckertown (Carlisle) 29031
Turbeville 29162
Twin Lake Hill (Columbia) . 29209
Ulmer 29849
Una (Lamar) 29069, 29378
Union 29379
Valley Falls 29303
    (Spartanburg)
Van Wyck 29744
Vance 29163
Varnville 29944
Vaucluse 29850
Wadmalaw Island 29487
Wagener 29164
Walhalla 29691
Wallace 29596
Walterboro 29488
Wando 29492
Ward 29166
Ware Shoals 29692
Warrenville 29851
Wateree (Eastover) 29044
Waterloo 29384
Watsonia (Monetta) 29105
Wedgefield 29168
Wellford 29385
West Columbia (Cayce) 29033
    29169-172
    Cayce-west Columbia 29169
    Cayce-west Columbia 29171
    Dixiana 29169
    Kathwood 29169
    Pineridge 29169
    Saluda Gardens 29169
    Springdale 29169
    Westover Acres 29169
West Union 29696
Westminster 29693
Westover Acres 29169
    (West Columbia)
Westville 29175
White Bluff (Kershaw) 29067
White Hall (Yemassee) 29945
White Oak 29176
White Pond (Williston) 29853
White Rock 29177
White Stone 29386
Whitmire 29178
Williams 29493
Williamston 29697
Willington (Mc Cormick) 29835
Williston 29853
Wilson (Manning) 29102
Windsor 29856
Windy Hill Beach 29582
    (North Myrtle Beach)
Winnsboro 29180
Woodford (North) 29112
Woodrow (Dalzell) 29040
Woodruff 29388
Woodward (Blackstock) 29014
Workman (New Zion) 29111
Yemassee 29945
Yonges Island (Hollywood) 29449
York 29745

ANDERSON

APARTMENTS

Anderson Vlg
200 MIRACLE MILE DR ... 29621

Caldwell Homes
1000 S TOWERS ST 29624

Fairview Gdns
1101 WILLIAMSTON RD .. 29621

Fortson Homes
1100 E MARKET ST 29624

Le Chateau
201 MIRACLE MILE DR ... 29621

Meadow Run
3301 ABBEVILLE HWY 29624

Mi Vernon Place
203 MIRACLE MILE DR ... 29621

North Gate
4115 LIBERTY HWY 29621

Oak Square
201 OAK SQUARE DR 29624

Raintree
2420 MARCHBANKS AVE 29621

Willow Wood
1110 W FRANKLIN ST 29624

Wilmary
223 E BENSON ST 29624

ARCADIA LAKES

APARTMENTS

Arborwood
308 PERCIVAL RD 29206

Carriage Hill Apts
5225 CLEMSON AVE 29206

Jamestown Apts
4214 Bethel Church Rd 29206

Lakeshore Condos
5516 LAKESHORE DR 29206

Quail Run Apts
3509 LAKE AVE 29206

Ravenwood Apts
4215 Bethel Church Rd 29206

Turnberry Lane Apts

305 PERCIVAL RD 29206

BATESVILLE

APARTMENTS

Halton Place
660 HALTON RD 29607

Jessie Jackson Townhomes
50 RAMSEY CT 29607

Park Haywood
245 CONGAREE RD 29607

Woodland Homes
100 PEARCE AVE 29607

BUILDINGS

Century Plaza
211 CENTURY DR 29607

BAYVIEW

APARTMENTS

Camelot Apts
3431 COVENANT RD 29204

Gonzales Gardens
1505 GARDEN PLZ 29204

Lamplight Apt
1730 WINDOVER RD 29204

Jaggers Terrace
2541 BARHAMVILLE 29204

Oak Read Apts
2211 READ ST 29204

The Carolina Apts
3201 MEADOWLARK DR . 29204

BUILDINGS

Landmark Center
3600 FOREST DR 29204

Landmark East
3700 FOREST DR 29204

Middleburg Mall
2700 MIDDLEBURG DR ... 29204

BENDALE

APARTMENTS

Bendale Town House
5610 FARROW RD 29203

Colonial Village
3700 WEST AVE 29203

Highland Park Apts
3800 WEST AVE 29203

Latimer Manor Apts
100 LORICK CIR 29203

Willow Lakes Apts
5313 FAIRFIELD RD 29203

BLUFF ESTATES

APARTMENTS

Cedarwood Apts
7648 Garners Ferry Rd 29209

Colonial Villa Apts
7645 Garners Ferry Rd 29209

Georgetown Sq Apt
1701 ELMTREE RD 29209

Villager Apts
401 BURNSIDE DR 29209

HOSPITALS

Dorn Veterans Hospital
6439 Garners Ferry Rd 29209

BON AIR

APARTMENTS

Harvin Apts
114 N WASHINGTON ST .. 29150

Savannah Sq
403 ALICE DR 29150

GOVERNMENT

City County Office Building
115 N HARVIN ST 29150

CHARLESTON

APARTMENTS

Amberwood Apts
4995 LAMBS RD 29418

Ansonborough House
71 SOCIETY ST 29401

Ashley House Apts
14 LOCKWOOD DR 29401

Ashley Oaks Apts
78 Ashley Hall Plantation .. 29407

Brackenbrook Apts
4775 APARTMENT BLVD . 29418

Briargreen Apts
3 SAWGRASS RD 29412

Brighton Place
1429 ORLEANS RD 29407

Broadmoor Apts
5820 N MURRAY AVE 29406

Chas Arms Apts
1551 Sam Rittenberg Blvd   29407

Colony Sq Apts
1100 RIVER RD 29406

Dockside Apts
330 CONCORD ST 29401

Dorchester Gardens Apts
5600 DORCHESTER RD .. 29418

Ft Sumter House
1 KING ST 29401

Georgetown Apts
1476 Orange Grove Rd 29407

Hampton Point Apts
1916 Sam Rittenberg Blvd   29407

Hawthorne City Mhp
1990 HAWTHORNE DR ... 29406

Indigo Creek Apts
1735 ASHLEY HALL RD ... 29407

Joseph Floyd Manor
2106 Mount Pleasant St 29403

Orleans Gdn Apts
1900 HAZELWOOD DR 29407

Plantation Apts
1840 CARRIAGE LN 29407

Planters Trace Apts
2222 ASHLEY RIVER RD . 29414

Point James Apts
1402 CAMP RD 29412

Quail Run Apts
6220 N MURRAY AVE 29406

Regency Square Apts
6601 DORCHESTER RD .. 29418

Riviera Apts
6240 OLD POINT RD 29406

Royal Oaks Apts
6600 RIVERS AVE 29406

Sawgrass Apts
35 CROSSCREEK DR 29412

Sergeant Jasper Apts
310 BROAD ST 29401

Spanish Oak Apts
1515 ASHLEY RIVER RD . 29407

The Oaks Apts
1850 Ashley Crossing Ln .. 29414

West Village Apts
1645 N WOODMERE DR . 29407

Willow Lake Apts
6834 WARD AVE 29406

Windjammer Apts
1742 SAM RITTENBERG . 29407

BUILDINGS

Amer Mutual Building
1 S PARK CIR 29407

Charleston City Hall
80 BROAD ST 29401

Charlestown Square Mall
2401 MALL DR 29406

Citadel Mall
2070 Sam Rittenberg Blvd   29407

Corporate Square Ii
4925 LA CROSS RD 29406

Harborview Tower
19 HAGOOD AVE 29403

N Chas City Hall
4900 LA CROSS RD 29406

Northwoods Mall
2150 Northwoods Blvd 29406

Pepperhill Square
7525 BRANDYWINE ST. .. 29420

Peoples Office Building
18 BROAD ST 29401

Rivergate Office Building
4975 LA CROSS RD 29406

GOVERNMENT

Courthouse
2 COURT HOUSE SQ 29401

Custom House
200 E BAY ST 29401

L Mendel Rivers Fedrl Bld
334 MEETING ST 29403

COLLEGES

Charleston Southern University
10087 PO BOX 29411

College Of Charleston
66 GEORGE ST 29424

Medical University Of Sc
171 ASHLEY AVE 29425

Trident Technical College
118067 PO BOX 29423

COLUMBIA

APARTMENTS

Broad River Township
1850 ATLANTIC DR 29210

Claire Towers Apts
1041 MARION ST 29201

Cloister Apts
3700 BUSH RIVER RD 29210

Columbia Gardens Apts
4000 PLOWDEN RD 29205

Cornell Arms Apts
1230 PENDLETON ST 29201

Creekside Apts
801 CHINQUAPIN RD 29212

Deerwood Knoll
319 S BELTLINE BLVD 29205

Essex Park Apts
1800 LONGCREEK DR 29210

Farrington Apts
1513 FARRINGTON WAY . 29210

Finley House
2100 BLOSSOM ST 29205

Garden Manor Apts
2400 ASHLAND RD 29210

Hammond Vil Apts
921 MARLBORO ST 29201

Hampton Park Apts
4427 BLOSSOM ST 29205

Heathwood Ct Apts
4103 DEVINE ST 29205

Hendley Homes
501 S BULL ST 29205

King Court Apts
1400 KING ST 29205

Lakeside Apts
401 HARBISON BLVD 29212

Lexington Green Condo
1208 BUSH RIVER RD 29210

Park Apts
1600 LONGCREEK DR 29210

Parklane Apts
8100 BAYFIELD RD 29223

Peachtree Place Apts
200 BERRYHILL RD 29210

Petan Apts
800 BEATTY RD 29210

Raintree Apts
3500 FERNANDINA RD ... 29210

River Chase Apts
3421 KAY ST 29210

Senate Plaza Apts
1520 SENATE ST 29201

Springtree Apts
250 SPRINGTREE DR 29223

The Hollow Apts
1521 LONGCREEK DR 29210

Timberlake Condos
405 HARBISON BLVD 29212

University Ter Apts
1415 BLOSSOM ST 29201

Waterford Apts
1340 LONGCREEK DR 29210

Wellspring Apts
500 HARBISON BLVD 29212

West Winds Apts
105 HILLPINE RD 29212

Willow Creek Apts
3200 FERNANDINA RD ... 29210

Woodland Terrace Apts
320 S BELTLINE BLVD 29205
Woodmere Apts
18 BERRYHILL RD 29210

BUILDINGS

Barringer Building
1338 MAIN ST 29201

IBM Building
1333 MAIN ST 29201

Jefferson Sq
1801 MAIN ST 29201

Keenan Building
1310 LADY ST 29201

Ncnb Tower
1301 GERVAIS ST 29201

Number One Main
1203 GERVAIS ST 29201

Palmetto Building
1400 MAIN ST 29201

Palmetto Center
1426 MAIN ST 29201

SCN Bank Building
1401 MAIN ST 29201

Security Federal Building
1233 WASHINGTON ST ... 29201

GOVERNMENT

Calhoun St Office Building
1222 SENATE ST 29201

Cola Judical Municipal Bl
1701 MAIN ST 29201

Edgar Brown Building
1205 PENDLETON ST 29201

Federal Building
1100 LAUREL ST 29201

Federal Land Bank Building
1401 HAMPTON ST 29201

Gressett Building
1101 PENDLETON ST 29201

Rembert C Dennis Building
1000 ASSEMBLY ST 29201

Rutledge Building
1429 SENATE ST 29201

S C State House
1200 GERVAIS ST 29201

Sol Blatt Building
1105 PENDLETON ST 29201

Strom Thurmond Building
1835 ASSEMBLY ST 29201

Wade Hampton Building
1200 SENATE ST 29201

HOSPITALS

Sc State Hospital
119 PO BOX 29202

GOVERNMENT

District Manager
29292 PO BOX 29292

COLLEGES

USC
0 UNIVERSITY OF SC 29208

GREENVILLE

APARTMENTS

Aladdin Manor
1008 WHITE HORSE RD . 29605

Botany Arms
702 EDWARDS RD 29615

Brockwood Senior Housing
800 W WASHINGTON ST . 29601

Century Oaks
10 DILLON DR 29609

City Heights
300 FURMAN HALL RD ... 29609

Continental
50 GLENWOOD RD 29615

Court Ridge Condos
2601 Duncan Chapel Rd .. 29609

Gandy Allmon Manor
210 S MEMMINGER ST ... 29601

Greenville Arms
200 ASHE DR 29611

Hampton Forest
2207 Wade Hampton Blvd 29615

Haywood Estates
1180 HAYWOOD RD 29615

Hillandale
2627 POINSETT HWY 29609

Howell Commons
150 HOWELL CIR 29615

Huntington Downs
1409 Roper Mountain Rd .. 29615

Lakeshore
1 LAKESIDE RD 29611

Lewis Village Condos
100 LEWIS DR 29605

Mcdaniel Heights
601 CLEVELAND ST 29601

Northway
3800 E NORTH ST 29615

Oak Forest Condos
2808 E NORTH ST 29615

Ohara
200 MITCHELL RD 29615

Overlook
65 VILLA RD 29615

Piedmont Manor
100 SHEMWOOD LN 29605

Ridgeview Condos
6526 WHITE HORSE RD .. 29611

Stratford Villa
200 EUNICE DR 29611

The Place
151 MITCHELL RD 29615

Town Park Condos
3706 E NORTH ST 29615

Turtle Creek
100 TURTLE CREEK DR . 29615

Woodstream
2735 ANDERSON RD 29611

Yorktown Condos
2530 E NORTH ST 29615

BUILDINGS

1 Insignia Financial Pl
55 BEATTIE PL 29601

C & S
75 BEATTIE PL 29601

Camperdown Building
1 CLEVELAND ST 29601

Daniel
301 N MAIN ST 29601

First Federal
301 COLLEGE ST 29601

Hyatt
220 N MAIN ST 29601

Medical Court
811 PENDLETON ST 29601

NCNB
7 N LAURENS ST 29601

Piedmont East
37 VILLA RD 29615

Piedmont West
33 VILLA RD 29615

Scn Bank
15 S MAIN ST 29601

GOVERNMENT

City Hall
206 S MAIN ST 29601

County Courthouse
305 E NORTH ST 29601

County Office
301 UNIVERSITY RDG 29601

GREENWOOD

BUILDINGS

Federal Building
120 MAIN ST 29646

Greenwood Medical Center
303 W ALEXANDER AVE . 29646

GOVERNMENT

Court House Building
528 MONUMENT ST 29646

MOUNT PLEAS-ANT

APARTMENTS

Fairmont Oaks
1226 FAIRMONT 29464

Fairmont Oaks
1240 FAIRMONT 29464

Palmetto Plantation
2011 HIGHWAY 17 29464

Simmons Pointe Condos
1551 BEN SAWYER 29464

MYRTLE BEACH

APARTMENTS

Briarcliffe West
10301 N KINGS HWY 29572

NORTH CHARLESTON

APARTMENTS

Cross Roads Apts
7910 CROSSROADS 29406

North Cove Apts
7950 CROSSROADS 29406

BUILDING

Ashley Center
4401 BELLE OAKS 29405

SPARTANBURG

APARTMENTS

Autumn Chase
1480 W O EZELL BLVD 29301

Bird Nest
345 BRYANT RD 29303

Corners
151 FERNWOOD DR 29307

Cross Key
311 POWELL MILL RD 29301

Fairforest Creek
350 NORRIS 29306

Heritage Court
425 CHURCH 29306

Hub City Cts
700 VANDERBILT RD 29301

Hunt Club
1010 HUNT CLUB LN 29301

Hunters Glen
350 BRYANT RD 29303

Huntington Woods
3040 W CROFT CIR 29302

Oakview Apts
650 HOWARD ST 29303

Park Place
110 SOUTHPORT 29306

Riverwind
200 HEYWOOD 29307
Schuyler
275 CHURCH 29306

Seville
1514 Fernwood Glendale .. 29307

Timerlane
106 KENSINGTON 29306

Villas At Raintree
323 E BLACKSTOCK RD . 29301

Villas At Woodcreek
701 MIKE DR 29303

Willow Oaks
2900 REIDVILLE RD 29301

Woodburn Place Condo
1000 WOODBURN 29302

Woodside
100 DUNWOODY DR 29307

Woodside
1631 FERNWOOD GLENDALE
RD 29307

Woodworth Homes
770 BALTIMORE ST 29301

BUILDINGS

City View
144 HENRY 29306

Corporate Sq
364 S PINE ST 29302

Country Club
2479 COUNTRY CLUB 29302

Ellen Watson
351 TEXTILE 29301

Georgetown Village
1421 REIDVILLE 29306

Physicians Center
100 E WOOD ST 29303

GOVERNMENT

City Hall
145 W BROAD ST 29306

County Administration
366 N CHURCH ST 29303

County Court House
180 MAGNOLIA ST 29306

Federal Building
201 MAGNOLIA ST 29306

SUMMERVILLE

APARTMENTS

Dorchester Crossing Apts
1660 OLD TROLLEY 29485

Waters Edge Apts
9989 DORCHESTER 29485

BUILDING

Presbyterian Home
201 9TH NORTH 29483

VALLEY FALL

APARTMENTS

Northside
695 HOWARD 29303

Pine Gate
1000 PINEGATE 29303

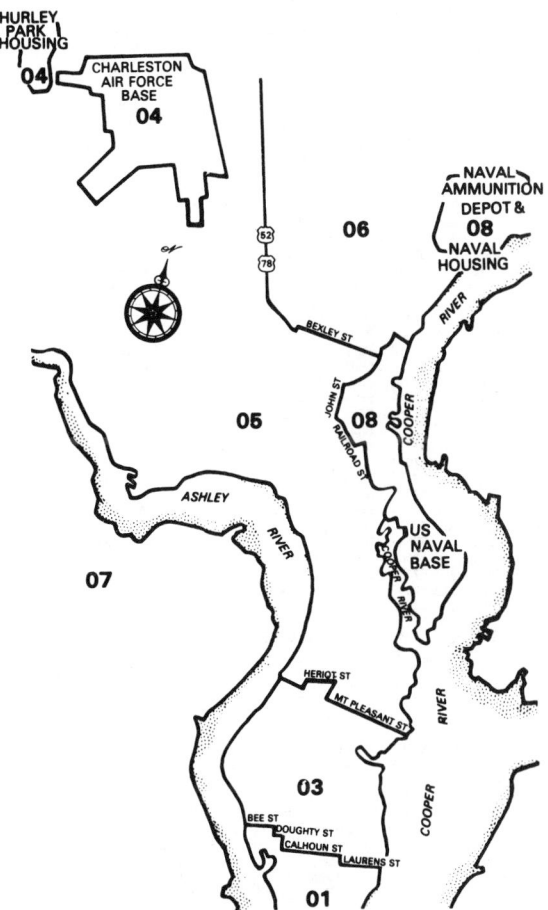

ZIP CODES
CHARLESTON, SC
294 + TWO DIGITS SHOWN = ZIP CODE

SOUTH DAKOTA
Abbreviation SD

Aberdeen	57401-402
Beebe	57401
Ordway	57401
Richmond Siding	57401
Academy (Platte)	57369
Ada (Bison)	57520
Agar	57520
Agency Village (Sisseton)	57262
Akaska	57420
Albee (Revillo)	57259
Alcester	57001
Alexandria	57311
Alfalfa Corner (Harrold)	57536
Allen	57714
Alpena	57312
Alsen (Beresford)	57004
Alsville (Lake Norden)	57248
Altamont (Clear Lake)	57226
Ames (Pierre)	57501
Amherst	57421
Anderson (Meadow)	57644
Andover	57422
Appleby (Watertown)	57201
Argonne (Howard)	57349
Arlington	57212
Armour	57313
Arpan (Nisland)	57762
Artas (Eureka)	57437
Artesian	57314
Ashton	57424
Astoria	57213
Athboy (Meadow)	57644
Athol (Ashton)	57424
Auance (Faith)	57626
Aurora	57002
Aurora Center (Stickney)	57375
Avon	57315
Bad Nation (Wood)	57585
Badger	57214
Bailey (Gann Valley)	57341
Bakerville (Custer)	57730
Baltic	57003
Bancroft	57316
Barnard	57426
Batesland	57716
Bath	57427
Bear Butte (Sturgis)	57785
Beardsley (Parkston)	57366
Beebe (Aberdeen)	57401
Belle Fourche	57717
Belvidere	57521
Bemis (Goodwin)	57238
Ben Claire	57068
(Valley Springs)	
Bend (Box Elder)	57719
Beresford	57004
Bethlehem	57708
Betts (Mitchell)	57301
Big Springs (Alcester)	57001
Big Stone	57216
(Big Stone City)	
Big Stone City	57216
Big Stone Lake (Wilmot)	57279
Bijou Hills (Chamberlain)	57325
Billsburg (Milesville)	57553
Bison	57620
Bixby (Bison)	57620
Black Hawk	57718

Blackpipe (Norris)	57560
Bloomfield (Carpenter)	57322
Blue Dog Lake (Waubay)	57273
Bluebell (Custer)	57730
Blumengard Colony	57438
(Faulkton)	
Blunt	57522
Bon Homme Colony	57063
(Tabor)	
Bonesteel	57317
Bonilla (Hitchcock)	57348
Bonita Springs (Enning)	57737
Bovee (Geddes)	57342
Bowdle	57428
Box Elder	57719
Bradley	57217
Brainard (Barnard)	57426
Brandon	57005
Brandt	57218
Brentford	57429
Brentwood Colony	57438
(Faulkton)	
Bridger (Howes)	57748
Bridgewater	57319
Bristol	57219
Britton	57430
Broadland (Huron)	57350
Brookdale Colony (Elkton)	57026
Brookings	57006-007
Bruce	57220
Bryant	57221
Buffalo	57720
Buffalo Gap	57722
Buffalo Ridge	57115
Bullhead	57621
Bullock (Buffalo)	57720
Burbank	57010
Burdock (Edgemont)	57735
Burke	57523
Burkmere (Faulkton)	57438
Bushnell (White)	57276
Butler (Bristol)	57219
Cactus Flats (Quinn)	57775
Calico (Pine Ridge)	57770
Camp Crook	57724
Campbell (Ree Heights)	57371
	57646
Canistota	57012
Canning (Pierre)	57501
Canova	57321
Canton	57013
Capa (Midland)	57552
Caputa	57725
Carlock (Gregory)	57533
Carpenter	57322
Carter	57526
Carthage	57323
Cash (Bison)	57620
Castle Rock (Newell)	57760
Castlewood	57223
Cavour	57324
Cedar Canyon (Newell)	57760
Center (Salem)	57058
Center Point (Viborg)	57070
Centerville	57014
Central City (Lead)	57754
Chalk Butte	57787
(Union Center)	
Chamberlain	57325-326
Chance (Bison)	57620
Chancellor	57015

Chelsea (Northville)	57465
Cherry Creek	57622
Chester	57016
Cheyenne Crossing (Lead)	57754
Claire City	57224
Claremont	57432
Clark	57225
Clark Colony (Raymond)	57258
Clayton (Emery)	57332
Clear Lake	57226
Clearfield (Winner)	57580
Clough (Sturgis)	57785
Clover Leaf Colony	57349
(Howard)	
Coal Springs (Meadow)	57644
Colman	57017
Colome	57528
Colton	57018
Columbia	57433
Como (Miller)	57362
Conata (Scenic)	57780
Conde	57434
Cooper (White Lake)	57383
	57626
Corona	57227
Corsica	57328
Corson (Brandon)	57005
Cottonwood (Quinn)	57775
Cottonwood Lake (Bowdle)	57428
Crandall (Conde)	57434
Craven (Ipswich)	57451
Crazy Horse (Custer)	57730
Creighton	57729
Cresbard	57435
Crocker	57229
Crooks	57020
Crow Creek	57339
(Fort Thompson)	
Custer	57730
Dakota Dunes	57049
(North Sioux City)	
Dalesburg (Centerville)	57014
Dallas	57529
Dalzell (Elm Springs)	57736
Danforth (Wessington)	57381
Dante	57329
Date (Prairie City)	57649
Davis	57021
De Smet	57231
Deadwood	57732
Deerfield (Hill City)	57745
Degray (Blunt)	57522
Dell Rapids	57022
Delmont	57330
Dempster (Estelline)	57234
Denby (Batesland)	57716
Dewey (Edgemont)	57735
Dimock	57331
Dixon (Gregory)	57533
Doland	57436
Dolton (Bridgewater)	57319
Dowling (Wall)	57790
Draper	57531
Dry Wood Lake (Sisseton)	57262
Dupree	57623
Eagle (Platte)	57369
Eagle Butte	57625
Eakin (Pierre)	57501
Eden	57232
Edgemont	57735
Edna (Presho)	57568

Edson (Faith)	57626	Gorman (Gettysburg)	57442	Humboldt	57035
Egan	57024	Govert (Bison)	57620	Huntimer (Colton)	57018
Elk Point	57025	Graceville Colony	57076	Hurley	57036
Elkton	57026	(Winfred)		Huron	57350, 57399
Ellis (Sioux Falls)	57107	Grashul (Piedmont)	57769	Ideal	57541
Elm Lake (Frederick)	57441	Grass Rope (Reliance)	57569	Igloo (Provo)	57774
Elm Springs	57736	Greenfield (Vermillion)	57069	Imlay (Scenic)	57780
Elm Springs Colony	57334	Greenway (Eureka)	57437	Imogene (Prairie City)	57649
(Ethan)		Greenwood (Wagner)	57380	Inland (Zeona)	57795
Elwood (Cherry Creek)	57622	Gregory	57533	Interior	57750
Emery	57332	Grenville	57239	Iona	57542
Emmet (Beresford)	57004	Gretna (Roscoe)	57471	Ipswich	57451
Enemy Swim Lake	57273	Groton	57445	Irene	57037
England Ranch (Midland)	57552	Grover (Watertown)	57201	Iron Mountain (Kennebec)	57544
Englewood (Lead)	57754	Gumbo (Wasta)	57791	Iroquois	57353
Enning	57737	Gustave (Camp Crook)	57724	Isabel	57633
Epiphany (Canova)	57321	Hamill	57534	James (Groton)	57445
Erwin	57233	Hammer (New Effington)	57255	James Valley (Huron)	57350
Esmond (Iroquois)	57353	Harding (Buffalo)	57720	Janesville (Utica)	57067
Estelline	57234	Harney Peak (Custer)	57730	Janousek (Tabor)	57063
Ethan	57334	Harrington (Martin)	57551	Java	57452
Eureka	57437	Harrisburg	57032	Jefferson	57038
Fairbank (Pierre)	57501	Harrison	57344	Joe Creek (Harrold)	57536
Fairburn	57738	Harrold	57536	Johnson Siding	57702
Fairfax	57335	Hartford	57033	(Rapid City)	
Fairpoint (Sturgis)	57785	Hartford Beach (Corona)	57227	Johnsonville (Toronto)	57268
Fairview	57027	Hartley (Milesville)	57553	Jolly Acres (Rapid City)	57701
Faith	57626	Hayes	57537	Joubert (New Holland)	57364
Farmer (Alexandria)	57311	Hayti	57241	Junction City (Elk Point)	57025
Farmingdale (Caputa)	57725	Hayward (Hermosa)	57744	Junius (Madison)	57042
Faulkton	57438	Hazel	57242	Kadoka	57543
Fedora	57337	Headlee Ranch (Interior)	57750	Kain (Buffalo Gap)	57722
Ferney	57439	Hecla	57446	Kampeska (Watertown)	57201
Firesteel	57628	Henry	57243	Karenin (Buffalo)	57720
Flandreau	57028	Heppner (Hot Springs)	57747	Kary (Murdo)	57559
Fleming (Fairburn)	57738	Hereford (Sturgis)	57785	Kasper (Onida)	57564
Florence	57235	Hermosa	57744	Kaylor	57354
Flyger (Hurley)	57036	Herreid	57632	Keldron	57634
Foley (Watertown)	57201	Herrick	57538	Kenel (Mc Laughlin)	57642
Folsom (Hermosa)	57744	Hetland	57244	Kennebec	57544
Forest City (Gettysburg)	57442	Hiawatha Beach (Wilmot)	57279	Keyapaha	57545
Forestburg (Artesian)	57314	Hidden Timber (Mission)	57555	Keystone	57751
Fort Meade	57741	Highmore	57345	Kidder (Britton)	57430
Fort Pierre	57532	Hiles (Wanblee)	57577	Kimball	57355
Fort Thompson	57339	Hill City	57745	Kingsbury (Tyndall)	57066
Foster (Mobridge)	57601	Hilland (Philip)	57567	Kirley (Midland)	57552
Francis (Pierre)	57501	Hillcrest (Oelrichs)	57763	Kones Corner	57223
Frankfort	57440	Hillcrest Colony	57236	Kranzburg	57245
Franklin (Chester)	57016	(Garden City)		Kyle	57752
Frederick	57441	Hillhead (Veblen)	57270	La Plant (Ridgeview)	57652
Freeman	57029	Hills (Eureka)	57437	Labolt	57246
Fruitdale	57742	Hillside Colony (Doland)	57436	Lacy (Fort Pierre)	57532
Fulton	57340	Hilmoe (Presho)	57568	Ladner (Buffalo)	57720
Game Lodge (Custer)	57730	Hisega (Rapid City)	57702	Lake Alvin (Harrisburg)	57032
Gann Valley	57341	Hisle (Wanblee)	57577	Lake Andes	57356
Garden City	57236	Hitchcock	57348	Lake Brandt (Chester)	57016
Garretson	57030	Holabird	57540	Lake Byron (Huron)	57350
Gary	57237	Holmquist (Webster)	57274	Lake Campbell (Brookings)	57006
Gayville	57031	Hooker (Viborg)	57070	Lake City	57247
Geddes	57342	Hoover (Newell)	57760	Lake Hendricks (White)	57276
Gettysburg	57442	Hosmer	57448	Lake Herman (Madison)	57042
Gill (Newell)	57760	Hot Springs	57747	Lake Madison (Wentworth)	57075
Glad Valley	57629	Houghton	57449	Lake Mitchell (Mitchell)	57301
Glen (Roscoe)	57471	Houston (Kennebec)	57544	Lake Norden	57248
Glencross	57630	Hoven	57450	Lake Poinsett (Arlington)	57212
Glendale Colony	57440	Howard	57349	Lake Preston	57249
(Frankfort)		Howell (Highmore)	57345	Lake Sinai (Sinai)	57061
Glendo (Prairie City)	57649	Howes	57748	Lake View Colony	57356
Glenham	57631	Hub City (Vermillion)	57069	(Lake Andes)	
Goodwin	57238	Hudson	57034	Lakeport (Tabor)	57063
Gopher (Mobridge)	57601	Huffton (Claremont)	57432	Lane	57358

Langford	57454	
Lantry	57636	
Laroche (Fort Pierre)	57532	
Lauzen (Edgemont)	57735	
Lead	57754	
Lebanon	57455	
Lemmon	57638	
Lennox	57039	
Leola	57456	
Lesterville	57040	
Letcher	57359	
Lewis And Clark (Yankton)	57078	
Lightcap (Isabel)	57633	
Lily (Webster)	57274	
Linden Beach (Corona)	57227	
Lindsey (Fort Pierre)	57532	
Little Eagle	57639	
Lodgepole	57640	
Long Valley	57547	
Longlake	57457	
Loomis (Mitchell)	57301	
Lower Brule	57548	
Lowry (Selby)	57472	
Loyalton (Roscoe)	57471	
Lucas (Burke)	57523	
Ludlow	57755	
Lyman (Reliance)	57569	
Lyons	57041	
Lyonville (Kimball)	57355	
Madison	57042	
Madsen Beach (Wilmot)	57279	
Mahto	57643	
Manchester (Iroquois)	57353	
Manderson	57756	
Mansfield	57460	
Maple Leaf (Mc Laughlin)	57642	
Marcus	57757	
Marcy Colony (Parkston)	57366	
Marietta (Provo)	57774	
Marion	57043	
Martin	57551	
Marty	57361	
Marvin	57251	
Mason (Belle Fourche)	57717	
Maurine (Faith)	57626	
Maverick (Hot Springs)	57747	
Maxwell Colony (Scotland)	57059	
Mayfield (Irene)	57037	
Mc Intosh	57641	
Mc Laughlin	57642	
Mcclure (Vivian)	57576	
Mccook Lake	57049	
(North Sioux City)		
Meadow	57644	
Meckling	57044	
Melham (Bancroft)	57316	
Mellette	57461	
Menno	57045	
Midland	57552	
Midway (Viborg)	57070	
Milbank	57252-253	
Milesville	57553	
Millboro (Winner)	57580	
Millbrook Colony	57301	
(Mitchell)		
Miller	57362	
Milltown (Parkston)	57366	
Mina	57462	
Minnekata (Hot Springs)	57747	
Miranda (Faulkton)	57438	
Mission	57555	

Mission Hill	57046	
Mission Ridge	57557	
Mitchell	57301	
Mobridge	57601	
Moe (Hudson)	57034	
Moenville (Midland)	57552	
Monroe	57047	
Montrose	57048	
Moreau (Faith)	57626	
Moreau Junction	57601	
(Mobridge)		
Morristown	57645	
Mosher (Winner)	57580	
Mound City	57646	
Mount Vernon	57363	
Mud Butte	57758, 57760	
Murdo	57559	
Mystic (Hill City)	57745	
Naomi (Lennox)	57039	
Naples (Vienna)	57271	
Nemo	57759	
New Effington	57255	
New Holland	57364	
New Underwood	57761	
Newark (Britton)	57430	
Newell	57760	
Newport Colony	57432	
(Claremont)		
Nisland	57762	
Nora (Alcester)	57001	
Norbeck (Faulkton)	57438	
Norman Ranch	57532	
(Fort Pierre)		
Norris	57560	
North Sioux City	57049	
North South Dakota	57601	
(Mobridge)		
Northville	57465	
Norway Center (Hudson)	57034	
Nowlin (Midland)	57552	
Nunda	57050	
Oacoma	57365	
Oahe (Pierre)	57501	
Oakwood Lake (Bruce)	57220	
Oelrichs	57763	
Oglala	57764	
Ohem (Dupree)	57623	
Okaton	57562	
Okobojo (Pierre)	57501	
Okreek	57563	
Ola (Chamberlain)	57325	
Old Town (Rapid City)	57701	
Oldham	57051	
Olivet	57052	
Olson (Ludlow)	57755	
Olsonville (Mission)	57555	
Onaka	57466	
Onida	57564	
Opal	57765	
Oral	57766	
Ordway (Aberdeen)	57401	
Orient	57467	
Orland (Madison)	57042	
Ortley	57256	
Orton (Fort Pierre)	57532	
Osceola (Bancroft)	57316	
Ottumwa (Midland)	57552	
Owanka	57767	
Pactola Lake (Rapid City)	57702	
Palisade (Garretson)	57030	
Parade	57647	

Parker	57053	
Parkston	57366	
Parmelee	57566	
Patricia (Martin)	57551	
Paxton (Dallas)	57529	
Pearl Creek Colony	57353	
(Iroquois)		
Pedro (Creighton)	57729	
Peever	57257	
Pelican (Watertown)	57201	
Peninsula Park	57075	
(Wentworth)		
Philip	57567	
Philip Junction (Philip)	57567	
Pickstown	57367	
Piedmont	57769	
Pierpont	57468	
Pierre	57501	
Pine Ridge	57770	
Pine Run (Mission)	57555	
Plainview (Howes)	57748	
Plankinton	57368	
Plano (Fulton)	57340	
Platte	57369	
Plum Creek (Philip)	57567	
Pluma (Deadwood)	57732	
Pollock	57648	
Polo (Orient)	57467	
Porcupine	57772	
Potato Creek (Interior)	57750	
Powell (Ipswich)	57451	
Prairie City	57649	
Prairie Village (Madison)	57042	
Presho	57568	
Pringle	57773	
Promise (Mobridge)	57601	
Provo	57774	
Pukwana	57370	
Pumpkin Center (Humboldt)	57035	
Putney (Groton)	57445	
Quinn	57775	
Ralph	57650	
Ramona	57054	
Ramsey (Montrose)	57048	
Randolph (Stratford)	57474	
Rapid City	57701-702	
	57706, 57708-709	
Hisega	57702	
Johnson Siding	57702	
Jolly Acres	57701	
Old Town	57701	
Pactola Lake	57702	
Rockerville	57701	
Silver City	57702	
Sulpher	57701	
Rauville (Watertown)	57201	
Ravinia	57357	
Raymond	57258	
Red Elm (Dupree)	57623	
Red Iron Lake (Lake City)	57247	
Red Scaffold (Howes)	57748	
Red Shirt (Hermosa)	57744	
Redfield	57469	
Redig	57776	
Redowl	57777	
Ree Heights	57371	
Reliance	57569	
Renner	57055	
Reva	57651	
Revillo	57259	
Richland (Elk Point)	57025	

HISEGA

APARTMENTS

Jackson Heights High Rise
1805 W FULTON ST 57702

BUILDINGS

Baken Park
2001 W MAIN ST 57702

Clock Tower Plaza
2525 W MAIN ST 57702

Rushmore Building
2040 W MAIN ST 57702

JOLLY ACRES

APARTMENTS

Country Bluff Apt
244 TEXAS ST 57701

Dahl Towers
824 COLUMBUS ST 57701

Knollwood Townhouses
1721 N MAPLE AVE 57701

River Ridge High Rise
330 PHILADELPHIA ST 57701

Upper Knollwood Townhouse
25 KNOLLWOOD DR 57701

Valley View High Rise
636 CATHEDRAL DR 57701

West Park Apt
1018 11TH ST 57701

Westhills Village Apt
255 TEXAS ST 57701

BUILDINGS

Centennial Square
2100 7TH ST 57701

First Federal Plaza
909 SAINT JOSEPH ST ... 57701

Prairie States Life Building
440 Mount Rushmore Rd .. 57701

Rushmore Mall
2200 N MAPLE AVE 57701

GOVERNMENT

Federal Building
515 9TH ST 57701

Penn County Court House
315 SAINT JOSEPH ST ... 57701

Public Safety Building
300 KANSAS CITY ST 57701

SIOUX FALLS

APARTMENTS

Country Club Estates
2505 S KIWANIS AVE 57105

Country Club Estates
2904 W 33RD ST 57105

Kenwood Mnr
2428 KENWOOD MNR 57104

Parkview
600 S KIWANIS AVE 57104

Rivertower
111 E 7TH ST 57102

BUILDINGS

Boyce Greely Building
231 S PHILLIPS AVE 57102

Empire East Mall
3800 S LOUISE AVE 57116

First Bank Of Sd
141 N MAIN AVE 57102

First National Bank Building
100 S PHILLIPS AVE 57102

Norwest Bank
101 N PHILLIPS AVE 57102

Security
101 S MAIN AVE 57102

Western Bank Building
100 N PHILLIPS AVE 57102

Western Mall
2101 W 41ST ST 57105

Western Surety Building
101 S PHILLIPS AVE 57102

GOVERNMENT

City Hall
224 W 9TH ST 57102

Federal Building
400 S PHILLIPS AVE 57102

Minnehaha County Ct House
415 N DAKOTA AVE 57102

Public Saftey Building
501 N DAKOTA AVE 57104

TENNESSEE
Abbreviation TN

Acklen (Nashville) 37212
Adams 37010
Adamsville 38310
Aetna (Centerville) 37033
Afton 37616
Alamo 38001
Alcoa 37701
Alexandria 37012
Algood (Cookeville) 38501
Allardt 38504
Allisona (College Grove) ... 37046
Allons 38541
Allred 38542
Alpine 38543
Altamont 37301
Am Qui (Madison) 37115
Andersonville 37705
Antioch 37011, 37013
Apison 37302
Ardmore 38449, 38453
      Dellrose 38449
      Dellrose 38453
Arlington 38002
Arrington 37014
Arthur 37707
Ashland City 37015
Athens 37303, 37371
Atoka 38004
Atwood 38220
Auburntown 37016
Bailey (Collierville) 38017
Baileyton (Greeneville) 37743
Bakewell 37304
Baneberry (White Pine) 37890
Baptist South South Board 37234
   (Nashville)
Barretville (Millington) 38053
Bartlett (Memphis) 38134
Bath Springs 38311
Baxter 38544
Bean Station 37708
Beech Bluff 38313
Beechgrove 37018
Beersheba Springs 37305
Belfast 37019
Bell Buckle 37020
Bellevue (Nashville) 37221
Bells 38006
Belvidere 37306
Bemis (Jackson) 38314
Benton 37307
Bethel Springs 38315
Bethesda (College Grove) . 37046
Bethpage 37022
Big Rock 37023
Big Sandy 38221
Birchwood 37308
Blaine 37709
Bloomingdale (Kingsport) .. 37660
Bloomington Springs 38545
Blountville 37617
Bluff City 37618
Bogota 38007
Bolivar 38008, 38074
Bon Aqua 37025
Bone Cave (Rock Island) .. 38581
Braden 38010
Bradford 38316

Bradyville 37026
Brentwood 37024, 37027
Briceville 37710
Brighton 38011
Bristol 37620-621, 37625
      Stephen Holston 37620
Brownsville 38012
Bruceton 38317
Brunswick 38014
Brush Creek 38547
Buchanan 38222
Buena Vista 38318
Buffalo Valley 38548
Bulls Gap 37711
Bumpus Mills 37028
Burlison 38015
Burns 37029
Burrville (Sunbright) 37872
Butler 37640
Bybee 37713
Byrdstown 38549
Calhoun 37309
Camden 38320
Campaign 38550
Carthage 37030
Caryville 37714
Castalian Springs 37031
Cedar Grove 38321
Cedar Hill 37032
Celina 38551
Centerville 37033
Chapel Hill 37034
Chapmansboro 37035
Charleston 37310
Charlotte 37036
Chattanooga 37400-412
      .... 37414-416, 37419
      .... 37421-422, 37424
      37499-450
      East Ridge 37412
Chestnut Mound 38552
Chewalla 38393
Christiana 37037
Chuckey 37641
Church Hill 37642, 37645
Clairfield 37715
Clarkrange 38553
Clarksburg 38324
Clarksville 37040-044
      Fredonia 37043
      Hickory Point 37043
      Hilldale 37043
      New Providence 37042
      Sango 37042
Cleveland 37311-312
      .... 37320, 37323, 37364
Clifton 38425
Clinton 37716-717
Cloverdale (Millington) 38053
Coalfield 37719
Coalmont 37313
Coble (Centerville) 37033
Cokercreek 37314
College Grove 37046
Collegedale 37315
Collierville 38017, 38027
      Bailey 38017
      Fisherville 38017
      Piperton 38017
Collinwood 38450
Colonial Heights 37663

   (Kingsport)
Columbia 38401-402
Como 38223
Conasauga 37316
Concord (Knoxville) 37922
Concord Farragut 37932-933
   (Knoxville)
Cookeville . 38501-503, 38505-06
      Algood 38501
Copperhill 37317
Cordova 38018
Cornersville 37047
Corryton 37721
Cosby 37722
Cottage Grove 38224
Cottontown 37048
Counce 38326
Covington 38019
Cowan 37318
Crab Orchard 37723
Crawford 38554
Crockett Mills 38021
Cross Plains 37049
Crosstown (Atoka) 38004
Crossville 38555, 38557
      Fairfield Glade 38555
Crump 38327
Cuba (Millington) 38053
Culleoka 38451
Cumberland City 37050
Cumberland Gap 37724
Cunningham 37052
Dandridge 37725
Darden 38328
Dayton 37321
Decatur 37322
Decaturville 38329
Decherd 37324
Deer Lodge 37726
Defeated (Carthage) 37030
Del Rio 37727
Delano 37325
Dellrose (Ardmore) . 38449, 38453
Denmark 38391
Denver 37054
Devonia (Briceville) 37710
Dickel (Tullahoma) 37388
Dickson 37055-056
Dixon Springs 37057
Dixonville (Millington) 38053
Donelson (Nashville) 37214
Dover 37058
Dowelltown 37059
Doyle 38559
Dresden 38225
Drummonds 38023
Duck River 38454
Ducktown 37326
Duff 37729
Dukedom 38226
Dunlap 37327
Dyer 38330
Dyersburg 38024-025
Eads 38028
Eagan 37730
Eagleville 37060
East (Nashville) 37206
East Acres (Millington) 38053
East Ridge (Chattanooga) . 37412
Eastside (Kingsport) 37664
Eaton 38331

Lupton City	37351	
Luray	38352	
Luttrell	37779	
Lutts	38471	
Lyles	37098	
Lynchburg	37352	
Lynn Garden (Kingsport)	37665	
Lynnville	38472	
Macon	38048	
Madison	37115-116	
Am Qui	37115	
Madisonville	37354	
Manchester	37355	
Mansfield	38236	
Martin	38237, 38238	
Maryville	37801-804	
Mascot	37806	
Mason	38049	
Masonhall (Kenton)	38233	
Maury City	38050	
Maynardville	37807	
Mc Clures Bend	37030	
(Carthage)		
Mc Donald	37353	
Mc Ewen	37101	
Mc Kenzie	38201	
Mc Lemoresville	38235	
Mc Minnville	37110	
Mcghee Tyson Ang Base	37777	
(Louisville)		
Medina	38355	
Medon	38356	
Melrose (Nashville)	37204	
	37220	
Memphis	37501, 38100-101	
	38103-120, 38122	
	38124-128, 38130-143	
	38145-148, 38150-152	
	38157, 38159, 38161, 38163	
	38165-168, 38173-175	
	38177, 38181-184	
	38186-188, 38190	
	38193-195, 38197	
Bartlett	38184	
Germantown	38138-38139	
Goldsmith	38143	
Goldsmiths	38143	
Hickory Hill	38115	
Mercer	38392	
Michie	38357	
Middleton	38052	
Midtown (Harriman)	37748	
Midway	37809	
Milan	38358	
Milledgeville	38359	
Millersville	37072	
(Goodlettsville)		
Millington	38053-054, 38083	
Barretville	38053	
Cloverdale	38053	
Cuba	38053	
Dixonville	38053	
East Acres	38053	
Kerrville	38053	
Locke	38053	
Lucy	38053	
Quito	38053	
Rosemark	38053	
Wilkinsville	38053	
Woodstock	38053	
Milton	37118	

Minor Hill	38473	
Miston	38056	
Mitchellville	37119	
Mohawk	37810	
Monroe	38573	
Monteagle	37356	
Monterey	38574	
Mooresburg	37811	
Morley (La Follette)	37766, 37812	
Morris Chapel	38361	
Morrison	37357	
Morristown	37813-816	
Moscow	38057	
Mosheim	37818	
Moss	38575	
Mount Carmel	37645	
Mount Juliet	37122	
Mount Pleasant	38474	
Mount Vernon	37358	
Mountain City	37683	
Mountain Home	37684	
Mulberry	37359	
Munford	38058	
Murfreesboro	37129-133	
Nashville	37200-222, 37224	
	37227-230, 37232	
	37234-250	
Acklen	37212	
Bellevue	37221	
Donelson	37214	
East	37206	
Glenview	37217	
Jere Baxter	37216	
Melrose	37204	
Melrose	37220	
Nashvle	37219	
National Life Center	37250	
North	37208	
Northeast	37207	
South	37210	
West	37209	
Woodbine	37211	
New Johnsonville	37134	
New Market	37820	
New Middleton	38563	
(Gordonsville)		
New Providence	37042	
(Clarksville)		
New River (Helenwood)	37755	
New Tazewell	37825	
Newbern	38059	
Newcomb	37819	
Newport	37821	
Niota	37826	
Nolensville	37135	
Norene	37136	
Norma (Huntsville)	37756	
Normandy	37360	
Norris	37828	
North (Nashville)	37208	
Northeast (Nashville)	37207	
Nunnelly	37137	
Oak Ridge	37830-831	
Oakdale	37829	
Oakfield	38362	
Oakland	38060	
Obion	38240	
Ocoee	37361	
Old Hickory	37138	
Oldfort	37362	
Olivehill	38475	

Oliver Springs	37840	
Oneida	37841	
Only	37140	
Ooltewah	37363	
Orlinda	37141	
Ozone	37842	
Pall Mall	38577	
Palmer	37365	
Palmersville	38241	
Palmyra	37142	
Paris	38242	
Parrottsville	37843	
Parsons	38363	
Pegram	37143	
Pelham	37366	
Petersburg	37144	
Petros	37845	
Peytonsville (Franklin)	37064	
Philadelphia	37846	
Pickwick Dam	38365	
Pigeon Forge	37863, 37868	
Pikeville	37367	
Piney Flats	37686, 37699	
Pinson	38366	
Pioneer	37847	
Piperton (Collierville)	38017	
Plaza (Mc Minnville)	37110	
Pleasant Hill	38578	
Pleasant Shade	37145	
Pleasant View	37146	
Pleasantville	37147	
Pocahontas	38061	
Portland	37148	
Postelle (Copperhill)	37317	
Powder Springs	37848	
Powell	37849	
Primm Springs	38476	
Prospect	38477	
Pruden	37851	
Pulaski	38478	
Puryear	38251	
Quebeck	38579	
Quito (Millington)	38053	
Ramer	38367	
Randolph (Burlison)	38015	
Ravenscroft (Sparta)	38583	
Readyville	37149	
Reagan	38368	
Red Boiling Springs	37150	
Reliance	37369	
Riceville	37370	
Rickman	38580	
Riddleton	37151	
Ridgely	38080	
Ridgetop	37152	
Ripley	38063	
Rives	38253	
Roan Mountain	37687	
Robbins	37852	
Rock Island	38581	
Rockford	37853	
Rockvale	37153	
Rockwood	37854	
Rogersville	37857	
Rosemark (Millington)	38053	
Rossville	38066	
Royal (Shelbyville)	37160	
Rudderville (Franklin)	37064	
Rugby	37733	
Russellville	37860	
Rutherford	38369	

Rutledge	37861	Speedwell	37870	Dickel	37388
Saint Andrews	37372	Spencer	38585	Turtletown	37391
Saint Bethlehem	37155	Spring City	37381	Unicoi	37692
Saint Joseph	38481	Spring Creek	38878	Union City	38261
Sale Creek (Bakewell)	37304	Spring Hill	37174	Unionville	37180
	37373	Springfield	37172	Vanleer	37181
Saltillo	38370	Springville	38256	Viola	37394
Samburg	38254	Stanton	38069	Vonore	37885
Sango (Clarksville)	37042	Stantonville	38379	Walland	37886
Santa Fe	38482	Stephen Holston (Bristol)	37620	Walling	38587
Sardis	38371	Stewart	37175	Wartburg	37887
Saulsbury	38067	Strawberry Plains	37871	Wartrace	37183
Savannah	38372	Sugar Tree	38380	Washburn	37888
Scotts Hill	38374	Summertown	38483	Watauga	37694
Sears (Memphis)	38140	Summitville	37382	Watertown	37184
Selmer	38375	Sunbright	37872	Watts Bar Dam	37395
Sequatchie	37374	Surgoinsville	37873	Waverly	37185
Sevierville .. 37862, 37864, 37876		Sweetwater	37874	Waynesboro	38485
Sewanee	37375, 37383	Taft	38488	West (Nashville)	37209
Seymour	37865	Talbott	37877	Westel (Rockwood)	37854
Shady Valley	37688	Tallassee	37878	Westmoreland	37186
Sharon	38255	Tate Springs	37708	Westpoint	38486
Sharps Chapel	37866	(Bean Station)		Westport	38387
Shawanee	37867	Tazewell	37879	White Bluff	37187
Shelbyville	37160-161	Telford	37690	White House	37188
Sherwood	37376	Tellico Plains	37385	White Pine	37890
Sheyborgan (Woodbury) ..	37190	Ten Mile	37880	Whites Creek	37189
Shiloh	38376	Tennessee Ridge	37178	Whitesburg	37891
Shipps Bend (Centerville) .	37033	Thompsons Station	37179	Whiteside	37396
Signal Mountain	37377	Thorn Hill	37881	Whiteville	38075
Silerton	38377	Tigrett	38070	Whitleyville	38588
Silver Point	38582	Tipton	38071	Whitwell	37397
Slayden	37165	Tiptonville	38079	Wilder	38589
Smartt	37378	Toone	38381	Wildersville	38388
Smithville	37166	Townsend	37882	Wilkinsville (Millington)	38053
Smyrna	37167, 38318	Tracy City	37387	Williamsport	38487
Snapps Ferry	37743	Trade	37691	Williston	38076
(Greeneville)		Treadway	37883	Winchester	37398
Sneedville	37869	Trenton	38382	Winfield	37892
Soddy Daisy	37379	Trezevant	38258	Winona	37893
Somerville	38068	Tri-city Airport	37617	Woodbine (Nashville)	37211
South (Nashville)	37210	(Blountville)		Woodbury	37190
South Fulton	38257	Trimble	38259	Woodland Mills	38271
South Pittsburg	37380	Triune (Arrington)	37014	Woodlawn	37191
Southside	37171	Troy	38260	Woodstock (Millington)	38053
Sparta	38583	Tullahoma	37388-389	Wrigley (Lyles)	37098
				Wynnburg	38077
				Yorkville	38389
				Yuma	38390

IMPORTANT BUILDINGS

ACKLEN

BUILDINGS

Medical Arts Building
1211 21ST AVE S 37212

BARTLETT

BUILDINGS

Shelby Oaks Corporate Ctr
5909 SHELBY OAKS DR .. 38134

BELLEVUE

APARTMENTS

Creekside Meadows
810 BELLEVUE RD 37221

CHATTANOOGA

APARTMENTS

Ayrshire Apts
418 MCCALLIE AVE 37402

Belemeade Apts
3725 FOUNTAIN AVE 37412

Bimini Apt
423 S SEMINOLE DR 37411

Boynton Terrace Apts
959 BOYNTON DR 37402

Boynton Village Apts
1205 BOYNTON DR 37402

Brainerd Apt
30 S GERMANTOWN RD .. 37411

Concorde Apt
7301 E BRAINERD RD 37421

El Cortijo
4515 OAK HILL RD 37416

Fontaine Village
3535 Mountain Creek Rd .. 37415

Foxfire Apts
4040 Mountain Creek Rd .. 37415

Hickory Valley Apts
1507 Hickory Valley Rd 37421

Hogshead Apts
600 GEORGIA AVE 37402

Jaycee Towers #2
959 GATEWAY AVE 37402

Jaycees Towers #1
500 W M L KING BLVD 37402

Jaycees Towers #1
500 W 9TH ST 37402

John Calvin Apts
100 NORTHGATE PARK .. 37415

Mary Walker Towers
2505 S MARKET ST 37408

Montclair Condominiums
1000 READS LAKE RD 37415

Montclair South Apts
4126 Mountain Creek Rd .. 37415

Morrison Springs Apts
701 Morrison Springs Rd .. 37415

Mountain Brook Apt
1185 Mountain Creek Rd .. 37405

Mountain Creek Apts
936 Mountain Creek Rd 37405

Napfe Apts
5465 HIGHWAY 58 37416

Normandy Apts
3501 DAYTON BLVD 37415

Patten Towers
1 E 11TH ST 37402

Pinewood Apt
3301 PINEWOOD AVE 37411

Robinson Apts
622 GEORGIA AVE 37402

Royal Arms Apt
314 MCBRIEN RD 37411

Shepherd Hills Apt
404 TUNNEL BLVD 37411

St Barnabas Apts
300 W 6TH ST 37402

The Gateway Towers
1100 GATEWAY AVE 37402

The Overlook Apts
1201 BOYNTON DR 37402

Thrippence Apts
3623 FOUNTAIN AVE 37412

Wind Ridge Apts
1175 PINEVILLE RD 37405

BUILDINGS

5700 Building
5700 BRAINERD RD 37411

5800 Building
5700 BRAINERD RD 37411

5900 Building
5700 BRAINERD RD 37411

6000 Building
5700 BRAINERD RD 37411

6100 Building
5700 BRAINERD RD 37411

6200 Building
5700 BRAINERD RD 37411

6300 Building
5700 BRAINERD RD 37411

6400 Building
5700 BRAINERD RD 37411

6500 Building
5700 BRAINERD RD 37411

6600 Building
5700 BRAINERD RD 37411

American Natl Bank Building
734 MARKET ST 37402

Blue Cross Building
801 PINE ST 37402

Chattanooga Bank Building
11 W 8TH ST 37402

Chestnut Street Towers
633 CHESTNUT ST 37450

Civic Forum
1001 MARKET ST 37402

Dome Building
736 GEORGIA AVE 37402

East Ridge Doctors Building
929 SPRING CREEK RD .. 37412

Eastgate Mall
5700 BRAINERD RD 37411

Emerson Building
100 E 10TH ST 37402

First Tennessee Bank Building
701 MARKET ST 37402

Foodlion Shpg. Center
321 BROWNS FERRY 37419

Franklin Building
5700 BRAINERD RD 37411

Hamilton Crossing
2200 Hamilton Place Blvd . 37421

Hamilton Place Mall
2100 Hamilton Place Blvd . 37421

James Building
735 BROAD ST 37402

Krystal Building
100 W M L KING BLVD 37402

Krystal Building
1 UNION SQ 37402

Krystal Building
100 W 9TH ST 37402

Maclellan Building
721 BROAD ST 37402

Medical Towers
1000 E 3RD ST 37403

Memorial Med Building
721 GLENWOOD DR 37404

Osborne Off Ctr
5700 BRAINERD RD 37411

Park Plaza
1010 MARKET ST 37402

Pioneer Bank Building
801 BROAD ST 37402

Provident Building
211 E 6TH ST 37402

Tallan Building
110 W M L KING BLVD 37402

Tallan Building
2 UNION SQ 37402

Tallan Building
100 W 9TH ST 37402

Uptain Building
5700 BRAINERD RD 37411

Volunteer Building
832 GEORGIA AVE 37402

West Building Maclellan
722 CHESTNUT ST 37402

Whitehall Building
960 E 3RD ST 37403

Zayre Building
401 W M L KING BLVD 37402

Zayre Building
401 W 9TH ST 37402

GOVERNMENT

City Hall
101 E 11TH ST 37402

City Hall Annex
100 E 11TH ST 37402

Federal Building
900 GEORGIA AVE 37402

Hamilton County Courthous
625 GEORGIA AVE 37402

HOSPITALS

Erlanger Med Ctr Plaza
979 E 3RD ST 37403

HOTELS

Radisson Read House
827 BROAD ST 37402

Sheraton Hotel
407 CHESTNUT ST 37402

CLARKSVILLE

APARTMENTS

American Vlg Mhp
510 TOBACCO RD 37042

Burkhart Trailer Park
922 POWER ST 37042

Creekbend Trailer Park
296 TOBACCO RD 37042

Emerald Hill Apts
371 PATRICK ST 37040

Ratchford Apts
500 PEACHERS MILL RD 37042

Shady Rest Trailer Park
708 POWER ST 37042

Woodland Trailer Park
3193 Fort Campbell Blvd .. 37042

BUILDINGS

Federal Building
116 N 2ND ST 37040

CLEVELAND

APARTMENTS

Horizon Square Apts
2324 Georgetown Rd NW .. 37311

Marquis Apts
3600 KEITH ST NW 37312

N Cleve Towers
1200 MAGNOLIA AVE NE . 37311

Pine Forest Apts
3005 Henderson Ave NW . 37312

Spring Brook Apts
2360 BLACKBURN RD SE 37311

Windsor Ct Apts
2075 CLINGAN DR NW 37311

BUILDINGS

Bradley Medical Center
2401 N OCOEE ST 37311

Cleveland Mall
2955 KEITH ST NW 37312

Cleveland Mun Building
190 CHURCH ST NE 37311

GOVERNMENT

Bradley Co Court Hse
155 N OCOEE ST 37311

DONELSON

BUILDINGS

Donelson Medical Center
3051 LEBANON RD 37214

Metro Airport Terminal
1 TERMINAL DR 37214

Professional Building
3053 LEBANON RD 37214

GLENVIEW

APARTMENTS

Harbour Town Condos
4001 ANDERSON RD 37217

JACKSON

GOVERNMENT

Federal Building
109 S HIGHLAND AVE 38301

Madison County Court Hous
100 E MAIN ST 38301

Madison County Jail
100 E MAIN ST 38301

KARNS

APARTMENTS

Cross Creek Apts
5000 WESTERN AVE 37921

Waterford Apts
5201 WESTERN AVE 37921

KIMBERLIN HEIGHTS

BUILDINGS

Baptist Professional Building
200 BLOUNT AVE SE 37920

Blount Professional Building
211 BLOUNT AVE SE 37920

Physicians Office Building
1928 ALCOA HWY 37920

KNOXVILLE

APARTMENTS

Bouldercrest Apts
2000 WILSON RD 37912

Canyon Apartments
600 E INSKIP DR 37912

Concept 21 Apts
401 GALLAHER VIEW RD 37919

Country Club Apts
8400 Middlebrook Plaza ... 37923

Creek Ridge Apts
5700 Pleasant Ridge Rd ... 37912

Deane Hill Apts
7700 GLEASON RD 37919

Eastowne Village
3100 E Towne Mall Cir 37924

Foxfire Apts
2300 MERCHANTS DR 37912

Guy B Love Towers
1171 ARMSTRONG AVE ... 37917

Isabella Towers
1515 ISABELLA CIR 37915

Kingston Sq Apts
6315 KINGSTON PIKE 37919

Knob Hill Apts
1307 WILSON RD 37912

Knox Landing
634 E INSKIP DR 37912

Londontown Apts
6401 NIGHTINGALE LN ... 37909

Meadowood Apartments
4000 Pleasant Ridge Rd ... 37912

North Gate Terrace
4301 Whittle Spring Rd 37917

Pine Ridge Apartments
4700 SCHUBERT RD 37912

Sans Souci
300 Walker Springs Rd 37923

Steeple Chase
5800 Central Avenue Pike 37912

Summitt Towers
201 LOCUST ST 37902

Sunchase Apts
790 N CEDAR BLUFF RD 37923

Tanglewood Apts
4501 TILLERY RD 37912

The Gables
2100 WILSON RD 37912

Tillery Ridge Apts
1716 MERCHANTS DR 37912

Townview Ter Apts
200 TOWNVIEW DR 37915

Townview Terrace Apts
300 MULVANEY ST 37915

Townview Towers
1100 TOWNVIEW DR 37915

Walker Springs Apts
721 Walker Springs Rd 37923

Warren House Apts
9015 TEN MILE RD 37923

Washington Ridge
4503 WASHINGTON PIKE 37917

Westview Tower
7823 GLEASON RD 37919

Windover Apts
301 CHESHIRE DR 37919

Windrush Apts
527 MORRELL RD 37919

BUILDINGS

1st Amer Natl Bank Building
505 S GAY ST 37902

1st Tennessee Bank Building
530 S GAY ST 37902

9040 Building
9040 Executive Park Dr 37923

Andrew Johnson Towers
912 S GAY ST 37902

Burwell Building
602 S GAY ST 37902

Charter Federal Building
531 S GAY ST 37902

Executive Office Plaza
9041 Executive Park Dr 37923

Fidelity Building
502 S GAY ST 37902

Fort Hill Building
901 E SUMMIT HILL DR ... 37915

Fort Sanders Prof Building
501 20TH ST 37916

Magdalene Clark Towers
939 E EMERALD AVE 37917

Medical Arts Building
603 W MAIN ST 37902

Newland Prof Building
2001 LAUREL AVE 37916

Northshore Center
1111 Northshore Dr NW 37919

One Centre Square
620 MARKET ST 37902

Riverview Tower
900 S GAY ST 37902

Sovran Bank Building
550 W MAIN ST 37902

St Marys Prof Building
930 E EMERALD AVE 37917

Third National Bank Building
700 E HILL AVE 37915

Third National Bank Building
623 MARKET ST 37902

Two Centre Square
625 S GAY ST 37902

Valley Fidelty Building
607 MARKET ST 37902

GOVERNMENT

City & County Building
400 W MAIN ST 37902

Federal Building
710 LOCUST ST 37902

Knox Co Court House
300 W MAIN ST 37902

State Office Building
531 HENLEY ST 37902

U S Federal Court House
501 W MAIN ST 37902

MELROSE

BUILDINGS

100 Oaks Tower
719 THOMPSON LN 37204

MEMPHIS

BUILDINGS

100 North Main Building
100 N MID AMERICA MALL 38103

Cotton Exchange
65 UNION AVE 38103

Exchange Building
9 N 2ND ST 38103

Falls
22 N FRONT ST 38103

First American Bank
44 N 2ND ST 38103

James Building
5350 POPLAR AVE 38119

Jefferson Court Building
46 N 3RD ST 38103

Lincoln America Towers
60 N MID AMERICA MALL 38103

Lincoln American Towers
60 N MAIN ST 38103

Nonconnah Corporate Ctr
2600 NONCONNAH BLVD 38132

One Commerce Sq Building
40 S MID AMERICA MALL 38103

Sterick Building
8 N 3RD ST 38103

Union Planters Bank
67 MADISON AVE 38103

White Station Towers
5050 POPLAR AVE 38157

GOVERNMENT

Clifford Davis Federal Of
167 N MID AMERICA MALL 38103

Criminal Justice Center
201 POPLAR AVE 38103

Donnley J Hill State Off
170 N Mid America MAll 38103

Memphis City Hall
125 N Mid America Mall 38103

Shelby County Courthouse
140 ADAMS AVE 38103

Shelby County Office
157 POPLAR AVE 38103

NASHVILLE

APARTMENTS

Bavaria Apts
4501 PACKARD DR 37211

Continental Apts
3415 W END AVE 37203

Dominion House
5099 LINBAR DR 37211

Gazebo Apts
141 NEESE DR 37211

Hadley Park Towers
2901 John A Merritt Blvd ... 37209

Harding Manor
441 HARDING PL 37211

Longwood Terrace Apts
371 WALLACE RD 37211

Metro Manor
500 5TH AVE N 37219

Riverbend Apts
6700 CABOT DR 37209

Rock Harbor Apts
515 BASSWOOD DR 37209

Royal Oaks Towers
4505 HARDING RD 37205

Southern Hills
370 WALLACE RD 37211

Sunrise Apts
189 WALLACE RD 37211

BUILDINGS

3rd National Finance Ctr
424 CHURCH ST 37219

American Trust Building
305 UNION ST 37201

Baker Building
110 21ST AVE S 37203

Church Street Center
706 CHURCH ST 37203

Citizens Bank Building
401 CHARLOTTE AVE 37219

Fidelity Federal Building
401 UNION ST 37219

Five Park Plaza
2545 PARK PLZ 37203

First Union Tower
150 4TH STREET 37219

Mid State Medical Center
2010 CHURCH ST 37203

Nashville Bank & Trust
315 UNION ST 37201

Nashville Convention Ctr
601 COMMERCE ST 37203

Noel Place
200 4TH AVE N 37219

One Belle Meade Place
4400 HARDING RD 37205

One Park Plaza
2501 PARK PLZ 37203

Parkview Towers
210 25TH AVE N 37203

St Cloud Corner
500 CHURCH ST 37219

St Thomas Doctors Building
4230 HARDING RD 37205

Stahlman Building
211 UNION ST 37201

GOVERNMENT

Customs Building
701 BROADWAY 37203

Metro Courthouse
1 PUBLIC SQ 37201

U S Courthouse
801 BROADWAY 37203

Us Courthouse Annex
110 9TH AVE S 37203

TEXAS
Abbreviation TX

A C Nielsen (El Paso)	79966
	79973-974
Abbott	76621
Abernathy	79311
Abilene 79600-608, 79697-699	
Hamby	79601
Impact	79603
McMurray	79605
Potosi	79601
Abram (Mission)	78572
Ac Nielsen Couponing 88587-589	
(El Paso)	
Acacia Lake (Brownsville) . 78520	
Academy (Little River)	76554
Ace	77326
Ackerly	79713
Adams Gardens	78550
(Harlingen)	
Addicks (Houston)	77079
Addicks Barker (Houston) . 77084	
Addison 75001, 75234, 75244	
	75248
Adkins	78101
Adrian	79001
Afton	79220
Aggieland	77844
(College Station)	
Agua Dulce	78330
Agua Nueva (Hebbronville) 78361	
Aguilares (Mirando City) ... 78369	
Aiken	79221
Alamo	78516
Alamo Heights	78209
(San Antonio)	
Alanreed	79002
Alazan (Nacogdoches)	75961
Alba	75410
Albany	76430
Albert (Stonewall)	78671
Aldine (Houston)	77039
Aledo	76008
Alexanders Store	75973
(Shelbyville)	
Alfred (Alice)	78332
Algerita (San Saba)	76877
Algoa (Alvin)	77510
Alice 78332-333, 78342	
Alfred	78332
Guajillo	78332
Palito Blanco	78332
San Jose	78332
Springfield	78332
Alief	77411
Allen	75002
Alleyton	78935
Allison	79003
Alpine	79830-832
Sul Ross	79832
Alta Loma (Santa Fe)	77510
Altair	77412
Alto	75925
Alto Springs (Kosse)	76653
Alton (Mission)	78572
Alvarado	76009
Alvin	77511-512
Algoa	77511
Alvord	76225
Amarillo 79100-111, 79114	

	79116-121, 79123-124
	79159-161, 79163-168
	79170-178, 79180-182
	79184-189
Diamond Shamrock	
	79161, 79173, 79188
Santa Fe Railway	79171
Ames (Gatesville) ... 76528, 77575	
Amherst	79312
Ammansville (La Grange) . 78945	
Anadarko (Laneville)	75667
Anahuac	77514
Anchor (Angleton)	77515
Ander (Goliad)	77963
Anderson 77830, 77875	
Carlos	77830
Andice (Georgetown)	78628
Andrews	79714
Angleton	77515-516
Anchor	77515
Baileys Prairie	77515
Bonney	77515
Mcbeth	77515
Anna	75409
Annona	75550
Anson	79501
Anthony	79821
Antioch (Atlanta) ... 75551, 75562	
	75758, 75852, 75935, 75975
Anton	79313
Apple Springs	75926
Appleby (Nacogdoches) ... 75961	
Aquilla	76622
Aransas Pass	78335-336
City By The Sea	78336
Arcadia (Santa Fe)	77517
Archer City	76351
Arcola (Rosharon)	77583
Argenta (Mathis)	78368
Argo (Cookville)	75558
Argyle	76226
Arlam (Garrison)	75946
Arlington 76000, 76003-007	
...... 76010-019, 76094, 76096	
Pantego	76013
Univ Of Texas At	
Arlington	76019
Armstrong	78338
Arneckeville (Cuero)	77954
Arnett (Gatesville)	76528
Arp	75750
Arroyo (Harlingen)	78550
Art	76820
Artesia Wells	78001
Arthur City	75411
Ash (Athens) 75751, 75835	
Asherton	78827
Ashland (Diana)	75640
Ashwood (Sweeny)	77480
Asia (Corrigan)	75939
Aspermont	79502
Astin (Hearne)	77859
Astrodome (Houston)	77025
AT&T (Dallas)	75350
Atascocita (Humble)	77346
Atascosa	78002
Ater (Gatesville)	76528
Athens	75751
Atlanta	75551
Attoyac (Nacogdoches) ... 75961	
Aubrey	76227

Augusta (Grapeland)	75844
Austin . 73301, 73344, 78700-705	
	78709-739, 78741-769
	78771-774, 78778-783
	78785-789
Balcones	78759
Bee Caves	78733
Bergstrom	78719
Bergstrom A FB	78743
Bluff Springs	78744
Brushy Creek	78717
Camp Mabry	78731
Capitol	78701
Circleville	78736
Colton	78744
Creedmoor	78747
Dessau	78753
Four Points	78732
Hornsby Bend	78725
Hudson Bend	78734
IRS Service Center	
	73301, 73344, 78788
Jollyville	78729
Lakeway 78734, 78738	
Marshall Ford	78732
Montopolis	78741
Moores Crossing	78719
Oak Hill	78749
Pilot Knob	78744
Rollingwood	78746
San Leanna	78748
Sprinkle	78754
Sunset Valley	78745
Tarrytown	78703
Travis Heights	78704
University Of Texas	78712
West Lake Hills	78746
West Lake	78746
Austonio (Crockett)	75835
Austwell	77950
Avalon	76623
Avery	75554
Avinger	75630
Avoca (Stamford)	79503
Avondale (Harlingen)	78550
Axtell	76624
Azle 76020, 76098	
Pelican Bay	76020
Bacliff	77518
Bagwell	75412
Bahia Mar (Port Isabel) 78578	
Bailey	75413
Baileys Prairie	77515
(Angleton)	
Baileyville (Rosebud)	76570
Baird	79504
Balch Springs (Mesquite) .. 75180	
Balcones (Austin)	78759
Balcones Heights	78201
(San Antonio)	
Bald Hill (Lufkin)	75901
Baldwin (Karnack)	75661
Ballinger	76821
Balmorhea	79718
Bammel (Houston)	77040
Bandera	78003
Bangs	76823
Bankersmith	78624
(Fredericksburg)	
Banquete	78339
Barclay (Lott)	76656

527

Bardwell	75101
Barker	77413
Barkman (Hooks)	75561
Barksdale	78828
Barnes (Moscow)	75960
Barnhart	76930
Barnum (Corrigan)	75939
Barrett (Crosby)	77532
Barry	75102
Barstow	79719
Bartlett	76511
Bascom (Tyler)	75705
Bassett (Simms)	75574
Bastrop	78602
Batesville	78829
Batson	77519
Battle (Mart)	76664
Baxter (Athens)	75751
Bay City	77404, 77414
Buckeye	77414
Cedar Lake	77414
Clemville	77414
Sargent	77404
Sargent	77414
Bay View (Bacliff)	77518
Bayside	78340
Baytown	77520-522
Bayway	77520
Beach City	77520
Cedar Point	77520
Cove	77520
Garth	77520
Lakewood	77520
Lynchburg	77520
Mcnair	77520
Stewart Heights	77520
Bayview (Los Fresnos)	78566
Bayway (Baytown)	77520
Beach (Conroe)	77301
Beach City (Baytown)	77520
Beasley	77417
Beaukiss (Elgin)	78621
Beaumont	77700-711
	77713, 77720, 77726
Cheek	77705
Fannett	77705
Beaver Dam (De Kalb)	75559
Bebe	78603
Beckville	75631
Bedford	76021-022, 76095
Bedias	77831
Bee Cave (Austin)	78733
Bee House (Evant)	76525
Beech Grove (Jasper)	75951
Beeville	78102, 78104
Belfalls (Troy)	76579
Bellaire	77401-402
Bellevue	76228
Bellmead (Waco)	76704-705
Bells	75414
Bellview (Bellville)	77418
Bellville	77418
Bellvue (Bellville)	77418
Belmont	78604
Belott (Crockett)	75835
Belton	76513
Ben Arnold	76517
Ben Bolt	78342
Ben Franklin	75415
Ben Hur (Mart)	76664
Ben Wheeler	75754

Benavides	78341
Benbrook (Fort Worth)	76126
Benchley (Bryan)	77801
Bend	76824
Benjamin	79505
Berclair	78107
Berea (Jefferson)	75657
Bergheim	78004
Bergstrom (Austin)	78719
Bernardo (Cat Spring)	78933
Berryville (Frankston)	75763
Bertram	78605
Best (Big Lake)	76932
Bethel (Athens)	75751
	75861, 76821
Bethlehem (De Kalb)	75559
	75644
Beverly Hills (Waco)	76711
Beyersville (Coupland)	78615
Big Bend National Park	79834
Big Lake	76932
Big Sandy	75755
Big Spring	79720-721
Vealmoor	79720
Big Wells	78830
Bigfoot	78005
Biggs Field (El Paso)	79908
	79918
Bighill (Thornton)	76687
Billington (Axtell)	76624
Birome	76625
Bishop	78343
Bivins	75555
Black (Friona)	79035
Black Jack (Troup)	75789
Blackfoot (Montalba)	75853
Blackwell	79506
Blair (Merkel)	79536
Blanco	78606
Blandlake (San Augustine)	75972
Blanket	76432
Blanton (Ballinger)	76821
Bleakwood (Kirbyville)	75956
Bledso (Bledsoe)	79314
Bledsoe	79314
Bleiblerville	78931
Blessing	77419
Blevins (Eddy)	76524
Blocker (Marshall)	75670
Blodgett (Pittsburg)	75686
Bloomburg	75556
Blooming Grove	76626
Bloomington	77951
Blossom	75416
Blue (Lexington)	78947
Blue Mound (Fort Worth)	76131
Blue Ridge	75424
Bluegrove	76352
Bluetown (Santa Maria)	78592
Bluff Dale	76433
Bluff Springs (Austin)	78744
Bluffton	78607
Blum	76627
Blumenthal	78624
(Fredericksburg)	
Bluntzer (Robstown)	78380
Bobville (Dobbin)	77333
Boca Chica (Brownsville)	78520
Boerne	78006
Bogata	75417
Boling	77420

Bolivar (Port Bolivar)	77650
Bon Ami (Kirbyville)	75956
Bon Wier	75928
Bonanza (Whitney)	76692
Bonham	75418
Bonner (Mcallen)	78501
Bonney (Angleton)	77515
Bonnie View (Woodsboro)	78393
Booker	79005
Booth (Richmond)	77469
Borden (Weimar)	78962
Bordersville (Humble)	77338
Borger	79007-008
Phillips	79007
Bosqueville (Waco)	76708
Boston (New Boston)	75570
Bovina	79009
Bowie	76230
Box Church (Groesbeck)	76642
Boyd	76023
Boys Ranch	79010, 79174
Valle De Oro	79010
Vega	79010
Brackettville	78832
Bradford (Montalba)	75853
Bradshaw (Winters)	79567
Brady (Center)	75935, 76825
Calf Creek	76825
Fife	76825
Katemcy	76825
Brandon	76628
Brashear	75420
Brazoria	77422
Brazos Point (Kopperl)	76652
Breckenridge	76424
Bremond	76629
Brenham	77833-834
Gay Hill	77833
Independence	77833
Breslau (Hallettsville)	77964
Briary (Rosebud)	76570
Bridge City	77611
Bridgeport	76426
Briggs	78608
Brileytown (Garrison)	75946
Briscoe	79011
Broaddus	75929
Bronson	75930
Bronte	76933
Brookeland	75931
Brookesmith	76827
Brookshire	77423
Brookside Village	77581
(Pearland)	
Brookston	75421
Browndell (Brookeland)	75931
Brownfield	79316
Brownsboro	75756, 78644
	76802
Edom	75756
New Hope	75756
Brownsville	78520-523, 78526
Acacia Lake	78520
Boca Chica	78520
Bville	78520
El Jardin	78520
Keller Corner	78520
Kennedy Shores	78520
Palm Village	78520
Portway Acres	78520
Villa Cavazos	78520

Villa Nueva 78520
Brownwood 76801, 76803-804
   Early 76801
   Grosvenor 76801
   Indian Creek 76801
   Lake Brownwood 76801
   Lake Shore 76801
   Shamrock Shores 76801
   Thrifty 76801
Bruceville 76630
Bruceville Eddy 76630
  (Bruceville)
Brumley (Pittsburg) 75686
Brundage 78834
  (Carrizo Springs)
Bruni 78344
Brushy Creek (Austin) 78717
Bryan 77801-803, 77805-808
   Benchley 77801
   Edge 77801
   Law 77801
   Reliance 77801
   Steep Hollow 77801
   Tabor 77801
Bryans Mill 75560, 75568
  (Douglassville)
Bryson 76427
Buchanan Dam 78609
Buckeye (Bay City) 77414
Buckholts 76518
Buckhorn (Bellville) 77418
Buckingham (Richardson) . 75080
Buda 78610
Buffalo 75831
Buffalo Gap 79508
Buford (Colorado City) 79512
Bula 79320
Bullard 75757
Bulverde 78163
Buna 77612
Bunker Hill Village 77024
  (Houston)
Burkburnett 76354
Burkett 76828
Burkeville 75932
Burleigh (Bellville) 77418
Burleson 76028, 76097
Burlington 76519
Burnet 78611
Burns (Hooks) 75561
Burr (Wharton) 77488
Burton 77835
Bushland 79012
Bustamante (Hebbronville) . 78361
Butler (Oakwood) 75855
Bville (Brownsville) 78520
Byers 76357
Bynum 76631
Cactus 79013
Caddo 76429
Caddo Mills 75135
Caldwell 77836
Caledonia (Timpson) 75975
Calf Creek (Brady) 76825
Call 75933
Calliham 78007
Calvert 77837
Calvin (Bastrop) 78602
Camden 75934
Cameron 76520
Camilla (Coldspring) 77331

Camp Mabry (Austin) 78731
Camp Strake (Conroe) 77301
Camp Verde (Center Point) 78010
Camp Wood 78833
Campbell 75422
Campbellton 78008
Campo Alto (Alamo) 78516
Campti (Center) 75935
Canadian 79014
Canton 75103
Canutillo 79835
Canyon 79015-016
Canyon Lake .. 78130, 78132-133
  (New Braunfels)
Capitol (Austin) 78701
Caplen (Gilchrist) 77617
Caradan (Goldthwaite) 76844
Carbon 76435
Carbondale (Maud) 75567
Cardinal Hall (Athens) 75751
Carey (Childress) ... 79201, 79222
Carlisle (Trinity) 75862
Carlos (Anderson) 77830
Carlsbad 76934
Carlsen Promotion Group
  (El Paso) 88540-544
Carlton 76436
Carmine 78932
Carmona (Corrigan) 75939
Caro (Nacogdoches) 75961
Carricitos (San Benito) 78586
Carrizo Springs 78834
Carrollton 75006-008
  75010-011
Carterville (Linden) 75563
Carthage 75633
Cason 75636
Castell 76831
Castle Hills 78213
  (San Antonio)
Castroville 78009, 78056
   Mico 78056
Cat Spring 78933
Catarina 78836
Cave Springs (Marshall) ... 75670
Cavitt (Oglesby) 76561
Cayuga 75832
Cedar Creek 78612
Cedar Grove (Lufkin) 75901
Cedar Hill 75104, 75106
Cedar Lake (Bay City) 77414
Cedar Lane 77415
Cedar Park 78613
Cedar Point (Baytown) 77520
Cedar Springs (Rosebud) .. 76570
Cee Vee 79223
Cego (Eddy) 76524
Cele (Manor) 78653
Celeste 75423
Celina 75009
Center 75935, 76642
   Antioch 75935
   Brady 75935
   Campti 75935
   Choice 75935
   East Liberty 75935
   Good Hope 75935
   Grigsby 75935
   James 75935
   Jericho 75935
   Neuville 75935

   Short 75935
   Waterman 75935
Center Point (Pittsburg) 75686
  78010
   Camp Verde 78010
Centerview (Centerville) 75833
Centerville 75833
Central (Pollok) 75969
Central Heights 75961
  (Nacogdoches)
Centralia 75834
Cestohowa (Falls City) 78113
Chaffee Vlliiage 76544
  (Killeen)
Chalk 79224, 79248
Chandler 75758
Channelview 77530
Channing 79018, 79058
   Masterson 79018
   Masterson 79058
Chapel Hill (Tyler) 75707
Chapman (Henderson) 75652
Chapman Ranch 78347
Chappell Hill 77426
Charco (Goliad) 77963
Charlotte 78011
Chat (Hillsboro) 76645
Chatfield 75105
Cheapside (Cuero) 77954
Cheek (Beaumont) 77705
Cherokee 76832
Cherry Spring 78624
  (Fredericksburg)
Chester 75936
Chesterville 77435
  (East Bernard)
Chico 76431
Chicota 75425
Chihuahua (Mission) 78572
Childress 79201
Chillicothe 79225
Chilton 76632
China 77613
China Spring 76633
Chireno 75937
Chita (Trinity) 75862
Choice (Center) 75935
Chriesman 77838
Christine 78012
Christoval 76935
Church Hill (Henderson) ... 75652
Cibolo 78108
Circleville (Taylor) ... 76574, 78736
Cisco 76437
Cistern (Flatonia) 78941
Citrus City (Mission) 78572
City By The Sea 78336
  (Aransas Pass)
City Of Amarillo 79165, 79186
City Of Lubbock (Lubbock) 79457
Clairemont (Snyder) 79549
Clarendon 79226
Clark (Cleveland) 77327
Clarks (Port Lavaca) 77979
Clarksville 75426, 78703
Clarksville City 75693
  (White Oak)
Claude 79019
Clawson (Lufkin) 75901
Clay 77839
Clay Hill (Teague) 75860

Glenn Heights 75115	
Deanville 77852	
Decatur 76234	
Decker Prairie (Magnolia) . 77355	
Deer Park 77536	
Del Rio (Carta Valley)	
.... 78840-843, 78847	
Del Valle 78617	
Delhi (Rosanky) 78953	
Dell City 79837	
Delmita 78536	
Delrose (Gilmer) 75644	
Denison 75020-021	
Denning (San Augustine) .. 75972	
Dennis 76439	
Denny (Kosse) 76653	
Denson Spring (Grapeland) 75844	
Denton 76201-208	
Corinth 76205	
Hickory Creek 76205	
Shady Shores 76205	
Denver City 79323	
Deport 75435	
Derby (Dilley) 78017	
Dermott (Snyder) 79549	
Desdemona 76445	
Desoto (De Soto) 75115	
Dessau (Austin) 78753	
Detmold (Thorndale) 76577	
Detroit 75436	
Devers 77538	
Devine 78016	
Dew (Buffalo) 75831, 75860	
Dewalt (Sugar Land) 77479	
Deweyville 77614	
Dialville (Rusk) 75785	
Diamond Shamrock (Amarillo)	
.... 79161, 79173, 79188	
Diana 75640	
Diboll 75941	
Dickens 79229	
Dickinson 77539	
Dies (Woodville) 75979	
Dike 75437	
Dilley 78017	
Dilworth (Gonzales) 78629	
Dime Box 77853	
Dimmitt 79027	
Dinero 78350	
Dinsmore (Wharton) 77488	
Dirgin (Tatum) 75691	
Divot (Dilley) 78017	
Doak Springs (Lincoln) 78948	
Dobbin 77333	
Dodd City 75438	
Dodge 77334	
Dodson 79230	
Dogwood (Woodville) 75979	
Dogwood Acres (Porter) 77365	
Dogwood City (Flint) 75762	
Domino (Queen City) 75572	
Donie 75838	
Donna 78537	
Doole 76836	
Dorchester (Howe) 75459	
Doss (Linden) 75563, 78618	
Dot (Eddy) 76524	
Dotson (Long Branch) 75669	
Double Oak (Lewisville) 75067	
Doucette 75942	
Dougherty 79231	

Douglass 75943	
Douglassville 75560	
Drasco (Winters) 79567	
Dreka (Shelbyville) 75973	
Dreyer (Shiner) 77984	
Driftwood 78619	
Dripping Springs 78620	
Driscoll 78351	
Dryden 78851	
Dubina (Schulenburg) 78956	
Dublin 76446	
Duffau (Hico) 76457	
Duke (Rosharon) 77583	
Dumas 79029	
Dumont 79232	
Duncanville 75116, 75137-138	
Dundee (Holliday) 76366	
Dunlay (Hondo) 78861	
Dunn 79516	
Durango (Lott) 76656	
Dyess Air Force Base 79607	
(Dyess AFB)	
Eagle Lake 77434	
Eagle Pass 78852-853	
Early (Brownwood) 76801	
Earth 79031	
East Bernard 77435	
East Columbia 77486	
(West Columbia)	
East Hamilton 75973	
(Shelbyville)	
East Liberty (Center) 75935	
East Mayfield (Hemphill) ... 75948	
East Mountain (Gilmer) 75644	
East Side (De Berry) 75639	
East Texas Center (Tyler) .. 75708	
East View (Kilgore) 75662	
Eastgate (Dayton) 77535	
Eastland 76448	
Easton 75641	
Ebenezer (Pittsburg) 75686	
Echo (Coleman) 76834	
Echols (Coolidge) 76635	
Eckert (Willow City) 78675	
Ecleto 78111	
Ector 75439	
Edcouch 78538	
Eddy 76524	
Eden 76837	
Edgar (Cuero) 77954	
Edge (Bryan) 77801	
Edgecliff (Fort Worth) 76134	
Edgewood 75117	
Edgeworth (Rogers) 76569	
Edinburg 78539-540	
Faysville 78539	
Lull 78539	
Palmview 78539	
Red Gate 78539	
San Carlos 78539	
Edmonson 79032	
Edna 77957	
Edom (Brownsboro) 75756	
Edroy 78352	
Egypt 77436	
El Campo 77437	
El Centro 78536, 78577	
(Delmita)	
El Gato (Alamo) 78516	
El Indio 78860	
El Jardin (Brownsville) 78520	

El Lago (Seabrook) 77586	
El Paso (Anthony) 79821	
.... 79900-908, 79910-918	
.... 79920, 79922-927	
.... 79930-932, 79934-938	
.... 79940-955, 79958	
.... 79960-961, 79966, 79968	
.... 79973-978, 79980	
.... 79982-999, 88510-521	
.... 88523-536, 88538-550	
.... 88553-563, 88565-589	
7 Oaks 88570-88574	
A C Nielsen 79966	
A C Nielsen 79973-79974	
Biggs Field 79908, 79918	
Fort Bliss 79906, 79916	
Gage Marketing 88575-88586	
Horizon City 79927	
Nielsen Corp 79977	
Socorro 79927	
Southern Union Gas Co 79976	
Texas Commerce Bank 79980	
Univ Of Tx At El Paso . 79968	
El Sauz (Rio Grande City) . 78582	
El Toro (Edna) 77957	
Elbert 76359	
Eldorado 76936	
Electra 76360	
Elevation (Milano) 76556	
Elgin 78621	
Elk (Axtell) 76624	
Elkhart 75839	
Ellinger 78938	
Ellington Field (Houston) ... 77209	
Elm Grove (Eagle Lake) 77434	
Elm Mott 76640	
Elmaton 77440	
Elmendorf 78112	
Elmo 75118	
Elmwood (Palestine) 75801	
Eloise (Reagan) 76680	
Elroy (Del Valle) 78617	
Elsa 78543	
Elwood (Midway) 75852	
Elysian Fields 75642	
Emerald Bay (Bullard) 75757	
Emilee (Woodville) 75979	
Emmett (Frost) 76641	
Emory 75440	
Encinal 78019	
Encino 78353	
Energas (Amarillo) 79163	
Energy 76452	
Engelman (Elsa) 78543	
Engle (Schulenburg) 78956	
Enloe 75441	
Ennis 75119-120	
Enoch (Gilmer) 75644	
Enochs 79324	
Enterprise (Jacksonville) ... 75766	
Eola 76937	
Era 76238	
Erin (Jasper) 75951	
Escobares 78582	
(Rio Grande City)	
Escobas (Hebbronville) 78361	
Estelline 79233	
Estes (Rockport) 78382	
Etoile 75944	
Eula (Clyde) 79510	
Eulalie (Timpson) 75975	

Euless 76039-040	
Eulogy (Kopperl) 76652	
Eustace 75124	
Evadale 77615	
Evant 76525	
Evergreen (Cleveland) 77327	
Everitt (Cleveland) 77327	
Everman (Fort Worth) 76140	
Ewell (Gilmer) 75644	
Eylau (Texarkana) 75501	
Ezzell (Hallettsville) 77964	
Fabens 79838	
Fair Oaks Ranch (Boerne) 78006	
Fair Play (Beckville) 75631	
Fairchilds (Needville) 77461	
Fairdale (Hemphill) 75948	
Fairfield 75840	
Fairmount (Hemphill) 75948	
Fairview (Mc Kinney) 75069	
.... 75784	
Faker (Pittsburg) 75686	
Falcon (Roma) 78584	
Falcon Heights 78545	
Falfurrias 78355	
Fallon (Mexia) 76667	
Falls City 78113	
Fannett (Beaumont) 77705	
Fannin 77960	
Farmers Branch (Dallas) .. 75234	
.... 75244	
Farmersville 75442	
Farnsworth 79033	
Farrar (Buffalo) 75831, 75838	
Farrsville (Wiergate) 75977	
Farwell 79325	
Fashing (Campbellton) 78008	
Fate 75132	
Fayetteville 78940	
Faysville (Edinburg) 78539	
Fedor (Lincoln) 78948	
Fentress 78622	
Ferris 75125	
Fieldton 79326	
Fife (Brady) 76825	
Figridge (Stowell) 77661	
Fincastle (Frankston) 75763	
Fink (Pottsboro) 75076	
Firm Cases 78284-286	
(San Antonio)	
Fischer 78623	
Fisk (Coleman) 76834	
Fitze (Garrison) 75946	
Flat 76526	
Flat Fork (Tenaha) 75974	
Flatonia 78941	
Flatwood (Ben Wheeler) .. 75754	
Flint 75762	
Flo (Buffalo) 75831	
Flomot 79234	
Florence 76527	
Floresville 78114	
Flowella (Falfurrias) 78355	
Flower Mound (Lewisville) 75028	
Flowermound (Lewisville) . 75028	
Floy (Flatonia) 78941	
Floyd (Greenville) 75401	
Floydada 79235	
Fluvanna 79517	
Flynn 77855	
Follett 79034	
Fondren (Webster) 77598	

Fords Corner 75972	
(San Augustine)	
Fordtran (Yoakum) 77995	
Forest (Alto) 75925	
Forest Glade (Mexia) 76667	
Forest Hill (Quitman) 75783	
.... 76119	
Forest Hills (Fort Worth) .. 76140	
Forestburg 76239	
Forney 75126	
Forreston 76041	
Forsan 79733	
Fort Bliss (El Paso) 79906	
.... 79908, 79916	
Fort Davis 79734	
Fort Gates (Gatesville) 76528	
Fort Hancock 79839	
Fort Hood (Killeen) 76544	
Fort Mc Kavett 76841	
Fort Ringgold 78582	
(Rio Grande City)	
Fort Sam Houston 78234	
(San Antonio)	
Fort Stockton 79735	
Fort Wolters 76067	
(Mineral Wells)	
Fort Worth 76100-124	
.... 76126-127, 76129-137	
... 76140, 76147-148, 76150	
.... 76155, 76161-164	
.... 76177-182, 76185	
.... 76191-193, 76195-199	
Benbrook 76126	
Blue Mound 76131	
Colonial Financial 76195	
Edgecliff 76134	
Everman 76140	
FAA 76193	
Forest Hill 76119, 76140	
Haltom City 76117	
Interfirst Bank 76197	
Lake Worth 76135-76136	
Lakeside 76108	
North Richland Hills	
.... 76118, 76180, 76182	
Richland Hills .. 76118, 76180	
River Oaks 76114	
Saginaw 76131, 76179	
Sansom Park 76114	
South W B T South ... 76122	
Tarrant County	
Courthouse 76196	
Watauga 76148	
Westover Hills 76107	
Westworth 76114	
White Settlement 76108	
Four Points (Austin) 78732	
Fowlerton 78021	
Frame Switch (Taylor) 76574	
Francitas 77961	
Franklin 77856	
Frankston 75763	
Frankston Lake 75763	
(Frankston)	
Fred 77616	
Fredericksburg 78624	
Fredonia (Kilgore) .. 75662, 76842	
Fredonia Hill 75961	
(Nacogdoches)	
Freeport 77541	
Freer 78357	

Freestone (Buffalo)	
.... 75831, 75838, 75860	
Fresno 77545	
Freyburg (Schulenburg) 78956	
Friar (Overton) 75684	
Friday (Groveton) 75845	
Friendship (Granger) 76530	
Friendswood 77546, 77549	
Frio Town (Pearsall) 78061	
Friona 79035	
Frisco 75034	
Fritch 79036	
Fronton (Roma) 78584	
Frost 76641	
Fruitland (Bowie) 76230	
Fruitvale 75127	
Frydek (Sealy) 77474	
Fuller Springs (Lufkin) 75901	
Fulshear 77441	
Fulton 78358	
Furney Richardson 75860	
(Teague)	
Fussel (Laneville) 75667	
Gail79738	
Gainesville 76240-241	
Lake Kiowa 76240	
Galena Park 77547	
Gallatin 75764	
Galloway (Atlanta) 75551	
Galveston 77550, 77552-555	
Island 77550	
Jamaica Beach 77550	
Virginia Point 77550	
West Galveston 77554	
Ganado 77962	
Gano (Thorndale) 76577	
Garceno (Rio Grande City) 78582	
Garciasville 78547	
Garden City (Houston) 77088	
.... 79739	
Garden Ridge 78266	
(San Antonio)	
Garden Valley (Lindale) 75771	
Gardendale 79758	
Garfield (Del Valle) 78617	
Garland 75040-049, 75559	
Sachse 75048	
Garrison 75946	
Garth (Baytown) 77520	
Garwood 77442	
Gary 75643	
Gatesville	
.... 76528, 76576, 76597-598	
Ames 76528	
Arnett 76528	
Ater 76528	
Fort Gates 76528	
Ireland 76528	
Levita 76528	
Mountain 76528	
Pidcoke 76528	
The Grove 76576	
Turnersville 76528	
White Hall 76528	
Gause 77857	
Gay Hill (Brenham) 77833	
Geneva 75947	
George West 78022	
Georgetown 78626-628	
Andice 78628	
Jonah 78626	

Gerald (Elm Mott)	76640	
Geronimo	78115	
Gholson (Waco)	76705	
Giddings	78942	
Gilbert (Lufkin)	75901	
Gilchrist	77617	
Gill (Marshall)	75670	
Gillett (Ecleto)	78111, 78116	
Gilmer	75644	
Girard	79518	
Girvin	79740	
Gladewater	75647	
Glass (Walnut Springs)	76690	
Glaze City (Shiner)	77984	
Glazier (Canadian)	79014	
Glecker (Schulenburg)	78956	
Glen Flora	77443	
Glen Rose	76043	
Glendale (Trinity)	75862	
Glenn Heights (De Soto)	75115	
Glenwood (Gilmer)	75644	
Glidden	78943	
Gober	75443	
Godley	76044	
Gold (Fredericksburg)	78624	
Golden	75444	
Golden Acres (Pasadena)	77503	
Goldsboro	79519	
Goldsmith	79741	
Goldthwaite	76844	
Goliad	77963	
Golinda (Lorena)	76655	
Gonzales	78629	
Goober Hill (Shelbyville)	75973	
Good Hope (Center)	75935	
Good Springs (Henderson)	75652	
Goodland (Sudan)	79371	
Goodrich	77335	
Goodville (Lott)	76656	
Gordon	76453	
Gordonville	76245	
Goree	76363	
Gorman	76454	
Gouldbusk	76845, 76889	
Graceton (Gilmer)	75644	
Graford	76449	
Graham	76450	
Granbury	76048-049	
Grand Bluff (Beckville)	75631	
Grand Prairie	75050-054	
Grand Saline	75140	
Grandfalls	79742	
Grandview (Texarkana)	75501	
	76050	
Grange Hall (Marshall)	75670	
Granger	76530	
Grangerland (Conroe)	77302	
Granite Shoals	78654	
(Marble Falls)		
Granjeno (Mission)	78572	
Grapeland	75844	
Grapevine	76051	
	76092, 76099	
Southlake	76092	
Gray (Jefferson)	75657	
Grayburg (Sour Lake)	77659	
Green Lake (Port Lavaca)	77979	
Greens Bayou (Houston)	77015	
Greenville	75401-404	
Floyd	75401	
Greenway Plaza (Houston)	77046	

Greenwood	76246	
Gregg (Manor)	78653	
Greggton (Longview)	75604-605	
Gregory	78359	
Gresham (Tyler)	75703, 75762	
Grey Forest (Helotes)	78023	
Grice (Gilmer)	75644	
Griffin (Troup)	75789	
Griffing (Port Arthur)	77640	
Grigsby (Center)	75935	
Grindstone (Fairfield)	75840	
Groesbeck	76642	
Groom	79039	
Grosvenor (Brownwood)	76801	
Groves	77619	
Groveton	75845	
Grulla	78548	
Gruver	79040	
Guadalupe (Victoria)	77901	
Guajillo (Alice)	78332	
Guerra	78360	
Gulf Oil (Dallas)	75323	
Gum Springs	75560, 75601	
(Douglassville)		
Gun Barrel City (Mabank)	75147	
Gunter	75058	
Gustine	76455	
Guthrie	79236	
Guy	77444	
Guys Store (Centerville)	75833	
Haid (Lane City)	77453	
Hainesville (Mineola)	75773	
Halbert (Shelbyville)	75973	
Hale Center	79041	
Hallettsville	77964	
Hallsburg (Waco)	76705	
Hallsville	75650	
Halsted (La Grange)	78945	
Haltom City (Fort Worth)	76117	
Hamby (Abilene)	79601	
Hamilton	76531	
Hamlin	79520	
Hammond (Bremond)	76629	
Hamon (Gonzales)	78629	
Hamshire	77622	
Hankamer	77560	
Hanson (Joaquin)	75954	
Happy	79042	
Happy Valley (Wingate)	79566	
Hardin	77561	
Hare (Taylor)	76574	
Hargill	78549	
Harker Heights	76541-543	
(Killeen)		
Harkeyville (San Saba)	76877	
Harleton	75651	
Harlingen	78550-553	
Adams Gardens	78550	
Arroyo	78550	
Avondale	78550	
Hgn	78550	
Kayare	78550	
Primera	78550	
Stuart Place	78550	
Harmony (Overton)	75684	
Harper	78631	
Harrisburg (Jasper)	75951	
Harrold	76364	
Hart	79043	
Hartley	79044	
Harvard (Pittsburg)	75686	

Harwood	78632	
Haskell	79521	
Haslam (Joaquin)	75954	
Haslet	76052	
Hasse	76456	
Hatchel (Winters)	79567	
Haukanier (Hankamer)	77560	
Havana (Mission)	78572	
Hawkins	75765	
Hawley	79525	
Headsville (Kosse)	76653	
Hearne	77859	
Heath (Rockwall)	75087	
Hebbronville	78361	
Hedley	79237	
Hedwig Village (Houston)	77024	
Heidelberg (Mercedes)	78570	
Heidenheimer	76533	
Heights (Houston)	77008	
Helmic (Groveton)	75845	
Helotes	78023	
Hemphill	75948	
Hempstead	77445	
Henderson	75652-653, 75680	
Antioch	75652	
Chapman	75652	
Church Hill	75652	
Craig	75652	
Crimcrest	75652	
Good Springs	75652	
Lake Cherokee	75652	
Liberty	75652	
Mcknight	75652	
New Prospect	75652	
New Salem	75652	
Oak Hill	75652	
Oakland	75652	
Pinehill	75652	
Pleasant Grove	75652	
Stewart	75652	
Henkhaus (Shiner)	77984	
Henly (Dripping Springs)	78620	
Henning (Garrison)	75946	
Henrietta	76365	
Henrys Chapel (Troup)	75789	
Hereford	79045	
Hermleigh	79526	
Herty (Lufkin)	75901	
Hewitt	76643	
Hext	76848	
Hgn (Harlingen)	78550	
Hickory Creek (Denton)	76205	
Hico	76457	
Hidalgo	78557	
Hidden Valley (Garrison)	75946	
Hide A Way Lake (Lindale)	75771	
Higgins	79046	
High Hill (Schulenburg)	78956	
High Island	77623	
Highland Park (Dallas)	75205	
Highland Village	75067	
(Lewisville)		
Highlands	77562	
Hill (Bastrop)	78602	
Hill Country Village	78232	
(San Antonio)		
Hillcrest (Columbus)	78934	
Hillister	77624	
Hillje (El Campo)	77437	
Hills (Paige)	78659	
Hillsboro	76645	

Hilltop Lakes (Normangee) 77871
Hilshire Village 77055
(Houston)
Hitchcock 77563
Hoard (Mineola) 75773
Hobson 78117
Hochheim 77967
Hockley 77447
Hockley Mine (Hockley) 77447
Hodgson (De Kalb) 75559
Holland 76534
Holliday 76366
Holly Springs (Jasper) 75951
Hollywood Park 78232
(San Antonio)
Holman (La Grange) 78945
Homer (Lufkin) 75901
Hondo 78861
Honey Grove 75446
Honey Island (Kountze) 77625
Hooks 75561
Hope (Yoakum) 77995
Hopewell (Crockett) 75835
Horizon City (El Paso) 79927
Hornsby Bend (Austin) 78725
Horseshoe Bay 78654
(Marble Falls)
Horton (De Berry) 75639
Houston .. 77000-099, 77201-210
.... 77212-213, 77215-231
.... 77233-238, 77240-245
.... 77248-263, 77265-275
.... 77277, 77279-282, 77284
.... 77287-293, 77297-299
    Addicks 77079
    Addicks Barker 77084
    Aldine 77039
    Astrodome 77025
    Astroworld 77025
    Bammel 77040
    Bunker Hill Village 77024
    Clear Lake City 77058
    Cloverleaf 77015
    Ellington Field 77209
    First City Nat Bank 77212
    Greens Bayou 77015
    Greenway Plaza 77046
    Hedwig Village 77024
    Heights 77008
    Hilshire Village 77055
    Hunters Creek Village . 77024
    Jacinto City 77029
    Jersey Village 77040
    Kohrville 77040
    Memorial Park . 77024, 77079
    .... 77094, 77224, 77279
    Nassau Bay 77058, 77258
    Piney Point 77024
    Satsuma 77040
    Sharpstown 77036
    Sheldon 77028
    Southside Place 77005
    Spring Valley 77024
    Texas Commerce Bank 77216
    Trammells 77045
    University Of Houston . 77204
    V A Hospital 77030
    West University Place . 77005
Howe 75459
Howellville (Alief) 77411
Hoxie (Taylor) 76574

Hoyte (Cameron) 76520
Hubbard 76648
Hubert (Mathis) 78368
Hudson (Lufkin) 75901
Hudson Bend (Austin) 78734
Huffman 77336
Hufsmith 77337
Hughes Springs 75656
Hull 77564
Humble 77325, 77338-339
.... 77345-347, 77396
    Atascocita 77346
    Bordersville 77338
    Kingwood 77325
    Kingwood 77339
    Kingwood 77345
Hungerford 77448
Hunt 78024
Hunter (New Braunfels) 78132
Hunters Creek Village 77024
(Houston)
Huntington 75949
Huntsville 77340-344, 77348-349
    Crabbs Prairie 77340
    Phelps 77340
    TX State Prison 77348-77349
Hurst 76053-054
Hurst Springs (Clifton) 76634
Hurstown (Shelbyville) 75973
Hutchins 75141
Hutto 78634
Huxley (Shelbyville) 75973
Hye 78635
Iago (Boling) 77420
Iatan (Westbrook) 79565
Idalou 79329
Impact (Abilene) 79603
Imperial 79743
Inadale (Roscoe) 79545
Independence (Brenham) . 77833
Indian Creek (Brownwood) 76801
Indian Gap (Hamilton) 76531
Indian Hill (Wiergate) 75977
Indian Rock (Gilmer) 75644
Indianola (Port Lavaca) 77979
Industry 78944
Inez 77968
Ingleside 78362
Ingram 78025
Inks Lake Village 78609
(Buchanan Dam)
Iola 77861
Iowa Beef Packers 79187
(Amarillo)
Iowa Colony (Rosharon) ... 77583
Iowa Park 76367
Ira 79527
Iraan 79744
Iredell 76649
Ireland (Gatesville) 76528
.... 76538
Irene 76650
Ironton (Jacksonville) 75766
Irving 75014-017, 75038-039
.... 75060-063, 75084
    Las Colinas ... 75038-75039
Isabel (Port Isabel) 78578
Island (Midway) 75852, 77550
Italy 76651
Itasca 76055
Ivanhoe 75447

Iverson (Milford) 76670
Izoro (Copperas Cove) 76522
Jacinto City (Houston) 77029
Jacksboro 76458
Jackson (Joaquin) 75954
Jacksonville 75766
Jacobs (Overton) 75684
Jamaica Beach 77550
(Galveston)
James (Center) 75935
Jamestown (Wiergate) 75977
Jarrell 76537
Jasper 75951
Jayton 79528
Jeddo (Rosanky) 78953
Jefferson 75657
Jenkins (Daingerfield) 75638
Jericho (Center) 75935
Jermyn 76459
Jersey Village (Houston) ... 77040
Jester (Purdon) 76679
Jewett 75846
Joaquin 75954
Johnson City 78636
Joinerville 75658
Joliet (Luling) 78648
Jollyville (Austin) 78729
Jonah (Georgetown) 78626
Jones Creek (El Campo) ... 77437
.... 77541
Jones Prairie (Cameron) ... 76520
Jonesboro 76538
Jonestown (Leander) 78645
Jonesville 75659
Joppa (Bertram) 78605
Jordans Store 75973
(Shelbyville)
Josephine 75164
Joshua 76058
Josserand (Groveton) 75845
Jourdanton 78026
Jud (Rochester) 79544
Judson 75660
Juliff (Rosharon) 77583
Junction 76849
Justiceburg 79330
Justin 76247
Kamay 76369
Kamey (Port Lavaca) 77979
Kane (Mcallen) 78501
Karnack 75661
Karnes City 78118
Katemcy (Brady) 76825
Katy 77449-450, 77491-494
    Park Row ... 77493-77494
Kaufman 75142
Kayare (Harlingen) 78550
Keechi (Buffalo) 75831
Keene 76059
Keller 76244, 76248
Keller Corner 78520
(Brownsville)
Kellerville (Mclean) 79057
Kelsay (Encino) 78353
Kelsey (Gilmer) 75644
Keltys (Lufkin) 75901
Kemah 77565
Kemp 75143
Kempner 76539
Kendalia 78027
Kendleton 77451

Kenedy 78119, 78125	(Rio Grande City)	Laredo 78040-044, 78049
Kenefick (Dayton) 77535	La Coste 78039	Rio Bravo 78043
Kennard 75847	La Feria 78559	Larue 75770
Kennedale 76060	La Gloria (Santa Elena) 78591	Las Colinas (Irving) 75038-039
Kennedy Shores 78520	La Grange 78945	Las Milpas (Pharr) 78577
(Brownsville)	La Joya 78560	Las Rusias (San Benito) ... 78586
Kenney 77452	La Marque 77568	Lasara 78561
Kent (Van Horn) 79855	La Paloma (San Benito) 78586	Latch (Gilmer) 75644
Kerens 75144	La Porte 77571-572	Latex (Panola) 75685
Kermit 79745	Lomax 77571	Latexo 75849
Kerrick 79051	Morgans Point 77571	Laureles (San Benito) 78586
Kerrville 78028-029	Shoreacres 77571	Lavon 75166
Kickapoo (Frankston) 75763	Sylvan Beach 77571	Law (Bryan) 77801
Kildare 75562	La Pryor 78872	Lawn 79530
Kilgore 75662-663	La Reforma (Delmita) 78536	Lazbuddie 79053
Cross Roads 75662	La Salle 77969	Lbb (Lubbock) 79400
Danville 75662	La Tijera (Donna) 78537	Lbk (Lubbock) 79400
East View 75662	La Vernia 78121	Leaday (Voss) 76888
Fredonia 75662	La Villa 78562	League City 77573-574
Liberty City 75662	La Ward 77970	Leagueville (Murchison) ... 75778
Melrose 75662	Lacy (Groveton) 75845	Leakey 78873
Monroe 75662	Lacy Lakeview (Waco) 76705	Leander 78641, 78645
New Hope 75662	Ladonia 75449	Jonestown 78645
Rolling Meadows 75662	Lafayette (Pittsburg) 75686	Lago Vista 78645
Killeen 76540-547	Lafkin (La Feria) 78559	Volente 78641
Chaffee Villiage 76544	Lago Vista (Leander) 78645	Whitestone 78641
Clear Creek 76544	Laguna Park (Clifton) 76634	Leary (Texarkana) .. 75501, 75561
Fort Hood 76544	Laguna Vista 78578	Ledbetter 78946
Harker Heights .. 76541-76543	(Port Isabel)	Leedale (Rogers) 76569
Maxdale 76542	Laird Hill 75666	Leesburg 75451
Mcnair Villiage 76544	Lake Brownwood 76801	Leesville 78122
Montague Village 76544	(Brownwood)	Lefors 79054
Oakalla 76543	Lake Cherokee 75652	Leggett 77350
Youngsport 76542	(Henderson)	Leigh (Karnack) 75661
Kimball (Kopperl) 76652	Lake Creek 75450	Lelia Lake 79240
Kimbro (Manor) 78653	Lake Dallas 75065	Leming 78050
Kingsbury 78638	Lake Jackson 77566	Lenorah 79749
Kingsland 78639	Lake Jacksonville 75766	Leo (Lexington) 78947
Kingsville 78363-364	(Jacksonville)	Leon Junction 76552
Ricardo 78363	Lake Kiowa (Gainesville) .. 76240	Leon Valley 78238, 78268
Kingwood (Humble) 77325	Lake Ransom Canyon 79364	(San Antonio)
.... 77339, 77345	(Slaton)	Leona 75850
Kinkler (Hallettsville) 77964	Lake Shore (Brownwood) . 76801	Leonard 75452
Kirby (San Antonio) 78219	Lake Victor (Lampasas) 76550	Leroy 76654
Kirbyville 75956	Lakehills (Pipe Creek) 78063	Levelland 79336, 79338
Kirk (Mart) 76664	Lakeland (Conroe) 77301	Pettit 79336
Kirkland 79201, 79238	Lakeport (Longview) 75603	Leveretts Chapel 75684
(Childress)	Lakeside (Fort Worth) 76108	(Overton)
Kirtley (Smithville) 78957	Lakeside City 76308	Levi (Lorena) 76655
Kirvin 75848	(Wichita Falls)	Levita (Gatesville) 76528
Kittrell (Trinity) 75862	Lakeside Village (Morgan) 76671	Lewisville 75028-029
Kleberg (Dallas) 75253	Lakeview (Waco) 76705	.... 75056-057, 75067
Klein (Spring) 77379, 77391	.... 77640, 77662, 79239	Double Oak 75067
Klondike 75448	Lakeway (Austin) .. 78734, 78738	Flower Mound 75028
Knickerbocker 76939	Lakewood (Baytown) 77520	Flowermound 75028
Knippa 78870	Lakewood Harbor (Clifton) 76634	Highland Village 75067
Knott 79748	Lakewood Village 75068	The Colony 75056
Knox City 79529	(Little Elm)	Lexington 78947
Knoxville (Harper) 78631	Lamar (Rockport) 78382	Libby (Nacogdoches) 75961
Koerth (Hallettsville) 77964	Lamesa 79331	Liberty (Henderson) 75652
Kohrville (Houston) 77040	Lampasas 76550	 77575
Kopperl 76652	Lanark (Queen City) 75572	Ames 77575
Kosse 76653	Lancaster 75134, 75146	Moss Bluff 77575
Kountze 77625	Landrum (San Benito) 78586	Moss Hill 77575
Kovar (Flatonia) 78941	Lane City 77453	Liberty City (Kilgore) 75662
Kress 79052	Lanely (Buffalo) 75831	Liberty Hill 78642
Krum 76249	Laneport (Taylor) 76574	Lilac (Thorndale) 76577
Kurten 77862	Laneville 75667	Lillian 76061
Kyle 78640	Langtry 78871	Lily Island (Camden) 75934
La Blanca 78558	Lanham (Jonesboro) 76538	Lincoln 78948
La Casita 78582	Lanier (Linden) 75563	Lindale 75771

Linden	75563
Lindenau (Cuero)	77954
Lindsay	76250
Lingleville	76441
Linn	78563
Linwood (Alto)	75925
Lipan	76462
Lipscomb	79056
Lissie	77454
Littig (Elgin)	78621
Little Elm	75068
Little River	76554
Littlefield	79339
Live Oak (San Antonio)	78233
Liverpool	77577
Livingston	77351
Llano	78643
Lochridge (Rosharon)	77583
Lockhart	78644
Lockney	79241
Lodi	75564
Loebau (Lincoln)	78948
Lohn	76852
Lolita	77971
Lomax (La Porte)	77571
Lometa	76853
London	76854
Lone Mountain (Gilmer)	75644
Lone Oak	75453, 78940
Lone Star	75558, 75668
(Cookville)	
Long Branch	75669
Long Mott	77972
Long Point	75661, 77461
(Karnack)	
Longview	75601-608, 75615
Greggton	75604-605
Gum Springs	75601
Lakeport	75603
Pinewood	75602
Spring Hill	75604
Tenneryville	75601
Longworth (Roby)	79543
Loop	79342
Lopeno	78564
Lopezville (San Juan)	78589
Loraine	79532
Lorena	76655
Lorenzo	79343
Los Angeles (Cotulla)	78014
Los Coyotes (Lyford)	78569
Los Cuates (San Benito)	78586
Los Ebanos	78565
Los Fresnos	78566
Los Indios	78567
Los Saenz (Roma)	78584
Lott	76656
Louise	77455
Lovelace (Hillsboro)	76645
Lovelady	75851
Loving	76460
Lowake	76855
Loyola Beach (Riviera)	78379
Lozano	78568
Lubbock	79400-416, 79423-424
...	79430, 79452-453, 79457
...	79464, 79489-491, 79493
	79499
City Of Lubbock	79457
Lucas (Allen)	75002
Luckenbach	78624

(Fredericksburg)	
Lueders	79533
Lufkin	75901-904, 75915
Bald Hill	75901
Cedar Grove	75901
Clawson	75901
Davisville	75901
Fuller Springs	75901
Gilbert	75901
Herty	75901
Homer	75901
Hudson	75901
Keltys	75901
Moffett	75901
Providence	75901
Red Town	75901
Redland	75901
Woodlawn	75901
Luling	78648
Lull (Edinburg)	78539
Lumberton	77711, 77657
Lund (Elgin)	78621
Lyford	78569
Lynchburg (Baytown)	77520
Lyons	77863
Lytle	78052
Lytton Springs (Dale)	78616
Mabank	75147
Macdona	78054
Macedonia (Texarkana)	75501
Mackay (Wharton)	77488
Macune (San Augustine)	75972
Madero (Mission)	78572
Madisonville	77864
Magnet (Wharton)	77488
Magnolia	77355
Magnolia Beach	77979
(Port Lavaca)	
Mahl (Nacogdoches)	75961
Mahomet (Bertram)	78605
Malakoff	75148
Malone	76660
Malta (New Boston)	75570
Manchaca	78652
Manda (Manor)	78653
Manheim (Paige)	78659
Manor	78653
Mansfield	76063
Manvel	77578
Maple	79344
Mapleton (Crockett)	75835
Marathon	79842
Marble Falls	78654, 78657
Marfa	79843
Marietta	75566
Marion	78124
Markham	77456
Marlin	76661
Marquez	77865
Marshall	75670-671
Blocker	75670
Cave Springs	75670
Crossroads	75670
Darco	75670
Gill	75670
Grange Hall	75670
Nesbitt	75670
Marshall Ford (Austin)	78732
Mart	76664
Martindale	78655
Martins Mills	75754

(Ben Wheeler)	
Martinsville	75958
Maryneal	79535
Mason	76856
Massey Lake	75861
(Tennessee Colony)	
Masterson (Channing)	79018
	79058
Matador	79244
Matagorda	77457
Mathis	78368
Matinburg (Pittsburg)	75686
Mattox (Wiergate)	75977
Maud	75567
Mauriceville	77626
Maurin (Gonzales)	78629
Maxdale (Killeen)	76542
Maxwell	78656
May	76857
Maydelle	75772
Mayflower (Wiergate)	75977
Maypearl	76064
Maysfield	76555
Mc Adoo	79243
Mc Allen	78501-505
Bonner	78501
Kane	78501
Mccoll	78501
Mc Beth (Angleton)	77515
Mc Camey	79752
Mc Caulley	79534
Mc Clanahan (Marlin)	76661
Mc Coll (Mcallen)	78501
Mc Coy	78053
Mc Dade	78650
Mc Faddin	77973
Mc Gregor	76657
Mc Kinney	75069-070
Fairview	75069
Mc Knight (Henderson)	75652
Mc Lean (Mclean)	79057
Mc Leod	75565
Mc Mahan (Dale)	78616
Mc Murray (Abilene)	79605
Mc Murry College (Abilene)	79697
Mc Nair (Baytown)	77520
Mc Nair Villiage (Killeen)	76544
Mc Nary (Fort Hancock)	79839
Mc Neil	78651
Mc Queeney	78123
Meador Grove (Moody)	76557
Meadow	79345
Medina	78055
Medina Lake (Pipe Creek)	78063
Meeks (Burlington)	76519
Megargel	76370
Meldrum (Tenaha)	75974
Melissa	75454
Melrose (Kilgore)	75662, 75961
Melvin	76858
Memorial Park	77024, 77079
	77094, 77224, 77279
(Houston)	
Memphis	79245
Menard	76859
Mendoza (Lockhart)	78644
Menlow (Abbott)	76621
Mentone	79754
Mercedes	78570
Mereta	76940
Meridian	76665

Merit	75458
Merkel	79536
Mertens	76666
Mertzon	76941
Meskill (Texas City)	77590
Mesquite	75149-150
	75180-182, 75185, 75187
Balch Springs	75180
Sunnyvale	75182
Mexia	76667
Meyersville	77974
Miami	79059
Mico (Castroville)	78056
Middleton (Centerville)	75833
Midfield	77458
Midkiff	79755
Midland	79701-712
Midline (Cleveland)	77327
Midlothian	76065
Midway (Winona)	75792, 75852
	76645, 77327
	77984, 78390
Antioch	75852
Elwood	75852
Island	75852
Milam (Geneva)	75947, 75959
Miland	75959
Milane	75959
Milano	75959
Mildland	75959
Miles	75959
Miland (Milam)	75959
Milane (Milam)	75959
Milano (Milam)	75959, 76556
Elevation	76556
Sandy Creek	76556
Mildland (Milam)	75959
Miles (Milam)	75959, 76861
Milford	76670
Mill Pond (Nacogdoches)	75961
Millersview	76862
Millheim (Sealy)	77474
Millican	77866
Millsap	76066
Minden	75680
Mineola	75773
Mineral	78125
Mineral Wells	76067-068
Fort Wolters	76067
Salesville	76067
Minerva (Rockdale)	76567
Mings Chapel (Gilmer)	75644
Mingus	76463
Mirando City	78369
Mission	78572-573
Abram	78572
Alton	78572
Chihuahua	78572
Citrus City	78572
Granjeno	78572
Havana	78572
Madero	78572
Palmhurst	78572
Perezville	78572
Sharyland	78572
Mission Valley (Victoria)	77901
Missouri City	77459, 77489
Mixon (Troup)	75789
Mobeetie	79061
Moffatt (Temple)	76501
Moffett (Lufkin)	75901

Monadale (Hutto)	78634
Monahans	79756
Monaville (Hempstead)	77445
Monroe (Kilgore)	75662
Monroe City (Anahuac)	77514
Mont (Hallettsville)	77964
Mont Belvieu	77580
Montague	76251
Montague Village	76544
(Killeen)	
Montalba	75853
Monte Alto (Edcouch)	78538
Montgomery	77356
Montgomery Ward (Dallas)	75353
Monthalia (Cost)	78614
Montopolis (Austin)	78741
Moody	76557
Moore	78057
Moore Station (Larue)	75770
Moores Crossing (Austin)	78719
Mooresville (Chilton)	76632
Morales (Edna)	77957
Moran	76464
Moravia (Schulenburg)	78956
Morgan	76671
Morgan Mill	76465
Morgans Point (La Porte)	77571
Morgans Point Resort	76513
(Belton)	
Morris Ranch	78624
(Fredericksburg)	
Morse	79062
Morton (Diana)	75640, 79346
Moscow	75960
Mosheim (Valley Mills)	76689
Moss Bluff (Liberty)	77575
Moss Hill (Liberty)	77575
Moulton	77975
Mound	76558
Mound City (Grapeland)	75844
Mount Belvieu	77580
Mount Calm	76673
Mount Enterprise	75681, 75773
Mount Lucas (Dinero)	78350
Mount Olive (Shiner)	77984
Mount Pleasant	75455-456
Mount Selman (Bullard)	75757
Mount Sharp	78620
(Dripping Springs)	
Mount Sylvan (Lindale)	75771
Mount Union (Kirbyville)	75956
Mount Vernon	75457
Mountain (Gatesville)	76528
Mountain Home	78058
Mozelle (Coleman)	76834
Muenster	76252
Muldoon	78949
Muleshoe	79347
Mullin	76864
Mullins Prairie	78945
(La Grange)	
Mumford	77867
Munday	76371
Murchison	75778
Murphy (Plano)	75074, 75094
Mustang (Coolidge)	76635
Myra	76253
Nacogdoches	75961-964
Alazan	75961
Appleby	75961
Attoyac	75961

Caro	75961
Central Heights	75961
Fredonia Hill	75961
Libby	75961
Mahl	75961
Melrose	75961
Mill Pond	75961
Oak Ridge	75961
Orton Hill	75961
Redfield	75961
Swift	75961
Trawick	75961
Union Springs	75961
University Place	75961
Nada	77460
Nancy (Zavalla)	75980
Naples	75568
Naruna (Lampasas)	76550
Nash	75569
Nassau (Round Top)	78961
Nassau Bay (Houston)	77058
	77258
Natalia	78059
Navarro (Corsicana)	75110
Navarro Mills (Purdon)	76679
Navasota	77868-869
Nazareth	79063
Nechanitz (Ledbetter)	78946
Neches	75779
Nederland	77627
Needa (Cost)	78614
Needville	77461
Nelsonville (Bellville)	77418
Nemo	76070
Nesbitt (Marshall)	75670, 76629
Neuville (Center)	75935
Nevada	75173
New Baden	77870
New Boston	75570
New Braunfels	78130-133
Canyon Lake	78130
Canyon Lake	78132-133
Hunter	78132
Sattler	78132-133
Solms	78130
Startzville	78132-133
New Caney	77357
New Clarkson (Rosebud)	76570
New Colony (Linden)	75563
New Corn Hill (Jarrell)	76537
New Deal	79350
New Diana (Diana)	75640
New Harmony (Shelbyville)	75973
New Home	79383
New Hope (Kilgore)	75662
	75756, 75766, 75773
New London	75682
New Mine (Pittsburg)	75686
New Mountain (Gilmer)	75644
New Prospect	75652, 75975
(Henderson)	
New Salem (Henderson)	75652
New Summerfield	75780
New Sweden (Manor)	78653
New Taiton (El Campo)	77437
New Ulm	78950
New Waverly	77358
New York (Larue)	75770
Newark	76071
Newby (Jewett)	75846
Newcastle	76372

Newgulf	77462
Newport (Bowie)	76230
Newton	75966
Nickel (Gonzales)	78629
Niederwald (Kyle)	78640
Nielsen Clearing Refunding (El Paso)	88510-521
	88523-536, 88538-539
Nielsen Corp (El Paso)	79977
Nigton (Apple Springs)	75926
Nile (Thorndale)	76577
Nineveh (Buffalo)	75831, 75833
Nix (Lampasas)	76550
Nixon	78140
Noack (Taylor)	76574
Nocona	76255
Nogalus (Groveton)	75845
Nolan	79537
Nolanville	76559
Nome	77629
Noodle (Merkel)	79536
Noonday (Flint)	75762
Nordheim	78141
Norias (Armstrong)	78338
Normangee	77871
Normanna	78142
Normans Crossing (Taylor)	76574
Norse (Clifton)	76634
North Cedar (Apple Springs)	75926
North Cleveland (Cleveland)	77327
North Houston	77315
North Port Arthur	77640
	77642-643
	(Port Arthur)
North Prairie (Chilton)	76632
North Richland Hills	76118
	76180
	(Fort Worth)
North Vidor (Vidor)	77662
North Zulch	77872
Northcrest (Waco)	76705
Northfield (Childress)	79201
Norton	76865
Norwood (San Augustine)	75972
Notrees	79759
Novice	79538
Novohrad (Moulton)	77975
Noxville (Harper)	78631
Nursery	77976
O' Brien (O Brien)	79539
Oak Forest (Gonzales)	78629
Oak Grove (Quitman)	75783
Oak Hill (Henderson)	75652
	78735-736, 78749
Oak Point (Little Elm)	75068
Oak Ridge (De Kalb)	75559
	75961
Oak Ridge North	77385-386
	(Conroe)
Oakalla (Killeen)	76543
Oakhurst	77359
Oakland (Henderson)	75652
	78951
Oaklawn (Texarkana)	75501
Oakville	78060
Oakwood	75855
Oatmeal (Bertram)	78605
Ocee (Crawford)	76638
Odds (Thornton)	76687

Odell	79247
Odem	78370
Odessa	79760-769
Odonnell	79351
Oenaville (Temple)	76501
Ofarrell (Atlanta)	75551
Oglesby	76561
Oilton	78371
Ojuelas (Mirando City)	78369
Oklaunion	76373
Old Boston (New Boston)	75570
Old Brazoria (Brazoria)	77422
Old Glory	79540
Old Larissa (Bullard)	75757
Old London (New London)	75682
Old Mobeetie (Mobeetie)	79061
Old Moulton (Moulton)	77975
Old Ocean	77463
Old Round Rock	78664
	(Round Rock)
Old Salem (Call)	75933
Old Union (Simms)	75574, 76687
Olden	76466
Oldenburg (Fayetteville)	78940
Oletha (Thornton)	76687
Olivia (Port Lavaca)	77979
Olmito	78575
Olmos (Skidmore)	78389
Olmos Park (San Antonio)	78212
Olney	76374
Olton	79064
Omaha	75571
Omen (Tyler)	75705
Onalaska	77360
Opelika (Murchison)	75778
Oquinn (La Grange)	78945
Orange	77630-632
West Orange	77630
Orange Grove	78372
Orangefield	77639
Orchard	77464
Ore City	75683
Orla	79770
Orton Hill (Nacogdoches)	75961
Osage (Weimar)	78962
Oscar (Temple)	76501
Otey (Rosharon)	77583
Ottine	78658
Otto	76675
Ovalo	79541
Overton	75684
Ovilla (Red Oak)	75154
Owentown (Tyler)	75708, 75792
Oyster Creek (Freeport)	77541
Ozona	76943
Paducah	79248
Pagoda (Trinity)	75862
Paige	78659
Paint Rock	76866
Palacios	77465
Palava (Sweetwater)	79556
Palestine	75801-802, 75882
Elmwood	75801
Palito Blanco (Alice)	78332
Palm Village	78520
	(Brownsville)
Palmer	75152
Palmhurst (Mission)	78572
Palmview (Edinburg)	78539
Palo Alto (Bishop)	78343
Palo Pinto	76484

Paluxy	76467
Pampa	79065-066
Pancake (Jonesboro)	76538
Pandora	78143
Panhandle	75560, 79068
(Douglassville)	
Panna Maria	78144
Panola	75685
Panorama Village (Conroe)	77304
Pantego (Arlington)	76013
Papalote (Sinton)	78387
Paradise	76073
Paris	75460-462
Reno	75462
Park (Fayetteville)	78940
Park Row (Katy)	77449-450
	77493-494
Parker (Allen)	75002
Pasadena	77501-508
Golden Acres	77503
Patroon (Shelbyville)	75973
Pattison	77466
Patton (Splendora)	77372
Pattonville	75468
Pauls Store (Shelbyville)	75973
Pawelekville (Falls City)	78113
Pawnee	78145
Paxton (Joaquin)	75954
Peacock (Aspermont)	79502
Pear Ridge (Port Arthur)	77640
Pear Valley	76867
Pearl City (Yoakum)	77995
Pearland	77581, 77584, 77588
Brookside Village	77581
Pearsall	78061
Peaster	76485
Pecan Gap	75469
Pecangrove (Oglesby)	76561
Pecos	79772
Pedigo (Woodville)	75979
Peggy	78062
Pelham (Hubbard)	76648
Pelican Bay (Azle)	76020
Pendleton	76564
Penelope	76676
Penitas	78576
Pennington	75856
Penwell	79776
Peoria (Hillsboro)	76645
Pep	79353
Percilla (Grapeland)	75844
Perezville (Mission)	78572
Pernitas Point (Sandia)	78383
Perrin	76486
Perry	76677
Perryton	79070
Perryville (Gilmer)	75644
Personville (Buffalo)	75831
	75838, 76642
Peters (Sealy)	77474
Petersburg	79250
Petersville (Yoakum)	77995
Petrolia	76377
Petronila (Robstown)	78380
Petteway (Bremond)	76629
Pettibone (Cameron)	76520
Pettit (Levelland)	79336
Pettus	78146
Petty	75470
Pflugerville	78660
Pharr	78577

Phelps (Huntsville)	77340	
Phillips (Borger)	79007	
Pickton	75471	
Pidcoke (Gatesville)	76528	
Pierce	77467	
Pierces Chapel	75766	
(Jacksonville)		
Pilot Knob (Austin)	78744	
Pilot Point	76258	
Pine (Pittsburg)	75686	
Pine Forest (Vidor)	77662	
Pine Hill (Jacksonville)	75766	
Pine Valley (Diboll)	75941	
Pinehill (Henderson)	75652	
Pinehurst	77362	
Pineland	75968	
Pinewood (Longview)	75602	
Piney Point (Houston)	77024	
Pioneer Town (Wimberley)	78676	
Pipe Creek	78063	
Pirtle (Overton)	75684	
Pisek (Fayetteville)	78940	
Pitner Junction (Overton)	75684	
Pittsburg	75686	
Placedo	77977	
Plains	79355	
Plainview	79072-073	
Plano	75023-026, 75074-075	
	75086, 75093-094	
Murphy	75074	
Murphy	75094	
Plantersville	77363	
Pleak (Richmond)	77469	
Pleasant Grove	75652, 76570	
(Henderson)		
Pleasant Hill (Corrigan)	75939	
Pleasant Ridge	75763, 75833	
(Frankston)		
Pleasanton	78064	
Pledger	77468	
Pluck (Corrigan)	75939	
Plum	78952	
Plum Grove (Cleveland)	77327	
Po Boxes (Corpus Christi)	78469	
Poesville (Morgan)	76671	
Point	75472	
Point Comfort	77978	
Point Enterprise (Mexia)	76667	
Pointblank	77364	
Pollok	75969	
Ponder	76259	
Pone (Laneville)	75667	
Ponta (Jacksonville)	75766	
Pontotoc	76869	
Pony (Ballinger)	76821	
Poolville	76487	
Porfirio (Raymondville)	78580	
Port Acres (Port Arthur)	77640	
Port Alto (Port Lavaca)	77979	
Port Aransas	78373	
Port Arthur	77640-643	
Griffing	77640	
Lakeview	77640	
North Port Arthur	77640	
North Port Arthur		
	77642-643	
Pear Ridge	77640	
Port Acres	77640	
Sabine	77640	
West Port Arthur	77640	
Port Bolivar	77650	

Port Isabel	78578, 78597	
Bahia Mar	78578	
Isabel	78578	
Laguna Vista	78578	
Port Lavaca (Long Mott)	77972	
	77979	
Clarks	77979	
Green Lake	77979	
Indianola	77979	
Kamey	77979	
Magnolia Beach	77979	
Olivia	77979	
Port Alto	77979	
Weedhaven	77979	
Port Mansfield	78580, 78598	
(Raymondville)		
Raymondville	78598	
Port Neches	77651	
Port O' Connor	77982	
Porter	77365	
Porter Springs (Crockett)	75835	
Portland	78374	
Portway Acres	78520	
(Brownsville)		
Post	79356	
Post Oak (Ledbetter)	78946	
Postoak (Bowie)	76230	
Poteet	78065	
Poth	78147	
Potosi (Abilene)	79601	
Pottsboro	75076	
Pottsville	76565	
Powderly	75473	
Powell	75153	
Powell Point (Kendleton)	77451	
Poynor	75782	
Praesel (Rockdale)	76567	
Praha (Flatonia)	78941	
Prairie Dell (Salado)	76571	
Prairie Grove (Mexia)	76667	
Prairie Hill	76678	
Prairie Lea	78661	
Prairie View	77446	
Premont	78375	
Presidio	79845-846	
Redford	79846	
Price	75687	
Priddy	76870	
Primera (Harlingen)	78550	
Primrose (Ben Wheeler)	75754	
Princeton	75407	
Pritchett (Big Sandy)	75755	
Proctor	76468	
Progreso	78579	
Prosper	75078	
Providence (Lufkin)	75901	
Provident City (Louise)	77455	
Pt Aransas (Port Aransas)	78373	
Puerto Rico (Linn)	78563	
Pumphrey (Winters)	79567	
Purdon	76679	
Purmela	76566	
Pursley (Purdon)	76679	
Putnam	76469	
Pyote	79777	
Pyron (Roscoe)	79545	
Quail	79251	
Quanah	79252	
Queen City	75572	
Quemado	78877	
Quinlan	75474	

Quintana (Freeport)	77541	
Quitaque	79255	
Quitman	75783	
Rabb (Robstown)	78380	
Rabbs (Hallettsville)	77964	
Rabbs Prairie (La Grange)	78945	
Raccoon Bend (Bellville)	77418	
Rachal (Encino)	78353	
Radium (Anson)	79501	
Rainbow	76077	
Raisin (Victoria)	77901	
Ralls	79357	
Ramah (Tenaha)	75974	
Ramirez (Realitos)	78376	
Ramona (Weslaco)	78596	
Ranchito (San Benito)	78586	
Rancho Viejo	78361	
(Hebbronville)		
Randolph	75475	
Ranger	76470	
Rangerville (San Benito)	78586	
Rankin	79778	
Ransom Canyon	79364, 79366	
(Slaton)		
Ratcliff	75858, 75972	
Ratibor (Temple)	76501	
Ravenna	75476	
Rayburn (Cleveland)	77327	
Rayford (Spring)	77373	
Raymondville	78580, 78598	
Porfirio	78580	
Port Mansfield	78580	
Santa Monica	78580	
Willamar	78580	
Raytown (Rotan)	79546	
Raywood	77582	
Reagan	76680	
Realitos	78376	
Red Cut Heights	75501	
(Texarkana)		
Red Gate (Edinburg)	78539	
Red Hill (Douglassville)	75560	
	75563	
Red Lake (Oakwood)	75855	
Red Oak	75154	
Red Ranger (Rogers)	76569	
Red Rock	78662	
Red Springs (Texarkana)	75501	
	75771	
Red Town (Lufkin)	75901	
Redbank (Hooks)	75561	
Redfield (Nacogdoches)	75961	
Redford (Presidio)	79846	
Redland (Ben Wheeler)	75754	
	75833, 75901	
Redlawn (Alto)	75925	
Redlick (Texarkana)	75501	
Redtown (Pollok)	75969	
Redwater	75573	
Reedville (Maxwell)	78656	
Reese (Jacksonville)	75766	
Refuge (Grapeland)	75844	
Refugio	78377	
Rek Hill (Fayetteville)	78940	
Reklaw	75784	
Relampago (Mercedes)	78570	
Reliance (Bryan)	77801	
Reno (Paris)	75462	
Reynard (Grapeland)	75844	
Rhome	76078	
Rhonesboro (Big Sandy)	75755	

.... 77414	
Sarita 78385	
Saspamco (Elmendorf) 78112	
Satin 76685	
Satsuma (Houston) 77040	
Sattler 78132-133	
(New Braunfels)	
Saturn (Harwood) 78632	
Savoy 75479	
Scallorn (Lometa) 76853	
Schertz 78154	
Schroeder (Goliad) 77963	
Schulenburg 78956	
Schwertner 76573	
Scotland 76379	
Scottsville 75688	
Scroggins 75480	
Scurry 75158	
Seabrook 77586	
Seadrift 77983	
Seagoville 75159	
Seagraves 79359	
Sealy 77474	
Sears (Dallas) 75368	
Sears Lockbox (Dallas) 75346	
Seaton (Temple) 76501	
Seawillow (Lockhart) 78644	
Sebastian 78594	
Sebastopol (Trinity) 75862	
Security (Cleveland) 77327	
Security Couriers 75389	
(Dallas)	
Segno (Livingston) 77351	
Segovia (Junction) 76849	
Seguin 78155-156	
Sejita (Realitos) 78376	
Selective Service 75387	
(Dallas)	
Selma (Schertz) 78154	
Selman City 75689	
Seminole 79360	
Seven Oaks (Leggett) 77350	
Seven Pines (Gilmer) 75644	
Seven Points (Kemp) 75143	
Seven Sisters (Freer) 78357	
Sexton (San Augustine) 75972	
Sexton (City) (Overton) 75684	
Seymour 76380	
Shady Grove (Diboll) 75941	
.... 76679	
Shady Shores (Denton) 76205	
Shafter 79850	
Shallowater 79363	
Shamrock 79077, 79079	
(Samnorwood)	
Twitty 79079	
Shamrock Shores 76801	
(Brownwood)	
Shankleville (Burkeville) 75932	
Sharp (Buckholts) 76518	
Sharpstown (Houston) 77036	
Sharyland (Mission) 78572	
Shavano Park 78231	
(San Antonio)	
Sheffield 79781	
Shelby (Fayetteville) 78940	
Shelbyville 75973	
Sheldon (Houston) 77028	
Shep (Wingate) 79566	
Shepherd 77371	
Shepphard (Buna) 77612	

Sheridan 77475	
Sherman 75090-092	
Sherwood (Mertzon) 76941	
Shiloh (Thrall) 76578, 76667	
Shiner 77984	
Shiro 77876	
Shive (Hamilton) 76531	
Shoreacres (La Porte) 77571	
Short (Center) 75935	
Sidney 76474	
Sierra Blanca 79851	
Silas (Timpson) 75975	
Siloam (De Kalb) 75559	
Silsbee 77656	
Silver 76949	
Silver City (Cameron) 76520	
.... 76679	
Silver Valley (Coleman) 76834	
Silverton 79257	
Simmonsville (Gilmer) 75644	
Simms 75574	
Simonton 77476	
Simsboro (Teague) 75860	
Sinclair City (Troup) 75789	
Singleton (Bedias) 77831	
Sinton 78387	
Sisterdale (Boerne) 78006	
Skellytown 79080	
Skidmore 78389	
Slaton 79364	
Slidell 76267	
Slocum (Elkhart) 75839	
Smiley 78159	
Smith Hill (Hooks) 75561	
Smithland (Jefferson) 75657	
Smiths Bend (Clifton) 76634	
Smithville 78957	
Smyer 79367	
Smyrna (Atlanta) 75551	
Snook 77878	
Snow Hill (Corrigan) 75939	
Snyder 79549-550	
Clairemont 79549	
Dermott 79549	
Union 79549	
Socorro (El Paso) 79927	
Sodville (Sinton) 78387	
Solms (New Braunfels) 78130	
Somerset 78069	
Somerville (Clay) ... 77839, 77879	
Sonora 76950	
Sorters (Porter) 77365	
Soules Chapel (Gilmer) 75644	
Sour Lake 77659	
South Bend 76481	
South Elm (Buckholts) 76518	
South Houston 77587	
South Padre Island 78597	
South Plains 79258	
South Purmela (Purmela) ... 76566	
South San Pedro 78380	
(Robstown)	
South Texarkana 75501	
(Texarkana)	
Southlake (Grapevine) 76092	
Southland (Slaton) 79364	
Southmayd 76268	
Southside Place (Houston) . 77005	
Southwestern Bankcard 75396	
(Dallas)	
Spade 79369	

Spanish Camp (Wharton) . 77488	
Sparks (Holland) 76534	
Speaks 77985	
Spearman 79081	
Speegleville (Waco) 76710	
Spicewood 78669	
Splendora 77372	
Spofford (Quemado) 78877	
Spring 77373, 77379-383	
.... 77386-389, 77391	
Klein 77379	
Klein 77391	
Oak Ridge North 77386	
Rayford 77373	
The Woodlands 77387	
Spring Branch 78070	
Spring Creek 78624	
(Fredericksburg)	
Spring Hill (De Kalb) .. 75559-560	
.... 75604	
Spring Valley (Moody) 76557	
.... 77024	
Springdale (Queen City) 75572	
Springfield (Montalba) 75853	
.... 78332	
Springhill (Dawson) 76639	
Springlake 79082	
Springtown 76082	
Sprinkle (Austin) 78754	
Spur 79370	
Spurger 77660	
Stafford 77477, 77497	
The Meadows 77477	
Stairtown (Luling) 78648	
Stamford 79503, 79553	
Avoca 79503	
Tuxedo 79553	
Stampede (Moody) 76557	
Stamps (Gilmer) 75644	
Stanton 79782	
Staples 78670	
Star 76880	
Starrville (Winona) 75792	
Startzville 78132-133	
(New Braunfels)	
Steeltown (Groves) 77619	
Steep Hollow (Bryan) 77801	
Stellar (Muldoon) 78949	
Stephen Creek 77331	
(Coldspring)	
Stephenville 76401-402	
Sterling City 76951	
Stewards Mill (Streetman) . 75859	
Stewart (Henderson) 75652	
Stewart Heights (Baytown) . 77520	
Stinnett 79083	
Stith (Merkel) 79536	
Stockdale 78160	
Stockholm (Lyford) 78569	
Stockman (Timpson) 75975	
Stoneburg (Bowie) 76230	
Stonewall 78671	
Stormville (Quitman) 75783	
Stowell 77661	
Stratford 79084	
Stratton (Cuero) 77954	
Strawn 76475	
Streeter (Mason) 76856	
Streetman 75859	
String Prairie (Rosanky) 78953	
Structure (Elgin) 78621	

Stuart Place (Harlingen)	78550
Sublime	77986
Sudan	79371
Suffolk (Gilmer)	75644
Sugar Land 77478-479, 77487	
Dewalt	77479
Sugar Valley (Sweeny)	77480
Sul Ross (Alpine)	79832
Sullivan City	78595
Sulphur Bluff	75481
Sulphur Springs 75482-483	
Summerfield	79085
Summerville (Gonzales) ..	78629
Sumner	75486
Sundown	79372
Sunny Side (Brookshire) ..	77423
Sunnyslope (Texarkana) ..	75501
Sunnyvale (Mesquite)	75182
Sunray	79086
Sunrise (Marlin)	76661
Sunrise Beach (Llano)	78643
Sunset	76270
Sunset Valley (Austin)	78745
Surfside Beach (Freeport) .	77541
Sutherland Springs	78161
Swan (Tyler)	75704
Sweeny	77480
Sweeny Switch (Mathis)	78368
Sweet Home	77987
Sweetwater	79556
Swift (Nacogdoches)	75961
Swiss Alp (Schulenburg) ...	78956
Sycamore (Burkeville)	75932
Sylvan Beach (La Porte)	77571
Sylvester	79560
Tabor (Bryan)	77801
Taft 78390	
Tahoka	79373
Taiton (El Campo)	77437
Talco	75487
Talpa	76882
Tamega (Bertram)	78605
Tamina (Conroe)	77301
Tanglewood (Lexington)	78947
Tarkington Prairie	77327
(Cleveland)	
Tarpley	78883
Tarrytown (Austin)	78703
Tarzan	79783
Tatum	75691
Tavener (East Bernard)	77435
Taylor	76574
Taylor Lake Village	77586
(Seabrook)	
Teague (Kirvin) 75848, 75860	
Clay Hill	75860
Cotton Gin	75860
Dew	75860
Freestone	75860
Furney Richardson	75860
Salem	75860
Simsboro	75860
Teaselville (Bullard)	75757
Tecula (Jacksonville)	75766
Tehuacana	76686
Telegraph	76883
Telephone	75488
Telferner	77988
Tell	79259
Temple 76501-505, 76508	
Moffatt	76501

Oenaville	76501
Oscar	76501
Ratibor	76501
Seaton	76501
Zabcikville	76501
Tenaha	75974
Tennessee Colony	
75861, 76880, 75884, 75886	
Tenneryville (Longview)	75601
Tennyson	76953
Tenoka (Tenaha)	75974
Terlingua	79852
Terrell	75160
Terrell Hills	78209
(San Antonio)	
Terrys Chapel (Rosebud) ..	76570
Terryville (Yoakum)	77995
Texaco (Dallas)	75326
Texarkana 75501, 75503-505	
75507, 75599	
Oaklawn	75501
Red River Army Depot	75501
Red River Army Depot	75507
South Texarkana	75501
Wake Village	75501
Texas City 77590-592	
Meskill	77590
Texline	79087
Texon (Big Lake)	76932
Thayer (Mercedes)	78570
The Colony (Lewisville)	75056
The Grove (Gatesville)	76576
The Meadows (Stafford)	77477
The Woodlands 77380-381	
....	77387
(Spring)	
Thedford (Lindale)	75771
Thelma (Groesbeck)	76642
Theon (Jarrell)	76537
Thicket	77374
Thomas (Pittsburg)	75686
Thomaston	77989
Thompsons	77481
Thompsonville (Waelder) ..	78959
Thorndale	76577
Thornton	76687
Thrall	76578
Three Point (Round Rock) .	78664
Three Rivers (Oakville)	78060
....	78071
Thrifty (Brownwood)	76801
Throckmorton	76483
Tidwell Prairie (Bremond) .	76629
Tilden	78072
Tilmon (Dale)	78616
Timber Cove (Seabrook) ...	77586
Timberlane Acres (Porter) .	77365
Timpson	75975
Tioga	76271
Tivoli	77990
Tivydale (Fredericksburg) .	78624
Tod (Seabrook)	77586
Tokio	79376
Tolar	76476
Toledo (Burkeville)	75932
Tom Bean	75489
Tomball (Hufsmith)	77337
.... 77375, 77377	
Rose Hill	77375
Topsey (Copperas Cove) ..	76522
Tornillo	79853

Tours (West)	76691
Tow	78672
Town Bluff (Woodville)	75979
Toyah	79785
Toyahvale	79786
Trammells (Houston)	77045
Travis (Lott)	76656
Travis Heights (Austin)	78704
Trawick (Nacogdoches)	75961
Trent	79561
Trenton	75490
Trevat (Groveton)	75845
Tri Cities (Athens)	75751
Trinidad	75163
Trinity	75862
Trophy Club (Roanoke)	76262
Troup	75789
Trout Creek (Call)	75933
Troy	76579
Truscott	79260
Tuleta	78162
Tulia	79088
Turkey	79261
Turlington (Fairfield)	75840
Turnersville (Gatesville)	76528
....	78610
Turnertown (Selman City) .	75689
Turney (Jacksonville)	75766
Tuscola	79562
Tuxedo (Stamford)	79553
Twitty (Shamrock)	79079
Tye	79563
Tyler 75701-713, 75798-799	
Bascom	75705
Chapel Hill	75707
East Texas Junction	75708
Omen	75705
Saint Louis	75701
Swan	75704
University Of Texas	
At Tyler	75799
Tynan	78391
Type (Elgin)	78621
Uhland (Kyle)	78640
Umbarger	79091
Uncertain (Karnack)	75661
Union (Snyder)	79549
Union Chapel	75560
(Douglassville)	
Union Hill (Gilmer)	75644
Union Springs	75961
(Nacogdoches)	
Universal City 78148, 78150	
University Park (Dallas)	75205
University Place	75961
(Nacogdoches)	
Upton (Smithville)	78957
Ut (Austin)	78712
Utopia	78884
Uvalde 78801-802	
Val Verde (Buckholts)	76518
Valentine	79854
Valera	76884
Valle De Oro (Boys Ranch)	79010
Valley Lodge (Simonton) ...	77476
Valley Mills	76689
Valley Spring	76885
Valley View (Gilmer)	75644
.... 76272, 76821	
.... 77954, 79512	
Van 75790	

Van Alstyne	75495
Van Horn	79855
Van Vleck	77482
Vance (Barksdale)	78828
Vancourt	76955
Vanderbilt	77991
Vanderpool	78885
Vanetia (Marquez)	77865
Vattmanville (Riviera)	78379
Vaughan (Hillsboro)	76645
Vealmoor (Big Spring)	79720
Vega (Boys Ranch)	79010
	79092
Venus	76084
Vera	76383
Verhalen (Pecos)	79772
Veribest	76886
Vernon	76384-385
Viboras (Hebbronville)	78361
Victoria	77901-905
Cologne	77901
Da Costa	77901
Guadalupe	77901
Mission Valley	77901
Raisin	77901
Victory City (Hooks)	75561
Vidor	77662, 77670
Lakeview	77662
North Vidor	77662
Pine Forest	77662
Rose City	77662
Vienna (Hallettsville)	77964
Vigo Park (Tulia)	79088
Vilas (Holland)	76534
Villa Cavazos	78520
(Brownsville)	
Villa Nueva (Brownsville)	78520
Village (Dallas)	75205
Village Mills	77663
Villareales	78582
(Rio Grande City)	
Violet (Robstown)	78380
Virginia Point	77550
(Galveston)	
Voca	76887
Volente (Leander)	78641
Von Ormy	78073
Voss	76888
Votaw	77376
Voth	77709
Waco	76700-708, 76710-712
	76714-716, 76795-799
Amer Income Life Ins	76797
Bellmead	76704-76705
Beverly Hills	76711
Bosqueville	76708
Gholson	76705
Hallsburg	76705
Lacy Lakeview	76705
Northcrest	76705
Robinson	76706
Robinson Plaza	76706
Rock Creek	76708
Speegleville	76710
V A Regional Office	76799
Woodway	76712
Word Record	76796
Wadsworth	77483
Waelder	78959
Waka	79093
Wake Village (Texarkana)	75501

Wakefield (Corrigan)	75939
Walburg	78673
Waldeck (Ledbetter)	78946
Waldrip (Lohn)	76852
Walhalla (Round Top)	78954
Walkers Mill (Hallsville)	75650
Wall	76957
Waller	77484
Wallis	77485
Wallisville	77597
Walnut Grove (Troup)	75789
Walnut Springs	76690
Walton (Athens)	75751
Wamba (Texarkana)	75501
Ward Prairie (Fairfield)	75840
Warda	78960
Wards Creek (Simms)	75574
Waring	78074
Warlock (Avinger)	75630
Warren	77664
Warrenton (Round Top)	78961
Washington	77880
Waskom	75692
Wastella (Roscoe)	79545
Watauga (Fort Worth)	76148
Water Valley	76958
Waterloo (Taylor)	76574
Waterman (Center)	75395
Waters Bluff (Winona)	75792
Watson (Lampasas)	76550
Watt (Mart)	76664
Watuaga (Fort Worth)	76148
Waxahachie	75165
Wayside	79094
Wbamc (El Paso)	79920
Weatherford	76086-088
Willow Park	76087
Webberville (Manor)	78653
Webster	77598
Weches (Grapeland)	75844
Weedhaven (Port Lavaca)	77979
Weesatche	77993
Weimar	78962
Weinert	76388
Weir	78674
Welch	79377
Welcome (Industry)	78944
Wellborn	77881
Wellington	79095
Wellman	79378
Wells	75976
Weser (Goliad)	77963
Weslaco	78596, 78599
Ramona	78596
West	76691
West Columbia	77486
West End (El Campo)	77437
West Galveston	77554
(Galveston)	
West Lake Hills (Austin)	78746
West Mineola (Mineola)	75773
West Orange (Orange)	77630
West Payne (El Campo)	77437
West Point	78963
West Port Arthur	77640
(Port Arthur)	
West University Place	77005
(Houston)	
Westbrook	79565
Westgate Mall (Amarillo)	79160
Westhoff	77994

Westlake (Austin)	78746
Westminster	75485
Weston	75097
Westover Hills	76107
(Fort Worth)	
Westphalia (Lott)	76656
Westville (Trinity)	75862
Westworth (Fort Worth)	76114
Wetmore (Bulverde)	78163
	78247
Whaley (New Boston)	75570
Wharton	77488
Wheeler	79096
Wheelock	77882
White Deer	79097
White Hall (Gatesville)	76528
	76557, 77868
White Oak	75693
White Rock	75972
(San Augustine)	
White Settlement	76108
(Fort Worth)	
Whiteface	79379
Whitehouse	75791
Whitesboro	76273
Whitestone (Leander)	78641
Whitewright	75491
Whitharral	79380
Whitney	76692
Whitsett	78075
Whitson (Moody)	76557
Whitt	76490
Whon	76889
Wichita Falls	76301-311
Lakeside City	76308
Wickett	79788
Wied (Hallettsville)	77964
Wiergate	75977
Wiggins (Bivins)	75555
Wild Peach Village	77422
(Brazoria)	
Wilderville (Rosebud)	76570
Wildorado	79098
Wildwood (Village Mills)	77663
Willamar (Raymondville)	78580
Williamsburg	77964
(Hallettsville)	
Willis	77378
Willow City	78675
Willow Grove	75954, 76557
(Joaquin)	
Willow Oak (Gilmer)	75644
Willow Park (Weatherford)	76087
Willow Springs	77331, 78940
(Coldspring)	
Wills Point	75169
Wilmer	75172
Wilmeth (Winters)	79567
Wilson	79381
Wimberley	78676
Winchester	78964
Windcrest (San Antonio)	78239
Windom	75492
Windthorst	76389
Winfield	75493
Winfree (Dayton)	77535
Wingate	79566
Wink	79789
Winkler (Streetman)	75859
Winnie	77665
Winnsboro	75494

Winona 75792	Woodlawn 75694, 75901	Yancey 78886
Winslow (Hillsboro) 76645	Woods (Tenaha) 75974	Yantis 75497
Winters 79567	Woodsboro 78393	Yard (Tennessee Colony) .. 75861
Witting (Moulton) 77975	Woodson 76491	Yarrelton (Buckholts) 76518
Woden 75978	Woodville 75979, 75990	Yescas (San Benito) 78586
Wolfe City 75496	Woodway (Waco) 76712	Yoakum 77995
Wolfforth 79382	Woody Acres (Porter) 77365	Yorktown 78164
Womack (Clifton) 76634	Word Record (Waco) 76796	Young (Fairfield) 75840
Wood Springs (Lindale) 75771	Wortham 76693	Youngsport (Killeen) 76542
Woodbranch (New Caney) 77357	Worthing (Hallettsville) 77964	Zabcikville (Temple) 76501
Woodbury (Hillsboro) 76645	Wright City (Overton) 75684	Zapata 78076
Woodcreek (Wimberley) 78676	Wrightsboro 78677	Zavalla 75980
Woodlake 75865	Wylie 75098, 79605	Zephyr 76890
		Zipperlenville (Rosebud) .. 76570

IMPORTANT BUILDINGS   TEXAS

ABILENE

BUILDINGS

Alexander Building
104 PINE ST 79601

Bank Of Commerce Building
3300 S 14TH ST 79605

Cockrell Building
1133 N 2ND ST 79601

Commerce Plaza
1290 S WILLIS ST 79605

Cresendo
1052 N 5TH ST 79601

First State Plaza
400 OAK ST 79602

Meadows Med Ctr
1325 HICKORY ST 79601

NCNB
402 CYPRESS ST 79601

New Courthouse
300 OAK ST 79602

Permian Building
317 N WILLIS ST 79603

Professional Building
1101 N 19TH ST 79601

Professional Center
1100 N 19TH ST 79601

ACACIA LAKE

GOVERNMENT

Cameron County Hall Of Ju
974 E HARRISON ST 78520

Federal Court House
1001 E ELIZABETH ST 78520

AMARILLO

BUILDINGS

Amarillo National Bank
410 S TAYLOR ST 79101

Bank One Building
600 TYLER ST. 79101

First National Building
700 FILLMORE ST. 79101

Fisk Building
724 S POLK ST 79101

Old Courthouse Annex
500 FILLMORE ST. 79101

Place One
801 FILLMORE ST. 79101

Place Two
905 FILLMORE ST. 79101

Plaza One
410 TAYLOR ST. 79101

Plaza Two
500 TAYLOR ST. 79101

Saint Anthonys
200 7TH STREET 79107

Western Plaza Mall
2101 WESTERN ST. 79109

Westgate Mall
7701 INTERSTATE 40 79160

HOSPITAL

High Plains Baptist Hospital
1600 WALLACE 79106

Northwest Texas Hospital
1501 COULTER 79106

GOVERNMENT

Federal Building
205 E 5TH AVE 79101

Potter County Courthouse
501 S FILLMORE ST 79101

Texas Dept Of Corrections
9601 NE 24TH AVE 79107

AUSTIN

GOVERNMENT

Federal Building
300 E 8TH ST 78701

State Archives Lib Pc
12927 PO BOX 78711

Texas Supreme Court
12248 PO BOX 78711

Travis County Courthouse
1000 GUADALUPE ST 78701

US Fed/dist Courthouse
200 W 8TH ST 78701

BEAUMONT

BUILDINGS

Beaumont Savings
470 ORLEANS ST 77701

Biscamp Building
2360 CALDER ST 77702

Calder Professional Building
2929 CALDER ST 77702

Drs Building
3155 STAGG DR 77701

Goodhue Building
398 PEARL ST 77701

Petroleum Building
550 FANNIN ST 77701

San Jacinto Building
595 ORLEANS ST 77701

GOVERNMENT

City Hall
801 MAIN ST 77701

County Court House
1149 PEARL ST 77701

Jack Brooks Building
300 WILLOW ST 77701

HOSPITALS

Bmt Neurological Center
3260 FANNIN ST 77701

BROWNSVILLE

HOSPITALS

Brownsville Med Center
3590 PO BOX 78523

COLOGNE

GOVERNMENT

Federal Building
312 S MAIN ST 77901

New Vic County Courthouse
115 N BRIDGE ST 77901

HOSPITALS

Citizen Hospital
2701 HOSPITAL DR 77901

COLLEGES

University Houston-victoria
2302 E RED RIVER ST 77901

CORPUS CHRISTI

BUILDINGS

600 Building
0 600 BUILDING 78473

600 Building
600 LEOPARD ST 78473

American Bank Plz
711 N CARANCAHUA ST . 78475

Bayview Federal Building
0 Bayview Federal Building 78474

Corpus Christi National Bank
500 N WATER ST 78471

First City Bank Tower
615 N Upper Broadway St 78477

First City Tower II
0 FIRST CITY TOWER II .. 78478

First City Tower II
555 N CARANCAHUA ST . 78478

Texas Commerce Plaza
802 N CARANCAHUA ST . 78470

Wilson Building
545 N Upper Broadway St 78476

Wilson Tower
606 N CARANCAHUA ST . 78476

GOVERNMENT

City Hall
1201 LEOPARD ST 78401

County Court House
901 LEOPARD ST 78401

Federal Us Courthouse
521 STARR ST 78401

Govt Plaza
400 MANN ST 78401

HOSPITALS

Memorial Medical Center
2606 HOSPITAL BLVD 78405

DALLAS

BUILDINGS

Arco Tower
1601 BRYAN ST 75201

Concourse Off Plaza
6310 LYNDON B JOHNSON
FWY 75240

County Criminal Ct Building
501 MAIN ST 75202

Dallas County Courthouse
600 COMMERCE ST 75202

Earle Cabell Federal Building
1114 COMMERCE ST 75242

Gibbs-Hill Building
5501 LYNDON B JOHNSON
FWY 75240

Lincoln Center III
5430 LYNDON B JOHNSON
FWY 75240

Lincoln Plaza
500 N AKARD ST 75201

Old Red Court House
100 S HOUSTON ST 75202

Provident Bank Building
5429 LYNDON B JOHNSON
FWY 75240

DEL RIO

BUILDINGS

Federal Courthouse
111 E BROADWAY ST 78840

DENTON

BUILDINGS

Federal Building
101 E MCKINNEY ST 76201

EL PASO

BUILDINGS

Banner Building
215 N MESA ST 79901

Bassett Tower
303 TEXAS AVE 79901

Caples Building
300 E SAN ANTONIO AVE 79901

El Paso Electric Co
303 N OREGON AVE 79901

Medical Center Plaza
1501 ARIZONA AVE 79902

State National Bank Building
221 N KANSAS ST 79901

Sunwest Bank Building
416 N STANTON ST 79901

Texas Commerce Bank Building
201 E MAIN DR 79901

University Towers
1900 N OREGON ST 79902

GOVERNMENT

Elp City-county Building
500 E SAN ANTONIO AVE 79901

Federal Building
700 E SAN ANTONIO AVE 79901

Federal Courthouse Building
511 E SAN ANTONIO AVE 79901

US Courthouse
511 E SAN ANTONIO AVE 79901

EYLAU

BUILDINGS

Pine Terrace Off Center
4310 MCKNIGHT RD 75501

Texarkana Nat'l Bank Building
100 W BROAD ST 75501

FORT WORTH

BUILDINGS

Baker Building
110 W 7TH ST 76102

Burk Burnett
500 MAIN ST 76102

City Center Tower
301 COMMERCE ST 76102

Commerce
307 W 7TH ST 76102

Continental Life
714 MAIN ST 76102

Continental Plaza
777 MAIN ST 76102

Electric Service
115 W 7TH ST 76102

Empire America Savings
1600 W 7TH ST 76102

Executive Plaza
210 W 6TH ST 76102

First City Bank Tower
201 MAIN ST 76102

First United
410 W 7TH ST 76102

Fort Worth Club
306 W 7TH ST 76102

Ft Worth Club Tower
777 TAYLOR ST 76102

Houston Place
910 HOUSTON ST 76102

Interfirst Tower
801 CHERRY ST 76102

Lawyers
100 MAIN ST 76102

Mallick Tower
1 SUMMIT AVE 76102

Moncrief
109 E 9TH ST 76102

NCNB
500 W 7TH ST 76102

Neil Anderson
411 W 7TH ST 76102

Oil & Gas
309 W 7TH ST 76102

One Tandy Center
100 Throckmorton St 76102

Sinclair
106 W 5TH ST 76102

Summit
1500 W 5TH ST 76102

Summit Tower
1200 SUMMIT AVE 76102

T & P
221 W LANCASTER AVE . 76102

T & P
1600 Throckmorton St 76102

Team Bank
500 Throckmorton St 76102

Texas
200 W 7TH ST 76102

Two Tandy Center
300 W 3RD ST 76102

United Savings
815 Throckmorton St 76102

US Court House
501 W 10TH ST 76102

US Life & Title
1200 WEST FWY 76102

W T Waggoner
810 HOUSTON ST 76102

Water Gardens
100 E 15TH ST 76102

Welborn
1203 LAKE ST 76102

GOVERNMENT

Lanham Federal
819 TAYLOR ST 76102

GALVESTON

BUILDINGS

American Natl Ins Building
1 MOODY PLZ 77550

County Court House
722 MOODY AVE 77550

GEORGETOWN

GOVERNMENT

Williamson Co Courthouse
0 COURTHOUSE 78626

GRESHAM

BUILDINGS

Broadway Square Mall
4601 S BROADWAY AVE . 75703

GRIFFING

GOVERNMENT

City Hall
444 4TH ST 77640

Federal Building
2875 75TH ST 77640

Sub Courthouse Building
525 LAKESHORE DR 77640

COLLEGES

Lamar University
1500 PROCTER ST 77640

GUM SPRINGS

BUILDINGS

Bank One Building
211 E TYLER ST 75601

Petroleum Building
202 E WHALEY ST 75601

GOVERNMENT

Courthouse
101 E METHVIN ST 75601

HARLINGEN

HOSPITALS

Valley Baptist Med Ctr
2588 PO BOX 78551

COLLEGES

Tx St Technical Institute
2628 PO BOX 78551

HOUSTON

GOVERNMENT

City Hall
900 BAGBY ST 77002

Civil Courthouse
301 FANNIN ST 77002

Criminal Courthouse
301 SAN JACINTO ST 77002

LAKESIDE CITY

BUILDINGS

One Parker Square Building
2525 KELL BLVD 76308

Southwest Natl Bank Building
4245 KEMP BLVD 76308

LUBBOCK

BUILDINGS

City Bank Building
5211 BROWNFIELD 79407

Court Place
1001 MAIN ST 79401

First National Bank Building
1500 BROADWAY ST 79401

Metro Tower
1220 BROADWAY ST 79401

Nationsbank
916 MAIN ST 79401

Plaza West
4630 50TH ST 79414

Pyramid Plaza
3223 S LOOP 289 79423

South Plains Mall
6002 SLIDE 79414

Texas Commerce Bank Bldg
1208 14TH ST. 79401

Tower Of The Plains
5010 UNIVERSITY AVE 79413

GOVERNMENT

Federal Building
1205 TEXAS AVE 79401

Lubbock County Courthouse
904 BROADWAY ST 79401

Lubbock State School
5396 PO BOX 79408

HOSPITALS

Methodist Hospital
1201 PO BOX 79408

University Medical
5980 PO BOX 79408

MILITARY

Reese Air Force Base
300 REESE BLVD 79489

MESQUITE

BUILDINGS

Galloway Plaza Contract
870001 PO BOX 75150

MIDLAND

BUILDINGS

Building Of The Southwest
310 W TEXAS AVE 79701

Briercroft Savings Building
200 N LORAINE ST 79701

Century Plaza Building
310 W WALL ST 79701

Empire Plaza
508 W WALL ST 79701

H B F Building
414 W TEXAS AVE 79701

Lexington Motor Inn
1003 S MIDKIFF RD 79701

Metro Building
119 N COLORADO ST 79701

Mid America Building
301 N COLORADO ST 79701

Midland Executive Center
310 W ILLINOIS AVE 79701

Midland Tower Building
223 W WALL ST 79701

NCNB
303 W WALL ST 79701

Oil & Gas Building
105 W WALL ST 79701

One Marienfeld Pl Building
110 N MARIENFELD ST ... 79701

One Wall Plaza
306 W WALL ST 79701

Patio Building
308 N COLORADO ST 79701

Permian Building
319 W TEXAS AVE 79701

Police Commission Building
601 N LORAINE ST 79701

Tx American Bank
2301 W WALL ST 79701

Union Oil Building
619 W TEXAS AVE 79701

Vaughn Building
400 W TEXAS AVE 79701

Wall Tower East
201 W WALL ST 79701

Wall Tower West
203 W WALL ST 79701

West Building
401 N COLORADO ST 79701

Western United Life Building
300 W TEXAS AVE 79701

Wilco Building
415 W WALL ST 79701

GOVERNMENT

County Courthouse Annex
218 W ILLINOIS AVE 79701

Courthouse
200 W WALL ST 79701

Federal Building
200 E WALL ST 79701

MURPHY

BUILDINGS

Nation Bank
101 E PARK BLVD 75074

GOVERNMENT

Collin County Government
651 18TH ST 75074

NORTH PORT ARTHUR

HOSPITALS

St Mary Hospital
3600 GATES BLVD 77642

ODESSA

BUILDINGS

First State Bank Plaza
1330 E 8TH ST 79761

Petroleum Building
400 W 4TH ST 79761

GOVERNMENT

Courthouse
300 N GRANT AVE 79761

HOSPITALS

Medical Center Hospital
500 W 4TH ST 79761

Women & Children's Hosp
520 E 6TH ST 79761

OLD ROUND ROCK

GOVERNMENT

Williamson Co Annex
211 COMMERCE BLVD 78664

SAINT LOUIS

BUILDINGS

Tyler Natl Bank Building
3301 GOLDEN RD 75701

SAN ANGELO

BUILDINGS

Central Natl Bank Building
36 W BEAUREGARD AVE 76903

GTE Tower
2702 LOOP 306 76904

Texas Bank Tower
2201 SHERWOOD WAY ... 76901

GOVERNMENT

Federal Building
33 E TWOHIG AVE 76903

T G County Courthouse
112 W Beauregard Ave 76903

SAN ANTONIO

BUILDING

Frost Bank Tower
100 HOUSTON 78205

M & S Tower
730 MAIN STREET 78205

Milam Building
115 TRAVIS 78205

Petroleum Commerce Bldg.
201 SAINT MARYS 78205

Tower Life Building
310 SAINT MARYS 78205

Travis Building
405 SAINT MARYS 78205

GOVERNMENT

Bexar County Courthouse
100 DOLOROSA 78205

Bexar County Justice Ctr
300 DOLOROSA 78205

Federal Building
727 E DURANGO BLVD ... 78206

Federal Building
727 E DURANGO BLVD ... 78206

Us Courthouse
655 E DURANGO BLVD ... 78206

TEXARKANA

GOVERNMENT

Federal Building
500 N STATE LINE AVE 75502

Miller Co Court House
0 MILLER CO Courthouse 75502

U S Post Office Building
500 N STATE LINE AVE 75502

TYLER

BUILDINGS

Fair Foundation Building
121 S BROADWAY AVE ... 75702

First Place
209 N BROADWAY AVE ... 75702

Ncnb Center Building
102 N COLLEGE AVE 75702

Petroleum Building
305 S BROADWAY AVE ... 75702

GOVERNMENT

Federal Building
211 W FERGUSON ST 75702

Smith County Courthouse
100 N BROADWAY AVE ... 75702

Smith County Office Building
106 E ELM ST 75702

VICTORIA

GOVERNMENT

City Hall
1758 PO BOX 77902

HOSPITALS

De Tar Hospital
2089 PO BOX 77902

WACO

BUILDING

Federal Building
800 FRANKLIN 76701

WEATHERFORD

GOVERNMENT

Courthouse Annex
1112 SANTA FE DR 76086

WICHITA FALLS

BUILDINGS

1st Wichita National Building
719 SCOTT AVE 76301

City National Building
807 8TH ST 76301

County Courthouse
900 7TH ST 76301

Energy Center
710 LAMAR ST 76301

Federal Building
1000 LAMAR ST 76301

First National Building
708 8TH ST 76301

First Texas Building
901 INDIANA AVE 76301

Hamilton Building
900 8TH ST 76301

Oil & Gas Building
813 8TH ST 76301

Wichita Tower
705 8TH ST 76301

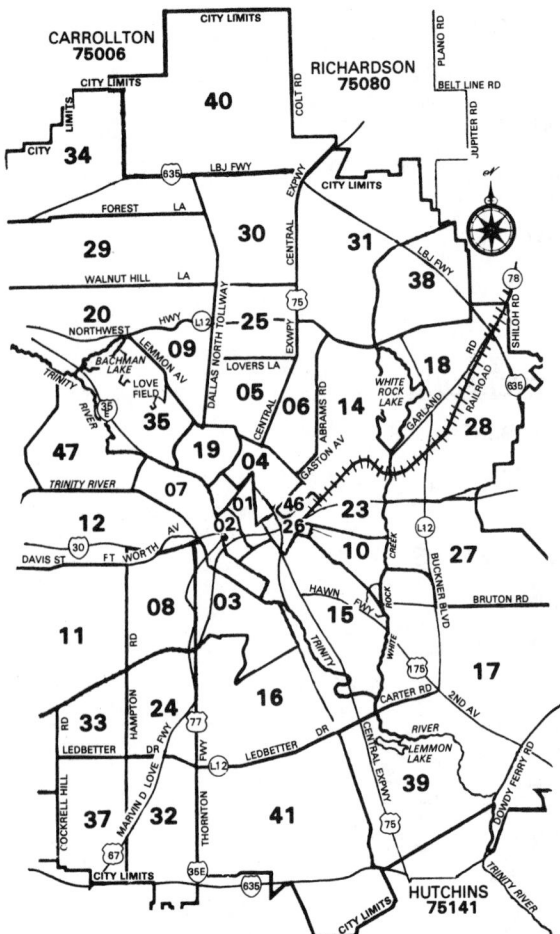

ZIP CODES
DALLAS, TX
572 + TWO DIGITS SHOWN = ZIP CODE

UTAH
Abbreviation UT

Abraham (Hinckley) 84635
Adamsville (Greenville) 84731
Alpine 84004
Alta (Sandy) 84092
Altamont 84001
Alton 84710
Altonah 84002
Amalga (Smithfield) 84335
American Fork 84003
Anchorage (Clearfield) 84015
Aneth 84510
Angle (Antimony) 84712
Annabella 84711
Antimony 84712
Apple Valley (Hurricane) ... 84737
Arcadia (Bridgeland) 84012
Arches (Moab) 84532
Arsenal (Clearfield) 84015
Aurora 84620
Austin (Monroe) 84754
Avon (Paradise) 84328
Axtell 84621
Bauer (Stockton) 84071
Bear River City 84301
Beaver 84713
Beaverdam (Collinston) 84306
Beeton (Deweyville) 84309
Belmont Heights 84070, 84092
(Sandy)
Benjamin (Spanish Fork) .. 84660
Bennion (Salt Lake City) 84118
Benson (Smithfield) 84335
Beryl 84714
Bethel (Garrison) 84728
Bicknell 84715
Big Water (Kanab) 84741
Bingham Canyon 84006
Birdseye (Fairview) 84629
Blanding 84511
Bloomington (St George) .. 84770
Bluebell 84007
Bluff 84512
Bluffdale (Riverton) 84065
Bonanza 84008
Boneta (Altamont) 84001
Bonnie (Orem) 84057-058
Bothwell (Tremonton) 84337
Bottle Hollow 84026
(Fort Duchesne)
Boulder 84716
Bountiful 84010-011
Val Verda 84010
Bowery Haven (Richfield) . 84701
Brian Head 84719
Bridgeland 84012
Brigham (Brigham City) 84302
Brigham City 84302
Brighton (Salt Lake City) ... 84121
Brookside (Veyo) 84782
Bryce 84764
Bryce Canyon 84717
Bullfrog (Lake Powell) 84533
Bunker (Orem) 84057-058
Burbank (Milford) 84751
Burmester (Grantsville) 84029
Burrville (Richfield) 84701
Bushnell (Brigham City) 84302
BYU (Provo) 84602

Cache Junction 84304
Caineville (Torrey) 84775
Cailao (Ibapah) 84034
Camp Williams (Riverton) . 84065
Cannonville 84718
Canyonlands (Moab) 84532
Capitol Reef (Torrey) 84775
Carbonville (Price) 84501
Castle Dale 84513
Castle Gate (Helper) 84526
Castleton (Moab) 84532
Cedar City 84720-721
Enoch 84720
Pintura 84720
Cedar Hills 84062
(Pleasant Grove)
Cedar Valley 84013
Cedarview (Roosevelt) 84066
Center Creek (Heber City) . 84032
Centerfield 84622
Centerville 84014
Central 84722
Central Valley (Monroe) 84754
Charleston (Heber City) 84032
Chester 84623
Circleville 84723
Cisco 84515
Clarkston 84305
Clawson 84516
Clearfield 84015-016
Anchorage 84015
Arsenal 84015
Clinton 84015
Sunset 84015
West Point 84015
Cleveland 84518
Clinton (Clearfield) 84015
Clover (Rush Valley) 84069
Clyde (Orem) 84057-058
Coalville 84017
College Ward (Logan) 84321
.... 84339
Collinston 84306
Como Springs (Morgan) 84050
Copperton 84006
(Bingham Canyon)
Corinne 84307
Cornish 84308
Cottonwood 84121
(Salt Lake City)
Cove (Lewiston) 84320
Cove Fort (Beaver) 84713
Covered Bridge 84660
(Spanish Fork)
Crescent (Sandy) ... 84070, 84092
Croydon 84018
Crystal Springs 84314
(Honeyville)
Cushing (Midvale) 84047
Dammeron Valley 84783
Daniels (Heber City) 84032
Defas Park (Hanna) 84031
Defense Depot (Ogden) 84407
Delta 84624
Deseret (Delta) 84624
Devils Slide (Morgan) 84050
Deweyville 84309
Diamond Valley 84770
(St George)
Draper 84020
Dry Fork (Vernal) 84078

Duchesne 84021
Duck Creek Village 84762
Dugway 84022
Dugway Proving Ground ... 84022
(Dugway)
Dutch John 84023
East Carbon 84520
East Layton (Layton) 84040
East Wellington 84542
(Wellington)
Echo 84024
Eden 84310
Elberta 84626
Elk Ridge (Payson) 84651
Elmo 84521
Elsinore 84724
Elwood (Tremonton) 84337
Emery 84522
Emory (Echo) 84024
Enoch (Cedar City) 84720
Enterprise (Morgan) 84050
.... 84725
Ephraim 84627
Erda (Tooele) 84074
Escalante 84726
Eskdale (Garrison) 84728
Etna (Grouse Creek) 84313
Eureka 84628
Fairfield (Cedar Valley) 84013
Fairview 84629
Farmington 84025
Farr West (Ogden) 84404
Faust (Vernon) 84080
Fayette 84630
Ferron 84523
Fielding 84311
Fillmore 84631
Fish Lake (Richfield) 84701
Flowell (Fillmore) 84631
Fort Douglas 84113
(Salt Lake City)
Fort Duchesne 84026
Fountain Green 84632
Francis (Kamas) 84036
Fremont (Loa) 84747
Fruit Heights (Kaysville) ... 84037
Fruita (Torrey) 84775
Fruitland 84027
Fry Canyon (Lake Powell) . 84533
Garden City 84028
Garland 84312
Garrison 84728
Genola (Santaquin) 84655
Glen Canyon (Kanab) 84741
Glendale 84729
Glenwood 84730
Gooseberry (Salina) 84654
Goshen 84633
Granger (Salt Lake City) ... 84119
Granite (Sandy) 84070, 84092
Grantsville 84029
Green Lake (Manila) 84046
Green River 84525
Greendale (Dutch John) 84023
Greenville 84731
Greenwich 84732
Grouse Creek 84313
Grover (Teasdale) 84773
Gunlock 84733
Gunnison 84634
Gusher 84030

Hailstone (Heber City) 84032	Lehi 84043	Nibley (Logan) 84321, 84332
Halls Crossing 84533	Leland (Spanish Fork) 84660	North Creek (Beaver) 84713
(Lake Powell)	Levan 84639	North Logan (Logan) 84321
Hanksville 84734	Lewiston 84320	North Ogden (Ogden) 84404
Hanna 84031	Liberty (Eden) 84310	North Salt Lake 84054
Harrisburg Junction 84770	Lincoln (Tooele) 84074	Oak City 84649
(St George)	Lindon 84042	Oak Creek (Fairview) 84629
Harrisville (Ogden) 84404	Littleton (Morgan) 84050	Oakley 84055
Hatch 84735	Loa 84747	Oasis 84650
Heber City 84032	Logan 84321-323, 84341	Ogden 84201, 84244, 84400-405
Helper 84526	College Ward 84321	.... 84407-409, 84412, 84414
Henefer 84033	Nibley 84321	Defense Depot 84407
Henrieville 84736	North Logan 84321	Farr West 84404
Herriman (Riverton) 84065	River Heights 84321	Harrisville 84404
Hiawatha 84527	Young Ward 84321	North Ogden 84404
Highland (American Fork) . 84003	Lyman 84749	Plain City 84404
Hildale 84784	Lynndyl 84640	Pleasant View 84404
Hillfield 84056	Madsen (Honeyville) 84314	Pleasant View 84414
(Hill Air Force Base)	Maeser (Vernal) 84078	Riverdale 84405
Hinckley 84635	Magna 84044	Slaterville 84404
Hite (Lake Powell) 84533	Mammoth (Provo) 84601	South Ogden 84403
Holden 84636	Manderfield (Beaver) 84713	South Weber 84403
Holladay 84117, 84124	Manila 84046	Taylor 84401
(Salt Lake City)	Manti 84642	Uintah 84403
Honeyville 84314	Mantua 84324	Warren 84404
Hooper 84315	Mapleton 84664	Washington Terrace 84405
Howell 84316	Marion (Kamas) 84036	West Haven 84401
Hoytsville (Coalville) 84017	Martin (Helper) 84526	West Warren 84404
Hunter (Salt Lake City) 84120	Marysvale 84750	West Weber 84401
Huntington 84528	Mayfield 84643	Wilson 84401
Huntsville 84317	Meadow 84644	Ophir (Stockton) 84071
Hurricane 84737	Meadowville (Laketown) ... 84038	Orangeville 84537
Hyde Park 84318	Mendon 84325	Orderville 84758
Hyrum 84319	Mexican Hat 84531	Orem 84057-059
Ibapah 84034	Middleton (St George) 84770	Bonnie 84057-058
Indianola (Fairview) 84629	Midvale 84047	Bunker 84057-058
Ioka (Roosevelt) 84066	Midway 84049	Clyde 84057-058
Irish Green (Lake Powell) . 84533	Milburn (Fairview) 84629	Lakeview 84058
Ivins 84738	Milford 84751	Vineyard 84057-058
Jensen 84035	Millville 84326	Ouray (Fort Duchesne) 84026
Joseph 84739	Milton (Morgan) 84050	Palmyra (Spanish Fork) 84660
Junction 84740	Minersville 84752	Panguitch 84759
Kamas 84036	Moab 84532	Paradise 84328
Kanab 84741	Modena 84753	Paragonah 84760
Kanarraville 84742	Mona 84645	Park City 84060, 84068
Kanesville (Hooper) 84315	Monarch (Roosevelt) 84066	Kimball Junction 84060
Kanosh 84637	Monroe 84754	Snyderville 84060
Kaysville 84037	Montezuma Creek 84534	Summit Park 84060
Kearns (Salt Lake City) 84118	Monticello 84535	Park Valley 84329
Keetley (Heber City) 84032	Monument Valley 84536	Parowan 84761
Kenilworth 84529	Morgan 84050	Partoun (Wendover) 84083
Kimball Junction 84060	Moroni 84646	Payson 84651
(Park City)	Mount Carmel 84755	Penrose (Tremonton) 84337
Kingston 84743	Mount Pleasant 84647	Peoa 84061
Koosharem 84744	Mountain Bell 84135	Perry (Brigham City) 84302
La Sal 84530	(Salt Lake City)	Petersboro (Mendon) 84325
La Verkin 84745	Mountain Fuel 84139	Peterson (Morgan) 84050
Lake Point (Tooele) 84074	(Salt Lake City)	Petra (Garrison) 84728
Lake Powell 84533	Mountain Green (Morgan) . 84050	Pickleville (Garden City) 84028
Lake Shore (Spanish Fork) 84660	Mountain Home 84051	Pine Cliff (Coalville) 84017
Laketown 84038	Murray (Salt Lake City) 84107	Pine Valley 84781
Lakeview (Orem) 84058	.... 84117, 84123, 84157	Pinto (Newcastle) 84756
Lapoint 84039	Myton 84052	Pintura (Cedar City) 84720
Lark (Riverton) 84065	Naples (Vernal) 84078	Plain City (Ogden) 84404
Lawrence (Huntington) 84528	Natural Bridges 84532-533	Pleasant Green (Magna) ... 84044
Layton 84040-041	(Moab)	Pleasant Grove 84062
East Layton 84040	Neola 84053	Pleasant View (Ogden) 84404
West Layton 84041	Nephi 84648	 84414
Leamington 84638	New Harmony 84757	Plymouth 84330
Leeds 84746	Newcastle 84756	Portage 84331
Leeton (Roosevelt) 84066	Newton 84327	Porterville (Morgan) 84050

Price	84501	
Promontory (Corinne)	84307	
Providence	84332	
Provo	84601-606	
BYU	84602	
Mammoth	84601	
Sundance	84604	
Randlett	84063	
Randolph	84064	
Redmond	84652	
Richfield	84701	
Richmond	84333	
Richville (Morgan)	84050	
River Heights (Logan)	84321	
Riverdale (Ogden)	84405	
Riverside	84334	
Riverton	84065, 84095	
Bluffdale	84065	
Camp Williams	84065	
Herriman	84065	
Lark	84065	
South Jordan	84065	
Rockville	84763	
Roosevelt	84066	
Rosette (Park Valley)	84329	
Round Valley (Laketown)	84038	
Roy	84067	
Rush Valley	84069	
Saint George	84783	
Saint John (Rush Valley)	84069	
Salem	84653	
Salina	84654	
Salt Lake City	84100-127
	84130-145, 84147-148
	84150-153, 84157-158
	84165, 84170, 84180
	84184-185, 84189-90, 84199
Bennion	84118	
Brighton	84121	
Cottonwood	84121	
Fort Douglas	84113	
Granger	84119	
Holladay	84117	
Holladay	84124	
Hunter	84120	
Kearns	84118	
Mountain Bell	84135	
Mountain Fuel	84139	
Murray	84107	
Murray	84117	
Murray	84123	
Murray	84157	
Salt Lake Cty Complex	84190	
South Salt Lake	84115	
South Salt Lake	84165	
Taylorsville	84119	
Taylorsville	84123	
West Valley City	84170	
Zcmi	84137	
Salt Lake County Complex	84190	
Sandy	84070, 84090-094	
Alta	84092	
Belmont Heights	84070	
Belmont Heights	84092	
Crescent	84070	
Crescent	84092	

Granite	84070	
Granite	84092	
Sherwood Park	84070	
Sherwood Park	84092	
Snowbird	84092	
White City	84070	
White City	84092	
Santa Clara	84765	
Santaquin	84655	
Saratoga (Lehi)	84043	
Scipio	84656	
Sevier	84766	
Sherwood Park (Sandy)	84070	
	84092	
Sigurd	84657	
Skull Valley	84029	
(Grantsville)		
Slaterville (Ogden)	84404	
Smithfield	84335	
Snowbird (Sandy)	84092	
Snowville	84336	
Snyderville (Park City)	84060	
South Jordan (Riverton)	84065	
	84095	
Riverton	84095	
South Ogden (Ogden)	84403	
South Salt Lake	84105-106	
	84115, 84165	
(Salt Lake City)		
South Weber (Ogden)	84403	
Spanish Fork	84660	
Spring City	84662	
Spring Glen (Helper)	84526	
Spring Lake (Payson)	84651	
Springdale	84767, 84779	
Springville	84663	
Spry (Panguitch)	84759	
Standardville (Helper)	84526	
Stansbury Park (Tooele)	84074	
Starr (Mona)	84645	
Sterling	84665	
Stockton	84071	
Stoddard (Morgan)	84050	
Sugarville (Delta)	84624	
Summit	84772	
Summit Park (Park City)	84060	
Sundance (Provo)	84604	
Sunnyside	84539	
Sunset (Clearfield)	84015	
Sutherland (Delta)	84624	
Swan Creek (Garden City)	84028	
Syracuse	84075	
Tabiona	84072	
Talmage	84073	
Taylor (Ogden)	84401	
Taylorsville	84119, 84123	
(Salt Lake City)		
Teasdale	84773	
Terra (Dugway)	84022	
Thatcher (Tremonton)	84337	
Thistle (Fairview)	84629	
Thompson	84540	
Ticaboo (Lake Powell)	84533	
Timpanogos	84003	
(American Fork)		
Tooele	84074	
Toquerville	84774	

Torrey	84775	
Tremonton	84337	
Trenton	84338	
Tridell	84076	
Tropic	84776	
Trout Creek (Wendover)	84083	
Uintah (Ogden)	84403	
Union (Midvale)	84047	
Upalco (Bluebell)	84007	
Upton (Coalville)	84017	
Utida (Cornish)	84308	
Uvada (Modena)	84753	
Val Verda (Bountiful)	84010	
Venice (Richfield)	84701	
Vernal	84078-079	
Dry Fork	84078	
Maeser	84078	
Naples	84078	
Vernon	84080	
Veyo	84782	
Vineyard (Orem)	84057-058	
Virgin	84779	
Wales	84667	
Wallsburg	84082	
Wanship (Coalville)	84017	
Warren (Ogden)	84404	
Washington	84780	
Washington Terrace	84405	
(Ogden)		
Wellington	84542	
Wellsville	84339	
Wendover	84083	
West Bountiful	84087	
(Woods Cross)		
West Haven (Ogden)	84401	
West Jordan	84084, 84088	
West Kaysville	84037	
(Kaysville)		
West Layton (Layton)	84041	
West Point (Clearfield)	84015	
West Valley City	84119-120	
	84170	
(Salt Lake City)		
West Warren (Ogden)	84404	
West Weber (Ogden)	84401	
Wheelon (Collinston)	84306	
White City	84070, 84092	
(Sandy)		
Whiterocks	84085	
Willard	84340	
Wilson (Ogden)	84401	
Winchester Hills	84770	
(St George)		
Woodland (Kamas)	84036	
Woodland Hills (Salem)	84653	
Woodrow (Delta)	84624	
Woodruff	84086	
Woods Cross	84087	
Young Ward (Logan)	84321	
	84339	
Zcmi (Salt Lake City)	84137	

MAMMOTH

GOVERNMENT

Utah County Building
51 S UNIVERSITY AVE 84601

OGDEN

GOVERNMENT

County Courthouse
2549 WASHINGTON BLVD 84401

Federal Building
324 25TH ST 84401

State Office Building
2540 WASHINGTON BLVD 84401

HOSPITALS

Mckay Dee Hospital
3939 HARRISON BLVD 84403

SALT LAKE CITY

GOVERNMENT

City & County Building
451 S STATE ST 84111

Federal Building
125 S STATE ST 84138

Federal Courts Building
350 S MAIN ST 84101

VERMONT
Abbreviation VT

Abnaki (North Hero)	05474
Adamant	05640
Adams Landing	05458
(Grand Isle)	
Addison (Vergennes)	05491
Albany	05820
Albany Center (Irasburg)	05845
Albertson (West Rutland)	05777
Alburg	05440
Alfrecha	05759
(North Clarendon)	
Alpine Haven	05471
(Montgomery Center)	
Alpine Village (Warren)	05674
Ames Hill (Marlboro)	05344
Amsden (Perkinsville)	05151
Andover (Bridport)	05734
Anthony (Bennington)	05201
Arlington	05250
Arnold Bay (Vergennes)	05491
Arrowhead Lake (Milton)	05468
Ascutney	05030
Athens (Chester)	05143
Avalon Beach (Hydeville)	05750
Averill	05901
Bakersfield	05441
Baltimore (Chester Depot)	05144
Barnard	05031
Barnet	05821
Barnumsville	05255, 05257
(Manchester Center)	
Barnumtown (New Haven)	05472
Barre	05641, 05678
Berlin	05641
Boutswells	05641
East Hill	05641
East Orange	05641
Lower Websterville	05641
Orange	05641
Trow Hill	05641
West Hill	05641
Barre Transfer	05602
(Montpelier)	
Barton	05822, 05839, 05875
Kimball	05822
Bartonsville (Chester)	05143
Basin Harbor (Vergennes)	05491
Beanville (Randolph)	05060
	05083
Beaulieus Corner	05459
(Highgate Center)	
Beaver (Fairfax)	05454
Beebe Plain	05823
Beecher Falls	05902
Beldons (Middlebury)	05753
Bellevue Hill	05478
(Saint Albans)	
Bellows Falls	05101
Belmont	05730
Belvidere Center	05442
Belvidere Corners	05464
(Jeffersonville)	
Belvidere Junction	05492
(Waterville)	
Bennington	05201
Benson	05731
Benson Landing	05743
(Fair Haven)	

Berkshire (East Berkshire)	05447
	05476
Berkshire Center	05450
(Enosburg Falls)	
Berlin (Montpelier) .. 05602,	05641
Bethel	05032
Bethel Gilead (Randolph) ..	05060
Binghamville (Cambridge)	05444
Birdland (North Hero)	05474
Bliss Pond (Adamant)	05640
Blissville (Poultney)	05764
Blossoms Corners	05775
(West Pawlet)	
Bolton (Waterbury)	05676
Bolton Valley (Richmond) ..	05477
Boltonville (Wells River) ..	05081
Bomoseen	05732
Bondville	05340
Bordoville	05450
(Enosburg Falls)	
Boutswells (Barre)	05641
Bowlsville	05742
(East Wallingford)	
Bradford	05033
Bragg (Norwich)	05055
Braintree (Randolph)	05060
Branch (Wolcott)	05680
Brandon	05733
Brattleboro	05301-304
Green River	05301
Guilford	05301
Harrisville	05301
Hinesburg	05301
West Brattleboro	05301
Bread Loaf (Middlebury) ..	05753
Bridgeport (Bridport)	05734
Bridgewater	05034
Bridgewater Corners	05035
Brighton (Island Pond)	05846
Brimstone Corner	05083
(West Fairlee)	
Brimstone Corners	05761
(Pawlet)	
Bristol	05443
Brockways Mills (Chester)	05143
Bromley Mountain .. 05148,	05254
(Londonderry)	
Brookfield	05036
Brookline (Newfane)	05345
Brookside (East Dover)	05341
	05452, 05494
Brooksville (Middlebury) ..	05753
Brookville (New Haven)	05472
Brownington (Orleans)	05860
Brownsville	05037
Buck (Johnson)	05656
Buck Hollow (Fairfax)	05454
Buell Hollow (Fairfax)	05454
Buels Gore (Starksboro) ...	05487
Burke (West Rutland)	05777
	05871
Burke Mountain	05832
(East Burke)	
Burlington	05401-407
Champlain	05401, 05406
Fort Ethan Island	05401
Foster Summit	05401
N Burlington	05401
S Burlington 05401,	05406
Burnham Hill (Hardwick) ...	05843
Burnham Hollow	05757

(Middletown Springs)	
Burtons Island	05481
(Saint Albans Bay)	
Button Bay (Vergennes) ...	05491
Cabot	05647
Cadys Falls (Morrisville) ...	05661
Calais	05648
Cambridge	05444
Cambridge Junction	05464
(Jeffersonville)	
Cambridgeport	05141
Camp Johnson	05446
(Colchester)	
Camp Warner (Brandon) ...	05733
Canaan (Averill) 05901,	05903
Wallispond	05903
Carver Falls (Fair Haven)..	05743
Castleton	05735
Cavendish	05142
Cedar Beach (Charlotte) ...	05445
Center Rutland	05736
Centerville (Hyde Park)	05655
Champlain (Burlington)	05401
	05406, 05468
Charleston	05872
(West Charleston)	
Charlotte	05445
Chelsea	05038
Chester	05143
Chester Depot	05144
Chickberry (Brandon)	05733
Chimney Corner (Milton) ...	05468
Chimney Point	05491
(Vergennes)	
Chipman Hill (Middlebury)	05753
Chipman Lake (Danby)	05739
Chipmans Point 05733,	05760
(Brandon)	
Chippenhook	05777
(West Rutland)	
Chiselville (Arlington)	05250
	05252
Chittenden	05737
Clarendon	05759
(North Clarendon)	
Clarendon Springs	05777
(West Rutland)	
Clay Point (Milton)	05468
Clementwood (Rutland)	05701
Cleveland Corner	05661
(Morrisville)	
Cloverdale (Cambridge)	05444
Colbyville (Waterbury)	05676
Colchester .. 05439, 05446,	05449
Camp Johnson	05446
Fort Ethan Allen	05446
Malletts Bay	05446
Porters Point	05446
Winooski Park	05446
Cold River 05738,	05759
(Cuttingsville)	
Cold Spring (Milton)	05468
Coles Corner	05819
(Saint Johnsbury)	
Concord	05824
Cookville (Corinth)	05039
Copperfield (Vershire)	05079
Corinth	05039
Cornwall (Middlebury)	05753
Coventry	05825
Cover Point (North Hero) ..	05474

Groton	05046
Grout	05159
(Westminster Station)	
Guildhall	05905
Guilford (Brattleboro)	05301
Guinea Road (Charlotte)	05445
Halifax (West Halifax)	05358
Halls Lake (Wells River)	05081
Hammondsville (Reading)	05062
Hancock	05748
Hanksville (Starksboro)	05487
Hardscrabble	05156
(Springfield)	
Hardwick	05843
Hardwick Steet	05836
(East Hardwick)	
Harmonyville (Townshend)	05353
Harrisville (Brattleboro)	05301
Hartford	05047
Hartland	05048
Hartland Four Corners	05049
Harvey (Danville)	05828
Harwood Hill (Bennington)	05201
Hathaways Point	05478
(Saint Albans)	
Healdville (Mount Holly)	05758
Heartwell (Rutland)	05701
Heartwellville	05350
(Readsboro)	
Hectorville	05471
(Montgomery Center)	
Herrick (Enosburg Falls)	05450
Hewitts Corners	05053
(North Pomfret)	
Highgate Center	05450
Hill West	05450
(Enosburg Falls)	
Hinesburg (Brattleboro)	05301
	05461
Lake Iroquois	05461
Mechanicsburg	05461
Rhode Island Corner	05461
Hog Island (Swanton)	05488
Holden (Pittsford)	05763
Holiday Hill (Rupert)	05768
Holiday Point	05474
(North Hero)	
Holland (Derby Line)	05830
Hollister (Florence)	05744
Hookerville (Marshfield)	05658
Hortonia (Orwell)	05760
Hortonville (Mount Holly)	05758
	05760
Houghs Crossing (Orwell)	05760
Houghtonville (Grafton)	05146
Hubbard Corner	05478
(Saint Albans)	
Hubbardton (Bomoseen)	05732
Huntington	05462
Huntsville (Fairfax)	05454
Hutchins	05471
(Montgomery Center)	
Hyde Manor (Brandon)	05733
Hyde Park	05655
Hydeville	05750
Indian Point (Newport)	05855
Inwood (Barnet)	05821
Ira (West Rutland)	05777
Irasburg	05845
Irasville (Waitsfield)	05673
Island Pond	05846

Isle La Motte	05463
Jacksonville	05342
Jamaica	05343
Jay (North Troy)	05859
Jeffersonville	05464
Jenneville (Windsor)	05089
Jericho	05465
Jerusalem (Bristol)	05443
Joes Pond (West Danville)	05873
Johnny Care Hills	05478
(Saint Albans)	
Johnsbury	05819
(Saint Johnsbury)	
Johnson	05656
Jones Brook (Montpelier)	05602
Jonesville	05466
Kansas (East Arlington)	05252
Keelers Bay (South Hero)	05486
Kendall (East Thetford)	05043
Kendricks Corner	05150
(North Springfield)	
Killington	05751
Kimball (Barton)	05822
Kimballs	05473
(North Ferrisburg)	
Kirby (Concord)	05824
Knights Point	05474
(North Hero)	
Kugg Flats	05677
(Waterbury Center)	
Lagrange (North Hero)	05474
Lake Arrowhead (Milton)	05468
Lake Bomoseen	05735
(Castleton)	
Lake Carmi (Franklin)	05457
Lake Dunmore (Salisbury)	05769
Lake Echo (Brandon)	05733
Lake Elmore	05657
Lake Emerald	05253
(East Dorset)	
Lake Fairlee (Ely)	05044
Lake Fern (Brandon)	05733
	05745
Lake Glen (Castleton)	05735
Lake Hinevah	05758
(Mount Holly)	
Lake Hortonia	05743, 05760
(Fair Haven)	
Lake Hurst	05463
(Isle La Motte)	
Lake Iroquois (Hinesburg)	05461
Lake Lamoille	05661
(Morrisville)	
Lake Morey (Fairlee)	05045
Lake Park (Newport)	05855
Lake Raponda	05363
(Wilmington)	
Lake Rescue (Ludlow)	05149
Lake Richville (Shoreham)	05770
Lake St Catherine	05764
(Poultney)	
Lake Sunset (Benson)	05731
Lake Valley (Woodbury)	05681
Lakeview House	05488
(Swanton)	
Lakewood (Swanton)	05488
Landgrove (Londonderry)	05148
Lanesboro (Marshfield)	05658
Langdons (Castleton)	05735
Lapham Bay (Bridport)	05734
Larrabees Point	05770

(Shoreham)	
Leicester (Brandon)	05733
Leicester Junction	05778
(Whiting)	
Lewiston (Norwich)	05055
Lillieville (Bethel)	05032
Lincoln (Bristol)	05443
Londonderry	05148
Long Point	05473
(North Ferrisburg)	
Lowell	05847
Lower Cabot (Marshfield)	05658
Lower Granville	05747
(Granville)	
Lower Narrows	05873
(West Danville)	
Lower Plain (Bradford)	05033
Lower Village (Stowe)	05672
Lower Waterford	05848
Lower Websterville	05641
(Barre)	
Ludlow	05149
Lunenburg	05906
Lyman	05001
(White River Junction)	
Lyndon	05849
Lyndon Center	05850
Lyndonville	05851
Mackville (Hardwick)	05843
Mad River Glen	05673
(Waitsfield)	
Madonna (Jeffersonville)	05464
Maidstone (Guildhall)	05905
Mallets Bay (Winooski)	05404
Malletts Bay (Colchester)	05446
Manchester	05254
Manchester Center	05255
Maple Dell (Springfield)	05156
Maquam (Swanton)	05488
Marlboro	05344
Marshfield	05658
Mary Meyer (Townshend)	05353
Marydown (Pittsford)	05763
Mc Indoe Falls	05050
Mechanicsburg (Hinesburg)	05461
Mechanicsville (Richmond)	05477
Medburyville (Wilmington)	05363
Melville (Saint Albans)	05478
Mendon (Rutland)	05701
Merrill Corner (Irasburg)	05845
Middlebury	05753, 05766
Beldons	05753
Bread Loaf	05753
Brooksville	05753
Chipman Hill	05753
Cornwall	05753
Ripton	05766
West Cornwall	05753
Weybridge	05753
Middlesex (Montpelier)	05602
Middletown (Chester)	05143
Middletown Springs	05757
Mile Point (Vergennes)	05491
Miles Pond	05858
(North Concord)	
Mill Village (Vershire)	05079
	05701, 05827
Milton	05468
Miltonboro (Milton)	05468
Missisquoi (Richford)	05476
Monkton	05469

557

Monkton Ridge 05473	
(North Ferrisburg)	
Montgomery 05470	
Montgomery Center 05471	
Montpelier 05601-604	
.... 05609, 05620, 05633	
Barre Transfer 05602	
Berlin 05602	
East Montpelier Center 05602	
Gould Hill 05602	
Jones Brook 05602	
Middlesex 05602	
Putnamville 05602	
Shady Hill 05602	
West Brookville 05602	
Wrightsville 05602	
Moretown 05660	
Morgan 05853	
Morristown (Morrisville) 05661	
Morrisville (Lake Elmore) .. 05657	
.... 05661	
Cadys Falls 05661	
Cleveland Corner 05661	
Garfield 05661	
Lake Lamoille 05661	
Morristown 05661	
Mud City 05661	
Morses Line (Franklin) 05457	
Morses Mills (Passumpsic) 05861	
Moscow 05662	
Mosquitoville 05042	
(East Ryegate)	
Mount Holly 05758	
Mount Mansfield (Stowe) .. 05672	
Mount Philo 05473	
(North Ferrisburg)	
Mount Snow (West Dover) . 05356	
Mount Tabor (Danby) 05739	
Mud City (Morrisville) 05661	
Mud Creek (Alburg) 05440	
Mutton Road (Charlotte) 05445	
Nashville (Jericho) 05465	
Nebraska Valley (Stowe) ... 05672	
Neshobe Back 05732	
New Boston (Norwich) 05055	
.... 05772	
New Haven 05472	
New Haven Mills (Bristol) .. 05443	
Newark (West Burke) 05871	
Newbury 05051	
Newbury Center 05069	
(South Ryegate)	
Newfane 05345	
Newport 05855	
Newport Center 05857	
North Bennington 05257	
North Burlington 05401	
(Burlington)	
North Calais 05650	
(East Calais)	
North Cambridge 05464	
(Jeffersonville)	
North Clarendon 05759	
North Concord 05858	
North Danville 05819	
(Saint Johnsbury)	
North Derby (Newport) 05855	
North Dorset 05253	
(East Dorset)	
North Duxbury (Waterbury) 05676	
North Fairfax (Fairfax) 05454	

North Fayston (Moretown) 05660	
North Ferrisburg 05473	
North Hartland 05052	
North Hero 05474	
North Hyde Park 05665	
North Landgrove 05148	
(Londonderry)	
North Montpelier 05666	
(East Montpelier)	
North Orwell (Orwell) 05760	
North Pawlet (Pawlet) 05761	
North Peacham 05873	
(West Danville)	
North Pomfret 05053	
North Pownal 05260	
North Randolph 05041	
(East Randolph)	
North Rupert (Pawlet) 05761	
North Shaftsbury 05262	
(Shaftsbury)	
North Sheldon 05485	
(Sheldon Springs)	
North Sherburne 05751	
(Killington)	
North Shrewsbury 05738	
(Cuttingsville)	
North Springfield 05150	
North Thetford 05054	
North Troy 05859	
North Tunbridge 05077	
(Tunbridge)	
North Underhill 05488-489	
(Swanton)	
North Westminster 05101	
(Bellows Falls)	
North Windham 05148	
(Londonderry)	
North Wolcott (Wolcott) 05680	
Northfield 05663	
Northfield Falls 05664	
Norton 05907	
Norwich 05055	
Oakland (Saint Albans) 05478	
Oil City (Strafford) 05072	
Old Bennington 05201	
(Bennington)	
Old Church (Randolph) 05060	
Olympus (Bethel) 05032	
Orange (Barre) 05641	
Orchard Lane 05156	
(Springfield)	
Orleans 05860	
Orwell 05760	
Otter Valley (Brandon) 05733	
Owls Head Harbor 05491	
(Vergennes)	
Palmers Corner (Bridport) . 05734	
Panton (Vergennes) 05491	
Paper Mill Village 05257	
(North Bennington)	
Passumpsic 05861	
Pawlet 05761	
Peach Four Corners 05085	
(West Newbury)	
Peacham 05862	
Pearl (Grand Isle) 05458	
Peaseville (Chester) 05143	
Pedden Acres 05156	
(Springfield)	
Pekin (Plainfield) 05667	
Perkinsville 05151	

Peru 05152	
Peth (Randolph) 05060	
Pierce Corner 05759	
(North Clarendon)	
Pikes Falls (Jamaica) 05343	
Piko Peak (Killington) 05751	
Pinewood (Essex Junction) 05452	
Pittsfield 05762	
Pittsford 05763	
Plainfield 05667	
Pleasant Valley 05444, 05489	
(Cambridge)	
Plymouth 05056	
Plymouth Union (Plymouth) 05056	
Point Farm (Grand Isle) 05458	
Pomfret (North Pomfret) ... 05053	
Popsquash (Swanton) 05488	
Porters Point 05446	
(Colchester)	
Portland (Lake Elmore) 05657	
Post Mills 05058	
Potash Bay (Vergennes) ... 05491	
Potash Point (Vergennes) . 05491	
Pottersville (Wolcott) 05680	
Poultney (East Poultney) .. 05741	
.... 05764	
Blissville 05764	
Eurlea 05764	
Lake St Catherine 05764	
Rareville 05764	
South Poultney 05764	
Pownal 05261	
Prindle Corner 05445	
(Charlotte)	
Proctor 05765	
Proctorsville 05153	
Prosper (Woodstock) 05091	
Pumpkin Village 05448, 05483	
(East Fairfield)	
Putnamville (Montpelier) ... 05602	
Putney 05346	
Quechee 05059	
Queen City 05403	
(South Burlington)	
Ralston Corner (Concord) . 05824	
Randolph 05060	
Randolph Center 05061	
Rareville (Poultney) 05764	
Rawsonville 05155	
(South Londonderry)	
Reading 05062	
Readsboro 05350, 05352	
Heartwellville 05350	
Stamford 05352	
Red Village (Lyndonville) .. 05851	
Reedville (Chester) 05143	
Rhode Island Corner 05461	
(Hinesburg)	
Rices Mills 05075	
(Thetford Center)	
Richford 05476	
Richmond 05477	
Ricker Mills (Groton) 05046	
Ripton (Middlebury) 05766	
Riverside (Hancock) ... 05488-489	
Riverton (Northfield) 05663	
Rixford (Highgate Center) . 05459	
Robinson (Rochester) 05767	
Rochester 05767	
Rochville (Bristol) 05443	
Rockingham 05101	

Rocky Dale (Bristol) 05443
Round Pond 05069, 05468
(South Ryegate)
Roxbury 05669
Royalton (South Royalton) 05068
Rupert 05768
Russellville 05738
(Cuttingsville)
Russtown 05001
(White River Junction)
Rutland 05701-702
   Clementwood 05701
   East Pittsford 05701
   Glen 05701
   Heartwell 05701
   Mendon 05701
   Mill Village 05701
Ryegate (East Ryegate) 05042
Saint Albans 05478-479
Saint Albans Bay 05481
Saint Albans Hill 05478
(Saint Albans)
Saint George (Williston) 05495
Saint Johnsbury 05819
Saint Johnsbury Center 05863
Saint Michaels College 05439
.... 05446
(Colchester)
Saint Rocks 05478, 05483
(Saint Albans)
Salisbury 05769
Samsonville 05450
(Enosburg Falls)
Sanderson Corner 05454
(Fairfax)
Sandgate (Arlington) 05250
Saxtons River 05154
Scotch Hill (Fair Haven) 05743
Scottsville (Danby) 05739
Searsburg (Wilmington) 05363
Shadow Lake (Glover) 05839
Shady Hill (Montpelier) 05602
Shaftsbury 05262
Sharon 05065
Shawville (Franklin) 05457
Sheddsville (Windsor) 05089
Sheffield 05866
Shelburne 05482
Sheldon 05483
Sheldon Springs 05485
Sherburne (Killington) 05751
Shoreham 05770
Shrewsbury 05738
(Cuttingsville)
Simonsville (Chester) 05143
Simpsonville (Townshend) 05353
Sky Acres (Washington) 05675
Smith Four Corners 05843
(Hardwick)
Smithville (Ludlow) 05149
Smugglers Notch 05464
(Jeffersonville)
Sodom (North Bennington) 05257
South Albany (Alburg) 05875
(West Glover)
South Alburg (Alburg) 05440
South Barre 05670
South Burlington 05401
.... 05403, 05406-407
   Burlington 05403, 05407
   Queen City 05403

South Cabot (Marshfield) .. 05658
South Cambridge 05464
(Jeffersonville)
South Corinth (Bradford) 05033
South Danville (Danville) 05828
South Dorset (Dorset) 05251
South Duxbury 05660, 05676
(Moretown)
South End (Danby) 05739
South Franklin 05450
(Enosburg Falls)
South Hero 05486
South Lincoln (Bristol) 05443
South Londonderry 05155
South Lunenburg 05906
(Lunenburg)
South Newbury (Newbury) 05051
South Newfane 05351
South Northfield 05663
(Northfield)
South Peacham (Barnet) 05821
South Pomfret 05067
South Poultney (Poultney) 05764
South Randolph 05068
(South Royalton)
South Reading 05153
(Proctorsville)
South Richford (Richford) . 05476
South Royalton 05068
South Ryegate 05069
South Shaftsbury 05262
(Shaftsbury)
South Starksboro 05487
(Starksboro)
South Strafford 05070
South Tunbridge 05068
(South Royalton)
South Vershire (Vershire) .. 05079
South Walden (Hardwick) . 05843
South Wallingford 05773
(Wallingford)
South Wardsboro 05355
(Wardsboro)
South Washington 05675
(Washington)
South Wheelock 05851
(Lyndonville)
South Windham 05359
(West Townshend)
South Woodbury 05650
(East Calais)
South Woodstock 05071
Spankerton (Pawlet) 05761
Spoonerville 05144
(Chester Depot)
Springfield 05156
Stamford (Readsboro) 05352
Stannard 05842
(Greensboro Bend)
Starksboro 05487
Stevens Mills (Richford) 05476
Stevensville (Underhill) 05489
Stockbridge 05772
Stowe (Moscow) 05662, 05672
   Lower Village 05672
   Mount Mansfield 05672
   Nebraska Valley 05672
   Upper Hollow Road 05672
   West Branch 05672
Strafford 05072
Stratton (W Wardsboro) 05360

Stratton Mountain 05155
(South Londonderry)
Stump Station (Shoreham) 05770
Sudbury (Brandon) 05733
Sugarbush Valley (Warren) 05674
Summer Point (Vergennes) 05491
Summit (Mount Holly) 05758
Sunderland (Arlington)
.... 05250, 05252
Sutton 05867
Swanton 05488
Sweek Hollow (Sheldon) ... 05483
Tafts Corner (Taftsville) 05073
Taftsville 05073
Talcott (Williston) 05495
Talcville (Rochester) 05767
Tarbellville 05742
(East Wallingford)
Taylorville (Hardwick) 05843
The Bluffs (Newport) 05855
The Hollow 05473
(North Ferrisburg)
The Island (Weston) 05161
Thetford 05074
Thetford Center 05075
Thompsonburg 05148
(Londonderry)
Tinmouth (Wallingford) 05773
Topsham (East Corinth) 05076
.... 05076
Topsham Four Corners 05040
(East Corinth)
Townshend 05353, 05359
   Harmonyville 05353
   Mary Meyer 05353
   Simpsonville 05353
Trow Hill (Barre) 05641
Troy 05868
True Blue (Proctor) 05765
Tunbridge 05077
Tyson (Ludlow) 05149
Una Bella (Bennington) 05201
Underhill 05489
Underhill Center 05490
Union Village 05043
(East Thetford)
Upper Graniteville 05654
(Graniteville)
Upper Hollow Road 05672
(Stowe)
Upper Narrows 05873
(West Danville)
Vergennes 05491
Vernon 05354
Vershire 05079
Victory (North Concord) 05858
Waits River 05086
(West Topsham)
Waitsfield 05673
Walden (West Danville) 05873
Wallingford 05773
Wallispond (Canaan) 05903
Waltham (Vergennes) 05491
Wardsboro 05355
Warren 05674
Washington 05675
Washington Heights 05657
(Lake Elmore)
Waterbury 05676, 05671
Waterbury Center 05677
Waterford 05848

(Lower Waterford)
Waterville 05492
Weathersfield 05151
(Perkinsville)
Weathersfield Bow 05156
(Springfield)
Websterville 05678
Wells 05774
Wells River 05081
West Addison (Vergennes) 05491
West Arlington 05250
(Arlington)
West Barnet (Barnet) 05821
West Berkshire 05450
(Enosburg Falls)
West Bolton (Jericho) 05465
West Branch (Stowe) 05672
West Brattleboro 05301
(Brattleboro)
West Bridgewater 05035
(Bridgewater Corners)
West Bridport (Bridport) 05734
West Brookfield 05060
(Randolph)
West Brookfield 05602
(Montpelier)
West Burke 05871
West Castleton 05743
(Fair Haven)
West Charleston 05872
West Corinth (Corinth) 05039
West Cornwall 05753
(Middlebury)
West Danville 05873
West Derby (Newport) 05855
West Dover 05351, 05356
(South Newfane)
Mount Snow 05356

West Dummerston 05357
West Enosburg 05450
(Enosburg Falls)
West Fairlee 05083
West Ferrisburg 05491
(Vergennes)
West Georgia 05478
(Saint Albans)
West Glover 05875
West Groton (Groton) 05046
West Halifax 05358
West Hartford 05084
West Haven (Fair Haven) .. 05743
West Hill 05450, 05641
(Enosburg Falls)
West Lincoln (Bristol) 05443
West Milton (Milton) 05468
West Newbury 05085
West Norwich (Norwich) ... 05055
West Pawlet 05775
West Rupert 05776
West Rutland 05777
West Salisbury 05769
(Salisbury)
West Springfield 05156
(Springfield)
West Swanton (Swanton) .. 05488
West Topsham 05086
West Townshend 05359
West Wardsboro 05360
West Waterford 05819
(Saint Johnsbury)
West Windsor 05037
(Brownsville)
West Woodstock 05091
(Woodstock)
Westfield 05874

Westford 05494
Westminster 05158
Westminster Station 05159
Westminster W. (Putney) ... 05346
Westmore (Orleans) 05860
Weston 05161
Weston Priory (Weston) ... 05161
Weybridge (Middlebury) ... 05753
Wheelock (Lyndonville) 05851
White River Junction 05001
.... 05009
Whitesville (Cavendish) 05142
Whiting 05778
Whitingham 05361
Wilder 05088
Williamstown 05679
Williamsville 05362
Williston 05495
Wilmington 05363
Windham (W. Townshend) 05359
Windsor 05089
Wings Point (Charlotte) 05445
Winhall (Bondville) 05340
Winooski 05404
Winooski Park 05446
(Colchester)
Wolcott 05680
Wolumsak 05257
(North Bennington)
Woodbury 05681
Woodford (Bennington) 05201
Woodmere (Bennington) ... 05201
Woodpecker Village 05450
(Enosburg Falls)
Woodstock 05091
Worcester 05682
Wrightsville (Montpelier) ... 05602

IMPORTANT BUILDINGS   VERMONT

BURLINGTON

APARTMENTS

Country Park Apts
635 HINESBURG RD 05403

Default
175 KENNEDY DR 05403

Dorset Commons
435 DORSET BLVD 05403

George Town
125 KENNEDY DR 05403

Horizon Heights
350 SPEAR ST 05403

Manor Woods
100 KENNEDY DR 05403

Meadow Brook
69 JOY DR 05403

Millyard
100 W CANAL ST 05404

Sugar Tree
200 KENNEDY DR 05403

The Courtyard
120 E SPRING ST 05404

Town Square
425 DORSET BLVD 05403

Village Green Apts
75 HINESBURG RD 05403

Wellesley Grove
630 HINESBURG RD 05403

BUILDINGS

Burlington Intl Airport
1200 AIRPORT DR 05403

Burlington Sq Mall
4 BURLINGTON SQ 05401

Champlain Mill
1 MAIN ST 05404

Chase Mill
1 MILL ST 05401

Dorset Square Mall
150 DORSET BLVD 05403

Executive Square
346 SHELBURNE RD 05401

Factory Outlet Mall
560 SHELBURNE RD 05401

Woolen Mill
20 W CANAL ST 05404

GOVERNMENT

City Hall
149 CHURCH ST 05401

Federal Bldg
11 ELMWOOD AVE 05401

So Burl City Offices
575 DORSET BLVD 05403

VIRGIN ISLANDS
Abbreviation VI

Charlotte Amalie	00801-804
(St Thomas)	
Christiansted	00820-824
Saint Croix	00820-824
Cruz Bay (St John)	00830-831
Frederiksted	00840-841
Saint Croix	00840-841
Kingshill	00850-851
Saint Croix	00850
Saint Croix	00820-824
....	00840-841, 00850
(Christiansted)	
Saint John (St John) ..	00830-831
Saint Thomas	00801-804

Irvington	22480
Isle Of Wight	23397
Ivanhoe	24350
Ivor	23866
Ivy	22945
Jamaica	23079
James Store	23080
Jamestown	23081
Jamesville	23398
Jarratt	23867, 23870
Java	24565
Jefferson Manor	22303
(Alexandria)	
Jeffersonton	22724
Jenkins Bridge	23399
Jersey	22481
Jetersville	23083
Jewell Ridge	24622
Jonesville	24263
Jordan Mines	24449
Keeling	24566
Keen Mountain	24624
Keene	22946
Keezletown	22832
Keller	23401
Kenbridge	23944
Kents Store	23084
Keokee	24265
Kesslers Mill (Salem)	24153
Keswick	22947
Keysville	23947
Kilmarnock	22482
Kimballton (Ripplemead)	24150
King George	22485
King William	23086
Kings Store (Copper Hill)	24079
Kinsale	22488
La Crosse	23950
Lacey Spring	22833
Lackey	23694
Ladysmith	22501
Lafayette (Elliston)	24087
Lahore	22502
Lake Anne (Reston)	22090
Lake Monticello (Palmyra)	22963
Lakeridge (Woodbridge)	22192
Lakeside (Richmond)	23228
Lambsburg	24351
Lancaster	22503
Laneview	22504
Lanexa	23089
Lansdowne (Leesburg)	22075
Laurel Fork	24352
Lawrenceville	23868
Leakesville Junction	24069
(Cascade)	
Lebanon	24266
Lee Hall (Newport News)	23603
Lee Mont	23403
Leesburg	22075
Lennig (Nathalie)	24577
Leon	22725
Lewisetta	22505
Lexington	24450
Lightfoot	23090
Lignum	22726
Lillian Vernon	23479
(Virginia Beach)	
Lincoln	22078
Lincolnia (Alexandria)	22312
Linden	22642

Lindsay (Gordonsville)	22942
Linville	22834
Lithia (Buchanan)	24066
Little Creek	23455
(Virginia Beach)	
Little Plymouth	23091
Littlevine (Hillsville)	24343
Lively	22507
Locust Dale	22948
Locust Grove	22508
Locust Hill	23092
Locustville	23404
Long Island	24569
Loretto	22509
Lorton	22079, 22199
Mason Neck	22079
Lottsburg	22511
Louisa	23093, 23170
Lovettsville	22080
Lovingston	22949
Lowesville	22951
Lowmoor (Low Moor)	24457
Lowry	24570
Lunenburg	23952
Luray	22835
Lynch Station	24571
Lynchburg	24501-06, 24512-515
Fort Hill	24502
Miller Park	24501
Rivermont	24503
Timberlake	24502
Lyndhurst	22952
Machipongo	23405
Macon	23101
Madison (Etlan)	22719
	22722, 22727
Aylor	22727
Criglersville	22727
Haywood	22727
Shelby	22727
Twymans Mill	22727
Madison Heights	24572
Madison Mills	22953
Madison Run	22942
(Gordonsville)	
Maidens	23102
Manakin (Manakin Sabot)	23103
Manakin Sabot	23103
Manassas	22110-111
Mangohick	23104
Mannboro	23105
Manquin	23106
Mappsville	23407
Marion	24354, 24373
Stony Battery	24354
The Cedars	24354
Thomas Bridge	24354
Marionville	23408
Markham	22643
Marshall	22115
Martinsville	24112-115
Maryus	23107
Mascot	23108
Mason Cove (Salem)	24153
Mason Neck (Lorton)	22079
Massies Mill	22954
Master Charge (Richmond)	23276
Mathews	23109
Matoaca (Petersburg)	23803
Mattaponi	23110
Maurertown	22644

Mavisdale	24627
Max Meadows	24360
Maxie	24628
Mc Clure	24269
Mc Coy	24111
Mc Dowell	24458
Mc Gaheysville	22840
Mc Kenney	23872
Mc Lean (Greenway)	22067
	22109, 22101-103, 22106
West Mclean	22102
Meadowcreek (Galax)	24333
Meadowview (Clinchburg)	24321
	24361
Clinchburg	24361
Mears	23409
Mechanicsville	23111
Meherrin	23954
Melfa	23410
Melrose (Roanoke)	24017
Melton (Gordonsville)	22942
Mendota	24270
Meredithville	23873
Merrifield	22081, 22116
Northern Virginia	22081
Northern Virginia Facility	
	22081
Merrimac (Williamsburg)	23185
Merry Point	22513
Middlebrook	24459
Middleburg	22117
Middletown	22645, 22649
Reliance	22649
Midland	22728
Midlothian	23112-113
Sycamore Square	23113
Milboro Sprgs (Millboro)	24460
Miles	23114
Milford	22514
Mill Gap (Monterey)	24465
Millboro	24460
Millboro Spring	24460
(Millboro)	
Millenbeck (Lancaster)	22503
Miller Park (Lynchburg)	24501
Millers (Richmond)	23231
Millers Tavern	23115
Millers Tavrn	23115
(Millers Tavern)	
Millwood	22646
Mine Run	22568
Mineral	23117
Mint Spring	24463
Mitchells	22729
Mobjack	23118
Modest Town	23412
Mollusk	22517
Moneta	24121
Monroe	24574
Montclair (Dumfries)	22026
Montebello	24464
Monterey	24465
Montevideo (Penn Laird)	22846
Montezuma (Dayton)	22821
Montford (Orange)	22960
Monticello	22902
(Charlottesville)	
Montpelier	23192
Montpelier Station	22957
Montrose (Richmond)	23231
Montross	22520

Rhoadesville 22542
Rice 23966
Rich Creek 24147
Richardson (Hillsville) 24343
Richardsville 22736
Richlands 24641
Richmond 23173, 23200-238
.... 23240-242, 23249-250
.... 23255, 23260-261, 23266
.... 23269-270, 23272-280
.... 23282, 23284-286
.... 23288-294, 23297-298
Ampthill 23234
Azalea 23227
Bellevue 23227
Bon Air 23235
Brookside 23227
Buford 23235
Business Reply 23286
C & P Tele 23272
Capitol 23201-23219
Central Station 23241
County Of Henrico 23273
East End 23223
Forest Hill 23225
Lakeside 23228
Main Office 23260-23261
Main Post Office 23232
Master Charge 23276
Millers 23231
Montrose 23231
Montrose Heights 23231
Northside 23222
Pocoshock 23235
Regency 23229
Ridge 23233
Saunders 23220
Southside 23224
Sovran Bank 23292
Sovran Center 23277
Staples Mill 23228
Stewart 23221
Tuckahoe 23229
United Virginia Bank ... 23291
Varina 23231
West End 23230
Westbury 23229
Westhampton 23226
Ridge (Richmond) 23233
.... 23294
Ridgeway 24148, 24597
Rileyville 22650
Riner 24149
Ringgold 24586
Ripplemead 24150
Rivermont (Lynchburg) 24503
Riverton (Front Royal) 22651
Rixeyville 22737
Roanoke . 24000-020, 24022-038
.... 24040, 24042-045, 24048
Bonsack 24012
Cave Spring 24018
Garden City 24014
Grandin Road 24015
Hollins 24019
Hollins College 24020
Melrose 24017
Norfolk West Rwy 24043
Poages Mill 24018
South Roanoke 24014
Rochelle 22738

Rockbridge Baths 24473
Rockfish (Shipman) 22971
Rockville 23146
Rocky Gap 24366
Rocky Mount 24151
Rollins Fork 22544
Rose Hill 24281
Rosedale 24280
Roseland 22967, 22976
Round Hill 22141
Rowe 24646
Ruby 22545
Ruckersville 22968
Rural Retreat 24368
Rustburg 24588
Ruther Glen 22546
Ruthville 23147
Sabot (Manakin Sabot) 23103
Saint Charles 24282
Saint Paul 24283
Salem 24153, 24156-157
Saltville 24370
Saluda 23149
Sandston 23150
Sandy Hook 23153
Sandy Level 24161
Sanford 23426
Sanville (Bassett) 24055
Saunders (Richmond) 23220
Saxe 23967
Saxis 23427
Schley 23154
Schoolfield (Danville) 24541
Schuyler 22969
Scottsburg 24589
Scottsville 24562, 24590
(Howardsville)
Scruggs (Moneta) 24121
Seaford 23696
Sealston 22547
Seaview 23429
Sedley 23878
Selma 24474
Seven Corners 22044
(Falls Church)
Seven Fountains 22652
(Fort Valley)
Seven Mile Ford 24373
Severn 23155
Shacklefords 23156
Shadow (Susan) 23163
Shadwell (Keswick) 22947
Shanghai (Mattaponi) 23110
Sharps 22548
Shawsville 24162
Shelby (Madison) 22727
Shenandoah 22849
Sherando (Lyndhurst) 22952
Shiloh 22549
Shipman 22971
Shirley Duke (Alexandria) . 22304
Shirlington (Arlington) 22206
Shortt Gap 24647
Simpsons (Check) 24072
Singers Glen 22850
Skippers 23879
Skipwith 23968
Smithfield 23430
Snell (Spotsylvania) 22553
Snowden (Big Island) 24526
Snowflake (Gate City) 24251

Snowville (Pulaski) 24301
Somerset 22972
Somerville 22739
South (Arlington) 22204
South Boston 24592, 24596
South Garden 22959
(North Garden)
South Hill 23970
South Jackson 22842
(Mount Jackson)
South Norfolk 23324
(Chesapeake)
South Roanoke (Roanoke) 24014
Southside (Richmond) 23224
Sovran Center (Richmond) 23277
Sparta 22552
Speedwell 24374
Spencer 24165
Sperryville 22740
Spotsylvania 22553
Spottswood 24475
Spout Spring 24593
Spring Grove 23881
Springfield (Burke) 22009
.... 22015, 22150-153, 22156
.... 22158-161
North Springfield 22151
North Springfld 22151
West Springfield 22152
Sprouses Corner (Dillwyn) 23936
Stafford 22554-555
Staffordsville 24167
Stanardsville 22973
Stanley 22851
Stanleytown 24168
Staples Mill (Richmond) 23228
Star Tannery 22654
State Farm 23160
Staunton 24401-402, 24407
Woodrum 24401
Steeles Tavern 24476
Stephens City 22655
Stephenson 22656
Sterling 20164-167, 22170
Dulles 20166
Stevens Creek (Fries) 24330
Stevensburg 22741
Stevensville 23161
Stewart (Richmond) 23221
Stewartsville (Vinton) 24179
Stonega 24285
Stones Mill (Wytheville) 24382
Stony Battery (Marion) 24354
Stony Creek 23882
Strasburg 22641, 22657
Stratford 22558
Stuart 24171
Studley 23162
Suffolk 23432-439
Chuckatuck 23432
Crittenden 23433
Driver 23435
Holland 23437
Whaleyville 23438
Sugar Grove 24375
Sumerduck 22742
Supply 22559
Surry 23883
Susan 23163
Sussex 23884
Sutherland 23885

Sutherlin	24594
Sweet Briar	24595
Swoope	24479
Swords Creek	24649
Sycamore Square	23113
(Midlothian)	
Syria	22743
Syringa (Topping)	23169
Tabb (Yorktown)	23693
Tamworth (Cartersville)	23027
Tangier	23440
Tannersville	24377
Tappahannock	22560
Tasley	23441
Tazewell (Burkes Garden)	24608
	24651
Temperanceville	23442
Thaxton	24174
The Cedars (Marion)	24354
The Plains	22171
Thelma (Gordonsville)	22942
Theological Seminary	22304
(Alexandria)	
Thomas Bridge (Marion)	24354
Thornburg	22565
Thornhill (Orange)	22960
Timberlake (Lynchburg)	24502
Timberville	22853
Tiptop (North Tazewell)	24630
Toano	23168
Toms Brook	22660
Topping	23169
Townsend	23443
Trammel	24289
Trevilians	23170
Triangle	22172
Triplet (Lawrenceville)	23868
Trout Dale	24378
Troutville	24175
Troy	22974
Tuckahoe (Richmond)	23229
Turbeville	24596
Turnpike (Fairfax)	22031
Twymans Mill (Madison)	22727
Tye River (Arrington)	22922
Tyro	22976
Tysons Corner	22103
(West Mclean)	
Union Hall	24176
Unionville	22567-568
Uno (Rochelle)	22738
Upperville	22176
Urbanna	23175
Valentines	23887
Vansant	24656
Varina (Richmond)	23231
Venia (Honaker)	24260
Vernon Hill	24597
Verona	24482
Vesta	24177
Vesuvius	24483
Victoria	23974
Vienna	22027, 22184-185
	22124, 22180-183
Dunn Loring	22027

Dunn Loring	22180
Viewtown	22746
Village	22570
Villamont	24178
Vint Hill (Warrenton)	22186
Vinton	24179
Virgilina	24598
Virginia Beach	23450-452
	23454-468, 23479
Backbay	23457
Beverly Enterprises	23468
Dam Neck	23461
Fleet Combat Training Ctr	
	23461
Fort Story	23459
Lillian Vernon	23479
Oceana NAS	23460
Princess Anne	23456
Pungo	23456
Volney	24379
Wachapreague	23480
Wake	23176
Wakefield	23888
Waldrop (Gordonsville)	22942
Walkerton	23177
Wallops Island	23337
(Chincoteague)	
Walmsley (Callao)	22435
Walnut Hill (Petersburg)	23805
Walters (Carrsville)	23481
Wardtown	23482
Ware Neck	23178
Warfield	23889
Warm Springs	24484
Warner	23179
Warrenton	22186
Warsaw	22572
Wash (Washington)	22747
Washington	22747
Water View	23180
Waterford	22190
Wattsville	23483
Waverly	23890
Waynesboro	22980
Weber City	24290
Weems	22576
Weirwood	23484
Wellington (Alexandria)	22308
West Augusta	24485
West End (Richmond)	23230
West Lexington	24450
(Lexington)	
West Mclean	22102-103
(Mc Lean)	
Mc Lean	22103
Tysons Corner	22103
West Point	23181
West Springfield	22152-153
(Springfield)	
Westbury (Richmond)	23229
Westhampton (Richmond)	23226
Westmoreland	22577
Weyers Cave	24486
Whaleyville (Suffolk)	23438
Whitacre (Cross Junction)	22625

White Hall	22987
White Marsh	23183
White Plains	23893
White Post	22663
White Stone	22578
Whitethorne (Blacksburg)	24060
Whitetop	24292
Whitewood	24657
Wicomico	23184
Wildwood (Palmyra)	22963
Williamsburg (Jamestown)	
	23081, 23185-188
Colonial Williamsburg	23185
Merrimac	23185
Williamsville	24487
Willis	24380
Willis Wharf	23486
Willow Tree (Ewing)	24248
Wilmington (Palmyra)	22963
Wilsons	23894
Winchester	22601-604, 22638
Hayfield	22638
Windmill Point	22578
(White Stone)	
Windsor	23487
Wingina	24599
Winston (Culpeper)	22701
Wintergreen (Nellysford)	22958
Wirtz	24184
Wise	24293
Withams	23488
Wodrow Wilson	22939
(Fishersville)	
Wolford	24658
Wolftown	22748
Woodberry Forest	22989
Woodbridge	22191-194
Dale City	22193
Lakeridge	22192
Prince William	22192
Woodford	22580
Woodlawn	24381
Woodrow Wilson	22939
(Fishersville)	
Woodrum (Staunton)	24401
Woods Cross Roads	23190
Woodstock	22664
Woodville	22749
Woolwine	24185
Wrights Shop	24572
(Madison Heights)	
Wylliesburg	23976
Wytheville	24382
Yale	23897
Yancey Mills (Crozet)	22932
Yards	24659
Yorktown	23690-693
Grafton	23692
Tabb	23693
Zacata	22581
Zanoni	23191
Zion (Gordonsville)	22942
Zion Crossroads	22942
(Gordonsville)	
Zuni	23898

ALEXANDRIA

HOSPITALS

Alexandria Hospital
4320 SEMINARY RD 22304

Mt Vernon Hospital
2501 PARKERS LN 22306

MILITARY

Cameron Station
5010 DUKE ST 22304

COLLEGES

Va Theological Seminary
3737 SEMINARY RD 22304

ARLINGTON

HOSPITALS

National Orthpaedic Hosp
2455 ARMY NAVY DR 22206

No Va Doctors Hospital
601 S Carlin Springs Rd ... 22204

AZALEA

APARTMENTS

Imperial Plaza
1717 BELLEVUE AVE 23227

Morningside/pcu
1600 WESTBROOK AVE .. 23227

BONSACK

APARTMENTS

Bowers Holiday Village
2715 10TH ST NW 24012

Friendship Manor East
320 Hershberger Rd NW .. 24012

Park Towne Apt
1716 EMPRESS DR NW .. 24012

Park Towne Apt
2524 MARR ST NW 24012

Valley View Village
4821 RUTGERS AVE NW . 24012

BUILDINGS

Crossroads Mall
5002 AIRPORT RD NW 24012

Valley View Mall
4802 Valley View Blvd NW 24012

BRISTOL

APARTMENTS

Bristol Mall
500 GATE CITY HWY 24201

CAPITOL

BUILDINGS

700 Building
700 E MAIN ST 23219

Centre Building
700 E FRANKLIN ST 23219

Eskimo Building
530 E MAIN ST 23219

Federal Reserve Building
701 E BYRD ST 23219

Heritage Building
1001 E MAIN ST 23219

James Monroe Building
101 N 14TH ST 23219

James River Plaza Building
1 JAMES RIVER PLZ 23219

Jefferson/blanton Building
1220 BANK ST 23219

Office Building
6 N 6TH ST 23219

Rich Fed Building
728 E MAIN ST 23219

Safety Health & Welfare B
501 N 9TH ST 23219

Travelers Building
1108 E MAIN ST 23219

Wash/old State Off Building
1100 BANK ST 23219

GOVERNMENT

State Capitol Building
0 CAPITOL SQ 23219

CAVE SPRING

APARTMENTS

Bent Tree Apts
3464 COLONIAL AVE 24018

Normandy Knoll Apts
3501 NORMANDY LN 24018

Stratford Village Apts
3780 Stratford Park Dr SW 24018

The Pines
4700 SUSSEX CT 24018

CHARLOTTESVILLE

APARTMENTS

1800 Jpa Hi-rise Apts
1800 Jefferson Park Ave ... 22903

600 Brandon Ave Apts
600 BRANDON AVE 22903

Alcove Apts
207 14TH ST NW 22903

Altamont Apts
11 ALTAMONT CIR 22902

Berkshire Apts
2410 N BERKSHIRE RD .. 22901

Cambridge Square Apts
826 CABELL AVE 22903

Carrollton Ter
101 CARROLLTON TER .. 22903

Charlottesville Towers
511 N 1ST ST 22902

Corner Village
1215 WERTLAND ST 22903

Country Green Apts
701 Mountainwood Rd 22903

Crestview Apts
2118 ANGUS RD 22901

Faculty Apts
203 RUGBY RD 22903

Gardenwood Apts
2204 N BERKSHIRE RD .. 22901

Garrett Square Apts
400 GARRETT ST 22902

Georgetown Sq Apts
166 GEORGETOWN RD .. 22901

Gordon Hall
583 BRANDON AVE 22903

Grady Apts
1410 GRADY AVE 22903

Greenleaf Apts
212 5TH ST SW 22903

Hearthwood Apts
2111 MICHIE DR 22901

Hessian Hills Apts
2400 BARRACKS RD 22901

High Rise For Elderly
500 S 1ST ST 22902

Hunters Creek Apt
2230 Commonwealth Dr ... 22901

Inglewood Sq Apts
1900 INGLEWOOD DR 22901

Jack Jouett Apts
68 UNIVERSITY WAY 22903

Landmark Apts
1904 Jefferson Park Ave ... 22903

Lynnhaven Court Apts
2206 N BERKSHIRE RD .. 22901

Madison Apts
512 BRANDON AVE 22903

Meadowview Apts
2201 ANGUS RD 22901

Monticello Plaza
500 COURT SQ 22902

Oakridge Gardens Apts
720 PROSPECT AVE 22903

Old Salem Apts
2617 BARRACKS RD 22901

Park Lane Apts
630 PARK ST 22902

Piedmont Faculty Apts
115 MIMOSA DR 22903

Preston Ct Apts
1600 GRADY AVE 22903

Raleigh Ct Apts
10 UNIVERSITY CIR 22903

Rugby Mcintire Apts
611 RUGBY RD 22903

Solomon Ct Apts
2517 HYDRAULIC RD 22901

Tarleton Square Apts
701 E HIGH ST 22902

Turtle Creek Apts
101 TURTLE CREEK RD . 22901

Univ Cir Apts
32 UNIVERSITY CIR 22903

University Forum
2021 IVY RD 22903

University Gdns
500 EMMET ST N 22903

Varsity Apts
311 15TH ST NW 22903

Venable Square Apts
312 13TH ST NW 22903

Wellington Ct Apts
1114 JOHN ST 22903

Westgate Apts
502 GEORGETOWN RD .. 22901

Whitewood Village Apts
141 WHITEWOOD RD 22901

Woodrow Apts
101 WOODROW ST 22903

BUILDINGS

Centel Building
1924 ARLINGTON BLVD .. 22903

HOTELS

Best Western Cavalier Inn
105 EMMET ST N 22903

Econo Lodge
400 EMMET ST N 22903

University Lodge
140 EMMET ST N 22903

DANVILLE

BUILDINGS

Municipal Building
418 PATTON ST 24541

ENON

APARTMENTS

Mill Park Terrace
2216 CAROLINE ST 22401

BUILDINGS

Medical Arts Building
2301 FALL HILL AVE 22401

Pratt Clinic
1701 FALL HILL AVE 22401

ETTRICK

BUILDINGS

Community Bank
212 N SYCAMORE ST 23803

HOSPITALS

Southside Regional Mccq
801 S ADAMS ST 23803

FAIRFAX

GOVERNMENT

Massey Building
4100 CHAIN BRIDGE RD . 22030

COLLEGES

George Mason University
4400 UNIVERSITY DR 22030

FALLS CHURCH

GOVERNMENT

City Hall
300 PARK AVE 22046

HOSPITALS

Fairfax Hospital
3300 GALLOWS RD 22042

FORT HILL

APARTMENTS

Mill Woods Apts
6224 OLD MILL RD 24502

Pinebrook Village Apts
220 MCCONVILLE RD 24502

BUILDINGS

River Ridge Shopping Ctr
3405 Candlers Mountain ... 24502

COLLEGES

Liberty Baptist Univ
3765 Candlers Mountain ... 24502

FRONT ROYAL

HOSPITALS

Warren Memorial Hospital
1000 N Shenandoah Ave .. 22630

GARDEN CITY

APARTMENTS

Cinnamon Ridge Apts
5127 OVERLAND DR 24014

Copper Croft Apts
4333 ELECTRIC RD 24014

Honeywood Apts
3101 HONEYWOOD LN ... 24014

Quail Valley Apts
5260 CROSS BOW CIR ... 24014

Summer Tree Apts
3701 SOUTHWAY DR SW 24014

Windy Hill Key Apts
5400 BERNARD DR SW .. 24014

GRANDIN ROAD

APARTMENTS

Brandon Ridge
2755 BRANDON AVE SW . 24015

Ruxton Apts
2840 COLONIAL AVE SW 24015

HOLLINS

APARTMENTS

Bent Creek Apts
6525 GREENWAY DR 24019

Brookside Apts
130 CLUBHOUSE DR 24019

LYNCHBURG

APARTMENTS

Boonsboro Village Apts
4715 BOONSBORO RD ... 24503

Greenfield Apts
1500 LONGVIEW DR 24501

Huntingwood Apts
225 COFFEE RD 24503

Lakeside Dr Apts
1125 LAKESIDE DR 24501

Mccausland Ridge Apts
2075 LANGHORNE RD 24501

Princeton Circle West Apt
18 W PRINCETON CIR 24503

The Forest Apts
3101 LINK RD 24503

Virginia Apts
718 CHURCH ST 24504

Westbury Apts
5001 BOONSBORO RD ... 24503

Westminster Cantebury Apt
501 VA Episcopal School .. 24503

MARTINSVILLE

BUILDINGS

City Municipal Building
1112 PO BOX 24114

Liberty Fair Mall
240 COMMONWEALTH BLVD
W 24112

HOSPITAL

Memorial Hospital
4788 PO BOX 24115

COLLEGE

Patrick Henry Community College
5311 PO BOX 24115

MELROSE

APARTMENTS

Countryside Est
2308 Highland Farm Rd NW24017

Sterling Wood Garden Apts
2215 MONTAUK RD NW .. 24017

NEWPORT NEWS

BUILDINGS

Nations Bank Building
2600 WASHINGTON AVE . 23607

Rouse Towers
6060 JEFFERSON AVE 23605

NORFOLK

APARTMENTS

Pembroke Towers Apts
601 PEMBROKE AVE 23507

BUILDINGS

4100 Building
4101 GRANBY ST 23504

Bankers Trust Building
109 W CITY HALL AVE 23510

Dominion Tower
999 WATERSIDE DR 23510

Greater Norfolk Plz Building
555 FENCHURCH ST 23510

JANAF Executive Building
1 JANAF Executive Building23502

Nations Bank
1 COMMERCIAL PL 23510

Norfolk Federal Building
200 GRANBY ST 23510

Public Safety Building
811 E CITY HALL AVE 23510

Sma Center
234 MONTICELLO AVE 23510

Southern Office Building
1 Southern Shopping Ctr .. 23505

World Trade Center
101 W MAIN ST 23510

GOVERNMENT

U S Court House
600 GRANBY ST 23510

HOSPITALS

De Paul Medical Building
110 KINGSLEY LN 23505

Medical Tower
400 GRESHAM DR 23507

HOTELS

Hotel Norfolk
700 MONTICELLO AVE 23510

PETERSBURG

APARTMENTS

Halcun Manor
1800 Boydton Plank Rd 23805

Tanglewood
1700 JOHNSON RD 23805

PORTSMOUTH

APARTMENTS

Colonial Manor Apts
3622 PRINCETON PL 23707

Edinburg Apts
344 COURT ST 23704

Effingham Plaza
715 MADISON ST 23704

Fort Nelson Towers
333 GREEN ST 23704

Glenshellah Apts
3610 HARTFORD ST 23707

Harbor Tower Apts
1 HARBOR CT 23704

Harbor View Apts
230 Swimming Point Walk 23704

One Crawford Pky Apts
1 CRAWFORD PKY 23704

Patio Plaza Apts
700 CRAWFORD PKY 23704

Portsmouth Garden Apts
1 LAWRENCE CIR 23707

Wilson Manor Apts
3501 COMMERCE ST 23707

BUILDINGS

Dominion Nat Bank Building
430 CRAWFORD ST 23704
Federal Building
431 CRAWFORD ST 23704

Midtown Professional Ctr
3315 COUNTY ST 23707

New Kirn Building
339 HIGH ST 23704

Professional Building
505 WASHINGTON ST 23704

Signet Bank Building
355 CRAWFORD ST 23704

GOVERNMENT

Circuit Court Building
601 CRAWFORD ST 23704

RICHMOND

APARTMENTS

Berkshire
300 W FRANKLIN ST 23220

Chesterfield Apt
900 W FRANKLIN ST 23220

Gresham Court Apt
1030 W FRANKLIN ST 23220

Lexington Tower
104 W FRANKLIN ST 23220

Stuart Ct Apt
1600 MONUMENT AVE 23220

BUILDINGS

Seaboard Building
3600 W BROAD ST 23230

HOSPITALS

Hosp Clinical Sup Building
403 N 13TH ST 23298

Massey Cancer Center
401 COLLEGE ST 23298

Mcquire Vet Adm Hosp
1201 BROAD ROCK BLVD 23249

Mcv East Hospital
1215 E MARSHALL ST 23298

Mcv Main Hospital
401 N 12TH ST 23298

Mcv North Hospital
1300 E MARSHALL ST 23298

Mcv West Hospital
1200 E BROAD ST 23298

Nelson Clinic
401 N 11TH ST 23298

COLLEGES

University Of Richmond
28 WESTHAMPTON WAY 23173

VA Commonwealth Univer
1000 VCU E 23298

ROANOKE

BUILDINGS

Colonial Plaza Building
10 FRANKLIN RD SE 24011

Coreast
406 1ST ST SW 24011

Crestar Bank Building
310 1ST ST SW 24011

Franklin Plaza (ibm)
111 FRANKLIN RD SE 24011

GOVERNMENT

Chamber Of Commerce
700 PO BOX 24004

Municipal Building
215 CHURCH AVE SW 24011

Poff Federal Building
210 FRANKLIN RD SW 24011

State City Building
104 CAMPBELL AVE SW .. 24011

HOSPITALS

Community Hospital
12946 PO BOX 24029

Roanoke Memorial Hospital
13367 PO BOX 24033

VIRGINIA BEACH

BUILDINGS

Columbus Center
1 COLUMBUS CTR 23462

Hilltop West Exec Office
1604 HILLTOP WEST SHOPPING
CTR 23451

WASHINGTON
Abbreviation WA

Aberdeen 98520
Abmps (Vancouver) 98667
Acme 98220
Adco (Soap Lake) 98851
Addy 99101
Adelaide (Redmond) 98052
Adelma Beach 98368
          (Port Townsend)
Adna 98522
Adrian (Soap Lake) 98851
Aeneas (Tonasket) 98855
Agate Beach (Joyce) 98343
Agnew (Port Angeles) 98362
Ahtanum (Yakima) 98902
Airport Boxes (Spokane) ... 99219
Airway Heights 99001
Ajlune (Mossyrock) 98564
Albion 99102
Alder (Eatonville) 98328
Alder Grove (Montesano) .. 98563
Alderton (Puyallup) 98371
Alderwood Manor 98036
          (Lynnwood)
Alger (Burlington) 98233
Algona (Auburn) 98001
Allen (Bow) 98232
Allentown (Seattle) 98178
Allyn 98524
Almira 99103
Aloha (Pacific Beach) 98571
Alpental 98068
          (Snoqualmie Pass)
Alpha (Onalaska) 98570
Amanda Park 98526
Amber (Cheney) 99004
Amboy 98601
American Lake (Tacoma) .. 98498
Ames Lake (Redmond) 98052
Anacortes 98221-222
          Guemes 98221
          Similk Beach 98221
Anatone 99401
Anderson Island 98303
Annapolis (Port Orchard) .. 98366
Appleton 98602
Appleyard (Wenatchee) 98801
Ardenvoir 98811
Argyle (Friday Harbor) 98250
Ariel 98603
Arletta (Gig Harbor) 98335
Arlington 98223
Artic (Cosmopolis) 98537
Artondale (Gig Harbor) 98335
Ashford 98304
Asotin 99402
Auburn 98001-003
          .... 98023, 98047, 98054
          .... 98063, 98071, 98092-093
          Algona 98001
Ault Field (Oak Harbor) 98277
Avondale (Redmond) 98052
Azwell (Pateros) 98846
Bainbridge Island 98110
          (Bainbridge Is)
Bakerview (Bellingham) 98226
Ballard (Seattle) 98107
Bangor (Silverdale) 98315
Baring 98224

Basin City (Mesa) 99343
Battle Ground 98604
Bay Center 98527
Bay City (Aberdeen) 98520
Beacon Hill (Seattle) 98144
Bear Creek (Belfair) 98528
Beaux Arts (Bellevue) 98004
Beaver 98305
Beaver Valley 98365
          (Port Ludlow)
Beckett Point 98368
          (Port Townsend)
Belfair 98528
Bellevue 98004-009, 98015
          Beaux Arts 98004
          Clyde Hill 98004
          Eastgate 98006-007
          Hunts Point 98004
          Lake Hills 98007
          Medina 98004
          Newport Hills 98006
          Yarrow Point 98004
Bellingham 98225-228
          Bakerview 98226
          Chuckanut 98225
          Edgemoor 98225
          Fairhaven 98225
          Marietta 98225
          Silver Beach 98226
          South Bellingham 98225
Belmont 99104
Bench Drive (Aberdeen) ... 98520
Benge 99105
Benton City 99320
Beverly 99321
Bickleton 99322
Bingen 98605
Birch Bay (Blaine) 98230
Bitter Lake (Seattle) 98133
          98177
Black Diamond 98010
Blaine 98230-231
          Birch Bay 98230
Blakely Island 98222
Blewett (Leavenworth) 98826
Blyn (Sequim) 98382
Bodie (Wauconda) 98859
Bogachiel (Forks) 98331
Boistfort (Chehalis) 98532
Bon Marche (Seattle) 98181
Bonney Lake (Sumner) 98390
Boston Harbor (Olympia) .. 98501
Bothell 98011-012
          .... 98021, 98041, 98082
          Inglewood 98011
          Kennard Corner 98021
          Mill Creek 98012
          Queensborough 98021
          Queensgate 98011
          Thrashers Corner 98021
Bow 98232, 98246
          Allen 98232
          Edison 98232
          Samish Island 98232
Boyds 99107
Brady (Montesano) 98563
Breidablick (Poulsbo) 98370
Bremerton
          .... 98310-312, 98314, 98337
          Brownsville 98310
          Camp Union 98312

Chico 98312
Crosby 98310
East Bremerton 98310
Enetai 98312
Erlands Point 98312
Gilberton 98310
Holly 98312
Kitsap Lake 98312
Manette 98310
Marine Drive 98312
Meadowdale 98310
Rocky Point 98312
Sheridan Park 98310
West Park 98312
Wildcat Lake 98312
Wycoff 98312
Brewster 98812
Bridgeport 98813
Brier (Lynnwood) 98036
Brinnon 98320
Broadway (Seattle) 98102
Brooklyn (Cosmopolis) 98537
Brownstown 98920
Brownsville (Bremerton) 98310
Brush Prairie 98606
Bryant (Arlington) 98223
Buckley 98321
Bucoda 98530
Buena 98921
Bunker (Chehalis) 98532
Burbank 99323
Burien (Seattle) 98146, 98148
          .... 98166, 98168
Burley 98322
Burlington 98233
Burnett (Buckley) 98321
Burton 98013, 98070
          Vashon 98013
Camano City (Stanwood) .. 98292
Camas 98607
Camp Murray (Tacoma) 98430
Camp Union (Bremerton) .. 98312
Cape Flattery (Neah Bay) . 98357
Capitol Hill (Seattle) 98102
Carbonado 98323
Carlisle 98536
          (Copalis Crossing)
Carlsborg 98324
Carlson (Mineral) 98355
Carlton 98814
Carnation 98014
Carriage Hill (Glenoma) 98336
Carrolls 98609
Carson 98610
Cascade (Renton) 98058
Cascade Park (Vancouver) 98684
Cashmere 98815
Castle Rock 98611
Cathlamet 98612
Cedar Falls (North Bend) .. 98045
Cedarview (Sumner) 98390
Cedarville (Oakville) 98568
Cedonia (Hunters) 99137
Center (Quilcene) 98376
Centerville 98613
Central (Yakima) 98901
Central Park (Aberdeen) ... 98520
Central Valley (Poulsbo) ... 98370
Centralia 98531
Ceres (Chehalis) 98532
Chattaroy 99003

Chehalis	98532
Chelan	98816
Chelan Falls	98817
Cheney	99004
Chenois Creek (Hoquiam)	98550
Chesaw (Oroville)	98844
Chewelah	99109
Chico (Bremerton)	98312
Chimacum	98325
Chinook	98614
Chuckanut (Bellingham)	98225
Chumstick (Leavenworth)	98826
Cinebar	98533
Clallam Bay	98326
Claquato (Chehalis)	98532
Clarkston	99403
Clayton	99110
Cle Elum	98922
Clearbrook (Sumas)	98295
Clearlake	98235
Clearview (Snohomish)	98290
Clearwater (Forks)	98331
Cliffdell (Naches)	98937
Clinton	98236
Clyde Hill (Bellevue)	98004
Coal Creek (Issaquah)	98027
Cohasset Beach	98595
(Westport)	
Colbert	99005
Colby (Port Orchard)	98366
Colchester (Port Orchard)	98366
Colfax	99111
College Place	99324
Colton	99113
Columbia (Seattle)	98118
Columbia Square	98684
(Vancouver)	
Colville	99114
Conconully	98819
Concrete	98237
Connell	99326
Conway	98238
Cook (Bingen)	98605
Copalis Beach	98535
Copalis Crossing	98536
Cosmopolis	98537
Cottage Lake	98072
(Woodinville)	
Cougar	98616
Coulee City	99115
Coulee Dam	99116
Coupeville	98239
Covington (Kent)	98042
Cowiche	98923
Crane (Joyce)	98343
Crescent Beach (Joyce)	98343
Crescent Valley	98335
(Gig Harbor)	
Creston	99117, 99147
Crewport (Granger)	98932
Crocker (Orting)	98360
Cromwell (Gig Harbor)	98335
Crosby (Bremerton)	98310
Crown Hill (Seattle)	98117
Crystal Mountain	98022
(Enumclaw)	
Cumberland (Enumclaw)	98022
Cunningham	99327
Curlew	99118
Curtis	98538
Cushman Dam (Hoodsport)	98548

Cusick	99119
Custer	98240
Dabob (Quilcene)	98376
Dallesport	98617
Danville	99121
Darrington	98241
Davenport	99122
Dayton	99328
Deckerville (Elma)	98541
Deer Harbor	98243
Deer Lake (Loon Lake)	99148
Deer Park	99006
Deming	98244
Denny Creek (North Bend)	98045
Des Moines (Seattle)	98198
Desert Aire (Othello)	99344
Diablo (Rockport)	98283
Diamond Point (Sequim)	98382
Dieringer (Sumner)	98390
Disautel (Omak)	98841
Discovery Bay	98368
(Port Townsend)	
Dixie	99329
Dockton (Vashon)	98070
Doebay (Olga)	98279
Donald (Wapato)	98951
Doris (Vantage)	98950
Doty	98539
Douglas (Waterville)	98858
Dryad (Chehalis)	98532
Dryden	98821
Dungeness (Sequim)	98382
Dupont (Du Pont)	98327
Duvall	98019
Duwamish (Seattle)	98188
Earlmount (Redmond)	98052
East Bremerton	98310
(Bremerton)	
East Farms	99025
(Newman Lake)	
East Olympia	98540
East Port Orchard	98366
(Port Orchard)	
East Quilcene (Quilcene)	98376
East Redmond (Redmond)	98052
East Selah (Yakima)	98901
East Union (Seattle)	98122
East Wenatchee	98802
(Wenatchee)	
Eastgate (Bellevue)	98006-007
Eastmont (Everett)	98204
Easton	98925
Eastsound	98245
Eatonville	98328
Edgemoor (Bellingham)	98225
Edgewood (Puyallup)	98371-372
Edison (Bow)	98232
Edmonds	98020, 98026
Woodway	98020
Edwall	99008
Eglon (Kingston)	98346
Elbe	98330
Eldon (Lilliwaup)	98555
Electron (Orting)	98360
Elger Bay (Stanwood)	98292
Elgin (Gig Harbor)	98335
Elk	99009
Elk Plain (Spanaway)	98387
Ellensburg	98926, 98950
Thrall	98926
Ellisford (Tonasket)	98855

Elma	98541
Elmer City	99124
Eltopia	99330
Endicott	99125
Enetai (Bremerton)	98312
Entiat	98822
Enumclaw	98022
Ephrata	98823
Erlands Point (Bremerton)	98312
Espanola (Medical Lake)	99022
Ethel	98542
Evaline (Winlock)	98596
Evans	99126
Everett	98200-201
	98203-208, 98271
Eastmont	98204
Lowell	98203
Pinehurst	98203
Silver Lake	98204
Evergreen Square	98684
(Vancouver)	
Everson	98247, 98276
Strandell	98247
Van Buren	98247
Ewan (Saint John)	99127
Fairfield	99012
Fairhaven (Bellingham)	98225
Fairholm (Port Angeles)	98362
Fairview (Yakima)	98903
Fairwood (Renton)	98058
Fall City	98024
Farmer (Waterville)	98858
Farmington (Belmont)	99104
	99128
Federal Way	98003, 98023
	98063, 98093
Auburn	98003
Auburn	98023
Auburn	98063
Auburn	98093
Westfair	98023
Felida (Vancouver)	98685
Ferndale	98248
Fernwood (Port Orchard)	98366
Fife (Tacoma)	98424
Finley (Kennewick)	99336
Fircrest (Tacoma)	98466
Firdale (Raymond)	98577
Firwood (Puyallup)	98371
Five Corners (Yelm)	98597
Fobes Hill (Sumner)	98390
Ford	99013
Fords Prairie (Centralia)	98531
Forest (Chehalis)	98532
Forest City	98366
(Port Orchard)	
Forest Park (Seattle)	98155
Forks	98331
Fort Flagler (Nordland)	98358
Fort Lawton (Seattle)	98199
Fort Lewis (Tacoma)	98433
Fort Steilacoom (Tacoma)	98494
Fort Worden	98368
(Port Townsend)	
Four Corners	98038
(Maple Valley)	
Four Lakes	99014
Fox Island	98333
Fragaria (Olalla)	98359
Frances (Raymond)	98577
Freeland	98249

Fort Lawton	98199
Goodwill Games 1990	98151
Greenwood	98103
Interbay	98119
International	98104
Kenmore	98155
Lake City	98125
Lake Forest Park	98155
Madison Park	98112
Magnolia	98199
Mcmicken Heights	98188
Normandy Park	98148, 98166, 98198
North City	98155
Northgate	98125
Poineer Square	98104
Queen Anne	98109
Reg Lib Handicapped	98129
Richmond Beach	98160
Richmond Beach	98177
Richmond Highlands	98133
Riverton	98188
Safco Plaza	98185
Shoreline	98133, 98155, 98177
Shorewood	98146
Skyway	98178
The Highlands	98177
Times Square	98101
Tukwila	98108, 98138, 98168, 98178, 98188
Wallingford	98103
Wedgwood	98115
West Seattle	98116
Westwood	98136
Westwood Village	98126
White Center	98106, 98146
Seattle Heights	98036
(Lynnwood)	
Seaview	98644
Sedro Woolley	98284
Sekiu	98381
Selah	98942
Sequim	98382
Shadle Garland (Spokane)	99205, 99209
Shaw Island	98286
Shelton	98584
Sheridan Park (Bremerton)	98310
Shine (Chimacum)	98325
Shore Acres (Gig Harbor)	98335
Shorewood (Seattle)	98146
Shorewood Beach	98333
(Fox Island)	
Silvana	98287
Silver Beach (Bellingham)	98226
Silver Creek	98585
Silver Lake (Everett)	98204
Silverdale	98315, 98383
Bangor	98315
Olympic View	98383
Silverlake	98645
Similk Beach (Anacortes)	98221
Skamania (Stevenson)	98648
Skamokawa	98647
Skykomish	98288
Skyway (Seattle)	98178
Smokey Point (Arlington)	98223
Snohomish	98290-291
Clearview	98290
Larimers Corner	98290

Machias	98290
Maltby	98290
Snoqualmie	98065
Snoqualmie Pass	98068
Snug Harbor	98262
(Lummi Island)	
Soap Lake	98851
Sol Duc Hot Springs	98362
(Port Angeles)	
South Aberdeen (Aberdeen)	98520
South Bay (Olympia)	98501
South Bellingham	98225
(Bellingham)	
South Bend	98586
South Broadway (Yakima)	98903
South Cle Elum	98943
South Colby	98384
South Elma (Elma)	98541
South Montesano	98563
(Montesano)	
South Park Village	98366
(Port Orchard)	
South Prairie	98385
South Sound (Olympia)	98501
Southworth	98386
Spanaway	98387
Spangle	99028, 99031
Rosalia	99170
Spokane	99200-216, 99218-220, 99223, 99228, 99251-252, 99254-256, 99258, 99260, 99299
Gonzaga Univ	99258
Hillyard	99207
Liberty Park	99202, 99220
Manito	99203, 99223
Millwood	99212
Shadle Garland	99205, 99209
Whitworth College	99251
Sprague (Lamont)	99017, 99032
Spring Glen (Fall City)	98024
Springdale	99173
Stanwood	98292
Starbuck	99359
Startup	98293
Stehekin	98852
Steilacoom	98388
Steptoe	99174
Stevenson	98648
Stiebels Corner	98392
(Suquamish)	
Stillwater (Carnation)	98014
Strandell (Everson)	98247
Stratford	98853
Sultan	98294
Sumach (Yakima)	98901, 98903
Sumas	98295
Summit (Puyallup)	98371
Sumner	98390, 98352
Sunny Bay (Gig Harbor)	98335
Sunnyside	98944
Sunnyslope (Port Orchard)	98366
Sunrise Beach	98335
(Gig Harbor)	
Suquamish	98392
Sylvan (Fox Island)	98333
Synarep (Riverside)	98849
Tacoma	98401-409, 98411-413, 98415-416, 98418, 98421-422, 98424, 98430-431, 98433-434

	98438-439, 98442-447, 98450, 98455, 98460, 98464-467, 98477, 98492-494, 98497-499
American Lake	98498
Camp Murray	98430
Fife	98424
Fircrest	98466
Fort Lewis	98433
Fort Steilacoom	98494
Lakewood Center	98439, 98498-98499
Madigan AMC	98431
Madigan Hospital	98431
Mcchord AFB	98438
North Fort Lewis	98434
Oakbrook	98497
Parkland	98444-98446
Ruston	98407
Tillicum	98492
University Place	98464
Weyerhaeuser Co	98477
Taholah	98587
Tahuya	98588
Tampico (Yakima)	98902
Tanglewild (Olympia)	98501, 98506
Tatoosh Island (Neah Bay)	98357
Teanaway (Cle Elum)	98922
Tekoa	99033
Telma (Leavenworth)	98826
Tenino	98589
Terrace Heights (Yakima)	98901
Thompson Place (Olympia)	98501
Thornton	99176
Thorp	98946
Thrali (Ellensburg)	98926
Thrashers Corner	98021
(Bothell)	
Thrift (Graham)	98338
Tieton	98947
Tillicum (Tacoma)	98492
Times Square (Seattle)	98101
Tokeland	98590
Toledo	98591
Tonasket	98855
Toppenish	98948
Totem Lake (Kirkland)	98033-034
Touchet	99360
Toutle	98649
Townsend (Port Townsend)	98368
Townwater (Olympia)	98501
Tracyton	98393
Trinidad (Quincy)	98848
Trout Lake	98650
Troutlake (Trout Lake)	98650
Tukwila (Seattle)	98108, 98138, 98168, 98178, 98188
Tulalip (Marysville)	98271
Tumtum	99034
Tumwater	98501-502, 98512
Twisp	98856
Tyler (Cheney)	99004
Underwood	98651
Union	98592
Union Gap (Yakima)	98903
Union Mills (Olympia)	98501
Uniontown	99179
University (Seattle)	98105
University Place (Tacoma)	98464
Upper Hoh (Forks)	98331

Usk99180

Vader	98593
Vail (Rainier)	98576
Valley	99181
Valleyford (Freeman)	99015
	99023, 99036
Van Buren (Everson)	98247
Vancouver 98660-668, 98682	
	98684-686
Abmps	98667
Cascade Park	98684
Columbia Square	98684
Evergreen Square	98684
Felida	98685
Hazel Dell	98665
Mercantile Center	98684
Orchards	98662
Salmon Creek	98686
Vantage	98950
Vashon (Burton) 98013, 98070	
Burton	98070
Dockton	98070
Vaughn	98394
Veradale	99037
Vesta (Cosmopolis)	98537
Victor (Gig Harbor)	98335
View Park (Port Orchard)	98366
Villa Beach	98303
(Anderson Island)	
Virginia (Poulsbo)	98370
Wabash (Enumclaw)	98022
Wahkiacus	98670
Waitsburg	99361
Waldron	98297
Walla Walla	99362
Wallingford (Seattle)	98103
Wallula	99363
Wapato	98951
Warden	98857
Warren (Gig Harbor)	98335
Washougal	98671
Washtucna	99371
Waterman (Port Orchard)	98366
Waterville	98858

Wauconda	98859
Wauna	98395
Waunch Prairie	98531
(Centralia)	
Wautauga Beach	98366
(Port Orchard)	
Waverly	99039
Wedgwood (Seattle)	98115
Weikel (Yakima)	98902
Welcome (Deming)	98244
Wellpinit	99040
Wenatchee 98801-802, 98807	
Appleyard	98801
East Wenatchee	98802
Kenroy	98801
Mission Square	98801
Pearcot	98801
West Wenatchee	98801
West Park (Bremerton)	98312
West Richland (Richland)	99352
West Seattle (Seattle)	98116
West Side (Yakima)	98902
West Wenatchee	98801
(Wenatchee)	
Westfair (Federal Way)	98023
Westport	98595
Westwood (Seattle)	98136
Westwood Village	98126
(Seattle)	
Wheeler (Moses Lake)	98837
White Center 98106, 98146	
White Pass (Naches)	98937
White Salmon	98672
White Swan	98952
Whites (Elma)	98541
Wide Hollow (Yakima)	98908
Wilbur	99185
Wildcat Lake (Bremerton)	98312
Wilderness Village	98038
(Maple Valley)	
Wildwood (Curtis)	98538
Wilkeson	98396
Willapa (Raymond)	98577
Wilson Creek	98860

Winchester (Quincy)	98848
Winlock	98596
Winslow (Bainbridge Is)	98110
Winthrop (Mazama)	98833
	98862
Winton (Leavenworth)	98826
Wishkah (Aberdeen)	98520
Wishram	98673
Withrow (Waterville)	98858
Wollochet (Gig Harbor)	98335
Woodinville	98072
Woodland	98674
Woodlawn (Hoquiam)	98550
Woodmont Beach (Kent)	98032
Woodway (Edmonds)	98020
Wycoff (Bremerton)	98312
Wye Lake (Port Orchard)	98366
Yacolt	98675
Yakima	98901-904
	98907-909
Ahtanum	98902
Central	98901
East Selah	98901
Fairview	98903
Fruitvale	98902
Gleed	98904
Gleed Station	98901
Harwood	98902
Pomona	98902
South Broadway	98903
Sumach	98901
Sumach	98903
Tampico	98902
Terrace Heights	98901
Union Gap	98903
Weikel	98902
West Side	98902
Wide Hollow	98908
Yale (Ariel)	98603
Yarrow Point (Bellevue)	98004
Yelm	98597
Yoman Ferry	98303
(Anderson Island)	
Zillah	98953

AMERICAN LAKE

APARTMENTS

Forest Village
8300 PHILLIPS RD SW 98498

Morning Tree
8101 83RD AVE SW 98498

APPLEYARD

BUILDINGS

Federal
301 YAKIMA ST 98801

Wenatchee City Hall
129 S CHELAN AVE 98801

ARLETTA

BUILDING

Gig Harbor City Hall
3105 JUDSON 98335

AUBURN

HOSPITALS

Auburn General Hospital
20 2ND ST NE 98002

St Francis Hospital
34515 9TH AVE S 98003

GOVERNMENT

Seattle Bulk Mail Center
5000 PO BOX 98063

BEACON HILL

HOSPITALS

Pacific Medical Center
1200 12TH AVE S 98144

BEAUX ARTS

BUILDINGS

400 Building
400 108TH AVE NE 98004

Bellevue Business Center
777 106TH AVE NE 98004

Bellevue City Hall
11511 MAIN ST 98004

Bellevue Corporate Plaza
600 108TH AVE NE 98004

Carlson Building
808 106TH AVE NE 98004

Cascade Building
855 106TH AVE NE 98004

Commons Building
1200 112TH AVE NE 98004

Ditty Building
612 BELLEVUE WAY NE .. 98004

First Interstate Financia
225 108TH AVE NE 98004

Key Bank Building
10655 NE 4TH ST 98004

Northwest Building
700 112TH AVE NE 98004

One Bellevue Center
411 108TH AVE NE 98004

Plaza Center
10900 NE 8TH ST 98004

Prudential Building
700 108TH AVE NE 98004

Redwood Building
845 106TH AVE NE 98004

Seafirst Bank Plaza
777 108TH AVE NE 98004

Skyline Tower
10900 NE 4TH ST 98004

Surrey Building
10777 MAIN ST 98004

Tally Building
200 112TH AVE NE 98004

US Bank Plaza
10800 NE 8TH ST 98004

HOSPITALS

Overlake Hospital Medical
1035 116TH AVE NE 98004

HOTELS

Bellevue Hilton Inn
100 112TH AVE NE 98004

Holiday Inn
11211 MAIN ST 98004

Red Lion Hotel
300 112TH AVE SE 98004

BELLEVUE

BUILDINGS

Benaroya Business Park
300 120TH AVE NE 98005

Century I
13401 BEL RED RD 98005

COLLEGES

Bellevue Community Colleg
3000 Landerholm Cir SE ... 98007

BELLINGHAM

BUILDINGS

Whatcom County Building
311 GRAND AVE 98225

HOSPITALS

St Josephs Hospital
3201 ELLIS ST 98225

COLLEGES

Western Washington Univ
516 HIGH ST 98225

BITTER LAKE

HOSPITALS

Northwest
330333 PO BOX 98133

COLLEGES

Shoreline Community Colle
16101 Greenwood Ave N .. 98133

BOSTON HARBOR

APARTMENTS

Aquarian
301 T ST SW 98501

Bellwether
1400 FONES RD SE 98501

Governor House
621 CAPITOL WAY S 98501

Maple Vista
1517 CAPITOL WAY S 98501

Sheraton Inn
900 CAPITOL WAY S 98501

BUILDINGS

Evergreen Plaza
711 CAPITOL WAY S 98501

Federal
801 CAPITOL WAY S 98501

BREMERTON

APARTMENTS

Bay View
100 SHERIDAN RD 98310

Cedar Park
4020 BLEDSOE AVE 98310

Edgewood Villa
1901 WINFIELD AVE 98310

Kona Village
1717 SHERIDAN RD 98310

Maple Manor
2700 MAPLE ST 98310

Southcourt
834 7TH ST 98310

BUILDINGS

Admiral
500 5TH ST 98310

Bremer
104 PACIFIC AVE 98310

Bremerton Professional
3421 KITSAP WAY 98312

Dietz
324 PACIFIC AVE 98310

Eastwood
2528 WHEATON WAY 98310

Medical Dental
423 PACIFIC AVE 98310

Sheridan Med Ctr
900 SHERIDAN RD 98310

Soriano
509 4TH ST 98310

BROWNSVILLE

BUILDING

Bremerton City Hall
239 4TH STREET 98310

BURIEN

HOSPITALS

Highline Community
16251 SYLVESTER RD SW98166'

CENTRAL

BUILDINGS

City Of Yakima
129 N 2ND ST 98901

Larson
6 S 2ND ST 98901

The Tower
402 E YAKIMA AVE 98901

William O Douglas
25 S 3RD ST 98901

Yakima County Courthouse
128 N 2ND ST 98901

DES MOINES

COLLEGES

Highline Community Colleg
2400 S 240TH ST 98198

EDMONDS

HOSPITALS

Stevens Memorial Hospital
21601 76TH AVE W 98026

EVERETT

HOSPITALS

General Hospital
1321 COLBY AVE 98201

HILLYARD

BUILDINGS

Franklin Park Mall
5628 N DIVISION ST 99207

North Spokane Proffesiona
5901 N Lidgerwood St 99207

Northtown Office Building
4407 N DIVISION ST 99207

INTERBAY

COLLEGES

Seattle Pacific Universit
3307 3RD AVE W 98119

INTERNATIONAL

BUILDINGS

Alaska
618 2ND AVE 98104

Arctic
700 3RD AVE 98104

At&t Gateway Tower
700 5TH AVE 98104

Cabrini Medical Tower
901 BOREN AVE 98104

Central
810 3RD AVE 98104

Coleman
811 1ST AVE 98104

Columbia Seafirst Center
701 5TH AVE 98104

Dexter Horton
710 2ND AVE 98104

Exchange
821 2ND AVE 98104

First Interstate Center
999 3RD AVE 98104

Hoge
705 2ND AVE 98104

Inn At Virginia Mason
1006 SPRING ST 98104

Key Tower
1000 2ND AVE 98104

King County Administratio
500 4TH AVE 98104

King County Courthouse
516 3RD AVE 98104

Lowman
107 CHERRY ST 98104

Lyon
607 3RD AVE 98104

National
1008 WESTERN AVE 98104

Norton
801 2ND AVE 98104

Pacific
720 3RD AVE 98104

Pioneer
600 1ST AVE 98104

Public Safety
610 3RD AVE 98104

Seafirst 5th Ave Plaza
800 5TH AVE 98104

Seattle Municipal
600 4TH AVE 98104

Smith Tower
506 2ND AVE 98104

GOVERNMENT

Federal
909 1ST AVE 98104

U S Courthouse
1010 5TH AVE 98104

HOSPITALS

Harborview Medical Center
325 9TH AVE 98104

HOTELS

Sorrento Hotel
900 MADISON ST 98104

Stouffer Madison Hotel
515 MADISON ST 98104

LACEY

APARTMENTS

Capitol Club
3800 14TH AVE SE 98503

Diamond Head
1510 COLLEGE ST SE 98503

BUILDING

Lacey City Hall
420 COLLEGE 98503

LAKEWOOD CENTER

HOSPITAL

Western State Hospital
9601 STEILACOOM 98498

LIBERTY PARK

BUILDINGS

Dwight D Eisenhower Building
110 S FERRALL ST 99202

St Lukes Med Building
715 S COWLEY ST 99202

Tapio Building
104 S FREYA ST 99202

OLYMPIA

APARTMENTS

Apple Tree
3200 Capitol Mall Dr SW ... 98502

RENTON

HOSPITAL

Valley Medical Center
400 43RD STREET 98055

HOTELS

Holiday Inn
9487 PO BOX 98057

RIVERSIDE

BUILDINGS

Bon Marche Building
214 N WALL ST 99201

Fernwell Building
505 W RIVERSIDE AVE 99201

Fidelity Building
522 W RIVERSIDE AVE 99201

Great Western Building
905 W RIVERSIDE AVE 99201

Lincoln Building
818 W RIVERSIDE AVE 99201

Old City Hall
221 N WALL ST 99201

Parkade Plaza
511 W MAIN AVE 99201

Parkade Plaza
112 N HOWARD ST 99201

Paulsen Medical Building
421 W RIVERSIDE AVE 99201

Peyton Building
10 N POST ST 99201

Review Tower Building
999 W RIVERSIDE AVE 99201

Rookery Building
14 N HOWARD ST 99201

Seafirst Financial Building
601 W RIVERSIDE AVE 99201

Sherwood Building
510 W RIVERSIDE AVE 99201

Us Bank Building
422 W RIVERSIDE AVE 99201

Wash Mutual Building
601 W MAIN AVE 99201

GOVERNMENT

City Hall Building
808 W Spokane Falls Blvd 99201

Federal Court House
920 W RIVERSIDE AVE 99201

Post Office Building
904 W RIVERSIDE AVE 99201

HOTELS

Sheraton-spokane
322 N Spokane Falls Ct 99201

SEATTLE

BUILDINGS

1001 Fourth Avenue Plaza
1001 4TH AVE 98154

1111 3rd Ave
1111 3RD AVE 98101

1411 4th Ave
1411 4TH AVE 98101

Arcade Plaza
1321 2ND AVE 98101

Bank Of California
900 4TH AVE 98164

Blanchard Plaza
2201 6TH AVE 98121

Century Square
1501 4TH AVE 98101

Cobb Medical Center
1305 4TH AVE 98101

Denny
2200 6TH AVE 98121

Fourth & Battery
2401 4TH AVE 98121

Fourth & Pike
1424 4TH AVE 98101

Fourth & Vine
2601 4TH AVE 98121

IBM
1200 5TH AVE 98101

Joseph Vance
1402 3RD AVE 98101

Joshua Green
1425 4TH AVE 98101

Labor Temple
2800 1ST AVE 98121

Lloyd
603 STEWART ST 98101

Logan
500 UNION ST 98101

Marsh & Mclennan
720 OLIVE WAY 98101

Medical Dental
509 OLIVE WAY 98101

Metropolitan Park East
1730 MINOR AVE 98101

Metropolitan Park West
1100 OLIVE WAY 98101

Northern Life
1110 3RD AVE 98101

One Union Square
600 UNIVERSITY ST 98101

Pacific First Center
1420 5TH AVE 98101

Park Place
1200 6TH AVE 98101

Pike Tower
520 PIKE ST 98101

Plaza 600
600 STEWART ST 98101

Puget Sound Plaza
1325 4TH AVE 98101

Seattle Tower
1218 3RD AVE 98101

Seattle Trade Center
2601 ELLIOTT AVE 98121

Securities
1904 3RD AVE 98101

Sedwick James
2101 4TH AVE 98121

Sixth & Pine
523 PINE ST 98101

Skinner
1326 5TH AVE 98101

Terminal Sales
1932 1ST AVE 98101

Times Square
414 OLIVE WAY 98101

Tower
1809 7TH AVE 98101

Two Union Square
601 UNION ST 98101

Unigard Financial Center
1215 4TH AVE 98161

United Airlines
2033 6TH AVE 98121

Washington Mutual Tower
1201 3RD AVE 98101

West One Bank Tower
1301 5TH AVE 98101

Westin
2001 6TH AVE 98121

Westlake Center
1601 5TH AVE 98101

GOVERNMENT

Henry M Jackson Federal
915 2ND AVE 98174

HOSPITALS

Children's
5371 PO BOX 98105

HOTELS

Sheraton Hotel
1400 6TH AVE 98101

SHADLE GARLAND

BUILDINGS

North Professional Building
4601 N MONROE ST 99205

SPOKANE

APARTMENTS

Alexandria Apts
623 S HOWARD ST 99204

Breslin Apts
729 S BERNARD ST 99204

Cambridge Crt
206 W 8TH AVE 99204

Cathedral Plaza
1120 W SPRAGUE AVE 99204

Comstock Arms
328 W 8TH AVE 99204

Knicker Bocker Apts
507 S HOWARD ST 99204

Lilac Plaza
7007 N WISCOMB ST 99208

Mary Cliff Manor
707 W 6TH AVE 99204

Mayfair Apts
726 W 6TH AVE 99204

Oxford Apts
702 S BERNARD ST 99204

Park Terrace
620 W 7TH AVE 99204

Roosevelt Apts
524 W 7TH AVE 99204

Westminister
2301 W PACIFIC AVE 99204

BUILDINGS

6th Ave Medical Building
508 W 6TH AVE 99204

Building
324 N PINES RD 99206

Chronicle Building
926 W SPRAGUE AVE 99204

Deaconess Medical Building
801 W 5TH AVE 99204

Farm Credit Bank Building
601 W 1ST AVE 99204

Fifth Ave Medical Building E
104 W 5TH AVE 99204

Freeway Plaza
1500 W 4TH AVE 99204

Medical Center Building
820 S MCCLELLAN ST 99204

Medicus Professional Ctr
12615 E MISSION AVE 99216

Sacred Heart Medical
105 W 8TH AVE 99204

Spokane House
4301 W SUNSET BLVD 99204

Symons Building
7 S HOWARD ST 99204

Valley Professional Building
12509 E MISSION AVE 99216

Washington Trust Building
717 W SPRAGUE AVE 99204

TACOMA

APARTMENTS

Commencement Terrace
29 SAINT HELENS AVE ... 98402

Holbert House
3502 92ND ST S 98409

Miramar
7320 6TH AVE 98406

Olympic Manor
7301 6TH AVE 98406

Park Towers
220 TACOMA AVE S 98402

Sky Terrace
235 BROADWAY 98402

Vista Del Ray
319 TACOMA AVE N 98403

BUILDINGS

Cedar St Medical
1901 S CEDAR ST 98405

Cornerstone
1148 BROADWAY 98402

Doctor's Professional
721 S FAWCETT AVE 98402

Fawcett Plaza One
950 S FAWCETT AVE 98402

First Interstate Plaza
1201 PACIFIC AVE 98402

Perkins
1103 A ST 98402

Seafirst Center
950 PACIFIC AVE 98402

Tacoma Financial Ctr
1145 BROADWAY 98402

Tacoma Mall Office
4301 S PINE ST 98409

Tacoma Medical Center
1212 S 11TH ST 98405

Tacoma Savings Center
820 A ST 98402

Union Station
1717 PACIFIC 98402

Washington
1019 PACIFIC AVE 98402

GOVERNMENT

County Annex
2401 S 35TH ST 98409

County-city
930 TACOMA AVE S 98402

Federal
1102 A ST 98402

Tacoma Municipal
747 MARKET ST 98402

HOSPITALS

Allenmore Medical Center
1901 S UNION AVE 98405

St Joseph's Hospital
1717 S J ST 98405

Tacoma General Hospital
315 Martin Luther Kings Jr. 98405

TUMWATER

BUILDING

Thurston County
2000 LAKERIDGE 98502

VANCOUVER

APARTMENTS

Columbia House
130 W 24TH ST 98660

Smith Tower
515 WASHINGTON ST 98660

GOVERNMENT

City Hall
210 E 13TH ST 98660

Clark County Courthouse
1200 FRANKLIN ST 98660

Federal Building
500 W 12TH ST 98660

State Office Building
800 FRANKLIN ST 98660

HOSPITALS

St Joseph Community
600 NE 92ND AVE 98664

Va Medical Center
1603 E Fourth Plain Blvd .. 98661

WEST VIRGINIA
Abbreviation WV

Abraham (Shady Spring) .. 25918
Accoville 25606
Adrian 26210
Advent 25231
Albright 26519
Alderson 24910
Alexander (French Creek) . 26218
Algoma (Northfork) 24868
Alkol 25501
Allen Junction 25810
Alloy 25002
Alma 26320
Alpoca 24710
Alum Bridge 26321
Alum Creek 25003
Alvy 26322
Amboy (Aurora) 26705
Ameagle 25004
Amelia (Pond Gap) 25160
Amherstdale 25607
Amigo 25811
Amma 25005
Anawalt 24808
Anmoore 26323
Ansted 25812
Anthony (Frankford) 24938
Apple Grove 25502
Arbovale 24915
Arbuckle (Leon) 25123
Arnett 25007
Arnoldsburg 25234
Arthur 26816
Arthurdale 26520
Artie 25008
Asbury 24916
Asco (Davy) 24828
Ashford 25009
Ashland 24810
Ashton 25503
Athens 24712
Auburn 26325
Augusta 26704
Aurora 26705
Auto 24917
Avondale 24811
Baisden 25608
Baker 26801
Bakerton 25410
Bald Knob 25010
Baldwin (Glenville) 26351
Ballard 24918
Ballengee 24919
Bancroft 25011
Bandytown (Twilight) 25204
Barboursville 25504
Barnabus (Omar) 25638
Barrackville 26559
Barrett 25013
Bartley 24813
Bartow 24920
Baxter 26560
Bayard 26707
Beards Fork 25014
Beaver 25813
Beckley 25801-802, 25926
     East Beckley 25801
     Neville 25801
Beckwith 25814

Beech Bottom 26030
Beeson 24714
Belington 26250
Belle 25015
Belleville 26133
Bellview (Fairmont) 26554
Belmont 26134
Belva 26656
Bens Run 26135
Bentree 25018
Benwood 26031
Berea 26327
Bergoo 26298
Berkeley Springs 25411
Berwind 24815
Bethany 26032
Beverly 26253
Bickmore 25019
Big Bend 26136
Big Chimney (Charleston) . 25302
Big Creek 25505
Big Otter (Ivydale) 25113
Big Run 26561
Big Sandy 24816
Big Springs 26137
Bim 25021
Birch River 26610
Blacksville 26521
Blair 25022
Blandville 26328
Bloomery 26817
Bloomingrose 25004
Blount 25025
Blue Creek 25026
Blue Jay 25816
Bluefield 24701
Bluewell (Bluefield) 24701
Bob White 25028
Bolair (Webster Springs) ... 26288
Bolt 25817
Bomont 25030
Boomer 25031
Booth 26522
Borderland 25665
Bowden 26254
Bozoo 24923
Bradley 25818
Bradshaw 24817
Bramwell 24715
Branchland 25506
Brandonville 26523
Brandywine 26802
Breeden 25666
Brenton 24818
Bretz 26524
Bridgeport 26330
Bristol 26332
Broaddus (Philippi) 26416
Brohard 26138
Brooks 25957
Brownton 26334
Bruceton Mills 26525
Bruno 25611
Buckeye 24924
Buckhannon 26201
Bud 24716
Buffalo 25033
Bunker Hill 25413
Burlington 26710
Burnsville 26335, 26615
     Gem 26335

Burnwell 25034
Burton 26562
Cabin Creek 25035
Cabins 26855
Cairo 26337
Caldwell 24925
Calvin 26660
Camden 26338
Camden On Gauley 26208
Cameron 26033
Camp Creek 25820
Canebrake 24819
Cannelton 25036
Canvas 26662
Capels 24820
Capon Bridge 26711
Capon Springs 26823
Carbon (Leewood) 25122
Caretta 24821
Carolina 26563
Cascade (Masontown) 26542
Cass 24927
Cassville 26527
Cedar Grove 25039
Cedarville 26611
Center Point 26339
Centralia 26612
Century 26214
Ceredo 25507
Chapmanville 25508
Charles Town 25414
Charleston 25300-306, 25309
          .... 25311-315, 25317
          .... 25320-339, 25350
          .... 25356-357, 25360-362
          ... 25364-365, 25375, 25387
          .... 25389, 25392, 25396
     Big Chimney 25302
     Cross Lanes 25313
     Malden 25306
     Marmet 25315
     Sissonville 25320
     South Charleston 25303
     South Charleston 25309
     South Hills 25314
     Spring Hill 25309
Charlton Heights 25040
Charmco 25958
Chattaroy 25667
Chauncey 25612
Cherry Run (Hedgesville) .. 25427
Chester 26034
Chloe 25235
Circleville 26804
Clarksburg 26301-302, 26461
     Nutter Fort 26301
     Stonewood 26301
Clay 25043
Clear Creek 25044
Clear Fork 24822
Clem (Frametown) 26623
Clendenin 25045
Cleveland 26215
Clifftop (Danese) 25831
Clifton 25237
Clintonville 24928
Clio 25046
Clothier 25047
Coal City 25823
Coal Mountain 24823
Coaldale (Freeman) 24724

Coalton	26257	
Coalwood	24824	
Coburn (Burton)	26562	
Colcord	25048	
Colfax	26566	
Colliers	26035	
Comfort	25049	
Cool Ridge	25825	
Copen	26615	
Cora	25614	
Core	26529	
Corinne	25826	
Corinth	26713	
Corley (Flatwoods)	26621	
Corton (Clendenin)	25045	
Costa	25051	
Cottageville	25239	
Cottle	26207	
Cove Gap (Kiahsville)	25534	
Covel	24719	
Cowen	26206	
Coxs Mills	26342	
Crab Orchard	25827	
Craigsville	26205	
Cranberry	25828	
Crawford	26343	
Crawley	24931	
Creston	26141	
Crichton	25961	
Cross Lanes (Charleston)	25313	
Crown Hill	25052	
Crum	25669	
Crumpler	24825	
Cucumber	24826	
Culloden	25510	
Cunard (Fayetteville)	25840	
Curtin (Webster Springs)	26288	
Cyclone	24827	
Dailey	26259	
Dallas	26036	
Danese	25831	
Daniels	25832	
Danville	25053	
Davin	25617	
Davis	26260	
Davisville	26142	
Davy	24828	
Dawes	25054	
Dawmont	26344	
Dawson (Alderson)	24910	
Decota (Leewood)	25122	
Deep Water	25057	
Dehue (Yolyn)	25654	
Delbarton	25670	
Dellslow	26531	
Delray	26714	
Diamond (Belle)	25015	
Diana	26217	
Dille	26617	
Dingess	25671	
Dixie	25059	
Dorcas (Petersburg)	26847	
Dorothy	25060	
Dothan	25833	
Dott (Matoaka)	24736	
Drennen	26667	
Droop (Hillsboro)	24946	
Dry Creek	25062	
Drybranch	25061	
Dryfork	26263	
Duck	25063	

Duhring (Rock)	24747	
Dunbar	25064	
Duncan (Le Roy)	25252	
Dunlow	25511	
Dunmore	24934	
Durbin	26264	
Earling (Lyburn)	25632	
East Bank	25067	
East Beckley (Beckley)	25801	
East Gulf (Rhodell)	25915	
East Lynn	25512	
Eastside (Fairmont)	26554	
Eccles	25836	
Eckman	24829	
Edgarton	25672	
Edmond	25837	
Eglon	26716	
Elbert	24830	
Eleanor	25070	
Elgood (Princeton)	24740	
Elizabeth	26143	
Elk Garden	26717	
Elkhorn	24831	
Elkins	26241	
Elkview	25071	
Ellamore	26267	
Ellenboro	26346	
Elm Grove (Wheeling)	26003	
Elmira	26618	
Elton	25965	
Emmett	25620	
English	24832	
Enterprise	26568	
Erbacon	26203	
Eskdale	25075	
Ethel	25076	
Eureka	26144	
Evans	25241	
Everettville	26533	
Exchange	26619	
Fairdale	25839	
Fairlea	24902	
Fairmont	26554-555	
Bellview	26554	
Eastside	26554	
Jordan	26554	
Monongah	26554	
Fairview	26570	
Falling Rock	25079	
Falling Waters	25419	
Falls Mill	26620	
Fanrock	24834	
Farmington	26571	
Fayetteville	25840	
Fenwick	26202	
Ferrellsburg (Harts)	25524	
Filbert (Elbert)	24830	
Fisher	26818	
Five Forks	26145	
Flat Top	25841	
Flatwoods	26621	
Flemington	26347	
Floe (Chloe)	25235	
Flower (Cedarville)	26611	
Fola (Bickmore)	25019	
Follansbee	26037	
Folsom	26348	
Forest Hill	24935	
Fort Ashby	26719	
Fort Gay	25514	
Fort Neal	26103	

Fort Seybert	26806	
Fort Spring	24936	
Foster	25081	
Four States	26572	
Frame (Elkview)	25071	
Frametown	26623	
Frankford	24938	
Franklin	26807	
Fraziers Bottom	25082	
Freeman	24724	
French Creek	26218	
Frenchton	26219	
Friars Hill (Frankford)	24938	
Friendly	26146	
Gallagher	25083	
Gallipolis Ferry	25515	
Galloway	26349	
Gandeeville	25243	
Gap Mills	24941	
Garrison (Whitesville)	25209	
Gary	24836	
Gassaway	26624	
Gatewood (Fayetteville)	25840	
Gauley Bridge	25085	
Gauley Mills	26208	
(Camden On Gauley)		
Gay	25244	
Gem (Burnsville)	26335	
Genoa	25517	
Gerrardstown	25420	
Ghent	25843	
Gilbert	25621	
Gilboa	26671	
Gilliam (Worth)	24897	
Gilmer	26350	
Given	25245	
Glace	24942	
Glady	26268	
Glasgow	25086	
Glen	25088	
Glen Dale	26038	
Glen Daniel	25844	
Glen Easton	26039	
Glen Ferris	25090	
Glen Fork	25845	
Glen Jean	25846	
Glen Morgan	25847	
Glen Rogers	25848	
Glen White	25849	
Glengary	25421	
Glenhayes	25519	
Glenville	26351	
Glenwood	25520	
Gordon	25093	
Gormania	26720	
Grafton	26354	
Grant Town	26574	
Grantsville	26147	
Granville	26534	
Grassy Meadows	24943	
Great Cacapon	25422	
Green Bank	24944	
Green Spring	26722	
Green Sulphur Springs	25966	
Green Valley (Bluefield)	24701	
Greenville	24945	
Greenwood	26360	
Griffithsville	25521	
Grimms Landing	25095	
Gypsy	26361	
Hacker Valley	26222	

Halltown	25423	Jacksonburg	26377	Letart	25253
Hambleton	26269	Jane Lew	26378	Letter Gap	25255
Hamlin	25523	Jeffrey	25114	Levels	25431
Hampden	25623	Jenkinjones	24848	Lewisburg	24901-902
Hancock	25411	Jesse	24849	Liberty	25124
(Berkeley Springs)		Job (Whitmer)	26296	Lillydale (Lynco)	24857
Handley	25102	Jodie	26674	Lima	26383
Hanover	24839	Jolo	24850	Linden	25256
Hansford	25103	Jonben	25856	Lindside	24951
Harman	26270	Jones Springs	25427	Linn	26384
Harmony	25246	(Hedgesville)		Little Birch	26629
Harper	25851	Jordan (Fairmont)	26554	Little Falls (Morgantown)	26505
Harpers Ferry	25410, 25425	Josephine	25857	Littleton	26581
(Bakerton)		Julian	25529	Liverpool (Le Roy)	25252
Harrison	25105	Jumping Branch	25969	Lizemores	25125
Harrisville	26362	Junction	26824	Lobata (Matewan)	25678
Hartford	25247	Junior	26275	Lochgelly	25866
Harts	25524	Justice	24851	Lockbridge	25973
Harvey (Oak Hill)	25901	Kanawha Falls	25115	Lockney	25258
Havaco	24841	Kanawha Head	26228	Logan	25601
Haywood	26366	Kasson (Moatsville)	26405	London	25126
Hazelgreen	26367	Kayford (Leewood)	25122	Long Branch	25867
Hazelton	26535	Kearneysville	24529-530	Longacre (Smithers)	25186
Heaters	26627	Kegley	24731	Lookout	25868
Hedgesville	25427	Kellysville	24732	Looneyville	25259
Helen	25853	Kenna	25248	Lorado	25630
Helvetia	26224	Kenova	25530	Lorentz	26229
Hemphill	24842	Kentuck	25249	Lost City	26810
Henderson	25106	Kerens	26276	Lost Creek	26385
Hendricks	26271	Kermit	25674	Lumberport	26386
Henlawson	25624	Keslers Cross Lanes	26675	Lundale	25631
Hensley	24843	Kessler (Rupert)	25984	Lyburn	25632
Hepzibah	26369	Keyser	26726	Lynco	24857
Herndon	24726	Keystone	24852	Maben	25870
Hernshaw	25107	Kiahsville	25534	Mabie	26278
Herold (Sutton)	26601	Kieffer	24950	Mabscott	25871
Hewett	25108	Kilsyth	25859	Mac Arthur	25873
Hiawatha	24729	Kimball	24853	Macfarlan	26148
Hico	25854	Kimberly	25118	Madison	25130
High View	26808	Kincaid	25119	Mahan	25131
Highland (Ellenboro)	26346	Kingmont	26578	Mahone (Harrisville)	26362
Hillsboro	24946	Kingston	25120	Maidsville	26541
Hilltop	25855	Kingwood	26537	Malden (Charleston)	25306
Hines	25967	Kirby	26729	Mallory	25634
Hinton	25951	Kistler	25628	Mammoth	25132
Holden	25625	Kopperston	24854	Man	25635
Hometown	25109	Kyle	24855	Manheim (Rowlesburg)	26425
Hopemont (Terra Alta)	26764	Lahmansville	26731	Mannington	26582
Horner	26372	Lake	25121	Maplewood	25874
Horse Shoe Run	26769	Lakin	25250	Marfrance (Quinwood)	25981
Hugheston	25110	Lanark	25860	Marianna	24859
Hundred	26575	Landville (Man)	25635	Marlinton	24954
Hunt (Man)	25635	Lanham (Poca)	25159	Marmet (Charleston)	25315
Huntington	25700-729	Lansing	25862	Martinsburg	25401
	25755, 25770-779	Lashmeet	24733	Mason	25260
Hurricane	25526	Lavalette	25535	Masontown	26542
Huttonsville	26273	Lawton (Layland)	25864	Matewan	25678
Iaeger	24844	Layland	25864	Matheny	24860
Idamay	26576	Le Roy	25252	Mathias	26812
Ikes Fork	24845	Leckie	24856	Matoaka	24736
Independence	26374	Leet (Harts)	25524	Maxwelton	24957
Indian Mills	24935	Leewood	25122	Maybeury	24861
(Forest Hill)		Left Hand	25251	Maysel	25133
Indore	25111	Lehew (Yellow Spring)	26865	Maysville	26833
Industrial	26375	Leivasy	26676	Mc Comas	24735
Institute	25112	Lenore	25676	Mc Connell (Stollings)	25646
Inwood	25428	Leon	25123	Mc Dowell (Ashland)	24810
Ireland	26376	Lerona	25971	Mc Graws	25875-876
Isaban	24846	Lesage	25537	Mc Mechen	26040
Itmann	24847	Leslie	25972	Mcalpin (Sophia)	25921
Ivydale	25113	Lester	25865	Mead (Rhodell)	25915

Meador	25682	
Meadow Bluff	24958	
Meadow Bridge	25966, 25976	
(Green Sulphur Springs)		
Meadow Creek	25977	
Meadowbrook	26404	
Medley	26734	
Metz	26585	
Miami	25134	
Middlebourne	26149	
Midkiff	25540	
Midway (Kearneysville)	25430	
	25878	
Milam	26838	
Mill Creek	26280	
Mill Point (Hillsboro)	24946	
Millstone	25261	
Millville	25432	
Millwood	25262	
Milton	25541	
Minden	25879	
Mingo	26281, 26294	
Minnehaha Springs	24954	
(Marlinton)		
Minnora (Orma)	25268	
Moatsville	26405	
Mohawk	24862	
Monaville	25636	
Monongah (Fairmont)	26554	
Montana Mines	26586	
Montcalm	24737	
Montcoal	25135	
Monterville	26282	
Montgomery	25136	
Montrose	26283	
Moorefield	26836	
Morgantown	26502-507	
Little Falls	26505	
Sabraton	26503	
Star City	26504-505	
Westover	26502	
Westover	26505	
Morrisvale	25565	
(Spurlockville)		
Moundsville	26041	
Mount Alto	25264	
Mount Carbon	25139	
Mount Clare	26408	
Mount Gay	25637	
Mount Hope	25880	
Mount Lookout	26678	
Mount Nebo	26679	
Mount Storm	26739	
Mount Zion	26151	
Mountain	26407	
Mouth Of Seneca	26884	
(Seneca Rocks)		
Mullens	25882	
Munday	26152	
Myra	25544	
Myrtle (Delbarton)	25670	
Nallen	26680	
Naoma	25140	
Napier	26631	
Naugatuck	25685	
Nebo	25141	
Nellis	25142	
Nemours	25142	
Neola	24961, 24986	
White Sulphur Springs	24961	
Nettie	26681	
Neville (Beckley)	25801	
New Creek	26743	
New Cumberland	26047	
New England (Washington)	26181	
New Haven	25265	
New Manchester	26056	
New Martinsville	26155	
New Milton	26411	
New Richmond	24867	
Newberne	26409	
Newburg	26410	
Newell	26050	
Newhall	24866	
Newton	25266	
Newtown	25686	
Newville (Sutton)	26601	
Nicut	26633	
Nimitz	25978	
Nitro	25143	
Nobe (Big Springs)	26137	
Nolan	25687	
Normantown	25267	
North Matewan	25688	
North Parkersburg	26104	
North Spring	24869	
Northfork	24868	
Norton	26285	
Nutter Fort (Clarksburg)	26301	
Oak Hill	25901	
Oakvale	24739	
Oceana	24870	
Odd	25902	
Ohley	25147	
Old Fields	26845	
Omar	25638	
Ona	25545	
Onego	26886	
Orgas	25148	
Orlando	26412	
Orma	25268	
Osage	26543	
Ottawa	25149	
Ovapa	25150	
Overbrook (Wheeling)	26003	
Packsville (Whitesville)	25209	
Paden City	26159	
Page	25152	
Pageton	24871	
Palermo	25546	
Palestine	26160	
Panther	24872	
Parcoal	26288	
(Webster Springs)		
Parkersburg	26101-106	
Parsons	26287	
Patterson Creek	26753	
(Ridgeley)		
Paw Paw	25434	
Pax	25904	
Paynesville	24873	
Peach Creek	25639	
Pecks Mill	25547	
Pemberton	25905	
Pence Springs	24962	
Pennsboro	26415	
Pentress	26544	
Perkins	26634	
Petersburg	26847	
Peterstown	24963	
Petroleum	26161	
Peytona	25154	
Philippi	26416	
Pickaway (Sinks Grove)	24976	
Pickens	26230	
Piedmont	26750	
Pierpont (Maben)	25870	
Pigeon (Procious)	25164	
Pinch	25156	
Pine Grove	26419	
Pineville (Marianna)	24859	
	24874	
Piney View	25906	
Pipestem	25979	
Pliny	25158	
Poca	25159	
Poe	26683	
Point Pleasant	25550	
Points	25437	
Pond Gap	25160	
Pool	26684	
Porters Falls	26162	
Powellton	25161	
Powhatan	24877	
Pratt	25162	
Premier	24878	
Prenter	25163	
Prichard	25555	
Prince	25907	
Princeton (Oakvale)	24739-740	
Elgood	24740	
Princewick	25908	
Procious	25164	
Proctor	26055	
Prosperity	25909	
Pullman	26421	
Purgitsville	26852	
Pursglove	26546	
Quick (Clendenin)	25045	
Quinnimont	25910	
Quinwood	25981	
Rachel	26587	
Racine	25165	
Radnor (Genoa)	25517	
Ragland	25690	
Rainelle	25962	
Raleigh	25911	
Ramage (Jeffrey)	25114	
Ramsey	25912	
Ranger	25557	
Ranson	25438	
Ravencliff	25913	
Ravenswood	26164	
Rawl	25691	
Raysal	24879	
Reader	26167	
Red Creek	26289	
Red House	25168	
Red Jacket	25692	
Redstar	25914	
Reedsville	26547	
Reedy	25270	
Renick	24966	
Replete (Hacker Valley)	26222	
Reynoldsville	26422	
Rhodell	25915	
Richwood	26261	
Ridgeley	26753	
Ridgeview	25169	
Ridgeway	25440	
Riffle (Exchange)	26619	
Rig (Moorefield)	26836	
Rio	26755	

BECKLEY

BUILDINGS

City Hall
409 S KANAWHA ST 25801

Court House
215 MAIN ST 25801

Federal Building
400 NEVILLE ST 25801

Police Station
340 W PRINCE ST 25801

HOSPITALS

Applachian Reg Hospital
306 STANAFORD RD 25801

Beckley Hospital
1007 S OAKWOOD AVE ... 25801

Raleigh General Hospital
1710 HARPER RD 25801

Veterans Hospital
200 VETERANS AVE 25801

COLLEGES

Southern Wv Comm College
609 S KANAWHA ST 25801

BIG CHIMNEY

BUILDINGS

City Center West
900 PENNSYLVANIA AVE 25302

HOSPITALS

Women & Childrens
800 PENNSYLVANIA AVE 25302

CHARLESTON

APARTMENTS

Argone Apartments
27 RUFFNER AVE 25311

Carroll Terrace
1546 KANAWHA BLVD E .. 25311

Chateau Apartments
24 BRADFORD ST 25301

Country Club Village
4009 KANAWHA TPKE 25309

Edgewater Apartments
1330 KANAWHA BLVD E . 25301

Imperial Towers
1800 ROUNDHILL RD 25314

Kanawha Village Apartment
3901 Maccorkle Ave SE 25304

Lee Terrace
1319 LEE ST E 25301

Lippert Terrace
4420 Maccorkle Ave SE 25304

One Morris Apartments
1 MORRIS ST 25301

Regal Apartments
1424 KANAWHA BLVD E . 25301

Riverview Terrace
1108 KANAWHA BLVD E .. 25301

Terrace Park East
2106 KANAWHA BLVD E .. 25311

Town House Apartments
1202 KANAWHA BLVD E . 25301

Victorian Arms
1500 BRIDGE RD 25314

BUILDINGS

Arcade Building
710 VIRGINIA ST E 25301

Atlas Building
1031 QUARRIER ST 25301

Boulevard Towers
1018 KANAWHA BLVD E . 25301

Camc Medical Building
3100 Maccorkle Ave SE 25304

City Center East
4700 Maccorkle Ave SE 25304

Commerce Square
900 LEE ST E 25301

Davidson Building
910 QUARRIER ST 25301

Embleton Building
922 QUARRIER ST 25301

Hoyer Building
901 QUARRIER ST 25301

Judicial Annex
111 COURT 25301

L&s Building
812 QUARRIER ST 25301

Lee Building
210 BROOKS ST 25301

Masonic Building
107 HALE ST 25301

Medical Arts Building
1021 QUARRIER ST 25301

Midtown Center
405 CAPITOL ST 25301

Morrison Building
815 QUARRIER ST 25301

Ordnance Center
3100 Maccorkle Ave SW ... 25303

Ott Building
215 DUNBAR ST 25301

Peoples Building
179 SUMMERS ST 25301

Professional Building
1036 QUARRIER ST 25301

Security Building
100 CAPITOL ST 25301

St Francis Medical Plz
331 LAIDLEY ST 25301

State Capitol Complex
1900 KANAWHA 25305

Terminal Building
8 CAPITOL ST 25301

Union Building
723 KANAWHA BLVD E ... 25301

United Center
500 VIRGINIA ST E 25301

GOVERNMENT

City Hall
501 VIRGINIA ST E 25301

Federal Building
500 QUARRIER ST 25301

Kanawha County Courthouse
409 VIRGINIA ST E 25301

HOSPITALS

Camc General Division
1200 WASHINGTON ST E 25301

Camc Memorial Division
3200 Maccorkle Ave SE 25304

Doctors Hospital
30 MACCORKLE AVE SW 25303

Eye And Ear Clinic
1306 KANAWHA BLVD E . 25301

Highland Hospital
300 56TH ST SE 25304

Saint Francis Hospital
333 LAIDLEY ST 25301

HOTELS

Executive Inn
3300 Maccorkle Ave SE 25304

HUNTINGTON

APARTMENTS

5th Avenue Apartments
917 5TH AVE 25701

Adams Landing Apartments
836 VIRGINIA AVE W 25704

Americana
824 9TH AVE 25701

Apollo
749 3RD ST 25701

Barclay Apartments
6050 E PEA RIDGE RD 25705

Belair Apartments
332 12TH ST 25701

Belford Village
612 11TH AVE 25701

Bertram
612 9TH AVE 25701

Biggs
902 11TH AVE 25701

Biggs
1030 9TH ST 25701

Bryan Apartments
1518 4TH AVE 25701

Burgess
1143 9TH AVE 25701

Bush
1011 6TH AVE 25701

Cabell Apartments
333 14TH ST 25701

Careyco Apartments
1005 WASHINGTON AVE . 25704

Carrie Ellen Apartments
2476 3RD AVE 25703

Cavalier Apartments
1434 6TH AVE 25701

Clark Apartments
918 6TH ST 25701

Cloister
911 9TH AVE 25701

Conley
1026 12TH AVE 25701

Del Mar
1018 12TH AVE 25701

Denning Apartments
817 10TH AVE 25701

Emmons Jr Apartments
1209 3RD AVE 25701

Emmons Sr Apartments
1201 3RD AVE 25701

Executive
1020 9TH AVE 25701

Executive House Apartment
1424 3RD AVE 25701

Fairfield Tower
1701 FRANKLIN AVE 25701

Forest Manor
5940 MAHOOD DR 25705

Fountain Apartments
323 5TH AVE 25701

French Colony
2309 ADAMS AVE 25704

Garden Lane Apartments
16 GARDEN LN 25705

Garden Park Apartments
6288 BEECH DR 25705

Golden
1300 KANAWHA TER 25701

Grace
940 11TH AVE 25701

Grace
1029 10TH ST 25701

Greenbriar Apartments
942 10TH AVE 25701

Greenbrier Apartments
1107 4TH AVE 25701

Greentree Apartments
1615 6TH AVE 25703

Hamill Apartments
815 10TH AVE 25701

Harlan
1134 9TH AVE 25701

Highlawn Place
1130 3RD AVE 25701

Holiday
419 6TH ST 25701

Huff
535 4TH AVE 25701

Imperial House
933 12TH AVE 25701

Keister
613 TRENTON PL 25701

Long Branch Apartments
1665 6TH AVE 25703

Madison Manor
1329 MADISON AVE 25704

Malone Apartments
625 6TH AVE 25701

Marshall Arms Apartments
411 HAL GREER BLVD 25701

Marshall Plaza Apartments
1540 4TH AVE 25701

Monica Lynn Apartments
6297 E PEA RIDGE RD 25705

Monticello Apartments
2209 ADAMS AVE 25704

Morgan
640 9TH AVE 25701

Oxford Apartments
1628 6TH AVE 25703

Park View Apartments
1320 12TH ST 25701

Presbyterian Manor
101 13TH ST 25701

Price Apartments
2823 COLLIS AVE 25702

Rhodes Apartments
345 6TH AVE 25701

Ritter Park
938 13TH AVE 25701

Riverview Manor
99 13TH ST 25701

Riverview Manor
225 SHORT ST 25702

Roxen
1001 11TH AVE 25701

Spice Tree Apartments
1655 6TH AVE 25703

Townhouse Apartments
609 20TH ST 25703

Traymore
339 6TH AVE 25701

Traymore
612 TRENTON PL 25701

Trowbridge Manor
101 8TH AVE 25701

University Apartments
329 HAL GREER BLVD 25701

University Apartments
329 16TH ST 25701

Uptowner Apartments
1344 4TH AVE 25701

Van Whitt Apartments
1739 6TH AVE 25703

Van Whitt Apartments
209 19TH ST 25703

Vinson
1122 13TH ST 25701

Virginian Apartments
427 7TH ST 25701

W K Elliott Garden Apts
510 BRIDGE ST 25702

Washington Arms
963 WASHINGTON AVE ... 25704

Wedgewood Villa
5701 PINECREST DR 25705

Westmoreland Estates
2950 AUBURN RD 25704

Westview Manor
601 Veterans Memorial 25701

Westwood Acres
2104 5TH AVE W 25704

Westwood Acres
604 26TH ST W 25704

Woodrum Terrace Apartment
6036 BAKER RD 25705

Woodwind Apartments
1108 11TH AVE 25701

BUILDINGS

Chafin Building
517 9TH ST 25701

Coal Exchange Building
401 11TH ST 25701

Frederick Building
940 4TH AVE 25701

Keith Albee Building
929 4TH AVE 25701

Morris Building
845 4TH AVE 25701

Polan Building
824 5TH AVE 25701

Prichard Building
605 9TH ST 25701

West Virginia Building
910 4TH AVE 25701

GOVERNMENT

Cabell County Court House
750 5TH AVE 25701

City Hall
802 5TH AVE 25701

Federal Building
502 8TH ST 25701

US Courthouse
845 5TH AVE 25701

HOSPITALS

St Marys Hospital
2900 1ST AVE 25702

Va Medical Center
1540 Spring Valley Dr 25704

HOTELS

Coachs Inn
1056 WASHINGTON AVE . 25704

Tourist Motel
343 WASHINGTON AVE ... 25701

WISCONSIN
Abbreviation WI

Abbotsford 54405
Abrams 54101
Adams 53910
Adell 53001
Afton 53501
Alban (Rosholt) 54473
Albany 53502
Albertville (Colfax) 54730
Alden (New Richmond) 54017
Algoma 54201, 54231
Allenton 53002
Allouez (Green Bay) 54301
Alma 54610
Alma Center 54611
Almena 54805
Almond 54909
Altdorf (Vesper) 54489
Altoona 54720
Alvin (Long Lake) 54542
Amberg 54102
Amery 54001
Amherst 54406
Amherst Junction 54407
Angelica (Pulaski) 54162
Aniwa 54408
Antigo 54409, 54464
   Elmhurst 54409
Appleton 54911-915, 54919
   Grand Chute 54915
Arbor Vitae (Woodruff) 54568
Arcadia 54612
Arena 53503
Argonne 54511
Argyle 53504
Arkansaw 54721
Arkdale 54613
Arland (Clayton) 54004
Arlington 53911
Armstrong Creek 54103
Arnott (Stevens Point) 54481
Arpin 54410
Ashippun 53003
Ashland 54806
Ashley (Mosinee) 54455
Ashwaubenon 54304, 54313
   (Green Bay)
Athelstane 54104
Athens 54411
Atwood (Owen) 54460
Auburndale 54412
Augusta 54722
Aurora (Gilman) 54433
Auroraville (Berlin) 54923
Avalon 53505
Avoca 53506
Babcock 54413
Bagley 53801
Baileys Harbor 54202
Bakerville (Marshfield) 54449
Baldwin 54002, 54028
   Erin Prairie 54002
   Hammond 54002
   New Centerville 54002
   Rush River 54002
Balsam Lake 54024, 54810
   (Saint Croix Falls)
Bancroft 54921
Bangor 54614

Bank One (Milwaukee) 53268
Baraboo 53913
Barnes (Solon Springs) 54873
Barneveld 53507
Barre Mills (La Crosse) 54601
Barron 54812
Barronett 54813
Bassett 53101
Bateman (Chippewa Falls) 54729
Bay City 54723
Bay Mills (Tomahawk) 54487
Bay View (Milwaukee) 53207
Bayfield 54814
Bayside (Milwaukee) 53217
Bear Creek 54922
Beaver (Crivitz) 54114
Beaver Dam 53916
Beecher (Pembine) 54156
Beetown 53802
Beldenville 54003
Belgium 53004
Bell Center (Gays Mills) 54631
Belleville 53508
Bellevue (Green Bay) 54311
Belmont 53510
Beloit 53511-512
   Shopiere 53511
   Tiffany 53511
Benet Lake 53102
Bennett (Solon Springs) 54873
Benoit 54816
Benton 53803
Berlin 54923
Bethel (Arpin) 54410
Bevent (Hatley) 54440
Big Bend 53103
Big Falls 54926
Big Flats (Arkdale) 54613
Birch (Irma) 54442
Birchwood 54817
Birnamwood 54414
Biron (Wisconsin Rapids) .. 54494
Black Brook (Clear Lake) .. 54005
Black Creek 54106
Black Earth 53515
Black River Falls 54615
Blackwell (Laona) 54541
Blair 54616
Blanchardville 53516
Blenker 54415
Bloom City 54617, 54634
Bloomer 54724
Bloomingdale (Westby) 54667
Bloomington 53804
Bloomville (Gleason) 54435
Blue Mounds 53517
Blue River 53518
Boardman (Hudson) 54016
Bonduel 54107, 54182
   Navarino 54107
Boscobel 53805
Boulder Junction 54512
Bowler 54416
Boyceville 54725
Boyd 54726
Brackett (Fall Creek) 54742
Branch 54203
Brandon 53919
Brantwood 54513
Briggsville 53920
Brill 54818

Brillion 54110
Bristol 53104
Brodhead 53520
Brokaw 54417
Brookfield 53005
   .... 53008, 53045
Brooklyn 53521
Brooks 53921
Brookville (Woodville) 54028
Brown Deer 53209, 53223
   (Milwaukee)
Brownsville 53006
Browntown 53522
Bruce 54819
Brule 54820
Brussels 54204
Bryant 54418
Buena Vista (Plover) 54467
Buffalo City (Cochrane) 54622
Burkhardt (Hudson) 54016
Burlington 53105
Burnett 53922
Butler 53007
Butte Des Morts 54927
Butternut 54514
Byron 53009
Cable 54821
Cadott 54727
Cady (Wilson) 54027
Caledonia 53108
Cambria 53923
Cambridge 53523
Cameron 54822
Camp Douglas 54618, 54637
   Cutler 54618
Camp Lake 53109
Camp Mccoy (Sparta) 54656
Campbell (La Crosse) 54601
Campbellsport 53010
Canton (Rice Lake) 54868
Carey (Hurley) 54534
Caroline 54928
Carson (Junction City) 54443
Carter (Wabeno) 54566
Caryville (Eau Claire) 54701
Cascade 53011
Casco 54205
Cashton 54619
Cassian (Harshaw) 54529
Cassville 53806
Cataract 54620
Catawba 54515
Cato 54206
Cavour (Argonne) 54511
Cayuga (Mellen) 54546
Cazenovia 53924
Cecil 54111
Cedar (Saxon) 54559
Cedar Falls (Menomonie) . 54751
Cedar Grove 53013
Cedar Rapids (Glen Flora) 54526
Cedarburg 53012
Center Valley 54106
   (Black Creek)
Centerville (Galesville) 54630
Centuria 54824
Chaseburg 54621
Chelsea 54419, 54451
Chetek 54728
Chili 54420
Chilton 53014

Chippewa Falls 54729, 54774
Christie (Neillsville) 54456
City Point (Pittsville) 54466
Clam Falls (Frederic) 54837
Clam Lake 54517
Clark (Withee) 54498
Clayton 54004
Clear Lake 54005
Clearwater Lake 54521, 54562
   (Eagle River)
Cleghorn (Eleva) 54738
Cleveland 53015
Clifton (River Falls) 54022
Clinton 53525
Clintonville 54929
Cloverland (Eagle River) ... 54521
Clyman 53016
Cobb 53526
Cochrane 54622
Coddington (Plover) 54467
Colby 54421
Coleman 54112
Colfax 54730
Colgate 53017
Collins 54207
Coloma 54930
Columbus 53925
Combined Locks 54113
Comstock 54826
Connorsville (Boyceville) .. 54725
Conover 54519
Conrath 54731
Coon Valley 54623
Cornell (Merrill) 54732
Corning (Merrill) 54452
Cornucopia 54827
Cosy Valley (Mellen) 54546
Cottage Grove 53527
Couderay 54828
Crandon 54520
Cream (Alma) 54610
Crescent 54501, 54727
   (Rhinelander)
Crivitz 54114
Cross Plains 53528
Cuba City 53807
Cudahy 53110
Cumberland 54829
Curtiss 54422
Cushing 54006
Custer 54423
Cutler 54618, 54646
   (Camp Douglas)
Cylon (New Richmond) 54017
Dairyland (Danbury) 54830
Dale 54931
Dallas 54733, 54744
Dalton 53926
Danbury 54830
Dancy (Mosinee) 54455
Dane 53529
Darien 53114
Darlington 53530
De Forest 53532
De Pere 54115
De Soto 54624
Deer Creek (Stetsonville) .. 54480
Deer Park 54007
Deerbrook 54424
Deerfield 53531
Delafield 53018

Delavan 53115
Dellwood 53927
Delta (Mason) 54856
Denmark 54208
Deronda (Amery) 54001
Dewey (Stevens Point) 54481
Dexterville (Pittsville) 54466
Diamond Bluff 54014
   (Hager City)
Dickeyville 53808
Dodge 54625
Dodgeville 53533, 53595
Donald (Gilman) 54433
Dorchester 54425
Dousman 53118
Downing 54734
Downsville 54735
Doylestown 53928
Dresser 54009
Drummond 54832
Dunbar 54119
Durand 54736
Dyckesville (Luxemburg) ... 54217
Eagle 53119
Eagle Point 54729
   (Chippewa Falls)
Eagle River 54521
Eagleton (Bloomer) 54724
Earl (Springbrook) 54875
East Ellsworth 54011
East Farmington (Osceola) 54020
East Troy 53120
Eastman 54626
Eaton (Greenwood) 54437
Eau Claire 54701-703
   Caryville 54701
   Hallie 54703
Eau Galle 54028, 54737
   (Woodville)
Eau Pleine 54443
   (Junction City)
Eden 53019
Edgar 54426
Edgerton 53534
Edgewater 54834
Edmund 53535
Edson (Boyd) 54726
Egg Harbor 54209
Eisenstein (Park Falls) 54552
El Paso (Beldenville) 54003
Eland 54427
Elcho 54428
Elderon 54429
Eldorado 54932
Eleva 54738
Elk (Phillips) 54555
Elk Creek (Independence) . 54747
Elk Mound 54739
Elkhart Lake 53020
Elkhorn 53121
Ellis (Stevens Point) 54481
Ellison Bay 54210
Ellsworth 54003, 54010-011
   (Beldenville)
   Lostcreek 54011
   Moeville 54011
   Trimbelle 54011
Elm Grove 53122
Elmhurst (Antigo) 54409
Elmwood 54740
Elroy 53929

Elton 54430
Embarrass 54933
Emerald 54012
Endeavor 53930
Ephraim 54211
Erin (New Richmond) 54017
Erin Prairie (Baldwin) 54002
Esadore Lake (Medford) 54451
Ettrick 54627
Eureka 54024, 54934
   (Saint Croix Falls)
Evansville 53536
Evergreen (Grantsburg) 54840
Exeland 54835
Fairchild 54741
Fall Creek 54742
Fall River 53932
Farmington 54017
   (New Richmond)
Fence 54120
Fennimore 53809
Fenwood (Edgar) 54426
Ferryville 54628, 54640
Fifield 54524
Figis (Marshfield) 54472
Fish Creek 54212
Fitchburg (Madison) 53713
Flambeau 54538, 54555
   (Lac Du Flambeau)
Florence 54121
Fond Du Lac 54935-937
   Taycheedah 54935
Fontana 53125
Footville 53537
Forest (Emerald) 54012
Forest Junction 54123
Forestville 54213
Fort Atkinson 53538
Foster (Osseo) 54758
Fountain City 54629
Fox Lake 53933
Fox Point (Milwaukee) 53217
Foxboro 54836
Francis Creek 54214
Franklin 53132
Franksville 53126
Franzen (Wittenberg) 54499
Frederic 54837
Fredonia 53021
Freedom 54131, 54566
   Kaukauna 54131
Freemans (Lily) 54445
Fremont 54940
French Island (La Crosse) 54601
Friendship 53927, 53934
   (Dellwood)
Friesland 53935
Galesville 54630
Galloway 54432
Gays Mills 54631
Genoa 54632
Genoa City 53128
Germantown 53022
Gile 54525
Gillett 54124, 54176
Gillingham 53581
   (Richland Center)
Gilman 54433-434
   Aurora 54433
   Donald 54433
   Polley 54433

Gilmanton	54743
Gleason	54435
Glen Flora	54526
Glen Haven	53810
Glenbeulah	53023
Glendale (Milwaukee)	53209
	53211-212, 53217
Glenwood (Emerald)	54012
Glenwood City	54013
Glidden	54527
Goodman	54125
Goodnow (Harshaw)	54529
Goodrich (Medford)	54451
Gordon	54838
Gotham	53540
Grafton	53024
Grand Chute (Appleton)	54915
Grand Marsh	53936
Grand Rapids	54494
(Wisconsin Rapids)	
Grand View	54839
Grant (Granton)	54436, 54494
Granton	54436
Grantsburg	54840
Gratiot	53541
Green Bay	54300-308
54311, 54313, 54324, 54344	
Allouez	54301
Ashwaubenon	54304
Ashwaubenon	54313
Bellevue	54311
Hobart	54313
Howard	54303
Howard	54313
Midway	54301
Preble	54302
Scott	54301
Green Grove (Owen)	54460
Green Lake	54941
Green Valley	54127
Greenbush	53026
Greendale	53129
Greenfield	53219-221, 53228
(Milwaukee)	
Greenleaf	54126
Greenville	54942
Greenwood	54437
Gresham	54128
Gurney	54528
Hackett (Phillips)	54555
Hager City	54014
Halder (Mosinee)	54455
Hales Corners	53130, 53132
Hallie (Eau Claire)	54703
	54729
Hamburg (Athens)	54411
Hammond (Baldwin)	54002
	54015
Pleasant Valley	54015
Hancock	54943
Hannibal	54439
Hanover	53542
Hansen (Vesper)	54489
Harding (Merrill)	54452
Harrison (Gleason)	54435
Harshaw	54529
Hartford	53027
Hartland	53029
Hatfield (Merrillan)	54754
Hatley	54440
Haugen	54841

Haven (Sheboygan)	53083
Hawkins	54530
Hawthorne	54842
Hayward	54843
Hazel Green	53811
Hazel Green	53811
Hazelhurst	54531
Heafford Junction	54532
Helenville	53137
Hendren (Willard)	54493
Herbster	54844
Herrschners	54492
(Stevens Point)	
Hersey (Wilson)	54027
Hertel	54845
Hewitt	54441
High Bridge	54846
Highland	53543
Hilbert	54129
Hiles (Argonne)	54511
Hillpoint	53937
Hillsboro	54634
Hillsdale	54744
Hingham	53031
Hixton	54635
Hoard (Curtiss)	54422
Hobart (Green Bay)	54313
Hofa Park (Seymour)	54165
Holcombe	54745
Hollandale	53544
Hollister (White Lake)	54491
Holmen	54636
Honey Creek	53138
Horicon	53032
Horse Creek	54026
(Star Prairie)	
Hortonville	54944, 54951
Houlton (Saint Joseph)	54082
Howard (Green Bay)	54303
	54313
Howards Grove	53083
Hubertus	53033
Hudson	54016
Hull (Stevens Point)	54481
Humbird	54746
Hunting (Tigerton)	54486
Huntington	54017
(New Richmond)	
Hurley	54534, 54565
Carey	54534
Kimball	54534
Oma	54534
Pine Lake	54534
Hustisford	53034
Hustler	54637
Independence	54747
Ingram (Glen Flora)	54526
Institute (Sturgeon Bay)	54235
Iola	54945, 54990
Irma	54442
Iron Belt	54536
Iron Ridge	53035
Iron River	54847
Ironton (La Valle)	53941
Isaar (Seymour)	54165
Island Lake (New Auburn)	54757
Ixonia	53036
Jackson	53037
Jacksonport	54235
(Sturgeon Bay)	
Janesville (Hanover)	53542
	53545-547

Jefferson	53549
Jeffris (Gleason)	54435
Jersey City (Tomahawk)	54487
Jewett (New Richmond)	54017
Jim Falls	54748
Joel (Amery)	54001
Johnson Creek	53038
Jordan (Stevens Point)	54481
Juda	53550
Jump River	54434
Junction City	54443
Juneau	53039
Kaiser (Park Falls)	54552
Kansasville	53139
Kaukauna	54130-131
Kellner	54494
(Wisconsin Rapids)	
Kellnersville	54215
Kelly (Schofield)	54476
Kempster	54444
Kendall	54638
Kennan	54537
Kenosha	53140-144
Keshena	54135
Kewaskum	53040
Kewaunee	54216
Kiel	53042
Kieler	53812
Kimball (Hurley)	54534
Kimberly	54136
King	54946
Kingston	53939
Kinnickinnic	54022
(River Falls)	
Knapp	54749
Knowles (Lomira)	53048
Knowlton (Mosinee)	54455
Kohler	53044
Krakow	54137, 54171
Kronenwetter (Mosinee)	54455
Kunesh (Pulaski)	54162
La Crosse	54601-603
Barre Mills	54601
Campbell	54601
French Island	54601
Shelby	54601
La Farge	54639
La Pointe	54850
La Valle	53941
Lac Du Flambeau	54538
Ladysmith	54848
Lafayette	54729
(Chippewa Falls)	
Lake (Park Falls)	54552
Lake Delton	53940
Lake Emily	54407
(Amherst Junction)	
Lake Geneva	53147
Lake George (Rhinelander)	54501
Lake Hallie	54729
(Chippewa Falls)	
Lake Holcombe (Holcombe)	54745
Lake Mills	53551
Lake Nebagamon	54849
Lake Tomahawk	54539
Lake Wazeecha	54494
(Wisconsin Rapids)	
Lake Windsor (Windsor)	53598
Lake Wissota	54729
(Chippewa Falls)	
Laketown (Cushing)	54006

Niagara	54151
Nichols	54152
Norrie (Birnamwood)	54414
North Freedom	53951
North Hudson (Hudson)	54016
North Lake	53064
North Menomonie (Menomonie)	54751
North Prairie	53153
North Woods Beach (Hayward)	54843
Northfield (Hixton)	54635
Norwalk	54648
Nye (Osceola)	54020
Oak Creek	53154
Oak Grove (Prescott)	54021
Oakdale	54649
Oakfield	53065
Oconomowoc	53066
Oconto	54153
Oconto Falls	54154
Odanah	54861
Ogdensburg	54962
Ogema	54459
Ojibwa	54862
Okauchee	53069
Oma (Hurley)	54534
Omro	54963
Onalaska	54650
Oneida	54155
Ontario	54651
Oostburg	53070
Oregon	53575
Orfordville	53576
Osceola	54020
Oshkosh	54901-904, 54906
Osseo	54758
Owen	54460
Oxford	53952
Packwaukee	53953
Padus (Wabeno)	54566
Palmyra	53156
Pardeeville	53954
Park Falls	54552
Park Ridge (Stevens Point)	54481
Parrish (Gleason)	54435
Patch Grove	53817
Pearson	54462
Pelican (Rhinelander)	54501
Pelican Lake	54463
Pell Lake	53157
Pembine (Dunbar)	54119, 54156
Beecher	54156
Pence (Montreal)	54550
Pensaukee (Oconto)	54153
Pepin	54759
Peplin (Mosinee)	54455
Perkinstown (Medford)	54451
Peshtigo	54157
Pewaukee	53072
Phelps	54554
Phillips	54555
Phlox	54464
Pickerel	54465
Pickett	54964
Pigeon Falls	54760
Pine Lake	54501, 54534
(Rhinelander)	
Pine River (Merrill)	54452, 54965
Pittsville	54466

Plain	53577
Plainfield	54966
Platteville	53818
Pleasant Lake (Coloma)	54930
Pleasant Prairie	53158
Pleasant Valley (Hammond)	54015
Plover	54467
Plum City	54761
Plum Lake (Sayner)	54560
Plymouth	53073
Polar (Bryant)	54418
Polley (Gilman)	54433
Polonia (Custer)	54423
Poniatowski (Edgar)	54426
Poplar	54864
Popple River (Long Lake)	54542
Port Edwards	54469
Port Washington	53074
Port Wing	54865
Portage	53901
Porterfield	54159
Poskin	54866
Post Lake (Elcho)	54428
Potosi	53820
Potter	54160
Pound	54161
Powers Lake	53159
Poy Sippi	54967
Poynette	53955
Prairie Du Chien	53821
Prairie Du Sac	53578
Prairie Farm	54762
Pray (Pittsville)	54466
Preble (Green Bay)	54302
Prentice	54556
Prescott	54021
Presque Isle	54557
Princeton	54968
Pulaski	54162
Racine	53400-408
Radisson	54867
Randall (Grantsburg)	54840
Randolph	53956-956
Random Lake	53075
Range (Amery)	54001
Readfield	54969
Readstown	54652
Red Cliff (Bayfield)	54814
Redgranite	54970
Redville (Withee)	54498
Reedsburg	53959
Reedsville	54230
Reeseville	53579
Reeve (Clayton)	54004
Remington (Babcock)	54413
Rewey	53580
Rhinelander	54501
Rib Falls (Edgar)	54426
Rib Lake	54470
Rib Mountain (Wausau)	54401
Rice Lake	54868
Richardson (Clayton)	54004
Richfield	53076
Richford (Coloma)	54930
Richland Center	53581
Richmond (New Richmond)	54017
Ridgeland	54763
Ridgeway	53582
Ringle	54471
Rio	53960
Rio Creek	54231

Riplinger (Spencer)	54479
Ripon	54971
River Falls	54022
River Hills	53209, 53217
(Milwaukee)	
Roberts	54023
Rochester	53167
Rock Falls (Irma)	54442, 54764
Mondovi	54764
Rock Springs	53961
Rockfield	53077
Rockland	54653
Rome (Nekoosa)	54457
Rosendale	54974
Rosholt	54473
Rothschild	54474
Royalton	54975
Rozellville (Stratford)	54484
Rubicon	53078
Rudolph	54475
Rush River (Baldwin)	54002
Rusk (Menomonie)	54751
Saint Cloud	53079
Saint Croix Falls	54024
Saint Francis	53207, 53235
(Milwaukee)	
Milwaukee	53235
Saint Germain	54558
Saint Joseph	54082
Saint Nazianz	54232
Salem	53168
Sanborn (Ashland)	54806
Sand Creek	54765
Sandlake (Dresser)	54009
Sarona	54870
Sauk City	53583
Saukville	53080
Saxeville	54976
Saxon	54559
Sayner	54560
Scandinavia	54977
Schley (Merrill)	54452
Schofield	54476
Scott (Green Bay)	54301, 54452
Seneca	54654
Sevastopol (Sturgeon Bay)	54235
Sextonville	53584
Seymour	54165
Sharon	53585, 54473
Shawano	54166
Sheboygan	53081-083
Haven	53083
Howards Grove	53083
Sheboygan Falls	53085
Shelby (La Crosse)	54601
Sheldon	54766
Shell Lake	54871
Shepley (Wittenberg)	54499
Sherman (Park Falls)	54552
Sherry (Milladore)	54454
Sherwood	54169, 54466
Shiocton	54170
Shopiere (Beloit)	53511
Shorewood (Milwaukee)	53211
Shorewood Hills (Madison)	53705
Shullsburg	53586
Silver Lake	53170
Sinsinawa	53824
Siren	54872
Sister Bay	54234
Skanawan (Irma)	54442

Wyocena 53969	Yuba (Hillsboro) 54634	
Yellow Lake (Danbury) 54830	Zachow 54182	
York (Granton) 54436	Zenda 53195	

WISCONSIN   IMPORTANT BUILDINGS

ALLOUEZ

APARTMENTS

N Monroe Plaza
400 N MONROE AVE 54301

BUILDINGS

Bellin Bldg
130 E WALNUT ST 54301

Columbus Bldg
414 E WALNUT ST 54301

Medical Arts Bldg
704 S WEBSTER AVE 54301

GOVERNMENT

Brown County Bldg
111 N JEFFERSON ST 54301

County Court House
100 S JEFFERSON ST 54301

Green Bay City Hall Bldg
100 N JEFFERSON ST 54301

Northern Bldg
305 E WALNUT ST 54301

Wis State Office Bldg
200 N JEFFERSON ST 54301

HOTELS

Residence Inn
335 W Saint Joseph St 54301

ASHWAUBENON

GOVERNMENT

Wisconsin Dept Of Transportation
944 Vanderperren Way 54304

BROWNSVILLE

GOVERNMENT

Postmaster
9998 PO BOX 53006

BYRON

GOVERNMENT

Byron Cpo
90 PO BOX 53009

CARYVILLE

GOVERNMENT

State Office Bldg
718 W Clairemount Ave 54701

EAU CLAIRE

GOVERNMENT

E C County Courthouse
721 OXFORD AVE 54703

GREEN BAY

APARTMENTS

Mason Manor
1424 ADMIRAL CT 54303

JANESVILLE

BUILDINGS

Fairview Mall
15 S HARMONY DR 53545

Hayes Block
20 E MILWAUKEE ST 53545

Helgeson Bldg
101 E MILWAUKEE ST 53545

Janesville Mall
2500 MILTON AVE 53545

Oleary Building
2004 W COURT ST 53545

Rock Co Bank Bldg
1 S MAIN ST 53545

Wi Power & Light Bldg
17 S RIVER ST 53545

KENOSHA

BUILDINGS

Factory Outlet Mall
7700 120TH AVE 53142

Lakeside Market Place
11211 120TH AVE 53142

GOVERNMENT

Kenosha Cnty Court House
912 56TH ST 53140

Municipal Office Bldg
625 52ND ST 53140

Safety Bldg
1000 55TH ST 53140

MADISON

BUILDINGS

30 On The Sq Bldg
30 W MIFFLIN ST 53703

Adams Hall
1520 TRIPP ST 53706

Bank Of Madison Bldg
1 W MAIN ST 53703

Firstar Bank Building
1 S PINCKNEY ST 53703

Hovde Building
122 W Washington Ave 53703

Insurance Building
119 MARTIN LUTHER KING
JR BLVD 53703

Lake Terrace
121 E WILSON ST 53703

Madison Medical Center
20 S PARK ST 53715

Manchester Place
2 E MIFFLIN ST 53703

Monona Executive Building
4915 MONONA DR 53716

Park Regent Medical Building
1 S PARK ST 53715

Pyare Sq Building
4610 UNIVERSITY AVE 53705

Steenbock Memorial Library
550 BABCOCK 53706

Tenney Building
110 E MAIN ST 53703

Wendt Kurt F Library
215 RANDALL 53706

White Hall
615 JOHNSON 53706

White Helen C Library
600 N PARK ST 53706

YWCA
101 MIFFLIN 53703

Zoe Bayliss House
915 JOHNSON 53715

GOVERNMENT

Federal Courthouse
120 N HENRY ST 53703

HOSPITAL

Meriter Hospital
309 WASHINGTON 53703

St. Marys Hospital
707 MILLS 53715

COLLEGES

Babcock Hall
1605 LINDEN 53706

Barnard Hall
970 UNIVERSITY 53706

Bascom Hall
500 LINCOLN 53706

Birge Hall
430 LINCOLN 53706

Bradley Hall
1900 WILLOW 53706

Chadbourne Hall
420 PARK 53706

Chamberlain House
665 ELM 53706

Cole Hall
625 ELM 53706

Conover House
1650 KRONSHAGE 53706

Crew House
680 BABCOCK 53706

Education Building
1000 BASCOM 53706

Elizabeth Waters Hall
1200 OBSERVATORY 53706

Friedrick Center
1950 WILLOW 53706

Gilman House
1650 KRONSHAGE 53706

Goodnight Hall
1975 WILLOW 53706

Gordon Commons
717 JOHNSON 53706

Hiram Smith Hall
1545 OBSERVATORY 53706

Holt Commons
1650 KRONSHAGE 53706

Humphrey Hall
640 BABCOCK 53706

Jones House
655 ELM 53706

Jorns Hall
650 BABCOCK DR 53706

Kronshage Commons/Hall
1650 KRONSHAGE DR 53706

Lathrop Hall
1050 UNIVERSITY 53706

Lowell Hall
610 LANGDON 53703

Mack House
1650 KRONSHAGE 53706

Medical Sciences Building
1215 LINDEN DR 53706

Medical Sciences Center
1300 UNIVERSITY AVE 53706

Moore Hall
1575 LINDEN DR 53706

Music Hall
925 BASCOM 53706

North Hall
1050 BASCOM 53706

Ogg Hall
716 DAYTON 53706

Pharmacy
425 N CHARTER ST 53706

Radio Hall
975 OBSERVATORY 53706

Science Hall
550 PARK 53706

Sellery Hall
821 JOHNSON 53706

Showerman House
1650 KRONSHAGE 53706

Slichter Hall
625 BABCOCK DR 53706

South Hall
1055 BASCOM 53706

Spooner House
1510 TRIPP 53706

Sterling Hall
475 CHARTER 53706

Sterling Hall
1150 UNIVERSITY 53706

Sullivan Hall
635 ELM 53706

Susan Davis House
917 JOHNSON 53715

Swenson House
645 ELM 53706

Tripp Hall
1510 TRIPP 53706

Turner House
1650 KRONSHAGE 53706

University of Wisconsin
500 LINCOLN 53706

UW Extention
432 N LAKE ST 53706

Van Hise Hall
1220 LINDEN DR 53706

Van Vleck Hall
480 LINCOLN 53706

Vilas Hall
821 UNIVERSITY 53706

MILWAUKEE

BUILDINGS

100 East Building
100 E WISCONSIN AVE ... 53202

411 Building
411 E WISCONSIN AVE 53202

Bradley Center
1001 N 4TH ST 53203

Firstar Center
777 E WISCONSIN AVE ... 53202

Milwaukee Center
111 E KILBOURN AVE 53202

War Memorial Building
750 N Lincoln Memorial Dr 53202

GOVERNMENT

City Hall
200 E WELLS ST 53202

Federal Building
517 E WISCONSIN AVE ... 53202

Milwaukee County Courthou
901 N 9TH ST 53233

Municipal Building
841 N BROADWAY 53202

Post Office
345 W SAINT PAUL AVE .. 53203

State Office Building
819 N 6TH ST 53203

HOSPITALS

Milwaukee Childrens Hosp
1997 PO BOX 53201

HOTELS

Astor Hotel
924 E JUNEAU AVE 53202

Belmont Hotel
751 N 4TH ST 53203

Marc Plaza Hotel
509 W WISCONSIN AVE .. 53203

Park East Hotel
916 E STATE ST 53202

Pfister Hotel & Tower
424 E WISCONSIN AVE ... 53202

Sheraton Mayfair
2303 N MAYFAIR RD 53226

Shorecrest Hotel
1962 N PROSPECT AVE .. 53202

RACINE

GOVERNMENT

City Hall
730 WASHINGTON AVE ... 53403

Court House
730 WISCONSIN AVE 53403

SHEBOYGAN

GOVERNMENT

Sheboygan City Hall
828 CENTER AVE 53081

SHOREWOOD HILLS

BUILDING

Waisman Center
1500 HIGHLAND 53705

HOSPITAL

Veterans Admin. Hospital
2500 OVERLOOK 53705

COLLEGE

Madison Business College
1110 SPRING HARBOR ... 53705

WAUKESHA

BUILDINGS

217 Wisconsin
217 WISCONSIN AVE 53186

State Office
141 NW BARSTOW ST 53188

GOVERNMENT

Courthouse
515 W MORELAND BLVD 53188

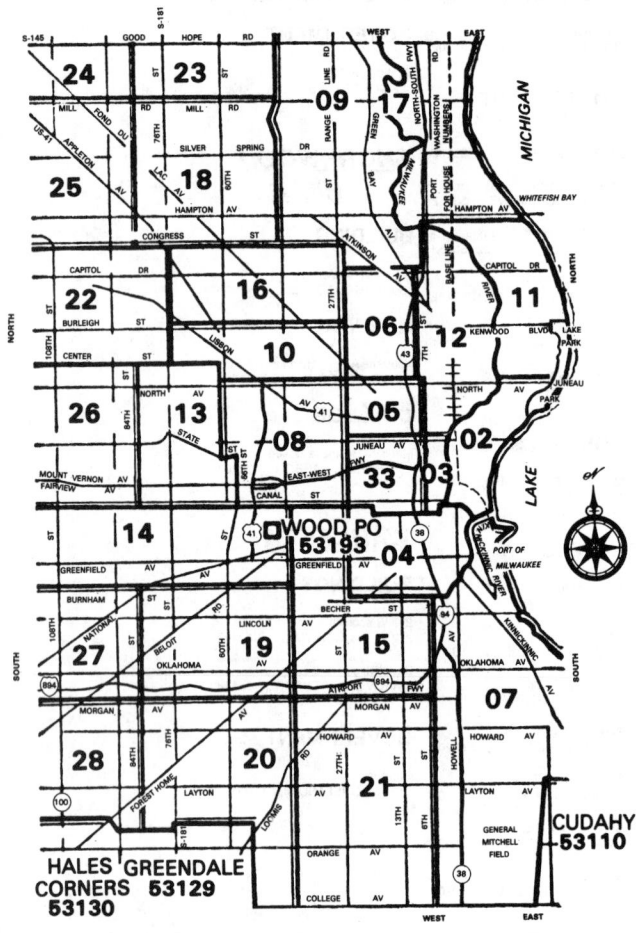

ZIP CODES
MILWAUKEE, WI
532 + TWO DIGITS SHOWN = ZIP CODE

WYOMING
Abbreviation WY

Acme (Ranchester)	82839
Afton	83110, 83112
	83118, 83128
Aladdin	82710
Albin	82050
Alcova	82620
Allendale (Casper)	82601
Alpine	83128
Alva	82711
Arapahoe	82510
Archer (Cheyenne)	82001
Arminto	82630
Arvada	82831
Atlantic City (Lander)	82520
Auburn	83111
Baggs	82321
Bairoil	82322
Banner	82832
Bar Nunn (Casper)	82601
Basin	82410
Bedford	83112
Beulah	82712
Big Horn	82833
Big Piney	83113
Bill	82633
Bitter Creek	82901
(Rock Springs)	
Bondurant	82922
Bordeaux (Wheatland)	82201
Boulder	82923
Buffalo	82834, 82840
Buford	82052
Burlington	82411
Burns	82053
Burris (Crowheart)	82512
Byron	82412
Canyon	82190
(Yellowstone National Park)	
Carlile	82713
Carpenter	82054
Casper	82601-602, 82604-605
	82609, 82615
	82630, 82638, 82646
Allendale	82601
Bar Nunn	82601
Centennial	82055
Cheyenne	82001-003
	82005-010
Archer	82001
Unicover Corp	82008
Chugwater	82210
Clearmont	82835
Cody	82414
Cokeville	83114
Colter Bay (Jackson)	83001
Cora	82925
Cowley	82420
Creston (Rawlins)	82301
Crowheart	82512
Daniel	83115
Dayton	82836
Deaver	82421
Devils Tower	82714
Diamond (Chugwater)	82210
Diamondville	83116
Dixon	82323
Douglas	82633
Dubois	82513

Eden	82926
Edgerton	82635
Egbert (Burns)	82053
Elk Mountain	82324
Elmo (Hanna)	82327
Emblem	82422
Encampment	82325
Ethete (Lander)	82520
Etna	83118
Evanston	82930-931
Evansville	82636
Fairview	83119
Farson	82932
Fishing Bridge	82190
(Yellowstone National Park)	
Fontenelle (Kemmerer)	83101
Fort Bridger	82933
Fort Laramie	82212
Fort Steele (Rawlins)	82301
Fort Washakie	82514
Four Corners	82715
Frannie	82423
Freedom	83120
Frontier	83121
Garland (Powell)	82435
Garrett	82058
Gas Hills (Riverton)	82501
Gillette	82716-718, 82731-732
Weston	82731
Glendo	82213
Glenrock	82637
Granger	82934
Granite Canon	82059
Grants Village	82190
(Yellowstone National Park)	
Grass Creek (Thermopolis)	82443
Green River	82935, 82938
Greybull	82426
Grover	83122
Guernsey	82214
Hamilton Dome	82427
Hamsfork (Kemmerer)	83101
Hanna	82327
Harriman (Granite Canon)	82059
Hartville	82215
Hawk Springs	82217
Heart Mountain (Powell)	82435
Hiland	82638
Hillsdale	82060
Horse Creek	82061
Hudson	82515
Hulett	82720
Huntley	82218
Hyattville	82428
Jackson	83001-002, 83025
Colter Bay	83001
Jay Em	82219
Jeffrey City	82310
Jelm	82063
Jenny Lake (Moose)	83012
Kaycee	82639
Keeline	82220
Kelly	83011
Kemmerer	83101
Kinnear	82516
Kirby	82430
Kirtley (Lusk)	82225
Kortes Dam (Hanna)	82327
La Barge	83123
Lagrange	82221
Lake	82190

(Yellowstone National Park)	
Lance Creek	82222
Lander	82520
Laramie	82051
	82063, 82070-071
Lookout	82051
Mountain Home	82070
University	82071
Leiter	82837
Leo (Hanna)	82327
Linch	82640
Lindbergh (Pine Bluffs)	82082
Lingle	82223
Little America	82929
Lonetree	82936
Lookout (Laramie)	82051
Lost Cabin (Lysite)	82642
Lost Springs	82224
Lovell	82431
Lucky Maccamp (Riverton)	82501
Lusk	82225
Lyman	82937
Lysite	82642
Mammoth Hot Springs	82190
(Yellowstone National Park)	
Manderson	82432
Mantua (Powell)	82435
Manville	82227
Marbleton (Big Piney)	83113
Mayoworth (Kaycee)	82639
Mc Fadden	82080
Mc Kinnon	82938
Medicine Bow	82329
Meeteetse	82433
Meriden	82081
Midval (Riverton)	82501
Midwest	82643
Mills	82644
Moorcroft (Carlile)	82713, 82721
Pine Haven	82721
Moose	83012
Moran	83001
Morton (Riverton)	82501
Mountain Home (Laramie)	82070
Mountain View	82939
Muddy Gap (Rawlins)	82301
Natrona	82646
New Haven (Hulett)	82720
Newcastle	82701, 82715
Odonnell Spur (Powell)	82435
Old Faithful	82190
(Yellowstone National Park)	
Opal	83124
Orin (Douglas)	82633
Osage	82723
Oshoto	82724
Otto	82434
Parkerton (Glenrock)	82637
Parkman	82838
Pavillion	82523
Piedmont (Fort Bridger)	82933
Pine Bluffs	82082
Pine Haven (Moorcroft)	82721
Pinedale	82941
Point Of Rocks	82942
Powder River	82648
Powell	82435
Prairie Center	82240
(Torrington)	
Quealy (Rock Springs)	82901
Ralston	82440

603

Ranchester 82839, 82844	Rozet 82727
Acme 82839	Ryan Park (Saratoga) 82331
Wolf 82844	Saddlestring 82840
Rawlins 82301, 82310	Saint Stephens 82524
Creston 82301	Sand Draw (Riverton) 82501
Fort Steele 82301	Saratoga 82331
Muddy Gap 82301	Savery 82332
Riner 82301	Shawnee 82229
Raymond (Cokeville) 83114	Shell 82441
Recluse 82725	Sheridan 82801
Red Desert (Wamsutter) ... 82336	Shirley Basin 82615
Reliance 82943	Shoshoni 82649
Riner (Rawlins) 82301	Sinclair 82334
Riverside (Encampment) .. 82325	Slater (Wheatland) 82201
Riverton 82501, 82510	Smoot 83126
Gas Hills 82501	South Pass City (Lander) .. 82520
Lucky Maccamp 82501	Story 82842
Midval 82501	Sundance (Aladdin) 82710
Morton 82501	 82729
Sand Draw 82501	Sunrise (Hartville) 82215
Robertson 82944	Superior 82945
Rock River (Garrett) 82058	Sussex (Kaycee) 82639
.... 82083	Sweetwater Station 82520
Rock Springs 82901-902	(Lander)
.... 82926, 82942	Ten Sleep 82442
Bitter Creek 82901	Teton Village 83025
Quealy 82901	Thayne 83127
Rockeagle (Lingle) 82223	Thermopolis 82443

Tie Siding 82084	
Tipton (Wamsutter) 82336	
Torrington 82240	
Turnerville (Bedford) 83112	
Unicover Corp (Cheyenne) 82008	
University (Laramie) 82071	
Upton 82730	
Urie (Lyman) 82937	
Uva (Wheatland) 82201	
Van Tassell 82242	
Veteran 82243	
Walcott 82335	
Wamsutter 82336	
Wapiti 82450	
West Thumb 82190	
(Yellowstone National Park)	
Weston (Gillette) 82731	
Wheatland 82201	
Willwood (Powell) 82435	
Wilson 83014	
Wolf (Ranchester) 82844	
Woods Landing (Jelm) 82063	
Worland 82401, 82430	
Wright 82732	
Wyarno 82845	
Yoder 82244	

IMPORTANT BUILDINGS

ALLENDALE

APARTMENTS

Pine Tree
4500 S POPLAR ST 82601

Skyline Towers
300 E COLLINS DR 82601

BUILDINGS

1st Interstate Bank
104 S WOLCOTT ST 82601

American Bank Building
123 W 1ST ST 82601

Intermountain
200 N WOLCOTT ST 82601

GOVERNMENT

Federal Bldg
100 E B ST 82601

Federal Court House
111 S WOLCOTT ST 82601

ARCHER

BUILDINGS

American Natl Bank
1912 CAPITOL AVE 82001

Boyd Bldg
1720 CAREY AVE 82001

City Center
1920 THOMES AVE 82001

Key Bank
1800 CAREY AVE 82001

Rocky Mtn Plaza
2020 CAREY AVE 82001

GOVERNMENT

County Bldg
1900 CAREY AVE 82001

Federal Bldg
2120 CAPITOL AVE 82001

BITTER CREEK

APARTMENTS

Southwest Rehab Center
1900 CHURCHILL 82901

CASPER

APARTMENTS

Sunridge
3900 E 12TH ST 82609

GOVERNMENT

Dept Of Employment
2760 PO BOX 82602

CHEYENNE

APARTMENTS

Westgate Village
5820 OSAGE AVE 82009

Westgate Village
5715 EDUCATION DR 82009

Westgate Village
320 W CARLSON ST 82009

HOSPITALS

Depaul Hospital
12006 PO BOX 82003

Assigned Zip & Area Codes

State	P.O. Abbr.	Assigned Zip Codes	Assigned Area Codes
Alabama	AL	35004-36925	205, 334
Alaska	AK	99501-99929	907
Arizona	AZ	85001-86556	520, 602
Arkansas	AR	71601-72959	501
California	CA	90001-96137	209, 213, 310, 408, 415, 510, 619, 707, 714, 805, 818, 862, 916
Colorado	CO	80001-81658	303, 719
Connecticut	CT	06001-06907	203, 860
Delaware	DE	19701-19980	302
Dist. of Columbia	DC	20000-20525	202
Florida	FL	32002-34698	305, 407, 813, 904, 941, 954
Georgia	GA	30001-31909	404, 706, 770, 912, 706
Hawaii	HI	96701-96898	808
Idaho	ID	83201-83876	208
Illinois	IL	60001-62999	217, 309, 312, 618, 630, 708, 815
Indiana	IN	46001-47997	219, 317, 812
Iowa	IA	50001-52809	319, 515, 712
Kansas	KS	66002-67954	316, 913
Kentucky	KY	40003-42788	502, 606
Louisiana	LA	70001-71496	318, 504
Maine	ME	03901-04992	207
Maryland	MD	20601-21930	301, 410
Massachusetts	MA	01001-02791	413, 508, 617
Michigan	MI	48001-49971	313, 517, 616, 810, 906
Minnesota	MN	55001-56763	218, 507, 612
Mississippi	MS	38601-39776	601
Missouri	MO	63001-65899	314, 417, 816
Montana	MT	59001-59937	406
Nebraska	NE	68001-69367	308, 402
Nevada	NV	89001-89883	702
New Hampshire	NH	03031-03897	603
New Jersey	NJ	07001-08999	201, 609, 908
New Mexico	NM	87001-88441	505
New York	NY	00400-00599	516, 914
		10001-14999	212, 315, 516, 518, 607, 716, 718, 914
North Carolina	NC	27006-28909	704, 917, 919
North Dakota	ND	58001-58856	701
Ohio	OH	43001-45899	216, 419, 513, 614
Oklahoma	OK	73001-74966	405, 918
Oregon	OR	97001-97920	503
Pennsylvania	PA	15001-19612	215, 412, 717, 814, 610
Rhode Island	RI	02801-02940	401
South Carolina	SC	29001-29945	803
South Dakota	SD	57001-57795	605
Tennessee	TN	37010-38589	421, 615, 901
Texas	TX	75001-79999	210, 214, 281, 409, 512, 713, 806, 817, 903, 915
Utah	UT	84001-84784	801
Vermont	VT	05001-05907	802
Virginia	VA	22001-24659	540, 703, 804
Washington	WA	98001-99403	206, 509, 360
West Virginia	WV	24701-26886	304
Wisconsin	WI	53001-54986	414, 608, 715
Wyoming	WY	82001-83128	307
Guam	GU	96910-96931	671
Puerto Rico	PR	00600-00999	809
Virgin Islands	VI	00800-00899	809

Numerical List of Area Codes

Area Code	State	Section of State*	Largest City Within Code Area
201	New Jersey	N	Newark
202	Dist. of Columbia	AP	Washington
203	Connecticut	AP	Hartford
204	Manitoba (Canada)	AP	Winnipeg
205	Alabama	AP	Birmingham
206	Washington	W	Seattle
207	Maine	AP	Portland
208	Idaho	AP	Boise
209	California	C	Fresno
210	Texas	C	San Antonio
212	New York	SE	New York City
213	California	SW	Los Angeles
214	Texas	NE	Dallas
215	Pennsylvania	SE	Philadelphia
216	Ohio	NE	Cleveland
217	Illinois	C	Springfield
218	Minnesota	N	Duluth
219	Indiana	N	Gary
281	Texas	SE	Houston
301	Maryland	C	Rockville
302	Delaware	AP	Wilmington
303	Colorado	N	Denver
304	West Virginia	AP	Huntington
305	Florida	SE	Miami
306	Saskatchewan (Canada)	AP	Regina
307	Wyoming	AP	Cheyenne
308	Nebraska	W	Grand Island
309	Illinois	NW	Peoria
310	California	SW	Long Beach
312	Illinois	NE	Chicago
313	Michigan	SE	Detroit
314	Missouri	E	St. Louis
315	New York	NC	Syracuse
316	Kansas	S	Wichita
317	Indiana	C	Indianapolis
318	Louisiana	W	Shreveport
319	Iowa	E	Davenport
334	Alabama	S	Montgomery
360	Washington	NW	Below Seattle
401	Rhode Island	AP	Providence
402	Nebraska	E	Omaha
403	Yukon (Canada)	AP	Whitehorse
	N.W. Territory (Canada)	AP	Yellowknife
	Alberta (Canada)	AP	Edmonton

*N = North   E = East   C = Central
S = South   W = West   AP = All Points

Area Code	State	Section of State*	Largest City Within Code Area
404	Georgia	N	Atlanta
405	Oklahoma	C	Oklahoma City
406	Montana	AP	Billings
407	Florida	EC	Orlando
408	California	WC	San Jose
409	Texas	SE	Beaumont
410	Maryland	AP	Baltimore
412	Pennsylvania	SW	Pittsburgh
413	Massachusetts	W	Springfield
414	Wisconsin	SE	Milwaukee
415	California	WC	San Francisco
416	Ontario (Canada)	SE	Toronto
417	Missouri	SW	Springfield
418	Quebec (Canada)	NE	Quebec
419	Ohio	NW	Toledo
423	Tennesee		Planned
441	Bermuda	AP	Hamilton
501	Arkansas	AP	Little Rock
502	Kentucky	W	Louisville
503	Oregon	AP	Portland
504	Louisiana	E	New Orleans
505	New Mexico	AP	Albuquerque
506	New Brunswick (Canada)	AP	Fredericton
507	Minnesota	S	Rochester
508	Massachusetts	C	Worcester
509	Washington	E	Spokane
510	California	WC	Oakland
512	Texas	S	San Antonio
513	Ohio	SW	Cincinnati
514	Quebec (Canada)	S	Montreal
515	Iowa	C	Des Moines
516	New York	SE	Levittown
517	Michigan	C	Lansing
518	New York	NE	Albany
519	Ontario (Canada)	SE	London
520	Arizona	S	Tuscon
540	Virginia	SW	Roanoke
562	California		Planned
601	Mississippi	AP	Jackson
602	Arizona	AP	Phoenix

---

*N = North   E = East   C = Central
S = South   W = West   AP = All Points

Area Code	State	Section of State*	Largest City Within Code Area
603	New Hampshire	AP	Concord
604	British Columbia (Canada)	AP	Victoria
605	South Dakota	AP	Sioux Falls
606	Kentucky	E	Lexington
607	New York	SC	Birmingham
608	Wisconsin	SW	Madison
609	New Jersey	S	Trenton
610	Pennsylvania	E	Philadelphia
612`	Minnesota	C	Minneapolis
613	Ontario (Canada)	SE	Ottawa
614	Ohio	SE	Columbus
615	Tennessee	E	Nashville
616	Michigan	W	Grand Rapids
617	Massachusetts	E	Boston
618	Illinois	S	East St. Louis
619	California	SW	San Diego
630	Illinois	NE	Chicago
701	North Dakota	AP	Grand Forks
702	Nevada	AP	Las Vegas
703	Virginia	W	Arlington
704	North Carolina	W	Charlotte
705	Ontario (Canada)	E	North Bay
706	Georgia	S	Augusta
707	California	NW	Santa Rosa
708	Illinois	NE	Oak Brook
709	Newfoundland (Canada)	AP	Saint Johns
712	Iowa	W	Sioux City
713	Texas	SE	Houston
714	California	SW	San Diego
715	Wisconsin	N	Eau Claire
716	New York	W	Buffalo
717	Pennsylvania	EC	Scranton
718	New York	SE	Brooklyn
719	Colorado	C	Colorado Springs
770	Georgia		Planned
801	Utah	AP	Salt Lake City
802	Vermont	AP	Burlington
803	South Carolina	AP	Columbia
804	Virginia	E	Norfolk

*N = North   E = East   C = Central
S = South   W = West   AP = All Points

Area Code	State	Section of State*	Largest City Within Code Area
805	California	SW	Bakersfield
806	Texas	NW	Lubbock
807	Ontario (Canada)	W	Fort William
808	Hawaii	AP	Honolulu
809	**Caribbean:**		
	Bahamas	AP	Nassau
	Dominican Republic	AP	Santo Domingo
	Jamaica	AP	Kingston
	Puerto Rice	AP	San Juan
	Virgin Islands	AP	Charlotte Amalie
810	Michigan	SE	Detroit
812	Indiana	S	Evansville
813	Florida	SW	Tampa
814	Pennsylvania	WC	Altoona
815	Illinois	N	Rockford
816	Missouri	NW	Kansas City
817	Texas	NC	Fort Worth
818	California	SW	Glendale
819	Quebec (Canada)	SW	Sherbrooke
860	Connecticut		Planned
901	Tennessee	W	Memphis
902	Nova Scotia (Canada)	AP	Halifax
	Prince Edward Is. (Canada)	AP	Charlottetown
903	Texas	NE	Tyler
904	Florida	N	Jacksonville
905	Mexico	S	Mexico City
906	Michigan	NW	Marquette
907	Alaska	AP	Anchorage
908	New Jersey	C	New Brunswick
909	California		Planned
910	North Carolina	W	Winston-Salem
912	Georgia	S	Macon
913	Kansas	N	Topeka
914	New York	SE	Yonkers
915	Texas	W	El Paso
916	California	NE	Sacramento
917	New York	AP	Beeper/Pager
918	Oklahoma	NE	Tulsa
919	North Carolina	E	Greensboro
941	Florida		Planned
954	Florida		Planned

---

*N = North   E = East   C = Central
S = South   W = West   AP = All Points

STATE LISTING OF COUNTIES

The three digits listed are for individual counties. For the last two digits, see individual state listings.

STATE LISTING OF COUNTIES

STATE LISTING OF COUNTIES

KANSAS
Abbreviation: KS

KENTUCKY
Abbreviation: KY

Muhlenberg	423
Nelson	400
Nicholas	403
Ohio	423
Oldham	400
Owen	403
Owsley	413
Pendleton	410
Perry	417
Pike	415
Powell	403
Pulaski	425
Robertson	410
Rockcastle	404
Rowan	403
Russell	426
Scott	403
Shelby	400
Simpson	421
Spencer	400
Taylor	427
Todd	422
Trigg	422
Trimble	400
Union	424
Warren	421
Washington	400
Wayne	426
Webster	424
Whitley	407
Wolfe	413
Woodford	403

LOUISIANA
Abbreviation: LA

Acadia	705
Allen	714
Ascension	707
Assumption	703
Avoyelles	713
Beauregard	706
Bienville	710
Bossier	710
Caddo	710
Calcasieu	706
Caldwell	714
Cameron	706
Catahoula	713
Claiborne	710
Concordia	713
De Soto	710
East Baton Rouge	708
East Carroll	712
East Feliciana	707
Evangeline	705
Franklin	713
Grant	714
Iberia	705
Iberville	707
Jackson	712
Jefferson	700
Jefferson Davis	705
La Salle	713
Lafayette	705
Lafourche	703
Lincoln	712
Livingston	707
Madison	712
Morehouse	712
Natchitoches	714
Orleans	701
Ouachita	712
Plaquemines	700
Pointe Coupee	707
Rapides	714
Red River	710

Richland	712
Sabine	714
Saint Bernard	700
Saint Charles	700
Saint Helena	704
Saint James	700
Saint Landry	713
Saint Martin	705
Saint Mary	703
Saint Tammany	704
St John The Baptist	700
Tangipahoa	704
Tensas	713
Terrebonne	703
Union	712
Vermilion	705
Vernon	714
Washington	704
Webster	710
West Baton Rouge	707
West Carroll	712
West Feliciana	707
Winn	714

MASSACHUSETTS
Abbreviation: MA

Barnstable	026
Berkshire	012
Bristol	027
Dukes	025
Essex	019
Franklin	013
Hampden	010
Hampshire	010
Middlesex	017
Nantucket	025
Norfolk	020
Plymouth	023
Suffolk	021
Worcester	016

MARYLAND
Abbreviation: MD

Allegany	215
Anne Arundel	211
Baltimore	212
Baltimore City	212
Calvert	206
Caroline	216
Carroll	217
Cecil	219
Charles	206
Dorchester	216
Frederick	217
Garrett	215
Harford	210
Howard	211
Kent	216
Montgomery	209
Prince Georges	207
Queen Annes	216
Saint Marys	206
Somerset	218
Talbot	216
Washington	217
Wicomico	218
Worcester	218

MAINE
Abbreviation: ME

Androscoggin	042
Aroostook	044
Cumberland	040
Franklin	042
Hancock	046
Kennebec	043
Knox	048
Lincoln	045
Oxford	042
Penobscot	044
Piscataquis	044
Sagadahoc	045
Somerset	049
Waldo	044
Washington	046
York	039

MICHIGAN
Abbreviation: MI

Alcona	487
Alger	498
Allegan	493
Alpena	497
Antrim	496
Arenac	487
Baraga	499
Barry	493
Bay	486
Benzie	496
Berrien	490
Branch	490
Calhoun	490
Cass	490
Charlevoix	497
Cheboygan	497
Chippewa	497
Clare	486
Clinton	488
Crawford	497
Delta	498
Dickinson	498
Eaton	490
Emmet	497
Genesee	484
Gladwin	486
Gogebic	499
Grand Traverse	496
Gratiot	486
Hillsdale	492
Houghton	499
Huron	484
Ingham	488
Ionia	488
Iosco	487
Iron	499
Isabella	493
Jackson	492
Kalamazoo	490
Kalkaska	496
Kent	495
Keweenaw	499
Lake	496
Lapeer	487
Leelanau	496
Lenawee	492
Livingston	481
Luce	498
Mackinac	497
Macomb	480

STATE LISTING OF COUNTIES

STATE LISTING OF COUNTIES

STATE LISTING OF COUNTIES

STATE LISTING OF COUNTIES

UTAH

Abbreviation: UT

STATE LISTING OF COUNTIES